# Physics

**COMBINED EDITION**

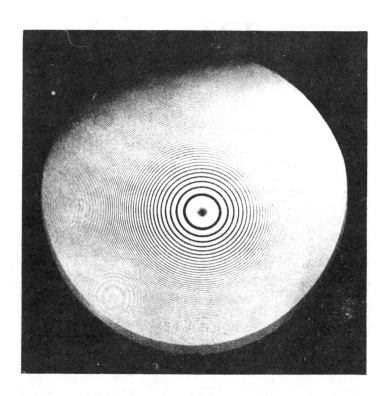

# S.ELECTED PHYSICAL PROPERTIES

| | |
|---|---|
| Density of air (STP) | $1.29$ kg/meter$^3$ |
| Density of water (20° C) | $1.00 \times 10^3$ kg/meter$^3$ |
| Density of mercury (20° C) | $13.5 \times 10^3$ kg/meter$^3$ |
| Speed of sound in dry air (STP) | 331 meters/sec $=$ 1090 ft/sec |
| Acceleration of gravity (standard) | $9.81$ meters/sec$^2$ $=$ 32.2 ft/sec$^2$ |
| Standard atmosphere | $1.01 \times 10^5$ nt/meter$^2$ $=$ 14.7 lb/in.$^2$ $=$ 760 mm-Hg |
| Mean radius of the earth | $6.37 \times 10^6$ meters $=$ 3960 miles |
| Mean earth-sun distance | $1.49 \times 10^8$ km $=$ $92.9 \times 10^6$ miles |
| Mean earth-moon distance | $3.80 \times 10^5$ km $=$ $2.39 \times 10^5$ miles |
| Mass of earth | $5.98 \times 10^{24}$ kg |
| Heat of fusion of water (0° C, 1 atm) | $79.7$ cal/gm |
| Heat of vaporization of water (100° C, 1 atm) | 539 cal/gm |
| Melting point of ice | $0.00°$ C $=$ 273.15° K |
| Ratio of specific heats ($\gamma$) for air (20° C) | $1.40$ |
| Wavelength of the sodium yellow doublet | 5892 A |
| Index of refraction of water (@ 5892 A) | $1.33$ |
| Index of refraction of crown glass (@ 5892 A) | 1.52 |

Wiley International Edition

# Physics

## PARTS I and II

**DAVID HALLIDAY**

Professor of Physics

University of Pittsburgh

**ROBERT RESNICK**

Professor of Physics

Rensselaer Polytechnic Institute

John Wiley & Sons, Inc.    New York • London • Sydney

TOPPAN COMPANY, LTD.,    TOKYO, JAPAN

BOOKS BY HALLIDAY (D.)
Introductory Nuclear Physics.  Second Edition

BOOKS BY HALLIDAY (D.) AND RESNICK (R.)
Physics for Students of Science and Engineering
Part II, Second Edition
Physics for Students of Science and Engineering
Parts I First Edition and II Second Edition Combined

BOOKS BY RESNICK (R.) AND HALLIDAY (D.)
Physics for Students of Science and Engineering
Part I

Library of Congress Catalog Card Number: 66-11527

Printed in Japan
By TOPPAN PRINTING COMPANY, LTD.

# Preface to Part I

This revision of Part I of *Physics for Students of Science and Engineering* (1960) is based on classroom experience at many institutions during the past six years. Although the changes are extensive, the basic outline of the book and its underlying philosophy remain unchanged. A great deal more has been done to help prepare the way smoothly for the treatment of relativistic and quantum physics that will follow Part II, while at the same time an even stronger foundation than before is laid in the classical areas.

Some of the principal changes that reflect this approach are: greater emphasis throughout on the role of reference frames in physical measurement and theory; an improved treatment of Newton's laws and the force laws, stressing the current views; a clearer analysis of the concepts of inertial and noninertial frames with specific applications to help fix the ideas; greater attention to microscopic models of macroscopic phenomena, from friction and collision phenomena to specific heats, thermal expansion and fluctuations; a much clearer presentation of the potential energy concept, whenever it occurs in various physical systems; a more central role for angular momentum in rotational systems and a generalization to unsymmetrical bodies and moving-axes; a somewhat more general treatment of oscillations, including two-body oscillations and the reduced mass concept and anharmonic oscillations; a correct treatment of systems of variable mass in classical physics; inclusion of quantum ideas where they naturally emerge in the "classical" domain; and more attention to statistical interpretations and modern views of thermodynamic processes.

Unit vectors are introduced in Chapter 2 and used thereafter where they simplify derivations or permit a clearer, more geometric, or improved analytic treatment of physical phenomena. More tables are used than previously to summarize and display ideas, equations, and physical data and to draw analogies. We continue to employ optional sections, indicated by smaller print, for specialized or advanced topics, but have included in new topical supplements some of the more specialized or advanced material. Naturally, wherever appropriate, we have systematically updated and modernized many features and topics—such as standards and units, nomenclature and symbols, references and appendices. And the figures have been carefully reworked to heighten their teaching value, to insure consistency, and to illustrate the greater number of applications to contemporary physics.

Most of the original illustrative worked-out examples have been retained from *Physics for Students of Science and Engineering*, with suitable changes and improvements. However, a significant number of new ones have been added to heighten interest and understanding at key places where teaching experience has shown the need. About 85 per cent of the original problems and thought questions remain, but more than one-half again as many new questions and problems have been added. Apart from providing what is probably the largest selection of questions and problems of any comparable text, this insures a wide choice of level of difficulty and area of interest and application. The increase in the length of the book can be fully attributed to such ancillary material—questions, problems, worked out examples, tables, appendices, and figures—all accruing, we believe, to the benefit of teacher and student.

We are indebted to the many teachers and students who have sent us constructive criticisms of the 1960 edition over the years and particularly to Kenneth Brownstein, Benjamin Chi, Ben Josephson, Jr., James C. Kemp, H. E. Rorschach, Jr., and Robert Weinstock, who have advised and assisted us in many ways. One of us (RR) wishes to thank Professor Gerald Holton for the many courtesies extended at Harvard University while the preparation of this book was in progress. We hope that our efforts have made it more useful and interesting to both students and instructors.

ROBERT RESNICK
DAVID HALLIDAY

*January 1966*
*Troy, New York*
*Pittsburgh, Pennsylvania*

# Preface to 1960 Edition

The time lag between developments in basic science and their application to engineering practice has shrunk enormously in the past few decades. The base of engineering, once largely empirical, is now largely scientific. Today the need is to stress principles rather than specific procedures, to select areas of contemporary interest rather than of past interest, and to condition the student to the atmosphere of change he will encounter during his career. These developments require a revision of the traditional course in general physics for engineers and scientists.

The most frequent criticisms made in varying degrees of textbooks used in such a course are these: (a) the content is encyclopedic in that topics are not treated with sufficient depth, the discussions are largely descriptive rather than explanatory and analytical, and too many topics are surveyed; (b) the content is not sufficiently "modern," and applications are drawn mostly from past engineering practice rather than from contemporary physics; (c) the organization of the material is too compartmentalized to reveal the essential unity of physics and its principles; (d) the approach is highly deductive and does not stress sufficiently the connection between theory and experiment. Of course, it is unlikely that a textbook will ever be written that is not criticized on one ground or another.

In writing this textbook we have been cognizant of these criticisms and have given much thought to ways of meeting them. We have considered the possibility of reorganizing the subject matter. The adoption of an atomic approach from the beginning or a structure built around energy in its various aspects suggest themselves. We have concluded that our goals can best be achieved by modifying the selection and treatment of topics within the traditional organization. To shuffle freely the cards of subject matter content or to abandon entirely a sequence which represents the growth of physical thought invites both a failure to appreciate the Newtonian and Maxwellian syntheses of classical physics and a superficial understanding of modern physics. A solid underpinning of classical physics is essential to build the superstructure of contemporary physics in our opinion.

To illustrate how we hope to achieve our goals within this framework, we present here the principal features of our book.

1. Many topics are treated in greater depth than has been customary heretofore, and much contemporary material has been woven into the body of the text. For example, gravitation, kinetic theory, electromagnetic waves, and physical optics, among others, are treated in greater depth. Contemporary topics, such as atomic standards, collision cross section, intermolecular forces, mass-energy conversion, isotope separation, the Hall effect, the free-electron model of conductivity, nuclear stability, nuclear resonance, and neutron diffraction, are discussed where they are pertinent.

To permit this greater depth and inclusion of contemporary material, we have omitted entirely or treated only indirectly much traditional material, such as simple machines, surface tension, viscosity, calorimetry, change of state, humidity, pumps, practical engines, musical scales, architectural acoustics, electrochemistry, thermoelectricity, motors, alternating-current circuits, electronics, lens aberrations, color, photometry, and others.

2. We have tried to reveal the unity of physics in many ways. Throughout the book we stress the general nature of key ideas common to all areas of physics. For example, the conservation laws of energy, linear momentum, angular momentum, and charge are used repeatedly. Wave concepts and properties of vibrating systems, such as resonance, are used in mechanics, sound, electromagnetism, optics, atomic physics, and nuclear physics. The field concept is applied to gravitation, fluid flow, electromagnetism, and nuclear physics.

The interrelation of the various disciplines of physics is emphasized by the use of physical and mathematical analogies and by similarity of method. For example, the correspondences between the mass-spring system and the $LC$ circuit or between the acoustic tube and the electromagnetic cavity are emphasized, and the interweaving of microscopic and macroscopic approaches is noted in heat phenomena and electrical and magnetic phenomena. We have tried to make a smooth transition between particle mechanics and kinetic theory, stressing that, in their classical aspects, both belong to the Newtonian synthesis. We have also sought a smooth transition between electromagnetism and wave optics, pointing frequently to the Maxwellian synthesis.

We discuss the limitations of classical ideas and the domain of their validity, and we emphasize the generalizing nature of contemporary ideas applicable in a broader domain. Throughout we aim to show the relation of theory to experiment and to develop an awareness of the nature and uses of theory.

3. Our approach to quantum physics is not the traditional descriptive one. Rather we seek to develop the contemporary concepts fairly rigorously, at a length and depth appropriate to an introductory course. In the early chapters we pave the way by pointing to the limitations of classical theory, by stressing the aspects of classical physics that bear on contemporary physics, and by choosing illustrative examples that have a modern flavor. Thus we stress fields rather than circuits, particles rather than extended bodies, and wave optics rather than geometrical optics. Among the illustrative examples are molecular potential energy curves, binding energy of a deuteron, nuclear collisions, the nuclear model of the atom, the Thomson atom model, molecular dipoles, drift speed of electrons, stability of betatron orbits, nuclear magnetic resonance, the red shift, and others too numerous to mention.

The point of view is that of developing the fundamental ideas of quantum physics. The customary descriptive chapter on nuclear physics is, for example, not present. Instead, the wave-particle duality, the uncertainty principle, the complementarity principle, and the correspondence principle are stressed.

4. The mathematical level of our book assumes a concurrent course in calculus. The derivative is introduced in Chapter 3 and the integral in Chapter 7. The related physical concepts of slope and area under a curve are developed steadily. Calculus is used freely in the latter half of the book. Simple differential equations are not avoided, although no formal procedures are needed or given for solving them. Vector notation and vector algebra, including scalar and vector products, are used throughout. Displacement is taken as the prototype vector, and the idea of invariance of vector relations is developed.

5. The number of problems is unusually large, but few are "plug-in" problems. Many involve extensions of the text material, contemporary applications, or derivations. The questions at the end of each chapter are intended to be thought-provoking; they may serve as the basis for class discussion, for essay papers, or for self-study. Only rarely can the questions be answered by direct quotation from the text.

6. The book contains an unusually large number of worked-out examples, with the "plug-in" variety used only to emphasize a numerical magnitude. Algebraic, rather than numerical, solutions are stressed. Examples sometimes extend the text treatment or discuss the fine points, but usually they are applications of the principles, often of contemporary physics.

7. The textbook has been designed to fit physics courses of various lengths. In small print there is a great deal of supplementary material of an advanced, historical, or philosophical character, to be omitted or included to varying degrees depending on interest and course length. In addition, many chapters may be regarded as optional. Each teacher will make his own choice. At our institutions Chapter 14 (statics of rigid bodies) and Chapters 41 and 42 (geometrical optics) are omitted. Other possibilities suggested, depending on emphasis or depth desired, or the nature of succeeding courses, are Chapter 12 (rotational dynamics), Chapters 17 and 18 (fluids), Chapter 24 (kinetic theory—II), Chapter 32 (emf and circuits), Chapter 46 (polarization), and Chapters 47 and 48 (quantum physics).

8. We have adopted the mks system of units throughout, although the British engineering system is also used in mechanics. Having observed the gradual exclusion, year by year, of the cgs system from advanced textbooks, we have seen fit to limit ourselves to the bare definition of the basic cgs quantities. An extensive list of conversion factors appears in Appendix G.

We wish to thank the engineering and science students at both Rensselaer Polytechnic Institute and the University of Pittsburgh who have borne with us through two successive preliminary editions. Constructive criticisms from our colleagues at each institution and from some eight reviewers have resulted in many changes. Benjamin Chi of R.P.I. has been of major service in all aspects of the preparation of the manuscript. Finally, we express our deep appreciation to our wives, not only for aid in typing and proofreading but for the patience and encouragement without which this book might never have been written.

DAVID HALLIDAY
ROBERT RESNICK

*January 1960*
*Pittsburgh, Pennsylvania*
*Troy, New York*

*Physics*, Part II, is a revised printing of the second edition of *Physics for Students of Science and Engineering*. In this (1966) new printing of Part II, the following revisions have been made.

1. A supplementary set of 142 problems has been provided. These have been carefully assembled so as to permit, when combined with the numerous problems in the original set, a wider choice of area of interest and level of difficulty than heretofore available.

2. A new Topical Supplement, on the differential form of Maxwell's equations and the electromagnetic wave equation, has been written for reference of students whose instructors choose to discuss this more advanced material.

3. The original appendices have been expanded and modernized and some new ones have been added in order to increase the usefulness and accuracy of such reference material. Front and back end-papers have been changed accordingly.

4. Pagination, numbered references, symbols and units, have been changed, where necessary, for consistency with the new Part I and the above revisions of Part II.

# Preface to Part II, Second Edition

This revision of Part II of *Physics for Students of Science and Engineering*, which we hope will make our book more useful to students and instructors, is based on classroom experience at many institutions during the last two years. The basic outline of the book and its underlying philosophy remain unchanged. We have, however, modified the treatment of many topics, among them Ampère's, Faraday's, Gauss's and Lenz's laws and Huygens' principle, to make them clearer and more explicit than before. The experimental basis of the laws of physics has received increased stress, and new experimental material, such as the radiation pressure measurements of Nichols and Hull, optical masers, relativistic particle accelerators, and fiber optics illustrate the basic concepts. More than half the figures have been redrawn for greater clarity, and new figures and photographs have been inserted in key places. The questions and problems have been re-evaluated, and more than 200 are new.

In a few places we have supplied new sections either to extend or to improve the understanding of the basic material. For example, there are sections in reduced type on the electric vectors ($\mathbf{E}$, $\mathbf{D}$, and $\mathbf{P}$) and on the magnetic vectors ($\mathbf{B}$, $\mathbf{H}$, and $\mathbf{M}$). $RC$ circuits are discussed, the Compton effect has been included in the treatment of the wave-particle duality, and a discussion of electromagnetic fields as seen by observers in relative motion has been added.

Other significant changes are (1) references to the literature available to students have been supplemented and brought up to date; (2) the sign

xiii

conventions for geometrical optics have been put on a more physical basis; (3) attention has been called to examples or problems that contain important new material by using italicized titles; and (4) we have further systemized and simplified the notation in several places, particularly in wave optics.

We continue to be indebted to Dr. Benjamin Chi for assistance in preparing the illustrations and for his detailed criticism of the optics chapters. One of us (DH) wishes to thank Professor G. Wataghin for courtesies extended at the University of Turin while this revision was in progress. Finally, we extend special thanks to those students and instructors who have been kind enough to write to us about their experiences with the first edition.

DAVID HALLIDAY
ROBERT RESNICK

*January 1, 1962*
*Pittsburgh, Pennsylvania*
*Troy, New York*

# Contents

# Physics PART I

# Measurement

## CHAPTER 1

### 1–1 Measurement

When plans were being made to lay the first Atlantic telegraph cable, the company in charge of the construction hired a young engineer, William Thomson (1824–1907), as a consultant. To solve some of the problems raised by this undertaking, Thomson made many accurate electrical measurements. Often he used instruments which he himself had invented. His advice, based on his own experiments, was ignored, chiefly because the principles involved were not clearly understood or accepted by those in authority. The subsequent failures of the project later led to a more careful consideration of Thomson's views. Their adoption led to the successful completion of the cable in 1858.* This experience may have helped Thomson form his often quoted view:

I often say that when you can measure what you are speaking about, and express it in numbers, you know something about it; but when you cannot express it in numbers, your knowledge is of a meagre and unsatisfactory kind; it may be the beginning of knowledge, but you have scarcely, in your thoughts, advanced to the stage of Science, whatever the matter may be.

Although other scientists would deny that they should deal only with ideas that are strictly measurable, none would deny the great importance of measurement to science. Often in the history of science small but significant discrepancies between theory and accurate measurements have led

---

* In 1892, Thomson, then one of Britain's foremost scientists, was raised to the peerage as Lord Kelvin. Among his other achievements, he was one of the founders of the science of thermodynamics.

1

to the development of new and more general theories.  Such advances in our understanding would not have occurred if scientists had been satisfied with only a qualitative explanation of the phenomena of nature.

### 1–2  Physical Quantities, Standards, and Units

The building blocks of physics are the physical quantities in terms of which the laws of physics are expressed.  Among these are force, time, velocity, density, temperature, charge, magnetic susceptibility, and numerous others.  Many of these terms, such as force and temperature, are part of our everyday vocabulary.  When these terms are so used, their meanings may be vague or may differ from their scientific meanings.

For the purposes of physics the basic quantities must be defined clearly and precisely.  One view is that the definition of a physical quantity has been given when the procedures for measuring that quantity have been given.  This is called the *operational point of view* because the definition is, at root, a set of laboratory operations leading to a number with a unit.  The operations may include mathematical calculations.

Physical quantities are often divided into *fundamental quantities* and *derived quantities*.  Such a division is arbitrary in that a given quantity can be regarded as fundamental in one set of operations and as derived in another.  Derived quantities are those whose defining operations are based on other physical quantities.  Examples of quantities usually viewed as derived are velocity, acceleration, and volume.  Fundamental quantities are not defined in terms of other physical quantities.  The number of quantities regarded as fundamental is the minimum number needed to give a consistent and unambiguous description of all the quantities of physics.  Examples of quantities usually viewed as fundamental are length and time.  Their operational definitions involve two steps: first, the choice of a *standard*, and second, the establishment of procedures for comparing the standard to the quantity to be measured so that a number and a unit are determined as the measure of that quantity.

An ideal standard has two principal characteristics: it is accessible and it is invariable.  These two requirements are often incompatible and a compromise has to be made between them.  At first greater emphasis was placed on accessibility, but the growing requirements of science and technology introduced the need for greater invariability.  The familiar yard, foot, and inch, for example, are descended directly from the human arm, foot, and upper thumb.  Today, such rough measures of length are not satisfactory and a much less variable standard must be used even at the expense of accessibility.

Suppose that we have chosen our standard of length to be a bar whose length we *define* as one meter.  If by direct comparison of this bar with a second bar we conclude that the second bar is three times as long as the standard, we say that the second bar has a length of three meters.  In practice, most quantities cannot be measured by direct comparison to a primary standard.  An indirect approach, using more involved procedures, is usually necessary.   Certain assumptions are made to relate the results of an indirect measurement to the direct operation.

Suppose, for example, that the distance from a rocket launching station to the surface of the moon must be known at a certain time.   One indirect way to determine this distance would be to send out a radar signal from the station which will be reflected from the surface of the moon back to a receiver at the sending station.   If the time between sending and receiving the signal is measured and the speed of the radar signal is known, the distance can be obtained as the product of the speed and one-half the time interval.   We assume here that the speed of the signal is constant and that the signal has traveled in a straight line.   The speed must be measured in a subsidiary experiment, and it is here that the standard of length appears in the operational procedure.

Astronomical distances, such as the distances of stars from the earth, cannot be measured in a direct way.   A few stars are close enough so that triangulation measurements can be made.   The position of the star with respect to the background of much more distant stars is observed at six-month intervals, when the earth has moved from one point of its orbit to a diametrically opposite point.   From these data the desired distance can be obtained using the diameter of the earth's orbit as a baseline.   Distances of nebulae many millions of light years from the earth are measured by indirect procedures more involved than triangulation (one light year is approximately $10^{16}$ meters; see Problem 6).

Just as we use indirect methods for measuring large distances, so we must also use an indirect approach to measure very small distances, such as those within atoms and molecules.   The effective radius of the proton, for example, has been measured by particle scattering experiments to be $1.2 \times 10^{-15}$ meter.   Table 1–1 shows the vast range over which length measurements can be made.

## 1–3   Reference Frames

The same physical quantity may have different values if it is measured by observers who are moving with respect to each other.   The velocity of a train has one value if measured by an observer on the ground, a different value if measured from a speeding car, and the value zero if measured by an observer sitting in the train itself.   None of these values has any fundamental advantage over any other; each is equally "correct" from the point of view of the observer making the measurement.

In general, the measured value of a physical quantity depends on the reference frame of the observer who is making the measurement.   This is clear enough if the physical quantity is a velocity, as above.   It is also true, however, if the physical quantity is, say, a displacement of a particle, a time interval between two events, an electric field, or a magnetic field, although a full appreciation of these four examples must await the study of the theory of relativity.

In the early days of physics it was believed that one particular reference

## Table 1–1

### SOME MEASURED LENGTHS

| | Meters |
|---|---|
| Distance to the most-distant quasar yet detected[1] (1964) | $6 \times 10^{25}$ |
| Distance to the nearest nebula (Great Nebula in Andromeda) | $2 \times 10^{22}$ |
| Radius of our galaxy | $6 \times 10^{19}$ |
| Distance to the nearest star (Alpha Centauri) | $4.3 \times 10^{16}$ |
| Mean orbit radius for the most distant planet (Pluto) | $5.9 \times 10^{12}$ |
| Radius of the sun | $6.9 \times 10^{8}$ |
| Radius of the earth | $6.4 \times 10^{6}$ |
| Highest free balloon ascension (1959) | $4.6 \times 10^{4}$ |
| Height of a man | $1.8 \times 10^{0}$ |
| Thickness of this book (Part I) | $4 \times 10^{-2}$ |
| Thickness of a page in this book | $1 \times 10^{-4}$ |
| Size of a poliomyelitis virus | $1.2 \times 10^{-8}$ |
| Radius of a hydrogen atom | $5.0 \times 10^{-11}$ |
| Effective radius of a proton | $1.2 \times 10^{-15}$ |

[1] *quasar* = quasi-stellar radio source.

frame, a so-called absolute frame, existed that had some fundamental advantage over all other frames. For an observer at rest in such a frame physical quantities would have their "true" or "absolute" values. This viewpoint has now been abandoned because, over many decades, experimental efforts to find this absolute reference frame have failed completely.

Consider reference frames moving with uniform velocity with respect to each other and with respect to the fixed stars. Such (unaccelerated, nonrotating) reference frames are called *inertial reference frames.* Experiment shows that all inertial reference frames are equivalent for the measurement of physical phenomena. Observers in different frames may obtain different numerical values for measured physical quantities, but *the relationships between the measured quantities, that is, the laws of physics, will be the same for all observers.*

Suppose, for example, that observers in different inertial frames measure the momenta of the particles involved in an atomic collision. They will obtain different numerical values both for the momenta of the individual particles and for the total momentum of the system of particles. Each observer, however, will note that the total momentum of the system of particles, whatever value he measured it to be, is the same after the collision as before. In other words, each observer will note that the collision obeys the *law of conservation of momentum;* we shall discuss this law in detail in Chapter 9.

Although physical laws are the same in all reference frames, the measured values of the physical quantities, as we have seen, may not be. It is important, therefore, that the student always realize what his reference frame is in a particular problem.

## 1–4  Standard of Length*

The first truly international standard of length was a bar of a platinum-iridium alloy called the *standard meter*, kept at the International Bureau of Weights and Measures near Paris, France. The distance between two fine lines engraved on gold plugs near the ends of the bar (when the bar was at 0.00° C and supported mechanically in a prescribed way) was defined to be *one meter*. Historically, the meter was intended to be a convenient fraction (one ten-millionth) of a distance from pole to equator along the meridian line through Paris. However, accurate measurements taken after the standard meter bar was constructed show that it differs slightly (about 0.023%) from its intended value.

Because the standard meter was not very accessible, accurate master copies of it were made and sent to standardizing laboratories throughout the civilized world. These secondary standards were used to calibrate other, still more accessible, measuring rods. Thus until recently every ruler, micrometer, or vernier caliper derived its legal authority from the standard meter through a complicated chain of comparisons using microscopes and dividing engines. This statement was also true for the *yard* used in English-speaking countries. Since 1959 one yard has been defined, by international agreement, to be

$$1 \text{ yard} = 0.9144 \text{ meter, exactly,}$$

which is equivalent to

$$1 \text{ in.} = 2.54 \text{ cm, exactly.}$$

There are several objections to the meter bar as the primary standard of length: It is potentially destructible, by fire or war, for example; it is not accurately reproducible; it is not very accessible. Most important, the accuracy with which the necessary intercomparisons of length can be made by the technique of comparing fine scratches, using a microscope, is no longer great enough to meet modern requirements of science and technology. The maximum accuracy obtainable with the standard meter as a reference is about 1 part in $10^7$; an error of this amount in the borehole of a guidance gyroscope could cause a space shot aimed at the moon to miss by a thousand miles.

The suggestion that the length of a light wave be used as a length standard was first made in 1864 by Hippolyte Louis Fizeau (1819–1896). The later development of the *interferometer* (see Chapter 43) provided scientists with a precision optical device in which light waves can be used as a length

---

* See "The Metre" by H. Barrell, in *Contemporary Physics*, Vol. 3, p. 415, 1962, for an excellent discussion of the standard of length.

**Fig. 1–1** A Kr⁸⁶ light source shown removed from the container in which it is housed. In operation the lamp is cooled with liquid nitrogen. (Courtesy the National Physical Laboratories, Teddington, England. Crown copyright reserved.)

comparison probe. Light waves are about $5 \times 10^{-5}$ cm long and length measurements of bars some centimeters long can be made to a very small fraction of a wavelength. An accuracy of 1 part in $10^9$ in the intercomparison of lengths using light waves is inherently possible. As the need for this increased accuracy in length comparisons arose, efforts were made to determine the best light source.

In 1961 an atomic standard of length was adopted by international agreement. The wavelength in vacuum of a particular orange radiation (identified by the spectroscopic notation $2p_{10} - 5d_5$) emitted by atoms of a particular isotope of krypton (Kr⁸⁶) in an electrical discharge was chosen. Specifically, one meter is now defined to be 1,650,763.73 wavelengths of this light. This number of wavelengths was arrived at by carefully measuring the length of the standard meter bar in terms of these light waves. This comparison was done so that the new standard, based on the wave length of light, would be as consistent as possible with the old standard, based on the meter bar. Figure 1–1 shows a krypton-86 light source, used as the basis of the length standard. The choice of an atomic standard offers advantages other than increased precision in length measurements. The atoms that generate light are available everywhere and all atoms of a given species are identical and emit light of the same wavelength. Hence such an atomic standard is both accessible and invariable. The particular wavelength chosen is uniquely characteristic of krypton-86 and is very sharply defined. This isotope can be obtained with great purity relatively easily and cheaply.

## 1–5 Standard of Time

The measurement of time has two different aspects. For civil and for some scientific purposes, we want to know the time of day so that we can order events in sequence. In most scientific work, we want to know how long an event lasts. Alternatively, if we are dealing with an oscillating system such as a microwave oscillator or an acoustic resonator, we want to know its frequency of oscillation. Thus any time standard must be able to answer both the question "What time is it?" and the two related questions "How long does it last?" or "What is its frequency?"* Table 1–2 shows the wide range of time intervals that can be measured.

Any phenomenon that repeats itself can be used as a measure of time;

---

* See "Accurate Measurement of Time" by Louis Essen, in *Physics Today*, July 1960, for an excellent discussion of the standard of time.

### Table 1–2

### SOME MEASURED TIME INTERVALS

|  | Seconds |
|---|---|
| Age of the earth | $1.3 \times 10^{17}$ |
| Age of the pyramid of Cheops | $1.5 \times 10^{11}$ |
| Human life expectancy (USA) | $2 \times 10^{9}$ |
| Time of earth's orbit around the sun (1 year) | $3.1 \times 10^{7}$ |
| Time of earth's rotation about its axis (1 day) | $8.6 \times 10^{4}$ |
| Period of the Echo II satellite | $5.1 \times 10^{3}$ |
| Half-life of the free neutron | $7.0 \times 10^{2}$ |
| Time between normal heartbeats | $8.0 \times 10^{-1}$ |
| Period of concert-A tuning fork | $2.3 \times 10^{-3}$ |
| Half-life of the muon | $2.2 \times 10^{-6}$ |
| Period of oscillation of 3-cm microwaves | $1.0 \times 10^{-10}$ |
| Typical period of rotation of a molecule | $1 \times 10^{-12}$ |
| Half-life of the neutral pion | $2.2 \times 10^{-16}$ |
| Period of oscillation of a 1-Mev gamma ray (calculated) | $4 \times 10^{-21}$ |
| Time for a fast elementary particle to pass through a medium-sized nucleus (calculated) | $2 \times 10^{-23}$ |

the measurement consists of counting the repetitions. An oscillating pendulum, coiled spring, or quartz crystal can be used, for example. Of the many repetitive phenomena occurring in nature, the rotation of the earth on its axis, which determines the length of the day, has been used as a time standard from earliest times. It is still the basis of our civil and legal time standard, one (mean solar) second being defined to be 1/86,400 of a (mean solar) day. Time defined in terms of the rotation of the earth is called *universal time* (*UT*).

In 1956, for reasons that will follow, the International Congress of Weights and Measures redefined the second, for scientific purposes requiring high precision, in terms of the earth's orbital motion about the sun. More particularly, they defined the second to be the fraction 1/31,556,925.9747 of the tropical year 1900; the selection of a particular earth orbit in the definition automatically makes the time standard *invariable*. Time defined in terms of the earth's orbital motion is called *ephemeris time* (*ET*).

Both *UT* and *ET* must be determined by astronomical observations. Since these observations must be extended over several weeks (for *UT*) or several years (for *ET*), a good secondary terrestrial clock, calibrated by the astronomical observations, is needed. *Quartz crystal clocks*, based on the electrically sustained natural periodic vibrations of a quartz wafer, serve

**Fig. 1–2** This cesium atomic clock at the Boulder Laboratories of the National Bureau of Standards measures frequency and time intervals to an accuracy equivalent to the loss of less than 1 sec in 3000 years.

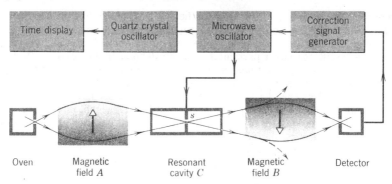

Oven      Magnetic          Resonant      Magnetic          Detector
          field A           cavity C      field B

**Fig. 1-3**  A schematic diagram of a cesium atomic clock. The vertical arrows in the shaded magnetic field areas point from the strong field to the weak field region of the (nonuniform) magnetic field, as the variable shading also suggests.

well as secondary time standards.   The best of these have kept time for a year with a maximum error of 0.02 sec.

One of the most common uses of a time standard is the determination of frequencies.   In the radio range, frequency comparisons to a quartz clock can be made electronically to a precision of at least 1 part in $10^{10}$ and, indeed, many situations require such precision.   However, this precision is about one hundred times greater than that with which a quartz clock itself can be calibrated by astronomical observations.   To meet the need for a better time standard, *atomic clocks* have been developed in several countries, using periodic atomic vibrations as a standard.

A particular type of atomic clock, based on a characteristic frequency associated with the cesium atom, has been in continuous operation at the National Physical Laboratory in England since 1955.   Figure 1-2 shows a similar clock at the U. S. Bureau of Standards.

A cesium atom behaves like a tiny magnet.   It experiences a sideways deflection as it moves through a nonuniform magnetic field; the amount and the direction of the deflection depend on the strength of this magnet and on the orientation of the axis of the magnet in this field.

In a cesium atomic clock, the oven in Fig. 1-3 serves as a source of cesium atoms, which enter and are deflected by nonuniform magnetic field A. The atoms then pass through slit S located in the center of a resonating cavity C and enter nonuniform magnetic field B.   If no change in the effective magnetic strength of the atoms occurs while they pass through the cavity, the field B just cancels out the deflections produced by field A and the moving atoms strike the detector.

If the cavity C is filled with radiation produced by a microwave oscillator and *if this radiation has a sharply defined critical frequency $\nu_{Cs}$*, the cesium atoms may change their effective magnetic strength as they pass through the cavity.*   If

---

* An atom can exist in a number of discrete configurations, or stationary states, each with a well-defined energy.   The atom can be induced to change from one of these states to another by irradiating it with, or by stimulating it to emit, light waves or other radiations with certain sharply defined frequencies.   Radiations with frequencies that do not belong to this discrete set will, in general, have no effect.   When such transitions between configurations occur, many properties of the atom, among them its effective magnetic strength, may change.

this occurs, the deflection of the atoms in field $B$ will change (see dashed lines) and the atomic beam will no longer strike the detector. Thus the atomic beam apparatus in Fig. 1–3 can be regarded as a sensitive device for determining whether the microwave oscillator has a particular, sharply defined frequency $\nu_{Cs}$. Indeed, it can be arranged that variations in the output of detector can be sent as correction signals to the microwave oscillator to insure that its frequency is always accurately maintained at the characteristic value $\nu_{Cs}$. This oscillator can, in turn, be used to control the frequency of a quartz crystal clock which, in its turn, can be made to control the motion of the hands of a standard clock or to provide other, more convenient timing signals.

The cesium atoms in the apparatus of Fig. 1–3 act like a pendulum in a pendulum clock; in each case, we have a characteristic frequency that is used to control a time-keeping device.

The fundamental atomic frequency $\nu_{Cs}$ on which the cesium clock is based has been measured in terms of the standard second defined in terms of the earth's orbital motion as: $\nu_{Cs} = 9{,}192{,}631{,}700 \pm 20$ vibrations/sec of ephemeris time, the particular earth orbit being the tropical year 1957.

Figure 1–4 shows, by comparison with the cesium clock, variations in the rate of rotation of the earth over nearly a three-year period. Note that the earth's rotation rate is high in summer and low in winter (northern hemisphere) and exhibits a steady decrease from year to year. It is because of this variability of the earth's rotation, pointed up so sharply in Fig. 1–4 but also known from astronomical observations, that $UT$ was replaced by $ET$ for precise scientific work.

In connection with Fig. 1–4, it is legitimate to ask how we can be sure that the rotating earth and not the cesium clock is "at fault." There are two answers. (1) The relative simplicity of the atom compared to the earth leads us to ascribe any differences between the two as timekeepers to physical phenomena on the earth. Tidal friction between the water and the land, for example, causes a slowing down of the earth's rotation. Also the seasonal motion of the winds introduces a regular seasonal variation in the rotation. Other variations may be associated with the melting of polar icecaps and shifts of other earth masses. (2) The solar system contains other timekeepers, such as the orbiting planets and the orbiting moons of the planets; the rotation of the earth shows variations with respect to these, too, which are similar to, but less accurately observable than, the variation exhibited in Fig. 1–4.

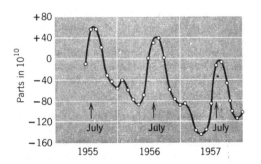

**Fig. 1–4** Variation in the rate of rotation of the earth as revealed by comparison with a cesium clock. (Adapted from L. Essen, *Physics Today*, July 1960.)

The time standard can be made available at remote locations by radio transmission. Many countries maintain radio stations for this purpose. Station WWV, located in Beltsville, Maryland, and operated by the National Bureau of Standards, is one of these. It broadcasts on carrier frequencies of 2.5, 5, 10, 15, and 25 $\times$ $10^6$ cycles/sec, stabilized to 1 part in $10^{10}$ by comparison to a cesium clock. At 5-min intervals, WWV alternately broadcasts an accurate 440-cycle/sec tone (concert $A$) and a 600-cycle/sec tone. Ten times per hour it broadcasts time signals, using a binary digit coding system; the signals are based on the earth's rotation, that is, they refer to universal time. Corrections are made for the wandering of the earth's axis and the annual variation in the earth's rotational speed.

In 1964, the second based on the cesium clock was *temporarily* adopted as an international standard by the Twelfth General Conference of Weights and Measures meeting in Paris. The action increases the accuracy of time measurements to 1 part in $10^{11}$, an improvement over the accuracy associated with astronomical methods of about 200. If two cesium clocks are operated at this precision, and if there are no other sources of error, the clocks will differ by only one second after running 5000 years.

Atomic clocks are still in a phase of rapid development as of 1965 and it is for this reason that the "cesium second" was adopted only temporarily. For example, the hydrogen maser gives promise of producing a clock with an error of only one second in 33,000,000 years.

## 1-6   Systems of Units

As already pointed out, there is a certain amount of arbitrariness in the choice of the fundamental quantities.* For example, length, time, and mass can be chosen as fundamental quantities; all other mechanical quantities, such as force, torque, density, etc., can be expressed in terms of these fundamental quantities. However, we might equally well choose force instead of mass as a fundamental quantity. However, having picked the fundamental quantities and determined units for them, we thereby automatically determine the units of the derived quantities.

Three different systems of units are most commonly used in science and engineering. They are the *meter-kilogram-second* or mks system, the Gaussian system, in which the fundamental mechanical units are the centimeter, the *gram*, and the *second* (a cgs system), and the British engineering system (a *foot-pound-second* or fps system). The gram and kilogram are mass units, and the pound is a force unit; these will be defined and discussed in Chapter 5.

We shall use the mks system principally throughout the text, except in mechanics where the fps system will also be used. The metric system is used universally in scientific work and provides the common units of commerce in most countries of the world.

* See "Dimensions, Units, and Standards" by A. G. McNish, in *Physics Today*, April 1957.

**Table 1–3**

PREFIXES USED FOR MULTIPLES AND SUBMULTIPLES
OF METRIC QUANTITIES

| $10^{-1}$ | deci- | deca- | $10^{1}$ |
|---|---|---|---|
| $10^{-2}$ | centi- | hecto- | $10^{2}$ |
| $10^{-3}$ | milli- | kilo- | $10^{3}$ |
| $10^{-6}$ | micro- | mega- | $10^{6}$ |
| $10^{-9}$ | nano- | giga- | $10^{9}$ |
| $10^{-12}$ | pico- | tera- | $10^{12}$ |

Some prefixes used to identify multiples and submultiples of metric quantities are shown in Table 1–3. Thus 1 millimeter = $10^{-3}$ meter, 1 nanosecond = $10^{-9}$ sec, 1 megavolt = $10^{6}$ volt, etc.

Much of the literature of physics is written in the Gaussian system. The student of physics must become familiar with several systems of units and must develop a facility for their manipulation. Appendix L shows how the equations of physics, given in this book in the form appropriate to the mks system, may be written in the form suitable to the Gaussian system; it also provides a Gaussian units table and gives their mks equivalents. The laws of physics, which express relations among observable physical quantities, are unchanged in physical content and significance, however, no matter what unit system is chosen to express them.

## QUESTIONS

**1.** Do you think that a definition of a physical quantity for which no method of measurement is known or given has meaning?

**2.** According to operational philosophy, if we cannot prescribe a feasible operation for determining a physical quantity, the quantity is undetectable by physical means and should be given up as having no physical reality. Not all scientists accept this view. What are the merits and drawbacks of this point of view in your opinion?

**3.** What characteristics, other than accessibility and invariability, would you consider desirable for a physical standard?

**4.** If someone told you that every dimension of every object had shrunk to half its former value overnight, how could you refute his statement?

**5.** How would you criticize the following statement: "Once you have picked a physical standard, by the very meaning of standard it is invariable?"

**6.** What does an observer on the earth mean by "up" and "down"? Do all such observers use the same reference frame? How could one make the meaning clearly understood to *any* observer?

**7.** Why was it necessary to specify the temperature at which comparisons with the standard meter bar were to be made? Can length be called a fundamental quantity if another physical quantity, such as temperature, must be specified in choosing a standard?

**8.** Can length be measured along a curved line? If so, how?

**9.** Can you suggest a way to measure (a) the radius of the earth; (b) the distance between the sun and the earth; (c) the radius of the sun?

**10.** Can you suggest a way to measure (a) the thickness of a sheet of paper; (b) the thickness of a soap bubble film; (c) the diameter of an atom?

**11.** What criteria should a good clock satisfy?

**12.** Name several repetitive phenomena occurring in nature which could serve as reasonable time standards.

**13.** The time it takes the moon to return to a given position as seen against the background of the fixed stars is called a siderial month. The time interval between identical phases of the moon is called a lunar month. The lunar month is longer than a siderial month. Why?

**14.** When man colonizes other planets, what drawbacks would our present standards of length and time have? What drawbacks would atomic standards have?

**15.** Can you think of a way to define a length standard in terms of a time standard or vice versa? (Think about a pendulum clock.) If so, can length and time both be considered as fundamental quantities?

## PROBLEMS

**1.** Express your height in the metric system of units.

**2.** In track meets both 100 yards and 100 meters are used as distances for dashes. Which is longer? By how many meters is it longer? By how many feet?

**3.** A rocket attained a height of 300 kilometers. What is this distance in miles?

**4.** Machine-tool men would like to have master gauges (1 in. long, say) good to 0.0000001 in. Show that the platinum-iridium meter is not measurable to this accuracy but that the krypton-86 meter is. Use data given in this chapter.

**5.** Assume that the average distance of the sun from the earth is 400 times the average distance of the moon from the earth. Now consider a total eclipse of the sun and state conclusions that can be drawn about (a) the relation between the sun's diameter and the moon's diameter; (b) the relative volumes of sun and moon. List the assumptions made in arriving at these answers. (c) Find the angle intercepted at the eye by a dime that just eclipses the full moon and from this experimental result and the given distance between sun and earth, estimate the diameter of the moon.

**6.** Astronomical distances are so large compared to terrestrial ones that much larger units of length are used for easy comprehension of the relative distances of astronomical objects. An *astronomical unit* (AU) is equal to the average distance from the earth to the sun, about $92.9 \times 10^6$ miles. A *parsec* is the distance at which one astronomical unit would subtend an angle of 1 sec of arc. A *light year* is the distance that light, traveling through a vacuum with a speed of 186,000 miles/sec, would cover in one year. (a) Express the distance from earth to sun in parsecs and in light years. (b) Express a light year and a parsec in miles.

**7.** Assuming that the length of the day uniformly increases by 0.001 sec in a century, calculate the cumulative effect on the measure of time over twenty centuries. Such a slowing down of the earth's rotation is indicated by observations of the occurrences of solar eclipses during this period.

**8.** (a) A unit of time sometimes used in microscopic physics is the *shake*. One shake equals $10^{-8}$ sec. Are there more shakes in a second than there are seconds in a year? (b) Mankind has existed for about $10^6$ years, whereas the universe is about $10^{10}$ years old. If the age of the universe is taken to be one day, for how many seconds has mankind existed?

**9.** (a) The radius of the proton is about $10^{-15}$ meter; the radius of the observable universe is about $10^{28}$ cm. Identify a physically meaningful distance which is approximately halfway between these two extremes on a logarithmic scale. (b) The mean life of a neutral pion (an elementary particle) is about $2 \times 10^{-16}$ sec. The age of the universe is about $4 \times 10^9$ years. Identify a physically meaningful time interval that is approximately halfway between these two extremes on a logarithmic scale.

**10.** From Fig. 1-4, calculate by what length of time the earth's rotation period in midsummer differs from that in the following spring.

**11.** A naval destroyer is testing five clocks. Exactly at noon, as determined by the WWV time signal, on the successive days of a week the clocks read as follows:

| Clock | Sun. | Mon. | Tues. | Wed. | Thurs. | Fri. | Sat. |
|-------|------|------|-------|------|--------|------|------|
| A | 12:36:40 | 12:36:56 | 12:37:12 | 12:37:27 | 12:37:44 | 12:37:59 | 12:38:14 |
| B | 11:59:59 | 12:00:02 | 11:59:57 | 12:00:07 | 12:00:02 | 11:59:56 | 12:00:03 |
| C | 15:50:45 | 15:51:43 | 15:52:41 | 15:53:39 | 15:54:37 | 15:55:35 | 15:56:33 |
| D | 12:03:59 | 12:02:52 | 12:01:45 | 12:00:38 | 11:59:31 | 11:58:24 | 11:57:17 |
| E | 12:03:59 | 12:02:49 | 12:01:54 | 12:01:52 | 12:01:32 | 12:01:22 | 12:01:12 |

How would you arrange these five clocks in the order of their relative value as good timekeepers? Justify your choice.

# Vectors

## CHAPTER 2

## 2–1  Vectors and Scalars

A change of position of a particle is called a *displacement*.  If a particle moves from position $A$ to position $B$ (Fig. 2–1a), we can represent its displacement by drawing a line from $A$ to $B$; the direction of displacement can be shown by putting an arrowhead at $B$ indicating that the displacement was *from $A$ to $B$*.  The path of the particle need not necessarily be a straight line from $A$ to $B$; the arrow represents only the net effect of the motion, not the actual motion.

In Fig. 2–1b, for example, we plot a path followed by a particle from $A$ to $B$.  The path is not the same as the displacement $AB$.  If we were to take snapshots of the particle when it was at $A$ and, later, when it was at some intermediate position $P$, we could obtain the displacement vector $AP$, representing the net effect of the motion during this interval, even though we would not know the actual path taken between these points.  Furthermore, a displacement such as $A'B'$ (Fig. 2–1a), which is parallel to $AB$, similarly directed, and equal in length to $AB$, represents the same *change* in position as $AB$.  We make no distinction between these two displacements.  A displacement is therefore characterized by a *length* and a *direction*.

In a similar way, we can represent a subsequent displacement from $B$ to $C$ (Fig. 2–1c).  The net effect of the two displacements will be the same as a displacement from $A$ to $C$.  We speak then of $AC$ as the *sum* or *resultant* of the displacements $AB$ and $BC$.  Notice that this sum is not an algebraic sum and that a number alone cannot uniquely specify it.

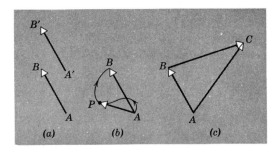

(a)          (b)          (c)

**Fig. 2–1**  Displacement vectors.  (a) Vectors $AB$ and $A'B'$ are identical since they have the same length and point in the same direction.  (b) The actual *path* of the particle in moving from $A$ to $B$ may be the curve shown; the *displacement* remains the vector $AB$. At some intermediate point $P$ the displacement from $A$ is the vector $AP$.  (c) After displacement $AB$ the particle undergoes another displacement $BC$. The net effect of the two displacements is represented by the vector $AC$.

Quantities that behave like displacements are called *vectors.** Vectors, then, are quantities that have both magnitude and direction and combine according to certain rules of addition. These rules are stated below. The displacement vector can be considered as the prototype. Some other physical quantities which are vectors are force, velocity, acceleration, electric field strength, and magnetic induction. Many of the laws of physics can be expressed in compact form using vectors; derivations involving these laws are often greatly simplified if this is done.

Quantities that can be completely specified by a number and unit and that therefore have magnitude only are called *scalars*. Some physical quantities which are scalars are mass, length, time, density, energy, and temperature. Scalars can be manipulated by the rules of ordinary algebra.

**2–2  Addition of Vectors, Geometrical Method**

To represent a vector on a diagram we draw an arrow. We choose the length of the arrow proportional to the magnitude of the vector (that is, we choose a scale), and we choose the direction of the arrow to be the direction of the vector, with the arrowhead giving the sense of the direction. For example, a displacement of 40 ft north of east on a scale of 1.0 in. per 10 ft would be represented by an arrow 4.0 in. long, drawn at an angle of 45° to the horizontal direction with the arrowhead at the top right extreme. A vector such as this is represented conveniently in printing by a boldface symbol such as **d**. In handwriting it is convenient to put an arrow above the symbol to denote a vector quantity, such as $\vec{d}$.

---

\* The word *vector* comes from the Latin and means *carrier*, which suggests a displacement. A good general reference on vectors is *Vector and Tensor Analysis* by G. E. Hay, Dover Publications, 1953.

Often we shall be interested only in the magnitude of the vector and not in its direction. The magnitude of **d** may be written as $|\mathbf{d}|$, called the absolute value of **d**; more frequently we represent the magnitude alone by the italic letter symbol, such as $d$. The boldface symbol is meant to signify both properties of the vector, magnitude and direction.

Consider now Fig. 2-2 in which we have redrawn and relabeled the vectors of Fig. 2-1c. The relation among these displacements (vectors) can be written as

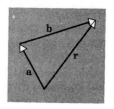

**Fig. 2-2** The vector sum **a** + **b** = **r**. Compare with Fig. 2-1c.

$$\mathbf{a} + \mathbf{b} = \mathbf{r}. \qquad (2\text{-}1)$$

The rules to be followed in performing this (vector) addition geometrically are these: On a diagram drawn to scale lay out the displacement vector **a**; then draw **b** with its tail at the head of **a**, and draw a line from the tail of **a** to the head of **b** to construct the vector sum **r**. This is a displacement equivalent in length and direction to the successive displacements **a** and **b**. This procedure can be generalized to obtain the sum of any number of successive displacements.

Since vectors are new quantities, we must expect new rules for their manipulation. The symbol "+" in Eq. 2-1 simply has a different meaning from arithmetic or ordinary algebra. It tells us to carry out a different set of operations.

Using Fig. 2-3 we can prove two important properties of vector addition:

$$\mathbf{a} + \mathbf{b} = \mathbf{b} + \mathbf{a}, \qquad \text{(commutative law)} \qquad (2\text{-}2)$$

and

$$\mathbf{d} + (\mathbf{e} + \mathbf{f}) = (\mathbf{d} + \mathbf{e}) + \mathbf{f}. \qquad \text{(associative law)} \qquad (2\text{-}3)$$

These laws assert that it makes no difference in what order or in what grouping we add vectors; the sum is the same. In this respect, vector addition and scalar addition follow the same rules.

The operation of subtraction can be included in our vector algebra by defining the negative of a vector to be another vector of equal magnitude

**Fig. 2-3** (a) The commutative law for vector sums, which states that **a** + **b** = **b** + **a**. (b) The associative law, which states that **d** + **e** + **f**.

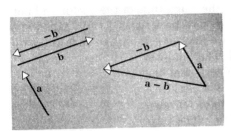

Fig. 2-4   The vector difference $\mathbf{a} - \mathbf{b}$
$= \mathbf{a} + (-\mathbf{b})$.

but opposite direction.   Then

$$\mathbf{a} - \mathbf{b} = \mathbf{a} + (-\mathbf{b}) \qquad\qquad (2\text{-}4)$$

as shown in Fig. 2-4.

Remember that, although we have used displacements to illustrate these operations, the rules apply to *all* vector quantities.

## 2-3   Resolution and Addition of Vectors, Analytic Method

The geometrical method of adding vectors is not very useful for vectors in three dimensions; often it is even inconvenient for the two-dimensional case.   Another way of adding vectors is the analytical method, involving the resolution of a vector into components with respect to a particular coordinate system.

Figure 2-5a shows a vector $\mathbf{a}$ whose tail has been placed at the origin of a rectangular coordinate system.   If we drop perpendicular lines from the head of $\mathbf{a}$ to the axes the quantities $a_x$ and $a_y$ so formed are called the *components* of the vector $\mathbf{a}$.   The process is called *resolving a vector into its components*.   Figure 2-5 shows a two-dimensional case for convenience; the extension of our conclusions to three dimensions will be clear.

A vector may have many sets of components.   For example, if we rotate the $x$-axis and $y$-axis in Fig. 2-5a by 10° counterclockwise, the components of $\mathbf{a}$ would be different.   Furthermore, we may use a nonrectangular coordinate system, that is, the angle between the two axes need not be 90°. Thus the components of a vector are only uniquely specified if we specify

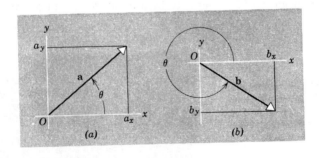

Fig. 2-5   Two examples of the resolution of a vector into its scalar components in a particular coordinate system.

the particular coordinate system being used. The vector need not be drawn with its tail at the origin of the coordinate system to find its components—although we have done so for convenience; the vector may be moved anywhere in the coordinate space and, as long as its angles with the coordinate directions are maintained, its components will be unchanged.

The components $a_x$ and $a_y$ in Fig. 2–5a are found readily from

$$a_x = a \cos \theta \quad \text{and} \quad a_y = a \sin \theta, \quad (2\text{–}5)$$

where $\theta$ is the angle that the vector **a** makes with the positive $x$-axis, measured counterclockwise from this axis. Note that, depending on the angle $\theta$, $a_x$ and $a_y$ can be positive or negative. For example, in Fig. 2–5b, $b_y$ is negative and $b_x$ is positive. The components of a vector behave like scalar quantities because, in any particular coordinate system of a given reference frame, only a number, with an algebraic sign, is needed to specify them.

Once a vector is resolved into its components, the components themselves can be used to specify the vector. Instead of the two numbers $a$ (magnitude of the vector) and $\theta$ (direction of the vector relative to the $x$-axis), we now have the two numbers $a_x$ and $a_y$. We can pass back and forth between the description of a vector in terms of its components $a_x$, $a_y$ and the equivalent description in terms of magnitude and direction $a$ and $\theta$. To obtain $a$ and $\theta$ from $a_x$ and $a_y$, we note from Fig. 2–5a that

$$a = \sqrt{a_x^2 + a_y^2} \quad (2\text{–}6a)$$

and

$$\tan \theta = a_y/a_x. \quad (2\text{–}6b)$$

The quadrant in which $\theta$ lies is determined from the sign of $a_x$ and $a_y$.

When resolving a vector into components it is sometimes useful to introduce a vector of unit length in a given direction. Thus vector **a** in Fig. 2–6a may be written, for example, as

$$\mathbf{a} = \mathbf{u}_a a, \quad (2\text{–}7)$$

where $\mathbf{u}_a$ is a *unit vector* in the direction of **a**. Often it is convenient to draw unit vectors along the particular coordinate axes chosen. In the rectangular coordinate system the special symbols **i**, **j**, and **k** are usually

**Fig. 2–6** (a) The vector **a** may be written as $\mathbf{u}_a a$ in which $\mathbf{u}_a$ is a unit vector in the direction of **a**. (b) The unit vectors **i**, **j**, and **k**, used to specify the positive $x$-, $y$-. and *y-directions respectively.*

(a)                    (b)

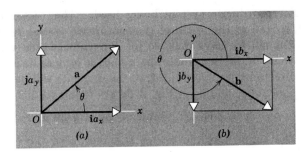

**Fig. 2–7** Two examples of the resolution of a vector into its vector components in a particular coordinate system; compare with Fig. 2-5.

used for unit vectors in the positive $x$-, $y$-, and $z$-directions, respectively; see Fig. 2–6$b$. Note that $\mathbf{i}$, $\mathbf{j}$, and $\mathbf{k}$ need not be located at the origin. Like all vectors, they can be translated anywhere in the coordinate space as long as their directions with respect to the coordinate axes are not changed.

The vectors $\mathbf{a}$ and $\mathbf{b}$ of Fig. 2–5 may be written in terms of their components and the unit vectors as

$$\mathbf{a} = \mathbf{i}a_x + \mathbf{j}a_y \tag{2-8a}$$

and

$$\mathbf{b} = \mathbf{i}b_x + \mathbf{j}b_y; \tag{2-8b}$$

see Fig. 2–7. The vector relation Eq. 2–8$a$ is equivalent to the scalar relation Eq. 2–6; each relates the vector ($\mathbf{a}$, or $a$ and $\theta$) to its components ($a_x$ and $a_y$). Sometimes we will call quantities such as $\mathbf{i}a_x$ and $\mathbf{j}a_y$ in Eq. 2–8$a$ the *vector components* of $\mathbf{a}$; they are drawn as vectors in Fig. 2–7$a$. The word *component* alone will continue to refer to the scalar quantities $a_x$ and $a_y$.

We now consider the addition of vectors by the analytical method. Let $\mathbf{r}$ be the sum of the two vectors $\mathbf{a}$ and $\mathbf{b}$ lying in the $x$-$y$ plane, so that

$$\mathbf{r} = \mathbf{a} + \mathbf{b}. \tag{2-9}$$

In a given coordinate system, two vectors such as $\mathbf{r}$ and $\mathbf{a} + \mathbf{b}$ can only be equal if their corresponding components are equal, or

$$r_x = a_x + b_x \tag{2-10a}$$

and

$$r_y = a_y + b_y. \tag{2-10b}$$

These two algebraic equations, taken together, are equivalent to the single vector relation Eq. 2–9. From Eqs. 2–6 we may find $r$ and the angle $\theta$ that $\mathbf{r}$ makes with the $x$-axis; that is,

$$r = \sqrt{r_x{}^2 + r_y{}^2}$$

and

$$\tan \theta = r_y/r_x.$$

Thus we have the following analytic rule for adding vectors: Resolve each vector into its components in a given coordinate system; the algebraic sum of the individual components along a particular axis is the component of the sum vector along that same axis; the sum vector can be reconstructed once its components are known.   This method for adding vectors may be generalized ·to many vectors and to three dimensions (see Problems 6 and 11).

The advantage of the method of breaking up vectors into components, rather than adding directly with the use of suitable trigonometric relations, is that we always deal with right triangles and thus simplify the calculations.

In adding vectors by the analytical method, the choice of coordinate axes determines how simple the process will be.   Sometimes the components of the vectors with respect to a particular set of axes are known to begin with, so that the choice of axes is obvious.   Other times a judicious choice of axes can greatly simplify the job of resolution of the vectors into components.   For example, the axes can be oriented so that at least one of the vectors lies parallel to an axis.

▶ **Example 1.**   An airplane travels 130 miles on a straight course making an angle of 22.5° east of due north.   How far north and how far east did the plane travel from its starting point?

We choose the positive $x$-direction to be east and the positive $y$-direction to be north.   Next (Fig. 2-8) we draw a displacement vector from the origin (starting point), making an angle of 22.5° with the $y$-axis (north) inclined along the positive $x$-direction (east). The length of the vector is chosen to represent a magnitude of 130 miles.   If we call this vector **d**, then $d_x$ gives the distance traveled east of the starting point and $d_y$ gives the distance traveled north of the starting point.   We have

$$\theta = 90.0° - 22.5° = 67.5°,$$

so that (see Eqs. 2–5)

$$d_x = d \cos \theta = (130 \text{ miles}) \cos 67.5° = 50 \text{ miles},$$

and

$$d_y = d \sin \theta = (130 \text{ miles}) \sin 67.5° = 120 \text{ miles}.$$

**Fig. 2–8**   Example 1.

**Example 2.**   An automobile travels due east on a level road for 30 miles.   It then turns due north at an intersection and travels 40 miles before stopping.   Find the resultant displacement of the car.

We choose a reference frame fixed with respect to the earth, with the positive $x$-direction of our coordinate system pointing east and the positive $y$-direction pointing north.   The two successive displacements, **a** and **b**, are then drawn as shown in Fig. 2–9.   The resultant displacement **r** is obtained from **r** = **a** + **b**.

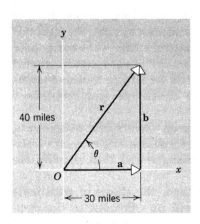

Fig. 2-9    Example 2.

Since **b** has no $x$-component and **a** has no $y$-component, we obtain (see Eqs. 2–10)

$$r_x = a_x + b_x = 30 \text{ miles} + 0 = 30 \text{ miles},$$

$$r_y = a_y + b_y = 0 + 40 \text{ miles} = 40 \text{ miles}.$$

The magnitude and direction of **r** are then (see Eqs. 2–6)

$$r = \sqrt{r_x{}^2 + r_y{}^2} = \sqrt{(30 \text{ miles})^2 + (40 \text{ miles})^2} = 50 \text{ miles},$$

$$\tan \theta = r_y/r_x = \frac{40 \text{ miles}}{30 \text{ miles}} = 1.33 \qquad \theta = \tan^{-1}(1.33) = 53°.$$

The resultant vector displacement **r** has a magnitude of 50 miles and makes an angle of 53° north of east.

**Example 3.**   Three coplanar vectors are expressed, with respect to a certain rectangular coordinate system of a given reference frame, as

$$\mathbf{a} = 4\mathbf{i} - \mathbf{j},$$

$$\mathbf{b} = -3\mathbf{i} + 2\mathbf{j},$$

and
$$\mathbf{c} = -3\mathbf{j},$$

in which the components are given in arbitrary units.   Find the vector **r** which is the sum of these vectors.

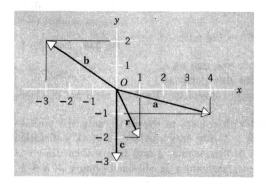

Fig. 2–10   Three vectors, **a**, **b**, and **c**, and their vector *sum* **r**.

From Eqs. 2–10 we have

$$r_x = a_x + b_x + c_x = 4 - 3 + 0 = 1,$$

and

$$r_y = a_y + b_y + c_y = -1 + 2 - 3 + -2.$$

Thus

$$\mathbf{r} = \mathbf{i}r_x + \mathbf{j}r_y$$

$$= \mathbf{i} - 2\mathbf{j}.$$

Figure 2–10 shows the four vectors. From Eqs. 2–6 we can calculate that the magnitude of $\mathbf{r}$ is $\sqrt{5}$ and that the angle that $\mathbf{r}$ makes with the positive $x$-axis, measured counterclockwise from that axis, is

$$\tan^{-1}(-2/1) = 297°. \qquad \blacktriangleleft$$

## 2–4   Multiplication of Vectors*

We have assumed in the previous discussion that the vectors being added together are of like kind; that is, displacement vectors are added to displacement vectors, or velocity vectors are added to velocity vectors. Just as it would be meaningless to add together scalar quantities of different kinds, such as mass and temperature, so it would be meaningless to add together vector quantities of different kinds, such as displacement and electric field strength.

However, like scalars, vectors of different kinds can be multiplied by one another to generate quantities of new physical dimensions. Because vectors have direction as well as magnitude, vector multiplication cannot follow exactly the same rules as the algebraic rules of scalar multiplication. We must establish new rules of multiplication for vectors.

We find it useful to define three kinds of multiplication operations for vectors: (1) multiplication of a vector by a scalar, (2) multiplication of two vectors in such a way as to yield a scalar, and (3) multiplication of two vectors in such a way as to yield another vector. There are still other possibilities, but we shall not consider them here.

The multiplication of a vector by a scalar has a simple meaning: The product of a scalar $k$ and a vector $\mathbf{a}$, written $k\mathbf{a}$, is defined to be a new vector whose magnitude is $k$ times the magnitude of $\mathbf{a}$. The new vector has the same direction as $\mathbf{a}$ if $k$ is positive and the opposite direction if $k$ is negative. To divide a vector by a scalar we simply multiply the vector by the reciprocal of the scalar.

When we multiply a vector quantity by another vector quantity, we must distinguish between the *scalar* (or *dot*) *product* and the *vector* (or *cross*) *product*. The *scalar product* of two vectors $\mathbf{a}$ and $\mathbf{b}$, written as $\mathbf{a} \cdot \mathbf{b}$, is defined to be

$$\mathbf{a} \cdot \mathbf{b} = ab \cos \phi, \qquad (2\text{–}11)$$

---

* The material of this section will be used later in the text. The scalar product is used first in Chapter 7 and the vector product in Chapter 11. The instructor can postpone this section accordingly if he wishes. Its presentation here gives a unified treatment of vector algebra and serves as a convenient reference for later work.

where $a$ is the magnitude of vector **a**, $b$ is the magnitude of vector **b**, and cos $\phi$ is the cosine of the angle $\phi$ between the two vectors* (see Fig. 2–11).

Since $a$ and $b$ are scalars and cos $\phi$ is a pure number, the *scalar product of two vectors is a scalar*. The scalar product of two vectors can be regarded as the product of the magnitude of one vector and the component of the other vector in the direction of the first. Because of the notation **a · b** is also called the dot product of **a** and **b** and is spoken as "a dot b."

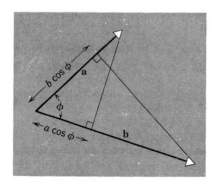

**Fig. 2–11** The scalar product **a · b** (= $a \, b$ cos $\phi$) is the product of the magnitude of either vector ($a$, say) by the component of the other vector in the direction of the first vector ($b$ cos $\phi$, say).

We could have defined **a · b** to be any operation we want, for example, to be $a^{\frac{1}{3}}b^{\frac{1}{3}}$ tan ($\phi/2$), but this would turn out to be of no use to us in physics. With our definition of the scalar product, a number of important physical quantities can be described as the scalar product of two vectors. Some of them are mechanical work, gravitational potential energy, electrical potential, electric power, and electromagnetic energy density. When such quantities are discussed later, their connection with the scalar product of vectors will be pointed out.

The *vector product* of two vectors **a** and **b** is written as **a ✕ b** and is another vector **c**, where **c** = **a ✕ b**. The *magnitude* of **c** is defined by

$$c = ab \sin \phi, \qquad (2\text{--}12)$$

where $\phi$ is the angle between **a** and **b**.

The *direction* of **c**, the vector product of **a** and **b**, is defined to be perpendicular to the plane formed by **a** and **b**. To specify the sense of the vector **c** we must refer to Fig. 2–12. Imagine rotating a right-handed screw whose axis is perpendicular to the plane formed by **a** and **b** so as to turn it *from* **a** *to* **b** through the angle $\phi$ between them. Then the direction of advance of the screw gives the direction of the vector product **a ✕ b** (Fig. 2–12a). Another convenient way to obtain the direction of a vector product is the following. Imagine an axis perpendicular to the plane of **a** and **b** through their origin. Now wrap the fingers of the *right hand* around this axis and push the vector **a** into the vector **b** through the smaller angle between them with the fingertips, keeping the thumb erect; the direction of the erect thumb then gives the direction of the vector product **a ✕ b**

---

* There are two different angles between a pair of vectors, depending on the sense of rotation. We always choose the *smaller* of the two in vector multiplication.

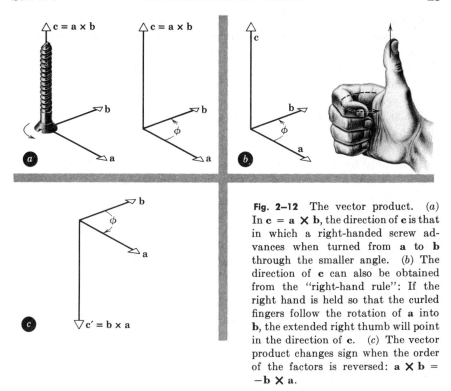

**Fig. 2–12**  The vector product.  (*a*) In **c** = **a** ✕ **b**, the direction of **c** is that in which a right-handed screw advances when turned from **a** to **b** through the smaller angle.  (*b*) The direction of **c** can also be obtained from the "right-hand rule": If the right hand is held so that the curled fingers follow the rotation of **a** into **b**, the extended right thumb will point in the direction of **c**.  (*c*) The vector product changes sign when the order of the factors is reversed: **a** ✕ **b** = −**b** ✕ **a**.

(Fig. 2–12*b*).* Because of the notation, **a** ✕ **b** is also called the cross product of **a** and **b** and is spoken as "**a** cross **b**."

Notice that **b** ✕ **a** is not the same vector as **a** ✕ **b**, so that the order of factors in a vector product is important. This is not true for scalars because the order of factors in algebra or arithmetic does not affect the resulting product. Actually, **a** ✕ **b** = −**b** ✕ **a** (Fig. 2–12*c*). This can be deduced from the fact that the magnitude $ab \sin \phi$ equals the magnitude $ba \sin \phi$, but the direction of **a** ✕ **b** is opposite to that of **b** ✕ **a**; this is so because the right-handed screw advances in one direction when rotated from **a** to **b** through $\phi$ but advances in the opposite direction when rotated from **b** to **a**, through $\phi$. The student can obtain the same result by applying the right-hand rule.

If $\phi$ is 90°, **a**, **b**, and **c** (= **a** ✕ **b**) are all at right angles to one another and give the directions of a three-dimensional right-handed coordinate system.

The reason for defining the vector product in this way is that it proves to be useful in physics. We often encounter physical quantities that are

---

* The procedure described in Fig. 2–12 is a convention. Two vectors such as **a** and **b** form a plane and there are *two* directions that point away from any plane. The one selected (by convention) employs the right hand or a right-hand'd screw; the left hand or a left-handed screw would have led to the other choice for the direction of **a** ✕ **b**.

vectors whose product, defined as above, is a vector quantity having important physical meaning. Some examples of physical quantities that are vector products are torque, angular momentum, the force on a moving charge in a magnetic field, and the flow of electromagnetic energy. When such quantities are discussed later, their connection with the vector product of two vectors will be pointed out.

The scalar product is the simplest product of two vectors. The order of multiplication does not affect the product. The vector product is the next simplest case. Here the order of multiplication does affect the product, but only by a factor of minus one, which implies a direction reversal. Other products of vectors are useful but more involved. For example, a tensor can be generated by multiplying each of the three components of one vector by the three components of another vector. Hence a tensor (of the second rank) has nine numbers associated with it, a vector three, and a scalar only one. Some physical quantities that can be represented by tensors are mechanical and electrical stress, moments and products of inertia, and strain. Still more complex physical quantities are possible. In this book, however, we are concerned only with scalars and vectors.

## 2–5  Vectors and the Laws of Physics

Vectors turn out to be very useful in physics. It will be helpful to look a little more deeply into why this is true. Suppose that we have three vectors **a**, **b**, and **r**, which have components $a_x$, $a_y$, $a_z$; $b_x$, $b_y$, $b_z$; and $r_x$, $r_y$, $r_z$, respectively in a particular coordinate system $xyz$ of our reference frame. Let us suppose further that the three vectors are related so that

$$\mathbf{r} = \mathbf{a} + \mathbf{b}. \tag{2–13}$$

By a simple extension of Eqs. 2–10 this means that

$$r_x = a_x + b_x; \qquad r_y = a_y + b_y; \qquad \text{and} \qquad r_z = a_z + b_z. \tag{2–14}$$

Now consider another coordinate system $x'y'z'$ which has these properties: (1) its origin does not coincide with the origin of the first, or $xyz$, system and (2) its three axes are not parallel to the corresponding axes in the first system. In other words, the second set of coordinates has been both *translated* and *rotated* with respect to the first.

The components of the vectors **a**, **b**, and **r** in the new system would all prove, in general, to be different; we may represent them by $a_{x'}$, $a_{y'}$, $a_{z'}$; $b_{x'}$, $b_{y'}$, $b_{z'}$; and $r_{x'}$, $r_{y'}$, $r_{z'}$, respectively. These new components would be found, however, to be related (see Problem 34) in that

$$r_{x'} = a_{x'} + b_{x'}; \qquad r_{y'} = a_{y'} + b_{y'}; \qquad \text{and} \qquad r_{z'} = a_{z'} + b_{z'}. \tag{2–15}$$

That is, in the new system we would find once again (see Eq. 2–13) that

$$\mathbf{r} = \mathbf{a} + \mathbf{b}.$$

In more formal language: *Relations among vectors*, of which Eq. 2–13 is only one example, *are invariant* (that is, *are unchanged*) *with respect to*

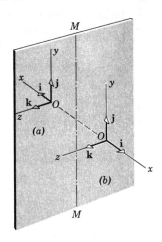

**Fig. 2–13** Showing (a) a left-handed and (b) a right-handed coordinate system. Notice that (a) and (b) are related in that each may be viewed as the image of the other in mirror $MM$. The "handedness" of a coordinate system cannot be changed by rotating it. Note that in (b), $\mathbf{i} \times \mathbf{j} = \mathbf{k}$, whereas in (a), $\mathbf{i} \times \mathbf{j} = -\mathbf{k}$.

*translation or rotation of the coordinates.* Now it is a fact of experience that the experiments on which the laws of physics are based and indeed the *laws of physics* themselves are similarly unchanged in form when we rotate or translate the reference system. Thus the language of vectors is an ideal one in which to express physical laws. If we can express a law in vector form, the invariance of the law for translation and rotation of the coordinate system is assured by this purely geometrical property of vectors.

It was thought until about 1956 that all laws of physics were invariant under another kind of transformation of coordinates, the substitution of a right-handed coordinate system for a left-handed one (see Fig. 2–13). In that year, however, some experiments involving the decay of certain elementary particles were studied in which the result of the experiment *did* turn out to depend on the "handedness" of the coordinate system used to express the results. In other words, the experiment and its image in a mirror would yield different results!* This surprising result led to a re-examination of the whole question of the symmetry of physical laws; as of 1965 these studies remain among the most challenging in modern physics.

## QUESTIONS

**1.** Can two vectors of different magnitude be combined to give a zero resultant? Can three vectors?

**2.** Can a vector be zero if one of its components is not zero?

**3.** Does it make any sense to call a quantity a vector when its magnitude is zero?

**4.** Name several scalar quantities. Is the value of a scalar quantity dependent on the reference frame chosen?

**5.** We can order events in time. For example, event $b$ may precede event $c$ but follow event $a$, giving us a time order of events $a$, $b$, $c$. Hence there is a sense of time, distinguishing past, present, and future. Is time a vector therefore? If not, why not?

---

* C. N. Yang and T. D. Lee were awarded the Nobel prize in 1957 for their theoretical prediction that this would be the case.

6. Do the commutative and associative laws apply to vector subtraction?

7. Can a scalar product be a negative quantity?

## PROBLEMS

1. Two vectors **a** and **b** are added. Show that the magnitude of the resultant cannot be greater than $a + b$ or smaller than $|a - b|$, where the vertical bars signify absolute value.

2. What are the properties of two vectors **a** and **b** such that

(a)            $\mathbf{a} + \mathbf{b} = \mathbf{c}$     and    $a + b = c,$

(b)            $\mathbf{a} + \mathbf{b} = \mathbf{a} - \mathbf{b},$

(c)            $\mathbf{a} + \mathbf{b} = \mathbf{c}$     and    $a^2 + b^2 = c^2.$

3. Consider two displacements, one of magnitude 3 meters and another of magnitude 4 meters. Show how the displacement vectors may be combined to get a resultant displacement of magnitude (a) 7 meters, (b) 1 meter, and (c) 5 meters.

4. Two vectors **a** and **b** have equal magnitudes, say 10 units. They are oriented as shown in Fig. 2–14 and their vector sum is **r**. Find (a) the $x$- and $y$-components of **r**; (b) the magnitude of **r**; and (c) the angle **r** makes with the $x$-axis.

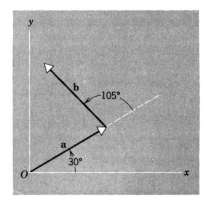

**Fig. 2–14**

5. Given two vectors $\mathbf{a} = 4\mathbf{i} - 3\mathbf{j}$ and $\mathbf{b} = 6\mathbf{i} + 8\mathbf{j}$, find the magnitude and direction of **a**, of **b**, of $\mathbf{a} + \mathbf{b}$, of $\mathbf{b} - \mathbf{a}$, and of $\mathbf{a} - \mathbf{b}$.

6. Generalize the analytical method of resolution and addition to the case of *three or more vectors.*

7. A car is driven eastward for a distance of 50 miles, then northward for 30 miles, and then in a direction 30° east of north for 25 miles. Draw the vector diagram and determine the total displacement of the car from its starting point.

8. A golfer takes three strokes to get his ball into the hole once he is on the green. The first stroke displaces the ball 12 ft north, the second stroke 6.0 ft southeast, and the third stroke 3.0 ft southwest. What displacement was needed to get the ball into the hole on the first stroke?

9. A particle undergoes three successive displacements in a plane, as follows: 4.0 meters southwest, 5.0 meters east, 6.0 meters in a direction 60° north of east. Choose

the $y$-axis pointing north and the $x$-axis pointing east and find (a) the components of each displacement, (b) the components of the resultant displacement, (c) the magnitude and direction of the resultant displacement, and (d) the displacement that would be required to bring the particle back to the starting point.

**10.** Use a scale of 2 meters to the inch and add the displacements of Problem 9 graphically. Determine *from your graph* the magnitude and direction of the resultant.

**11.** Generalize the analytical method of resolving and adding two vectors to *three dimensions*.

**12.** (a) A man leaves his front door, walks 1000 ft east, 2000 ft north, and then takes a penny from his pocket and drops it from a cliff 500 ft high. Set up a coordinate system and write down an expression, using unit vectors, for the displacement of the penny. (b) The man then returns to his front door, following a different path on the return trip. What is his resultant displacement for the round trip?

**13.** Find the sum of the vector displacements **c** and **d** whose components in miles along three perpendicular directions are

$$c_x = 5.0, \; c_y = 0, \; c_z = -2.0; \; d_x = -3.0, \; d_y = 4.0, \; d_z = 6.0.$$

**14.** A vector **d** has a magnitude 2.5 meters and points due north. What are the magnitudes and directions of the vectors

$$(a) \; -\mathbf{d}, \; (b) \; \mathbf{d}/2.0, \; (c) \; -2.5\mathbf{d} \quad \text{and} \quad (d) \; 4.0\mathbf{d}?$$

**15.** A room has the dimensions 10 ft $\times$ 12 ft $\times$ 14 ft. A fly starting at one corner ends up at a diametrically opposite corner. (a) What is the magnitude of its displacement? (b) Could the length of its path be less than this distance? Greater than this distance? Equal to this distance? (c) Choose a suitable coordinate system and find the components of the displacement vector in this frame.

**16.** In Problem 15, if the fly does not fly but crawls, what is the length of the shortest path it can take?

**17.** A man flies from Washington to Manila. Describe the displacement vector. What is its magnitude if the latitude and longitude of the two cities are 39° N, 77° W and 15° N, 121° E?

**18.** Two vectors of lengths a and b make an angle $\theta$ with each other when placed tail to tail. Prove, by taking components along two perpendicular axes, that the length of the resultant vector is

$$r = \sqrt{a^2 + b^2 + 2ab \cos \theta}.$$

**19.** Show for any vector **a** that $\mathbf{a} \cdot \mathbf{a} = a^2$ and that $\mathbf{a} \times \mathbf{a} = 0$.

**20.** Use the standard (right-hand) $xyz$ system of coordinates. Given vector **a** in the $+x$-direction, vector **b** in the $+y$-direction, and the scalar quantity $d$: (a) What is the direction of $\mathbf{a} \times \mathbf{b}$? (b) What is the direction of $\mathbf{b} \times \mathbf{a}$? (c) What is the direction of $\mathbf{b}/d$? (d) What is the magnitude of $\mathbf{a} \cdot \mathbf{b}$?

**21.** A vector **a** of magnitude ten units and another vector **b** of magnitude six units point in directions differing by 60°. Find (a) the scalar product of the two vectors and (b) the vector product of the two vectors.

**22.** In the coordinate system of Fig. 2–6b show that

$$\mathbf{i} \cdot \mathbf{i} = \mathbf{j} \cdot \mathbf{j} = \mathbf{k} \cdot \mathbf{k} = 1$$

and

$$\mathbf{i} \cdot \mathbf{j} = \mathbf{j} \cdot \mathbf{k} = \mathbf{k} \cdot \mathbf{i} = 0.$$

**23.** In the right-handed coordinate system of Fig. 2–6b show that

$$\mathbf{i} \times \mathbf{i} = \mathbf{j} \times \mathbf{j} = \mathbf{k} \times \mathbf{k} = 0$$

$$\mathbf{i} \times \mathbf{j} = \mathbf{k}; \quad \mathbf{k} \times \mathbf{i} = \mathbf{j}; \quad \mathbf{j} \times \mathbf{k} = \mathbf{i}.$$

**24.** (*a*) We have seen that the commutative láw does *not* apply to vector products, that is, a × b does not equal b × a. Show that the commutative law *does* apply to scalar products, that is, a · b = b · a. (*b*) Show that the distributive law applies to both scalar products and vector products, that is, show that

a · (b + c) = a · b + a · c and that a × (b + c) = a × b + a × c.

(*c*) Does the associative law apply to vector products, i.e., does a × (b × c) equal (a × b) × c? Does it make any sense to talk about an associative law for scalar products?

**25.** *Scalar product in unit vector notation.* Let two vectors be represented in terms of their coordinates as

$$a = ia_x + ja_y + ka_z$$

and

$$b = ib_x = jb_y + kb_z$$

Show analytically that

$$a \cdot b = a_x b_x + a_y b_y + a_z b_z.$$

(Hint: See Problem 22.)

**26.** Use the definition of scalar product a · b = $ab \cos \phi$ and the fact that a · b = $a_x b_x + a_y b_y + a_z b_z$ (see Problem 25) to obtain the angle between the two vectors given by a = 3i + 3j − 3k and b = 2i + j + 3k.

**27.** *Vector product in unit vector notation.* Show analytically that a × b = $i(a_y b_z - a_z b_y) + j(a_z b_x - a_x b_z) + k(a_x b_y - a_y b_x)$. (Hint: See Problem 23.)

**28.** Show that the magnitude of a vector product gives numerically the area of the parallelogram formed with the two component vectors as sides (see Fig. 2–15). Does this suggest how an element of area oriented in space could be represented by a vector?

**Fig. 2–15**

**29.** Show that the area of the triangle contained between the vectors a and b is $\frac{1}{2}|a \times b|$, where the vertical bars signify absolute value (see Fig. 2–15).

**30.** Show that a · (b × c) is equal in magnitude to the volume of the parallelepiped formed on the three vectors a, b, and c.

**31.** Let b and c be the intersecting face diagonals of a cube of edge *a*, as shown in

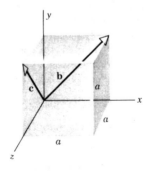

**Fig. 2–16**

Fig. 2–16. (a) Find the components of the vector **d**, where

$$\mathbf{d} = \mathbf{b} \times \mathbf{c}.$$

(b) Find the values of $\mathbf{b} \cdot \mathbf{c}$, of $\mathbf{d} \cdot \mathbf{c}$, and of $\mathbf{d} \cdot \mathbf{b}$.

**32.** Suppose **a**, **b**, and **c** are any three noncoplanar vectors. They are not necessarily mutually at right angles. (a) show that

$$\mathbf{a} \cdot (\mathbf{b} \times \mathbf{c}) = \mathbf{b} \cdot (\mathbf{c} \times \mathbf{a}) = \mathbf{c} \cdot (\mathbf{a} \times \mathbf{b}).$$

(b) Let

$$\mathbf{A} = \frac{\mathbf{b} \times \mathbf{c}}{v}, \qquad \mathbf{B} = \frac{\mathbf{c} \times \mathbf{a}}{v}, \qquad \mathbf{C} = \frac{\mathbf{a} \times \mathbf{b}}{v},$$

where $v = \mathbf{a} \cdot (\mathbf{b} \times \mathbf{c})$. Evaluate the dot product of each of **a**, **b**, **c** with each of **A**, **B**, **C**. (c) If **a**, **b**, **c** have dimensions of length, what are the dimensions of **A**, **B**, **C**?

**33.** Let $N$ be an integer greater than one; then

$$\cos 0 + \cos \frac{2\pi}{N} + \cos \frac{4\pi}{N} + \cdots + \cos (N - 1) \frac{2\pi}{N} = 0;$$

that is,

$$\sum_{n=0}^{n=N-1} \cos \frac{2\pi n}{N} = 0.$$

Also

$$\sum_{n=0}^{n=N-1} \sin \frac{2\pi n}{N} = 0.$$

Prove these two statements by considering the sum of $N$ vectors of equal length, each vector making an angle of $2\pi/N$ with that preceding.

**34.** *Invariance of vector addition under rotation of the coordinate system.* Figure 2–17 shows two vectors **a** and **b** and two systems of coordinates which differ in that the $x$ and $x'$ axes and the $y$ and $y'$ axes each make an angle $\phi$ with each other. Prove analytically that $\mathbf{a} + \mathbf{b}$ has the same magnitude and direction no matter which system is used to carry out the analysis.

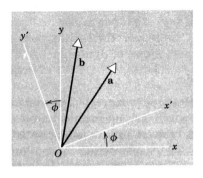

**Fig. 2–17**

# Motion in One Dimension

## CHAPTER 3

### 3–1 Mechanics

Mechanics, the oldest of the physical sciences, is the study of the motion of objects. The calculation of the path of an artillery shell or of a space probe sent from Earth to Mars are among its problems. So too is the analysis of tracks formed in bubble chambers, representing the collisions, decay, and interactions of elementary particles (see Fig. 10–11 and Appendix E).

When we describe motion we are dealing with that part of mechanics called *kinematics*. When we relate motion to the forces associated with it and to the properties of the moving objects, we are dealing with *dynamics*. In this chapter we shall define some kinematical quantities and study them in detail for the special case of motion in one dimension. In Chapter 4 we discuss some cases of two- and three-dimensional motion. Chapter 5 deals with the more general case of dynamics.

### 3–2 Particle Kinematics

A real object can rotate as it moves. For example, a baseball may be spinning while it is moving as a whole in some trajectory. Also, a body may vibrate as it moves, as, for example, a falling water droplet. These complications can be avoided by considering the motion of a very small body called a *particle*. Mathematically, a particle is treated as a point, an object without extent, so that rotational and vibrational considerations are not involved.

Actually, there is no such thing in nature as an object without extent. The concept of "particle" is nevertheless very useful because real objects

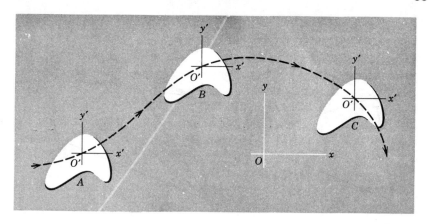

**Fig. 3–1** Translational motion of an object. Translation can occur in three dimensions, but only two are shown for simplicity.

often behave to a very good approximation as though they were particles. A body need not be "small" in the usual sense of the word in order to be treated as a particle. For example, if we consider the distance from the earth to the sun, with respect to this distance the earth and the sun can usually be considered to be particles. We can find out a great deal about the motion of the sun and planets, without appreciable error, by treating these bodies as particles. Baseballs, molecules, protons, and electrons can be often treated as particles. Even if a body is too large to be considered a particle for a particular problem, it can always be thought of as made up of a large number of particles, and the results of particle motion may be useful in analyzing the problem. As a simplification, therefore, we confine our present treatment to the motion of a particle.

Bodies that have only motion of translation behave like particles. An observer will call motion *translational* if the axes of a reference frame which is imagined rigidly attached to the object, say $x'$, $y'$, and $z'$, always remain parallel to the axes of his own reference frame, say $x$, $y$, and $z$. In Fig. 3–1, for example, we show the translational motion of an object moving from positions $A$ to $B$ to $C$. Notice that the path taken is not necessarily a straight line. Notice too that throughout the motion every point of the body undergoes the same displacements as every other point. We can assume the body to be a particle because in describing the motion of one point on the body we have described the motion of the body as a whole.

## 3–3   Average Velocity

*The velocity of a particle is the rate at which its position changes with time.* The position of a particle in a particular reference frame is given by a *position vector* drawn from the origin of that frame to the particle. At time $t_1$, let a particle be at point $A$ in Fig. 3–2a, its position in the $x$-$y$ plane

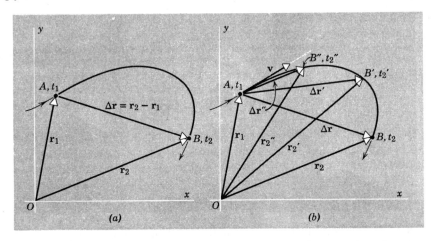

**Fig. 3–2**   (a) A particle moves from $A$ to $B$ in time $\Delta t$ ($= t_2 - t_1$) undergoing a displacement $\Delta r$ ($= r_2 - r_1$). *The average velocity* $\bar{v}$ between $A$ and $B$ is in the direction of $\Delta r$.   (b) As $B$ moves closer to $A$ the average velocity approaches the *instantaneous velocity* $v$ at $A$; $v$ is tangent to the path at $A$.

being described by position vector $r_1$.   For simplicity we treat motion in two dimensions only; the extension to three dimensions will not be difficult.

At a later time $t_2$ let the particle be at point $B$, described by position vector $r_2$.   The *displacement vector* describing the *change* in position of the particle as it moves from $A$ to $B$ is $\Delta r$ ($= r_2 - r_1$) and the elapsed time for the motion between these points is $\Delta t$ ($= t_2 - t_1$).   The *average velocity* for the particle during this interval is defined by

$$\bar{v} = \frac{\Delta r}{\Delta t} = \frac{\text{displacement (a vector)}}{\text{elapsed time (a scalar)}} \qquad (3\text{–}1)$$

A bar above a symbol indicates an average value for the quantity in question.

The quantity $\bar{v}$ is a vector, for it is obtained by dividing the vector $\Delta r$ by the scalar $\Delta t$.   Velocity, therefore, involves both direction and magnitude.   Its direction is the direction of $\Delta r$ and its magnitude is $|\Delta r/\Delta t|$.   The magnitude is expressed in distance units divided by time units, as, for example, meters per second or miles per hour.

The velocity defined by Eq. 3–1 is called an *average* velocity because the measurement of the net displacement and the elapsed time does not tell us anything at all about the motion between $A$ and $B$.   The path may have been curved or straight; the motion may have been steady or erratic.   The average velocity involves simply the total displacement and the total elapsed time.   For example, suppose a man leaves his house and goes on an automobile trip, returning to his house in a time $\Delta t$ after he left it.   His average velocity for the trip is zero because his displacement *for this particular time interval* $\Delta t$ is zero.

If we were to measure the time of arrival of the particle at each of many points along the actual path between $A$ and $B$ in Fig. 3–2a, we could describe the motion in more detail.  If the average velocity turned out to be the same (in magnitude and direction) between any two points along the path, we would conclude that the particle moved with *constant velocity*, that is, along a straight line (constant direction) at a uniform rate (constant magnitude).

## 3–4   Instantaneous Velocity

Suppose that a particle is moving in such a way that its average velocity, measured for a number of different time intervals, does *not* turn out to be constant.  This particle is said to move with variable velocity.  Then we must seek to determine a velocity of the particle at any given instant of time, called the *instantaneous velocity*.

Velocity can vary by a change in magnitude, by a change in direction, or both.  For the motion portrayed in Fig. 3–2a, the average velocity during the time interval $t_2 - t_1$ may differ both in magnitude and direction from the average velocity obtained during another time interval $t_2' - t_1$.  In Fig. 3–2b we illustrate this by choosing the point $B$ to be successively closer to point $A$.  Points $B'$ and $B''$ show two intermediate positions of the particle corresponding to the times $t_2'$ and $t_2''$ and described by position vectors $\mathbf{r}_2'$ and $\mathbf{r}_2''$, respectively.  The vector displacements $\Delta\mathbf{r}$, $\Delta\mathbf{r}'$, and $\Delta\mathbf{r}''$ differ in direction and become successively smaller.  Likewise, the corresponding time intervals $\Delta t$ $(= t_2 - t_1)$, $\Delta t'$ $(= t_2' - t_1)$, and $\Delta t''$ $(= t_2'' - t_1)$ become successively smaller.

As we continue this process, letting $B$ approach $A$, we find that the ratio of displacement to elapsed time approaches a definite limiting value.  Although the displacement in this process becomes extremely small, the time interval by which we divide it becomes small also and the ratio is not necessarily a small quantity.  Similarly, while growing smaller, the displacement vector approaches a limiting direction, that of the tangent to the path of the particle at $A$.  This limiting value of $\Delta\mathbf{r}/\Delta t$ is called the *instantaneous* velocity at the point $A$, or the velocity of the particle at the instant $t_1$.

If $\Delta\mathbf{r}$ is the displacement in a small interval of time $\Delta t$, following the time $t$, the velocity at the time $t$ is the limiting value approached by $\Delta\mathbf{r}/\Delta t$ as both $\Delta\mathbf{r}$ and $\Delta t$ approach zero.  That is, if we let $\mathbf{v}$ represent the instantaneous velocity,

$$\mathbf{v} = \lim_{\Delta t \to 0} \frac{\Delta\mathbf{r}}{\Delta t}.$$

The direction of $\mathbf{v}$ is the limiting direction that $\Delta\mathbf{r}$ takes as $B$ approaches $A$ or as $\Delta t$ approaches zero.  As we have seen, this limiting direction is that of the tangent to the path of the particle at point $A$.

In the notation of the calculus, the limiting value of $\Delta\mathbf{r}/\Delta t$ as $\Delta t$ approaches zero is written $d\mathbf{r}/dt$ and is called the *derivative* of $\mathbf{r}$ with respect to $t$. We have then

$$\mathbf{v} = \lim_{\Delta t \to 0} \frac{\Delta \mathbf{r}}{\Delta t} = \frac{d\mathbf{r}}{dt}. \tag{3-2}$$

The magnitude $v$ of the instantaneous velocity is called the *speed* and is simply the absolute value of $\mathbf{v}$. That is,

$$v = |\mathbf{v}| = |d\mathbf{r}/dt|. \tag{3-3}$$

Speed, being the magnitude of a vector, is intrinsically positive.

Just as a particle is a physical concept making use of the mathematical concept of a point, so here velocity is a physical concept using the mathematical concept of differentiation. In fact, the calculus was invented originally by Isaac Newton (1642–1727) in order to have a proper mathematical tool for treating fundamental mechanical problems.

In the next section we shall examine the concept of instantaneous velocity in detail for the special case of motion in one dimension, sometimes called rectilinear motion.

### 3–5   One-Dimensional Motion—Variable Velocity

Figure 3–3 shows a particle moving along a path in the $x$-$y$ plane. At time $t$ its position with respect to the origin is described by position vector $\mathbf{r}$ (see Fig. 3–3$a$) and it has a velocity $\mathbf{v}$ (see Fig. 3–3$b$) tangent to its path as shown. We can write (see Eq. 2–8)

$$\mathbf{r} = \mathbf{i}x + \mathbf{j}y, \tag{3-4}$$

where $\mathbf{i}$ and $\mathbf{j}$ are unit vectors in the positive $x$- and $y$-directions, respectively, and $x$ and $y$ are the (scalar) components of vector $\mathbf{r}$. Because $\mathbf{i}$ and $\mathbf{j}$ are constant vectors, we have, on combining Eqs. 3–2 and 3–4,

$$\mathbf{v} = \frac{d\mathbf{r}}{dt} = \mathbf{i}\frac{dx}{dt} + \mathbf{j}\frac{dy}{dt},$$

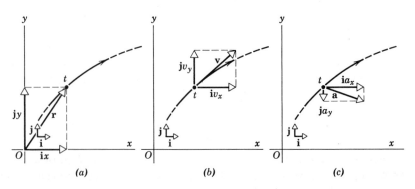

(a)                    (b)                    (c)

**Fig. 3–3**   A particle at time $t$ has ($a$) a position described by $\mathbf{r}$, ($b$) an instantaneous velocity $\mathbf{v}$, and ($c$) an instantaneous acceleration $\mathbf{a}$. The vector components $\mathbf{i}x$ and $\mathbf{j}y$ of Eq. 3-4, $\mathbf{i}v_x$ and $\mathbf{j}v_y$ of Eq. 3-5, and $\mathbf{i}a_x$ and $\mathbf{j}a_y$ of Eq. 3-10 are also shown, as are the unit vectors $\mathbf{i}$ and $\mathbf{j}$.

**Fig. 3–4**    A particle is moving to the right along the $x$-axis.

which we can express as

$$\mathbf{v} = \mathbf{i}v_x + \mathbf{j}v_y \quad \text{(two-dimensional motion)}, \qquad (3\text{–}5)$$

where $v_x\ (= dx/dt)$ and $v_y\ (= dy/dt)$ are the (scalar) components of the vector $\mathbf{v}$.

We now consider motion in one dimension only, chosen for convenience to be the $x$-axis. We must then have $v_y = 0$ so that Eq. 3–5 reduces to

$$\mathbf{v} = \mathbf{i}v_x \quad \text{(one-dimensional motion)}. \qquad (3\text{–}6)$$

Since $\mathbf{i}$ points in the positive $x$-direction, $v_x$ will be positive (and equal to $+v$) when $\mathbf{v}$ points in that direction, and negative (and equal to $-v$) when it points in the other direction. Since, in one-dimensional motion, there are only two choices as to the direction of $\mathbf{v}$, the full power of the vector method is not needed; we can work with the velocity component $v_x$ alone.

▶ **Example 1.** *The limiting process.* As an illustration of the limiting process in one dimension, consider the following table of data taken for motion along the $x$-axis. The first four columns are experimental data. The symbols refer to Fig. 3–4 in which the particle is moving from left to right, that is, in the positive $x$-direction. The particle was at position $x_1$ (100 cm from the origin) at time $t_1$ (1.00 sec). It was at position $x_2$ at time $t_2$. As we consider different values for $x_2$, and different corresponding times $t_2$, we find

| $x_1$, cm | $t_1$, sec | $x_2$, cm | $t_2$, sec | $x_2 - x_1$ $= \Delta x$, cm | $t_2 - t_1$ $= \Delta t$, sec | $\Delta x/\Delta t$, cm/sec |
|---|---|---|---|---|---|---|
| 100.0 | 1.00 | 200.0 | 11.00 | 100.0 | 10.00 | 10.0 |
| 100.0 | 1.00 | 180.0 | 9.60 | 80.0 | 8.60 | 9.3 |
| 100.0 | 1.00 | 160.0 | 7.90 | 60.0 | 6.90 | 8.7 |
| 100.0 | 1.00 | 140.0 | 5.90 | 40.0 | 4.90 | 8.2 |
| 100.0 | 1.00 | 120.0 | 3.56 | 20.0 | 2.56 | 7.8 |
| 100.0 | 1.00 | 110.0 | 2.33 | 10.0 | 1.33 | 7.5 |
| 100.0 | 1.00 | 105.0 | 1.69 | 5.0 | 0.69 | 7.3 |
| 100.0 | 1.00 | 103.0 | 1.42 | 3.0 | 0.42 | 7.1 |
| 100.0 | 1.00 | 101.0 | 1.14 | 1.0 | 0.14 | 7.1 |

Equation 3–2, which holds for the general case of motion in three dimensions, is

$$\mathbf{v} = \lim_{\Delta t \to 0} \frac{\Delta \mathbf{r}}{\Delta t} = \frac{d\mathbf{r}}{dt}.$$

For one-dimensional motion along the $x$-axis we have a similar relation, scalar in character, in which each vector quantity is replaced by its corresponding component or

$$v_x = \lim_{\Delta t \to 0} \frac{\Delta x}{\Delta t} = \frac{dx}{dt}. \tag{3-7}$$

It is clear from the table that as we select values of $x_2$ closer to $x_1$, $\Delta t$ approaches zero and the ratio $\Delta x / \Delta t$ approaches the apparent limiting value $+7.1$ cm./sec. At time $t_1$, therefore, $v_x = +7.1$ cm/sec, as closely as we are able to determine from the data. Since $v_x$ is positive, the velocity **v** ($= i v_x$; see Eq. 3–6) points to the right in Fig. 3–4. This is tangent to the path in the direction of motion, as it must be.

**Example 2.** Figure 3–5a shows six successive "snapshots" of a particle moving along the $x$-axis with variable velocity. At $t = 0$ it is at position $x = +1.00$ ft to the right of the origin; at $t = 2.5$ sec it has come to rest at $x = +5.00$ ft; at $t = 4.0$ sec it has returned to $x = +1.40$ ft. Figure 3–5b is a plot of position $x$ versus time $t$ for this motion. The *average velocity* for the entire 4.0-sec interval is the net displacement or change of position ($+0.40$ ft) divided by the elapsed time (4.0 sec) or $\overline{v}_x = +0.10$ ft/sec. (We call $\overline{v}_x$ average velocity and $v_x$ velocity, for one-dimensional motion, even though velocity is a vector and not a scalar. This conforms to common usage and should cause no misunderstandings. These quantities are not speeds because they may be negative, whereas speed is intrinsically positive.) The average velocity vector **v** points in the positive $x$-direction (that is, to the right in Fig. 3–5a) because the net displacement points in this direction. The quantity $\overline{v}_x$ can be obtained directly from the slope of the dashed line $af$ in Fig. 3–5b, where by slope we mean the ratio of the net displacement $gf$ to the elapsed time $ga$. (The slope is *not* the tangent of the angle $fag$ measured on the graph with a protracter. This angle is arbitrary because it depends on the scales we choose for $x$ and $t$.)

The velocity $v_x$ at any instant is found from the slope of the curve of Fig. 3–5b at that instant. Equation 3–7 is in fact the relation by which the slope of the curve is defined in the calculus. In our example the slope at $b$, which is the value of $v_x$ at $b$, is $+1.7$ ft/sec; the slope at $d$ is zero and the slope at $f$ is $-6.2$ ft/sec. When we determine the slope $dx/dt$ at each instant $t$, we can make a plot of $v_x$ versus $t$, as in Fig. 3–5c. Note that for the interval $0 < t < 2.5$ sec, $v_x$ is positive so that the velocity vector **v** points to the right in Fig. 3–5a; for the interval $2.5$ sec $< t < 4.0$ sec $v_x$ is negative so that **v** points to the left in Fig. 3–5a. ◀

## 3–6   Acceleration

Often the velocity of a moving body changes either in magnitude, in direction, or both as the motion proceeds. The body is then said to have an acceleration. *The acceleration of a particle is the rate of change of its velocity with time.* Suppose that at the instant $t_1$ a particle, as in Fig. 3–6, is at point $A$ and is moving in the $x$-$y$ plane with the instantaneous velocity $\mathbf{v}_1$, and at a later instant $t_2$ it is at point $B$ and moving with the instantaneous velocity $\mathbf{v}_2$. The *average acceleration* $\overline{\mathbf{a}}$ during the motion from $A$ to $B$ is defined to be the *change of velocity* divided by the time interval, or

$$\overline{\mathbf{a}} = \frac{\mathbf{v}_2 - \mathbf{v}_1}{t_2 - t_1} = \frac{\Delta \mathbf{v}}{\Delta t}. \tag{3-8}$$

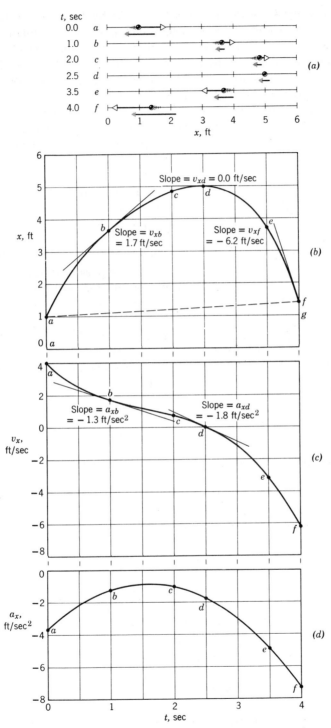

**Fig. 3-5** (a) Six consecutive "snapshots" of a particle moving along the x-axis. The vector joined to the particle is its instantaneous velocity; that below the particle is its instantaneous acceleration. (b) A plot of x versus t for the motion of the particle. (c) A plot of $v_x$ versus t. (d) A plot of $a_x$ versus t.

The quantity $\bar{\mathbf{a}}$ is a vector, for it is obtained by dividing a vector $\Delta\mathbf{v}$ by a scalar $\Delta t$. Acceleration is therefore characterized by magnitude and direction. Its direction is the direction of $\Delta\mathbf{v}$ and its magnitude is $|\Delta\mathbf{v}/\Delta t|$. The magnitude of the acceleration is expressed in velocity units divided by time units, as for example meter/sec per sec (written meters/sec$^2$ and read "meters per second squared"), cm/sec$^2$, and ft/sec$^2$.

We call $\bar{\mathbf{a}}$ of Eq. 3–8 the *average* acceleration because nothing has been said about the time variation of velocity *during* the interval $\Delta t$. We know only the net change in velocity and the total elapsed time. If the change in velocity (a vector) divided by the corresponding elapsed time, $\Delta\mathbf{v}/\Delta t$, were to remain constant, regardless of the time intervals over which we measured the acceleration, we would have *constant* acceleration. Constant acceleration, therefore, implies that the *change* in velocity is uniform with time in direction and magnitude. If there is *no change* in velocity, that is, if the velocity were to remain constant both in magnitude and direction, then $\Delta\mathbf{v}$ would be zero for all time intervals and the acceleration would be zero.

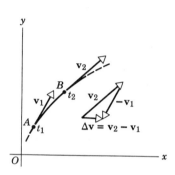

**Fig. 3–6** A particle has velocity $\mathbf{v}_1$ at point $A$ and moves to point $B$, where its velocity is $\mathbf{v}_2$. The triangle shows the (vector) change in velocity $\Delta\mathbf{v}$ ($= \mathbf{v}_2 - \mathbf{v}_1$) experienced by the particle as it moves from $A$ to $B$.

If a particle is moving in such a way that its average acceleration, measured for a number of different time intervals, does *not* turn out to be constant, the particle is said to have a variable acceleration. The acceleration can vary in magnitude, or in direction, or both. In such cases we seek to determine the acceleration of the particle at any given time, called the instantaneous acceleration.

The *instantaneous acceleration* is defined by

$$\mathbf{a} = \lim_{\Delta t \to 0} \frac{\Delta\mathbf{v}}{\Delta t} = \frac{d\mathbf{v}}{dt}. \qquad (3\text{–}9)$$

That is, the acceleration of a particle at time $t$ is *the limiting value of $\Delta\mathbf{v}/\Delta t$* at time $t$ as both $\Delta\mathbf{v}$ and $\Delta t$ approach zero. The direction of the instantaneous acceleration $\mathbf{a}$ is the limiting direction of the vector change in velocity $\Delta\mathbf{v}$. The magnitude $a$ of the instantaneous acceleration is simply $a = |\mathbf{a}| = |d\mathbf{v}/dt|$. When the acceleration is constant the instantaneous acceleration equals the average acceleration. The student should note that the relation of $\mathbf{a}$ to $\mathbf{v}$, in Eq. 3–9, is the same as that of $\mathbf{v}$ to $\mathbf{r}$, in Eq. 3–2.

Two special cases illustrate that acceleration can arise from a change in either the magnitude or the direction of the velocity. In one case we have motion along a straight line with uniformly changing speed (as in Section 3–8). Here the velocity does not change in direction but its magnitude changes uniformly with time. This is a case of constant acceleration. In the second case we have motion in a circle at constant speed (Section 4–4). Here the velocity vector changes continuously in direction but its magnitude remains constant. This, too, is accelerated motion, though the direction of the acceleration vector is not constant. Later we will encounter other important cases of accelerated motion.

### 3–7   One-Dimensional Motion—Variable Acceleration

From Eqs. 3–5 and 3–9 we can write, for motion in two dimensions as in Fig. 3–3,

$$\mathbf{a} = \frac{d\mathbf{v}}{dt} = \mathbf{i}\,\frac{dv_x}{dt} + \mathbf{j}\,\frac{dv_y}{dt}$$

or

$$\mathbf{a} = \mathbf{i}a_x + \mathbf{j}a_y, \tag{3–10}$$

where $a_x$ ($= dv_x/dt$) and $a_y$ ($= dv_y/dt$) are the (scalar) components of the acceleration vector $\mathbf{a}$ (see Fig. 3–3c).

We again restrict ourselves to motion in one dimension only, chosen for convenience to be the $x$-axis. Since $v_y$ for such motion does not change with time (and is, in fact, zero), $a_y$, which is $dv_y/dt$, must also be zero so that

$$\mathbf{a} = \mathbf{i}a_x. \tag{3–11}$$

Since $\mathbf{i}$ points in the positive $x$-direction, $a_x$ will be positive when $\mathbf{a}$ points in this direction and negative when it points in the other direction.

▶ **Example 3.**   The motion of Fig. 3-5a is one of variable acceleration along the $x$-axis. To find the acceleration* $a_x$ at each instant we must determine $dv_x/dt$ at each instant. This is simply the slope of the curve of $v_x$ versus $t$ at that instant. The slope of Fig. 3–5c at point $b$ is $-1.3$ ft/sec$^2$ and that at point $d$ is $-1.8$ ft/sec$^2$, as shown in the figure. The result of calculating the slope for all points is shown in Fig. 3–5d. Notice that $a_x$ is negative at all instants, which means that the acceleration vector $\mathbf{a}$ points in the negative $x$-direction. This means that $v_x$ is always decreasing with time, as is clearly seen from Fig. 3–5c. The motion is one in which the acceleration vector has a constant direction but varies in magnitude (see Fig. 3–5a).                                                                 ◀

### 3–8   One-Dimensional Motion—Constant Acceleration

Let us now further restrict our considerations to motion which not only occurs in one dimension (the $x$-axis) but for which $a_x = $ a constant. For such *constant acceleration* the *average* acceleration for any time interval is equal to the (constant) instantaneous acceleration $a_x$. Let $t_1 = 0$ and let

---

* As for velocity, we commonly call $a_x$ for one-dimensional motion the acceleration even though acceleration is a vector and $a_x$ is correctly an acceleration component. For one-dimensional motion there is only one component if the axis is chosen along the line of the motion.

$t_2$ be any arbitrary time $t$. Let $v_{x0}$ be the value of $v_x$ at $t = 0$ and let $v_x$ be its value at the arbitrary time $t$. With this notation we find $a_x$ (see Eq. 3–8) from

$$a_x = \frac{\Delta v}{\Delta t} = \frac{v_x - v_{x0}}{t - 0}$$

or

$$v_x = v_{x0} + a_x t. \tag{3–12}$$

This equation states that the velocity $v_x$ at time $t$ is the sum of its value $v_{x0}$ at time $t = 0$ plus the change in velocity during time $t$, which is $a_x t$.

Figure 3–7c shows a graph of $v_x$ versus $t$ for constant acceleration; it is a graph of Eq. 3–12. Notice that the slope of the velocity curve is constant, as it must be because the acceleration $a_x$ $(= dv_x/dt)$ has been assumed to be constant, as Fig. 3–7d shows.

When the velocity $v_x$ changes uniformly with time, its average value over any time interval equals one-half the sum of the values of $v_x$ at the beginning and at the end of the interval. That is, the average velocity $\overline{v_x}$ between $t = 0$ and $t = t$ is

$$\overline{v_x} = \tfrac{1}{2}(v_{x0} + v_x). \tag{3–13}$$

This relation would not be true if the acceleration were not constant, for then the curve of $v_x$ versus $t$ would not be a straight line.

If the position of the particle at $t = 0$ is $x_0$, the position $x$ at $t = t$ can be found from

$$x = x_0 + \overline{v_x} t$$

which can be combined with Eq. 3–13 to yield

$$x = x_0 + \tfrac{1}{2}(v_{x0} + v_x)t. \tag{3–14}$$

The displacement due to the motion in time $t$ is $x - x_0$. Often the origin is chosen so that $x_0 = 0$.

Notice that aside from initial conditions of the motion, that is, the values of $x$ and $v_x$ at $t = 0$ (taken here as $x = x_0$ and $v_x = v_{x0}$), there are four parameters of the motion. These are $x$, the displacement; $v_x$, the velocity; $a_x$, the acceleration; and $t$, the elapsed time. If we know only that the acceleration is constant, but not necessarily its value, from any two of these parameters we can obtain the other two. For example, if $a_x$ and $t$ are known, Eq. 3–12 gives $v_x$, and having obtained $v_x$, we find $x$ from Eq. 3–14.

In most problems in uniformly accelerated motion, two parameters are known and a third is sought. It is convenient, therefore, to obtain relations between any three of the four parameters. Equation 3–12 contains $v_x$, $a_x$, and $t$, but *not* $x$; Eq. 3–14 contains $x$, $v_x$, and $t$ but *not* $a_x$. To complete our system of equations we need two more relations, one containing $x$, $a_x$, and $t$ but *not* $v_x$ and another containing $x$, $v_x$, and $a_x$ but *not* $t$. These are easily obtained by combining Eqs. 3–12 and 3–14.

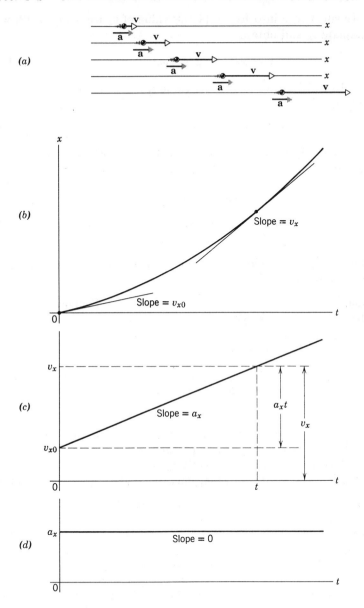

**Fig. 3-7**   (a) Five successive "snapshots" of rectilinear motion with constant acceleration.   The arrows on the spheres represent **v**; those below represent **a**.   (b) The displacement increases quadratically according to $x = v_{x0} t + \frac{1}{2} a_x t^2$.   Its slope increases
uniformly and at each instant has the value $v_x$, the velocity.   (c) The velocity $v_x$
increases uniformly according to $v_x = v_{x0} + a_x t$.   Its slope is constant and at each
instant has the value $a_x$, the acceleration.   (d) The acceleration $a_x$ has a constant
value; its slope is zero.   Figure 3-5 shows similar plots for one-dimensional motion
in which the acceleration is *not* constant.

Thus, if we substitute into Eq. 3–14 the value of $v_x$ from Eq. 3–12, we thereby eliminate $v_x$ and obtain

$$x = x_0 + v_{x0}t + \tfrac{1}{2}a_x t^2. \tag{3-15}$$

When Eq. 3–12 is solved for $t$ and this value for $t$ is substituted into Eq. 3–14, we obtain

$$v_x{}^2 = v_{x0}{}^2 + 2a_x(x - x_0). \tag{3-16}$$

Equations 3–12, 3–14, 3–15, and 3–16 (see Table 3–1) are the complete set of equations for motion along a straight line with constant acceleration.

### Table 3–1

KINEMATIC EQUATIONS FOR STRAIGHT LINE MOTION
WITH CONSTANT ACCELERATION

(The position $x_0$ and the velocity $v_{x0}$ at the initial instant $t = 0$ are the given initial conditions)

| Equation Number | Equation | $x$ | $v_x$ | $a_x$ | $t$ |
|---|---|---|---|---|---|
| 3–12 | $v_x = v_{x0} + a_x t$ | ✗ | ✓ | ✓ | ✓ |
| 3–14 | $x = x_0 + \tfrac{1}{2}(v_{x0} + v_x)t$ | ✓ | ✓ | ✗ | ✓ |
| 3–15 | $x = x_0 + v_{x0}t + \tfrac{1}{2}a_x t^2$ | ✓ | ✗ | ✓ | ✓ |
| 3–16 | $v_x{}^2 = v_{x0}{}^2 + 2a_x(x - x_0)$ | ✓ | ✓ | ✓ | ✗ |

A special case of motion with constant acceleration is one in which the acceleration is zero, that is, $a_x = 0$. In this case the four equations in Table 3–1 reduce to the expected results $v_x = v_{x0}$ (the velocity does not change) and $x = x_0 + v_{x0}t$ (the displacement changes linearly with time).

▶ **Example 4.** The curve of Fig. 3-7b is a displacement-time graph for motion with constant acceleration; that is, it is a graph of Eq. 3–15 in which $x_0 = 0$. The slope of the tangent to the curve at time $t$ equals the velocity $v_x$ at that time. Notice that the slope increases continuously with time from $v_{x0}$ at $t = 0$. The *rate of increase* of this slope should give the acceleration $a_x$, which is *constant* in this case. The curve of Fig. 3-7b is a *parabola* since Eq. 3–15 is the equation for a parabola having slope $v_{x0}$ at $t = 0$. We obtain, on successive differentiation of Eq. 3–15,

$$x = x_0 + v_{x0}t + \tfrac{1}{2}a_x t^2$$

$$dx/dt = v_{x0} + a_x t \quad \text{or} \quad v_x = v_{x0} + a_x t,$$

which gives the velocity $v_x$ at time $t$ (compare Eq. 3–12), and

$$dv_x/dt = a_x,$$

the constant acceleration. The displacement-time graph for uniformly accelerated rectilinear motion will therefore always be parabolic.     ◀

### 3–9    Consistency of Units and Dimensions

The student should not feel compelled to memorize relations such as those of Table 3–1.  The important thing is to be able to follow the line of reasoning used to obtain the results.  These relations will be recalled automatically after the student has used them repeatedly to solve problems, partly as a result of the familiarity acquired but chiefly as a result of the better understanding obtained through application.

We can use any convenient *units* of time and distance in these equations. If we choose to express time in seconds and distance in feet, for self-consistency we must express velocity in ft/sec and acceleration in ft/sec$^2$. If we are given data in which the units of one quantity, as velocity, are not consistent with the units of another quantity, as acceleration, then before using the data in our equations we should transform both quantities to units that are consistent with one another.   Having chosen the units of our fundamental quantities, we automatically determine the units of our derived quantities consistent with them.   In carrying out any calculation, always remember to attach the proper units to the final result, for the result is meaningless without this label.

▶ **Example 5.**  Suppose we wish to find the speed of a particle which has a uniform acceleration of 5.00 cm/sec$^2$ for an interval of $\frac{1}{2}$ hr if the particle has a speed of 10.0 ft/sec at the beginning of this interval.  We decide to choose the foot as our length unit and the second as our time unit.   Then

$$a_x = 5.00 \text{ cm/sec}^2 = 5.00 \text{ cm/sec}^2 \times \left(\frac{1 \text{ in.}}{2.54 \text{ cm}}\right) \times \left(\frac{1 \text{ ft}}{12 \text{ in.}}\right)$$

$$= \frac{5.00}{30.5} \text{ ft/sec}^2 = 0.164 \text{ ft/sec}^2.$$

The time interval

$$\Delta t = t - t_0 = \frac{1}{2} \text{ hr} \times \left(\frac{60 \text{ min}}{1 \text{ hr}}\right) \times \left(\frac{60 \text{ sec}}{1 \text{ min}}\right) = 1800 \text{ sec.}$$

Note that the conversion factors in large parentheses are equal to unity.   Taking the initial time $t_0 = 0$, as in Eq. 3–12, we then have

$$v_x = v_{x0} + a_x t = 10.0 \text{ ft/sec} + (0.164 \text{ ft/sec}^2)(1800 \text{ sec})$$

$$= 305 \text{ ft/sec.} \qquad ◀$$

One way to spot an erroneous equation is to check the *dimensions* of all its terms.   The dimensions of any physical quantity can always be expressed as some combination of the fundamental quantities, such as mass, length, and time, from which they are derived.   The dimensions of velocity are length $(L)$ divided by time $(T)$; the dimensions of acceleration are length divided by time squared, etc.   *In any legitimate physical equation the dimensions of all the terms must be the same.*   This means, for example, that we cannot equate a term whose total dimension is a velocity to one whose total dimension is an acceleration.   The dimensional labels attached to various quantities may be treated just like algebraic quantities and may be combined, canceled, etc., just as if they were factors in the equation. For example, to check Eq. 3–15, $x = x_0 + v_{x0}t + \frac{1}{2}a_x t^2$, dimensionally, we note that $x$ and $x_0$ have the dimension of a length. Therefore the two remaining terms must also have the dimension of a length. The dimension of the term $v_{x0}t$ is

$$\frac{\text{length}}{\text{time}} \times \text{time} = \text{length} \qquad \text{or} \qquad \frac{L}{T} \times T = L,$$

and that of $\frac{1}{2}a_x t^2$ is

$$\frac{\text{length}}{\text{time}^2} \times \text{time}^2 = \text{length} \qquad \text{or} \qquad \frac{L}{T^2} \times T^2 = L.$$

The equation is therefore *dimensionally correct*. The student should check the dimensions of all the equations he uses.

▶ **Example 6.** The speed of an automobile traveling due east is uniformly reduced from 45.0 miles/hr to 30.0 miles/hr in a distance of 264 ft.

(a) What is the magnitude and direction of the constant acceleration?

We choose, arbitrarily, the direction from west to east to be the positive $x$-direction. We are given $x$ and $v_x$ and we seek $a_x$. The time is not involved. Equation 3–16 is therefore appropriate (see Table 3–1). We have $v_x = +30.0$ miles/hr, $v_{x0} = +45.0$ miles/hr, $x - x_0 = +264$ ft $= 0.0500$ mile. From Eq. 3–16, $v_x^2 = v_{x0}^2 + 2a_x(x - x_0)$, we obtain

$$a_x = \frac{v_x^2 - v_{x0}^2}{2(x - x_0)},$$

or

$$a_x = \frac{(30.0 \text{ miles/hr})^2 - (45.0 \text{ miles/hr})^2}{2(0.0500 \text{ mile})} = -1.13 \times 10^4 \text{ miles/hr}^2$$

$$= -4.58 \text{ ft/sec}^2.$$

The direction of the acceleration **a** is due west, that is, in the negative $x$-direction because $a_x$ is negative. The car is slowing down as it moves eastward, as it must do if it is being accelerated toward the west. When the speed of a body is decreasing, we often say that it is decelerating.

(b) How much time has elapsed during this deceleration?

If we use only the original data, Table 3–1 shows that Eq. 3–14 is appropriate. From Eq. 3–14, $x = x_0 + \frac{1}{2}(v_{x0} + v_x)t$, we obtain

$$t = \frac{2(x - x_0)}{v_{x0} + v_x},$$

or

$$t = \frac{(2)(0.0500 \text{ mile})}{(45.0 + 30.0) \text{ miles/hr}} = \frac{1}{750} \text{ hr} = 4.80 \text{ sec.}$$

If we use the derived data of part (a), Eq. 3–12 is appropriate. This gives us a check. From Eq. 3–12, $v_x = v_{x0} + a_x t$, we have

$$t = \frac{v_x - v_{x0}}{a_x}$$

or

$$t = \frac{(30.0 - 45.0) \text{ miles/hr}}{-1.13 \times 10^4 \text{ miles/hr}^2} = 1.33 \times 10^{-3} \text{ hr} = 4.80 \text{ sec.}$$

(c) If one assumes that the car continues to decelerate at the same rate, how much time would elapse in bringing it to rest from 45.0 miles/hr?

Equation 3–12 is useful here. We have $v_{x0} = 45.0$ miles/hr, $a_x = -1.13 \times 10^4$ miles/hr², and the final velocity $v_x = 0$. Then from Eq. 3–12, $v_x = v_{x0} + a_x t$, we obtain

$$t = \frac{v_x - v_{x0}}{a_x},$$

or

$$t = \frac{(0 - 45.0) \text{ miles/hr}}{-1.13 \times 10^4 \text{ miles/hr}^2} = 4.00 \times 10^{-3} \text{ hr} = 14.4 \text{ sec.}$$

(d) What total distance is required to bring the car to rest from 45.0 miles/hr? Equation 3–15 is appropriate here. We have $v_{x0} = 45.0$ miles/hr, $a_x = -1.13 \times 10^4$ miles/hr², $t = 4.00 \times 10^{-3}$ hr. From Eq. 3–15, $x = x_0 + v_{x0}t + \frac{1}{2}a_x t^2$, we obtain

$$x - x_0 = v_{x0}t + \tfrac{1}{2}a_x t^2$$

$$= (45.0 \text{ miles/hr})(4.00 \times 10^{-3} \text{ hr})$$
$$+ \tfrac{1}{2}(-1.13 \times 10^4 \text{ miles/hr}^2)(4.00 \times 10^{-3} \text{ hr})^2$$
$$= 0.0900 \text{ mile} = 475 \text{ ft.}$$

**Example 7.** The nucleus of a helium atom (alpha-particle) travels along the inside of a straight hollow tube 2.0 meters long which forms part of a particle accelerator. (a) If one assumes uniform acceleration, how long is the particle in the tube if it enters at a speed of 1000 meters/sec and leaves at 9000 meters/sec? (b) What is its acceleration during this interval?

(a) We choose an $x$-axis parallel to the tube, its positive direction being that in which the particle is moving and its origin at the tube entrance. We are given $x$ and $v_x$ and we seek $t$. The acceleration $a_x$ is not involved. Hence we use Eq. 3–14, $x = x_0 + \frac{1}{2}(v_{x0} + v_x) t$ with $x_0 = 0$ or

$$t = \frac{2x}{v_{x0} + v_x},$$

$$t = \frac{(2)(2.0 \text{ meters})}{(1000 + 9000) \text{ meters/sec}} = 4.0 \times 10^{-4} \text{ sec,}$$

or 400 microseconds.

(b) The acceleration follows from Eq. 3–12, $v_x = v_{x0} + a_x t$, or

$$a_x = \frac{v_x - v_{x0}}{t} = \frac{(9000 - 1000) \text{ meters/sec}}{4.0 \times 10^{-4} \text{ sec}} = +2.0 \times 10^7 \text{ meters/sec}^2,$$

or 20 million meters per second per second! Although this acceleration is enormous by standards of the previous example, it occurs over an extremely short time. The acceleration **a** is in the positive $x$-direction, that is, in the direction in which the particle is moving, because $a_x$ is positive.        ◀

## 3-10   Freely Falling Bodies

The most common example of motion with (nearly) constant acceleration is that of a body falling toward the earth. In the absence of air resistance it is found that all bodies, regardless of their size, weight, or composition, fall with the same acceleration at the same point of the earth's surface, and if the distance covered is not too great, the acceleration remains constant throughout the fall. This ideal motion, in which air resistance and the small change in acceleration with altitude are neglected, is called "free fall."

The acceleration of a freely falling body is called the acceleration due to gravity and is denoted by the symbol **g**. Near the earth's surface its magnitude is approximately 32 ft/sec$^2$, 9.8 meters/sec$^2$, or 980 cm/sec$^2$, and it is directed down toward the center of the earth. The variation of the exact value with latitude and altitude will be discussed later (Chapter 16).

The nature of the motion of a falling object was long ago a subject of interest in natural philosophy. Aristotle had asserted that "the downward movement . . . of any body endowed with weight is quicker in proportion to its size." It was not until many centuries later when Galileo Galilei (1564–1642), an Italian scientist of the Renaissance, appealed to experiment to discover the truth, and then publicly proclaimed it, that Aristotle's authority on the matter was seriously challenged. In the later years of his life, Galileo wrote the treatise entitled *Dialogues Concerning Two New Sciences* in which he detailed his studies of motion.* This treatise may be considered as marking the beginning of the science of dynamics.

Aristotle's belief that a heavier object will fall faster is a commonly held view. It appears to receive support from a well-known lecture demonstration in which a ball and a sheet of paper are dropped at the same instant, the ball reaching the floor much sooner than the paper. However, when the lecturer first crumples the paper tightly and then repeats the demonstration, both ball and paper strike the floor at essentially the same time. In the former case, it is the effect of greater resistance of the air which makes the paper fall more slowly than the ball. In the latter case, the effect of air resistance on the paper is reduced and is about the same for both bodies, so that they fall at about the same rate. Of course, a direct test can be made by dropping bodies in vacuum. Even in easily obtainable partial vacuums we can show that a feather and a ball of lead thousands of times heavier drop at rates that are practically indistinguishable.

In Galileo's time, however, there was no effective way to obtain a partial vacuum, nor did equipment exist to time freely falling bodies with sufficient precision to obtain reliable numerical data. Nevertheless, Galileo proved his result by showing

---

* Galileo made noteworthy contributions to astronomy by the application of his telescope. His strong evidence in favor of the Copernican hypothesis of the solar system served to refute the Ptolemaic system and on this account raised strong feelings against him in the minds of the leaders of the Church. Twice he was brought before the Inquisition. He was ordered not to publish anything in support of the Copernican system and was compelled to publicly disclaim his belief in it. It was during a period of fear and uncertainty that he wrote his dialogue on motion, not published until after his death.

first that the character of the motion of a ball rolling down an incline was the same as that of a ball in free fall. The incline merely served to reduce the effective acceleration of gravity and to slow the motion thereby. Time intervals measured by the volume of water discharged from a tank could then be used to test the speed and acceleration of this motion. Galileo showed that if the acceleration along the incline is constant, the acceleration due to gravity must also be constant; for the acceleration along the incline is simply a component of the vertical acceleration of gravity, and along an incline of constant slope the ratio of the two accelerations remains fixed.

He found from his experiments that the distances covered in consecutive time intervals were proportional to the odd numbers 1, 3, 5, 7, . . . , etc. Total distances for consecutive intervals thus were proportional to $1 + 3$, $1 + 3 + 5$, $1 + 3 + 5 + 7$, etc., that is, to the squares of the integers 1, 2, 3, 4, etc. But if the distance covered is proportional to the square of the elapsed time, velocity acquired is proportional to the elapsed time, a result which is true only if motion is uniformly accelerated. He found that the same results held regardless of the mass of the ball used.

### 3–11   Equations of Motion in Free Fall

We shall select a reference frame rigidly attached to the earth. The $y$-axis will be taken as positive vertically upward. Then the acceleration due to gravity **g** will be a vector pointing vertically down (toward the center of the earth) in the negative $y$-direction. (This choice is arbitrary. In other problems it may be convenient to choose down as positive.) Our equations for constant acceleration are applicable here. We simply replace $x$ by $y$ and set $y_0 = 0$ in Eqs. 3–12, 3–14, 3–15, and 3–16, obtaining

$$v_y = v_{y0} + a_y t,$$

$$y = \tfrac{1}{2}(v_{y0} + v_y)t,$$

$$y = v_{y0}t + \tfrac{1}{2}a_y t^2, \tag{3–17}$$

$$v_y{}^2 = v_{y0}{}^2 + 2a_y y,$$

and, for problems in free fall, we set $a_y = -g$. Notice that we have chosen the initial position as the origin, that is we have chosen $y_0 = 0$ at $t = 0$. Note also that $g$ is the magnitude of the acceleration due to gravity.

▶ **Example 8.** A body is dropped from rest and falls freely. Determine the position and speed of the body after 1.0, 2.0, 3.0, and 4.0 sec have elapsed.

We choose the starting point as the origin. We know the initial speed and the acceleration and we are given the time. To find the position we use

$$y = v_{y0}t - \tfrac{1}{2}gt^2.$$

Then, $v_{y0} = 0$ and $g = 32$ ft/sec$^2$, and with $t = 1.0$ sec we obtain

$$y = 0 - \tfrac{1}{2}(32 \text{ ft/sec}^2)(1.0 \text{ sec})^2 = -16 \text{ ft}.$$

To find the speed with $t = 1.0$ sec, we use

$$v_y = v_{y0} - gt$$

and obtain     $v_y = 0 - (32 \text{ ft/sec}^2)(1.0 \text{ sec}) = -32 \text{ ft/sec}.$

| $t$ sec | $y$ ft | $v_y$ ft/sec | $a_y$ ft/sec$^2$ |
|---|---|---|---|
| 0 | 0 | 0 | −32 |
| 1.0 | −16 | −32 | −32 |
| 2.0 | −64 | −64 | −32 |
| 3.0 | −144 | −96 | −32 |
| 4.0 | −256 | −128 | −32 |

**Fig. 3–8** A body in free fall; showing $y$, $v_y$, and $a_y$ at particular times $t$.

After 1.0 sec of falling from rest, the body is 16 ft below its starting point and has a velocity directed downward whose magnitude is 32 ft/sec; the negative signs for $y$ and $v_y$ show that the associated vectors each point in the negative $y$-direction, that is, downward.

The student should now show that the values of $y$, $v_y$, and $a_y$ obtained at times $t = 2.0$, 3.0, and 4.0 sec are those shown in Fig. 3–8.

**Example 9.** A ball is thrown vertically upward from the ground with a speed of 80 ft/sec.

(*a*) How long does it take to reach its highest point?

At its highest point, $v_y = 0$, and we have $v_{y0} = +80$ ft/sec. To obtain the time $t$ we use $v_y = v_{y0} - gt$, or

$$t = \frac{v_{y0} - v_y}{g}$$

$$t = \frac{(80 - 0)\ \text{ft/sec}}{32\ \text{ft/sec}^2} = 2.5\ \text{sec.}$$

(*b*) How high does the ball rise? Using only the original data, we choose the relation $v_y{}^2 = v_{y0}{}^2 - 2gy$, or

$$y = \frac{v_{y0}{}^2 - v_y{}^2}{2g},$$

$$= \frac{(80\ \text{ft/sec})^2 - 0}{2 \times 32\ \text{ft/sec}^2} = +100\ \text{ft.}$$

(c) At what times will the ball be 96 ft above the ground? Using $y = v_{y0}t - \frac{1}{2}gt^2$, we have

$$\tfrac{1}{2}gt^2 - v_{y0}t + y = 0,$$

$$\tfrac{1}{2}(32 \text{ ft/sec}^2)t^2 - (80 \text{ ft/sec})t + 96 \text{ ft} = 0,$$

or

$$t^2 - 5.0t + 6.0 = 0,$$

which yields $t = 2.0$ sec and $t = 3.0$ sec.

At $t = 2.0$ sec, the ball is moving upward with a speed of 16 ft/sec, for

$$v_y = v_{y0} - gt = 80 \text{ ft/sec} - (32 \text{ ft/sec}^2)(2.0 \text{ sec}) = +16 \text{ ft/sec.}$$

At $t = 3.0$ sec, the ball is moving downward with the same speed, for

$$v_y = v_{y0} - gt = 80 \text{ ft/sec} - (32 \text{ ft/sec}^2)(3.0 \text{ sec}) = -16 \text{ ft/sec.}$$

Notice that in this 1.0-sec interval the velocity changed by $-32$ ft/sec, corresponding to an acceleration of $-32$ ft/sec$^2$.

The student should be able to convince himself that in the absence of air resistance the ball will take as long to rise as to fall the same distance, and that it will have the same speed going down at each point as it had going up. ◄

## QUESTIONS

**1.** Can you think of physical phenomena involving the earth in which the earth cannot be treated as a particle?

**2.** Each second a rabbit moves half the remaining distance from his nose to a head of lettuce. Does he ever get to the lettuce? What is the limiting value of his average velocity? Draw graphs showing his velocity and position as time increases.

**3.** Average speed can mean the magnitude of the average velocity vector. Another meaning given to it is that average speed is the total length of path traveled divided by the elapsed time. Are these meanings different? If so, give an example.

**4.** When the velocity is constant, does the average velocity over any time interval differ from the instantaneous velocity at any instant?

**5.** Is the average velocity of a particle moving along the $x$-axis $\frac{1}{2}(v_{x0} + v_x)$ when the acceleration is not uniform? Prove your answer with the use of graphs.

**6.** Does the speedometer on an automobile register speed as we defined it?

**7.** (a) Can a body have zero velocity and still be accelerating? (b) Can a body have a constant speed and still have a varying velocity? (c) Can a body have a constant velocity and still have a varying speed?

**8.** Can an object have an eastward velocity while experiencing a westward acceleration?

**9.** Can the direction of the velocity of a body change when its acceleration is constant?

**10.** Devise a scheme for keeping time with a "water clock" such as Galileo used. Can you avoid repetitive operations and still keep accurate time?

**11.** If a particle is released from rest $(v_{y0} = 0)$ at $y_0 = 0$ at the time $t = 0$, Eq. 3-17 for constant acceleration says that it is at position $y$ at two different times, namely, $+\sqrt{2y/a_y}$ and $-\sqrt{2y/a_y}$. What is the meaning of the negative root of this quadratic equation?

**12.** What happens to our kinematic equations under the operation of time reversal, that is, replacing $t$ by $-t$? Explain.

**13.** Consider a ball thrown vertically up. Taking air resistance into account, would you expect the time during which the ball rises to be longer or shorter than the time during which it falls?

**14.** Can there be motion in two dimensions with an acceleration in only one dimension?

**15.** A man standing on the edge of a cliff at some height above the ground below throws one ball straight up with initial speed $u$ and then throws another ball straight down with the same initial speed. Which ball, if either, has the larger speed when it hits the ground? Neglect air resistance.

**16.** From what you know about angular measure, what *dimensions* would you assign to an angle? Can a quantity have units without having dimensions?

**17.** If $m$ is a light stone and $M$ is a heavy one, according to Aristotle $M$ should fall faster than $m$. Galileo attempted to show that Aristotle's belief was logically inconsistent by the following argument. Tie $m$ and $M$ together to form a double stone. Then, in falling, $m$ should retard $M$, since it tends to fall more slowly, and the combination would fall faster than $m$ but more slowly than $M$; but according to Aristotle the double body $(M + m)$ is heavier than $M$ and hence should fall faster than $M$.

If you accept Galileo's reasoning as correct, can you conclude that $M$ and $m$ must fall at the same rate? What need is there for experiment in that case?

If you believe Galileo's reasoning is incorrect, explain why.

## PROBLEMS

**1.** Compare your average speed in the following two cases. (a) You walk 240 ft at a speed of 4.0 ft/sec and then run 240 ft at a speed of 10 ft/sec along a straight track. (b) You walk for 1.0 min at a speed of 4.0 ft/sec and then run for 1.0 min at 10 ft/sec along a straight track.

**2.** A train moving at an essentially constant speed of 60 miles/hr moves eastward for 40 min, then in a direction 45° east of north for 20 min, and finally westward for 50 min. What is the average velocity of the train during this run?

**3.** Two trains, each having a speed of 30 miles/hr, are headed at each other on the same straight track. A bird that can fly 60 miles/hr flies off one train when they are 60 miles apart and heads directly for the other train. On reaching the other train it flies directly back to the first train, and so forth. (a) How many trips can the bird make from one train to the other before they crash? (b) What is the total distance the bird travels?

**4.** A particle moving along a horizontal line has the following positions at various instants of time:

| $x$(meters) = 0.080 | 0.050 | 0.040 | 0.050 | 0.080 | 0.13 | 0.68 |
|---|---|---|---|---|---|---|
| $t$(sec) = 0.0 | 1.0 | 2.0 | 3.0 | 4.0 | 5.0 | 10 |

(a) Plot displacement (not position) versus time. (b) Find the average velocity of the particle in the intervals 0.0 to 1.0 sec, 0.0 to 2.0 sec, 0.0 to 3.0 sec, 0.0 to 4.0 sec. (c) Find the slope of the curve drawn in part a at the points $t = 1.0$, 2.0, 3.0, 4.0, and 5.0. (d) Plot the slope (units?) versus time. (e) From the curve of part d determine the acceleration of the particle at times $t = 2.0$, 3.0 and 4.0 sec.

**5.** A tennis ball is dropped onto the floor from a height of 4.0 ft. It rebounds to a height of 3.0 ft. If the ball was in contact with the floor for 0.010 sec, what was its average acceleration during contact?

**6.** The graph of $x$ versus $t$ (see Fig. 3–9a) is for a particle in straight line motion. State for each interval whether the velocity $v_x$ is $+$, $-$, or 0, and whether the acceleration $a_x$ is $+$, $-$, or 0. The intervals are $OA$, $AB$, $BC$, and $CD$. From the curve is there any *interval* over which the acceleration is obviously *not constant*? (Ignore the behavior at the end points of the intervals.)

(a)     (b)

**Fig. 3–9**

**7.** Answer the previous questions for the motion described by the graph of Fig. 3–9b.

**8.** An arrow while being shot from a bow was accelerated over a distance of 2.0 ft. If its speed at the moment it left the bow was 200 ft/sec what was the average acceleration imparted by the bow? Justify any assumptions you need to make.

**9.** An electron with initial velocity $v_{x0} = 1.0 \times 10^4$ meters/sec enters a region where it is electrically accelerated (Fig. 3–10). It emerges with a velocity $v_x = 4.0 \times 10^6$ meters/sec. What was its acceleration, assumed constant? (Such a process occurs in the electron gun in a cathode-ray tube, used in television receivers and oscilloscopes.)

**Fig. 3–10**

**10.** Suppose that you were called upon to give some advice to a lawyer concerning the physics involved in one of his cases. The question is whether a driver was exceeding a 30 miles/hr speed limit before he made an emergency stop, brakes locked and wheels sliding. The length of skid marks on the road was 19.2 ft. The policeman made the reasonable assumption that the maximum deceleration of the car would not exceed the acceleration of a freely falling body and arrested the driver for speeding. Was he speeding? Explain.

**11.** A meson is shot with constant speed $5.00 \times 10^6$ meters/sec into a region where an electric field produces an acceleration on the meson of magnitude $1.25 \times 10^{14}$ meters/sec$^2$ directed opposite to the initial velocity. How far does the meson travel before coming to rest? How long does the meson remain at rest?

**12.** A rocketship in free space moves with constant acceleration equal to 32 ft/sec$^2$. (a) If it starts from rest, how long will it take to acquire a speed one-tenth that of light? (b) How far will it travel in so doing?

**13.** A train started from rest and moved with constant acceleration. At one time it was traveling 30 ft/sec, and 160 ft farther on it was traveling 50 ft/sec. Calculate (a) the acceleration, (b) the time required to travel the 160 ft mentioned, (c) the time required to attain the speed of 30 ft/sec, (d) the distance moved from rest to the time the train had a speed of 30 ft/sec.

**14.** At the instant the traffic light turns green, an automobile starts with a constant acceleration $a_x$ of 6.0 ft/sec$^2$. At the same instant a truck, traveling with a constant speed of 30 ft/sec, overtakes and passes the automobile. (a) How far beyond the starting point will the automobile overtake the truck? (b) How fast will the car be traveling at that instant? (It is instructive to plot a qualitative graph of $x$ versus $t$ for each vehicle.)

**15.** A car moving with constant acceleration covers the distance between two points 180 ft apart in 6.0 sec. Its speed as it passes the second point is 45 ft/sec. (a) What is its speed at the first point? (b) What is its acceleration? (c) At what prior distance from the first point was the car at rest?

**16.** The engineer of a train moving at a speed $v_1$ sights a freight train a distance $d$ ahead of him on the same track moving in the same direction with a slower speed $v_2$. He puts on the brakes and gives his train a constant deceleration $a$. Show that

$$\text{if} \quad d > \frac{(v_1 - v_2)^2}{2a}, \quad \text{there will be no collision;}$$

$$\text{if} \quad d < \frac{(v_1 - v_2)^2}{2a}, \quad \text{there will be a collision.}$$

(It is instructive to plot a qualitative graph of $x$ versus $t$ for each train.)

**17.** Two trains, one traveling at 60 miles/hr and the other at 80 miles/hr, are headed toward one another along a straight level track. When they are 2.0 miles apart, both engineers simultaneously see the other's train and apply their brakes. If the brakes decelerate each train at the rate of 3.0 ft/sec$^2$, determine whether there is a collision.

**18.** A rocket-driven sled running on a straight level track is used to investigate the physiological effects of large accelerations on humans. One such sled can attain a speed of 1000 miles/hr in 1.8 sec starting from rest. (a) Assume the acceleration is constant and compare it to $g$. (b) What is the distance traveled in this time?

**19.** (a) With what speed must a ball be thrown vertically upward in order to rise to a height of 50 ft? (b) How long will it be in the air?

**20.** Water drips from the nozzle of a shower onto the stall floor 81 in. below. The drops fall at regular intervals of time, the first drop striking the floor at the instant the fourth drop begins to fall. Find the location of the individual drops when a drop strikes the floor.

**21.** If a body travels half its total path in the last second of its fall from rest, find the time and height of its fall. Explain the physically unacceptable solution of the quadratic time equation.

**22.** An artillery shell is fired directly up from a gun; a rocket, propelled by burning fuel, takes off vertically from a launching area. Plot qualitatively (numbers not required) *possible* graphs of $a_y$ versus $t$, of $v_y$ versus $t$, and of $y$ versus $t$ for each. Take $t = 0$ at the instant the shell leaves the gun barrel or the rocket leaves the ground. Continue the plots until the rocket and the shell fall back to earth; neglect air resistance; assume that up is positive and down is negative.

**23.** A rocket is fired vertically and ascends with a constant vertical acceleration of 64 ft/sec$^2$ for 1.0 min. Its fuel is then all used and it continues as a free particle. (a) What is the maximum altitude reached? (b) What is the total time elapsed from take-off until the rocket strikes the earth?

**24.** A lead ball is dropped into a lake from a diving board 16 ft above the water. It hits the water with a certain velocity and then sinks to the bottom with this same constant velocity. It reaches the bottom 5.0 sec after it is dropped. (a) How deep is the lake? (b) What is the average velocity of the ball? (c) Suppose all the water is drained from the lake. The ball is thrown from the diving board so that it again reaches the bottom in 5.0 sec. What is the initial velocity of the ball?

**25.** A stone is dropped into the water from a bridge 144 ft above the water. Another stone is thrown vertically down 1.0 sec after the first is dropped. Both stones strike the water at the same time. (a) What was the initial speed of the second stone? (b) Plot speed versus time on a graph for each stone, taking zero time as the instant the first stone was released.

**26.** A steel ball bearing is dropped from the roof of a building (the initial velocity of the ball is zero). An observer standing in front of a window 4.0 ft high notes that the ball takes $\frac{1}{8}$ sec to fall from the top to the bottom of the window. The ball bearing continues to fall, makes a completely elastic collision with a horizontal sidewalk, and reappears at the bottom of the window 2.0 sec after passing it on the way down. How tall is the building? (The ball will have the same speed at a point going up as it had going down after a completely elastic collision.)

**27.** A dog sees a flowerpot sail up and then back down past a window 5.0 ft high. If the total time the pot is in sight is 1.0 sec, find the height above the window that the pot rises.

**28.** A balloon is ascending at the rate of 12 meters/sec at a height 80 meters above the ground when a package is dropped. How long does it take the package to reach the ground?

**29.** A parachutist after bailing out falls 50 meters without friction. When the parachute opens, he decelerates downward 2.0 meters/sec². He reaches the ground with a speed of 3.0 meters/sec. (a) How long is the parachutist in the air? (b) At what height did he bail out?

**30.** An elevator ascends with an upward acceleration of 4.0 ft/sec². At the instant its upward speed is 8.0 ft/sec, a loose bolt drops from the ceiling of the elevator 9.0 ft from the floor. Calculate (a) the time of flight of the bolt from ceiling to floor and (b) the distance it has fallen relative to the elevator shaft.

**31.** The position of a particle moving along the x-axis depends on the time according to the equation

$$x = at^2 - bt^3,$$

where x is in feet and t in seconds. (a) What dimensions and units must a and b have? For the following, let their numerical values be 3.0 and 1.0, respectively. (b) At what time does the particle reach its maximum positive x-position? (c) What total length of path does the particle cover in the first 4.0 sec? (d) What is its displacement during the first 4.0 sec? (e) What is the particle's speed at the end of each of the first four seconds? (f) What is the particle's acceleration at the end of each of the first four seconds?

**32.** An electron, starting from rest, has an acceleration that increases linearly with time, that is, $a = kt$, the change in acceleration being $k = (1.5 \text{ meters/sec}^2)/\text{sec}$. (a) Plot a versus t during the first 10-sec interval. (b) From the curve of part (a) plot the corresponding v versus t curve and estimate the electron's velocity 5.0 sec after its motion starts. (c) From the v versus t curve of part (b) plot the corresponding x versus t curve and estimate how far the electron moved during the first 5.0 sec of its motion.

**33.** The position of a particle moving along the x-axis depends on the time according to the relation

$$x = \frac{v_{x0}}{k} (1 - e^{-kt})$$

in which $v_{x0}$ and k are constants. (a) Plot a curve of x versus t. Notice that $x = 0$ at $t = 0$ and that $x = v_{x0}/k$ at $t = \infty$; that is, the total distance through which the particle moves is $v_{x0}/k$.   (b) Show that the velocity $v_x$ is given by

$$v_x = v_{x0}e^{-kt}$$

so that the velocity decreases exponentially with time from its initial value of $v_{x0}$, coming to rest only in infinite time.   (c) Show that the acceleration $a_x$ is given by

$$a_x = -kv_x$$

so that the acceleration is directed opposite to the velocity and has a magnitude proportional to the speed.   (d) This particular motion is one with variable acceleration. Give a plausible physical argument explaining how it can take an infinite time to bring to rest a particle that travels a finite distance.

# Motion in a Plane

## CHAPTER 4

## 4–1 Displacement, Velocity, and Acceleration

In this chapter we return to a consideration of motion in two dimensions taken, for convenience, to be the $x$-$y$ plane. Figure 4–1 shows a particle at time $t$ moving along a curved path in this plane. Its *position*, or displacement from the origin, is measured by the vector **r**; its *velocity* is indicated by the vector **v** which, as we have seen in Section 3–4, must be tangent to the path of the particle. The *acceleration* is indicated by the vector **a**; the direction of **a**, as we shall see more explicitly later, does not bear any unique relationship to the path of the particle but depends rather on the rate at which the velocity **v** changes with time as the particle moves along its path.

The vectors **r**, **v**, and **a** are interrelated (see Eqs. 3–4, 3–5, and 3–10) and can be expressed in terms of their components, using unit vector notation, as

$$r = ix + jy, \qquad (4\text{--}1)$$

$$v = \frac{dr}{dt} = iv_x + jv_y, \qquad (4\text{--}2)$$

and

$$a = \frac{dv}{dt} = ia_x + ja_y. \qquad (4\text{--}3)$$

**Fig. 4–1** A particle moves along a curved path in the $x$-$y$ plane. Its position **r**, velocity **v**, and acceleration **a** are shown at time $t$, along with the vector components of those vectors. Note that $x$, $y$, $v_x$, $v_y$, and $a_x$ are positive but that $a_y$ is negative. Compare to Fig. 3-3.

These equations can easily be extended to three dimensions by adding to them the terms $kz$, $kv_z$, and $ka_z$, respectively in which $\mathbf{k}$ is a unit vector in the $z$-direction.

In Chapter 3 we considered the special case in which the particle moved in one dimension only, say along the $x$-axis, where the vectors $\mathbf{r}$, $\mathbf{v}$, and $\mathbf{a}$ were directed along this axis, either in the positive $x$-direction or the negative $x$-direction. The components $y$, $v_y$, and $a_y$ were zero and we described the motion in terms of equations relating the scalar quantities $x$, $v_x$, and $a_x$. Or, when the particle moved along the $y$-axis, the components $x$, $v_x$, and $a_x$ were zero and the motion was described in terms of equations relating the scalar quantities $y$, $v_y$, and $a_y$. In this chapter we consider motion in the $x$-$y$ plane so that, in general, both sets of components have nonzero values.

#### 4–2  Motion in a Plane with Constant Acceleration

Let us consider first the special case of motion in a plane with *constant* acceleration. Here, as the particle moves, the acceleration $\mathbf{a}$ does not vary either in magnitude or in direction. Hence the components of $\mathbf{a}$ in any particular reference frame also will not vary, that is, $a_x =$ constant and $a_y =$ constant. We then have a situation which can be described as the sum of two component motions occurring simultaneously with constant acceleration along each of two perpendicular directions. The particle will move, in general, along a curved path in the plane. This may be so even if one component of the acceleration, say $a_x$, is zero, for then the corresponding component of the velocity, say $v_x$, may have a constant, nonzero value. An example of this latter situation is the motion of an artillery shell which follows a curved path in a vertical plane and, neglecting the effects of air resistance, is subject to a constant acceleration $\mathbf{g}$ directed down along the $y$-axis only.

We can obtain the general equations for plane motion with constant $\mathbf{a}$ simply by setting

$$a_x = \text{constant} \quad \text{and} \quad a_y = \text{constant}.$$

The equations for constant acceleration, summarized in Table 3–1, then apply to both the $x$- and $y$-components of the position vector $\mathbf{r}$, the velocity vector $\mathbf{v}$, and the acceleration vector $\mathbf{a}$ (see Table 4–1).

The two sets of equations in Table 4–1 are related in that the time parameter $t$ is the same for each, since $t$ represents the time at which the particle, moving in a curved path in the $x$-$y$ plane, occupied a position described by the position components $x$ and $y$.

The equations of motion in Table 4–1 may also be expressed in vector form. For example, substituting Eqs. 4–4a, 4a' into Eq. 4–2 yields

$$\mathbf{v} = \mathbf{i}v_x + \mathbf{j}v_y$$

$$= \mathbf{i}(v_{x0} + a_x t) + \mathbf{j}(v_{y0} + a_y t)$$

$$= (\mathbf{i}v_{x0} + \mathbf{j}v_{y0}) + (\mathbf{i}a_x + \mathbf{j}a_y)t.$$

## Table 4–1

MOTION WITH CONSTANT ACCELERATION IN THE $x$-$y$ PLANE

| Equation No. | $x$-Motion Equations | Equation No. | $y$-Motion Equations |
|---|---|---|---|
| 4–4a | $v_x = v_{x0} + a_x t$ | 4–4a' | $v_y = v_{y0} + a_y t$ |
| 4–4b | $x = x_0 + \frac{1}{2}(v_{x0} + v_x)t$ | 4–4b' | $y = y_0 + \frac{1}{2}(v_{y0} + v_y)t$ |
| 4–4c | $x = x_0 + v_{x0}t + \frac{1}{2}a_x t^2$ | 4–4c' | $y = y_0 + v_{y0}t + \frac{1}{2}a_y t^2$ |
| 4–4d | $v_x{}^2 = v_{x0}{}^2 + 2a_x(x - x_0)$ | 4–4d' | $v_y{}^2 = v_{y0}{}^2 + 2a_y(y - y_0)$ |

The first quantity in parentheses is the initial velocity vector $\mathbf{v}_0$ (see Eq. 4–2) and the second is the (constant) acceleration vector $\mathbf{a}$ (see Eq. 4–3). Thus the vector relation

$$\mathbf{v} = \mathbf{v}_0 + \mathbf{a}t \qquad (4\text{–}5a)$$

is equivalent to the two scalar relations Eqs. 4–4a, a' in Table 4–1. It shows simply and compactly that the velocity $\mathbf{v}$ at time $t$ is the sum of the initial velocity $\mathbf{v}_0$ which the particle would have in the absence of acceleration plus the (vector) change in velocity, $\mathbf{a}t$, acquired during the time $t$ under the constant acceleration $\mathbf{a}$. Similarly, the scalar equations 4–4c, c' are equivalent to the single vector equation

$$\mathbf{r} = \mathbf{r}_0 + \mathbf{v}_0 t + \frac{1}{2}\mathbf{a}t^2, \qquad (4\text{–}5b)$$

which is also easily interpreted. The proof of this and other relations is left to Problem 17.

### 4–3   Projectile Motion

An example of curved motion with constant acceleration is projectile motion. This is the two-dimensional motion of a particle thrown obliquely into the air. The ideal motion of a baseball, a golf ball, or a bullet is an example of projectile motion.* We assume that the effect the air itself would have on their motions can be neglected.

The motion of a projectile is one of constant acceleration $\mathbf{g}$, directed downward, and thus should be described by the equations in Table 4–1. There is no horizontal component of acceleration. If we choose a reference frame with the positive $y$-axis vertically upward, we may put $a_y = -g$ and $a_x = 0$ in these equations.

Let us further choose the origin of our reference frame to be the point at which the projectile begins its flight (see Fig. 4–2). Hence the origin will be the point at which the ball leaves the thrower's hand or the fuel in the rocket burns out, for example. In Table 4–1 this choice of origin implies

---

* See Galileo Galilei, *Dialogues Concerning Two New Sciences*, the "Fourth Day," for a fascinating discussion of Galileo's research on projectiles.

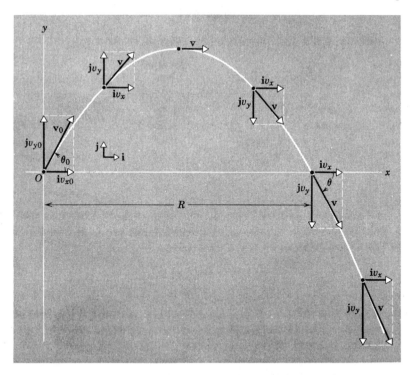

**Fig. 4–2** The trajectory of a projectile, showing the initial velocity $v_0$ and its vector components and also the velocity $v$ and its vector components at five later times. Note that $v_x = v_{x0}$ throughout the flight. The distance $R$ is the horizontal range.

that $x_0 = y_0 = 0$. The velocity at $t = 0$, the instant the projectile begins its flight, is $v_0$, which makes an angle $\theta_0$ with the positive $x$-direction. The $x$- and $y$-components of $v_0$ (see Fig. 4–2) are then

$$v_{x0} = v_0 \cos \theta_0 \quad \text{and} \quad v_{y0} = v_0 \sin \theta_0.$$

Because there is no horizontal component of acceleration, the horizontal component of the velocity will be constant. In Eq. 4–4a we set $a_x = 0$ and $v_{x0} = v_0 \cos \theta_0$, so that

$$v_x = v_0 \cos \theta_0. \tag{4–6a}$$

The horizontal velocity component retains its initial value throughout the flight.

The vertical component of the velocity will change with time in accordance with vertical motion with constant downward acceleration. In Eq. 4–4a' we set

$$a_y = -g \quad \text{and} \quad v_{y0} = v_0 \sin \theta_0,$$

so that

$$v_y = v_0 \sin \theta_0 - gt. \tag{4–6a'}$$

The vertical velocity component is that of free fall. Indeed, if we view the motion of Fig. 4-2 from a reference frame that moves to the right with a speed $v_{x0}$, the motion will be that of an object thrown vertically upward with an initial speed $v_0 \sin \theta_0$.

The *magnitude* of the resultant velocity vector at any instant is

$$v = \sqrt{v_x{}^2 + v_y{}^2}. \tag{4-7}$$

The angle $\theta$ that the velocity vector makes with the horizontal at that instant is given by

$$\tan \theta = \frac{v_y}{v_x}.$$

The velocity vector is tangent to the path of the particle at every point, as shown in Fig. 4-2.

The $x$-coordinate of the particle's position at any time, obtained from Eq. 4-4c with $x_0 = 0$, $a_x = 0$, and $v_{x0} = v_0 \cos \theta_0$, is

$$x = (v_0 \cos \theta_0)t. \tag{4-6c}$$

The $y$-coordinate, obtained from Eq. 4-4c' with $y_0 = 0$, $a_y = -g$, and $v_{y0} = v_0 \sin \theta_0$, is

$$y = (v_0 \sin \theta_0)t - \tfrac{1}{2}gt^2. \tag{4-6c'}$$

Equations 4-6c, c' give us $x$ and $y$ as functions of the common parameter $t$, the time in flight. By combining and eliminating $t$ from them, we obtain

$$y = (\tan \theta_0)x - \frac{g}{2(v_0 \cos \theta_0)^2} x^2, \tag{4-8}$$

which relates $y$ to $x$ and is the equation of the trajectory of the projectile. Since $v_0$, $\theta_0$, and $g$ are constants, this equation has the form

$$y = bx - cx^2,$$

the equation of a parabola. Hence the trajectory of a projectile is parabolic.

▶ **Example 1.** A bomber is flying at a constant horizontal velocity of 820 miles/hr at an elevation of 52,000 ft toward a point directly above its target. At what angle of sight $\phi$ should a bomb be released to strike the target (Fig. 4-3)?

We choose a reference frame fixed with respect to the earth, its origin $O$ being the bomb release point. The motion of the bomb at the instant of release is the same as that of the bomber. Hence the initial projectile velocity $\mathbf{v}_0$ is horizontal and its magnitude is 820 miles/hr or 1200 ft/sec. The angle of projection $\theta_0$ is zero.

The time of fall is obtained from Eq. 4-6c'. With $\theta_0 = 0$ and $y = -52,000$ ft, this gives

$$t = \sqrt{-\frac{2y}{g}} = \sqrt{-\frac{2(-52,000)\text{ft}}{32 \text{ ft/sec}^2}} = 57 \text{ sec.}$$

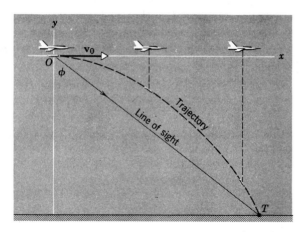

**Fig. 4–3**    Example 1.    A bomb is released from an airplane with horizontal velocity $v_0$.

Note that the time of fall of the bomb does *not* depend on the speed of the plane for a *horizontal* projection.    (See, however, Problem 10.)

The horizontal distance traveled by the bomb in this time is given by Eq. 4–6c, $x = (v_0 \cos \theta_0)t$, or $x = (1200 \text{ ft/sec})(57 \text{ sec}) = 68,000$ ft so that the angle of sight (Fig. 4–3) should be

$$\phi = \tan^{-1} \frac{x}{|y|} = \tan^{-1} \frac{68,000}{52,000} = 53°.$$

Does the motion of the bomb appear to be parabolic when viewed from a reference frame fixed with respect to the bomber?

**Example 2.**    A soccer player kicks a ball at an angle of 37° from the horizontal with an initial speed of 50 ft/sec.    (A right triangle, one of whose angles is 37°, has sides in the ratio 3:4:5, or 6:8:10.)    Assuming that the ball moves in a vertical plane:

(*a*)  Find the time $t_1$ at which the ball reaches the highest point of its trajectory. At the highest point, the vertical component of velocity $v_y$ is zero.    Solving Eq. 4–6a′ for $t$, we obtain

$$t = \frac{v_0 \sin \theta_0 - v_y}{g}.$$

With

$$v_y = 0, \qquad v_0 = 50 \text{ ft/sec}, \qquad \theta_0 = 37°, \qquad g = 32 \text{ ft/sec}^2,$$

we have

$$t_1 = \frac{[50(\tfrac{6}{10}) - 0] \text{ ft/sec}}{32 \text{ ft/sec}^2} = \frac{15}{16} \text{ sec}.$$

(*b*)  How high does the ball go?    The maximum height is reached at $t = 15/16$ sec.    By using Eq. 4–6c′,

$$y = (v_0 \sin \theta_0)t - \tfrac{1}{2}gt^2,$$

we have

$$y_{\text{max}} = (50 \text{ ft/sec})(\tfrac{6}{10})(\tfrac{15}{16} \text{ sec}) - \tfrac{1}{2}(32 \text{ ft/sec}^2)(\tfrac{15}{16})^2 \text{ sec}^2 = 14 \text{ ft}.$$

(c) What is the horizontal range of the ball and how long is it in the air?

The horizontal distance from the starting point at which the ball returns to its original elevation (ground level) is the *range* R.   We set $y = 0$ in Eq. 4–6c' and find the time $t_2$ required to traverse this range.   We obtain

$$t_2 = \frac{2v_0 \sin \theta_0}{g} = \frac{2(50 \text{ ft/sec})(\frac{6}{10})}{32 \text{ ft/sec}^2} = \frac{15}{8} \text{ sec.}$$

Notice that $t_2 = 2t_1$.   This corresponds to the fact that the same time is required for the ball to go up (reach its maximum height from ground) as is required for the ball to come down (reach the ground from its maximum height).

The range R can then be obtained by inserting this value $t_2$ for $t$ in Eq. 4–6c. We obtain, from $x = (v_0 \cos \theta_0)t$,

$$R = (v_0 \cos \theta_0)t_2 = (50 \text{ ft/sec})(\tfrac{8}{10})(\tfrac{15}{8} \text{ sec}) = 75 \text{ ft.}$$

(d) What is the velocity of the ball as it strikes the ground?   From Eq. 4–6a we obtain

$$v_x = v_0 \cos \theta_0 = (50 \text{ ft/sec})(\tfrac{8}{10}) = 40 \text{ ft/sec.}$$

From Eq. 4–6a' we obtain for $t = t_2 = \frac{15}{8}$ sec,

$$v_y = v_0 \sin \theta_0 - gt = (50 \text{ ft/sec})(\tfrac{6}{10}) - (32 \text{ ft/sec}^2)(\tfrac{15}{8} \text{ sec}) = -30 \text{ ft/sec.}$$

Hence, from Eq. 4–7,

$$v = \sqrt{v_x{}^2 + v_y{}^2} = \sqrt{(40 \text{ ft/sec})^2 + (-30 \text{ ft/sec})^2} = 50 \text{ ft/sec,}$$

and                            $\tan \theta = v_y/v_x = -\tfrac{30}{40},$

so that $\theta = -37°$, or 37° *clockwise* from the x-axis.   Notice that $\theta = -\theta_0$, as we expect from symmetry (Fig. 4–2).

**Example 3.**   In a favorite lecture demonstration a gun is sighted at an elevated target which is released in free fall by a trip mechanism as the bullet leaves the muzzle.   No matter what the initial speed of the bullet, it always hits the falling target.

The simplest way to understand this is the following.   If there were no accleration due to gravity, the target would not fall and the bullet would move along the line of sight directly into the target (Fig. 4–4).   The effect of gravity is to cause each body to accelerate down at the same rate from the position it would otherwise have had.   Therefore, in the time $t$, the bullet will fall a distance $\frac{1}{2}gt^2$ from the position it would have had along the line of sight and the target will fall the same distance from its starting point.   When the bullet reaches the line of fall of the target, it will be the same distance below the target's initial position as the target is and hence the collision.   If the bullet moves faster than shown in the figure ($v_0$ larger), it will have a greater range and will cross the line of fall at a higher point; but since it gets there sooner, the target will fall a correspondingly smaller distance in the same time and collide with it.   A similar argument holds for slower speeds.

For an equivalent analysis, let us use Eq. 4–5b

$$\mathbf{r} = \mathbf{r}_0 + \mathbf{v}_0 t + \tfrac{1}{2}\mathbf{a}t^2$$

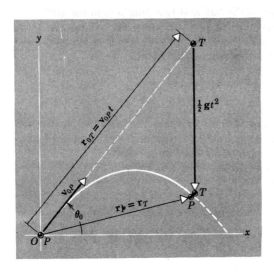

**Fig. 4–4** Example 3. In the motion of a projectile, its displacement from the origin at any time $t$ can be thought of as the sum of two vectors: $v_{0P}t$, directed along $v_{0P}$, and $gt^2/2$, directed downward.

to describe the positions of the projectile and the target at any time $t$. For the projectile $P$, $r_0 = 0$ and $a = g$, and we have

$$r_P = v_{0P}t + \tfrac{1}{2}gt^2.$$

For the target $T$, $r_0 = r_{0T}$, $v_0 = 0$, and $a = g$, leading to

$$r_T = r_{0T} + \tfrac{1}{2}gt^2.$$

If there is a collision, we must have $r_P = r_T$. Inspection shows that this will always occur at a time $t$ given by $r_{0T} = v_{0P}t$, that is, in the time $t$ ($= r_{0T}/v_{0P}$) required for the projectile to travel to the target position along the line of sight, assuming that its initial velocity remains unchanged. ◀

## 4–4 Uniform Circular Motion

In Section 3–6 we saw that acceleration arises from a change in velocity. In the simple case of free fall the velocity changed in magnitude only, but not in direction. In a particle moving in a circle with constant speed, called uniform circular motion, the velocity vector changes continuously in direction but not in magnitude. We seek now to obtain the acceleration in uniform circular motion.

The situation is shown in Fig. 4–5a. Let $P$ be the position of the particle at the time $t$ and $P'$ its position at the time $t + \Delta t$. The velocity at $P$ is $v$, a vector tangent to the curve at $P$. The velocity at $P'$ is $v'$, a vector tangent to the curve at $P'$. Vectors $v$ and $v'$ are equal in magnitude, the speed being constant, but their directions are different. The length of path traversed during $\Delta t$ is the arc length $PP'$, which is equal to $v \, \Delta t$, $v$ being the constant speed.

Now redraw the vectors $v$ and $v'$, as in Fig. 4–5b, so that they originate at a common point. We are free to do this as long as the magnitude and direction of each vector are the same as in Fig. 4–5a. This diagram (Fig. 4–5b) enables us to see clearly the *change in velocity* as the particle moved from $P$ to $P'$. This change, $\mathbf{v}' - \mathbf{v} = \Delta\mathbf{v}$, is the vector which must be added to $\mathbf{v}$ to get $\mathbf{v}'$. Notice that it points inward, approximately toward the center of the circle.

Now the triangle $OQQ'$ formed by $\mathbf{v}$, $\mathbf{v}'$, and $\Delta\mathbf{v}$ is similar to the triangle $CPP'$ formed by the chord $PP'$ and the radii $CP$ and $CP'$. This is so because both are isosceles triangles having the same vertex angle; the angle $\theta$ between $\mathbf{v}$ and $\mathbf{v}'$ is the same as the angle $PCP'$ because $\mathbf{v}$ is perpendicular to $CP$ and $\mathbf{v}'$ is perpendicular to $CP'$. We can therefore write

$$\frac{\Delta v}{v} = \frac{v\,\Delta t}{r}, \quad \text{approximately,}$$

the chord $PP'$ being taken equal to the arc length $PP'$. This relation becomes more nearly exact as $\Delta t$ is diminished, since the chord and the arc then approach each other. Notice also that $\Delta\mathbf{v}$ approaches closer and closer to a direction perpendicular to $\mathbf{v}$ and $\mathbf{v}'$ as $\Delta t$ is diminished and therefore approaches closer and closer to a direction pointing to the exact center of the circle. It follows from this relation that

$$\frac{\Delta v}{\Delta t} = \frac{v^2}{r}, \quad \text{approximately,}$$

and in the limit when $\Delta t \to 0$ this expression becomes exact. We therefore obtain

$$a = \lim_{\Delta t \to 0} \frac{\Delta v}{\Delta t} = \frac{v^2}{r} \qquad (4\text{–}9)$$

as the magnitude of the acceleration. The direction of $\mathbf{a}$ is instantaneously along a radius inward toward the center of the circle.

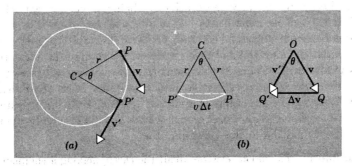

**Fig. 4–5** Uniform circular motion. The particle travels around a circle at constant speed. Its velocity at two points $P$ and $P'$ is shown. Its change in velocity in going from $P$ to $P'$ is $\Delta\mathbf{v}$.

Figure 4–6 shows the instantaneous relation between **v** and **a** at various points of the motion. The magnitude of **v** is constant, but its direction changes continuously. This gives rise to an acceleration **a** which is also constant in magnitude (but not zero) but continuously changing in direction. The velocity **v** is always tangent to the circle in the direction of motion; the acceleration **a** is always directed radially inward. Because of this, **a** is called a *radial*, or *centripetal*, acceleration. *Centripetal* means "seeking a center."

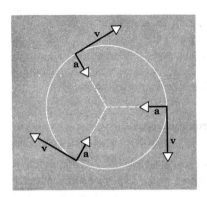

**Fig. 4–6** In uniform circular motion the acceleration **a** is always directed toward the center of the circle and hence is perpendicular to **v**.

Both in free fall and in projectile motion **a** is constant in direction and magnitude and we can use the equations developed for constant acceleration (see Table 4–1). We cannot use these equations for uniform circular motion because **a** varies in direction and is therefore not constant.

The units of centripetal acceleration are the same as those of an acceleration resulting from a change in the magnitude of a velocity. Dimensionally, we have

$$\frac{v^2}{r} = \left(\frac{\text{length}}{\text{time}}\right)^2 \bigg/ \text{length} = \frac{\text{length}}{\text{time}^2} \quad \text{or} \quad \frac{L}{T^2},$$

which are the dimensions of acceleration. The units therefore may be ft/sec², meters/sec², among others.

The acceleration resulting from a change in direction of a velocity is just as real and just as much an acceleration in every sense as that arising from a change in magnitude of a velocity. By definition, acceleration is the time rate of change of velocity, and velocity, being a vector, can change in direction as well as magnitude. If a physical quantity is a vector, its directional aspects cannot be ignored, for their effects will prove to be every bit as important and real as those produced by changes in magnitude.

It is worth emphasizing at this point that there need not be any motion in the direction of an acceleration and that there is no fixed relation in general between the directions of **a** and **v**. In Fig. 4–7 we give examples in which the angle between **v** and **a** varies from 0 to 180°. Only in one case, $\theta = 0°$, is the motion in the direction of **a**.

▶ **Example 4.** The moon revolves about the earth, making a complete revolution in 27.3 days. Assume that the orbit is circular and has a radius of 239,000 miles. What is the magnitude of the acceleration of the moon toward the earth? We have $r = 239,000$ miles $= 3.85 \times 10^8$ meters. The time for one complete

| $\theta = 180°$ | $180° > \theta > 90°$ | $\theta = 90°$ | $90° > \theta > 0°$ | $\theta = 0°$ |
|---|---|---|---|---|
| Ball thrown up | Rise of a projectile | Uniform circular motion | Fall of a projectile | Ball thrown down |

revolution, called the period, is $T = 27.3$ days $= 2.36 \times 10^6$ sec. The speed of the moon (assumed constant) is therefore

$$v = 2\pi r/T = 1020 \text{ meters/sec.}$$

The centripetal acceleration is

$$a = \frac{v^2}{r} = \frac{(1020 \text{ meters/sec})^2}{3.85 \times 10^8 \text{ meters}} = 0.00273 \text{ meter/sec}^2, \quad \text{or only } 2.78 \times 10^{-4}g.$$

**Example 5.** Calculate the speed of an artificial earth satellite, assuming that it is traveling at an altitude $h$ of 140 miles above the surface of the earth where $g = 30$ ft/sec$^2$. The radius of the earth $R$ is 3960 miles.

Like any free object near the earth's surface the satellite has an acceleration $g$ toward the earth's center. It is this acceleration that causes it to follow the circular path. Hence the centripetal acceleration is $g$, and from Eq. 4–9, $a = v^2/r$, we have

$$g = v^2/(R + h),$$

or

$$v = \sqrt{(R + h)g} = \sqrt{(3960 \text{ miles} + 140 \text{ miles})(5280 \text{ ft/mile})(30 \text{ ft/sec}^2)}$$

$$= 2.55 \times 10^4 \text{ ft/sec} = 17,400 \text{ miles/hr.} \quad \blacktriangleleft$$

Let us now derive Eq. 4–9 using vector methods. Figure 4–8a shows a particle in uniform circular motion about the origin $O$ of a reference frame. For this motion the polar coordinates $r$, $\theta$ are more useful than the rectangular coordinates $x$, $y$ because $r$ remains constant throughout the motion and $\theta$ increases in a simple linear way with time; the behavior of $x$ and $y$ during such motion is more complex. The two sets of coordinates are related by

$$r = \sqrt{x^2 + y^2} \quad \text{and} \quad \theta = \tan^{-1} y/x \qquad (4\text{--}10a)$$

or by the reciprocal relations

$$x = r \cos \theta \quad \text{and} \quad y = r \sin \theta. \qquad (4\text{--}10b)$$

In rectangular reference frames we used the unit vectors $\mathbf{i}$ and $\mathbf{j}$ to describe motion in the $x$-$y$ plane. Here we find it more convenient to introduce two new unit vectors $\mathbf{u}_r$ and $\mathbf{u}_\theta$. These, like $\mathbf{i}$ and $\mathbf{j}$, have unit length and are dimensionless; they designate direction only.

The unit vector $\mathbf{u}_r$ at any point is in the direction of increasing $\mathbf{r}$ at that point; it is directed radially outward from the origin. The unit vector $\mathbf{u}_\theta$ at any point is in the direction of increasing $\theta$ at that point; it is always tangent to a circle

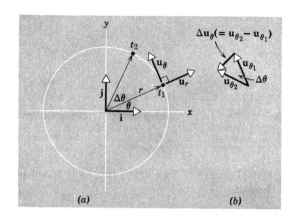

Fig. 4–8  (a)  A particle moving counterclockwise in a circle of radius $r$.  (b) The unit vectors $\mathbf{u}_{\theta_1}$ and $\mathbf{u}_{\theta_2}$ at times $t_1$ and $t_2$ respectively, and the change $\Delta\mathbf{u}_\theta$ ($= \mathbf{u}_{\theta_2} - \mathbf{u}_{\theta_1}$).

through the point in a counterclockwise direction.  As Fig. 4–8a shows, $\mathbf{u}_r$ and $\mathbf{u}_\theta$ are at right angles to each other.  The unit vectors $\mathbf{u}_r$ and $\mathbf{u}_\theta$ differ from the unit vectors $\mathbf{i}$ and $\mathbf{j}$ in that the directions of $\mathbf{u}_r$ and $\mathbf{u}_\theta$ vary from point to point in the plane; the unit vectors $\mathbf{u}_r$ and $\mathbf{u}_\theta$ are thus *not constant* vectors.

In terms of $\mathbf{u}_r$ and $\mathbf{u}_\theta$ the motion of a particle moving counterclockwise at uniform speed $v$ in a circle about the origin in Fig. 4–8a can be described by the vector equation

$$\mathbf{v} = \mathbf{u}_\theta v. \tag{4–11}$$

This relation tells us, correctly, that the direction of $\mathbf{v}$ (which is the same as the direction of $\mathbf{u}_\theta$) is tangent to the circle and that the magnitude of $\mathbf{v}$ is the constant quantity $v$ (because the magnitude of $\mathbf{u}_\theta$ is unity).

To find the acceleration we combine Eqs. 4–3 and 4–11, yielding

$$\mathbf{a} = \frac{d\mathbf{v}}{dt} = \frac{d\mathbf{u}_\theta}{dt} v. \tag{4–12}$$

Note that $v$ in Eq. 4–11 is a constant, but $\mathbf{u}_\theta$ is not since its direction changes as the particle moves.  To evaluate $d\mathbf{u}_\theta/dt$, consider Fig. 4–8b which shows the unit vectors $\mathbf{u}_{\theta_1}$ and $\mathbf{u}_{\theta_2}$ corresponding to an elapsed time $\Delta t$ ($= t_2 - t_1$) for the moving particle.  The vector $\Delta\mathbf{u}_\theta$ ($= \mathbf{u}_{\theta_2} - \mathbf{u}_{\theta_1}$) points radially inward toward the origin in the limiting case as $\Delta t \to 0$.  In other words, $d\mathbf{u}_\theta$ at any point has the direction of $-\mathbf{u}_r$.  The angle between $\mathbf{u}_{\theta_2}$ and $\mathbf{u}_{\theta_1}$ in the figure is $\Delta\theta$, which is the angle swept out by a radial line from the origin to the particle in time $\Delta t$.  The magnitude of $\Delta\mathbf{u}_\theta$ is simply $\Delta\theta$; bear in mind that the vectors $\mathbf{u}_{\theta_1}$ and $\mathbf{u}_{\theta_2}$ in Fig. 4–8b have the magnitude unity.  Thus

$$\frac{d\mathbf{u}_\theta}{dt} = -\mathbf{u}_r \lim_{\Delta t \to 0} \frac{\Delta\theta}{dt} = -\mathbf{u}_r \frac{d\theta}{dt}$$

and, from Eq. 4–12,

$$\mathbf{a} = \frac{d\mathbf{u}_\theta}{dt} v = -\mathbf{u}_r \frac{d\theta}{dt} v. \tag{4–13}$$

Now, $d\theta/dt$ is the uniform angular rotation rate of the particle and is given by

$$\frac{d\theta}{dt} = \frac{2\pi \text{ radians}}{\text{time for one revolution}} = \frac{2\pi}{2\pi r/v} = \frac{v}{r}.$$

Putting this into Eq. 4–13 leads us finally to

$$a = -u_r \frac{v^2}{r} \tag{4-14}$$

which tells us that the acceleration in uniform circular motion has a magnitude $v^2/r$ (see Eq. 4–9) and points radially inward (note the factor $-u_r$). The vector relation Eq. 4–14 thus tells us *both* the magnitude *and* the direction of the centripetal acceleration $a$. Note that, as expected, $a$ has a constant magnitude but changes continually in direction because $u_r$ changes continually in direction.

### 4–5   Tangential Acceleration in Circular Motion

We now consider the more general case of circular motion in which the speed $v$ of the moving particle is *not* constant. We shall use vector methods in polar coordinates.

As before, the velocity is given by Eq. 4–11, or

$$v = u_\theta v$$

except that, in this case, not only $u_\theta$ but also $v$ varies with time. Recalling the formula for the derivative of a product, one obtains for the acceleration

$$a = \frac{dv}{dt} = u_\theta \frac{dv}{dt} + v \frac{du_\theta}{dt} \tag{4-15}$$

In Eq. 4–12 the first term in this equation was not present because, $v$ being there assumed to be constant, $dv/dt$ was zero. The last term in Eq. 4–15 reduces, as we saw in the last section, to $-u_r(v^2/r)$. We can now write Eq. 4–15 as

$$a = u_\theta a_T - u_r a_R, \tag{4-16}$$

in which $a_T = dv/dt$ and $a_R = v^2/r$   The first term, $u_\theta a_T$, is the vector component of $a$ that is tangent to the path of the particle and arises from a change in the magnitude of the velocity in circular motion (see Fig. 4–9). This term and $a_T$ are called the *tangential acceleration*. The second term $-u_r a_R$ is the vector component of $a$ directed radially in toward the center of the circle and arises from a

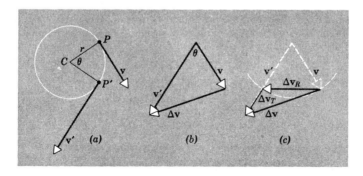

**Fig. 4–9**   In nonuniform circular motion the speed is variable. The change in velocity $\Delta v$ in going from $P$ to $P'$ is made up of two parts: $\Delta v_R$ caused by the change in direction of $v$, and $\Delta v_T$ caused by the change in magnitude of $v$. In the limit as $\Delta t \to 0$, $\Delta v_R$ points toward the center $C$ of the circle and $\Delta v_T$ is tangent to the circular path.

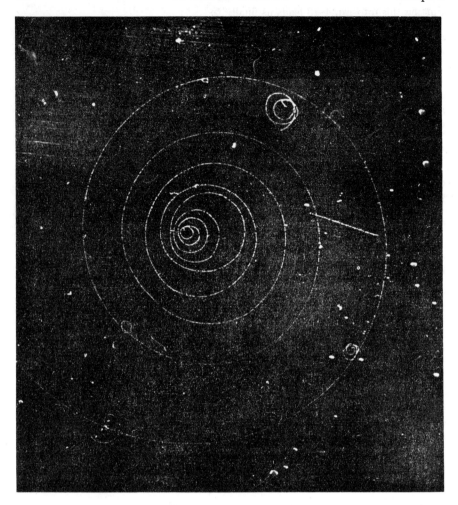

**Fig. 4–10** A track left in a 10-in. liquid-hydrogen-filled bubble chamber by an energetic spiralling electron. (Courtesy Lawrence Radiation Laboratory.) This picture is one of a number in a collection prepared for easy stereoscopic viewing and published, with explanatory material, as *Introduction to the Detection of Nuclear Particles in a Bubble Chamber*, The Ealing Press, Cambridge 40, Massachusetts (1964). When viewed stereoscopically the electron is seen to be moving toward the reader as it moves in along the spiral. Its velocity vector at any point, thus, does not lie in the plane of the figure, but tilts up out of it; its motion is thus three-dimensional, rather than two-dimensional as we assumed for other examples in this chapter.

change in the direction of the velocity in circular motion (see Fig. 4–9). This term and $a_R$ are called the *centripetal acceleration*.

The magnitude of the instantaneous acceleration is

$$a = \sqrt{a_T{}^2 + a_R{}^2} \tag{4–17}$$

If the speed is constant, then $a_T = dv/dt = 0$ and Eq. 4–16 reduces to Eq. 4–14. When the speed $v$ is not constant, $a_T$ is not zero and $a_R$ varies from point to point. If the speed changes at a rate that is not constant, then $a_T$ will also vary from point to point.

If the motion is not circular, the formulas for $a_T$ ($= dv/dt$) and for $a_R$ ($= v^2/r$) can still be applied if instead of using for $r$ the magnitude of the radius vector from the origin we substitute the radius of curvature of the path at the instantaneous position of the particle. Then $a_T$ gives the component of acceleration tangent to the curve at that position, and $a_R$ gives the component of acceleration normal to the curve at that position. Figure 4–10 shows the track left in a liquid-hydrogen-filled bubble chamber by an energetic electron that spirals inward. The electron loses energy as it traverses the liquid in the chamber so that its speed $v$ is being reduced steadily. Thus there is at every point a *tangential acceleration* given by $dv/dt$. The *centripetal acceleration* $a_R$ at any point is given by $v^2/r$, where $r$ is the radius of curvature of the track at the point in question; both $v$ and $r$ become smaller as the particle loses energy. The force causing the electron to spiral is produced by a magnetic field present in the bubble chamber and at right angles to the plane of Fig. 4–10 (see Chapter 33).

## 4–6   Relative Velocity and Acceleration

In earlier sections we considered the addition of velocities in a particular reference frame. Let us now consider the relation between the velocity of an object as determined by one observer $S$ ($=$ reference frame $S$) and the velocity of the same object as determined by another observer $S'$ ($=$ reference frame $S'$) who is moving with respect to the first.

Consider observer $S$ fixed to the earth, so that his reference frame is the earth. The other observer $S'$ is moving on the earth—for example, a passenger sitting on a moving train—so that his reference frame is the train. They each follow the motion of the same object, say an automobile on a road or a man walking through the train. Each observer will record a displacement, a velocity, and an acceleration for this object measured *relative to his reference frame*. How will these measurements compare? In this section we consider only the case in which the second frame is in motion with respect to the first with a *constant* velocity $\mathbf{u}$.

In Fig. 4–11 the reference frame $S$ represented by the $x$- and $y$-axes can

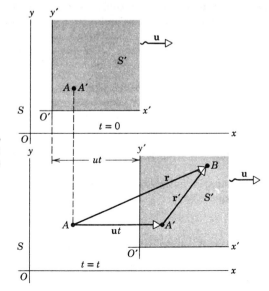

**Fig. 4–11**  Two reference frames, $S$ ($= x, y$) and $S'$ ($= x', y'$); $S'$ moves to the right, relative to $S$, with speed $u$.

be thought of as fixed to the earth. The shaded region indicates another reference frame $S'$, represented by $x'$- and $y'$-axes, which moves along the $x$-axis with a constant velocity $\mathbf{u}$, as measured in the $S$-system; it can be thought of as drawn on the floor of a railroad flatcar.

Initially, a particle (say a ball on the flatcar) is at a position called $A$ in the $S$-frame and called $A'$ in the $S'$-frame. At a time $t$ later the flatcar and its $S'$ reference frame have moved a distance $ut$ to the right and the particle has moved to $B$. The *displacement* of the particle from its initial position *in the S-frame* is the vector $\mathbf{r}$ from $A$ to $B$. The *displacement* of the particle from its initial position *in the S'-frame* is the vector $\mathbf{r}'$ from $A'$ to $B$. These are different vectors because the reference point $A'$ of the moving frame has been displaced a distance $ut$ along the $x$-axis during the motion. From the figure we see that $\mathbf{r}$ is the vector sum of $\mathbf{r}'$ and $\mathbf{u}t$:

$$\mathbf{r} = \mathbf{r}' + \mathbf{u}t. \tag{4–18}$$

Differentiating Eq. 4–18 leads to

$$\frac{d\mathbf{r}}{dt} = \frac{d\mathbf{r}'}{dt} + \mathbf{u}.$$

But $d\mathbf{r}/dt = \mathbf{v}$, the instantaneous velocity of the particle measured in the $S$-frame, and $d\mathbf{r}'/dt = \mathbf{v}'$, the instantaneous velocity of the same particle measured in the $S'$ frame, so that

$$\mathbf{v} = \mathbf{v}' + \mathbf{u}. \tag{4–19}$$

Hence the velocity of the particle relative to the $S$-frame, $\mathbf{v}$, is the vector sum of the velocity of the particle relative to the $S'$-frame, $\mathbf{v}'$, and the velocity $\mathbf{u}$ of the $S'$-frame relative to the $S$-frame.

▶ **Example 6.** (a) The compass of an airplane indicates that it is heading due east. Ground information indicates a wind blowing due north. Show on a diagram the velocity of the plane with respect to the ground.

The object is the airplane. The earth is one reference frame ($S$) and the air is the other reference frame ($S'$) moving with respect to the first. Then

    $\mathbf{u}$ is the velocity of the air with respect to the ground.
    $\mathbf{v}'$ is the velocity of the plane with respect to the air.
    $\mathbf{v}$ is the velocity of the plane with respect to the ground.

In this case $\mathbf{u}$ points north and $\mathbf{v}'$ points east. Then the relation $\mathbf{v} = \mathbf{v}' + \mathbf{u}$ determines the velocity of the plane with respect to the ground, as shown in Fig. 4–12a.

The angle $\alpha$ is the angle N of E of the plane's course with respect to the ground and is given by

$$\tan \alpha = u/v'.$$

The airplane's speed with respect to the ground is given by

$$v = \sqrt{(v')^2 + u^2}.$$

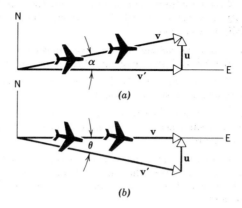

**Fig. 4–12** Example 6.

For example, if the air-speed indicator shows that the plane is moving relative to the air at a speed of 200 miles/hr, and if the speed of the wind with respect to the ground is 40.0 miles/hr, then

$$v = \sqrt{(200)^2 + (40.0)^2} \text{ miles/hr} = 204 \text{ miles/hr}$$

is the ground speed of the plane and

$$\alpha = \tan^{-1} \frac{40.0}{200} = 11° \, 20'$$

gives the course of the plane N of E.

(b) Now draw the vector diagram showing the direction the pilot must steer the plane through the air for the plane to travel due east with respect to the ground.

He would naturally head partly into the wind. His speed relative to the earth will therefore be less than before. The vector diagram is shown in Fig. 4–12b. The student should calculate $\theta$ and $v$, using the previous data for $u$ and $v'$. ◀

We have seen that different velocities are assigned to a particle by different observers when the observers are in relative motion. These velocities *always differ by* the relative velocity of the two observers, which here is *a constant velocity.* It follows that when the particle velocity changes, the *change will be the same* for both observers. Hence they each measure the *same acceleration* for the particle. The acceleration of a particle is the same in *all* reference frames moving relative to one another with constant velocity; that is, $a = a'$. This result follows in a formal way if we differentiate Eq. 4–19. Thus $dv/dt = dv'/dt + du/dt$; but $du/dt = 0$ when $u$ is constant, so that $a = a'$.

## QUESTIONS

1. In projectile motion when air resistance is negligible, is it ever necessary to consider three-dimensional motion rather than two-dimensional?

2. In broad jumping does it matter how high you jump? What factors determine the span of the jump?

3. Why doesn't the electron in the beam from an electron gun fall as much because of gravity as a water molecule in the stream from a hose? Assume horizontal motion initially in each case.

4. An aviator, pulling out of a dive, follows the arc of a circle. He was said to have "experienced $3g$'s" in pulling out of the dive. Explain what this statement means.

5. Describe qualitatively the acceleration acting on a bead which moves inward with constant speed along a spiral.

6. Could the acceleration of a projectile be represented in terms of a radial and a tangential component at each point of the motion? If so, is there any advantage to this representation?

7. A boy sitting in a railroad car moving at constant velocity throws a ball straight up into the air. Will the ball fall behind him? In front of him? Into his hand? What happens if the car accelerates forward or goes around a curve while the ball is in the air?

8. A man on the observation platform of a train moving with constant velocity drops a coin while leaning over the rail. Describe the path of the coin as seen by (a) the man on the train, (b) a person standing on the ground near the track, and (c) a person in a second train moving in the opposite direction to the first train on a parallel track.

9. A bus with a vertical windshield moves along in a rainstorm at speed $v_b$. The raindrops fall vertically with a terminal speed $v_r$. At what angle do the raindrops strike the windshield?

10. Drops are falling vertically in a steady rain. In order to go through the rain from one place to another in such a way as to encounter the least number of raindrops, should you move with the greatest possible speed, the least possible speed, or some intermediate speed?

11. An elevator is descending at a constant speed. A passenger takes a coin from his pocket and drops it to the floor. What accelerations would (a) the passenger and (b) a person at rest with respect to the elevator shaft observe for the falling coin?

## PROBLEMS

1. Prove that for a vector $\mathbf{a}$ defined by

$$\mathbf{a} = \mathbf{i}a_x + \mathbf{j}a_y + \mathbf{k}a_z$$

the scaler components are given by

$$a_x = \mathbf{i} \cdot \mathbf{a}, \qquad a_y = \mathbf{j} \cdot \mathbf{a}, \qquad \text{and} \qquad a_z = \mathbf{k} \cdot \mathbf{a}.$$

2. A ball rolls off the edge of a horizontal table top 4.0 ft high. If it strikes the floor at a point 5.0 ft horizontally away from the edge of the table, what was its speed at the instant it left the table?

3. A ball rolls off the top of a stairway with a horizontal velocity of magnitude 5.0 ft/sec. The steps are 8.0 in. high and 8.0 in. wide. Which step will the ball hit first?

4. A shell is fired horizontally from a powerful gun located 144 ft above a horizontal plane with a muzzle speed of 800 ft/sec. (a) How long does the shell remain in the air? (b) What is its range? (c) What is the magnitude of the vertical component of its velocity as it strikes the target?

5. Show that the maximum height reached by a projectile is $y_{\max} = (v_0 \sin \theta_0)^2/2g$.

**6.** Show that the horizontal range of a projectile having an initial speed $v_0$ and angle of projection $\theta_0$ is $R = (v_0^2/g) \sin 2\theta_0$. Then show that a projection angle of 45° gives the maximum horizontal range (Fig. 4–13).

**7.** Find the angle of projection at which the horizontal range and the maximum height of a projectile are equal.

**8.** In Galileo's *Two New Sciences* the author states that "for elevations (angles of projection) which exceed or fall short of 45° by equal amounts, the ranges are equal . . . ". Prove this statement.

**9.** A rifle with a muzzle velocity of 1500 ft/sec shoots a bullet at a small target 150 ft away. How high above the target must the gun be aimed so that the bullet will hit the target?

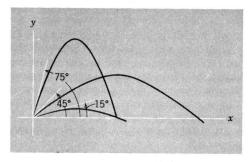

**Fig. 4–13**

**10.** A dive bomber, diving at an angle of 53° with the vertical, releases a bomb at an altitude of 2400 ft. The bomb hits the ground 5.0 sec after being released. (a) What is the speed of the bomber? (b) How far did the bomb travel horizontally during its flight? (c) What were the horizontal and vertical components of its velocity just before striking the ground?

**11.** A batter hits a pitched ball at a height 4.0 ft above ground so that its angle of projection is 45° and its horizontal range is 350 ft. The ball is fair down the left field line where a 24-ft-high fence is located 320 ft from home plate. Will the ball clear the fence?

**12.** A football is kicked off with an initial speed of 64 ft/sec at a projection angle of 45°. A receiver on the goal line 60 yd away in the direction of the kick starts running to meet the ball at that instant. What must his speed be if he is to catch the ball before it hits the ground?

**13.** In a cathode-ray tube a beam of electrons is projected horizontally with a speed of $1.0 \times 10^9$ cm/sec into the region between a pair of horizontal plates 2.0 cm long. An electric field between the plates exerts a constant downward acceleration on the electrons of magnitude $1.0 \times 10^{17}$ cm/sec². Find (a) the vertical displacement of the beam in passing through the plates and (b) the velocity of the beam (direction and magnitude) as it emerges from the plates.

**14.** (a) Show that if the acceleration of gravity changes by an amount $dg$, the range of a projectile (see Problem 6) of given initial speed $v_0$ and angle of projection $\theta_0$ changes by $dR$ where $dR/R = -dg/g$. (b) If the acceleration of gravity changes by a small amount $\Delta g$ (say by going from one place to another), the range for a given projectile system will change as well. Let the change in range be $\Delta R$. If $\Delta g$, $\Delta R$ are small enough, we may write $\Delta R/R = -\Delta g/g$. In 1936, Jesse Owens (United States) established a world's running broad jump record of 8.09 meters at the Olympic games at Berlin ($g = 9.8128$ meters/sec²). By how much would his record have differed if he had competed instead in 1956 at Melbourne ($g = 9.7999$ meters/sec²)? (In this connection see "Bad Physics in Athletic Measurements," by P. Kirkpatrick, *American Journal of Physics*, February 1944.)

**15.** Electrons, nuclei, atoms and molecules, like all forms of matter, will fall under the influence of gravity. Consider separately a beam of electrons, of nuclei, of atoms, and of molecules traveling a horizontal distance of 1.0 meter. Let the average speed be for an electron $3.0 \times 10^7$ meters/sec, for a thermal neutron $2.2 \times 10^3$ meters/sec, for a neon atom $5.8 \times 10^2$ meters/sec, and for an oxygen molecule $4.6 \times 10^2$ meters/sec. Let the beams move through vacuum with initial horizontal velocities and find by how much their paths deviate from a straight line (vertical displacement in 1.0 meter) due to gravity.   How do these results compare to that for a beam of golf balls (use reasonable data)?   What is the controlling factor here?

**16.** A radar observer on the ground is "watching" an approaching projectile.   At a certain instant he has the following information: (a) the projectile has reached maximum altitude and is moving horizontally with a speed $v$; (b) the straight-line distance to the projectile is $l$; (c) the line of sight to the projectile is an angle $\theta$ above the horizontal. Find the distance $D$ between the observer and the point of impact of the projectile. Does the projectile pass over his head or strike the ground before reaching him?   $D$ is to be expressed in terms of the observed quantities $v$, $l$, and $\theta$ and the known value of $g$. Assume a flat earth; assume also that the observer lies in the plane of the projectile's trajectory.

**17.** Show that Eqs. 4–4d, $d'$ in Table 4–1 can be expressed in vector form as

$$\mathbf{v} \cdot \mathbf{v} = \mathbf{v}_0 \cdot \mathbf{v}_0 + 2\mathbf{a} \cdot (\mathbf{r} + \mathbf{r}_0),$$

that Eqs. 4–4b, $b'$ can be expressed as

$$\mathbf{r} = \mathbf{r}_0 + \tfrac{1}{2}(\mathbf{v}_0 + \mathbf{v})t,$$

and Eqs. 4–4c, $c'$ as

$$\mathbf{r} = \mathbf{r}_0 + \mathbf{v}_0 t + \tfrac{1}{2}\mathbf{a}t^2.$$

**18.** Projectiles are hurled at a horizontal distance $R$ from the edge of a cliff of height $h$ in such a way as to land a horizontal distance $x$ from the bottom of the cliff.   If you want $x$ to be as small as possible, how would you adjust $\theta_0$ and $v_0$, assuming that $v_0$ can be varied from zero to some maximum finite value and that $\theta_0$ can be varied continuously?   Only one collision with the ground is allowed (see Fig. 4–14).

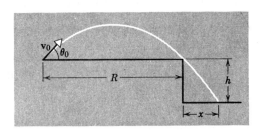

**Fig. 4–14**

**19.** Consider a projectile at the top of its trajectory.   (a) What is its speed in terms of $v_0$ and $\theta_0$?   (b) What is its acceleration?   (c) How is the direction of its acceleration related to that of its velocity?   (d) Over a short distance a circular arc is a good approximation to a parabola.   What then is the radius of the circular arc approximating the projectile's motion near the top of its path?

**20.** A particle rests on the top of a hemisphere of radius $R$.   Find the smallest horizontal velocity that must be imparted to the particle if it is to leave the hemisphere without sliding down it.

**21.** A magnetic field will deflect a charged particle perpendicular to its direction of motion.   An electron experiences a radial acceleration of $3.0 \times 10^{14}$ meters/sec$^2$ in one such field.   What is its speed if the radius of its curved path is 0.15 meter?

**22.** In Bohr's model of the hydrogen atom an electron revolves around a proton in a circular orbit of radius $5.28 \times 10^{-11}$ meter with a speed of $2.18 \times 10^6$ meters/sec. What is the acceleration of the electron in the hydrogen atom?

**23.** Find the magnitude of the centripetal acceleration of a particle on the tip of a fan blade, 0.30 meter in diameter, rotating at 1200 rev/min.

**24.** By what factor would the speed of the earth's rotation have to increase for a body on the equator to require a centripetal acceleration of $g$ to keep it on the earth? Such a body now requires a centripetal acceleration of only about 3.0 cm/sec$^2$.

**25.** A particle travels with constant speed on a circle of radius 3.0 meters and completes one revolution in 20 sec (Fig. 4–15). Starting from the origin $O$, find (a) the magnitude and direction of the displacement vectors 5.0 sec, 7.5 sec, and 10 sec later; (b) the magnitude and direction of the displacement in the 5.0-sec interval from the fifth to the tenth second; (c) the average velocity vector in this interval; (d) the instantaneous velocity vector at the beginning and at the end of this interval; (e) the average acceleration vector in this interval; and (f) the instantaneous acceleration vector at the beginning and at the end of this interval.

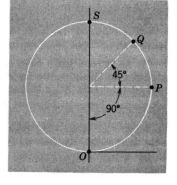

**26.** An earth satellite moves in a circular orbit 400 miles above the earth's surface. The time for one revolution (the period) is found to be 98 min. Find the acceleration of gravity at the orbit from these data.

**27.** The earth revolves about the sun in a (nearly) circular orbit with a (nearly) constant speed of 30 km/sec. What is the acceleration of the earth toward the sun?

**Fig. 4–15**

**28.** A particle moves in a plane according to

$$x = R \sin \omega t + \omega R t,$$

$$y = R \cos \omega t + R,$$

where $\omega$ and $R$ are constants. This curve, called a *cycloid*, is the path traced out by a point on the rim of a wheel which rolls without slipping along the $x$-axis. (a) Sketch the path. (b) Calculate the instantaneous velocity and acceleration when the particle is at its maximum and minimum value of $y$.

**29.** (a) Write an expression for the position vector $\mathbf{r}$ for a particle describing uniform circular motion, using rectangular coordinates and the unit vectors $\mathbf{i}$ and $\mathbf{j}$. (b) From (a) derive vector expressions for the velocity $\mathbf{v}$ and the acceleration $\mathbf{a}$. (c) Prove that the acceleration is directed toward the center of the circular motion.

**30.** Write an expression, using the unit vectors $\mathbf{u}_\theta$ and $\mathbf{u}_r$, for the position vector $\mathbf{r}$ for a particle describing uniform circular motion and from it derive Eq. 4–11, $\mathbf{v} = \mathbf{u}_\theta v$.

**31.** Express the unit vectors $\mathbf{u}_r$ and $\mathbf{u}_\theta$ in terms of $\mathbf{i}$, $\mathbf{j}$, and the angle $\theta$ in Fig. 4–8.

**32.** A person walks up a stalled escalator in 90 sec. When standing on the same escalator, now moving, he is carried up in 60 sec. How much time would it take him to walk up the moving escalator?

**33.** Find the speed of two objects if, when they move uniformly toward each other, they get 4.0 meters closer each second, and, when they move uniformly in the same direction with the original speeds, they get 4.0 meters closer each 10 sec.

**34.** A man can row a boat 4.0 miles/hr in still water. (*a*) If he is crossing a river where the current is 2.0 miles/hr, in what direction will his boat be headed if he wants to reach a point directly opposite from his starting point? (*b*) If the river is 4.0 miles wide, how long will it take him to cross the river? (*c*) How long will it take him to row 2.0 miles *down* the river and then back to his starting point? (*d*) How long will it take him to row 2.0 miles *up* the river and then back to his starting point? (*e*) In what direction should he head the boat if he wants to cross in the smallest possible time?

**35.** A man wants to cross a river 500 meters wide. His rowing speed (relative to the water) is 3000 meters/hr. The river flows at a speed of 1200 meters/hr. If the man's walking speed on shore is 5000 meters/hr, (*a*) find the path (combined rowing and walking) he should take to get to the point directly opposite his starting point in the shortest time. (*b*) How long does it take?

**36.** A train travels due south at 88.2 ft/sec (relative to ground) in a rain that is blown toward the south by the wind. The path of each raindrop makes the angle 21.6° with the vertical, as measured by an observer stationary on the earth. An observer seated in the train, however, sees perfectly vertical tracks of rain on the windowpane. Determine the speed of each raindrop relative to the earth.

**37.** An airplane has a speed of 135 miles/hr in still air. It is flying straight north so that it is at all times directly above a north-south highway. A ground observer tells the pilot by radio that a 70-miles/hr wind is blowing, but neglects to tell him the wind direction. The pilot observes that in spite of the wind he can travel 135 miles *along* the highway in one hour. In other words, his ground speed is the same as if there were no wind. (*a*) What is the direction of the wind? (*b*) What is the heading of the plane, that is, the angle between its axis and the highway?

**38.** A pilot is supposed to fly due east from $A$ to $B$ and then back again to $A$ due west. The velocity of the plane in air is $\mathbf{v}'$ and the velocity of the air with respect to the ground is $\mathbf{u}$. The distance between $A$ and $B$ is $l$ and the plane's air speed $v'$ is constant. (*a*) If $u = 0$ (still air), show that the time for the round trip is $t_0 = 2l/v'$. (*b*) Suppose that the air velocity is due east (or west). Show that the time for a round trip is then

$$t_E = \frac{t_0}{1 - u^2/(v')^2}.$$

(*c*) Suppose that the air velocity is due north (or south). Show that the time for a round trip is then

$$t_N = \frac{t_0}{\sqrt{1 - u^2/(v')^2}}.$$

(*d*) In parts (*b*) and (*c*) one must assume that $u < v'$. Why?

# Particle Dynamics—I

## 5–1 Classical Mechanics

In Chapters 3 and 4, we studied the motion of a particle, with emphasis on motion along a straight line or in a plane. We did not ask what "caused" the motion; we simply described it in terms of the vectors **r**, **v**, and **a**. Our discussion was thus largely geometrical. In this chapter and the next we discuss the causes of motion, an aspect of mechanics called *dynamics*. As before, bodies will be treated as though they were single particles. Later in the book we shall treat groups of particles and extended bodies as well.

The motion of a given particle is determined by the nature and the arrangement of the other bodies that form its *environment*. In general, only nearby objects need to be included in the environment, the effects of more distant objects usually being negligible. Table 5–1 shows some "particles" and possible environments for them.

In what follows, we limit ourselves to the very important special case of gross objects moving at speeds that are small compared to $c$, the speed of light; this is the realm of *classical mechanics*. Specifically, we shall not inquire here into such questions as the motion of an electron in a uranium atom or the collision of two protons whose speeds are, say, $0.90c$. The first inquiry would involve us with the quantum theory and the second with the theory of relativity. We leave consideration of these theories, of which classical mechanics is a special case (see Section 6–4), to later.

The central problem of classical particle mechanics is this; (1) We are given a particle whose characteristics (mass, charge, magnetic dipole

## Table 5-1

| System | The "Particle" | The Environment |
|---|---|---|
| 1. | A block | The spring; the rough surface |
| 2. | A golf ball | The earth |
| 3. | An artificial satellite | The earth |
| 4. | An electron | A large uniformly charged sphere |
| 5. | A bar magnet | A second bar magnet |

moment, etc.) we know.   (2) We place this particle, with a known initial velocity, in an environment of which we have a complete description. (3) Problem: what is the subsequent motion of the particle? .

This problem was solved, at least for a large variety of environments, by Isaac Newton (1642–1727) when he put forward his laws of motion and formulated his law of universal gravitation.   The program for solving this problem, in terms of our present understanding of classical mechanics,* is: (1) We introduce the concept of *force* **F** and define it in terms of the acceleration **a** experienced by a particular standard body.   (2) We develop a procedure for assigning a *mass m* to a body so that we may understand the fact that different particles of the same kind experience different accelerations in the same environment.   (3) Finally, we try to find ways of calculating the forces that act on particles from the properties of the particle and of its environment; that is, we look for *force laws*.   Force, which is at

---

* See "Presentation of Newtonian Mechanics" by Norman Austern, *American Journal of Physics*, September 1961, "On the Classical Laws of Motion" by Leonard Eisenbud, *American Journal of Physics*, March 1958, and "The Laws of Classical Motion: What's *F*?   What's *m*?   What's *a*?" by Robert Weinstock, *American Journal of Physics*, October 1961, for expositions of the laws of classical mechanics as we now view them, almost 300 years after Newton.

root a technique for relating the environment to the motion of the particle, appears both in the laws of motion (which tell us what acceleration a given body will experience under the action of a given force) and in the force laws (which tell us how to calculate the force that will act on a given body in a given environment). The laws of motion and the force laws, taken together, constitute the laws of mechanics.

The program of mechanics cannot be tested piecemeal. We must view it as a unit and we shall judge it to be successful if we can say "yes" to these two questions. (1) Does the program yield results that agree with experiment? (2) Are the force laws simple in form? It is the crowning glory of Newtonian mechanics that we can indeed answer each of these questions in the affirmative.

In this section we have used the terms force and mass rather unprecisely, having identified force with the influence of the environment, and mass with the resistance of a body to be accelerated when a force acts on it, a property often called inertia. In later sections we shall refine these primitive ideas about force and mass.

## 5–2  Newton's First Law

For centuries the problem of motion and its causes was a central theme of natural philosophy. It was not until the time of Galileo and Newton, however, that dramatic progress was made. Isaac Newton, born in England in the year of Galileo's death, is the principal architect of classical mechanics.* He carried to full fruition the ideas of Galileo and others who preceded him. His three laws of motion were first presented (in 1686) in his *Principia Mathematica Philosophiae Naturalis*.

Before Galileo's time most philosophers thought that some influence or "force" was needed to keep a body moving. They thought that a body was in its "natural state" when it was at rest. For a body to move in a straight line at constant speed, for example, they believed that some external agent had to continually propel it; otherwise it would "naturally" stop moving.

If we wanted to test these ideas experimentally, we would first have to find a way to free a body from all influences of its environment or from all forces. This is hard to do, but in certain cases we can make the forces very small. If we study the motions as we make the forces smaller and smaller, we shall have some idea of what the motion would be like if the external forces were truly zero.

Let us place our test body, say a block, on a rigid horizontal plane. If we let the block slide along this plane, we notice that it gradually slows down and stops. This observation was used, in fact, to support the idea that motion stopped when the external force, in this case the hand initially

---

* Newton also invented the (fluxional) calculus, conceived the idea of universal gravitation and formulated its law, and discovered the composition of white light. He was a skillful experimenter, a mathematician of first rank, and a biblical scholar as well as what today would be called theoretical physicist.

pushing the block, was removed.  Galileo argued against this idea, however, reasoning as follows: Let us repeat our experiment, now using a smoother block and a smoother plane and providing a lubricant.  We notice that the velocity decreases more slowly than before.  Let us use still smoother blocks and surfaces and better lubricants.  We find that the block decreases in velocity at a slower and slower rate and travels farther each time before coming to rest.*  We can now extrapolate and say that if all friction could be eliminated, the body would continue indefinitely in a straight line with constant speed.  This was Galileo's conclusion.  Galileo asserted that some external force was necessary to *change* the velocity of a body but that no external force was necessary to *maintain* the velocity of a body.  Our hand, for example, exerts a force on the block when it sets it in motion.  The rough plane exerts a force on it when it slows it down.  Both of these forces produce a change in the velocity, that is, they produce an acceleration.

This principle of Galileo was adopted by Newton as the first of his three laws of motion.  Newton stated his first law in these words: *"Every body persists in its state of rest or of uniform motion in a straight line unless it is compelled to change that state by forces impressed on it."*

Newton's first law is really a statement about reference frames.  For, in general, the acceleration of a body depends on the reference frame relative to which it is measured.  The first law tells us that, if there are no nearby objects (and by this we mean that there are no forces because every force must be associated with an object in the environment) then it is possible to find a family of reference frames in which a particle has no acceleration.  The fact that bodies stay at rest or retain their uniform linear motion in the absence of applied forces is often described by assigning a property to matter called inertia.  Newton's first law is often called the law of inertia and the reference frames to which it applies are therefore called inertial frames.  Such frames are either fixed with respect to the distant stars or moving at uniform velocity with respect to them.

In nearly all cases in this book we will apply the laws of classical mechanics from the point of view of an observer in an inertial frame.  It is possible to solve problems in mechanics using a noninertial frame, such as a frame rotating with respect to the fixed stars, but to do so we have to introduce forces (often called *pseudo-forces*) that cannot be associated with objects in the environment.  We will discuss this in Chapters 6, 11, and 16.  A reference frame attached to the earth can be considered to be an inertial frame for most practical purposes.  We shall see in Chapter 16 how good an approximation this is.

Notice that there is no distinction in the first law between a body at rest and one moving with a constant velocity.  Both motions are "natural" in the absence of forces.  That this is so becomes clear when a body at rest

---

* The student may have experimented in the laboratory with a "dry ice puck."  This is a device which can be made to move over a smooth horizontal surface, floating on a layer of $CO_2$ gas.  The friction between the puck and the surface is very low indeed and it is hard to measure any reduction in speed for path lengths of practical dimensions.

in one inertial frame is viewed from a second inertial frame, that is, a frame moving with constant velocity with respect to the first.    An observer in the first frame finds the body to be at rest; an observer in the second frame finds the same body to be moving with uniform velocity.    Both observers find the body to have no acceleration, that is, no change in velocity, and both may conclude from the first law that no force acts on the body.

Notice, too, that by implication there is no distinction in the first law between the absence of all forces and the presence of forces whose resultant is zero.    For example, if the push of our hand on the book exactly counteracts the force of friction on it, the book will move with uniform velocity. Hence another way of stating the first law is: *If no net force acts on a body its acceleration* **a** *is zero.*

If there *is* an interaction between the body and objects present in the environment, the effect may be to change the "natural" state of the body's motion.    To investigate this we must now examine carefully the concept of force.

### 5–3   Force

Let us refine our concept of force by defining it operationally.    In our everyday language force is associated with a push or a pull, perhaps exerted by our muscles.    In physics, however, we need a more precise definition.    We define force here in terms of the acceleration that a given standard body experiences when placed in a suitable environment.

As a standard body we find it convenient to use (or rather to imagine that we use!) a particular platinum cylinder carefully preserved at the International Bureau of Weights and Measures near Paris, and called the *standard*

**Fig. 5–1** The national standard kilogram No. 4, kept at the United States National Bureau of Standards. It is an accurate copy of the International standard kept at the International Bureau of Weights and Measures near Paris. The standard kilogram is the platinum cylinder housed under the double bell-jar.

*kilogram* (see Fig. 5–1).    For use in later sections we state here that this body has been selected as our standard of *mass* and has been assigned, by definition, a mass $m_0$ of exactly 1 kg.    Later we will describe how masses are assigned to other bodies.

As for an environment we place the standard body on a horizontal table having negligible friction and we attach a spring to it.    We hold the other end of the spring in our hand, as in Fig. 5–2a.    Now we pull the spring horizontally to the right so that by trial and error the standard body experiences a measured uniform acceleration of 1.00 meter/sec$^2$.    We then declare, *as a matter of definition*, that the spring (which is the significant

**Fig. 5–2** (a) A "particle" $P$ (the standard kilogram) at rest on a horizontal frictionless surface. (b) The body is accelerated by pulling the spring to the right.

(b)

body in the environment) is exerting a constant force whose magnitude we will call "1.00 newton" on the standard body. We note that, in imparting this force, the spring is kept stretched an amount $\Delta l$ beyond its normal unextended length, as Fig. 5–2b shows.

We can repeat the experiment, either stretching the spring more or using a stiffer spring, so that we measure an acceleration of 2.00 meters/sec² for the standard body. We now declare that the spring is exerting a force of 2.00 newtons on the standard body. In general, if we observe this particular standard body to have an acceleration $a$ in a particular environment, we then say that the environment is exerting a force $F$ on the standard body, where $F$ (in newtons) is numerically equal to $a$ (in meters/sec²).

Now let us see whether force, as we have defined it, is a *vector* quantity. In Fig. 5–2b we assigned a magnitude to the force $F$, and it is a simple matter to assign a direction to it as well, namely, the direction of the acceleration that the force produces. However, to be a vector it is not enough for a quantity to have magnitude and direction; it must also obey the laws of vector addition described in Chapter 2. We can learn only from experiment whether forces, as we defined them, do indeed obey these laws.

Let us arrange to exert a 4.00-newton force along the $x$-axis and a 3.00-newton force along the $y$-axis and let us apply these forces *simultaneously* to the standard body placed, as before, on a horizontal, frictionless surface. What will be the acceleration of the standard body? We would find by experiment that it was 5.00 meters/sec², directed along a line that makes an angle of 37° with the $x$-axis. In other words, we would say that the standard body was experiencing a force of 5.00 newtons in this same direction. This same result can be obtained by adding the 4.00-newton and 3.00-newton forces vectorially according to the parallelogram method. Experiments of this kind show conclusively that forces are vectors; they have magnitude; they have direction; they add according to the parallelogram law.

The result of experiments of this general type is often stated as follows: *When several forces act on a body, each produces its own acceleration independently. The resulting acceleration is the vector sum of the several independent accelerations.*

## 5–4   Mass; Newton's Second Law

In Section 5–3 we considered only the accelerations given to one particular object, the standard kilogram. We were able thereby to define forces quantitatively. What effect would these forces have on other objects? Since our standard body was chosen arbitrarily in the first place, we know that for any given object the acceleration will be directly proportional to the force applied. The significant question remaining then is: What effect will the *same force* have on *different objects?* Everyday experience gives us a qualitative answer. The same force will produce different accelerations on different bodies. A baseball will be accelerated more by a given force than will an automobile. In order to obtain a quantitative answer to this question we need a method to measure mass, the property of a body which determines its resistance to a change in its motion.

Let us attach a spring to our standard body (the standard kilogram, to which we have arbitrarily assigned a mass $m_0 = 1.00$ kg, exactly) and arrange to give it an acceleration $a_0$ of, say 2.00 meters/sec$^2$, using the method of Fig. 5–2b. Let us measure carefully the extension $\Delta l$ of the spring associated with the force that the spring is exerting on the block.

Now we remove the standard kilogram and substitute an arbitrary body, whose mass we label $m_1$. We apply the *same force* (the one that accelerated the standard kilogram 2.00 meters/sec$^2$) to the arbitrary body (by stretching the spring by the same amount) and we measure an acceleration $a_1$ of, say, 0.50 meter/sec$^2$.

We *define* the ratio of the masses of the two bodies to be the inverse ratio of the accelerations given to these bodies by the same force, or

$$m_1/m_0 = a_0/a_1 \qquad \text{(same force } \mathbf{F} \text{ acting).}$$

In this example we have, numerically,

$$m_1 = m_0(a_0/a_1) = 1.00 \text{ kg } [(2.00 \text{ meters/sec}^2)/(0.50 \text{ meters/sec}^2)]$$

$$= 4.00 \text{ kg.}$$

The second body, which has only one-fourth the acceleration of the first body when the same force acts on it, has, by definition, four times the mass of the first body. Hence mass may be regarded as a quantitative measure of inertia.

If we repeat the preceding experiment with a different common force acting, we find the ratio of the accelerations, $a_0'/a_1'$, to be the same as in the previous experiment, or

$$m_1/m_0 = a_0/a_1 = a_0'/a_1'.$$

The ratio of the masses of two bodies is thus independent of the common force used.

Furthermore, experiment shows that we can consistently assign masses to any body by this procedure. For example, let us compare a second arbitrary body with the standard body, and thus determine its mass, say $m_2$. We can now compare the two arbitrary bodies, $m_2$ and $m_1$, directly, obtaining accelerations $a_2''$ and $a_1''$ when the same force is applied. The mass ratio, defined as usual from

$$m_2/m_1 = a_1''/a_2'', \quad \text{(same force acting)}$$

turns out to have the same value that we obtain by using the masses $m_2$ and $m_1$ determined previously by direct comparison with the standard.

We can show, in still another experiment of this type, that if objects of mass $m_1$ and $m_2$ are fastened together they behave mechanically as a single object of mass $(m_1 + m_2)$. In other words, masses add like (and are) scalar quantities.

Table 5–2 shows the range of values over which masses can be determined, using various techniques.

**Table 5–2**

SOME MEASURED MASSES

| Object | Mass (kg) |
| --- | --- |
| Our galaxy | $2.2 \times 10^{41}$ |
| The sun | $2.0 \times 10^{30}$ |
| The earth | $6.0 \times 10^{24}$ |
| The moon | $7.4 \times 10^{22}$ |
| Mass of all the water in the oceans | $1.4 \times 10^{21}$ |
| An ocean liner | $7.2 \times 10^{7}$ |
| An elephant | $4.5 \times 10^{3}$ |
| A man | $7.3 \times 10^{1}$ |
| A grape | $3.0 \times 10^{-3}$ |
| A tobacco mosaic virus | $6.7 \times 10^{-10}$ |
| A speck of dust | $2.3 \times 10^{-13}$ |
| A penicillin molecule | $5.0 \times 10^{-17}$ |
| A uranium atom | $4.0 \times 10^{-25}$ |
| A proton | $1.7 \times 10^{-27}$ |
| An electron | $9.1 \times 10^{-31}$ |

We can now summarize all the experiments and definitions described above in one equation, the fundamental equation of classical mechanics,

$$\mathbf{F} = m\mathbf{a}. \quad (5\text{–}1)$$

In this equation $\mathbf{F}$ is the (vector) *sum* of *all* the forces acting *on* the body, $m$ is the mass of the body, and $\mathbf{a}$ is its (vector) acceleration. Equation 5–1 may be taken as a statement of Newton's second law. If we write it in the form $\mathbf{a} = \mathbf{F}/m$, we can see easily that the acceleration of the body is directly proportional to the resultant force acting on it and parallel in direction to this force and that the acceleration, for a given force, is inversely proportional to the mass of the body.

Notice that the first law of motion is contained in the second law as a special case, for if $\mathbf{F} = 0$, then $\mathbf{a} = 0$. In other words, if the resultant force on a body is zero, the acceleration of the body is zero. Therefore in the absence of applied forces a body will move with constant velocity or be at rest (zero velocity), which is what the first law of motion says. Therefore of Newton's three laws of motion only two are independent, the second and the third (Section 5–5). The division of translational particle dynamics that includes only systems for which the resultant force $\mathbf{F}$ is zero is called *statics*.

Equation 5-1 is a vector equation. We can write this single vector equation as three scalar equations,

$$F_x = ma_x, \qquad F_y = ma_y, \qquad \text{and} \quad F_z = ma_z, \qquad (5\text{–}2)$$

relating the $x$, $y$, and $z$ components of the resultant force ($F_x$, $F_y$, and $F_z$) to the $x$, $y$, and $z$ components of acceleration ($a_x$, $a_y$, and $a_z$) for the mass $m$. It should be emphasized that $F_x$ is the *sum* of the $x$-components of *all* the forces, $F_y$ is the sum of the $y$-components of *all* the forces, and $F_z$ is the *sum* of the $z$-components of *all* the forces acting on $m$.

## 5–5   Newton's Third Law of Motion

Forces acting on a body originate in other bodies that make up its environment. Any single force is only one aspect of a mutual interaction between *two* bodies. We find by experiment that when one body exerts a force on a second body, the second body always exerts a force on the first. Furthermore, we find that these forces are equal in magnitude but opposite in direction. A single isolated force is therefore an impossibility.

If one of the two forces involved in the interaction between two bodies is called an "action" force, the other is called the "reaction" force. *Either* force may be considered the "action" and the other the "reaction." Cause and effect is *not* implied here, but a mutual simultaneous interaction *is* implied.

This property of forces was first stated by Newton in his third law of motion: "*To every action there is always opposed an equal reaction; or, the mutual actions of two bodies upon each other are always equal, and directed to contrary parts.*"

In other words, if body $A$ exerts a force on body $B$, body $B$ exerts an equal but oppositely directed force on body $A$; and furthermore the forces lie along the line joining the bodies. Notice that the action and reaction forces, which always occur in pairs, act on *different* bodies. If they were to act on the same body, we could never have accelerated motion because the resultant force on every body would always be zero.

Imagine a boy kicking open a door. The force exerted by the boy $B$ on the door $D$ accelerates the door (it flies open); at the same time, the door $D$ exerts an equal but opposite force on the boy $B$, which decelerates the

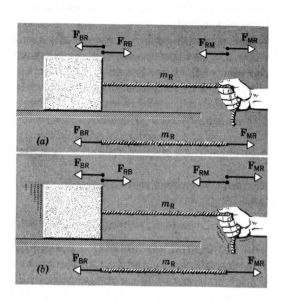

**Fig. 5–3** Example 1. A man pulls on a rope attached to a block. (*a*) The forces exerted on the rope by the block and by the man are equal and opposite. Thus the resultant horizontal force on the rope is zero, as is shown in the free-body diagram. The rope does not accelerate. (*b*) The force exerted on the rope by the man exceeds that exerted by the block. The net horizontal force has magnitude $F_{MR}$ $- F_{BR}$ and points to the right. Thus the rope is accelerated to the right. The block is also acted upon by a frictional force not shown here.

boy (his foot loses forward velocity). The boy will be painfully aware of the "reaction" force to his "action," particularly if his foot is bare.

The following examples illustrate the application of the third law and clarify its meaning.

▶ **Example 1.** Consider a man pulling horizontally on a rope attached to a block on a horizontal table as in Fig. 5–3. The man pulls on the rope with a force $\mathbf{F}_{MR}$. The rope exerts a reaction force $\mathbf{F}_{RM}$ on the man. According to Newton's third law, $\mathbf{F}_{MR} = -\mathbf{F}_{RM}$. Also, the rope exerts a force $\mathbf{F}_{RB}$ on the block, and the block exerts a reaction force $\mathbf{F}_{BR}$ on the rope. Again according to the third law, $\mathbf{F}_{RB} = -\mathbf{F}_{BR}$.

Suppose that the rope has a mass $m_R$. Then, in order to start the block and rope moving from rest, we must have an acceleration, say **a**. The only forces acting *on the rope* are $\mathbf{F}_{MR}$ and $\mathbf{F}_{BR}$, so that the resultant force on it is $\mathbf{F}_{MR} + \mathbf{F}_{BR}$, and this must be different from zero if the rope is to accelerate. In fact, from the second law we have

$$\mathbf{F}_{MR} + \mathbf{F}_{BR} = m_R\mathbf{a}$$

Since the forces and the acceleration are along the same line, we can drop the vector notation and write the relation between the *magnitudes* of the vectors, namely

$$F_{MR} - F_{BR} = m_R a.$$

We see therefore that in general $\mathbf{F}_{MR}$ does not have the same magnitude as $\mathbf{F}_{BR}$ (Fig. 5–3*b*). These two forces act on the *same* body and are *not* action and reaction pairs.

According to Newton's third law the magnitude of $\mathbf{F}_{MR}$ always equals the magnitude of $\mathbf{F}_{RM}$, and the magnitude of $\mathbf{F}_{RB}$ always equals the magnitude of $\mathbf{F}_{BR}$. However, only if the acceleration **a** of the system is zero will we have the pair of forces $F_{MR}$ and $F_{RM}$ equal in magnitude to the pair of forces $F_{RB}$ and $F_{BR}$ (Fig. 5–3a). In this special case only, we could imagine that the rope merely transmits the force exerted by the man to the block without change. This same result holds in principle if $m_R = 0$. In practice, we never find a massless rope. However, we can often neglect the mass of a rope, in which case the rope is assumed to transmit a force unchanged. The force exerted at any point in the rope is called the *tension* at that point. We may measure the tension at any point in the rope by cutting a suitable length from it and inserting a spring scale; the tension is the reading of the scale. The tension is the same at all points in the rope only if the rope is unaccelerated or assumed to be massless.

**Example 2.** Consider a spring attached to the ceiling and at the other end holding a block at rest (Fig. 5–4a). Since no body is accelerating, all the forces on any body will add vectorially to zero.

For example, the forces on the suspended block are **T**, the tension in the stretched spring, pulling vertically up on the mass, and **W**, the pull of the earth acting vertically down on the body, called its weight. These are drawn in Fig. 5–4b, where we show only the block for clarity. There are no other forces on the block.

In Newton's second law, **F** represents the *sum* of *all* the forces acting *on* a body, so that for the block

$$F = T + W.$$

The block is at rest so that its acceleration is zero, or $a = 0$. Hence, from the relation $F = ma$, we obtain $T + W = 0$, or

$$T = -W.$$

The forces act along the same line, so that their magnitudes are equal, or

$$T = W.$$

Therefore the tension in the spring is an exact measure of the weight of the block. We shall use this result later in presenting a static procedure for measuring forces.

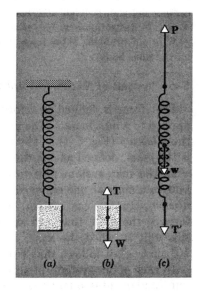

**Fig. 5–4** Example 2. (*a*) A block is suspended by a spring. (*b*) A free-body diagram showing all the vertical forces exerted on the block. (*c*) A similar diagram for the vertical forces on the spring.

It is instructive to examine the forces exerted on the spring; they are shown in Fig. 5–4c. **T'** is the pull of the block on the spring and is the reaction force of the action force **T**. **T'** therefore has the same magnitude as **T**, which is $W$. **P** is the upward pull of the ceiling on the spring, and **w** is the weight of the spring, that is, the pull of the earth on it. Since the spring is at rest and all forces act along the same line, we have

$$P + T' + w = 0,$$

or

$$P = W + w.$$

The ceiling therefore pulls up on the spring with a force whose magnitude is the sum of the weights of the block and spring.

From the third law of motion, the force exerted by the spring on the ceiling, $\mathbf{P'}$, must be equal in magnitude to $\mathbf{P}$, which is the reaction force to the action force $\mathbf{P'}$. $\mathbf{P'}$ therefore has a magnitude $W + w$.

In general, the spring exerts different forces on the bodies attached at its different ends, for $P' \neq T$. In the special case in which the weight of the spring is negligible, $w = 0$ and $P' = W = T$. Therefore a *weightless* spring (or cord) may be considered to transmit a force from one end to the other without change.

It is instructive to classify all the forces in this problem according to action and reaction pairs. The reaction to $\mathbf{W}$, a force exerted by the earth on the block, must be a force exerted by the block on the earth. Similarly, the reaction to $\mathbf{w}$ is a force exerted by the spring on the earth. Because the earth is so massive, we do not expect these forces to impart a noticeable acceleration to the earth. Since the earth is not shown in our diagrams, these forces have not been shown. The forces $\mathbf{T}$ and $\mathbf{T'}$ are action-reaction pairs, as are $\mathbf{P}$ and $\mathbf{P'}$. Notice that although $\mathbf{T} = -\mathbf{W}$ in our problem, these forces are *not* an action-reaction pair because they act on the *same* body.                                                                          ◀

### 5–6   Systems of Mechanical Units

Unit force is defined as a force that causes a unit of acceleration when applied to a unit mass. The mks (meter, kilogram, second) unit of mass is the *kilogram* (Fig. 5–1). The cgs (centimeter, gram, second) unit of mass is the *gram*, defined as one-thousandth of the kilogram mass.

In the mks system unit force is the force that will accelerate a one-kilogram mass at one meter/sec$^2$; we have seen that this unit is called the *newton*. In the cgs system, which includes the Gaussian system, unit force is the force that will accelerate a one-gram mass at one cm/sec$^2$; this unit is called the *dyne*. Since $1 \text{ kg} = 10^3$ gm and $1 \text{ meter/sec}^2 = 10^2 \text{ cm/sec}^2$, it follows that $1 \text{ nt} = 10^5$ dynes.

In each of our systems of units we have chosen mass, length, and time as our fundamental quantities. Standards were adopted for these fundamental quantities and units defined in terms of these standards. Force appears as a derived quantity, determined from the relation $F = ma$.

In the British engineering system of units, however, *force*, length, and time are chosen as the fundamental quantities and mass is a derived quantity. In this system, mass is determined from the relation $m = F/a$. The standard and unit of force in this system is the *pound*. Actually, the pound of force was originally defined to be the pull of the earth on a certain standard body at a certain place on the earth. We can get this force in an operational way by hanging the standard body from a spring at the particular point where the earth's pull on it is defined to be 1 lb of force. If the body is at rest, the earth's pull on the body, its weight $W$, is balanced by the tension in the spring. Therefore $T = W = 1$ lb, in this instance. We can now use this spring (or any other one thus calibrated) to exert a force of 1 lb on any other body; to do this we simply attach the spring to another body and stretch it the same amount as the pound force had stretched it. The standard body can be compared to the kilogram and it is found to have the mass 0.45359237 kg. The acceleration due to gravity at the certain place on the earth is found to be 32.1740 ft/sec². The pound of force can therefore be defined from $F = ma$ as the force that accelerates a mass of 0.45359237 kg at the rate of 32.1740 ft/sec².

This procedure enables us to compare the pound-force with the newton. Using the fact that 32.1740 ft/sec² equals 9.8066 meters/sec², we find that

$$1 \text{ lb} = (0.45359237 \text{ kg})(32.1740 \text{ ft/sec}^2)$$

$$= (0.45359237 \text{ kg})(9.8066 \text{ meters/sec}^2)$$

$$\cong 4.45 \text{ nt.}$$

The unit of mass in the British engineering system can now be derived. It is defined as the mass of a body whose acceleration is 1 ft/sec² when the force on it is 1 lb; this mass is called the *slug*. Thus, in this system

$$F[\text{lb}] = m \text{ [slugs]} \times a \text{ [ft/sec}^2].$$

Legally the pound is a unit of mass but in engineering practice the pound is treated as a unit of force or weight. This has given rise to the terms pound-mass and pound-force. The pound-mass is a body of mass 0.45359237 kg; no standard block of metal is preserved as the pound-mass, but, like the yard, it is defined in terms of the mks standard. The pound-force is the force that gives a standard pound an acceleration equal to the standard acceleration of gravity, 32.1740 ft/sec². As we shall see later, the acceleration of gravity varies with distance from the center of the earth, and this "standard acceleration" is, therefore, the value at a particular distance from the center of the earth. (Any point at sea level and 45°N latitude is a good approximation.)

In this book only forces will be measured in pounds. Thus the corresponding unit of mass is the slug. The units of force, mass, and acceleration in the three systems are summarized in Table 5–3.

The *dimensions* of force are the same as those of mass times acceleration. In a system in which mass, length, and time are the fundamental quantities,

**Table 5–3**

UNITS IN $F = ma$

| Systems of Units | Force | Mass | Acceleration |
|---|---|---|---|
| Mks | newton (nt) | kilogram (kg) | meter/sec² |
| Cgs (Gaussian) | dyne | gram (gm) | cm/sec² |
| Engineering | pound (lb) | slug | ft/sec² |

the dimensions of force are, therefore, mass $\times$ length/time$^2$, or $MLT^{-2}$. We shall arbitrarily adopt mass, length, and time as our fundamental mechanical quantities.

Recalling that our length and time standards are atomic standards, some have speculated that the standard kilogram may some day be replaced by an atomic standard of mass. This new standard might consist of a specification of a number of atoms of a certain type whose collective mass under suitable circumstances is 1 kg. At the present time, however, the accuracy with which masses can be compared, as on a balance, exceeds the accuracy with which we can determine the exact number of atoms that make up a given mass.

## 5–7 The Force Laws

The three laws of motion that we have described are only part of the program of mechanics that we outlined in Section 5–1. It remains to investigate the *force laws*, which are the procedures by which we calculate the force acting on a given body in terms of the properties of the body and its environment. Newton's second law

$$\mathbf{F} = m\mathbf{a} \qquad (5\text{–}3)$$

is essentially not a law of nature but a definition of force. We need to identify various functions of the type:

$$\mathbf{F} = \text{a function of the properties of the particle} \\ \text{and of the environment} \qquad (5\text{–}4)$$

so that we can, in effect, eliminate $\mathbf{F}$ between Eqs. 5–3 and 5–4, thus obtaining an equation that will let us calculate the acceleration of a particle in terms of the properties of the particle and its environment. We see here clearly that force is a concept that connects the acceleration of the particle on the one hand with the properties of the particle and its environment on the other. We indicated earlier that one criterion for declaring the program of mechanics to be successful would be the discovery that *simple* laws of the type of Eq. 5–4 do indeed exist. This turns out to be the case, and this fact constitutes the essential reason that we "believe" the laws of classical mechanics. If the force laws had turned out to be very complicated, we would not be left with the feeling that we had gained much insight into the workings of nature.

The number of possible environments for an accelerated particle is so great that a detailed discussion of all the force laws is not feasible in this chapter. We shall, however, indicate in Table 5–4 the force laws that apply to the five particle-plus-environment situations of Table 5–1. At appropriate places throughout the text we will discuss these and other force laws in detail; several of the laws in Table 5–4 are approximations or special cases.

## Table 5–4

### THE FORCE LAWS FOR THE SYSTEMS OF TABLE 5–1

| System | Force Law |
|---|---|
| 1. A block propelled by a stretched spring over a rough horizontal surface | (a) Spring force: $F = -kx$, where $x$ is the extension of the spring and $k$ is a constant that describes the spring; $\mathbf{F}$ points to the right; see Chapter 15<br>(b) Friction force: $F = \mu mg$, where $\mu$ is the coefficient *of friction* and $mg$ is the weight of the block; $\mathbf{F}$ points to the left; see Chapter 6 |
| 2. A golf ball in flight | $F = mg$; $\mathbf{F}$ points down (see Section 5–8) |
| 3. An artificial satellite | $F = GmM/r^2$, where $G$ is the *gravitational constant*, $M$ the mass of the earth, and $r$ the orbit radius; $\mathbf{F}$ points toward the center of the earth; see Chapter 16. This is *Newton's law of universal gravitation* |
| 4. An electron near a charged sphere | $F = (1/4\pi\epsilon_0)eQ/r^2$, where $\epsilon_0$ is a constant, $e$ is the electron charge, $Q$ is the charge on the sphere, and $r$ is the distance from the electron to the center of the sphere; $\mathbf{F}$ points to the right; see Chapter 26. This is *Coulomb's law of electrostatics* |
| 5. Two bar magnets | $F = (3\mu_0/2\pi)\mu^2/r^4$, where $\mu_0$ is a constant, $\mu$ is the *magnetic dipole* moment of each magnet, and $r$ is the center-to-center separation of the magnets; we assume that $r \gg l$, where $l$ is the length of each magnet; $\mathbf{F}$ points to the right |

### 5–8 Weight and Mass

The *weight* of a body is the gravitational force exerted on it by the earth. Weight, being a force, is a vector quantity. The direction of this vector is the direction of the gravitational force, that is, toward the center of the earth. The magnitude of the weight is expressed in force units, such as pounds or newtons.

When a body of mass $m$ is allowed to fall freely, its acceleration is that of gravity $\mathbf{g}$ and the force acting on it is its weight $\mathbf{W}$. Newton's second law, $\mathbf{F} = m\mathbf{a}$, when applied to a freely falling body, gives us $\mathbf{W} = m\mathbf{g}$. Both $\mathbf{W}$ and $\mathbf{g}$ are vectors directed toward the center of the earth. We can therefore write

$$W = mg, \tag{5–5}$$

where $W$ and $g$ are the magnitudes of the weight and acceleration vectors. To keep an object from falling we have to exert on it an upward force equal in magnitude to $W$, so as to make the net force zero. In Fig. 5–4a the tension in the spring supplies this force.

We stated previously that $g$ is found experimentally to have the same value for all objects *at the same place*. From this it follows that the ratio of the weights of two objects must be equal to the ratio of their masses. Therefore a chemical balance, which actually is an instrument for comparing two downward forces, can be used in practice to compare masses. If a sample of salt in one pan of a balance is pulling down on that pan with the same force as is a standard one gram-mass on the other pan, we know* that the mass of salt is equal to one gram. We are likely to say that the salt "weighs" one gram, although a gram is a unit of mass, not weight. However, it is always important to distinguish carefully between weight and mass.

We have seen that the weight of a body, the downward pull of the earth on that body, is a vector quantity. The mass of a body is a scalar quantity. The quantitative relation between weight and mass is given by $\mathbf{W} = m\mathbf{g}$. Because $\mathbf{g}$ varies from point to point on the earth, $\mathbf{W}$, the weight of a body of mass $m$, is different in different localities. Thus, the weight of a one kg-mass in a locality where $g$ is 9.80 meters/sec$^2$ is 9.80 nt; in a locality where $g$ is 9.78 meters/sec$^2$, the same one kg-mass weighs 9.78 nt. If these weights were determined by measuring the amount of stretch required in a spring to balance them, the difference in weight of the same one kg-mass at the two different localities would be evident in the slightly different stretch of the spring at these two localities. Hence, unlike the mass of a body, which is an intrinsic property of the body, the weight of a body depends on its location relative to the center of the earth. Spring scales read differently, balances the same, at different parts of the earth.

We shall generalize the concept of weight in Chapter 16 in which we discuss universal gravitation. There we shall see that the weight of a body is zero in regions of space where the gravitational effects are nil, although the inertial effects, and hence the mass of the body, remain unchanged from those on earth. In a space ship free from the influence of gravity it is a simple matter to lift a large block of lead ($\mathbf{W} = 0$), but the astronaut would still stub his toe if he were to kick the block ($m \neq 0$).

It takes the same force to accelerate a body in gravity-free space as it does to accelerate it along a horizontal frictionless surface on earth, for its mass is the same in each place. But it takes a greater force to hold the body up against the pull of the earth on the earth's surface than it does high up in space, for its weight is different in each place.

Often, instead of being given the mass, we are given the weight of a body on which forces are exerted. The acceleration $\mathbf{a}$ produced by the force $\mathbf{F}$ acting on a body whose weight has a magnitude $W$ can be obtained by combining Eq. 5–3 and Eq. 5–5. Thus from $\mathbf{F} = m\mathbf{a}$ and $W = mg$ we obtain

$$m = W/g, \qquad \text{so that} \qquad \mathbf{F} = (W/g)\mathbf{a}. \qquad (5\text{–}6)$$

The quantity $W/g$ plays the role of $m$ in the equation $F = ma$ and is, in fact, the mass of a body whose weight has the magnitude $W$. For example, a man whose weight is 160 lb at a point where $g = 32.0$ ft/sec$^2$ has a

---

* Corrections for buoyancy, owing to the different volumes of air displaced by the salt and the standard, must be made. These are discussed in Chapter 17.

mass $m = W/g = (160 \text{ lb})/(32.0 \text{ ft/sec}^2) = 5.00$ slugs. Notice that his weight at another point where $g = 32.2 \text{ ft/sec}^2$ is $W = mg = (5.00 \text{ slugs})$ $(32.2 \text{ ft/sec}^2) = 161$ lb.

## 5–9    A Static Procedure for Measuring Forces

In Section 5–3 we defined force by measuring the acceleration imparted to a standard body by pulling on it with a stretched spring. That may be called a dynamic method for measuring force. Although convenient for the purposes of definition, it is not a particularly practical procedure for the measurement of forces. Another method for measuring forces is based on measuring the change in shape or size of a body (a spring, say) on which the force is applied when the body is unaccelerated. This may be called the static method of measuring forces.

The idea of the static method is to use the fact that when a body, under the action of several forces, has zero acceleration, the vector sum of all the forces acting on the body must be zero. This is, of course, just the content of the first law of motion. A single force acting on a body would produce an acceleration; this acceleration can be made zero if we apply another force to the body equal in magnitude but oppositely directed. In practice we seek to keep the body at rest. If now we choose some force as our unit force, we are in a position to measure forces. The pull of the earth on a standard body at a particular point can be taken as the unit force, for example.

The instrument most commonly used to measure forces in this way is the spring balance. It consists of a coiled spring having a pointer at one end that moves over a scale. A force exerted on the balance changes the length of the spring. If a body weighing 1.00 lb is hung from the spring, the spring stretches until the pull of the spring on the body is equal in magnitude but opposite in direction to its weight. A mark can be made on the scale next to the pointer and labeled "1.00-lb force." Similarly, 2.00-lb, 3.00-lb, etc., weights may be hung from the spring and corresponding marks can be made on the scale next to the pointer in each case. In this way the spring is calibrated. We assume that the force exerted on the spring is always the same when the pointer stands at the same position. The calibrated balance can now be used to measure any suitable unknown force, not merely the pull of the earth on some body.

The third law is tacitly used in our static procedure because we assume that the force exerted by the spring on the body is the same in magnitude as the force exerted by the body on the spring. This latter force is the force we wish to measure. The first law is used too, because we assume $\mathbf{F}$ is zero when $\mathbf{a}$ is zero. It is worth noting again here that if the acceleration were not zero, the body of weight $W$ would not stretch the spring to the same length as it did with $\mathbf{a} = 0$. In fact, if the spring and attached body of weight $W$ were to fall freely under gravity so that $\mathbf{a} = \mathbf{g}$, the spring would not stretch at all and its tension would be zero.

### 5–10    Some Applications of Newton's Laws of Motion

It will be helpful to write down some procedures for solving problems in classical mechanics and to illustrate them by several examples. Newton's second law states that the vector sum of all the forces acting on a body is equal to its mass times its acceleration. The first step in problem solving is therefore: (1) Identify the body to whose motion the problem refers. As obvious as this seems, lack of clarity on the point as to what has been or should be picked as "the body" is a major source of mistakes. (2) Having selected "the body," we next turn our attention to the objects in "the environment" because these objects (inclined planes, springs, cords, the earth, etc.) exert forces on the body. We must be clear as to the nature of these forces. (3) The next step is to select a suitable (inertial) reference frame. We should position the origin and orient the coordinate axes so as to simplify the task of our next step as much as possible. (4) We now make a separate diagram of the body alone, showing the reference frame and *all* of the forces acting *on* the body. This is called a *free-body* diagram. (5) Finally we apply Newton's second law, in the form of Eq. 5–2, to each component of force and acceleration.

The following examples illustrate the method of analysis used in applying Newton's laws of motion. Each body is treated as if it were a particle of definite mass, so that the forces acting on it may be assumed to act at a point. Strings and pulleys are considered to have negligible mass. Although some of the situations picked for analysis may seem simple and artificial, they are the prototypes for many interesting real situations; but, more important, the method of analysis—which is the chief thing to understand—is applicable to all the modern and sophisticated situations of classical mechanics, even sending a spaceship to Mars.

▶ **Example 3.** Figure 5–5$a$ shows a weight $W$ hung by strings. Consider the knot at the junction of the three strings to be "the body." The body remains at rest under the action of the three forces shown in Fig. 5–5$b$. Suppose we are given

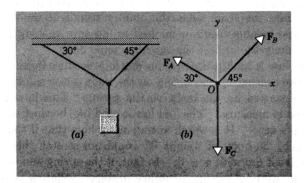

**Fig. 5–5** Example 3. ($a$) A mass is suspended by strings. ($b$) A free-body diagram showing all the forces acting on the knot. The strings are assumed to be weightless.

the magnitude of one of these forces.   How can we find the magnitude of the other forces?

$F_A$, $F_B$, and $F_C$ are *all* the forces acting *on* the body.   Since the body is unaccelerated (actually at rest), $F_A + F_B + F_C = 0$.   Choosing the $x$- and $y$-axes as shown, we can write this vector equation as three scalar equations:

$$F_{Ax} + F_{Bx} = 0,$$

$$F_{Ay} + F_{By} + F_{Cy} = 0,$$

using Eq. 5–2.   The third scalar equation for the $z$-axis is simply

$$F_{Az} = F_{Bz} = F_{Cz} = 0.$$

That is, the vectors all lie in the $x$-$y$ plane so that they have no $z$-components.
From the figure we see that

$$F_{Ax} = -F_A \cos 30° = -0.866F_A,$$

$$F_{Ay} = F_A \sin 30° = 0.500F_A,$$

and

$$F_{Bx} = F_B \cos 45° = 0.707F_B,$$

$$F_{By} = F_B \sin 45° = 0.707F_B.$$

Also,

$$F_{Cy} = -F_C = -W,$$

because the string $C$ merely serves to transmit the force on **one end** to the junction at its other end.   Substituting these results into our original equations, we obtain

$$-0.866F_A + 0.707F_B = 0,$$

$$0.500F_A + 0.707F_B - W = 0.$$

If we are given the magnitude of any one of these three forces, we can solve these equations for the other two.   For example, if $W = 100$ lb, we obtain $F_A = 73.3$ lb and $F_B = 89.6$ lb.

**Example 4.**   We wish to analyze the motion of a block on a smooth incline.
(a) *Static case.*   Figure 5–6a shows a block of mass $m$ kept at rest on a smooth plane, inclined at an angle $\theta$ with the horizontal, by means of a string attached to the vertical wall.   The forces acting *on* the block are shown in Fig. 5–6b.   $F_1$ is the force exerted *on* the block by the string; $mg$ is the force exerted *on* the block by the earth, that is, its weight; and $F_2$ is the force exerted *on* the block by the inclined surface.   $F_2$, called the normal force, is normal to the surface of contact because there is no frictional force between the surfaces.*   If there were a frictional force, $F_2$ would have a component parallel to the incline.   Because we wish to analyze the motion of *the block,* we choose *ALL the forces acting ON the block.*   The student will note that the block will exert forces on other bodies in its environment (the string, the earth, the surface of the incline) in accordance with the action-reaction

---

* The normal force is an example of a constraining force, one which limits the freedom of movement a body might otherwise have.   It is an elastic force arising from small deformations of the bodies in contact, which are never perfectly rigid as we often tacitly assume.

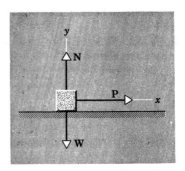

**Fig. 5–6** Example 4. (a) A block is held on a smooth inclined plane by a string. (b) A free-body diagram showing all the forces acting on the block.

**Fig. 5–7** Example 5. A block is being pulled along a smooth table. The forces acting on the block are shown.

principle; these forces, however, are not needed to determine the motion of the block because they do not act on the block.

Suppose $\theta$ and $m$ are given. How do we find $F_1$ and $F_2$? Since the block is unaccelerated, we obtain

$$\mathbf{F}_1 + \mathbf{F}_2 + m\mathbf{g} = 0.$$

It is convenient to choose the $x$-axis of our reference frame to be along the incline and the $y$-axis to be normal to the incline (Fig. 5–6b). With this choice of coordinates, only one force, $m\mathbf{g}$, must be resolved into components in solving the problem. The two scalar equations obtained by resolving $m\mathbf{g}$ along the $x$- and $y$-axes are

$$F_1 - mg \sin \theta = 0, \quad \text{and} \quad F_2 - mg \cos \theta = 0,$$

from which $F_1$ and $F_2$ can be obtained if $\theta$ and $m$ are given.

(b) *Dynamic case.* Now suppose that the string is cut. Then the force $\mathbf{F}_1$, the pull of the string on the block, will be removed. The resultant force on the block will no longer be zero, and the block will accelerate. What is its acceleration?

From Eq. 5–2 we have $F_x = ma_x$ and $F_y = ma_y$. Using these relations we obtain

$$F_2 - mg \cos \theta = ma_y = 0,$$

and                                 $$-mg \sin \theta = ma_x,$$

which yield                         $$a_y = 0, \quad a_x = -g \sin \theta.$$

The acceleration is directed down the incline with a magnitude of $g \sin \theta$.

**Example 5.** Consider a block of mass $m$ pulled along a smooth horizontal surface by a horizontal force $\mathbf{P}$, as shown in Fig. 5–7. N is the normal force exerted on the block by the frictionless surface and **W** is the weight of the block.

(a) If the block has a mass of 2.0 kg, what is the normal force?

From the second law of motion with $a_y = 0$, we obtain

$$F_y = ma_y \quad \text{or} \quad N - W = 0.$$

Hence, $N = W = mg = (2.0 \text{ kg})(9.8 \text{ meters/sec}^2) = 20 \text{ nt}.$

(b) What force $P$ is required to give the block a horizontal velocity of 4.0 meters/sec in 2.0 sec starting from rest?

The acceleration $a_x$ follows from

$$a_x = \frac{v_x - v_{x0}}{t} = \frac{4.0 \text{ meters/sec} - 0}{2.0 \text{ sec}} = 2.0 \text{ meters/sec}^2.$$

From the second law, $F_x = ma_x$ or $P = ma_x$. The force $P$ is then

$$P = ma_x = (2.0 \text{ kg})(2.0 \text{ meters/sec}^2) = 4.0 \text{ nt.}$$

**Example 6.**   Figure 5–8a shows a block of mass $m_1$ on a smooth horizontal surface pulled by a string which is attached to a block of mass $m_2$ hanging
over a pulley. We assume that the
pulley has no mass and is frictionless
and that it merely serves to change the
direction of the tension in the string at
that point. Find the acceleration of
the system and the tension in the string.

Suppose we choose the block of mass
$m_1$ as the body whose motion we investigate. The forces on this block, taken
to be a particle, are shown in Fig. 5–8b.
**T**, the tension in the string, pulls on the
block to the right; $m_1g$ is the downward
pull of the earth on the block and **N** is
the vertical force exerted on the block by
the smooth table. The block will accelerate in the $x$-direction only, so that
$a_{1y} = 0$. We, therefore, can write

$$N - m_1g = 0 = m_1a_{1y},$$

and $\qquad\qquad T = m_1a_{1x}.$   (5–7)

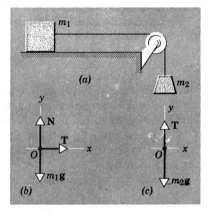

**Fig. 5–8** Example 6. (a) Two masses are connected by a string; $m_1$ lies on a smooth table, $m_2$ hangs freely. (b) A free-body diagram showing all the forces acting on $m_1$. (c) A similar diagram for $m_2$.

From these equations we conclude that $N = m_1g$. We do not know $T$, so we cannot solve for $a_{1x}$.

To determine $T$ we must consider the motion of the block $m_2$. The forces acting
on $m_2$ are shown in Fig. 5–8c. Because the string and block are accelerating, we
cannot conclude that $T$ equals $m_2g$. In fact, if $T$ were to equal $m_2g$, the resultant
force on $m_2$ would be zero, a condition holding only if the system is not accelerated.
The equation of motion for the suspended block is

$$m_2g - T = m_2a_{2y}.$$   (5–8)

The direction of the tension in the string changes at the pulley and, because the
string has a fixed length, it is clear that

$$a_{2y} = a_{1x},$$

so that we can represent the acceleration of the system as simply $a$. We then obtain from Eqs. 5–7 and 5–8

$$m_2 g - T = m_2 a, \tag{5-9}$$

and

$$T = m_1 a.$$

These yield

$$m_2 g = (m_1 + m_2)a, \tag{5-10}$$

or

$$a = \frac{m_2}{m_1 + m_2} g,$$

and

$$T = \frac{m_1 m_2}{m_1 + m_2} g, \tag{5-11}$$

which gives us the acceleration of the system $a$ and the tension in the string $T$.

Notice that the tension in the string is always less than $m_2 g$. This is clear from Eq. 5–11, which can be written

$$T = m_2 g \, \frac{m_1}{m_1 + m_2}.$$

Notice also that $a$ is always less than $g$, the acceleration due to gravity. Only when $m_1$ equals zero, which means that there is no block at all on the table, do we obtain $a = g$ (from Eq. 5–10). In this case $T = 0$ (from Eq. 5–9).

We can interpret Eq. 5–10 in a simple way. The net unbalanced force on the system of mass $m_1 + m_2$ is represented by $m_2 g$. Hence, from $F = ma$, we obtain Eq. 5–10 directly.

To make the example specific, suppose $m_1 = 2.0$ kg and $m_2 = 1.0$ kg. Then

$$a = \frac{m_2}{m_1 + m_2} g = \tfrac{1}{3} g = 3.3 \text{ meters/sec}^2,$$

and

$$T = \frac{m_1 m_2}{m_1 + m_2} g = (\tfrac{2}{3})(9.8) \text{ kg-m/sec}^2 = 6.5 \text{ nt.}$$

**Example 7.** Consider two unequal masses connected by a string which passes over a frictionless and massless pulley, as shown in Fig. 5–9a. Let $m_2$ be greater than $m_1$. Find the tension in the string and the acceleration of the masses.

We consider an *upward* acceleration *positive*. If the acceleration of $m_1$ is $a$, the acceleration of $m_2$ must be $-a$. The forces acting on $m_1$ and on $m_2$ are shown in Fig. 5–9b in which $T$ represents the tension in the string.

The equation of motion for $m_1$ is

$$T - m_1 g = m_1 a$$

and for $m_2$ is

$$T - m_2 g = -m_2 a.$$

Combining these equations, we obtain

$$a = \frac{m_2 - m_1}{m_2 + m_1} g, \tag{5-12}$$

and

$$T = \frac{2 m_1 m_2}{m_1 + m_2} g.$$

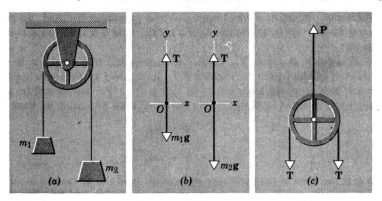

**Fig. 5–9** Example 7. (*a*) Two unequal masses are suspended by a string from a pulley (Atwood's machine). (*b*) Free-body diagrams for $m_1$ and $m_2$. (*c*) Free-body diagram for the pulley, assumed massless.

For example, if $m_2$ = 2.0 slugs and $m_1$ = 1.0 slug,

$$a = (32/3.0) \text{ ft/sec}^2 = g/3,$$

$$T = (\tfrac{4}{3})(32) \text{ slug-ft/sec}^2 = 43 \text{ lb.}$$

Notice that the magnitude of $T$ is always intermediate between the weight of the mass $m_1$ (32 lb in our example) and the weight of the mass $m_2$ (64 lb in our example). This is to be expected, since $T$ must exceed $m_1 g$ to give $m_1$ an upward acceleration, and $m_2 g$ must exceed $T$ to give $m_2$ a downward acceleration. In the special case when $m_1 = m_2$, we obtain $a = 0$ and $T = m_1 g = m_2 g$, which is the static result to be expected.

Figure 5–9*c* shows the forces acting on the massless pulley. If we treat the pulley as a particle, all the forces can be taken to act through its center. $P$ is the upward pull of the support on the pulley and $T$ is the downward pull of each segment of the string on the pulley. Since the pulley has no translational motion,

$$P = T + T = 2T.$$

If we were to drop our assumption of a massless pulley and assign a mass $m$ to it, we would then be required to include a downward force $mg$ on the support. Also, as we shall see later, the rotational motion of the pulley results in a different tension in each segment of the string. Friction in the bearings also affects the rotational motion of the pulley and the tension in the strings.

**Example 8.** Consider an elevator moving vertically with an acceleration **a**. We wish to find the force exerted by a passenger on the floor of the elevator.

Acceleration will be taken *positive upward* and *negative downward*. Thus positive acceleration in this case means that the elevator is either moving upward with increasing speed or is moving downward with decreasing speed. Negative acceleration means that the elevator is moving upward with decreasing speed or downward with increasing speed.

From Newton's third law the force exerted by the passenger on the floor will always be equal in magnitude but opposite in direction to the force exerted by the floor on the passenger. We can therefore calculate either the action force or the reaction force. When the forces acting on the passenger are used, we solve for the latter force. When the forces acting on the floor are used, we solve for the former force.

The situation is shown in Fig. 5–10: The passenger's true weight is **W** and the force exerted on him by the floor, called **P**, is his *apparent* weight in the accelerating elevator. The resultant force acting on him is **P** + **W**. Forces will be taken as positive when directed upward. From the second law of motion we have

$$F = ma,$$

or

$$P - W = ma, \tag{5–13}$$

where $m$ is the mass of the passenger and $a$ is his (and the elevator's) acceleration.

Suppose, for example, that the passenger weighs 160 lb and the acceleration is 2.0 ft/sec² upward. We have

$$m = \frac{W}{g} = \frac{160 \text{ lb}}{32 \text{ ft/sec}^2} = 5.0 \text{ slugs},$$

and from Eq. 5–13,

$$P - 160 \text{ lb} = (5.0 \text{ slugs})(2.0 \text{ ft/sec}^2)$$

or

$$P = \text{apparent weight} = 170 \text{ lb}.$$

If we were to measure this force directly by having the passenger stand on a spring scale fixed to the elevator floor (or suspended from the ceiling), we would find the scale reading to be 170 lb for a man whose weight is 160 lb. The passenger feels himself pressing down on the floor with greater force (the floor is pressing upward on him with greater force) than when he and the elevator are at rest. Everyone experiences this feeling when an elevator starts upward from rest.

**Fig. 5–10** Example 8. (*a*) A passenger stands on the floor of an elevator. (*b*) A free-body diagram for the passenger.

(*a*)     (*b*)

If the acceleration were taken as 2.0 ft/sec$^2$ downward, then $a = -2.0$ ft/sec$^2$ and $P = 150$ lb for the passenger. The passenger who weighs 160 lb feels himself pressing down on the floor with less force than when he and the elevator are at rest.

If the elevator cable were to break and the elevator were to fall freely with an acceleration $a = -g$, then $P$ would equal $W + (W/g)(-g) = 0$. Then the passenger and floor would exert no forces on each other. The passenger's apparent weight, as indicated by the spring scale on the floor, would be zero. ◄

## QUESTIONS

**1.** What is your mass in slugs? Your weight in newtons?

**2.** Why do you fall forward when a moving train decelerates to a stop and fall backward when a train accelerates from rest? What would happen if the train rounded a curve at constant speed?

**3.** A horse is urged to pull a wagon. The horse refuses to try, citing Newton's third law as his defense: "'The pull of the horse on the wagon is equal but opposite to the pull of the wagon on the horse.' If I can never exert a greater force on the wagon than it exerts on me, how can I ever start the wagon moving?" asks the horse. How would you reply?

**4.** A block of mass $m$ is supported by a cord $C$ from the ceiling, and another cord $D$ is attached to the bottom of the block (Fig. 5–11). Explain this: If you give a sudden jerk to $D$ it will break, but if you pull on $D$ steadily, $C$ will break.

Fig. 5–11

Fig. 5–12

**5.** Two 10-lb weights are attached to a spring scale as shown in Fig. 5–12. Does the scale read 0 lb, 10 lb, 20 lb, or give some other reading?

**6.** Criticize the statement, often made, that the mass of a body is a measure of the "quantity of matter" in it.

**7.** Using force, length, and time as fundamental quantities, what are the dimensions of mass?

**8.** Is the definition of mass that we have given limited to objects initially at rest?

**9.** Is the current standard of mass accessible, invariable, reproducible, indestructible? Does it have simplicity for comparison purposes? Would an atomic standard be better in any respect?

**10.** Suppose the carbon atom was chosen as the standard of mass. What information would be needed to express the mass of the standard kilogram in terms of this atomic standard? How could this information be obtained?

**11.** Suggest practical ways by which one could determine the masses of the various objects listed in Table 5–2.

**12.** In a tug of war, three men pull on a rope to the left at $A$ and three men pull to the right at $B$ with forces of equal magnitude. Now a weight of 5.0 lb is hung vertically from the center of the rope. (a) Can the men get the rope $AB$ to be horizontal? (b) If not, explain. If so, determine the magnitude of the forces required at $A$ and $B$ to do this.

**13.** Both the following statements are true; explain them. Two teams having a tug of war must always pull equally hard on one another. The team that pushes harder against the ground wins.

**14.** Under what circumstances would your weight be zero? Does your answer depend on the choice of a reference system?

**15.** Two objects of equal mass rest on opposite pans of a trip scale. Does the scale remain balanced when it is accelerated up or down in an elevator?

**16.** A massless rope is strung over a frictionless pulley. A monkey holds onto one end of the rope and a mirror, having the same weight as the monkey, is attached to the other end of the rope at the monkey's level. Can the monkey get away from his image seen in the mirror (a) by climbing up the rope, (b) by climbing down the rope, (c) by releasing the rope?

**17.** A student standing on the large platform of a spring scale notes his weight. He then takes a step on this platform and notices that the scale reads less than his weight at the beginning of the step and more than his weight at the end of the step. Explain.

## PROBLEMS

**1.** Two blocks, mass $m_1$ and $m_2$ are connected by a light spring on a horizontal frictionless table. Find the ratio of their accelerations $a_1$ and $a_2$ after they are pulled apart and then released.

**2.** Let the only forces acting on two bodies be their mutual interactions. If both bodies start from rest, show that the distances traveled by each are inversely proportional to the respective masses of the bodies.

**3.** A body of mass $m$ is acted on by two forces $\mathbf{F}_1$ and $\mathbf{F}_2$, as shown in Fig. 5–13. If $m = 5.0$ kg, $F_1 = 3.0$ nt, and $F_2 = 4.0$ nt, find the vector acceleration of the body.

**Fig. 5–13**

**Fig. 5–14**

**4.** A block of mass $M$ is pulled along a horizontal frictionless surface by a rope of mass $m$, as in Fig. 5–14. A force $\mathbf{P}$ is applied to one end of the rope. (a) Find the acceleration of the block and the rope. (b) Find the force that the rope exerts on the block $M$ in terms of $P$, $M$, and $m$.

5. A car moving initially at a speed of 50 miles/hr and weighing 3000 lb is brought to a stop in a distance of 200 ft. (a) Find the braking force and the time required to stop. (b) Assuming the same braking force, find the distance and time required to stop if the car were going 25 miles/hr initially.

6. An electron travels in a straight line from the cathode of a vacuum tube to its anode, which is exactly 1.0 cm away. It starts with zero speed and reaches the anode with a speed of $6.0 \times 10^6$ meters/sec. (a) Assume constant acceleration and compute the force on the electron. Take the electron's mass to be $9.1 \times 10^{-31}$ kg. This force is electrical in origin. (b) Compare it with the gravitational force on the electron, which we neglected when we assumed straight-line motion. Is this assumption valid?

7. A body of mass 2.0 slugs is acted on by the downward force of gravity and a horizontal force of 130 lb. Find its acceleration and its velocity as a function of time, assuming it starts from rest.

8. An electron is projected horizontally from an electron gun at a speed of $1.2 \times 10^7$ meters/sec into an electric field which exerts a constant vertical force of $4.5 \times 10^{-15}$ nt on it. The mass of the electron can be taken to be $9.1 \times 10^{-31}$ kg. Determine the vertical distance the electron is deflected during the time it has moved forward 3.0 cm horizontally.

9. A space traveler whose mass is 75 kg leaves the earth. Compute his weight (a) on the earth, (b) 400 miles above the earth (where $g = 8.1$ meters/sec$^2$), and (c) in interplanetary space. What is his mass at each of these locations?

10. Two blocks are in contact on a frictionless table. A horizontal force is applied to one block, as shown in Fig. 5–15. (a) If $m_1 = 2.0$ kg, $m_2 = 1.0$ kg, and $F = 3.0$ nt, find the force of contact between the two blocks. (b) Show that if the same force is applied to $m_2$ rather than to $m_1$, the force of contact between the blocks is 2.0 nt, which is not the same as the value derived in (a). Explain.

Fig. 5–15

11. Three blocks are connected, as shown in Fig. 5–16, on a horizontal frictionless table and pulled to the right with a force $T_3 = 60$ nt. If $m_1 = 10$ kg, $m_2 = 20$ kg, and $m_3 = 30$ kg, find the tensions $T_1$ and $T_2$. Draw an analogy to bodies being pulled in tandem, such as an engine pulling a train of coupled cars.

Fig. 5–16

**12.** A charged sphere of mass $3.0 \times 10^{-4}$ kg is suspended from a string. An electric force acts horizontally on the sphere so that the string makes an angle of 37° with the vertical when at rest (Fig. 5–17). Find (a) the magnitude of the electric force and (b) the tension in the string.

**13.** How could a 100-lb object be lowered from a roof using a cord with a breaking strength of 87 lb without breaking the rope?

**Fig. 5–17**

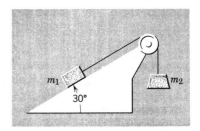

**Fig. 5–18**

**14.** Compute the initial upward acceleration of a rocket of mass $1.3 \times 10^4$ kg if the initial upward thrust of its engine is $2.6 \times 10^5$ nt. Can you neglect the weight of the rocket (the downward pull of the earth on it)?

**15.** A block of mass $m_1 = 3.0$ slugs on a smooth inclined plane of angle 30° is connected by a cord over a small frictionless pulley to a second block of mass $m_2 = 2.0$ slugs hanging vertically (Fig. 5–18). (a) What is the acceleration of each body? (b) What is the tension in the cord?

**16.** A 10-kg monkey is climbing a massless rope attached to a 15-kg mass over a (frictionless!) tree limb. (a) Explain quantitatively how the monkey can climb up the rope so that he can raise the 15-kg mass off the ground. (b) If, after the mass has been raised off the ground, the monkey stops climbing and holds on to the rope, what will his acceleration and the tension in the rope now be?

**17.** A block is released from rest at the top of a frictionless inclined plane 16 meters long. It reaches the bottom 4.0 sec later. A second block is projected up the plane from the bottom at the instant the first block is released in such a way that it returns to the bottom simultaneously with the first block. (a) Find the acceleration of each block on the incline. (b) What is the initial velocity of the second block? (c) How far up the inclined plane does it travel?

**18.** A block is projected up a frictionless inclined plane with a speed $v_0$. The angle of incline is $\theta$. (a) How far up the plane does it go? (b) How long does it take to get there? (c) What is its speed when it gets back to the bottom? Find numerical answers for $\theta = 30°$ and $v_0 = 8.0$ ft/sec.

**19.** A block slides down a frictionless incline making an angle $\theta$ with an elevator floor. Find its acceleration relative to the incline in the following cases. (a) Elevator descends at constant speed $v$. (b) Elevator ascends at constant speed $v$. (c) Elevator descends with acceleration $a$. (d) Elevator descends with deceleration $a$. (e) Elevator cable breaks.

**20.** An elevator weighing 6000 lb is pulled upward by a cable with an acceleration of 4.0 ft/sec². (a) What is the tension in the cable? (b) What is the tension when the elevator is accelerating downward at 4.0 ft/sec²?

**21.** A lamp hangs vertically from a cord in a descending elevator. The elevator has a deceleration of 8.0 ft/sec² before coming to a stop. (*a*) If the tension in the cord is 20 lb, what is the mass of the lamp? (*b*) What is the tension in the cord when the elevator ascends with an acceleration of 8.0 ft/sec²?

**22.** A plumb bob hanging from the ceiling of a railroad car acts as an accelerometer. (*a*) Derive the general expression relating the horizontal acceleration $a$ of the car to the angle $\theta$ made by the bob with the vertical. (*b*) Find $a$ when $\theta = 20°$. Find $\theta$ when $a = 5.0$ ft/sec².

**23.** Refer to Fig. 5–6. Let the mass of the block be 2.0 slugs and the angle $\theta$ equal 30°. (*a*) Find the tension in the string and the normal force acting on the block. (*b*) If the string is cut, find the acceleration of the block. Neglect friction.

**24.** Refer to Fig. 5–8a. Let $m_1 = 4.0$ slugs and $m_2 = 2.0$ slugs. Find the tension in the string and the acceleration of the two blocks.

**25.** Refer to Fig. 5–9a. Let $m_1 = 0.50$ kg and $m_2 = 1.0$ kg. Find the acceleration of the two blocks and the tension in the string.

**26.** A uniform flexible chain of length $l$, with weight per unit length $\lambda$, passes over a small, frictionless, massless pulley. It is released from a rest position with a length of chain $x$ hanging from one side and a length $l - x$ from the other side. (*a*) Under what circumstances will it accelerate? (*b*) Assuming these circumstances are met, find the acceleration $a$ as a function of $x$.

**27.** A triangular block of mass $M$ with angles 30°, 60°, and 90° rests with its 30°-90° side on a horizontal table. A cubical block of mass $m$ rests on the 60°-30° side (Fig. 5–19). (*a*) What horizontal acceleration $a$ must $M$ have relative to the table to keep $m$ stationary relative to the triangular block, assuming frictionless contacts? (*b*) What horizontal force $F$ must be applied to the system to achieve this result, assuming a frictionless table top? (*c*) Suppose no force is supplied to $M$ and both surfaces are frictionless. Describe the resulting motion.

**Fig. 5–19**

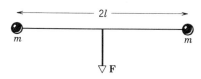

**Fig. 5–20**

**28.** Two particles, each of mass $m$, are connected by a light string of length $2l$, as shown in Fig. 5–20. A continuous force **F** is applied at the midpoint of the string ($x = 0$) at right angles to the initial position of the string. Show that the acceleration of $m$ in the direction at right angles to **F** is given by

$$a_x = \frac{F}{2m}\frac{x}{\sqrt{l^2 - x^2}}$$

in which $x$ is the perpendicular distance of one of the particles from the line of action of **F**. Discuss the situation when $x = l$.

**29.** *Terminal velocity.* The resistance of the air to the motion of bodies in free fall depends on many factors, such as the size of the body and its shape, the density and temperature of the air, and the velocity of the body through the air. A useful assumption, only approximately true, is that the resisting force $f_R$ is proportional to the velocity and oppositely directed; that is, $f_R = -kv$, where $k$ is a constant whose value in any particular case is determined by factors other than velocity.

Consider free fall of an object from rest through the air.

(a) Show that Newton's second law gives

$$mg - kv = ma \qquad \text{or} \qquad mg - k\frac{dy}{dt} = m\frac{d^2y}{dt^2}.$$

(b) Show that the body ceases to accelerate when it reaches a velocity $v_T = mg/k$, called the *terminal velocity*.

(c) Prove, by substituting it in the equation of motion of part (a), that the velocity varies with time as

$$v = v_T(1 - e^{-kt/m})$$

and plot $v$ versus $t$.

(d) Sketch qualitatively curves of $y$ versus $t$ and $a$ versus $t$ for this motion, noting that the initial acceleration is $g$ and the final acceleration is zero.

# Particle Dynamics—II

## CHAPTER 6

### 6–1 Introduction

In Chapter 5 we considered particle dynamics for bodies subject to a force that was constant in both magnitude and direction. The forces that we dealt with were exerted by the earth or by taut cords, that is, they were either gravitational or elastic in nature. In this chapter we consider another kind of force, that resulting from friction.

We shall also discuss the dynamics of uniform circular motion, in which the force, although constant in magnitude, changes in direction with time. In Chapter 10 we shall consider problems in which the force, although constant in direction, changes in magnitude with time, as when one body exerts a transient force on another during a collision. Finally, in Chapter 15, we shall consider problems in which the force changes in *both* magnitude *and* direction with time, such as the force exerted by a spring on an oscillating mass suspended from it.

### 6–2 Frictional Forces*

If we project a block of mass $m$ with initial velocity $v_0$ along a long horizontal table, it eventually comes to rest. This means that, while it is moving, it experiences an average acceleration $\bar{a}$ that points in the direction opposite to its motion. If (in an inertial frame) we see that a body is being accelerated, we always associate a force, defined from Newton's

---

* See "The Friction of Solids" by E. H. Freitag, in *Contemporary Physics*, Vol. 2, 1961, p. 198, for a good general reference; see also the article "Friction" in the Encyclopedia Brittanica.

second law, with the motion. In this case we declare that the table exerts a *force of friction*, whose average value is $m\bar{a}$, on the sliding block.

Actually, whenever the surface of one body slides over that of another, each body exerts a frictional force on the other, parallel to the surfaces. The frictional force on each body is in a direction opposite to its motion relative to the other body. Frictional forces automatically oppose the motion and never aid it. Even when there is no relative motion, frictional forces may exist between surfaces.

Although we have ignored its effects up to now, friction is very important in our daily lives. Left to act alone it brings every rotating shaft to a halt. In an automobile, about 20% of the engine power is used to counteract frictional forces (only 1 or 2% in a turbojet engine, however). Friction causes wear and seizing of moving parts and many engineering man-hours are devoted to reducing it. On the other hand, without friction we could not walk as we now do; we could not hold a pencil in our hand and if we could it would not write; wheeled transport as we know it would not be possible.

We want to know how to express frictional forces in terms of the properties of the body and its environment; that is, we want to know the *force law* for frictional forces. In what follows we consider the sliding (not rolling) of one dry (unlubricated) surface over another. As we shall see later, friction, viewed at the microscopic level, is a very complicated phenomenon* and the force laws for dry, sliding friction are empirical in character and approximate in their predictions. They do not have the elegant simplicity and accuracy that we find for the gravitational force law (Chapter 16) or for the electrostatic force law (Chapter 26). It is remarkable, however, considering the enormous diversity of surfaces one encounters, that many aspects of frictional behavior can be understood qualitatively on the basis of a few simple mechanisms.

Consider a block at rest on a horizontal table as in Fig. 6–1. Attach a spring to it to measure the force required to set the block in motion. We find that the block will not move even though we apply a small force. We say that our applied force is balanced by an opposite frictional force exerted on the block by the table, acting along the surface of contact. As we increase the applied force we find some definite force at which the block just begins to move. Once motion has started, this same force produces accelerated motion. By reduci•g the force once motion has started, we find that it is possible to keep the block in uniform motion without acceleration; this force may be small, but it is never zero.

The frictional forces acting between surfaces at rest with respect to each other are called forces of *static friction*. The maximum force of static friction will be the same as the smallest force necessary to start motion. Once motion is started, the frictional forces acting between the surfaces

---

* See, for example, "Stick and Slip" by Ernest Rabinowicz, in *Scientific American*, May 1956.

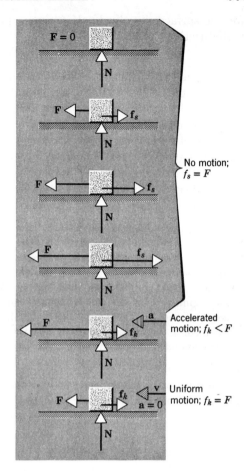

**Fig. 6–1** A block being put into motion as applied force F overcomes frictional forces. In the first four drawings the applied force is gradually increased from zero to magnitude $\mu_s N$. No motion occurs until this point because the frictional force always just balances the applied force. The instant $F$ becomes greater than $\mu_s N$, the block goes into motion, as is shown in the fifth drawing. In general, $\mu_k N < \mu_s N$; this leaves an unbalanced force to the left and the block accelerates. In the last drawing $F$ has been reduced to equal $\mu_k N$. The net force is zero, and the block continues with constant velocity.

usually decrease so that a smaller force is necessary to maintain uniform motion. The forces acting between surfaces in relative motion are called forces of *kinetic friction*.

The maximum force of static friction between any pair of dry unlubricated surfaces follows these two empirical laws. (1) It is approximately independent of the area of contact, over wide limits and (2) it is proportional to the normal force. The normal force, sometimes called the loading force, is the one which either body exerts on the other at right angles to their mutual interface. It arises from the elastic deformation of the bodies in contact, such bodies never really being entirely rigid. For a block resting on a horizontal table or sliding along it, the normal force is equal in magnitude to the weight of the block. Because the block has no vertical acceleration, the table must be exerting a force on the block that is directed upward and is equal in magnitude to the downward pull of the earth on the block, that is, equal to the block's weight.

The ratio of the magnitude of the maximum force of static friction to the magnitude of the normal force is called the *coefficient of static friction* for the surfaces involved. If $f_s$ represents the magnitude of the force of static friction, we can write

$$f_s \le \mu_s N, \qquad (6\text{-}1)$$

where $\mu_s$ is the coefficient of static friction and $N$ is the magnitude of the normal force. The equality sign holds only when $f_s$ has its maximum value.

The force of kinetic friction $f_k$ between dry, unlubricated surfaces follows the same two laws as those of static friction. (1) It is approximately independent of the area of contact over wide limits and (2) it is proportional to the normal force. The force of kinetic friction is also reasonably independent of the relative speed with which the surfaces move over each other.

The two laws of friction above were discovered experimentally by Leonardo da Vinci (1452–1519) and rediscovered, in 1699, by the French engineer G. Amontons. Leonardo's statement of the two laws was remarkable, coming as it did about two centuries before the concept of force was fully developed by Newton. Leonardo's formulation was: (1) "Friction made by the same weight will be of equal resistance at the beginning of the movement though the contact may be of different breadths or lengths" and (2) "Friction produces double the amount of effort if the weight be doubled." The French scientist, Charles A. Coulomb, (1736–1806) did many experiments on friction and pointed out the difference between static and kinetic friction.

The ratio of the magnitude of the force of kinetic friction to the magnitude of this normal force is called the *coefficient of kinetic friction*. If $f_k$ represents the magnitude of the force of kinetic friction,

$$f_k = \mu_k N, \qquad (6\text{-}2)$$

where $\mu_k$ is the coefficient of kinetic friction.

Both $\mu_s$ and $\mu_k$ are dimensionless constants, each being the ratio of (the magnitudes of) two forces. Usually, for a given pair of surfaces $\mu_s > \mu_k$. The actual values of $\mu_s$ and $\mu_k$ depend on the nature of both the surfaces in contact. Both $\mu_s$ and $\mu_k$ can exceed unity, although commonly they are less than one. Notice that Eqs. 6–1 and 6–2 are relations between the *magnitudes only* of the normal and frictional forces. These forces are always directed perpendicularly to one another.

On the atomic scale even the most finely polished surface is far from plane. Figure 6-2,

**Fig. 6–2** A highly magnified view of a section of a finely polished steel surface. The section was cut at an angle so that vertical distances are exaggerated by a factor of ten with respect to horizontal distances. The surface irregularities are several thousand atomic diameters high. From *Friction and Lubrication of Solids*, by F. P. Bowden and D. Tabor, Clarendon Press, 1950.

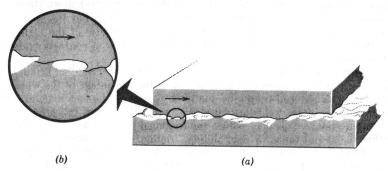

**Fig. 6–3** Sliding friction. (*a*) The upper body is sliding to the right over the lower body in this enlarged diagram. (*b*) A further enlarged view showing two spots where surface adhesion has occurred. Force is required to break these welds apart and maintain the motion.

for example, shows an actual profile, highly magnified, of a steel surface that would be considered to be highly polished. One can readily believe that when two bodies are placed in contact, the actual microscopic area of contact is much less than apparent macroscopic area of contact; in a particular case these areas can be easily in the ratio of 1 to $10^4$.

The actual (microscopic) area of contact is proportional to the normal force, because the contact points deform plastically under the great stresses that develop at these points. Many contact points actually become "cold-welded" together. This phenomenon, *surface adhesion*, occurs because at the contact points the molecules on opposite sides of the surface are so close together that they exert strong intermolecular forces on each other.

When one body (a metal, say) is pulled across another, the frictional resistance is associated with the rupturing of these thousands of tiny welds, which continually reform as new chance contacts are made (see Fig. 6-3). Radioactive tracer experiments have shown that, in the rupturing process, small fragments of one metallic surface may be sheared off and adhere to the other surface. If the relative speed of the two surfaces is great enough, there may be local melting at certain contact areas even though the surface as a whole may feel only moderately warm.

The coefficient of friction depends on many variables, such as the nature of the materials, surface finish, surface films, temperature, and extent of contamination. For example, if two carefully cleaned metal surfaces are placed in a highly evacuated chamber so that surface oxide films do not form, the coefficient of friction rises to enormous values and the surfaces actually become firmly "welded" together. The admission of a small amount of air to the chamber so that oxide films may form on the opposing surfaces reduces the coefficient of friction to its "normal" value.

With these complications it is not surprising that there is no exact theory of dry friction and that the laws of friction are empirical. The surface adhesion theory of friction for metals leads to a ready understanding of the two laws of friction mentioned above however. (1) The microscopic contact area, which determines the frictional force $f_k$, is proportional to the normal force $N$ and thus $f_k$ is proportional to $N$, as Eq. 6-2 shows. (2) The fact that the frictional force is independent of the apparent area of contact means, for example, that the force required to drag a metal "brick" along a metal table is the same no matter which face of the brick is in contact with the table. We can understand this only if the microscopic area of contact is the same for all positions of the brick, and this is indeed the case. With the largest face down, there are a relatively large number of relatively small area contacts supporting the load; with the smallest face down there are fewer contacts (because the apparent contact area is smaller), but the area of an individual contact is larger by just the same factor because of the higher pressure exerted by the up-ended brick on this smaller number of contacts supporting the same load.

The frictional force that opposes one body *rolling* over another is much less than that for a sliding motion and this, indeed, is the advantage of the wheel over the sledge.   This reduced friction is due in large part to the fact that, in rolling, the microscopic contact welds are "peeled" apart rather than "sheared" apart as in sliding friction.   This may reduce the frictional force by as much as 1000-fold.

Frictional resistance in dry, sliding, friction can be considerably reduced by lubrication.   A mural in a grotto in Egypt dating back to 1900 B.C. shows a large stone statue being pulled on a sledge while a man in front of the sledge pours lubricating oil in its path.   A still more effective technique is to introduce a layer of gas between the sliding surfaces; the "dry ice puck" mentioned on page 82 and the gas-supported bearing are two examples.   Friction can be reduced still further by suspending a rotating object in an evacuated space by means of magnetic forces.   J. W. Beams, for example, has spun a 30-lb rotor of this type at 1000 rev/sec; when the drive was cut off, the rotor lost speed at the rate of only 1 rev/sec in a day.*

Examples of the application of the empirical force law for friction follow. The coefficients of friction given are assumed to be constant.   Actually $\mu_k$ can be regarded as a good average value that is not greatly different from the value at any particular speed in the range.

▶ **Example 1.**   A block is at rest on an inclined plane making an angle $\theta$ with the horizontal, as in Fig. 6–4a.   As the angle of incline is raised, it is found that slipping just begins at an angle of inclination $\theta_s$.   What is the coefficient of static friction between block and incline?

The forces acting on the block, considered to be a particle, are shown in Fig. 6–4b.  $\mathbf{W}$ is the weight of the block, $\mathbf{N}$ the normal force exerted on the block by the inclined surface, and $\mathbf{f}_s$ the tangential force of friction exerted by the inclined surface on the block.   Notice that the resultant force exerted by the inclined surface on the block, $\mathbf{N} + \mathbf{f}_s$, is no longer perpendicular to the surface of contact, as was true for smooth surfaces $(\mathbf{f}_s = 0)$.   The block is at rest, so that

$$\mathbf{N} + \mathbf{f}_s + \mathbf{W} = 0.$$

Resolving our forces into $x$- and $y$-components, along the plane and the normal to

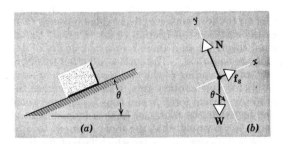

(a)                                        (b)

**Fig.  6–4** Example  1.  (a) A block at rest on a rough inclined plane.  (b) A free-body force diagram for the block.

---

*See "Ultrahigh—Speed Rotation," Jesse W. Beams in *Scientific American*, April 1961.

the plane, respectively, we obtain

$$N - W \cos \theta = 0,$$
$$f_s - W \sin \theta = 0. \tag{6-3}$$

However, $f_s \leqq \mu_s N$. If we increase the angle of incline slowly until slipping just begins, then for that angle, $\theta = \theta_s$ and we can use $f_s = \mu_s N$. Substituting this into Eqs. 6–3, we obtain

$$N = W \cos \theta_s$$

and

$$\mu_s N = W \sin \theta_s,$$

so that

$$\mu_s = \tan \theta_s.$$

Hence measurement of the angle of inclination at which slipping just starts provides a simple experimental method for determining the coefficient of static friction between two surfaces.

The student can make use of similar arguments to show that the angle of inclination $\theta_k$ required to maintain a *constant speed* for the block as it slides down the plane, once it has been started by tapping, is given by

$$\mu_k = \tan \theta_k,$$

where $\theta_k < \theta_s$. With the aid of a ruler the student can now determine $\mu_s$ and $\mu_k$ for a coin sliding down his textbook.

**Example 2.**  Consider an automobile moving along a straight horizontal road with a speed $v_0$. If the coefficient of static friction between the tires and the road is $\mu_s$, what is the shortest distance in which the automobile can be stopped?

The forces acting on the automobile, considered to be a particle, are shown in Fig. 6–5. The car is assumed to be moving in the positive $x$-direction. If we assume that $f_s$ is a constant force, we have uniformly decelerated motion.

From the relation (see Eq. 3–16)

$$v^2 = v_0{}^2 + 2ax,$$

with the final speed $v = 0$, we obtain

$$x = -v_0{}^2/2a,$$

where the minus sign means that **a** points in the negative $x$-direction.

To determine $a$, apply the second law of motion to the $x$-component of the motion:

$$-f_s = ma = (W/g)a \quad \text{or} \quad a = -g(f_s/W).$$

From the $y$ components we obtain

$$N - W = 0 \quad \text{or} \quad N = W,$$

so that          $$\mu_s = f_s/N = f_s/W$$

and              $$a = -\mu_s g.$$

Then the distance of stopping is

$$x = -v_0^2/2a = v_0^2/2g\mu_s. \tag{6-4}$$

The greater the initial speed, the longer the distance required to come to a stop; in fact, this distance varies as the square of the initial velocity. Also, the greater the coefficient of static friction between the surfaces, the less the distance required to come to a stop.

We have used the coefficient of static friction in this problem, rather than the coefficient of sliding friction, because we assume there is no sliding between the tires and the road. We have neglected rolling friction. Furthermore, we have assumed that the maximum force of static friction ($f_s = \mu_s N$) operates because the problem seeks the shortest distance for stopping. With a smaller static frictional force the distance for stopping would obviously be greater. The correct braking technique required here is to keep the car just on the verge of skidding. If the surface is smooth and the brakes are applied fully, sliding may occur. In this case $\mu_k$ replaces $\mu_s$, and the distance required to stop is seen to increase from Eq. 6–4. As a specific example, if $v_0 = 60$ miles/hr $= 88$ ft/sec, and $\mu_s = 0.60$ (a typical value), we obtain

$$x = \frac{v_0^2}{2\mu_s g} = \frac{(88 \text{ ft/sec})^2}{2(0.60)(32 \text{ ft/sec}^2)} = 200 \text{ ft.}$$

Notice that the mass of the car does not appear in Eq. 6–4. How can you explain the practice of "weighing down" a car in order to increase safety in driving on icy roads?

The student should now investigate how, in principle, forces of friction would modify the results of the examples of Section 5–10.          ◄

### 6–3   The Dynamics of Uniform Circular Motion

In Section 4–4 we pointed out that if a body is moving at uniform speed $v$ in a circle of radius $r$, it experiences a centripetal acceleration **a** whose magnitude is $v^2/r$. The direction of **a** is always radially inward toward the center of rotation. Thus **a** is a variable vector because, even though its magnitude remains constant, its direction changes continuously as the motion progresses.

Recall that there need not be any motion in the direction of an acceleration. In general, there is no fixed relation between the directions of the acceleration **a** and the velocity **v** of a particle, as Fig. 4–7 shows. For a particle in uniform circular motion the acceleration **a** and velocity **v** are always at right angles to each other.

Every accelerated body must have a force **F** acting on it, defined by Newton's second law (**F** $= m$**a**). Thus (assuming that we are in an inertial frame), if we see a body undergoing uniform circular motion, we can be

**Fig. 6-6** A disk $m$ moves with constant speed in a circular path on a horizontal frictionless surface. The only horizontal force acting on $m$ is the centripetal force **T** with which the string pulls on the body.

*certain* that a net force **F**, given in magnitude by

$$F = ma = mv^2/r$$

*must* be acting on the body; the body is *not* in equilibrium. The direction of **F** at any instant must be the direction of **a** at that instant, namely, radially inward. We must always be able to account for this force by pointing to a particular object in the environment that is exerting the force on the accelerating, circulating body.

If the body in uniform circular motion is a disc on the end of a string moving in a circle on a frictionless horizontal table as in Fig. 6-6, the force **F** on the disc is provided by the tension **T** in the string. This force **T** is the net force acting on the disc. It accelerates the disc by constantly changing the direction of its velocity so that the disc moves in a circle. **T** is always directed toward the pin at the center and its magnitude is $mv^2/R$. If the string were to be cut where it joins the disc, there would be no net force exerted on the disc. The disc would then move with constant speed in a straight line along the direction of the tangent to the circle at the point at which the string was cut. Hence, to keep the disc moving in a circle, a force must be supplied to it pulling it *inward* toward the center.

Forces responsible for uniform circular motion are called *centripetal* forces because they are directed "toward the center" of the circular motion. To label a force as "centripetal," however, simply means that it always points radially inward; the name tells us nothing about the nature of the force or about the body that is exerting it. Thus, for the revolving disc of Fig. 6-6, the centripetal force is an elastic force provided by the string; for the moon revolving around the earth (in an approximately circular orbit) the centripetal force is the gravitational pull of the earth on the moon; for an electron circulating about an atomic nucleus the centripetal force is electrostatic. A centripetal force is *not* a new kind of force but simply a way of describing the behavior with time of forces that are attributable to specific bodies in the environment. Thus a force can be centripetal *and* elastic, centripetal *and* gravitational, or centripetal *and* electrostatic, among other possibilities.

Let us consider some examples of forces that act centripetally.

▶ **Example 3.** *The Conical Pendulum.* Figure 6–7a represents a small body of mass $m$ revolving in a horizontal circle with constant speed $v$ at the end of a string of length $L$. As the body swings around, the string sweeps over the surface of a cone. This device is called a *conical pendulum.* Find the time required for one complete revolution of the body.

If the string makes an angle $\theta$ with the vertical, the radius of the circular path is $R = L \sin \theta$. The forces acting on the body of mass $m$ are **W**, its weight, and **T**, the pull of the string, as shown in Fig. 6–7b. It is clear that $\mathbf{T} + \mathbf{W} \neq 0$. Hence, the resultant force acting on the body is non-zero, which is as it should be because a force is required to keep the body moving in a circle with constant speed.

We can resolve **T** at any instant into a radial and a vertical component

$$T_r = T \sin \theta \quad \text{and} \quad T_z = T \cos \theta.$$

Since the body has no vertical acceleration,

$$T_z - W = 0.$$

But

$$T_z = T \cos \theta \quad \text{and} \quad W = mg,$$

so that

$$T \cos \theta = mg.$$

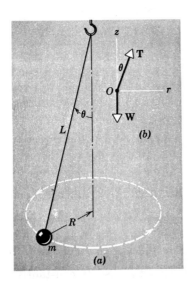

**Fig. 6–7** Example 3. (a) A mass $m$ suspended from a .string of length $L$ swings so as to describe a circle. The string describes a right circular cone of semiangle $\theta$. (b) A free-body force diagram for $m$.

The radial acceleration is $v^2/R$. This acceleration is supplied by $T_r$, the radial component of **T**, which is the centripetal force acting on $m$. Hence

$$T_r = T \sin \theta = mv^2/R.$$

Dividing this equation by the preceding one, we obtain

$$\tan \theta = v^2/Rg, \quad \text{or} \quad v^2 = Rg \tan \theta,$$

which gives the constant speed of the bob. If we let $\tau$ represent the time for one complete revolution of the body, then

$$v = \frac{2\pi R}{\tau} = \sqrt{Rg \tan \theta}$$

or

$$\tau = \frac{2\pi R}{v} = \frac{2\pi R}{\sqrt{Rg \tan \theta}} = 2\pi \sqrt{R/(g \tan \theta)}.$$

But $R = L \sin \theta$, so that

$$\tau = 2\pi \sqrt{(L \cos \theta)/g}.$$

This equation gives the relation between $\tau$, $L$, and $\theta$. Notice that $\tau$, called the *period* of motion, does not depend on $m$.

If $L = 3.0$ ft and $\theta = 30°$, what is the period of the motion?    We have

$$\tau = 2\pi \sqrt{\frac{(3.0 \text{ ft})(0.866)}{32 \text{ ft/sec}^2}} = 1.8 \text{ sec.}$$

**Example 4.**  *The Rotor.*  In many amusement parks we find a device called the *rotor*.  The rotor is a hollow cylindrical room which can be set rotating about the central vertical axis of the cylinder.  A person enters the rotor, closes the door, and stands up against the wall.  The rotor gradually increases its rotational speed from rest until, at a predetermined speed, the floor below the person is opened downward, revealing a deep pit. The passenger does not fall but remains "pinned up" against the wall of the rotor. Find the coefficient of friction necessary to prevent falling.

The forces acting on the passenger are shown in Fig. 6–8.  $W$ is the passenger's weight, $f_s$ is the force of static friction between passenger and rotor wall, and $P$ is the centripetal force exerted by the wall on the passenger necessary to keep him moving in a circle.  Let the radius of the rotor be $R$ and the final speed of the passenger be $v$.  Since the passenger does not move vertically, but experiences a radial acceleration $v^2/R$ at any instant, we have

$$f_s - W = 0$$

and

$$P(=ma) = (W/g)(v^2/R).$$

**Fig. 6–8**  The forces on a person in a "rotor" of radius $R$.

If $\mu_s$ is the coefficient of static friction between passenger and wall necessary to prevent slipping, then $f_s = \mu_s P$ and

$$f_s = W = \mu_s P$$

or

$$\mu_s = \frac{W}{P} = \frac{gR}{v^2}.$$

This equation gives the minimum coefficient of friction necessary to prevent slipping for a rotor of radius $R$ when a particle on its wall has a speed $v$.  Notice that the result does not depend on the passenger's weight.

As a practical matter the coefficient of friction between the textile material of clothing and a typical rotor wall (canvas) is about 0.40.  For a typical rotor the radius is 7.0 ft, so that $v$ must be about 24 ft/sec or 16 miles/hr or more.

**Example 5.**  Let the block in Fig. 6–9a represent an automobile or railway car moving at constant speed $v$ on a *level* road-bed around a curve having a radius of curvature $R$.  In addition to two vertical forces, namely the force of gravity $W$ and a normal force **N**, a horizontal centripetal force **P** acts on the car. In the case of the automobile this centripetal force is supplied by a sidewise frictional force exerted by the road on the tires; in the case of the railway car the centripetal force is supplied by the rails exerting a sidewise force on the inner rims of the car's wheels. Neither of these sidewise forces can be safely relied upon to be large enough at all times and both cause unnecessary wear. Hence, the roadbed is *banked* on curves, as shown in Fig. 6–9*b*. In this case, the normal force **N** has not only a vertical component, as before, but also a horizontal component which supplies the centripetal force necessary for uniform circular motion; no additional sidewise forces are needed, therefore, with a properly banked roadbed.

(a)

(b)

**Fig. 6–9**

The correct angle $\theta$ of banking can be obtained as follows. There is no vertical acceleration, so that

$$N \cos \theta = W.$$

The centripetal force is $N \sin \theta$, so that $N \sin \theta = mv^2/R$. Dividing the latter equation by the former and setting $W = mg$, we obtain

$$\tan \theta = v^2/Rg$$

Notice that the proper angle of banking depends upon the speed of the car and the curvature of the road. For a given curvature, the road is banked at an angle corresponding to an expected average speed. Often curves are marked by signs giving the proper speed for which the road was banked.

The student should check the banking formula for the limiting cases $v = 0$; $R \to \infty$; $v$ large; and $R$ small. He should also note the great similarity between Fig. 6–7 of Example 3 and Fig. 6–9*b* of this example.     ◀

## 6–4   Forces and Pseudo-Forces

All forces in nature can be classified under three headings, each with a different relative strength: (1) gravitational forces, which are relatively very weak, (2) electromagnetic forces, which are of intermediate strength, and (3) nuclear forces. Nuclear forces are of two types, those which bind neutrons and protons in the nucleus (very strong) and those responsible for beta decay (weak). These forces are "real" in the sense that we can associate them with specific objects in the environment. Such forces as the tension in a rope, the force of friction, the force that we exert on a wall by pushing on it, or the force exerted by a compressed spring are electromagnetic forces; all are macroscopic manifestations of the (electromagnetic) attractions and repulsions between atoms.

In our treatment of classical mechanics so far we have assumed that our measurements and observations were made from an inertial frame. This, we recall, is a reference frame that is either at rest or is moving at constant velocity with respect to the fixed stars; it is the set of reference frames defined by Newton's first law, namely, that set of frames in which a body will not be accelerated ($a = 0$) if there are no identifiable force-producing bodies in its environment ($\mathbf{F} = 0$). The choice of a reference frame is always ours to make, so that if we choose to select only inertial frames, we do not restrict in any way our ability to apply classical mechanics to natural phenomena.

Nevertheless we can, if we find it convenient, apply classical mechanics from the point of view of an observer in a *noninertial frame*. Such a frame might be one that is rotating (and therefore accelerating) with respect to the fixed stars. We sometimes choose an accelerating reference frame when we consider, for example, the separation of liquids of different density in a spinning centrifuge, the global circulation of the winds on the rotating earth, or the experiences of an astronaut in an orbiting satellite.

We can apply classical mechanics in noninertial frames if we introduce forces called *pseudo-forces* (or *inertial forces*). They are so named because, unlike the forces that we have examined so far, we cannot associate them with any particular body in the environment of the particle on which they act; we cannot classify them into any of the categories listed in the first paragraph of this section. Finally, if we view the particle from an inertial frame, the pseudo-forces disappear. These forces are, then, simply a technique that permits us to apply classical mechanics in the normal way to events if we insist on viewing the events from an accelerating reference frame.

Consider a rotating merry-go-round on which a marble is lodged against a raised rim at the outer edge. An observer on the merry-go-round is in a noninertial system. As he kneels down and examines the marble he sees that, with respect to him, it is not moving; if he pulls it away a bit from the rim toward the center of rotation, he observes that it moves back again, as if under the influence of a force directed radially outward. He would declare the marble to be in equilibrium under the action of this outward force (a *pseudo-force* called, in this case, a *centrifugal force*) and the radially inward force exerted by the rim.

An observer on the ground (an inertial frame) watching the marble would describe it differently. He would declare the marble to be in uniform circular motion, accelerated radially inward with $a = v^2/R$. The inward force $\mathbf{F}$ exerted by the rim on the marble accounts for this acceleration from Newton's second law, or $F = ma = mv^2/R$. The marble is definitely *not* in equilibrium from the point of view of this observer or of an observer in any inertial frame. Only if the rim were *not* exerting this inward force would the marble move with uniform speed in a straight line and be in equilibrium. This observer would find no trace of a force directed radially outward (the pseudo-force) and, indeed, there is no room for such a force in his analysis of the motion.

It is clear from this simple example that the radially outward pseudo-force (or centrifugal force) noted by the observer on the rotating merry-go-round must have a magnitude $mv^2/R$. Thus the magnitude of the pseudo-force depends on the speed of the particle *as seen from another reference frame*, namely, the ground; the speed of the particle in its own (rotating) reference frame is zero.

In mechanical problems, then, we have two choices: (1) select an *inertial frame* as a reference frame and consider only "real" forces, that is, forces that we can associate with definite bodies in the environment or (2) select a *noninertial frame* as a reference frame and consider not only the "real" forces but suitably defined pseudo-forces. Although we usually choose the first alternative, we sometimes choose the second; both are completely equivalent and the choice is a matter of convenience. We shall discuss noninertial frames and pseudo-forces further in Chapters 11 and 16.

## 6–5 Classical Mechanics, Relativistic Mechanics, and Quantum Mechanics

In these first chapters we have laid the groundwork of classical mechanics. We have presented the laws of motion and have given several examples of the force laws. In later chapters we shall discuss other kinds of forces and shall continue to develop the structure of the theory. Here we want to point out where classical mechanics stands in the framework of modern physics.

Physics is not a static body of doctrine but a developing science. Historically there have been long periods of deep concern with a certain class of problem, culminating, often rather suddenly and in unexpected ways, in a "breakthrough" in the form of a new, more comprehensive theory. This occured about 1670 (Newtonian mechanics), about 1870 (Maxwell's theory of electromagnetism), 1905 (Einstein's theory of relativity), and about 1925 (quantum mechanics). Some physicists believe that our present concern for problems in the area of elementary particles (see Appendix E) will lead us eventually to another major "breakthrough."

As physics has evolved, many things have changed, such as the problems to be solved and the tools we use to investigate them. But through it all the general method of inquiry or process of solution remains basically the same. Thus earlier theories of physics are found to have limited ranges of validity and to be special cases of more comprehensive theories, which in turn are found to have limitations, and so on. However, independent of any particular area or problem in physics, we always demand that theory meet the test of experiment, we search for quantities that are invariant, we are guided by a belief in the simplicity and symmetry of nature, and we seek and use analogies and models. Major unifying concepts arise which are valid in all domains of physics, such as the conservation laws. All this is important to understand for its own sake, independent of mastery of any particular special topic, and is exemplified throughout the book. If, in addition to mastering classical mechanics, the student comes to understand this process, he will find it much easier to understand and master such theories as relativity theory and quantum theory, wherein the same method of inquiry applies but whose areas of application, unlike those of classical mechanics, are not a familiar part of his daily life experience.

Classical mechanics, like all theories in physics, is based on observations of things that happen in nature. It will help to point out how limited are our normal experiences of natural phenomena. This is particularly true during our formative years which is the period during which we develop our intuitive notions (often false!) of what is "common sense" in natural events and what is not.

For example, the highest speed that can be used to transmit signals from one point to another is the speed of light ($c = 186,000$ miles/sec $= 3.00 \times 10^8$ meters/sec) and this seems to set an upper limit to the speeds of material objects. However, gross objects, even the fastest of them, such as jet planes or earth satellites, have speeds $v$ that are very much less than $c$. For an earth satellite moving at 17,000 miles/hr, $v/c$ is only 0.00025. Classical mechanics was built up over several centuries on a body of observations of relatively slow-moving objects such as planets, balls rolling down inclined planes, and falling bodies. Our experience with moving objects has indeed been limited, until the last few decades, to a tiny fraction of the range of possible speeds.

During these last decades it has become possible to make measurements on small particles, of potentially high speed, such as electrons, protons, and other fundamental particles. A proton accelerated in the 30-billion electron volt accelerator at the Brookhaven National Laboratories has, for example, $v/c = 0.98$. Are we to expect that the laws of classical mechanics, which work so beautifully when $v/c \ll 1$, will also describe correctly the collisions, decays, and interactions of these elementary particles moving at such high speeds? This is the grossest kind of extrapolation and indeed we find by experiment that it simply does not work; classical mechanics gives answers that do not agree with experiment if the speeds of the objects involved are appreciable compared to the speed of light.  This does not make us think less of classical mechanics, which serves so well in the region of low speed, precisely the very important region of our daily experiences.  We are led, however, to view classical mechanics as a special case of a more general theory which would hold for all speeds up to the speed of light.

Einstein, in 1905, first proposed this more general theory, the *special theory of relativity*.  We shall discuss it in depth later but will state here its fundamental postulate.  This is that the speed of light $c$ is the *same* for all observers in inertial frames, no matter what the motion of the light source may be.  In other words, if a light source is moving directly toward you at a speed $v$, you would measure the same value for $c$, if you observed a light pulse passing you, no matter what the value of $v$; you would also obtain speed $c$ for the light pulse if the source were rushing away from you at speed $v$.  If this basic assumption seems to violate "common sense," we must realize that our intuitive feelings are based on "common sense at low speeds."  We have no direct experience in our daily activities about what really happens in nature at high speeds.  Furthermore, all of Einstein's predictions (1) agree with experiment and (2) reduce to the predictions of classical mechanics at low speeds.

We list here just one of the predictions of the theory of relativity that is at variance with classical mechanics.  If two observers watch an object moving parallel to the common $x - x'$-axis in Fig. 4–11 they will find, from Eq. 4–19,

$$v = v' + u, \tag{6-5}$$

where $v'$ is the speed as measured by observer $S'$, $v$ is that measured by observer $S$, and $u$ is the relative speed of separation of the two reference frames.  Note that there is nothing in Eq. 6–5 to prevent $v$ from exceeding $c$ if $v'$ and $u$ are large enough.

The theory of relativity predicts that Eq. 6–5 is a special case of a more general formula, namely,

$$v = \frac{v' + u}{1 + v'u/c^2}. \tag{6-6}$$

Note that for $v' \ll c$ and $u \ll c$ Eq. 6–6 does indeed reduce to Eq. 6–5.  Also, if $v' < c$ and $u < c$, then $v$ cannot exceed $c$.  If $v' = u = 0.8\ c$, for example, Eq. 6–6 yields $v = 0.975\ c$; Eq. 6–5, on the other hand, yields $v = 1.6\ c$, which is contrary to experience.

For gross objects, Eqs. 6–5 and 6–6 give the same results within experimental error, so that we naturally use the simpler, Eq. 6–5.  If two satellites moving in opposite directions have speeds $v' = u = 17,000$ miles/hr, the denominator in Eq. 6–6 has the value 1.0000000007, so that the speed $v$ of one satellite as seen from the other differs very slightly indeed from the value $v' + u$ predicted by Eq. 6–5.  It would take speeds almost 3000 *times* as great as above, nearly 50 million miles/hr, generally achievable only in the subatomic domain, to obtain a difference as great as one-half of one percent in the two formulas.

We point out a second way in which our daily experiences are limited, namely, that all the objects that we normally deal with have masses that greatly exceed, for example, the electron mass ($m = 9.11 \times 10^{-31}$ kg).  This turns out to have an interesting consequence, closely related to the very concept of "particle" on which classical mechanics is based.  We have not hesitated to assign a mass $m$, a position $x$, and a velocity $v_x$ to a particle, assumed to be moving along the $x$-axis.*  If we

---

* We assume $v_x \ll c$ so that considerations of relativity do not enter this new discussion.

are asked within what accuracy $\Delta x$ and $\Delta v_x$ we could measure the position $x$ and the velocity $v_x$ respectively, we would be inclined to say that, although there might be limits in practice there are none in principle and, with sufficient attention to methods of measurement, we can specify $x$ and $v_x$ as closely as we wish. Experiment seems to confirm this view for large objects like golf balls or rifle bullets.

When we deal with objects of very small mass, however, such as electrons, we learn that the very procedures of measurement introduce fundamental uncertainties and that, in fact, the more precise our knowledge of $x$ becomes the less precise is our knowledge of $v_x$ and conversely. We can express this in terms of the famous Heisenberg uncertainty relation, which we write as

$$\Delta x \cong \frac{h}{m \, \Delta v_x} \tag{6-7}$$

in which $h$ (Planck's constant) is a fundamental constant of nature and has the value $h = 6.63 \times 10^{-34}$ kg meter$^2$/sec. Equation 6-7 shows clearly that if $\Delta v_x$ is very small (which means that we know $v_x$ very precisely), then $\Delta x$ must be relatively large (which means that we do not know $x$ very precisely). Thus it does not seem possible to measure *both* the position *and* the velocity of a particle to any given precision at the same time. If we cannot do this, then our whole concept of a particle as a mass point following a trajectory, which is a basic concept of classical mechanics, is open to question.

Just as for relativity theory, these considerations of quantum mechanics simply do not make any difference for the gross objects of our daily experience. Consider a bullet with a speed of $10^3$ meters/sec and a mass of 1.0 gm ($= 10^{-3}$ kg). Let us assume that we know the speed to be accurate to 0.1%, which means that $\Delta v_x = 0.001 \times 10^3 = 1$ meter/sec. The uncertainty in the position of the bullet is now given by Eq. 6-7 as

$$\Delta x \cong \frac{6.63 \times 10^{-34} \text{ kg meter}^2/\text{sec}}{(10^{-3} \text{ kg})(1 \text{ meter/sec})} \cong 7 \times 10^{-31} \text{ meter}$$

This is such a small distance (being $10^{-15}$ times smaller than an atomic nucleus!) that we could not possibly detect any limitation on the measurement of $x$ set by Eq. 6-7.

Consider, however, not a bullet but an electron ($m = 9.11 \times 10^{-31}$ kg) whose velocity is measured to be $2 \times 10^6$ meters/sec, which is about the speed of an electron in a hydrogen atom. If we assume that we know this velocity to be accurate to, say, 1%, then $\Delta v_x = 0.01 \times 2 \times 10^6$ meters/sec $= 2 \times 10^4$ meters/sec. The uncertainty in position predicted by Eq. 6-7 is then

$$\Delta x \cong \frac{6.63 \times 10^{-34} \text{ kg meter}^2/\text{sec}}{(9.11 \times 10^{-31} \text{ kg})(2 \times 10^{-4} \text{ meter/sec})} = 3 \times 10^{-8} \text{ meter.}$$

Since the radius of a hydrogen atom is about $5 \times 10^{-11}$ meter we see that the uncertainty with which we can locate the electron in the hydrogen atom, assuming that we have measured its speed as accurately as we claim, is 600 times the radius of the atom! The concept of "particle" does not mean much under these circumstances. This simply means that we cannot use classical mechanics to describe the motions of electrons in atoms; we need quantum mechanics.

The situation is very much like that of relativity theory. Ideas that we find acceptable in a certain region of experience (bullets) fall down when we apply them to a region outside our direct normal experience (electrons in atoms). Once again the solution is the same: Classical mechanics turns out to be an important special case of a more general theory. In this case the general theory is that of quantum mechanics developed about 1925 to 1926 by Heisenberg, Schrödinger, Born, and others. Once again, quantum mechanics does not detract from the merit of classical mechanics, which continues to give results that agree admirably with experiment for particles of relatively large mass.

The situation most remote from our daily experience deals with particles that have *both* small mass *and* high speed. Here we must use a still more general theory, *relativistic quantum mechanics*, which combines both relativity theory and quantum mechanics; such a theory was first developed by Dirac in 1927.

In the rest of our treatment of mechanics we return to the familiar special case of our daily experience, that of relatively massive and relatively slow-moving objects (classical mechanics). From time to time we will point out parenthetically how the predictions of classical mechanics must be modified when we depart from this region of experience.

## QUESTIONS

**1.** There is a limit beyond which further polishing of a surface *increases* rather than decreases frictional resistance. Can you explain this?

**2.** Is it unreasonable to expect a coefficient of friction to exceed unity?

**3.** How could a person who is at rest on completely frictionless ice covering a pond reach shore? Could he do this by walking, rolling, swinging his arms, or kicking his feet? How could a person be placed in such a position in the first place?

**4.** Explain how the range of your car's headlights limits the safe driving speed at night.

**5.** Your car skids across the center line on an icy highway. Should you turn the front wheels in the direction of skid or in the opposite direction (*a*) when you want to avoid a collision with an oncoming car, (*b*) when no other car is near but you want to regain control of the steering?

**6.** If you want to stop the car in the shortest distance on an icy road, should you (*a*) push hard on the brakes to lock the wheels, (*b*) push just hard enough to prevent slipping, or (*c*) "pump" the brakes?

**7.** A cube of weight $W$ rests on a rough inclined plane which makes an angle $\theta$ with the horizontal. Compare the minimum force necessary to start the cube moving down the plane with that necessary to start the cube moving up the plane. How do these compare with the minimum *horizontal* force (transverse to the slope) that will cause the cube to move down the plane?

**8.** Why are the train roadbeds and highways banked on curves?

**9.** How does the earth's rotation affect the apparent weight of a body at the equator?

**10.** A car is riding on a country road that resembles a roller coaster track. If the car travels with uniform speed, compare the force it exerts on a horizontal section of the road to the force it exerts on the road at the top of a hill and at the bottom of a hill. Explain.

**11.** Suppose you need to measure whether a table top in a train is truly horizontal. If you use a spirit level can you determine this when the train is moving down or up a grade? When the train is moving along a curve? (Hint: there are two horizontal components.)

**12.** In the conical pendulum of Example 3 what happens to the period $\tau$ and the speed $v$ when $\theta = 90°$? Why is this angle not achievable physically? Discuss the case for $\theta = 0°$.

**13.** A coin is put on a phonograph turntable. The motor is started, but before the final speed of rotation is reached, the coin flies off. Explain.

**14.** A passenger in the front seat of a car finds himself sliding toward the door as the driver makes a sudden left turn. Describe the forces on the passenger and on the car at this instant if (*a*) the motion is viewed from a reference frame attached to the earth and (*b*) if attached to the car.

**15.** What is the distinction between inertial reference frames and those differing only by a translation or rotation of the axes?

## PROBLEMS

**1.** A fireman weighing 160 lb slides down a vertical pole with an average acceleration of 10 ft/sec². What is the average vertical force he exerts on the pole?

**2.** A railroad flatcar is loaded with crates having a coefficient of static friction 0.25 with the floor. If the train is moving at 30 miles/hr, in how short a distance can the train be stopped without letting the crates slide?

**3.** Frictional heat generated by the moving ski is the chief factor promoting sliding in skiing. The ski sticks at the start, but once in motion will melt the snow beneath it. Waxing the ski makes it water repellent and reduces friction with the film of water. A magazine reports that a new type of plastic ski is even more water repellent and that on a gentle 700-ft slope in the Alps, a skier reduced his time from 61 to 42 sec with new skis. (a) Determine the average accelerations for each pair of skis. (b) Assuming a 3°-slope compute the coefficient of kinetic friction for each case.

**4.** A student wants to determine the coefficients of static friction and kinetic friction between a box and a plank. He places the box on the plank and gradually raises the plank. When the angle of inclination with the horizontal reaches 30°, the box starts to slip and slides 4.0 meters down the plank in 4.0 sec. Show how he can determine the coefficients from these observations.

**5.** A hockey puck weighing 0.25 lb slides on the ice for 50 ft before it stops. (a) If its initial speed was 20 ft/sec, what is the force of friction between puck and ice? (b) What is the coefficient of kinetic friction?

**6.** A 10-lb block of steel is at rest on a horizontal table. The coefficient of static friction between block and table is 0.50. (a) What is the magnitude of the horizontal force that will just start the block moving? (b) What is the magnitude of a force acting upward 60° from the horizontal that will just start the block moving? (c) If the force acts down at 60° from the horizontal, how large can it be without causing the block to move?

**7.** A piece of ice slides down a 45°-incline in twice the time it takes to slide down a frictionless 45°-incline. What is the coefficient of kinetic friction between the ice and the incline?

**8.** A horizontal force $F$ of 12 lb pushes a block weighing 5.0 lb against a vertical wall (Fig. 6–10). The coefficient of static friction between the wall and the block is 0.60

**Fig. 6–10**

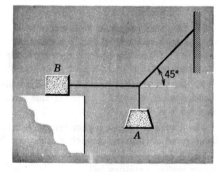

**Fig. 6–11**

and the coefficient of kinetic friction is 0.40.    Assume the block is not moving initially.
(a) Will the block start moving?    (b) What is the force exerted on the block by the wall?

**9.** Block $B$ in Fig. 6–11 weighs 160 lb.    The coefficient of static friction between block and table is 0.25.    Find the maximum weight of block $A$ for which the system will be in equilibrium.

**10.** A 4.0-kg block is put on top of a 5.0-kg block.    In order to cause the top block to slip on the bottom one, a horizontal force of 12 nt must be applied to the top block (Fig. 6–12).    Assume a frictionless table and find (a) the maximum horizontal force $F$ which can be applied to the lower block so that the blocks will move together and (b) the resulting acceleration of the blocks.

**Fig. 6–12**                            **Fig. 6–13**

**11.** In Fig. 6–13, $A$ is a 10-lb block and $B$ is a 5.0-lb block.    (a) Determine the minimum weight (block $C$) which must be placed on $A$ to keep it from sliding, if $\mu_s$ between $A$ and the table is 0.20.    (b) The block $C$ is suddenly lifted off $A$.    What is the acceleration of block $A$, if $\mu_k$ between $A$ and the table is 0.20?

**12.** The handle of a floor mop of mass $m$ makes an angle $\theta$ with the vertical direction. Let $\mu_k$ be the coefficient of kinetic friction between mop and floor, and $\mu_s$ be the coefficient of static friction between mop and floor.    Neglect the mass of the handle.    (a) Find the magnitude of the force $F$ directed along the handle required to slide the mop with uniform velocity across the floor.    (b) Show that if $\theta$ is smaller than a certain angle $\theta_0$, the mop cannot be made to slide across the floor no matter how great a force is directed along the handle.    (c) What is the angle $\theta_0$?

**13.** A block slides down an inclined plane of slope angle $\phi$ with constant velocity. It is then projected up the same plane with an initial speed $v_0$.    How far up the incline will it move before coming to rest?    Will it slide down again?

**14.** Body $B$ weighs 100 lb and body $A$ weighs 32 lb (Fig. 6–14).    Given $\mu_s = 0.56$ and $\mu_k = 0.25$, (a) find the acceleration of the system if $B$ is initially at rest and (b) find the acceleration if $B$ is moving initially.

**15.** Two masses, $m_1 = 1.65$ kg and $m_2 = 3.30$ kg, attached by a massless rod parallel to the incline on which both slide, as shown in Fig. 6–15, travel down along the plane with $m_1$ trailing $m_2$.    The angle of incline is $\theta = 30°$.    The coefficient of kinetic friction between $m_1$ and the incline is $\mu_1 = 0.226$; between $m_2$ and the incline the corresponding coefficient is $\mu_2 = 0.113$.    Compute (a) the tension in the rod linking $m_1$ and $m_2$ and (b) the common acceleration of the two masses.    (c) Would the answers to (a) and (b) be changed if $m_2$ trails $m_1$?

Fig. 6—14

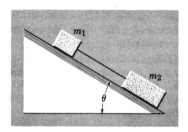

Fig. 6—15

**16.** An 8.0-lb block and a 16-lb block connected together by a string slide down a 30° inclined plane. The coefficient of kinetic friction between the 8.0-lb block and the plane is 0.10; between the 16-lb block and the plane it is 0.20. Find (a) the acceleration of the blocks and (b) the tension in the string, assuming that the 8.0-lb block leads. (c) Describe the motion if the blocks are reversed.

Fig. 6—16

**17.** A block of mass $m$ slides in an inclined right-angled trough as in Fig. 6–16. If the coefficient of kinetic friction between the block and the material composing the trough is $\mu_k$, find the acceleration of the block.

**18.** A block of mass $m$ at the end of a string is whirled around in a vertical circle of radius $R$. Find the critical speed below which the string would become slack at the highest point.

**19.** A 5000-lb airplane loops the loop at a speed of 200 miles/hr. Find (a) the radius of the largest circular loop possible and (b) the force on the plane at the bottom of this loop.

**20.** In the Bohr model of the hydrogen atom, the electron revolves in a circular orbit around the nucleus. If the radius of the orbit is $5.3 \times 10^{-11}$ meter and the electron makes $6.6 \times 10^{15}$ rev/sec, find (a) the acceleration (magnitude and direction) of the electron and (b) the centripetal force acting on the electron. (This force is due to the attraction between the positively charged nucleus and the negatively charged electron.) The mass of the electron is $9.1 \times 10^{-31}$ kg.

**21.** Assume that the standard kilogram would weigh exactly 9.80 nt at sea level on the earth's equator if the earth did not rotate about its axis. Then take into account the fact that the earth does rotate so that this mass moves in a circle of radius $6.40 \times 10^6$ meters (earth's radius) at a constant speed of 465 meters/sec. (a) Determine the centripetal force needed to keep the standard moving in its circular path. (b) Determine the force exerted by the standard kilogram on a spring balance from which it is suspended at the equator (its weight).

**22.** Because of the rotation of the earth, a plumb bob may not hang exactly along the direction of the earth's gravitational pull (its weight) but deviates slightly from this direction. Calculate the deviation (a) at 40° latitude, (b) at the poles, and (c) at the equator.

**23.** A circular curve of highway is designed for traffic moving at 40 miles/hr. (a) If the radius of the curve is 400 ft, what is the correct angle of banking of the road? (b) If the curve is not banked, what is the minimum coefficient of friction between tires and road that would keep traffic from skidding at this speed?

**24.** An old streetcar rounds a corner on unbanked tracks. If the radius of the tracks is 30 ft and the car's speed is 10 miles/hr, what angle with the vertical will be made by the loosely hanging hand straps? Is there a force acting on these straps? If so, is it a centripetal or a centrifugal force? Do your answers depend on what reference frame you choose?

**25.** A mass $m$ on a frictionless table is attached to a hanging mass $M$ by a cord through a hole in the table (Fig. 6–17). Find the conditions ($v$ and $r$) with which $m$ must spin for $M$ to stay at rest.

**Fig. 6–17**

**26.** Imagine that the disk of Fig. 6–6 is attached to a spring rather than a string. The unstretched length of the spring is $l_0$ and the tension in the spring increases in direct proportion to its elongation, the tension per unit elongation being $k$. If the disk rotates with a frequency $f$ (revolutions per unit time), show that (a) the radius $R$ of the uniform circular motion is $kl_0/(k - 4\pi^2 mf^2)$ and (b) the tension $T$ in the spring is $4\pi^2 mkl_0f^2/(k - 4\pi^2 mf^2)$.

**27.** (a) What is the smallest radius of a circle at which a bicyclist can travel if his speed is 18 mi/hr and the coefficient of static friction between the tires and the road is 0.32? (b) Under these conditions what is the largest angle of inclination to the vertical at which the bicyclist can ride without falling?

**28.** A small coin is placed on a flat, horizontal turntable. The turntable is observed to make three revolutions in 3.14 sec. (a) What is the speed of the coin when it rides without slipping at a distance 5.0 cm from the center of the turntable? (b) What is the acceleration (magnitude and direction) of the coin in part (a)? (c) What is the frictional-force acting on the coin in part (a) if the coin has a mass $m$? (d) What is the coefficient of static friction between the coin and the turntable if the coin is observed to slide off the turntable when it is greater than 10 cm from the center of the turntable?

**29.** A very small cube of mass $m$ is placed on the inside of a funnel (Fig. 6–18) rotating about a vertical axis at a constant rate of $\nu$ rev/sec. The wall of the funnel makes an angle $\theta$ with the horizontal. If the coefficient of static friction between the cube and the funnel is $\mu$ and the center of the cube is a distance $r$ from the axis of rotation, what are the largest and smallest values of $\nu$ for which the block will not move with respect to the funnel?

Fig. 6–18

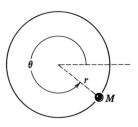

Fig. 6–19

30. A particle of mass $M = 0.305$ kg moves counterclockwise in a horizontal circle of radius $r = 2.63$ meters with uniform speed $v = 0.754$ meter/sec as in Fig. 6–19. Determine at the instant $\theta = 322°$ (measured counterclockwise from the positive $x$-direction) the following quantities: (a) the $x$-component of the velocity; (b) the $y$-component of the acceleration; (c) the total force on the particle; (d) the component of total force on the particle in the direction of its velocity.

# Work and Energy

## CHAPTER 7

## 7–1  Introduction

A fundamental problem of particle dynamics is to find how a particle will move when we know the forces that act on it.  By "how a particle will move" we mean how its position varies with time.  If the motion is one-dimensional, the problem is to find $x$ as a function of time, $x(t)$.  In the previous two chapters we solved this problem for the special case of a constant force.  The method used is this.  We find the resultant force $\mathbf{F}$ acting on the particle from the appropriate force law.  We then substitute $\mathbf{F}$ and the particle mass $m$ into Newton's second law of motion.  This gives us the acceleration $\mathbf{a}$ of the particle; or

$$\mathbf{a} = \mathbf{F}/m.$$

If the force $\mathbf{F}$ and the mass $m$ are constant, the acceleration $\mathbf{a}$ must be constant.  Let us choose the $x$-axis to be along the direction of this constant acceleration.  We can then find the speed of the particle from Eq. 3–12,

$$v = v_0 + at,$$

and the position of the particle from Eq. 3–15 (with $x_0 = 0$), or

$$x = v_0 t + \tfrac{1}{2}at^2;$$

note that, for simplicity and convenience, we have dropped the subscript $x$ in these equations.  The last equation gives us directly what we usually want to know, namely $x(t)$, the position of the particle as a function of time.  The problem is more difficult, however, when the force acting on a particle is *not constant*. In such a case we still obtain the acceleration of the particle, as before, from Newton's second law of motion. However, in order to get the speed or position of the particle, we can no longer use the formulas previously developed for constant acceleration because the acceleration now is *not* constant. To solve such problems, we use the mathematical process of integration, which we consider in this chapter.

We confine our attention to forces that vary with the position of the particle in its environment. This type of force is common in physics. Some examples are the gravitational forces between bodies, such as the sun and earth or earth and moon, and the force exerted by a stretched spring on a body to which it is attached. The procedure used to determine the motion of a particle subject to such a force leads us to the concepts of work and kinetic energy and to the development of the work-energy theorem, which is the central feature of this chapter. In Chapter 8 we consider a broader view of energy, embodied in the law of conservation of energy, a concept which has played a major role in the development of physics.

### 7–2  Work Done by a Constant Force

Consider a particle acted on by a force. In the simplest case the force **F** is constant and the motion takes place in a straight line in the direction of the force. In such a situation we define the *work done by the force on the particle* as the product of the magnitude of the force $F$ and the distance $d$ through which the particle moves. We write this as

$$W = Fd.$$

However, the constant force acting on a particle may not act in the direction in which the particle moves. In this case we define the *work done by the force on the particle* as the product of the component of the force along the line of motion by the distance $d$ the body moves along that line. In Fig. 7–1 a constant force **F** makes an angle $\phi$ with the $x$-axis and acts on a particle whose displacement along the $x$-axis is **d**. If $W$ represents the work done by **F** during this displacement, then according to our definition

$$W = (F \cos \phi)d. \qquad (7\text{--}1)$$

Of course, other forces must act on a particle that moves in this way (its

**Fig. 7–1** A force **F** makes the block undergo a displacement **d**. The component of **F** that does the work has magnitude $F \cos \phi$; the work done is $Fd \cos \phi$ ($= \mathbf{F} \cdot \mathbf{d}$).

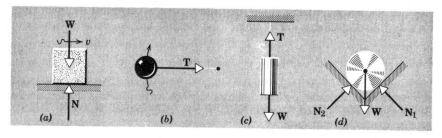

**Fig. 7–2**  Work is not always done by a force that is applied to a body.  (a) The block is moving to the right at constant speed $v$ over a frictionless surface.  Work is not done by either the weight **W** or the normal force **N**.  (b) The ball moves in a circle under the influence of a centripetal force **T**.  There is a centripetal acceleration **a** but no work is done by **T**.  In both (a) and (b) the forces being considered (**W**, **N**, and **T**) are at right angles to the displacement so that $W = \mathbf{F} \cdot \mathbf{d} = Fd \cos \phi = Fd \cos 90° = 0$.  (c) A cylinder hangs from a cord.  No work is done either by **T**, the tension in the cord, or by **W** the weight of the cylinder.  (d) A cylinder rests in a groove; no work is done by **W**, $\mathbf{N}_1$ or $\mathbf{N}_2$.  In both (c) and (d) the work done by the individual forces is zero because the displacement is zero.

weight and the frictional force exerted by the plane, to name two).  A particle acted on by only a single force may have a displacement in a direction other than that of this single force, as in projectile motion.  But it cannot move in a straight line unless the line has the same direction as that of the single force applied to it.  *Equation 7–1 refers only to the work done on the particle by the particular force* **F**.  *The work done on the particle by the other forces must be calculated separately.*  The total work done on the particle is the sum of the works done by the separate forces.

When $\phi$ is zero, the work done by **F** is simply $Fd$, in agreement with our previous equation.  Thus, when a horizontal force draws a body horizontally, or when a vertical force lifts a body vertically, the work done by the force is the product of the magnitude of the force by the distance moved.  When $\phi$ is 90°, the force has no component in the direction of motion.  That force then does no work on the body.  For instance, the vertical force holding a body a fixed distance off the ground does no work on the body, even if the body is moved horizontally over the ground.  Also, the centripetal force acting on a body in motion does no work on that body because the force is always at right angles to the direction in which the body is moving.  Of course, a force does no work on a body that does not move, for its displacement is then zero.  In Fig. 7–2 we illustrate common examples in which a force applied to a body does no work on that body.

Notice that we can write Eq. 7–1 either as $(F \cos \phi)d$ or $F(d \cos \phi)$.  This suggests that the work can be calculated in two different ways: Either we multiply the magnitude of the displacement by the component of the force in the direction of the displacement or we multiply the magnitude of the force by the component of the displacement in the direction of the force.  These two methods always give the same result.

Work is a *scalar*, although the two quantities involved in its definition, force and displacement, are vectors. In Section 2–4 we defined the *scalar product* of two vectors as the scalar quantity that we find when we multiply the magnitude of one vector by the component of a second vector along the direction of the first. We promised in that section that we would soon run across physical quantities that behave like scalar products. Equation 7–1 shows that work is such a quantity. In the terminology of vector algebra we can write this equation as

$$W = \mathbf{F} \cdot \mathbf{d}, \qquad (7\text{–}2)$$

where the dot indicates a scalar (or dot) product. Equation 7–2 for $\mathbf{F}$ and $\mathbf{d}$ corresponds to Eq. 2–11 for $\mathbf{a}$ and $\mathbf{b}$.

Work can be either positive or negative. If the particle on which a force acts has a component of motion opposite to the direction of the force, the work done by that force is negative. This corresponds to an obtuse angle between the force and displacement vectors. For example, when a person lowers an object to the floor, the work done on the object by the upward force of his hand holding the object is negative. In this case $\phi$ is 180°, for $\mathbf{F}$ points up and $\mathbf{d}$ points down.

Work as we have defined it (Eq. 7–2) proves to be a very useful concept in physics. Our special definition of the word *work* does not correspond to the colloquial usage of the term. This may be confusing. A person holding a heavy weight at rest in the air may say that he is doing hard work— and he may work hard in the physiological sense—but from the point of view of physics we say that he is not doing any work. We say this because the applied force causes no displacement. The word *work* is used only in the strict sense of Eq. 7–2. In many scientific fields words are borrowed from our everyday language and are used to name a very specific concept. The words *basic* and *cell*, for example, mean quite different things in chemistry and biology than in everyday language.

The *unit* of work is the work done by a unit force in moving a body a unit distance in the direction of the force. In the mks system the unit of work is 1 *newton-meter*, called 1 *joule*. In the British engineering system the unit of work is the *foot-pound*. In cgs systems the unit of work is 1 *dyne-centimeter*, called 1 *erg*. Using the relations between the newton, the dyne and the pound, and the meter, the centimeter, and foot, we obtain 1 joule = $10^7$ ergs = 0.7376 ft-lb.

▶ **Example 1.** A block of mass 10.0 kg is to be raised from the bottom to the top of an incline 5.00 meters long and 3.00 meters off the ground at the top. Assuming frictionless surfaces, how much work must be done by a force parallel to the incline pushing the block up at *constant speed* at a place where $g = 9.80$ meters/sec$^2$.

The situation is shown in Fig. 7–3a. The forces acting on the block are shown in Fig. 7–3b. We must first find $P$, the magnitude of the force pushing the block up the incline. Because the motion is not accelerated, the resultant force parallel to

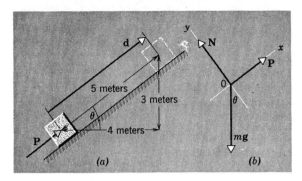

**Fig. 7–3**   Example 1.   (a) A force **P** displaces a block a distance **d** up an inclined plane which makes an angle $\theta$ with the horizontal.   (b) A free-body force diagram for the block.

the plane must be zero.   Thus

$$P - mg \sin \theta = 0,$$

or

$$P = mg \sin \theta = (10.0 \text{ kg})(9.80 \text{ meters/sec}^2)(\tfrac{3}{5}) = 58.8 \text{ nt}.$$

Then the work done by **P**, from Eq. 7–1 with $\phi = 0°$, is

$$W = \mathbf{P} \cdot \mathbf{d} = Pd \cos 0° = Pd = (58.8 \text{ nt})(5.00 \text{ meters}) = 294 \text{ joules}.$$

If a man were to raise the block vertically without using the incline, the work he would do would be the vertical force $mg$ times the vertical distance or

$$(98.0 \text{ nt})(3.00 \text{ meters}) = 294 \text{ joules},$$

the same as before.   The only difference is that with the incline he could apply a smaller force ($P = 58.8$ nt) to raise the block than is required without the incline ($mg = 98.0$ nt); on the other hand, he had to push the block a greater distance (5.00 meters) up the incline than he had to raise the block directly (3.00 meters).

**Example 2.**   A boy pulls a 10-lb sled 30 ft along a horizontal surface at a *constant speed*.   What work does he do on the sled if the coefficient of kinetic friction is 0.20 and his pull makes an angle of 45° with the horizontal?

The situation is shown in Fig. 7–4a and the forces acting on the sled are shown in Fig. 7–4b.   **P** is the boy's pull, **w** the sled's weight, **f** the frictional force, and **N** the normal force exerted by the surface on the sled.   The work done by the boy on the sled is

$$W = \mathbf{P} \cdot \mathbf{d} = Pd \cos \phi.$$

To evaluate this we first must determine $P$, whose value has not been given.   To obtain $P$ we refer to the force diagram.

The sled is unaccelerated, so that from the second law of motion we obtain

$$P \cos \phi - f = 0,$$

and

$$P \sin \phi + N - w = 0.$$

**Fig. 7–4**   Example 2.   (a) A boy displaces a sled an amount **d** by pulling with a force **P** on a rope that makes an angle $\phi$ with the horizontal.   (b) A free-body force diagram for the sled.

We know also that $f$ and $N$ are related by

$$f = \mu_k N.$$

These three equations contain three unknown quantities, $P$, $f$, and $N$.   To find $P$ we eliminate $f$ and $N$ from these equations and solve the remaining equation for $P$.   The student should verify that

$$P = \mu_k w/(\cos \phi + \mu_k \sin \phi).$$

With $\mu_k = 0.20$, $w = 10$ lb, and $\phi = 45°$ we obtain

$$P = (0.20)(10 \text{ lb})/(0.707 + 0.141) = 2.4 \text{ lb}.$$

Then with $d = 30$ ft, the work done by the boy on the sled is

$$W = Pd \cos \phi = (2.4 \text{ lb})(30 \text{ ft})(0.707) = 51 \text{ ft-lb}.$$

The vertical component of the boy's pull **P** does no work on the sled.   Notice, however, that it reduces the normal force between the sled and the surface ($N = w - P \sin \phi$) and thereby reduces the magnitude of the force of friction ($f = \mu_k N$).

Would the boy do more work, less work, or the same amount of work on the sled if he pulled horizontally instead of at 45° from the horizontal?   Do any of the other forces acting on the sled do work on it?     ◀

## 7–3   Work Done by a Variable Force—One Dimensional Case

Let us now consider the work done by a force that is not constant.   We consider first a force that varies in magnitude only.   Let the force be given as a function of position $F(x)$ and assume that the force acts in the $x$-direction.   Suppose a body is moved along the $x$-direction by this force.   What is the work done by this variable force in moving the body from $x_1$ to $x_2$?

In Fig. 7–5 we plot $F$ versus $x$.   Let us divide the total displacement into a large number of small equal intervals $\Delta x$ (Fig. 7–5a).   Consider the small displacement $\Delta x$ from $x_1$ to $x_1 + \Delta x$.   During this small displacement the force $F$ has a nearly constant value and the work it does, $\Delta W$, is approximately

$$\Delta W = F\,\Delta x, \qquad (7\text{-}3)$$

where $F$ is the value of the force at $x_1$. Likewise, during the small displacement from $x_1 + \Delta x$ to $x_1 + 2\Delta x$, the force $F$ has a nearly constant value and the work it does is approximately $\Delta W = F\,\Delta x$, where $F$ is the value of the force at $x_1 + \Delta x$. The total work done by $F$ in displacing the body from $x_1$ to $x_2$, $W_{12}$, is approximately the sum of a large number of terms like that of Eq. 7-3, in which $F$ has a different value for each term. Hence

$$W_{12} = \sum_{x_1}^{x_2} F\,\Delta x, \qquad (7\text{-}4)$$

where the Greek letter sigma ($\Sigma$) stands for sum over all intervals from $x_1$ to $x_2$.

To make a better approximation we can divide the total displacement from $x_1$ to $x_2$ into a larger number of equal intervals, as in Fig. 7-5b, so that $\Delta x$ is smaller and the value of $F$ at the beginning of each interval is more typical of its values within the interval. It is clear that we can obtain better and better approximations by taking $\Delta x$ smaller and smaller so as to have a larger and larger number of intervals. We can obtain an exact result for the work done by $F$ if we let $\Delta x$ go to zero and the number of intervals go to infinity. Hence the exact result is

$$W_{12} = \lim_{\Delta x \to 0} \sum_{x_1}^{x_2} F\,\Delta x. \qquad (7\text{-}5)$$

The relation

$$\lim_{\Delta x \to 0} \sum_{x_1}^{x_2} F\,\Delta x = \int_{x_1}^{x_2} F\,dx,$$

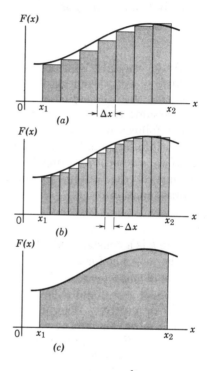

**Fig. 7-5** Computing $\displaystyle\int_{x_1}^{x_2} F(x)\,dx$ amounts to finding the area under the curve $F(x)$ between the limits $x_1$ and $x_2$. This can be done approximately as in the top drawing $(a)$ by dividing the area into a few strips, each of width $\Delta x$. The areas of the rectangles are then summed to give a rough value of the area. In the middle drawing $(b)$ the strips are narrower and the value for the area becomes more exact as the errors at the tops of the rectangles become smaller. In the bottom drawing $(c)$ the strips are only infinitesimal in width. The measurement of area is exact, since the errors at the tops of the rectangles go to zero as the strip width $dx$ goes to zero.

as the student may have learned in his calculus course, *defines the integral* of $F$ with respect to $x$ from $x_1$ to $x_2$. Numerically, this quantity is exactly equal to the area between the force curve and the $x$-axis between the limits $x_1$ and $x_2$ (Fig. 7–5c). Hence, graphically an integral can be interpreted as an area. The symbol $\int$ is a distorted $S$ (for *sum*) and symbolizes the integration process. We can write the total work done by $F$ in displacing a body from $x_1$ to $x_2$ as

$$W_{12} = \int_{x_1}^{x_2} F(x)\, dx. \tag{7–6}$$

As an example, consider a spring attached to a wall. Let the (horizontal) axis of the spring be chosen as an $x$-axis, and let the origin, $x = 0$, coincide with the endpoint of the spring in its normal, unstretched state. We assume that the positive $x$-direction points away from the wall. In what follows we imagine that we stretch the spring so slowly that it is essentially in equilibrium at all times ($\mathbf{a} = 0$).

If we stretch the spring so that its endpoint moves to a position $x$, the spring will exert a force on the agent doing the stretching given to a good approximation by

$$F = -kx, \tag{7–7}$$

where $k$ is a constant called the *force constant* of the spring. Equation 7–7 is the *force law* for springs. The direction of the force is always opposite to the displacement of the endpoint from the origin. When the spring is stretched, $x > 0$ and $F$ is negative; when the spring is compressed, $x < 0$ and $F$ is positive. The force exerted by the spring is a *restoring force* in that it always points toward the origin. Real springs will obey Eq. 7–7, known as *Hooke's law*, if we do not stretch them beyond a limited range. We can think of $k$ as the magnitude of the force per unit elongation. Thus very stiff springs have large values of $k$.

To stretch a spring we must exert a force $F'$ on it equal but opposite to the force $F$ exerted by the spring on us. The applied force* is therefore $F' = kx$ and the work done by the applied force in stretching the spring so that its endpoint moves from $x_1$ to $x_2$ is†

$$W_{12} = \int_{x_1}^{x_2} F'(x)\, dx = \int_{x_1}^{x_2} (kx)\, dx = \tfrac{1}{2}kx_2{}^2 - \tfrac{1}{2}kx_1{}^2.$$

---

\* If the applied force were different from $F' = kx$, we would have a net unbalanced force acting on the spring and its motion would be accelerated. To compute the work done we would have to specify exactly what the applied force is at each point. No matter what the force turned out to be, the work done would always be the same for the same displacement $x_1$ to $x_2$, providing the spring has the same speed initially and finally. However, it is much easier to use the simple force $F' = kx$ in calculating the work done. Such an applied force leads to unaccelerated motion. It is in order to be able to use this simple force that we specified unaccelerated motion in the first place.

† The student just becoming familiar with calculus should consult the list of integrals in Appendix I.

If we let $x_1 = 0$ and $x_2 = x$, we obtain

$$W = \int_0^x (kx)\, dx = \tfrac{1}{2}kx^2. \tag{7-8}$$

This is the work done in stretching a spring so that its endpoint moves from its unstretched position to $x$. Note that the work to *compress* a spring by $x$ is the same as that to stretch it by $x$ because the displacement $x$ is squared in Eq. 7-8; either sign for $x$ gives a positive value for $W$.

We can also evaluate this integral by computing the area under the force-displacement curve and the $x$-axis from $x = 0$ to $x = x$. This is drawn as the white area in Fig. 7-6. The area is a triangle of base $x$ and altitude $kx$. The white area is therefore

$$\tfrac{1}{2}(x)(kx) = \tfrac{1}{2}kx^2.$$

in agreement with Eq. 7-8.

**Fig. 7–6** The force exerted in stretching a spring is $F' = kx$. The area under the force curve is the work done in stretching the spring a distance $x$ and can be found by integrating or by using the formula for the area of a triangle.

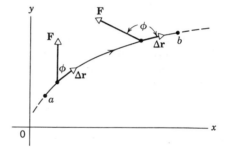

**Fig. 7–7** How **F** and $\phi$ might change along a path. As $\Delta\mathbf{r} \to 0$ we may replace it by the differential $d\mathbf{r}$, which always points in the direction of the velocity of the moving object, since $\mathbf{v} = d\mathbf{r}/dt$, and hence is tangent to the path at all points.

## 7–4  Work Done by a Variable Force—Two-Dimensional Case

The force **F** acting on a particle may vary in direction as well as in magnitude, and the particle may move along a curved path. To compute the work in this general case we divide the path up into a large number of small displacements $\Delta\mathbf{r}$, each pointing along the path in the direction of motion. Figure 7-7 shows two selected displacements for a particular situation; it also shows the value of **F** and the angle $\phi$ between **F** and $\Delta\mathbf{r}$ at each location. We can find the amount of work done on the particle during a displacement $\Delta\mathbf{r}$ from

$$dW = \mathbf{F} \cdot \Delta\mathbf{r} = F\cos\phi\, \Delta r \tag{7-9}$$

The work done by the variable force **F** on the particle as the particle moves, say, from $a$ to $b$ in Fig. 7-7 is found very closely by adding up (summing) the elements of work done over each of the line segments that make it up. As the line segments $\Delta\mathbf{r}$ become smaller they may be replaced by differentials $d\mathbf{r}$ and the sum over the line segments may be replaced by an integral, as in Eq. 7–6. The work is then found from

$$W_{ab} = \int_a^b \mathbf{F} \cdot d\mathbf{r} = \int_a^b F \cos \phi \, dr. \tag{7–10a}$$

We cannot evaluate this integral until we are able to say how $F$ and $\phi$ in Eq. 7–10a vary from point to point along the path; both are functions of the $x$- and $y$-coordinates of the particle in Fig. 7–7.

We can obtain another equivalent expression for Eq. 7–10a by expressing $\mathbf{F}$ and $d\mathbf{r}$ in terms of their components. Thus $\mathbf{F} = \mathbf{i}F_x + \mathbf{j}F_y$ and $d\mathbf{r} = \mathbf{i} \, dx + \mathbf{j} \, dy$, so that $\mathbf{F} \cdot d\mathbf{r} = F_x \, dx + F_y \, dy$. In this evaluation recall (see Problem 22, Chapter 2) that $\mathbf{i} \cdot \mathbf{i} = \mathbf{j} \cdot \mathbf{j} = 1$ and $\mathbf{i} \cdot \mathbf{j} = \mathbf{j} \cdot \mathbf{i} = 0$. Substituting this result into Eq. 7–10a, we obtain

$$W_{ab} = \int_a^b (F_x \, dx + F_y \, dy) \tag{7–10b}$$

Integrals such as those in Eqs. 7-10a and 7-10b are called *line integrals*.

▶ **Example 3.** As an example of a variable force consider a particle of mass $m$ suspended from a weightless cord of length $l$. This is called a simple pendulum. Let us displace the particle along a circular path of radius $l$ from $\phi = 0$ to $\phi = \phi_0$ by applying a force that is always *horizontal*. We can apply such a force by pulling horizontally on the particle with an attached string, for example. The particle will then have been displaced a vertical distance $h$. Figure 7–8a shows the situation and Fig. 7–8b shows the forces acting on the particle in the arbitrary position $\phi$. The applied force is $\mathbf{F}$, $\mathbf{T}$ is the tension in the cord, and $m\mathbf{g}$ the weight of the particle.

Again we assume that there is no acceleration (the reason is the same as before), so that in practice the motion must be very slow. The force $\mathbf{F}$ is always horizontal, but the displacement $d\mathbf{r}$ is along the arc. The direction of $d\mathbf{r}$ depends on the value of $\phi$ and is tangent to the circle at each point. $\mathbf{F}$ will vary in magnitude in such a way as to balance the horizontal component of the tension. Notice that the angle between $\mathbf{F}$ and $d\mathbf{r}$ is equal to the angular displacement $\phi$ in this case.

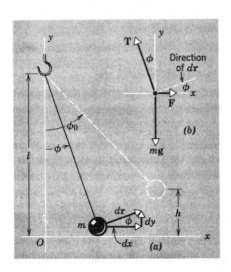

**Fig. 7–8** (a) A simple pendulum. A mass point $m$ is suspended on a string of length $l$. Its maximum displacement is $\phi_0$. (b) A free-body force diagram for the mass subjected to an applied horizontal force.

The work done as the mass $m$ moves from $\phi = 0$ to $\phi = \phi_0$ under the action of the force $\mathbf{F}$ is

$$W = \int_{\phi=0}^{\phi=\phi_0} \mathbf{F} \cdot d\mathbf{r} = \int_{\phi=0}^{\phi=\phi_0} F \cos \phi \, dr \qquad (7\text{-}10a)$$

or

$$W = \int_{x=0,y=0}^{x=(l-h) \tan \phi_0, y=h} (F_x \, dx + F_y \, dy). \qquad (7\text{-}10b)$$

Let us evaluate Eq. 7-10b.

Note that, from Newton's first law (see Fig. 7-8b)

$$F_x = T \sin \phi \quad \text{and} \quad mg = T \cos \phi.$$

Eliminating $T$ between these relations gives us

$$F_x = mg \tan \phi.$$

We also note in Fig. 7-8b that $F_y = 0$. Substituting these values for $F_x$ and $F_y$ into Eq. 7-10b yields

$$W = \int_{x=0,y=0}^{x=(l-h) \tan \phi_0, y=h} mg \tan \phi \, dx.$$

Now from Fig. 7-8a we see that

$$\tan \phi = dy/dx \quad \text{or} \quad \tan \phi \, dx = dy.$$

Making this substitution and noting that the integral depends only on the variable $y$, we obtain finally

$$W = \int_{y=0}^{y=h} (mg) \, dy = mg \int_0^h dy = mgh.$$

The student should now try to compute the work done in displacing the particle along the arc with constant speed by applying a force that is always directed along the arc. Here it will be simpler to work with Eq. 7-10a, using the tangential force and taking $dr = l\,d\phi$. The result will be the same as before, $W = mgh$. Notice that both these results are the same as the work that would be done in raising a mass $m$ vertically through a height $h$.

What work has been done on the particle by the tension $T$ in the string?   ◀

## 7-5   Kinetic Energy and the Work-Energy Theorem

In our previous examples of work done by forces, we dealt with *unaccelerated* objects. In such cases the *resultant force* acting on the object is zero. Let us suppose now that the *resultant force* acting on an object is *not zero*, so that the object is *accelerated*. The conditions are the same in all respects to those that exist when a single unbalanced force acts on the object.

The simplest situation to consider is that of a *constant resultant force* $\mathbf{F}$. Such a force, acting on a particle of mass $m$, will produce a constant acceleration $\mathbf{a}$. Let us choose the $x$-axis to be in the common direction of $\mathbf{F}$ and $\mathbf{a}$. What is the work done by this force on the particle in causing a displacement $x$? We have (for constant acceleration) the relations

$$a = \frac{v - v_0}{t}$$

and

$$x = \frac{v + v_0}{2} \cdot t,$$

which are Eqs. 3–12 and 3–14 respectively (in which we have dropped the subscript $x$, for convenience, and chosen $x_0 = 0$ in the last equation). Here $v_0$ is the particle's speed at $t = 0$ and $v$ its speed at the time $t$. Then the work done is

$$= Fx = max$$

$$= m\left(\frac{v - v_0}{t}\right)\left(\frac{v + v_0}{2}\right)t = \tfrac{1}{2}mv^2 - \tfrac{1}{2}mv_0^2. \tag{7–11}$$

*We call one-half the product of the mass of a body and the square of its speed the kinetic energy of the body.* If we represent kinetic energy by the symbol $K$, then

$$K = \tfrac{1}{2}mv^2. \tag{7–12}$$

We may then state Eq. 7–11 in this way: *The work done by the resultant force acting on a particle is equal to the change in the kinetic energy of the particle.*

Although we have proved this result for a constant force only, it holds whether the resultant force is constant or variable. Let the resultant force vary in magnitude (but not in direction), for example. Take the displacement to be in the direction of the force. Let this direction be the $x$-axis. The work done by the resultant force in displacing the particle from $x_0$ to $x$ is

$$W = \int \mathbf{F} \cdot d\mathbf{r} = \int_{x_0}^{x} F \, dx.$$

But from Newton's second law we have $F = ma$, and the acceleration $a$ can be written as

$$a = \frac{dv}{dt} = \frac{dv}{dx} \cdot \frac{dx}{dt} = \frac{dv}{dx}v = v\frac{dv}{dx}.$$

Hence

$$W = \int_{x_0}^{x} F \, dx = \int_{x_0}^{x} mv\frac{dv}{dx} \, dx = \int_{v_0}^{v} mv \, dv = \tfrac{1}{2}mv^2 - \tfrac{1}{2}mv_0^2. \tag{7–13}$$

A more general case is that in which the force varies both in direction and magnitude and the motion is along a curved path, as in Fig. 7–7. (See Problem 7.) Once again we find that the work done on a particle by the resultant force is equal to the change in the kinetic energy of the particle.

The work done *on* a particle by the *resultant* force is *always* equal to the change in the kinetic energy of the particle:

$$W \text{ (of the } resultant \text{ force)} = K - K_0 = \Delta K. \tag{7–14}$$

Equation 7–14 is known as the *work-energy theorem* for a particle.

Notice that when the speed of the particle is constant, there is no change in kinetic energy and the work done by the resultant force is zero. With uniform circular motion, for example, the speed of the particle is constant and the centripetal force does no work on the particle. A force at right angles to the direction of motion merely changes the *direction* of the velocity and not its magnitude. Only when the *resultant* force has a component along the direction of motion does it change the speed of the particle or its kinetic energy. Work is done on a particle only by that component of the resultant force along the line of motion. This agrees with our definition of work in terms of a scalar product, for in $\mathbf{F} \cdot d\mathbf{r}$ only the component of $\mathbf{F}$ along $d\mathbf{r}$ contributes to the product.

If the kinetic energy of a particle decreases, the work done on it by the resultant force is negative. The displacement and the component of the resultant force along the line of motion are oppositely directed. The work done *on* the particle by the force is the negative of the work done *by* the particle on whatever produced the force. This is a consequence of Newton's third law of motion. Hence Eq. 7–14 can be interpreted to say that the kinetic energy of a particle *decreases* by an amount just equal to the amount of work which the particle *does*. A body is said to have energy stored in it because of its motion; as it does work it slows down and loses some of this energy. Therefore, *the kinetic energy of a body in motion is equal to the work it can do in being brought to rest.* This result holds whether the applied forces are constant or variable.

The units of kinetic energy and of work are the same. Kinetic energy, like work, is a scalar quantity. The kinetic energy of a group of particles is simply the (scalar) sum of the kinetic energies of the individual particles in the group.

▶ **Example 4.** A neutron, one of the constituents of a nucleus, is found to pass two points 6.0 meters apart in a time interval of $1.8 \times 10^{-4}$ sec. Assuming its speed was constant, find its kinetic energy. The mass of a neutron is $1.7 \times 10^{-27}$ kg.

The speed is obtained from

$$v = \frac{d}{t} = \frac{6.0 \text{ meters}}{1.8 \times 10^{-4} \text{ sec}} = 3.3 \times 10^4 \text{ meters/sec.}$$

The kinetic energy is

$$K = \tfrac{1}{2}mv^2 = (\tfrac{1}{2})(1.7 \times 10^{-27} \text{ kg})(3.3 \times 10^4 \text{ meters/sec})^2 = 9.3 \times 10^{-19} \text{ joule.}$$

For purposes of nuclear physics the joule is a very large energy unit. A unit more commonly used is the electron volt (ev), which is equal to $1.60 \times 10^{-19}$ joule. The kinetic energy of the neutron in our example can then be expressed as

$$K = (9.3 \times 10^{-19} \text{ joule}) \left( \frac{1 \text{ ev}}{1.60 \times 10^{-19} \text{ joule}} \right) = 5.8 \text{ ev.}$$

**Example 5.** Assume the force of gravity to be constant for small distances above the surface of the earth. A body is dropped from rest at a height $h$ above the earth's surface. What will its kinetic energy be just before it strikes the ground?

The gain in kinetic energy is equal to the work done by the resultant force, which here is the force of gravity. This force is constant and directed along the line of motion, so that the work done by gravity is

$$W = \mathbf{F} \cdot \mathbf{d} = mgh.$$

Initially the body has a speed $v_0 = 0$ and finally a speed $v$. The gain in kinetic energy of the body is

$$\tfrac{1}{2}mv^2 - \tfrac{1}{2}mv_0^2 = \tfrac{1}{2}mv^2 - 0.$$

Equating these two equivalent terms we obtain

$$K = \tfrac{1}{2}mv^2 = mgh$$

as the kinetic energy of the body just before it strikes the ground.

The speed of the body is then

$$v = \sqrt{2gh}.$$

The student should show that in falling from a height $h_1$ to a height $h_2$ a body will increase its kinetic energy from $\tfrac{1}{2}mv_1^2$ to $\tfrac{1}{2}mv_2^2$, where

$$\tfrac{1}{2}mv_2^2 - \tfrac{1}{2}mv_1^2 = mg(h_1 - h_2).$$

In this example we are dealing with a constant force and a constant acceleration. The methods developed in previous chapters should be useful here too. Can you show how the results obtained by energy considerations could be obtained directly from the laws of motion for uniformly accelerated bodies?

**Example 6.**   A block weighing 8.0 lb slides on a horizontal frictionless table with a speed of 4.0 ft/sec. It is brought to rest in compressing a spring in its path. By how much is the spring compressed if its force constant is 0.25 lb/ft?

The kinetic energy of the block is

$$K = \tfrac{1}{2}mv^2 = \tfrac{1}{2}(w/g)v^2.$$

This kinetic energy is equal to the work $W$ that the block can do before it is brought to rest. The work done in compressing the spring a distance $x$ beyond its unstretched length is

$$W = \tfrac{1}{2}kx^2,$$

so that

$$\tfrac{1}{2}kx^2 = \tfrac{1}{2}(w/g)v^2$$

or

$$x = \sqrt{\frac{w}{gk}}\, v = \sqrt{\frac{8.0}{(32)(0.25)}}\, 4.0 \text{ ft} = 4.0 \text{ ft.} \quad \blacktriangleleft$$

## 7–6   Significance of the Work-Energy Theorem

The work-energy theorem does *not* represent a new, independent law of classical mechanics. We have simply *defined* work and kinetic energy and *derived* the relation between them directly from Newton's second law. The work-energy theorem is useful, however, for solving problems in which the work done by the resultant force is easily computed and in which we are interested in finding the particle's speed at certain positions. Of greater significance, perhaps, is the fact that the work-energy theorem is the starting point for a sweeping generalization in physics. It has been emphasized that the work-energy theorem is valid when $W$ is interpreted as the work done by the *resultant* force acting on the particle. However, it is helpful in many problems to compute separately the work done by certain types of force and give special names to the work done by each type. This leads to the concepts of different types of energy and the principle of the conservation of energy, which is the subject of the next chapter.

### 7–7　Power

Let us now consider the time involved in doing work. The same amount of work is done in raising a given body through a given height whether it takes one second or one year to do so. However, the *rate at which work is done* is often more interesting to us than the total work performed.

We define *power* as the time rate at which work is done. The average power delivered by an agent is the total work done by the agent divided by the total time interval, or

$$\bar{P} = W/t.$$

The instantaneous power delivered by an agent is

$$P = dW/dt. \tag{7–15}$$

If the power is constant in time, then $P = \bar{P}$ and

$$W = Pt.$$

In the mks system the unit of power is 1 joule/sec, which is called 1 *watt*. This unit of power is named in honor of James Watt whose steam engine is the predecessor of today's more powerful engines. In the British engineering system, the unit of power is 1 ft-lb/sec. Because this unit is quite small for practical purposes, a larger unit, called the *horsepower*, has been adopted. Actually Watt himself suggested as a unit of power the power delivered by a horse as an engine. One horsepower was chosen to equal 550 ft-lb/sec. One horsepower is equal to about 746 watts or about three-fourths of a kilowatt. A horse would not last very long at that rate.

Work can also be expressed in units of power × time. This is the origin of the term *kilowatt-hour*, for example. One kilowatt-hour is the work done in 1 hr by an agent working at a constant rate of 1 kw.

▶ **Example 7.** An automobile uses 100 hp and moves at a uniform speed of 60 miles/hr (= 88 ft/sec). What is the forward thrust exerted by the engine on the car?

$$P = \frac{W}{t} = \frac{\mathbf{F} \cdot \mathbf{d}}{t} = \mathbf{F} \cdot \mathbf{v}.$$

The forward thrust $\mathbf{F}$ is in the direction of motion given by $\mathbf{v}$, so that

$$P = Fv,$$

and
$$F = \frac{P}{v} = \left(\frac{100 \text{ hp}}{88 \text{ ft/sec}}\right)\left(\frac{550 \text{ ft-lb/sec}}{1 \text{ hp}}\right) = 630 \text{ lb}.$$

Why doesn't the car accelerate?　　　　　　　　　　　　　　◀

## QUESTIONS

**1.** Can you think of other words like "work" whose colloquial meanings are often different from their scientific meanings?

**2.** In a tug of war one team is slowly giving way to the other. What work is being done and by whom?

**3.** The inclined plane (see Example 1) is a simple machine which enables us to do work with the application of a smaller force than is otherwise necessary. The same statement applies to a wedge, a lever, a screw, a gear wheel, and a pulley. Do such machines save us work?

**4.** Springs $A$ and $B$ are identical except that $A$ is stiffer than $B$, that is, $k_A > k_B$. On which spring is more work expended if ($a$) they are stretched by the same amount, ($b$) they are stretched by the same force?

**5.** A man rowing a boat upstream is at rest with respect to the shore. ($a$) Is he doing any work? ($b$) If he stops rowing and moves down with the stream, is any work being done on him?

**6.** The work done by the resultant force is always equal to the change in kinetic energy. Can it happen that the work done by one of the component forces alone will be greater than the change in kinetic energy? If so, give examples.

**7.** When two children play catch on a train, does the kinetic energy of the ball depend on the speed of the train? Does the reference frame chosen affect your answer? If so, would you call kinetic energy a scalar quantity? (See Problem 19.)

**8.** Does the work done in raising a box onto a platform depend on how fast it is raised?

## PROBLEMS

**1.** A 100-lb block of ice slides down an incline 5.0 ft long and 3.0 ft high. A man pushes up on the ice parallel to the incline so that it slides down at constant speed. The coefficient of friction between the ice and the incline is 0.10. Find ($a$) the force exerted by the man, ($b$) the work done by the man on the block, ($c$) the work done by gravity on the block, ($d$) the work done by the surface of the incline on the block, ($e$) the work done by the resultant force on the block, and ($f$) the change in kinetic energy of the block.

**2.** A man pushes a 60-lb block 30 ft along a level floor at constant speed with a force directed 45° below the horizontal. If the coefficient of kinetic friction is 0.20, how much work does the man do on the block?

**3.** A crate weighing 500 lb is suspended from the end of a rope 40 ft long. The crate is then pushed aside 4.0 ft from the vertical and held there. ($a$) What is the force needed to keep the crate in this position? ($b$) Is work being done in holding it there? ($c$) Was work done in moving it aside? If so, how much? ($d$) Does the tension in the rope perform any work on the crate?

**4.** A cord is used to lower vertically a block of mass $M$ a distance $d$ at a constant downward acceleration of $g/4$. Find the work done by the cord on the block.

**5.** A block of mass $m = 3.57$ kg is drawn at constant speed a distance $d = 4.06$ meters along a horizontal floor by a rope exerting a constant force of magnitude $F = 7.68$ nt making an angle $\theta = 15.0°$ with the horizontal. Compute ($a$) the total work done on the block; ($b$) the work done by the rope on the block; ($c$) the work done by friction on the block; ($d$) the coefficient of kinetic friction between block and floor.

**6.** (*a*) Estimate the work done by the force shown on the graph (Fig. 7–9) in displacing a particle from $x = 1$ to $x = 3$ meters. Refine your method to see how close you can come to the exact answer of 6 joules. (*b*) The curve is given analytically by $F = a/x^2$ where $a = 9$ nt-meters$^2$. Show how to get the work done by the rules of integration.

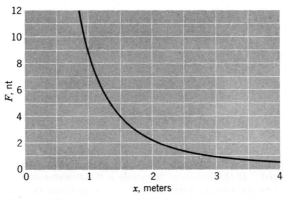

**Fig. 7–9**

**7.** When the force $\mathbf{F}$ varies both in direction and magnitude and the motion is along a curved path the work done by $\mathbf{F}$ is obtained from $dW = \mathbf{F} \cdot d\mathbf{r}$, the subsequent integration being taken along the curved path. Notice that both $F$ and $\phi$, the angle between $\mathbf{F}$ and $d\mathbf{r}$, may vary from point to point (see Fig. 7–7). Using Example 3 as a guide, show that for two-dimensional motion

$$W = \tfrac{1}{2}mv^2 - \tfrac{1}{2}mv_0{}^2,$$

where $v$ is the final speed and $v_0$ the initial speed.

**8.** Generalize the results of the previous problem to three dimensions.

**9.** A running man has half the kinetic energy that a boy of half his mass has. The man speeds up by 1.0 meter/sec and then has the same kinetic energy as the boy. What were the original speeds of man and boy?

**10.** From what height would an automobile have to fall to gain the kinetic energy equivalent to what it would have when going 60 miles/hr?

**11.** A proton (nucleus of the hydrogen atom) is being accelerated in a linear accelerator. In each stage of such an accelerator the proton is accelerated along a straight line by $3.6 \times 10^{15}$ meters/sec$^2$. If a proton enters such a stage moving initially with a speed of $2.4 \times 10^7$ meters/sec and the stage is 3.5 cm long, compute (*a*) its speed at the end of the stage and (*b*) the gain in kinetic energy resulting from the acceleration. Take the mass of the proton to be $1.67 \times 10^{-27}$ kg and express the energy in electron volts.

**12.** A 30-gm bullet initially traveling 500 meters/sec penetrates 12 cm into a wooden block. What average force does it exert?

**13.** Show *from considerations of work and kinetic energy* that the minimum stopping distance for a car of mass $m$ moving with speed $v$ along a level road is $v^2/2\mu_s g$, where $\mu_s$ is the coefficient of static friction between tires and road. (See Example 2, Chapter 6.)

**14.** A single force acts on a body in rectilinear motion. A plot of velocity versus time for the body is shown in Fig. 7-10. Find the sign (positive or negative) of the work done *by* the force *on* the body in each of the intervals *AB, BC, CD,* and *DE.*

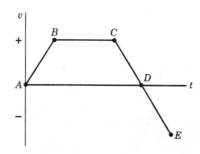

**Fig. 7-10**

**15.** (*a*) A mass of 0.675 kg on a frictionless table is attached to a string which passes through a hole in the table at the center of the horizontal circle in which the mass moves with constant speed. If the radius of the circle is 0.500 meter and the speed is 10.0 meters/sec, compute the tension in the string. (*b*) It is found that drawing an additional 0.200 meter of the string down through the hole, thereby reducing the radius of the circle to 0.300 meter, has the effect of multiplying the original tension in the string by 4.63. Compute the total work done by the string on the revolving mass during the reduction of the radius.

**16.** A proton starting from rest is accelerated in a cyclotron to a final speed of $3.0 \times 10^7$ meters/sec (about one-tenth the speed of light). How much work, in electron volts, is done on the proton by the electrical force of the cyclotron which accelerates it?

**17.** An outfielder throws a baseball with an initial speed of 60 ft/sec. An infielder at the same level catches the ball when its speed is reduced to 40 ft/sec. What work was done in overcoming the resistance of the air? The weight of a baseball is 9.0 oz.

**18.** The block of mass $M$ shown in Fig. 7-11 initially has a velocity $v_0$ to the right and its position is such that the spring exerts no force on it, i.e., the spring is not stretched or compressed. The block moves to the right a distance $l$ before stopping in the dotted position shown. The spring constant is $k$ and the coefficient of kinetic friction between block and table is $\mu_k$. As the block moves the distance $l$, (*a*) what is the work done on it by the friction force? (*b*) What is the work done on it by the spring force? (*c*) Are there other forces acting on the block, and, if so, what work do they do? (*d*) What is the total work done on the block? (*e*) Use the work-energy theorem to find the value of $l$ in terms of $M$, $v_0$, $\mu_k$, $g$, and $k$.

**Fig. 7-11**

**19.** *Work and Kinetic Energy In Moving Reference Frames.* Consider two observers, one whose frame is attached to the ground and another whose frame is attached, say, to a train moving with uniform velocity **u** with respect to the ground. Each observes that a particle, initially at rest with respect to the train, is accelerated by a constant force applied to it for time $t$ in the forward direction.

(a) Show that for each observer the work done by the force is equal to the gain in kinetic energy of the particle, but that one observer measures these quantities to be $\frac{1}{2}ma^2t^2$, whereas the other observer measures them to be $\frac{1}{2}ma^2t^2 + maut$. Here $a$ is the common acceleration of the particle of mass $m$.

(b) Explain the differences in work done by the same force in terms of the different distances through which the observers measure the force to act during the time $t$. Explain the different final kinetic energies measured by each observer in terms of the work the particle could do in being brought to rest relative to each observer's frame.

**20.** A net force of 5.0 nt acts on a 15-kg body initially at rest. Compute the work done by the force in the first, second, and third second and the instantaneous power exerted by the force at the end of the third second.

**21.** A satellite rocket weighing 100,000 lb acquires a speed of 4000 miles/hr in 1.0 min after launching. (a) What is its kinetic energy at the end of the first minute? (b) What is the average power expended during this time, neglecting frictional and gravitational forces?

**22.** A truck can move up a road having a grade of 1.0-ft rise every 50 ft with a speed of 15 miles/hr. The resisting force is equal to one-twenty-fifth the weight of the truck. How fast will the same truck move down the hill with the same horsepower?

**23.** A horse pulls a wagon with a force of 40 lb at an angle of 30° with the horizontal and moves along at a speed of 6.0 miles/hr. (a) How much work does the horse do in 10 min? (b) What is the power output of the horse?

**24.** The force required to tow a boat at constant velocity is proportional to the velocity. If it takes 10 hp to tow a certain boat at a speed of 2.5 miles/hr, how much horsepower does it take to tow it at a speed of 7.5 miles/hr?

**25.** What power is developed by a grinding machine whose wheel has a radius of 8.0 in and runs at 2.5 rev/sec when the tool to be sharpened is held against the wheel with a force of 40 lb? The coefficient of friction between the tool and the wheel is 0.32.

**26.** A boy whose mass is 51.0 kg climbs, with constant speed, a vertical rope 6.00 meters long in 10.0 sec. (a) How much work does the boy perform? (b) What is the boy's power output during the climb?

**27.** A body of mass $m$ accelerates uniformly from rest to a speed $v_f$ in time $t_f$. (a) Show that the work done on the body as a function of time $t$, in terms of $v_f$ and $t_f$, is

$$\frac{1}{2}m\frac{v_f^2}{t_f^2}t^2.$$

(b) As a *function of time t*, what is the instantaneous power delivered to the body? (c) What is the instantaneous power at the end of 10 sec delivered to a 3200-lb body which accelerates to 60 miles/hr in 10 sec?

# The Conservation of Energy

**CHAPTER 8**

## 8–1  Introduction

In Chapter 7 we derived the *work-energy theorem* from Newton's second law of motion.  This theorem says that the work $W$ done by the resultant force $\mathbf{F}$ acting on a particle as it moves from one point to another is equal to the change $\Delta K$ in the kinetic energy of the particle, or

$$W = \Delta K. \tag{8–1}$$

Often several forces act on a particle, the resultant force $\mathbf{F}$ being their vector sum, that is, $\mathbf{F} = \mathbf{F}_1 + \mathbf{F}_2 + \cdots \mathbf{F}_n$, in which we assume that $n$ forces act.  The work done by the resultant force $\mathbf{F}$ is the algebraic sum of the work done by these individual forces, or $W = W_1 + W_2 + \cdots W_n$.  Thus we can write the work-energy theorem (Eq. 8–1) as

$$W_1 + W_2 + \cdots + W_n = \Delta K. \tag{8–2}$$

In this chapter we shall consider systems in which a single particle is acted upon by various kinds of forces and we shall compute $W_1$, $W_2$, etc., for these forces; this will lead us to define different kinds of energy such as potential energy and heat energy.  The process culminates in the formulation of one of the great principles of science, the *conservation of energy principle*.

## 8–2  Conservative Forces

Let us first distinguish between two types of forces, *conservative* and *nonconservative*.  We shall consider an example of each type and we discuss each example from several different, but related, points of view.

Imagine a spring fastened at one end to a rigid wall as in Fig. 8–1. Let us slide a block of mass $m$ with velocity $\mathbf{v}$ directly toward the spring; we assume that the horizontal plane is frictionless and that the spring is ideal, that is, that it obeys Hooke's law (Eq. 7–7)

$$F = -kx, \qquad (8\text{–}3)$$

where $F$ is the force exerted by the spring when its free end is displaced through a distance $x$; we assume further that the mass of the spring is so small compared to that of the block that we can neglect the kinetic energy of the spring. Thus, in the system (mass + spring), all the kinetic energy is concentrated in the mass.

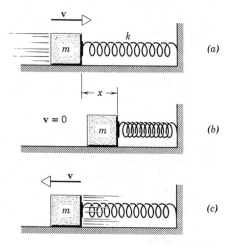

After the block touches the spring, the speed and hence the kinetic energy of the block decrease until finally the block is brought to rest by the action of the spring force, as in Fig. 8–1b. The block now reverses its motion as the compressed spring expands. It gains speed and kinetic energy and, when it comes once again to its position of initial contact with the spring, we find that it has the same speed and kinetic energy as it had originally; only the direction of motion has changed. The block loses kinetic energy during

**Fig. 8–1** (a) A block of mass $m$ is projected with speed $v$ against a spring. (b) The block is brought to rest by the action of the spring force. (c) The block has regained its initial speed $v$ as it returns to its starting point.

one part of its motion but gains it all back during the other part of its motion as it returns to its starting point (Fig. 8–1c).

We have interpreted the kinetic energy of a body as its ability to do work by virtue of its motion. It is clear that at the completion of a round trip the ability of the block in Fig. 8–1 to do work remains the same; it has been *conserved*. The elastic force exerted by an ideal spring, and other forces that act in this same way, are called *conservative*. The force of gravity is also conservative; if we throw a ball vertically upward, it will (if we assume air resistance to be negligible) return to our hand with the same kinetic energy that it had when it left our hand.

If, however, a particle on which one or more forces act returns to its initial position with either more or less kinetic energy than it had initially, then in a round trip its ability to do work has been changed. In this case the ability to do work has *not* been conserved and at least one of the forces acting is labeled *nonconservative*.

To illustrate a nonconservative force let us assume that the surfaces of the block and the plane in Fig. 8–1 are not frictionless but rather that a force of friction **f** is exerted by the plane on the block. The frictional force opposes the motion of the block no matter which way the block is moving and we find that the block returns to its starting point with *less* kinetic energy than it had initially. Since we showed in our first experiment that the spring force was conservative, we must attribute this new result to the action of the friction force.* We say that this force, and other forces that act in this same way, are *nonconservative*. The induction force in a betatron (Section 35–6) is also a nonconservative force. Instead of dissipating kinetic energy, however, it generates it, so that an electron moving in the circular betatron orbit will return to its initial position with *more* kinetic energy than it had there originally. In a round trip the electron gains kinetic energy, as it must do if the betatron is to be effective.

We can define conservative force from another point of view, that of the work done by the force on the particle. In our first example above, the work done by the elastic spring force on the block while the spring was being compressed was negative, because the force exerted on the block by the spring (to the left in Fig. 8–1a) was directed opposite to the displacement of the block (to the right in Fig. 8–1a). While the spring was being extended the work that the spring force did on the block was positive (force and displacement in the same direction). In our first example the net work done on the block by the spring force during a complete cycle, or round trip, is zero.

In our second example we considered the effect of the frictional force. The work done on the block by this force was negative for each portion of the cycle because the frictional force always opposed the motion. Hence the work done by friction in a round trip cannot be zero. In general, then: *A force is conservative if the work done by the force on a particle that moves through any round trip is zero. A force is nonconservative if the work done by the force on a particle that moves through any round trip is not zero.*

The work-energy theorem shows that this second way of defining conservative and nonconservative forces is fully equivalent to our first definition. If there is no change in the kinetic energy of a particle moving through any round trip then $\Delta K = 0$ and, from Eq. 8–1, $W = 0$ and the resultant force acting must be conservative. Similarly, if $\Delta K \neq 0$ then, from Eq. 8–1, $W \neq 0$ and at least one of the forces acting must be nonconservative.

We can look into this matter in a little more detail. When friction is present in the system of Fig. 8–1, four forces act on the block, the resultant force being

$$\mathbf{F} = \mathbf{F}_s + \mathbf{W} + \mathbf{N} + \mathbf{f}$$

in which the forces are the spring force $\mathbf{F}_s$, the weight of the block $\mathbf{W}$, the normal

---

* Actually two other forces act on the block in Fig. 8–1, its weight $\mathbf{W}$ and the normal force $\mathbf{N}$ exerted by the plane. Since these act at right angles to the motion, they cannot change the kinetic energy of the block and hence do not enter into this discussion.

force exerted on the block by the plane $N$, and the frictional force $f$. We can write Eq. 8–2, the work-energy theorem, as

$$W_s + W_W + W_N + W_f = \Delta K,$$

where the terms on the left are the work done on the block by the four forces above. We have seen that for a round trip $W_s = 0$. Similarly, $W_W = W_N = 0$ because the corresponding forces are at right angles to the displacement of the block. Thus the change in kinetic energy is due entirely to $W_f$, the work done by the frictional force.

We can consider the difference between conservative and nonconservative forces in still a third way. Suppose a particle goes from $a$ to $b$ along path 1 and back from $b$ to $a$ along path 2 as in Fig. 8–2a. Several forces may act on the particle during this round trip; we consider each force separately. If the force being considered is conservative, the work done on the particle by that particular force for the round trip is zero, or

$$W_{ab,1} + W_{ba,2} = 0,$$

which we can write as

$$W_{ab,1} = -W_{ba,2}.$$

(a)             (b)

**Fig. 8–2**

That is, the work in going from $a$ to $b$ along path 1 is the negative of the work in going from $b$ to $a$ along path 2. However, if we cause the particle to go from $a$ to $b$ along path 2, as shown in Fig. 8–2b, we merely reverse the direction of the previous motion along 2, so that

$$W_{ab,2} = -W_{ba,2}.$$

Hence

$$W_{ab,1} = W_{ab,2},$$

which tells us that the work done on the particle by a conservative force in going from $a$ to $b$ is the same for either path.

Paths 1 and 2 can be any paths at all as long as they go from $a$ to $b$; and $a$ and $b$ can be chosen to be any two points at all. We always find the same result if the force is conservative. Hence, we have another equivalent definition of conservative and nonconservative forces: *A force is conservative if the work done by it on a particle that moves between two points depends only on these points and not on the path followed. A force is nonconservative if the work done by that force on a particle that moves between two points depends on the path taken between those points.*

To illustrate this third (equivalent) definition of conservative forces, let us consider a second kind of conservative force, that due to gravity. Suppose that we take a stone of mass $m$ in our hand and raise it to a height $h$ above the ground, going from $a$ to $b$ by several different paths as in Fig. 8–3. We already know that in a round trip the total work done by a con-

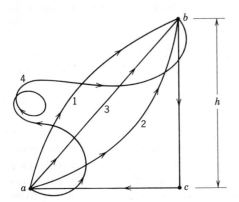

servative force is zero and that the gravitational force is conservative.
The work done *on* the stone by gravity along the return path $bca$ is simply
$mgh$. Hence, because gravity is a conservative force, the work done by
gravity *on* the stone along any of the paths from $a$ to $b$ must be $-mgh$, for
only if this is true can the total work done by gravity in a round trip be
zero. This means that gravity does negative work on the stone as it
moves from $a$ to $b$, or, to put it another way, work must be done *against*
gravity along any of the paths $ab$. The student can compute directly the
result that the work done by gravity along any path $ab$ equals $-mgh$.
For any of these paths can be decomposed into infinitesimal displacements
which are alternately horizontal and vertical; no work is done by gravity
in horizontal displacements, and the net vertical displacement is the same
in all cases. Hence the work done by gravity on the stone moving from
$a$ to $b$ depends only on the positions of $a$ and $b$ and not at all on the path
taken.

For a nonconservative force, such as friction, the work done is *not* independent of the path taken between two fixed points. We need only point
out that as we push a block over a (rough) table between any two points
$a$ and $b$ by various paths, the distance traversed varies and so does the work
done by the frictional force. It depends on the path.

The definitions of conservative force which we have given are equivalent
to one another. Which one we use depends only on convenience. The
round-trip approach shows clearly that kinetic energy is conserved when
conservative forces act. To develop the idea of potential energy, however,
the path independence statement is preferable.

### 8–3  Potential Energy

In this section we shall focus attention not on the moving block of
Fig. 8–1 but rather on the (isolated) system (block + spring). Instead
of saying that the block is moving we prefer, from this point of view, to
say that the configuration of the system is changing. We measure both
the position of the block and the configuration of the system at any instant
by the same parameter $x$, namely, the displacement of the free end of the

spring from its normal position, corresponding to an unstretched spring. The kinetic energy of the system is the same as that of the block because we have assumed the spring to be massless.

We have seen that the kinetic energy of the system of Fig. 8–1 decreases during the first half of the motion, becomes zero, and then increases during the second half of the motion. If there is no friction, the kinetic energy of the system when it has regained its initial configuration returns to its initial value.

Under these circumstances (conservative forces acting) it makes sense to introduce the concept of *energy of configuration*, or *potential energy U*, and to say that if $K$ for the system changes by $\Delta K$ as the configuration of the system changes (that is, as the block moves in the system of Fig. 8–1), then $U$ for the system must change by an equal but opposite amount so that the sum of the two changes is zero, or

$$\Delta K + \Delta U = 0. \tag{8–4a}$$

Alternatively, we can say that any change in kinetic energy $K$ of the system is compensated for by an equal but opposite change in the potential energy $U$ of the system so that their sum remains constant throughout the motion, or

$$K + U = \text{a constant.} \tag{8–4b}$$

The potential energy of a system represents a form of stored energy which can be fully recovered and converted into kinetic energy. We cannot associate a potential energy with a nonconservative force such as the force of friction because the kinetic energy of a system in which such forces act does *not* return to its initial value when the system returns to its initial configuration.

Equations 8–4 apply to a closed system of interacting objects, such as the (mass + spring) system of Fig. 8–1. In this example, because we have taken the spring to be effectively massless, the kinetic energy may be associated with the moving mass alone. The block slows down (or speeds up) because a force is exerted on it *by the spring;* it is appropriate, then, to associate the potential energy of the system with this force, that is to say, with the spring. Thus in this simple case we say that kinetic energy, localized in the mass, decreases during the first part of the motion while potential energy, localized in the spring, increases during this same time.*

Equations 8–4 are essentially bookkeeping statements about energy. They, and the concept of potential energy, have no real meaning, however, until we have shown how to calculate $U$ as a function of the configuration of the system within which the conservative forces act; in the example of Fig. 8–1 this means that we must be able to calculate $U(x)$, where $x$ is the spring displacement.

---

* Just as we assumed the spring to be effectively massless we also assume the block to be rigid, that is, effectively "springless." In a more general system, kinetic and potential energy could each be present in various portions of the system, in varying proportions as the system configuration changed.

To refine our concept of potential energy $U$ let us consider the work-energy theorem, $W = \Delta K$, in which $W$ is the work done by the resultant force on a particle as it moves from $a$ to $b$. For simplicity let us assume that only a single force $\mathbf{F}$ is acting on the particle; this is effectively true in the system of Fig. 8–1. If $\mathbf{F}$ is conservative we can combine the work-energy theorem (Eq. 8–1) with Eq. 8–4a, obtaining

$$W = \Delta K = -\Delta U. \tag{8–5a}$$

The work $W$ done by a conservative force depends only on the starting and the end points of the motion and not on the path followed between them. Such a force can depend only on the position of a particle; it does not depend on the velocity of the particle or on the time, for example.

For motion in one dimension, Eq. 8–5a becomes

$$\Delta U = -W = -\int_{x_0}^{x} F(x)\, dx, \tag{8–5b}$$

the particle moving from $x_0$ to $x$. Equation 8–5b shows how to calculate the change in potential energy $\Delta U$ when a particle, acted on by a conservative force $F(x)$, moves from point $a$, described by $x_0$, to point $b$, described by $x$. The equation shows that we can only calculate $\Delta U$ if the force $\mathbf{F}$ depends only on the position of the particle (that is, on the system configuration), which is equivalent to saying that potential energy has meaning only for conservative forces.

Now that we know that the potential energy $U$ depends on the position of the particle only, we can write Eq. 8–4b as

$$\tfrac{1}{2}mv^2 + U(x) = E \quad \text{(one-dimension)} \tag{8–6a}$$

in which $E$, which remains constant as the particle moves, is called the *total mechanical energy*. Suppose that the particle moves from point $a$ (where its position is $x_0$ and its speed is $v_0$) to point $b$ (where its position is $x$ and its speed is $v$); the total mechanical energy $E$ must be the same for each system configuration when the force is conservative, or, from Eq. 8–6a,

$$\tfrac{1}{2}mv^2 + U(x) = \tfrac{1}{2}mv_0^2 + U(x_0). \tag{8–6b}$$

The quantity on the right depends only on the initial position $x_0$ and the initial speed $v_0$, which have definite values; it is, therefore, *constant during the motion*. This is the constant total mechanical energy $E$. Notice that force and acceleration do not appear in this equation, only position and speed. Equations 8–6 are often called the *law of conservation of mechanical energy* for conservative forces.

In many problems we find that although some of the individual forces are not conservative, they are so small that we can neglect them. In such cases we can use Eqs. 8–6 as a good approximation. For example, air resistance may be present but may have so little effect on the motion that we can ignore it.

Notice that, instead of starting with Newton's laws, we can simplify problem solving when conservative forces alone are involved by starting with Eqs. 8–6. This relation is derived from Newton's laws, of course, but it is one step closer to the solution (the so-called first integral of the motion). We often solve problems without analyzing the forces or writing down Newton's laws by looking instead for something in the motion that is constant; here the mechanical energy is constant and we can write down Eqs. 8–6 as the first step.

For one-dimensional motion we can also write the relation between force and potential energy (Eq. 8–5b) as

$$F(x) = -\frac{dU(x)}{dx}. \tag{8–7}$$

To show this, substitute this expression for $F(x)$ into Eq. 8–5b and observe that you get an identity. Equation 8–7 gives us another way of looking at potential energy. *The potential energy is a function of position whose negative derivative gives the force.*

The student may have noticed that we wrote down the quantity $U(x)$ in Eqs. 8–6 although we are only able to calculate *changes* in $U$ (from Eq. 8–5b) and not $U$ itself. Let us imagine that a particle moves from $a$ to $b$ along the $x$-axis and that a single conservative force $F(x)$ acts on it. To assign a value to $U_b$, the potential energy at point $b$, let us write

$$\Delta U = U_b - U_a,$$

or (see Eq. 8–5b),

$$U_b = \Delta U + U_a = -\int_{x_a}^{x_b} F(x)\, dx + U_a. \tag{8–8}$$

We cannot assign a value to $U_b$ until we have assigned one to $U_a$. If point $b$ is any arbitrary position $x$, so that $U_b = U(x)$, we give meaning to $U(x)$ by choosing point $a$ to be some convenient reference position, described by $x_a = x_0$, and by arbitrarily assigning a value to the potential energy $U_a = U(x_0)$ when the body is at that point. Thus Eq. 8–8 becomes

$$U(x) = -\int_{x_0}^{x} F(x)\, dx + U(x_0). \tag{8–9}$$

The potential energy when the body is at the reference position, that is, $U(x_0)$, is usually given the arbitrary value zero.

It is often convenient to choose the reference position $x_0$ to be that at which the force acting on the particle is zero. Thus the force exerted by a spring is zero when the spring has its normal unstretched length; we usually say that the potential energy is also zero for this condition. Also, the attraction of the earth on a body decreases as the body moves away from the earth, becoming zero at an infinite distance. We usually take infinity as our reference position and assign the value zero to the potential energy associated with the gravitational force at that position (see Chapter 16). So far, however, we have been more concerned with the gravitational pull on bodies such as baseballs, etc., which, in comparison to the earth's radius, never move very far from the earth's surface. Here the gravitational force ($= m\mathbf{g}$) is essentially constant and we find it convenient to take the zero of potential energy to be, not at infinity, but at the surface of the earth.

The effect of changing the coordinate of the standard reference position $x_0$, or of the arbitrary value assigned to $U(x_0)$, is simply to change the value of $U(x)$ by an added constant. The presence of an arbitrary added constant in the potential energy expression (Eq. 8–9) makes no difference to the equations that we have written so far. This simply adds the same constant term to each side of Eq. 8–6b, for example, leaving that equation unchanged. Furthermore, changing $U(x)$ by an added constant does not change the force calculated from Eq. 8–7 because the derivative of a constant is zero. All this simply means that the choice of a reference point for potential energy is immaterial because we are always concerned with *differences* in potential energy, rather than with any absolute value of potential energy at a given point.

There is a certain arbitrariness in specifying kinetic energy also. In order to determine speed, and hence kinetic energy, we must specify a reference frame. The speed of a man sitting on a train is zero if we take the train as a reference frame, but it is not zero to an observer on the ground who sees the man move by with uniform velocity. The value of the kinetic energy depends on the reference frame used by the observer. Hence the important thing about mechanical energy $E$, which is the sum of the kinetic and the potential energies, is *not* its actual value during a given motion (this depends on the observer) but the fact that this value *does not change* during the motion for any particular observer when the forces are conservative.

### 8–4  One-Dimensional Conservative Systems

Let us now calculate the potential energy in one-dimensional motion for two examples of conservative forces, the force of gravity for motions near the earth's surface and the elastic restoring force of an (ideal) stretched spring.

For the force of gravity we take the one-dimensional motion to be vertical, along the $y$-axis. We take the positive direction of the $y$-axis to be upward; the force of gravity is then in the negative $y$-direction, or downward. We have $F(y) = -mg$, a constant. The potential energy at position $y$ is found from Eq. 8–9, or

$$U(y) = - \int_0^y F(y)\, dy + U(0) = - \int_0^y (-mg)\, dy + U(0) = mgy + U(0).$$

The potential energy can be taken as zero where $y = 0$, so that $U(0) = 0$, and

$$U(y) = mgy. \qquad (8\text{–}10)$$

The gravitational potential energy is then $mgy$. The relation $F(y) =$

$-dU/dy$ (Eq. 8–7) is satisfied, for $-d(mgy)/dy = -mg$. We choose $y = 0$ to be at the surface of the earth for convenience, so that the gravitational potential energy is zero at the earth's surface and increases linearly with altitude $y$.

If we compare points $y$ and $y = 0$, the conservation of kinetic plus potential energy, Eq. 8–6$b$, gives us the relation

$$\tfrac{1}{2}mv^2 + mgy = \tfrac{1}{2}mv_0{}^2.$$

This is equivalent mathematically to the well-known result (see Eq. 3–17),

$$v^2 = v_0{}^2 - 2gy.$$

If our particle moves from a height $h_1$ to a height $h_2$, we can use Eq. 8–6$b$ to obtain

$$\tfrac{1}{2}mv_1{}^2 + mgh_1 = \tfrac{1}{2}mv_2{}^2 + mgh_2.$$

This result is equivalent to that of Example 5, Chapter 7. The total mechanical energy $E$ is constant and is conserved during the motion, even though the kinetic energy and the potential energy vary as the configuration of the system (particle + earth) changes.

A second example of a conservative force is that exerted by an elastic spring on a body of mass $m$ attached to it moving on a horizontal frictionless surface. If we take $x_0 = 0$ as the position of the end of the spring when unextended, the force exerted *on* the mass when the spring is stretched a distance $x$ from its unextended length is $F = -kx$. The potential energy is obtained from Eq. 8–9,

$$U(x) = - \int_0^x F(x)\, dx + U(0) = - \int_0^x (-kx)\, dx + U(0).$$

If we choose $U(0) = 0$, the potential energy, as well as the force, is zero when the spring is unextended, and

$$U(x) = - \int_0^x (-kx)\, dx = \tfrac{1}{2}kx^2.$$

The result is the same whether we stretch or compress the spring, that is, whether $x$ is plus or minus.

The relation $F(x) = -dU/dx$ (Eq. 8–7) is satisfied, for $-d(\tfrac{1}{2}kx^2)/dx = -kx$. The elastic potential energy of the spring is then

$$U(x) = \tfrac{1}{2}kx^2. \tag{8–11}$$

The body of mass $m$ will undergo a motion in which the total energy $E$ is conserved (Fig. 8–4). From Eq. 8–6$b$ we have

$$\tfrac{1}{2}mv^2 + \tfrac{1}{2}kx^2 = \tfrac{1}{2}mv_0{}^2.$$

Here $v_0$ is the speed of the particle for $x = 0$. Physically we achieve such a result by stretching the spring with an applied force to some position, $x_m$, and then releasing the spring. Notice that at $x = 0$ the energy of the system (particle + spring) is all kinetic. At $x = x_m$ (the maximum value

**Fig. 8–4** A mass attached to a spring slides back and forth on a frictionless surface. The system is called a harmonic oscillator. The motion of the mass through one cycle is illustrated. Starting at the left (9 o'clock) the mass is in its extreme left position and momentarily at rest: $K = 0$. The spring is extended to its maximum length: $U = U_{max}$. ($K$ and $U$ are illustrated in the bar graphs below each sketch.) An eighth-cycle later (next drawing) the mass has gained kinetic energy, but the spring is no longer so elongated; $K$ and $U$ have here the same value, $K = U = U_{max}/2$. At the top the spring is neither elongated nor compressed and the speed is a maximum: $U = 0$, $K = K_{max} = U_{max}$. The cycle continues, with the total energy $E = K + U$ always the same: $E = K_{max} = U_{max}$. The harmonic oscillator will be analyzed more closely in Chapter 15.

of $x$), $v$ must be zero, so that here the system energy is all potential. At $x = x_m$, we have

$$\tfrac{1}{2}kx_m{}^2 = \tfrac{1}{2}mv_0{}^2$$

or

$$x_m = \sqrt{m/k}\, v_0.$$

For positions between $x_1$ and $x_2$, Eq. 8–6b gives

$$\tfrac{1}{2}kx_1{}^2 + \tfrac{1}{2}mv_1{}^2 = \tfrac{1}{2}kx_2{}^2 + \tfrac{1}{2}mv_2{}^2.$$

We have seen that *the kinetic energy of a body is the work that a body can do by virtue of its motion.* We express the kinetic energy by the formula $K = \frac{1}{2}mv^2$. We cannot give a similar universal formula by which potential energy can be expressed. *The potential energy of a system of bodies is the work that the system of bodies can do by virtue of the relative position of its parts, that is, by virtue of its configuration.* In each case we must determine how much work the system can do in passing from one configuration to another and then take this as the difference in potential energy of the system between these two configurations.

The potential energy of the spring depends on the relative position of the parts of the spring. Work can be obtained by allowing the spring to return from its extended to its unextended length, during which time it exerts a force through a distance. If a mass is attached to the spring, as in our example, the mass will be accelerated by this force and the potential energy will be converted to kinetic energy. In the gravitational case an object occupies a position with respect to the earth. The potential energy is a property of the object and the earth, considered as a system of bodies. It is the relative position of the parts of this system that determines its potential energy. The potential energy is greater when the parts are far apart than when they are close together. The loss of potential energy is equal to the work done in this process. This work is converted into kinetic energy of the bodies. In our example we ignored the kinetic energy acquired by the earth itself as an object fell toward it. In principle, this object exerts a force on the earth and causes it to acquire an acceleration, relative to some inertial frame. The resulting change in speed, however, is extremely small, and in spite of the enormous mass of the earth, its additional kinetic energy is negligible compared to that acquired by the falling object. This will be proved in a later chapter. In other cases, such as in planetary motion where the masses of the objects in our system may be comparable, we cannot ignore any part of the system. In general, *potential energy* is not assigned to either body separately but *is considered a joint property of the system.*

▶ **Example 1.** What is the change in gravitational potential energy when a 1600-lb elevator moves from street level to the top of the Empire State Building, 1250 ft above street level?

The gravitational potential energy of the system (elevator + earth) is $U = mgy$. Then

$$\Delta U = U_2 - U_1 = mg(y_2 - y_1).$$

But    $mg = W = 1600$ lb    and    $y_2 - y_1 = 1250$ ft,

so that    $\Delta U = 1600 \times 1250$ ft-lb $= 2.00 \times 10^6$ ft-lb.

**Example 2.** As an example of the simplicity and usefulness of the energy method of solving dynamical problems, consider the problem illustrated in Fig. 8–5. A block of mass $m$ slides down a curved frictionless surface. The force exerted by the surface on the block is always normal to the surface and to the direction of the motion of the block, so that this force does no work. Only the gravitational force

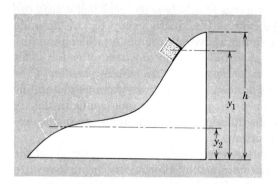

**Fig. 8–5** A block sliding down a frictionless curved surface.

does work on the block and that force is conservative. The mechanical energy $E$ is, therefore, conserved and we can write at once

$$\tfrac{1}{2}mv_1{}^2 + mgy_1 = \tfrac{1}{2}mv_2{}^2 + mgy_2.$$

This gives

$$v_2{}^2 = v_1{}^2 + 2g(y_1 - y_2).$$

The speed at the bottom of the curved surface depends only on the initial speed and the change in vertical height but does not depend at all on the shape of the surface. In fact, if the block is initially at rest at $y_1 = h$, and if we set $y_2 = 0$, we obtain

$$v_2 = \sqrt{2gh}.$$

At this point the student should recall the independence of path feature of work done by conservative forces and should be able to justify applying the ideas developed for one-dimensional motion to this two-dimensional example.

In this problem the value of the force depends on the slope of the surface at each point. Hence, the acceleration is not constant but is a function of position. To obtain the speed by starting with Newton's laws we would first have to determine the acceleration at each point and then integrate the acceleration over the path. We avoid all this labor by starting at once from the fact that the mechanical energy is constant throughout the motion.

**Example 3.** The spring in a spring gun has a force constant of 4.0 lb/in. It is compressed 2.0 in. from its natural length, and a ball weighing 0.030 lb is put into the barrel against it. Assuming no friction and a horizontal gun barrel, with what speed will the ball leave the gun when released?

The force is conservative so that mechanical energy is conserved in the process. The initial mechanical energy is the elastic potential energy of the spring, $\tfrac{1}{2}kx^2$, and the final mechanical energy is the kinetic energy of the ball, $\tfrac{1}{2}mv^2$. Hence,

$$\tfrac{1}{2}kx^2 = \tfrac{1}{2}mv^2$$

or

$$v = \sqrt{\frac{k}{m}}\, x = \sqrt{\frac{48 \text{ lb/ft}}{(0.030 \text{ lb})/(32 \text{ ft/sec}^2)}} \; (\tfrac{1}{6}\text{ft}) = 38 \text{ ft/sec.} \quad \blacktriangleleft$$

## 8–5   The Complete Solution of the Problem for One-Dimensional Forces Depending on Position Only

Equation 8–6$a$ gives the relation between coordinate and speed for one-dimensional motion when the force depends on position only. The force and the acceleration have been eliminated in arriving at this equation.   To complete the solution of the dynamical problem we must eliminate the speed and determine position as a function of time.

We can do this in a formal way, as follows.   From Eq. 8–6a we have

$$\tfrac{1}{2}mv^2 + U(x) = E.$$

Solving for $v$, we obtain

$$v = \frac{dx}{dt} = \sqrt{\frac{2}{m}\,[E - U(x)]}, \tag{8–12}$$

or

$$\frac{dx}{\sqrt{\dfrac{2}{m}\,[E - U(x)]}} = dt$$

Then the function $x(t)$ may be found by solving for $x$ the equation

$$\int_{x_0}^{x} \frac{dx}{\sqrt{\dfrac{2}{m}\,[E - U(x)]}} = \int_{t_0}^{t} dt = t - t_0. \tag{8–13}$$

Here the particle is taken to be at $x_0$ at the time $t_0$ and $E$ is the constant total energy.   In applying this equation, the sign of the square root taken corresponds to whether **v** points in the positive or in the negative $x$-direction.   When **v** changes direction during the motion it may be necessary to carry out the integration separately for each part of the motion.

Even when this integral cannot be evaluated or when the resulting equation cannot be solved to give an explicit solution for $x(t)$, the equation of energy conservation gives us useful information about the solution.   For example, for a given total energy $E$, Eq. 8–12 tells us that the particle is restricted to those regions on the $x$-axis where $E > U(x)$.   We cannot have an imaginary speed or a negative kinetic energy physically, so that $E - U(x)$ must be zero or greater. Furthermore, we can obtain a good qualitative description of the types of motion possible by plotting $U(x)$ versus $x$.   This description depends on the fact that the speed is proportional to the square root of the difference between $E$ and $U$.

For example, consider the potential energy function shown in Fig. 8–6.   This could be thought of as an actual profile of a frictionless roller coaster, but in general

**Fig. 8–6**   A potential energy curve.

it can represent the potential energy of a nongravitational system. Since we must have $E \geq U(x)$ for real motion, the lowest total energy possible is $E_0$. At this value of the total energy, $E_0 = U$ and the kinetic energy must be zero. The particle must be at rest at the point $x_0$. At a slightly higher energy $E_1$ the particle can move between $x_1$ and $x_2$ only. As it moves from $x_0$ its speed decreases on approaching either $x_1$ or $x_2$. At $x_1$ or $x_2$ the particle stops and reverses its direction. These points $x_1$ and $x_2$ are, therefore, called *turning points* of the motion. At a total energy $E_2$ there are four turning points, and the particle can oscillate in either one of the two potential valleys. At the total energy $E_3$ there is only one turning point of the motion, at $x_3$. If the particle is initially moving in the negative $x$-direction, it will stop at $x_3$ and then move in the positive $x$-direction. It will speed up as $U$ decreases and slow down as $U$ increases. At energies above $E_4$ there are no turning points, and the particle will not reverse direction. Its speed will change according to the value of the potential at each point.

At a point where $U(x)$ has a minimum value, such as at $x = x_0$, the slope of the curve is zero so that the force is zero, that is, $F(x_0) = -(dU/dx)_{x=x_0} = 0$. A particle at rest at this point will remain at rest. Furthermore, if the particle is displaced slightly in either direction, the force, $F(x) = -dU/dx$, will tend to return it, and it will oscillate about the equilibrium point. This equilibrium point is, therefore, called a point of *stable equilibrium*.

At a point where $U(x)$ has a maximum value, such as at $x = x_4$, the slope of the curve is zero so that the force is again zero, that is, $F(x_4) = -(dU/dx)_{x=x_4} = 0$. A particle at rest at this point will remain at rest. However, if the particle is displaced even the slightest distance from this point, the force, $F(x) = -dU/dx$, will tend to push it farther away from the equilibrium position. Such an equilibrium point is, therefore, called a point of *unstable equilibrium*.

In an interval in which $U(x)$ is constant, such as near $x = x_5$, the slope of the curve is zero so that the force is zero, that is, $F(x_5) = -(dU/dx)_{x=x_5} = 0$. Such an interval is called one of neutral equilibrium, since a particle can be displaced slightly without experiencing either a repelling or a restoring force.

From this it is clear that if we know the potential energy function for the region of $x$ in which the body moves, we know a great deal about the motion of the body.

▶ **Example 4.** The potential energy function for the force between two atoms in a diatomic molecule can be expressed approximately as follows:

$$U(x) = \frac{a}{x^{12}} - \frac{b}{x^6}$$

where $a$ and $b$ are positive constants and $x$ is the distance between atoms.

(a) At what values of $x$ is $U(x)$ equal to zero? At what value of $x$ is $U(x)$ a minimum?

In Fig. 8–7a we show $U(x)$ versus $x$. The values of $x$ at which $U(x)$ equals zero are found from

$$\frac{a}{x^{12}} - \frac{b}{x^6} = 0.$$

Hence

$$x^6 = \frac{a}{b} \qquad x = \sqrt[6]{\frac{a}{b}}.$$

$U(x)$ also becomes zero as $x \to \infty$ [see figure or put $x = \infty$ into equation for $U(x)$], so that $x = \infty$ is also a solution.

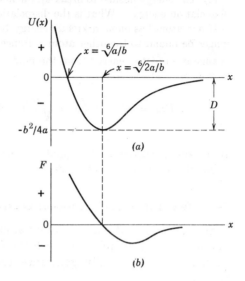

**Fig. 8–7** Example 4. (*a*) The potential energy and (*b*) the force between two atoms in a diatomic molecule as a function of the distance $x$ between atoms.

The value of $x$ at which $U(x)$ is a minimum is found from

$$\frac{d}{dx} U(x) = 0.$$

That is,

$$\frac{-12a}{x^{13}} + \frac{6b}{x^7} = 0$$

or

$$x^6 = \frac{2a}{b} \qquad x = \sqrt[6]{\frac{2a}{b}}.$$

(*b*) Determine the force between the atoms.
From Eq. 8–7

$$F(x) = -\frac{d}{dx} U(x),$$

$$F = \frac{-d}{dx}\left(\frac{a}{x^{12}} - \frac{b}{x^6}\right) = \frac{12a}{x^{13}} - \frac{6b}{x^7}.$$

We plot the force as a function of the separation between the atoms in Fig. 8–7b. When the force is positive (from $x = 0$ to $x = \sqrt[6]{2a/b}$), the atoms are repelled from one another (force directed toward increasing $x$). When the force is negative (from $x = \sqrt[6]{2a/b}$ to $x = \infty$), the atoms are attracted to one another (force directed toward decreasing $x$). At $x = \sqrt[6]{2a/b}$ the force is zero; this is the equilibrium point and is a point of stable equilibrium.

(*c*) Assume that one of the atoms remains at rest and that the other moves along $x$. Describe the possible motions.

From the analysis of this section it is clear that the atom oscillates about the equilibrium separation at $x = \sqrt[6]{2a/b}$, much as a particle sliding up and down the frictionless hills of the potential valley.

(d) The energy needed to break up the molecule into separate atoms is called the dissociation energy. What is the dissociation energy of the molecule?

If one atom has enough kinetic energy to get over the potential hill, it will no longer be bound to the other atom. Hence, the dissociation energy $D$ equals the change in potential energy from the minimum value at $x = \sqrt[6]{2a/b}$ to the value at $x = \infty$. This is simply

$$U(x = \infty) - U\left(x = \sqrt[6]{\frac{2a}{b}}\right) = 0 - \left(\frac{a}{4a^2/b^2} - \frac{b}{2a/b}\right) = \frac{b^2}{4a}.$$

If the kinetic energy at the equilibrium position is equal to or greater than this value, the molecule will dissociate.

◀

## 8–6 Two and Three-Dimensional Conservative Systems

So far we have discussed potential energy and energy conservation for one-dimensional systems in which the force was directed along the line of motion. We can easily generalize the discussion to three-dimensional motion.

If the work done by the force **F** depends only on the end points of the motion and is independent of the path taken between these points, the force is conservative. We define the potential energy $U$ by analogy with the one-dimensional system and find that it is a function of three space coordinates, that is, $U = U(x,y,z)$. Again we obtain an expression for the conservation of mechanical energy.

The generalization of Eq. 8–5b to motion in three dimensions is

$$\Delta U = - \int_{x_0}^{x} F_x \, dx - \int_{y_0}^{y} F_y \, dy - \int_{z_0}^{z} F_z \, dz \qquad (8\text{–}5c)$$

or, more compactly in vector notation,

$$\Delta U = - \int_{\mathbf{r}_0}^{\mathbf{r}} \mathbf{F}(\mathbf{r}) \cdot d\mathbf{r} \qquad (8\text{–}5d)$$

in which $\Delta U$ is the change in potential energy for the system as the particle moves from the point $(x_0,y_0,z_0)$, described by the position vector $\mathbf{r}_0$, to the point $(x,y,z)$, described by the position vector $\mathbf{r}$. $F_x$, $F_y$, and $F_z$ are the components of the conservative force $\mathbf{F}(\mathbf{r}) = \mathbf{F}(x,y,z)$.

The generalization of Eq. 8–6b to three-dimensional motion is

$$\tfrac{1}{2}mv^2 + U(x,y,z) = \tfrac{1}{2}mv_0^2 + U(x_0,y_0,z_0) \qquad (8\text{–}6c)$$

which can be written in vector notation as

$$\tfrac{1}{2}m\mathbf{v} \cdot \mathbf{v} + U(\mathbf{r}) = \tfrac{1}{2}m\mathbf{v}_0 \cdot \mathbf{v}_0 + U(\mathbf{r}_0) \qquad (8\text{–}6d)$$

in which $\mathbf{v} \cdot \mathbf{v} = v_x^2 + v_y^2 + v_z^2 = v^2$ and $\mathbf{v}_0 \cdot \mathbf{v}_0 = v_{0x}^2 + v_{0y}^2 + v_{0z}^2 = v_0^2$. Likewise Eq. 8–6a becomes

$$\tfrac{1}{2}mv^2 + U(x,y,z) = E$$

in three dimensions, $E$ being the constant total mechanical energy.

Finally, the generalization of Eq. 8–7 to three dimensions is

$$\mathbf{F}(\mathbf{r}) = -\mathbf{i}\frac{\partial U}{\partial x} - \mathbf{j}\frac{\partial U}{\partial y} - \mathbf{k}\frac{\partial U}{\partial z}$$

If we substitute this expression for $\mathbf{F}$ into Eq. 8–5$d$ we again obtain an identity. In vector language the conservative force $\mathbf{F}$ is said to be the negative of the *gradient* of the potential energy $U(x,y,z)$.

The student can show that all these expressions reduce to the correct one-dimensional equations for motion along the $x$-axis.

▶ **Example 5.** Consider the simple pendulum, Section 7–4, Fig. 7–8$a$. The motion of the system is in the $x$–$y$ plane, that is, it is a two-dimensional motion. The tension in the cord is always at right angles to the motion of the suspended particle, so that this force does no work on the particle. If the pendulum is displaced through some angle and is then released, only the gravitational force of attraction exerted on the particle by the earth does work on it. Since this force is conservative, we can use the equation of energy conservation in two dimensions,

$$\tfrac{1}{2}mv^2 + U(x,y) = E.$$

But $U(x,y)$ equals $mgy$, where $y$ is taken as zero at the lowest point of the arc ($\phi = 0°$). Then,

$$\tfrac{1}{2}mv^2 + mgy = E.$$

The particle is pulled through an angle $\phi_0$ before being released. The potential energy there is $mgh$, corresponding to a height $y = h$ above the reference point. At the release point ($\phi = \phi_0$) the speed and the kinetic energy are zero so that the potential energy equals the total mechanical energy at that point.

Hence,

$$E = mgh$$

and

$$\tfrac{1}{2}mv^2 + mgy = mgh,$$

or

$$\tfrac{1}{2}mv^2 = mg(h - y).$$

The maximum speed occurs at $y = 0$, where $v = \sqrt{2gh}$.
The minimum speed occurs at $y = h$, where $v = 0$.
At $y = 0$ the energy is entirely kinetic, the potential energy being zero.
At $y = h$ the energy is entirely potential, the kinetic energy being zero.
At intermediate positions the energy is partly kinetic and partly potential.

Notice that $U \leqq E$ at all points of the motion; the pendulum cannot rise higher than $y = h$, its initial release point.     ◀

## 8–7 Nonconservative Forces

So far we have considered only the action of a single conservative force on a particle. Starting from the work-energy theorem, or

$$W_1 + W_2 + \cdots + W_n = \Delta K \qquad (8\text{--}2)$$

we saw that, if only one force, say $\mathbf{F}_1$, was acting and if it was conservative, then we could represent the work $W_1$ that it did on the particle as a decrease in potential energy $\Delta U_1$ of the system (see Eq. 8–5a), or

$$W_1 = -\Delta U_1.$$

Combining this with Eq. 8–2 yielded

$$\Delta K + \Delta U_1 = 0.$$

If several conservative forces such as gravity, an elastic spring force, an electrostatic force, etc., are acting, we can easily extend these two equations to

$$\Sigma W_c = -\Sigma \Delta U \qquad (8\text{–}14a)$$

and $$\Delta K + \Sigma \Delta U = 0 \qquad (8\text{–}14b)$$

in which $\Sigma W_c$ is the sum of the work done by the various (conservative) forces and the $\Delta U$'s are the changes in the potential energy of the system associated with these forces. The quantity on the left of Eq. 8–14b is simply $\Delta E$, the change in the total mechanical energy, for the case in which several conservative forces are acting on a particle. We can write this equation then as

$$\Delta E = 0 \qquad \text{(conservative forces)}, \qquad (8\text{–}15)$$

which tells us that, as the system configuration changes the total mechanical energy $E$ for the system remains constant.

Let us now suppose that, in addition to the several conservative forces, a single nonconservative force due to friction acts on the particle. We can then write Eq. 8–2 as

$$W_f + \Sigma W_c = \Delta K,$$

where $\Sigma W_c$ is again the sum of the work done by the conservative forces and $W_f$ is the work done by friction. We can recast this (see Eq. 8–14b) as

$$\Delta K + \Sigma \Delta U = W_f. \qquad (8\text{–}16)$$

Equation 8–16 shows that, if a frictional force acts, the total mechanical energy is *not* constant, but changes by the amount of work done by the frictional force. We can write Eq. 8–16 as

$$\Delta E = E - E_0 = W_f. \qquad (8\text{–}17)$$

Since $W_f$, the work done by friction *on* the particle, is always negative, it follows from Eq. 8–17 that the final mechanical energy $E (= K + \Sigma U)$ is less than the initial mechanical energy $E_0 (= K_0 + \Sigma U_0)$.

Friction is an example of a dissipative force, one which does negative work on a body and tends to diminish the total mechanical energy of the system. If we had used another nonconservative force, then $W_f$ in Eqs. 8–16 and 8–17 would be replaced by a term $W_{nc}$, showing again that the total mechanical energy $E$ of the system is *not* constant, but changes by the amount of work done by the nonconservative force. Hence, *only when there are no nonconservative forces, or when we can neglect the work they do, can we assume conservation of mechanical energy.*

What happened to the "lost" mechanical energy in the case of friction? It is transformed into heat. Heat is developed when surfaces are rubbed together, for example. The heat energy developed is exactly equal to the mechanical energy dissipated. We shall have much more to say about heat energy in later chapters.

Just as the work done by a conservative force *on* an object is the negative of the potential energy gain, so the work done by a frictional force *on* an object is the negative of the heat energy gained. In other words, the heat energy produced is equal to the work done *by* the object. Then we can replace $W_f$ in Eq. 8–17 by $-Q$, in which $Q$ is the heat energy produced, or

$$\Delta E + Q = 0. \tag{8–18}$$

This asserts that there is no change in the sum of the mechanical and heat energy of the system when only conservative and frictional forces act on the system. Writing this equation as $Q = -\Delta E$ we see that the loss of mechanical energy equals the gain in heat energy.

▶ **Example 6.** A 10-lb block is thrust up a 30° inclined plane with an initial speed of 16 ft/sec. It is found to travel 5.0 ft along the plane, stop, and slide back to the bottom. Compute the force of friction **f** (assumed to have a constant magnitude) acting on the block and find the speed $v$ of the block when it returns to the bottom of the inclined plane.

Consider first the upward motion. At the top, where this motion ends,

$$E = K + U = 0 + (10 \text{ lb})(5.0 \text{ ft})(\sin 30°) = 25 \text{ ft-lb}.$$

At the bottom, where this motion begins,

$$E_0 = K_0 + U_0 = \frac{1}{2}\left(\frac{10 \text{ lb}}{32 \text{ ft/sec}^2}\right)(16 \text{ ft/sec})^2 + 0 = 40 \text{ ft-lb},$$

But

$$W_f = -fs = -f(5.0 \text{ ft}).$$

and

$$E - E_0 = W_f,$$

so that

$$25 \text{ ft-lb} - 40 \text{ ft-lb} = -f(5.0 \text{ ft})$$

and

$$f = 3.0 \text{ lb}.$$

Now consider the downward motion. The block returns to the bottom of the inclined plane with a speed $v$. Then, at the bottom, where this motion ends,

$$E = K + U = \frac{1}{2}\left(\frac{10 \text{ lb}}{32 \text{ ft/sec}^2}\right)v^2 + 0 = (\tfrac{5}{32} \text{ lb sec}^2/\text{ft})v^2.$$

At the top, where this motion begins,

But    $$E_0 = K_0 + U_0 = 0 + (10 \text{ lb})(5.0 \text{ ft})(\sin 30°) = 25 \text{ ft-lb},$$

$$W_f = -(3.0 \text{ lb})(5.0 \text{ ft}) = -15 \text{ ft-lb}.$$

and

$$E - E_0 = W_f,$$

so that
$$(\tfrac{5}{32} \text{ lb sec}^2/\text{ft})v^2 - 25 \text{ ft-lb} = -15 \text{ ft-lb},$$
and
$$v = 8.0 \text{ ft/sec.} \qquad \blacktriangleleft$$

## 8–8   The Conservation of Energy

We can extend the discussion of the previous section by considering not only conservative forces and the force of friction but also other, nonfrictional, nonconservative forces. We can regroup the work-energy theorem (Eq. 8–2)

$$W_1 + W_2 + \cdots + W_n = \Delta K$$

as

$$\Sigma W_c + W_f + \Sigma W_{nc} = \Delta K \qquad (8\text{--}19)$$

in which $\Sigma W_c$ is the total work done on the particle by conservative forces, $W_f$ is the work done by friction, and $\Sigma W_{nc}$ is the total work done by nonconservative forces other than friction. We have seen that each conservative force can be associated with a potential energy and that friction is associated with heat energy, or

$$\Sigma W_c = -\Sigma \Delta U$$

and

$$W_f = -Q,$$

so that Eq. 8–19 becomes

$$\Sigma W_{nc} = \Delta K + \Sigma \Delta U + Q.$$

Now whatever the $W_{nc}$ are, it has always been possible to find new forms of energy which corresponds to this work. We can then represent $\Sigma W_{nc}$ by another change of energy term on the right-hand side of the equation, with the result that we can always write the work-energy theorem as

$$0 = \Delta K + \Sigma \Delta U + Q + \text{(change in other forms of energy)}.$$

In other words, the total energy—kinetic plus potential plus heat plus all other forms—does not change. *Energy may be transformed from one kind to another, but it cannot be created or destroyed; the total energy is constant.*

This statement is a generalization from our experience, so far not contradicted by observation of nature. It is called the *principle of the conservation of energy.* Often in the history of physics this principle seemed to fail. But its apparent failure stimulated the search for the reasons. Experimentalists searched for physical phenomena besides motion that accompany the forces of interaction between bodies. Such phenomena have always been found. With work done against friction, heat is produced; in other interactions energy in the form of sound, light, electricity, etc., may be produced. Hence the concept of energy was generalized to include forms other than kinetic and potential energy of directly observable bodies. This procedure, which relates the mechanics of bodies observed to be in motion to phenomena which are not mechanical or in which motion is not directly detected, has linked mechanics to all other areas of physics. The energy concept now permeates all of physical science and has become one of the unifying ideas of physics.*

In subsequent chapters we shall study various transformations of energy —from mechanical to heat, mechanical to electrical, nuclear to heat, etc. It is during such transformations that we measure the energy changes in terms of work, for it is during these transformations that forces arise and do work.

Although the principle of the conservation of kinetic plus potential energy is often useful, we see that it is a restricted case of the more general principle of the conservation of energy. Kinetic and potential energy is conserved only when conservative forces act. Total energy is *always* conserved.

### 8–9 Mass and Energy

One of the great conservation laws of science has been the law of conservation of matter. From a philosophical point of view an early statement of this general principle was given by the Roman poet Lucretius, a contemporary of Julius Caesar, in his celebrated work *De Rerum Natura*. Lucretius wrote "Things cannot be born from nothing, cannot when begotten be brought back to nothing." It was a long time before this concept was established as a firm scientific principle. The principal experimental contribution was made by Antoine Lavoisier (1743–1794), regarded by many as the father of modern chemistry. He wrote in 1789 "We must lay it down as an incontestable axiom, that in all the operations of art and nature, nothing is created; an equal quantity of matter exists both before and after the experiment . . . and nothing takes place beyond changes and modifications in the combinations of these elements."

This principle, subsequently called the conservation of mass, proved extremely fruitful in chemistry and physics. Serious doubts as to the general validity of this principle were raised by Albert Einstein in his papers introducing the theory of relativity. Subsequent experiments on fast-moving electrons and on nuclear matter confirmed his conclusions.

Einstein's findings suggested that, if certain physical laws were to be retained, the mass of a particle had to be redefined as

$$m = \frac{m_0}{\sqrt{1 - v^2/c^2}}. \tag{8–20}$$

Here $m_0$ is the mass of the particle when at rest with respect to the observer, called the *rest mass;* $m$ is the mass of the particle measured as it moves at a speed $v$ relative to the observer; and $c$ is the speed of light, having a constant value of approximately $3 \times 10^8$ meters/sec. Experimental checks of this equation can be made, for example, by deflecting high-speed elec-

---

* See for example, "Concept of Energy in Mechanics," by R. B. Lindsay in *The Scientific Monthly*, October 1957.

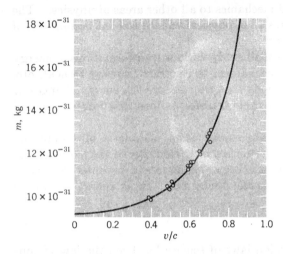

**Fig. 8-8** The way an electron's mass increases as its speed relative to the observer increases. The solid line is a plot of $m = m_0(1 - v^2/c^2)^{-\frac{1}{2}}$, and the circles are adapted from experimental values obtained by Bucherer and Neumann in 1914. The curve tends toward infinity as $v \to c$.

trons in magnetic fields and measuring the radii of curvature of their path. The paths are circular and the magnetic force a centripetal one ($F = mv^2/r$, $F$ and $v$ being known). At ordinary speeds the difference between $m$ and $m_0$ is too small to be detectable. Electrons, however, can be emitted from radioactive nuclei with speeds greater than nine-tenths that of light. In such cases the results (Fig. 8-8) confirm Eq. 8-20.

It is convenient to let the ratio $v/c$ be represented by $\beta$. Then Eq. 8-20 becomes

$$m = m_0(1 - \beta^2)^{-\frac{1}{2}}.$$

To find the kinetic energy of a body, we compute the work done by the resultant force in setting the body in motion. In Section 7-5 we obtained

$$K = \int_0^v \mathbf{F} \cdot d\mathbf{r} = \frac{1}{2} m_0 v^2$$

for kinetic energy, when we assumed a constant mass $m_0$. Suppose now instead we take into account the variation of mass with speed and use $m = m_0(1 - \beta^2)^{-\frac{1}{2}}$ in our previous equation. We find (Problem 29, Chapter 9) that the kinetic energy is no longer given by $\frac{1}{2}m_0 v^2$ but instead is

$$K = mc^2 - m_0 c^2 = (m - m_0)c^2 = \Delta mc^2. \tag{8-21}$$

The kinetic energy of a particle is, therefore, the product of $c^2$ and the increase in mass $\Delta m$ resulting from the motion.

Now, at small speeds we expect the relativistic result to agree with the classical result. By the binomial theorem we can expand $(1 - \beta^2)^{-\frac{1}{2}}$ as

$$(1 - \beta^2)^{-\frac{1}{2}} = 1 + \tfrac{1}{2}\beta^2 + \tfrac{3}{8}\beta^4 + \tfrac{5}{16}\beta^6 + \cdots.$$

At small speeds $\beta = v/c \ll 1$ so that all terms beyond $\beta^2$ are negligible.

Then

$$K = (m - m_0)c^2 = m_0c^2[(1 - \beta^2)^{-\frac{1}{2}} - 1]$$
$$= m_0c^2(1 + \tfrac{1}{2}\beta^2 + \cdots - 1) \cong \tfrac{1}{2}m_0c^2\beta^2 = \tfrac{1}{2}m_0v^2,$$

which is the classical result. Notice also that when $K$ equals zero, $m = m_0$ as expected.

The basic idea that energy is equivalent to mass can be extended to include energies other than kinetic. For example, when we compress a spring and give it elastic potential energy $U$, its mass increases from $m_0$ to $m_0 + U/c^2$. When we add heat in amount $Q$ to an object, its mass increases by an amount $\Delta m$, where $\Delta m$ is $Q/c^2$. We arrive at a principle of *equivalence of mass and energy*: For every unit of energy $E$ of *any* kind supplied to a material object, the mass of the object increases by an amount

$$\Delta m = E/c^2.$$

This is the famous Einstein formula

$$E = \Delta mc^2. \tag{8–22}$$

In fact, since mass itself is just one form of energy, we can now assert that a body at rest has an energy $m_0c^2$ by virtue of its rest mass. This is called its rest energy. If we now consider a closed system, the principle of the conservation of energy, as generalized by Einstein, becomes

$$\Sigma \, (m_0c^2 + \mathcal{E}) = \text{constant}$$

or          $$\Delta(\Sigma \, m_0c^2 + \Sigma \, \mathcal{E}) = 0,$$

where $\Sigma \, m_0c^2$ is the total rest energy and $\Sigma \, \mathcal{E}$ is the total energy of *all other* kinds. As Einstein wrote, "Pre-relativity physics contains two conservation laws of fundamental importance, namely the law of conservation of energy and the law of conservation of mass; these two appear there as completely independent of each other. Through relativity theory they melt together into *one* principle."

Because the factor $c^2$ is so large, we would not expect to be able to detect changes in mass in ordinary mechanical experiments. A change in mass of 1 gm would require an energy of $9 \times 10^{13}$ joules. But when the mass of a particle is quite small to begin with and high energies can be imparted to it, the relative change in mass may be readily noticeable. This is true in nuclear phenomena, and it is in this realm that classical mechanics breaks down and relativistic mechanics receives its most striking verification.

A beautiful example of exchange of energy between mass and other forms is given by the phenomenon of pair annihilation or pair production. In this phenomenon an electron and a positron, elementary material particles differing only in the sign of their electric charge, can combine and literally disappear. In their place we find high-energy radiation, called $\gamma$-radiation, whose radiant energy is exactly equal to the rest mass plus kinetic energies of the disappearing particles. The process is reversible, so that a materialization of mass from radiant energy can occur when a high enough energy γ-ray, under proper conditions, disappears; in its place appears a positron-electron pair whose total energy (rest mass + kinetic) is equal to the radiant energy lost.

▶ **Example 7.** Consider a quantitative example. On the atomic mass scale the unit of mass is $1.66 \times 10^{-27}$ kg approximately. On this scale the mass of the proton (the nucleus of a hydrogen atom) is 1.00731 and the mass of the neutron (a neutral particle, one of the constituents of all nuclei except hydrogen) is 1.00867. A deuteron (the nucleus of heavy hydrogen) is known to consist of a neutron and a proton; the mass of the deuteron is found to be 2.01360. The mass of the deuteron is *less than* the combined masses of neutron and proton by 0.00238 atomic mass units. The discrepancy is equivalent in energy to

$$E = \Delta mc^2 = (0.00238 \times 1.66 \times 10^{-27} \text{ kg})(3.00 \times 10^8 \text{ meters/sec})^2$$

$$= 3.57 \times 10^{-13} \text{ joules} = 2.22 \times 10^6 \text{ ev.}$$

When a neutron and a proton combine to form a deuteron, this exact amount of energy is given off in the form of γ-radiation. Similarly, it is found that the same amount of energy must be *added* to the deuteron to break it up into a proton and a neutron. This energy is therefore called the *binding energy* of the deuteron. ◀

## QUESTIONS

1. Mountain roads rarely go straight up the slope but wind up gradually. Explain why.

2. Is any work being done on a car moving with constant speed along a straight level road?

3. What happens to the potential energy an elevator loses in coming down from the top of a building to a stop at the ground floor?

4. In Example 2 (see Fig. 8–5) we asserted that the speed at the bottom does not depend at all on the *shape* of the surface. Would this still be true if friction were present?

5. Give physical examples of unstable equilibrium. Of neutral equilibrium. Of stable equilibrium.

6. Explain, using work and energy ideas, how a child pumps a swing up to large amplitudes from a rest position.

7. Two disks are connected by a stiff spring. Can one press the upper disk down enough so that when it is released it will spring back and raise the lower disk off the table (see Fig. 8–9)? Can mechanical energy be conserved in such a case?

**Fig. 8–9**

**8.** In the case of work done against friction, the amount of heat generated is independent of the velocity (or inertial reference frame) of the observer. That is, different observers would assign the same quantity of mechanical energy transformed into heat due to friction. How can this be explained, considering that such observers measure different quantities of total work done and different changes in kinetic energy in general (see Problem 19, Chapter 7)?

**9.** An object is dropped and observed to bounce to one and one-half times its original height. What conclusion can you draw from this observation?

**10.** The driver of an automobile traveling at speed $v$ suddenly sees a brick wall at a distance $d$ directly in front of him. To avoid crashing, is it better for him to slam on the brakes or to turn the car sharply away from the wall? (Hint: consider the force required in each case.)

**11.** A spring is kept compressed by tying its ends together tightly. It is then placed in acid and dissolves. What happened to its stored potential energy?

## PROBLEMS

**1.** Show that for the same initial speed $v_0$, the speed $v$ of a projectile will be the same at all points at the same elevation, regardless of the angle of projection.

**2.** The string in Fig. 8–10 has a length $l = 4.0$ ft. When the ball is released, it will swing down the dotted arc. How fast will it be going when it reaches the lowest point in its swing?

**Fig. 8–10**

**3.** The nail in Fig. 8–10 is located a distance $d$ below the point of suspension. Show that $d$ must be at least $0.6l$ if the ball is to swing completely around in a circle centered on the nail.

**4.** Suppose that the string of Fig. 8–10 is very elastic, made of rubber, say, and that the string is unextended at length $l$ when the ball is released. (a) Explain why you would expect the ball to reach a low point greater than a distance $l$ below the point of suspension. (b) Show, using dynamic and energy considerations, that if $\Delta l$ is small compared to $l$ the string will stretch by an amount $\Delta l = 3\,mg/k$, where $k$ is the assumed force constant of the string. Notice that the larger $k$ is, the smaller $\Delta l$ is, and the better the approximation $\Delta l \ll l$. (c) Show, under these circumstances, that the speed of the ball at the bottom is $v = \sqrt{2g(l - 3mg/2k)}$, *less* than it would be for an inelastic string ($k = \infty$). Give a physical explanation for this result using energy considerations.

**5.** (a) A light rigid rod of length $l$ has a mass $m$ attached to its end, forming a simple pendulum. It is inverted and then released. What is its speed $v$ at the lowest point and what is the tension $T$ in the suspension at that instant? (b) The same pendulum is next put in a horizontal position and released from rest. At what angle from the vertical will the tension in the suspension equal the weight in magnitude?

**6.** A simple pendulum of length $l$, the mass of whose bob is $m$, is observed to have a speed $v_0$ when the cord makes the angle $\theta_0$ with the vertical ($0 < \theta_0 < \pi/2$), as in Fig. 8–11. In terms of $g$ and the foregoing given quantities, determine (a) the total mechanical energy of the system; (b) the speed $v_1$ of the bob when it is at its lowest position; (c) the least value $v_2$ that $v_0$ could have if the cord is to achieve a horizontal position during the motion; (d) the speed $v_3$ such that if $v_0 > v_3$ the pendulum will not oscillate but rather will continue to move around in a vertical circle.

**Fig. 8–11**

**7.** An object is attached to a vertical spring and slowly lowered to its equilibrium position. This stretches the spring by an amount $d$. If the same object is attached to the same vertical spring but permitted to fall instead, through what distance does it stretch the spring?

**8.** A 2.0-kg block is dropped from a height of 0.40 meter onto a spring of force constant $k = 1960$ nt/meter. Find the maximum distance the spring will be compressed (neglect friction).

**9.** A frictionless roller coaster of mass $m$ starts at point $A$ with speed $v_0$, as in Fig. 8–12. Assume that the roller coaster can be considered as a point particle and that it always remains on the track. (a) What will be the speed of the roller coaster at points $B$ and $C$? (b) What constant deceleration is required to stop it at point $E$ if the brakes are applied at point $D$? (c) Suppose $v_0 = 0$; how long will it take the roller coaster to reach point $B$?

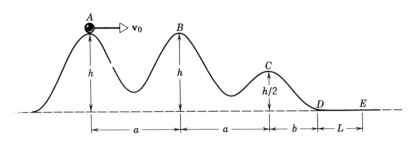

**Fig. 8–12**

**10.** A small block of mass $m$ slides along the frictionless loop-the-loop track shown in Fig. 8–13. (a) If it starts from rest at $P$, what is the resultant force acting on it at $Q$? (b) At what height above the bottom of the loop should the block be released so that the force it exerts against the track at the top of the loop is equal to its weight?

Fig. 8–13

Fig. 8–14

**11.** The particle $m$ in Fig. 8–14 is moving in a vertical circle of radius $R$ inside a track. There is no friction. When $m$ is at its lowest position, its speed is $v_0$. (a) What is the minimum value $v_m$ of $v_0$ for which $m$ will go completely around the circle without losing contact with the track? (b) Suppose $v_0$ is $0.775v_m$. The particle will move up the track to some point at $P$ at which it will lose contact with the track and travel along a path shown roughly by the dashed line. Find the angular position $\theta$ of point $P$.

**12.** A point mass $m$ starts from rest and slides down the surface of a frictionless solid sphere of radius $r$ as in Fig. 8–15. Measure angles from the vertical and potential energy from the top. Find (a) the change in potential energy of the mass with angle; (b) the kinetic energy as a function of angle; (c) the radial and tangential accelerations as a function of angle; (d) the angle at which the mass flies off the sphere. (e) If there is friction between the mass and the sphere, does the mass fly off at a greater or lesser angle than in part (d)?

Fig. 8–15

Fig. 8–16

**13.** An ideal massless spring $S$ can be compressed 1.0 meter by a force of 100 nt. This same spring is placed at the bottom of a frictionless inclined plane which makes an angle of $\theta = 30°$ with the horizontal (see Fig. 8–16). A 10-kg mass $M$ is released from rest at the top of the incline and is brought to rest momentarily after compressing the spring 2.0 meters. (a) Through what distance does the mass slide before coming to rest? (b) What is the speed of the mass just before it reaches the spring?

**14.** A body moving along the $x$-axis is subject to a force repelling it from the origin, given by $F = kx$. (a) Find the potential energy function $U(x)$ for the motion and write down the conservation of energy condition. (b) Describe the motion of the system and show that this is the kind of motion we would expect near a point of unstable equilibrium.

**15.** If the magnitude of the force of attraction between a particle of mass $m_1$ and one of mass $m_2$ is given by

$$F = k \frac{m_1 m_2}{x^2}$$

where $k$ is a constant and $x$ is the distance between the particles, find (a) the potential energy function and (b) the work required to increase the separation of the masses from $x = x_1$ to $x = x_1 + d$.

**16.** The magnitude of the force of attraction between the positively charged nucleus and the negatively charged electron in the hydrogen atom is given by

$$F = k \frac{e^2}{r^2}$$

where $e$ is the charge of the electron, $k$ is a constant, and $r$ is the separation between electron and nucleus. Assume that the nucleus is fixed. The electron, initially moving in a circle of radius $R_1$ about the nucleus, jumps suddenly into a circular orbit of smaller radius $R_2$. (a) Calculate the change in kinetic energy of the electron, using Newton's second law. (b) Using the relation between force and potential energy, calculate the decrease in potential energy of the atom. (c) Show by how much the total energy of the atom has decreased in this process. (This energy is given off in the form of radiation.)

**17.** The potential energy corresponding to a certain two-dimensional force field is given by $U(x,y) = \frac{1}{2}k(x^2 + y^2)$. (a) Derive $F_x$ and $F_y$ and describe the vector force at each point in terms of its Cartesian coordinates $x$ and $y$. (b) Derive $F_r$ and $F_\theta$ and describe the vector force at each point in terms of the polar coordinates $r$ and $\theta$ of the point. (c) Can you think of a physical model of such a force?

**18.** The so-called Yukawa potential

$$U(r) = -\frac{r_0}{r} U_0 e^{-r/r_0}$$

gives a fairly accurate description of the interaction between nucleons (that is, neutrons and protons, the constituents of the nucleus). The constant $r_0$ is about $1.5 \times 10^{-15}$ meter and the constant $U_0$ is about 50 Mev. (a) Find the corresponding expression for the force of attraction. (b) To show the short range of this force, compute the ratio of the force at $r = 2r_0$, $4r_0$, and $10r_0$ to the force at $r = r_0$.

**19.** An $\alpha$-particle (helium atom nucleus) in a large nucleus is bound by a potential like that shown in Fig. 8–17. (a) Construct a function of $x$, which has this general shape, with a minimum value $U_0$ at $x = 0$ and a maximum value $U_1$ at $x = x_1$ and

$x = -x_1$.  (b) Determine the force between the $\alpha$-particle and the nucleus as a function of $x$.  (c) Describe the possible motions.

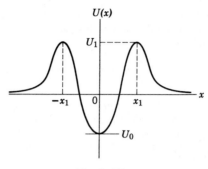

**Fig. 8–17**

**20.** A particle moves along a line in a region in which its potential energy varies as in Fig. 8–18.  (a) Sketch, with the same scale on the abscissa, the force $F(x)$ acting on the particle.  Indicate on the graph the approximate numerical scale for $F(x)$.  (b) If the particle has a constant total energy of 4.0 joules, sketch the graph of its kinetic energy. Indicate the numerical scale on the $K(x)$ axis.

**Fig. 8–18**

**21.** A certain peculiar spring is found *not* to conform to Hooke's law.  The force (in newtons) it exerts when stretched a distance $x$ (in meters) is found to have magnitude $52.8x + 38.4x^2$ in the direction opposing the stretch.  (a) Compute the total work required to stretch the spring from $x = 0.50$ to $x = 1.00$ meter. (b) With one end of the spring fixed, a particle of mass 2.17 kg is attached to the other end of the spring when it is extended by an amount $x = 1.00$ meter. If the particle is then released from rest, compute its *speed* at the instant the spring has returned to the configuration in which the extension is $x = 0.50$ meter. (c) Is the force exerted by the spring conservative or nonconservative? Explain.

**22.** Show that when friction is present in an otherwise conservative mechanical system, the rate at which mechanical energy is dissipated equals the frictional force times the speed at that instant, or

$$\frac{d}{dt}(K + U) = -fv$$

**23.** A body of mass $m$ starts from rest down a plane of length $l$ inclined at an angle $\theta$ with the horizontal. (a) Take the coefficient of friction to be $\mu$ and find the body's speed at the bottom. (b) How far, $d$, will it slide horizontally on a similar surface after reaching the bottom of the incline. Solve by using energy methods and solve again using Newton's laws directly.

**24.** A particle slides along a track with elevated ends and a flat central part, as shown in Fig. 8–19. The flat part has a length $l = 2.0$ meters. The curved portions of the track are frictionless. For the flat part the coefficient of kinetic friction is $\mu_k = 0.20$. The particle is released at point $A$ which is a height $h = 1.0$ meter above the flat part of the track. Where does the particle finally come to rest?

**Fig. 8–19**

**25.** A 1.0-kg block collides with a horizontal weightless spring of force constant 2.0 nt/meters (Fig. 8–20). The block compresses the spring 4.0 meters from the rest position. Assuming that the coefficient of kinetic friction between block and horizontal surface is 0.25, what was the speed of the block at the instant of collision?

**Fig. 8–20**

**26.** The cable of a 4000-lb elevator in Fig. 8–21 snaps when the elevator is at rest at the first floor so that the bottom is a distance $d = 12$ ft above a cushioning spring whose spring constant is $k = 10,000$ lb/ft. A safety device clamps the guide rails so that a constant friction force of 1000 lb opposes the motion of the elevator. (a) Find the speed of the elevator just before it hits the spring. (b) Find the distance s that the spring is compressed. (c) Find the distance that the elevator will "bounce" back up the shaft. (d) Using the conservation of energy principle, find the total distance that the elevator will move before coming to rest.

**Fig. 8–21**

**27.** A 40-lb body is pushed up a frictionless 30° inclined plane 10 ft long by a horizontal force **F**. (a) If the speed at the bottom is 2.0 ft/sec and at the top is 10 ft/sec, how much work is done by **F**? (b) Suppose the plane is not frictionless and that $\mu_k = 0.15$. What work will this same force do? How far up the plane does the body go?

**28.** A chain is held on a frictionless table with one-fifth of its length hanging over the edge. If the chain has a length $l$ and a mass $m$, how much work is required to pull the hanging part back on the table?

**29.** An escalator joins one floor with another one 25 ft above. The escalator is 40 ft long and moves along its length at 2.0 ft/sec. (a) What power must its motor deliver if it is required to carry a maximum of 100 persons per minute, of average mass 5.0 slugs? (b) A 160-lb man walks up the escalator in 10 sec. How much work does the motor do on him? (c) If this man turned around at the middle and walked down the escalator so as to stay at the same level in space, would the motor do work on him? If so, what power does it deliver for this purpose? (d) Is there any (other?) way the man could walk along the escalator without consuming power from the motor?

**30.** Show that $mc^2$ has the dimensions of energy.

**31.** An electron (rest mass $9.1 \times 10^{-31}$ kg) is moving with a speed $0.99c$. (a) What is its total energy? (b) Find the ratio of the Newtonian kinetic energy to the relativistic kinetic energy in this case.

**32.** What is the speed of an electron with a kinetic energy of (a) 100,000 ev, (b) 1,000,000 ev?

**33.** (a) The rest mass of a body is 0.010 kg. What is its mass when it moves at a speed of $3.0 \times 10^7$ meters/sec relative to the observer? At $2.7 \times 10^8$ meters/sec? (b) Compare the classical and relativistic kinetic energies for these cases. (c) What if the observer, or measuring apparatus, is riding on the body?

**34.** The United States consumed about $10^{15}$ watt-hr of electrical energy in 1960. How many kilograms of matter would have to be completely destroyed to yield this energy?

**35.** It is believed that the sun obtains its energy by a fusion process in which four hydrogen atoms are transformed into a helium atom with the emission of energy in various forms of radiation.   If a hydrogen atom has a rest mass of 1.0081 atomic mass units (see Example 7) and a helium atom has a rest mass of 4.0039 atomic mass units, calculate the energy released in each fusion process.

**36.** A vacuum diode consists of a cylindrical anode enclosing a cylindrical cathode. An electron with a potential energy relative to the anode of $4.8 \times 10^{-16}$ joule leaves the surface of the cathode with zero initial speed. Assume that the electron does not collide with any air molecules and that the gravitational force is negligible. (a) What kinetic energy would the electron have when it strikes the anode?   (b) Take $9.1 \times 10^{-31}$ kg as the mass of the electron and find its final speed.   (c) Were you justified in using classical relations for kinetic energy and mass rather than the relativistic ones?

# Conservation of Linear Momentum

## CHAPTER 9

### 9–1 Center of Mass

So far we have treated objects as though they were particles, having mass but no size. In translational motion each point on a body experiences the same displacement as any other point as time goes on, so that the motion of one particle represents the motion of the whole body. But even when a body rotates or vibrates as it moves, there is one point on the body, called the *center of mass*, that moves in the same way that a single particle subject to the same external forces would move. Figure 9–1 shows the simple parabolic motion of the center of mass of an Indian club thrown from one performer to another; no other point in the club moves in such a simple way. Note that, if the club were moving in pure translation (see Fig. 3–1), then *every* point in it would experience the same displacements as does the center of mass in Fig. 9–1. For this reason the motion of the center of mass of a body is called the translational motion of the body.

When the system with which we deal is not a rigid body, a center of mass, whose motion can also be described in a relatively simple way, can be assigned, even though the particles that make up the system may be changing their positions with respect to each other in a relatively complicated way as the motion proceeds. In this section we define the center of mass and show how to calculate its position. In the next section we discuss the properties that make it useful in describing the motion of extended objects or systems of particles.

Consider first the simple case of a system of two particles $m_1$ and $m_2$ at distances $x_1$ and $x_2$ respectively, from some origin $O$. We define a point $C$,

**Fig. 9–1**   An Indian club is thrown from one performer to another.   Even though it rotates and spins around its axis, as shown, there is one point on its axis, the *center of mass*, that follows a simple parabolic path.

the center of mass of the system, as a distance $x_{cm}$ from the origin $O$, where $x_{cm}$ is defined by

$$x_{cm} = \frac{m_1 x_1 + m_2 x_2}{m_1 + m_2}. \tag{9–1}$$

This point (Fig. 9–2) has the property that the product of the total mass of the system $M( = m_1 + m_2)$ times the distance of this point from the origin is equal to the sum of the products of the mass of each particle by its distance from the origin; that is,

$$(m_1 + m_2)x_{cm} = Mx_{cm} = m_1 x_1 + m_2 x_2.$$

In Eq. 9–1, $x_{cm}$ can be regarded as the *mass-weighted mean* of $x_1$ and $x_2$.

An analogy might help to fix this idea.   Suppose, for example, that we are given two boxes of nails.   In one box we have $n_1$ nails all having the same length $l_1$; in the other box we have $n_2$ nails all having the same length $l_2$.   We are asked to get the mean length of the nails.   If $n_1 = n_2$, the mean length is simply $(l_1 + l_2)/2$.   But if $n_1 \neq n_2$, we must allow for the fact that there are more nails of one length than another by a "weighting" factor for each length. For $l_1$ this factor is $n_1/(n_1 + n_2)$ and for $l_2$ this factor is $n_2/(n_1 + n_2)$, the fraction of the total number of nails in each box. Then the weighted-mean length is

$$\bar{l} = \left(\frac{n_1}{n_1 + n_2}\right)l_1 + \left(\frac{n_2}{n_1 + n_2}\right)l_2$$

or

$$\bar{l} = \frac{n_1 l_1 + n_2 l_2}{n_1 + n_2}.$$

The center of mass, defined in Eq. 9-1, is then a weighted-mean displacement where the "weighting" factor for each particle is the fraction of the total mass that each particle has.

If we have $n$ particles, $m_1, m_2, \cdots, m_n$, *along a straight line,* by definition the center of mass of these particles relative to some origin is

$$x_{\text{cm}} = \frac{m_1 x_1 + m_2 x_2 + \cdots + m_n x_n}{m_1 + m_2 + \cdots + m_n} = \frac{\Sigma\, m_i x_i}{\Sigma\, m_i}, \qquad (9\text{-}2)$$

where $x_1, x_2, \cdots, x_n$ are the distances of the masses from the origin from which $x_{\text{cm}}$ is measured. The symbol $\Sigma$ represents a summation operation, in this case over all $n$ particles. The sum

$$\Sigma\, m_i = M$$

is the total mass of the system. We can then rewrite Eq. 9-2 in the form

$$M x_{\text{cm}} = \Sigma\, m_i x_i. \qquad (9\text{-}2a)$$

Suppose now that we have three particles *not in a straight line;* they will lie in a plane, as in Fig. 9-3. The center of mass $C$ is defined and located by

**Fig. 9-2** The center of mass of the two masses $m_1$ and $m_2$ lies on the line joining $m_1$ and $m_2$ at $C$, a distance $x_{\text{cm}}$ from the origin.

**Fig. 9-3** The center of mass of the three masses $m_1$, $m_2$, and $m_3$ lies at point $C$, with coordinates $x_{\text{cm}}$, $y_{\text{cm}}$. $C$ lies in the same plane as that of the triangle formed by the three masses.

the coordinates $x_{cm}$ and $y_{cm}$, where

$$x_{cm} = \frac{m_1 x_1 + m_2 x_2 + m_3 x_3}{m_1 + m_2 + m_3}, \qquad (9\text{-}3)$$

$$y_{cm} = \frac{m_1 y_1 + m_2 y_2 + m_3 y_3}{m_1 + m_2 + m_3},$$

in which $x_1$, $y_1$ are the coordinates of the particle of mass $m_1$; $x_2$, $y_2$ are those of $m_2$; and $x_3$, $y_3$ are those of $m_3$. The coordinates $x_{cm}$, $y_{cm}$ of the center of mass are measured from the same arbitrary origin.

For a large number of particles lying in a plane, the center of mass is at $x_{cm}$, $y_{cm}$, where

$$x_{cm} = \frac{\Sigma\, m_i x_i}{\Sigma\, m_i} = \frac{1}{M} \sum m_i x_i \quad \text{and} \quad y_{cm} = \frac{\Sigma\, m_i y_i}{\Sigma\, m_i} = \frac{1}{M} \sum m_i y_i \quad (9\text{-}4)$$

in which $M$ $(= \Sigma\, m_i)$ is the total mass of the system.

For a large number of particles not necessarily confined to a plane but *distributed in space*, the center of mass is at $x_{cm}$, $y_{cm}$, $z_{cm}$, where

$$x_{cm} = \frac{1}{M} \sum m_i x_i, \quad y_{cm} = \frac{1}{M} \sum m_i y_i, \quad z_{cm} = \frac{1}{M} \sum m_i z_i \quad (9\text{-}5a)$$

In vector notation each particle in the system can be described by a position vector $\mathbf{r}_i$ in a particular reference frame and the center of mass can be located by a position vector $\mathbf{r}_{cm}$. These vectors are related to $x_i$, $y_i$, $z_i$ and $x_{cm}$, $y_{cm}$, $z_{cm}$ in Eq. 9-5a by

$$\mathbf{r}_i = \mathbf{i} x_i + \mathbf{j} y_i + \mathbf{k} z_i$$

and

$$\mathbf{r}_{cm} = \mathbf{i} x_{cm} + \mathbf{j} y_{cm} + \mathbf{k} z_{cm}.$$

Thus the three scalar equations of Eq. 9-5a can be replaced by a single vector equation

$$\mathbf{r}_{cm} = \frac{1}{M} \sum m_i \mathbf{r}_i \qquad (9\text{-}5b)$$

in which the sum is a vector sum. The student can prove that Eq. 9-5b is true by substituting the expressions given for $\mathbf{r}_i$ and $\mathbf{r}_{cm}$ just above into Eq. 9-5b. Note the economy of expression permitted by the use of vectors. Equation 9-5b shows that, if the origin of our reference frame is at the center of mass (which means that $\mathbf{r}_{cm} = 0$), then $\Sigma\, m_i \mathbf{r}_i = 0$ for the system.

Equations 9-5 are the most general case for a collection of particles. Equations 9-1 through 9-4 are special instances of this one. The location of the center of mass is independent of the reference frame used to locate it (see Problem 1). *The center of mass of a system of particles depends only on the masses of the particles and the positions of the particles relative to one another.*

A rigid body, such as a meter stick, can be thought of as a system of closely packed particles. Hence it also has a center of mass. The number of particles (atoms, for example) in the body is so large and their spacing so small, however, that we can treat the body as though it has a continuous distribution of mass. To obtain the expression for the center of mass of a continuous body, let us begin by subdividing the body into $n$ small elements of mass $\Delta m_i$ located approximately at the points $x_i, y_i, z_i$. The coordinates of the center of mass are then given approximately, by

$$x_{\text{cm}} = \frac{\Sigma \, \Delta m_i x_i}{\Sigma \, \Delta m_i} \qquad y_{\text{cm}} = \frac{\Sigma \, \Delta m_i y_i}{\Sigma \, \Delta m_i} \qquad z_{\text{cm}} = \frac{\Sigma \, \Delta m_i z_i}{\Sigma \, \Delta m_i}.$$

Now let the elements of mass be further subdivided so that the number of elements $n$ tends to infinity. The points $x_i, y_i, z_i$ will locate the mass elements more precisely as $n$ is increased and will locate them exactly as $n$ becomes infinite. The continuous body is then subdivided into an infinite number of infinitesimal mass elements. The coordinates of the center of mass can now be given precisely as

$$x_{\text{cm}} = \lim_{\Delta m_i \to 0} \frac{\Sigma \, \Delta m_i x_i}{\Sigma \, \Delta m_i} = \frac{\int x \, dm}{\int dm} = \frac{1}{M} \int x \, dm,$$

$$y_{\text{cm}} = \lim_{\Delta m_i \to 0} \frac{\Sigma \, \Delta m_i y_i}{\Sigma \, \Delta m_i} = \frac{\int y \, dm}{\int dm} = \frac{1}{M} \int y \, dm, \qquad (9\text{-}6a)$$

$$z_{\text{cm}} = \lim_{\Delta m_i \to 0} \frac{\Sigma \, \Delta m_i z_i}{\Sigma \, \Delta m_i} = \frac{\int z \, dm}{\int dm} = \frac{1}{M} \int z \, dm.$$

In these expressions $dm$ is the differential element of mass at the point $x, y, z$, and $\int dm$ equals $M$, where $M$ is the total mass of the object. For a continuous body the summation of Eq. 9-5a is replaced by the integration of Eq. 9-6a.

The vector expression that is equivalent to the three scalar expressions of Eq. 9-6a is

$$\mathbf{r}_{\text{cm}} = \frac{1}{M} \int \mathbf{r} \, dm \qquad (9\text{-}6b)$$

As before, the summation of Eq. 9-5b has been replaced by an integration. Once again we see that if the origin of our reference frame is at the center of mass (that is, if $\mathbf{r}_{\text{cm}} = 0$), then $\int \mathbf{r} \, dm = 0$ for the body. This integral, and the corresponding sum $\Sigma \, m_i \mathbf{r}_i$ of Eq. 9-5b, is called the *first moment of mass for the system.*

Often we deal with homogeneous objects having a point, a line, or a plane of symmetry. Then the center of mass will lie at the point, on the line, or in the plane of symmetry. For example, the center of mass of a homogeneous sphere (which has a point of symmetry) will be at the center of the sphere, the center of mass of a cone (which has a line of symmetry) will be on the axis of the cone, etc. We can understand that this is so because, from symmetry, the first moment of mass $(\int \mathbf{r} \, dm)$ is zero at the center of a sphere, somewhere along the axis of a cone, etc. It follows from Eq. 9–6b that $\mathbf{r}_{cm} = 0$ for such points which means that the center of mass is located at these points.

▶ **Example 1.**  Locate the center of mass of three particles of mass $m_1 = 1.0$ kg, $m_2 = 2.0$ kg, and $m_3 = 3.0$ kg at the corners of an equilateral triangle 1.0 meter on a side.

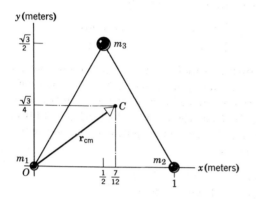

**Fig. 9–4**  Example 1. Finding the center of mass $C$ of three unequal masses forming an equilateral triangle.

Choose the $x$-axis along one side of the triangle as shown in Fig. 9–4. Then,

$$x_{cm} = \frac{\Sigma \, m_i x_i}{\Sigma \, m_i} = \frac{(1.0 \text{ kg})(0) + (2.0 \text{ kg})(1.0 \text{ meter}) + (3.0 \text{ kg})(\tfrac{1}{2} \text{ meter})}{(1.0 + 2.0 + 3.0) \text{ kg}} = \tfrac{7}{12} \text{ meter,}$$

$$y_{cm} = \frac{\Sigma \, m_i y_i}{\Sigma \, m_i} = \frac{(1.0 \text{ kg})(0) + (2.0 \text{ kg})(0) + (3.0 \text{ kg})(\sqrt{3}/2 \text{ meter})}{(1.0 + 2.0 + 3.0) \text{ kg}} = \tfrac{\sqrt{3}}{4} \text{ meter.}$$

The center of mass $C$ is shown in the figure. Why is it not at the geometric center of the triangle?

**Example 2.**  Find the center of mass of the triangular plate of Fig. 9–5.

If a body can be divided into parts such that the center of mass of each part is known, the center of mass of the body can usually be found simply. The triangular plate may be divided into narrow strips parallel to one side. The center of mass of each strip lies on the line which joins the middle of that side to the opposite vertex. But we can divide up the triangle in three different ways, using this process for each of three sides. Hence the center of mass lies at the intersection of the

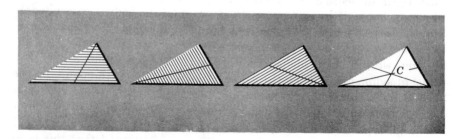

**Fig. 9–5**  Example 2. Finding the center of mass $C$ of a triangular plate.

three lines which join the middle of each side with the opposite vertices.  This is the only point that is common to the three lines.    ◀

## 9–2  Motion of the Center of Mass

Now we can discuss the physical importance of the center-of-mass concept.  Consider the motion of a group of particles whose masses are $m_1, m_2, \ldots, m_n$ and whose total mass is $M$.  For the time being we will assume that mass neither enters nor leaves the system so that the total mass $M$ of the system remains constant with time.  In Section 9–7 we shall consider systems in which $M$ is not constant; a familiar example is a rocket, which expels hot gases as its fuel burns, thus reducing its mass.

From Eq. 9–5b we have, for our fixed system of particles,

$$M\mathbf{r}_{cm} = m_1\mathbf{r}_1 + m_2\mathbf{r}_2 + \cdots + m_n\mathbf{r}_n,$$

where $\mathbf{r}_{cm}$ is the position vector identifying the center of mass in a particular reference frame.  Differentiating this equation with respect to time, we obtain

$$M\frac{d\mathbf{r}_{cm}}{dt} = m_1\frac{d\mathbf{r}_1}{dt} + m_2\frac{d\mathbf{r}_2}{dt} + \cdots + m_n\frac{d\mathbf{r}_n}{dt}$$

or

$$M\mathbf{v}_{cm} = m_1\mathbf{v}_1 + m_2\mathbf{v}_2 + \cdots + m_n\mathbf{v}_n,$$

(9–7)

where $\mathbf{v}_1$ is the velocity of the first particle, etc., and $d\mathbf{r}_{cm}/dt$ ($= \mathbf{v}_{cm}$) is the velocity of the center of mass.

Differentiating Eq. 9–7 with respect to time, we obtain

$$M\frac{d\mathbf{v}_{cm}}{dt} = m_1\frac{d\mathbf{v}_1}{dt} + m_2\frac{d\mathbf{v}_2}{dt} + \cdots + m_n\frac{d\mathbf{v}_n}{dt}$$

$$= m_1\mathbf{a}_1 + m_2\mathbf{a}_2 + \cdots + m_n\mathbf{a}_n,$$

(9–8)

where $\mathbf{a}_1$ is the acceleration of the first particle, etc., and $d\mathbf{v}_{cm}/dt$ ($= \mathbf{a}_{cm}$) is the acceleration of the center of mass of the system.  Now, from Newton's second law, the force $\mathbf{F}_1$ acting on the first particle is given by $\mathbf{F}_1 = m_1\mathbf{a}_1$.  Likewise, $\mathbf{F}_2 = m_2\mathbf{a}_2$, etc.  We can then write Eq. 9–8 as

$$M\mathbf{a}_{cm} = \mathbf{F}_1 + \mathbf{F}_2 + \cdots + \mathbf{F}_n.$$

(9–9)

Hence *the total mass of the group of particles times the acceleration of its center of mass is equal to the vector sum of all the forces acting on the group of particles.*

Among all these forces will be *internal* forces exerted by the particles on each other.  However, from Newton's third law, these internal forces will occur in equal and opposite pairs, so that they contribute nothing to the sum.  Hence the internal forces can be removed from the problem.  The right-hand sum in Eq. 9–9 represents the sum of only the *external* forces acting on all the particles.  We can then rewrite Eq. 9–9 as simply

$$M\mathbf{a}_{cm} = \mathbf{F}_{ext}.$$

(9–10)

This states that *the center of mass of a system of particles moves as though all the mass of the system were concentrated at the center of mass and all the external forces were applied at that point.*

Notice that we obtain this simple result without specifying the nature of the system of particles. The system can be a rigid body in which the particles are in fixed positions with respect to one another, or it can be a collection of particles in which there may be all kinds of internal motion. Whatever the system is, and however its individual parts may be moving, its center of mass moves according to Eq. 9–10.

Hence, instead of treating bodies as single particles as we have done in previous chapters, we can treat them as collections of particles. Then we can obtain the translational motion of the body, that is, the motion of its center of mass, by assuming that all the mass of the body is concentrated at its center of mass and all the external forces are applied at that point.* This, in fact, is the procedure that we followed implicitly in all our force diagrams and problem solving.

Aside from justifying and making more concrete our previous procedure, we have now found how to describe the translational motion of a *system* of particles and how to describe the *translational* motion of a body which may be rotating as well. In this chapter and the next we apply this result to the linear motion of a system of particles. In later chapters we shall see how it simplifies the analysis of rotational motion.

▶ **Example 3.** Consider three particles of different masses acted on by external forces, as shown in Fig. 9–6. Find the acceleration of the center of mass of the system.

First we find the coordinates of the center of mass. From Eq. 9–3,

$$x_{cm} = \frac{(8.0 \times 4) + (4.0 \times -2) + (4.0 \times 1)}{16} \text{ meters} = 1.8 \text{ meters},$$

$$y_{cm} = \frac{(8.0 \times 1) + (4.0 \times 2) + (4.0 \times -3)}{16} \text{ meters} = 0.25 \text{ meter}.$$

These are shown as $C$ in Fig. 9–6.

To obtain the acceleration of the center of mass, we first determine the resultant external force acting on the system consisting of the three particles. The $x$-component of this force is

$$F_x = 14 \text{ nt} - 6.0 \text{ nt} = 8.0 \text{ nt},$$

and the $y$-component is

$$F_y = 16 \text{ nt}.$$

Hence the resultant external force has a magnitude

$$F = \sqrt{(8.0)^2 + (16)^2} \text{ nt} = 18 \text{ nt},$$

---

* When the external force is gravity, it acts through the *center of gravity* of the body. In every case we have considered, the center of gravity coincides with the center of mass, which is a more general concept. The conditions under which these points are different for a body will be discussed in Chapter 14.

and makes an angle $\theta$ with the $x$-axis given by

$$\tan \theta = \frac{16 \text{ nt}}{8.0 \text{ nt}} = 2.0 \quad \text{or} \quad \theta = 63°.$$

Then, from Eq. 9-10, the acceleration of the center of mass is

$$a_{cm} = \frac{F}{M} = \frac{18 \text{ nt}}{16 \text{ kg}} = 1.1 \text{ meters/sec}^2,$$

making an angle of 63° with the $x$-axis.

Although the three particles will change their relative positions as time goes on, the center of mass will move, as shown, with this constant acceleration.     ◄

## 9-3   Linear Momentum of a Particle

The *momentum* of a single particle is a vector **p** defined as the product of its mass $m$ and its velocity **v**.   That is,

**Fig. 9–6**   Example 3.   Finding the motion of the center of mass of three masses, each subjected to a different force.   The forces all lie in the plane defined by the particles.   The distances indicated along the axes are in meters.

$$\mathbf{p} = m\mathbf{v}. \tag{9–11}$$

Momentum, being the product of a scalar by a vector, is itself a vector. Because it is proportional to **v**, the momentum **p** of a particular particle depends on the reference frame of the observer; we must always specify this frame.

Newton, in his famous *Principia*, expressed the second law of motion in terms of momentum (which he called "quantity of motion").   Expressed in modern terminology Newton's second law reads: *The rate of change of momentum of a body is proportional to the resultant force acting on the body and is in the direction of that force.*   In symbolic form this becomes

$$\mathbf{F} = \frac{d\mathbf{p}}{dt}. \tag{9–12}$$

If our system is a single particle of (constant) mass $m$, this formulation of the second law is equivalent to the form $\mathbf{F} = m\mathbf{a}$, which we have used up to now.   That is, if $m$ is a constant, then

$$\mathbf{F} = \frac{d\mathbf{p}}{dt} = \frac{d}{dt}(m\mathbf{v}) = m\frac{d\mathbf{v}}{dt} = m\mathbf{a}.$$

The relations $\mathbf{F} = m\mathbf{a}$ and $\mathbf{F} = d\mathbf{p}/dt$ for single particles are completely equivalent in classical mechanics.

In relativity theory the second law for a single particle in the form $\mathbf{F} = m\mathbf{a}$ is not valid.   However, it turns out that Newton's second law in the form $\mathbf{F} = d\mathbf{p}/dt$ *is* still a valid law *if* the momentum **p** for a single particle is defined not as $m_0\mathbf{v}$ but as

$$\mathbf{p} = \frac{m_0\mathbf{v}}{\sqrt{1 - v^2/c^2}}. \tag{9-13}$$

This result suggested a new definition of mass (compare Eqs. 9–11 and 9–13)

$$m = \frac{m_0}{\sqrt{1 - v^2/c^2}},$$

so that the momentum could still be written as $\mathbf{p} = m\mathbf{v}$; see Section 8–9.   In this equation $v$ is the speed of the particle, $c$ is the speed of light, and $m_0$ is the "rest mass" of the body (its mass when $v = 0$).   From this definition we must expect the mass of a particle to increase with its speed.   In atomic and nuclear systems particles may acquire enormous speeds, comparable to the speed of light.   This concept can be put to a direct test in such systems because the increase in mass over the rest mass for such particles is large enough to measure accurately.   Results of all such experiments indicate that this effect is real and given exactly by the equation above.   (See for example, Fig. 8–8.)

### 9–4   Linear Momentum of a System of Particles

Suppose that instead of a single particle we have a system of $n$ particles, with masses $m_1$, $m_2$, etc.   *We shall continue to assume,* as we did in Section 9–2, *that no mass enters or leaves the system,* so that the mass $M$ ($= \Sigma\, m_i$) of the system remains constant with time.   The particles may interact with each other and external forces may act on them as well.   Each particle will have a velocity and a momentum.   Particle 1 of mass $m_1$ and velocity $\mathbf{v}_1$ will have a momentum $\mathbf{p}_1 = m_1\mathbf{v}_1$, for example.   The system as a whole will have a *total momentum* **P** in a particular reference frame, which is defined to be simply the vector sum of the momenta of the individual particles in that same frame, or

$$\mathbf{P} = \mathbf{p}_1 + \mathbf{p}_2 + \cdots + \mathbf{p}_n \tag{9-14}$$

$$= m_1\mathbf{v}_1 + m_2\mathbf{v}_2 + \cdots + m_n\mathbf{v}_n.$$

If we compare this relation with Eq. 9–7 we see at once that

$$\mathbf{P} = M\mathbf{v}_{\mathrm{cm}}, \tag{9-15}$$

which is an equivalent definition for the momentum of a system of particles. In words, Eq. 9–15 states: *The total momentum of a system of particles is equal to the product of the total mass of the system and the velocity of its center of mass.*

We have seen (Eq. 9–10) that Newton's second law for a system of particles can be written as

$$\mathbf{F}_{\mathrm{ext}} = M\mathbf{a}_{\mathrm{cm}} \tag{9-10}$$

in which $\mathbf{F}_{\mathrm{ext}}$ is the vector sum of all the *external* forces acting on the system; we recall that the internal forces acting between particles cancel in pairs because of Newton's third law (see Fig. 9–7).   If we differentiate

**Fig. 9–7** Relationship between the forces acting on a system of three masses $m_1$, $m_2$, and $m_3$. (a) All the forces acting on each mass are shown here, as well as the location of the center of mass. On $m_1$ act forces $f_{21}$ and $f_{31}$ exerted by $m_2$ and $m_3$ respectively, as well as $\mathbf{F}_1$, a force from some external agent. Similar sets of forces act on $m_2$ and $m_3$. However, according to Newton's third law, internal forces $f_{31}$ and $f_{13}$ must be equal and opposite and must both lie along the line of centers of $m_1$ and $m_3$. Similar statements hold for the other two pairs of action-reaction forces. (b) If we are interested only in the motion of the system as a whole, we may consider all the forces to act on a mass $M = m_1 + m_2 + m_3$, located at the center of mass. Owing to the equality of the action-reaction pairs of internal forces as just stated, they cancel each other identically, leaving only the three external forces $\mathbf{F}_1$, $\mathbf{F}_2$, and $\mathbf{F}_3$. These are added graphically in (c) to yield a net force $\mathbf{F}_{\mathrm{ext}}$ acting on the center of mass of the system.

Eq. 9–15 with respect to time we obtain, for an assumed constant mass $M$,

$$\frac{d\mathbf{P}}{dt} = M\frac{d\mathbf{v}_{\mathrm{cm}}}{dt} = M\mathbf{a}_{\mathrm{cm}}. \tag{9–16}$$

Comparison of Eqs. 9–10 and 9–16 allows us to write Newton's second law for a system of particles in the form

$$\mathbf{F}_{\mathrm{ext}} = \frac{d\mathbf{P}}{dt}. \tag{9–17}$$

This equation is the generalization of the single-particle equation $\mathbf{F} = d\mathbf{p}/dt$ (Eq. 9–12) to a system of many particles, no mass entering or leaving the system. Equation 9–17 reduces to Eq. 9–12 for the special case of a single particle, there being only external forces on a one-particle system.

**9–5  Conservation of Linear Momentum**

Suppose that the sum of the external forces acting on a system is zero. Then, from Eq. 9–17,

$$\frac{d\mathbf{P}}{dt} = 0 \quad \text{or} \quad \mathbf{P} = \text{constant}.$$

*When the resultant external force acting on a system is zero, the total vector momentum of the system remains constant.* This simple but quite general result is called *the principle of the conservation of linear momentum.* We shall see that it is applicable to many important physical situations.

The conservation of linear momentum principle is the second of the great conservation principles that we have met so far, the first being the conservation of energy principle. Later we shall meet several others, among them the conservation of electric charge and of angular momentum. Conservation principles are of theoretical and practical importance in physics because they are simple and universal. They are all cast in the form: While the system is changing there is one aspect of the system that remains unchanged. Different observers, each in his own reference frame, would all agree, if they watched the same changing system, that the conservation laws applied to the system. For the conservation of linear momentum, for example, observers in different reference frames would assign different values of $\mathbf{P}$ to the linear momentum of the system, but each would agree (assuming $\mathbf{F}_{ext} = 0$) that his own value of $\mathbf{P}$ remained unchanged as the particles that make up the system move about.

The total momentum of a system can only be changed by external forces acting on the system. The internal forces, being equal and opposite, produce equal and opposite changes in momentum which annul one another. For a system of particles

$$\mathbf{p}_1 + \mathbf{p}_2 + \cdots + \mathbf{p}_n = \mathbf{P},$$

so that when the total momentum $\mathbf{P}$ is constant we have

$$\mathbf{p}_1 + \mathbf{p}_2 + \cdots + \mathbf{p}_n = \text{constant} = \mathbf{P}_0. \tag{9–18}$$

The momenta of the individual particles may change, but their sum remains constant if there is no net external force.

Momentum is a vector quantity. Equation 9–18 is therefore equivalent to three scalar equations, one for each coordinate direction. Hence the conservation of linear momentum supplies us with three conditions on the motion of a system to which it applies. The conservation of energy on the other hand supplies us with only one condition on the motion of a system to which it applies, because energy is a scalar.

The law of the conservation of linear momentum holds true even in atomic and nuclear physics, although Newtonian mechanics does not. Hence this conservation law must be more fundamental than the Newtonian principles. In our derivation of this principle we must have made more rigid assumptions than we needed to. This is true even in the framework of classical mechanics. The student should recall the key role played by Newton's third law in this deduction of momentum conservation. This law was used to justify the assumption that the sum of the internal forces acting on all the particles is zero. However, it is somewhat artificial to regard the internal forces in a piece of matter as resulting from pairs of equal and opposite forces between the various pairs of atoms. These internal forces are actually many-body forces, depending on not only the relative separation and orientation of two atoms but also on the positions and orientations of neighboring atoms. If it were possible to prove our assumption without using Newton's third law, the law of conservation of linear momentum would not depend on the validity of the third law of motion. Actually we can prove this assumption on the basis of a much less stringent requirement than that the third law should hold. The proof lies outside the scope of this text.*

---

* See "On Newton's Third Law and the Conservation of Momentum" E. Gerjuoy, *American Journal of Physics*, November 1949.

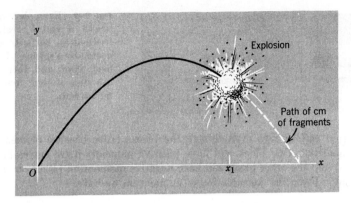

**Fig. 9–8**   Example 4. A projectile, following the usual parabolic trajectory, bursts at $x_1$. The center of mass of the fragments continues along the same parabolic path.

## 9–6   Some Applications of the Momentum Principle

▶ **Example 4.** Consider first a problem in which an external force acts on a system of particles. Recall our previous discussion of projectile motion (Chapter 4). Now let us imagine that our projectile is a shell that explodes while in flight. The path of the shell is shown in Fig. 9–8. We assume that the air resistance is negligible. The system is the shell, the earth is our reference frame, and the external force is that of gravity. At the point $x_1$ the shell explodes and shell fragments are blown in all directions. What can we say about the motion of this system thereafter?

The forces of the explosion are all *internal forces;* they are forces exerted by part of the system on other parts of the system. These forces may change the momenta of all the *individual fragments* from the values they had when they made up the shell, but they cannot change the *total* vector momentum of the system. Only an external force can change the total momentum. The external force, however, is simply that due to gravity. Since a system of particles as a whole moves as though all its mass were concentrated at the center of mass with the external force applied there, the center of mass of the fragments will continue to move in the parabolic trajectory that the unexploded shell would have followed. The change in the total momentum of the system attributable to gravity is the same whether the shell explodes or not.

What can you say about the *mechanical energy* of the system before and after the explosion?

**Example 5.** Consider now two blocks $A$ and $B$, of masses $m_A$ and $m_B$, coupled by a spring and resting on a horizontal frictionless table. Let us pull the blocks apart and stretch the spring, as in Fig. 9–9, and then release the blocks. Describe the subsequent motion.

If the system consists of the two blocks and spring, then after we have released the blocks there is no net *external* force acting on the system. We can therefore apply the conservation of linear momentum to the motion. The momentum of the system before the blocks were released was zero in the reference frame shown attached to the table, so the momentum must remain zero thereafter. The total momentum can be zero even though the blocks move because momentum is a *vector* quantity. One block will have positive momentum ($A$ moves in the $+x$ direction) and the other block will have negative momentum ($B$ moves in the $-x$ direction). From the conservation of momentum we have

$$\text{initial momentum} = \text{final momentum.}$$

$$0 = m_B\mathbf{v}_B + m_A\mathbf{v}_A.$$

Therefore

$$m_B\mathbf{v}_B = -m_A\mathbf{v}_A$$

or

$$\mathbf{v}_A = -\frac{m_B}{m_A}\,\mathbf{v}_B.$$

For example, if $m_A$ is 2 slugs and $m_B$ is 1 slug, then $\mathbf{v}_A$ will always be one-half $\mathbf{v}_B$ in magnitude and oppositely directed as the blocks move.

The kinetic energy of block $A$ is $\frac{1}{2}m_A v_A{}^2$ and can be written as $(m_A v_A)^2/2m_A$ and that of block $B$ is $\frac{1}{2}m_B v_B{}^2$ and can be written as $(m_B v_B)^2/2m_B$. But

$$\frac{K_A}{K_B} = \frac{2m_B(m_A v_A)^2}{2m_A(m_B v_B)^2} = \frac{m_B}{m_A},$$

in which $m_A v_A$ equals $m_B v_B$ because of momentum conservation. The kinetic energies of the blocks at any instant are inversely proportional to their respective masses. Because mechanical energy is conserved also, the blocks will continue to oscillate back and forth, the energy being partly kinetic and partly potential. What is the motion of the center of mass of this system?

If mechanical energy is not conserved, as would be true if friction were present, the motion will die out as the energy is dissipated. Can we apply the conservation of linear momentum in this case? Explain.

**Example 6.** As an example of recoil, consider radioactive decay. An $\alpha$-particle (the nucleus of a helium atom) is emitted from a uranium-238 nucleus, originally at rest, with a speed of $1.4 \times 10^7$ meters/sec and a kinetic energy of 4.1 Mev (million electron volts). Find the recoil speed of the residual nucleus (thorium-234).

We think of the system (thorium + $\alpha$-particle) as initially bound and forming the uranium nucleus. The system then fragments into two separate parts. The momentum of the system before fragmentation is zero. In the absence of external forces, the momentum after fragmentation is also zero. Hence,

$$\text{initial momentum} = \text{final momentum,}$$

$$0 = M_\alpha\mathbf{v}_\alpha + M_{\text{Th}}\mathbf{v}_{\text{Th}},$$

$$\mathbf{v}_{\text{Th}} = -\frac{M_\alpha}{M_{\text{Th}}}\,\mathbf{v}_\alpha.$$

The ratio of the $\alpha$-particle mass to the thorium nucleus mass, $M_\alpha/M_{\text{Th}}$, is $4/234$ and $v_\alpha = 1.4 \times 10^7$ meters/sec. Hence,

$$v_{\text{Th}} = -(4/234)(1.4 \times 10^7 \text{ meters/sec}) = -2.4 \times 10^5 \text{ meters/sec.}$$

The minus sign indicates that the residual thorium nucleus recoils in a direction exactly opposite to the motion of the $\alpha$-particle, so as to give a resultant vector momentum of zero.

How can we compute the kinetic energy of the recoiling nucleus (see previous example)? Where does the energy of the fragments come from?

**Example 7.** Consider now the apparently simple example of a ball thrown up from the earth by a person and then caught by him on its return. To simplify matters we can consider the person to be part of the earth since he does not lose contact with it. We also assume that air resistance is negligible.

The system being considered consists of the earth and the ball. The gravitational forces between the parts of the system are now internal forces. Let us choose a reference frame in which the system (earth + ball) is at rest. When the ball is thrown up, the earth must recoil as seen by an observer in this reference frame. The momentum of the system (earth + ball) is zero initially and no external forces act. Therefore, momentum is conserved and the total momentum remains zero throughout the motion. The upward momentum acquired by the ball is balanced by an equal and opposite downward momentum of the earth. We have

$$\text{initial momentum} = \text{final momentum,}$$

$$0 = m_B \mathbf{v}_B + m_E \mathbf{v}_E,$$

$$m_B \mathbf{v}_B = -m_E \mathbf{v}_E.$$

Here $m_B$ and $m_E$ are the masses of ball and earth respectively and $\mathbf{v}_B$ and $\mathbf{v}_E$ are the velocities of the ball and the earth in our selected reference frame. Owing to the enormous mass of the earth in comparison with the ball, the recoil speed of the earth is negligibly small.

As the ball and earth separate, the internal force of gravitational attraction pulls them together until they cease separating and begin to approach one another. As the ball falls toward the earth, the earth falls toward the ball with an equal but oppositely directed momentum. As the ball is caught, its momentum is neutralized by (and it neutralizes) the momentum of the earth. Both objects lose their relative motion, the total momentum is still zero, and the original situation before throwing is restored.

You will recall that when we discussed the conservation of energy in the presence of gravitational potential, we neglected to consider the motion of the earth itself. We took the surface of the earth as our zero level of gravitational potential energy. The reference position did not matter, since we were concerned only with *changes* in potential energy. However, in computing changes in kinetic energy, we assumed that the earth remained stationary, as in the case of the ball thrown up from the earth.

In principle, we cannot ignore the change in the kinetic energy of the earth itself. For example, when the ball falls toward the earth, the earth is slightly accelerated toward the ball. We neglected this fact before because we assumed that the change in kinetic energy of the earth is negligible. This result is not obvious, because although the earth's speed will certainly be small, its mass is enormous and the kinetic energy acquired may be significant. To settle the point we compute the ratio of the kinetic energy of the earth to that of the ball.   Using $m_E v_E = m_B v_B$ from momentum conservation, we have

$$\frac{K_E}{K_B} = \frac{\frac{1}{2} m_E v_E{}^2}{\frac{1}{2} m_B v_B{}^2} = \frac{\frac{1}{2}(m_E v_E)^2}{\frac{1}{2}(m_B v_B)^2} \cdot \frac{m_B}{m_E} = \frac{m_B}{m_E}.$$

Since the mass of the ball $m_B$ is negligibly small compared to the mass of the earth $m_E$, the kinetic energy acquired by the earth, $K_E$, is negligibly small compared to that of the ball, $K_B$.   For example, if $m_B = 6$ kg (a rather massive ball), then, since $m_E = 6 \times 10^{24}$ kg, $K_E/K_B = 10^{-24}$!

Notice that this problem is identical in principle to Example 5.   The differences are only those of detail; in one the potential energy is elastic and in the other the potential energy is gravitational; in one the masses are pictured as of the same order of magnitude, and in the other they are of very different orders of magnitude.

◀

### 9–7   Systems of Variable Mass

So far we have dealt only with systems in which the total system mass $M$ remained constant with time.   Now we consider systems in which mass enters or leaves the system while we are observing it, $dM/dt$ being positive in the former case and negative in the latter.

Figure 9–10$a$ shows a system of mass $M$ whose center of mass is moving with velocity $\mathbf{v}$ as seen from a particular reference frame.   An external force $\mathbf{F}_{\text{ext}}$ acts on the system.   At a time $\Delta t$ later the configuration has changed to that shown in Fig. 9–10$b$.   A mass $\Delta M$ has been ejected from the system, its center of mass moving with velocity $\mathbf{u}$ as seen by our observer.   The system mass is reduced to $M - \Delta M$ and the velocity $\mathbf{v}$ of the center of mass of the system is changed to $\mathbf{v} + \Delta \mathbf{v}$.

The student may imagine the system of Fig. 9–10 to represent a rocket.   It ejects hot gas from its orifice at a fairly high speed, decreasing its own mass and increasing its own speed.   In a rocket the loss of mass is continuous during the burning process.   The external force $\mathbf{F}_{\text{ext}}$ is *not* the thrust of the rocket but is the force of gravity on the rocket and the resisting force of the atmosphere.

To analyze the situation let us, for the time being, define the system to be one of constant mass.   This means that in Fig. 9–10$b$, we shall include in our system not only the mass $M - \Delta M$ of the body but also the ejected mass $\Delta M$, the total mass of the system being the $M$ of Fig. 9–10$a$.   Doing so permits us to apply the results that we have derived so far for constant mass systems.   We shall see that this approach leads us to the form of Newton's second law for systems in which the mass is not constant.

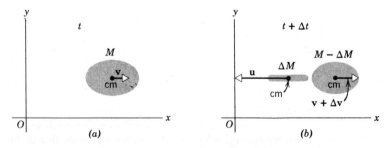

**Fig. 9–10**   A mass $M$ moving with velocity $\mathbf{v}$ ejects a mass $\Delta M$ during a time interval $\Delta t$.   An external force $\mathbf{F}_{\text{ext}}$ (not shown) acts on the system.

From Eq. 9–17

$$\mathbf{F}_{ext} = \frac{d\mathbf{P}}{dt} \tag{9-17}$$

we can write, as an approximate result for the finite time interval $\Delta t$,

$$\mathbf{F}_{ext} \cong \frac{\Delta \mathbf{P}}{\Delta t} = \frac{\mathbf{P}_f - \mathbf{P}_i}{\Delta t}$$

in which $\mathbf{P}_f$ is the (final) system momentum in Fig. 9–10b and $\mathbf{P}_i$ is the (initial) system momentum for Fig. 9–10a. But $\mathbf{P}_f = (M - \Delta M)(\mathbf{v} + \Delta \mathbf{v}) + \Delta M \mathbf{u}$ and $\mathbf{P}_i = M\mathbf{v}$. This leads to

$$\mathbf{F}_{ext} \cong \frac{[(M - \Delta M)(\mathbf{v} + \Delta \mathbf{v}) + \Delta M \mathbf{u}] - [M\mathbf{v}]}{\Delta t}$$

$$= M \frac{\Delta \mathbf{v}}{\Delta t} + [\mathbf{u} - (\mathbf{v} + \Delta \mathbf{v})] \frac{\Delta M}{\Delta t}. \tag{9-19}$$

Now, if we let $\Delta t$ approach zero, the configuration of Fig. 9–10b approaches that of Fig. 9–10a; that is, $\Delta \mathbf{v}/\Delta t$ approaches $d\mathbf{v}/dt$, the acceleration of the body in Fig. 9–10a. The quantity $\Delta M$ is the mass ejected in $\Delta t$: this leads to a decrease in the mass $M$ of the original body. Since $dM/dt$, the change in mass of the body with time, is intrinsically negative in this case, the positive quantity $\Delta M/\Delta t$ is replaced by $-dM/dt$ as $\Delta t$ approaches zero. Finally, $\Delta \mathbf{v}$ goes to zero as $\Delta t$ approaches zero. Making these changes in Eq. 9–19 leads to

$$\mathbf{F}_{ext} = M \frac{d\mathbf{v}}{dt} + \mathbf{v} \frac{dM}{dt} - \mathbf{u} \frac{dM}{dt} \tag{9-20a}$$

or

$$\mathbf{F}_{ext} = \frac{d}{dt}(M\mathbf{v}) - \mathbf{u} \frac{dM}{dt}, \tag{9-20b}$$

which is Newton's second law, defining the external forces on a body (like that of Fig. 9–10a) whose mass is changing.

Note that these equations reduce to the familiar forms $\mathbf{F}_{ext} = M\mathbf{a}$ and $\mathbf{F}_{ext} = (d/dt)(M\mathbf{v})$ respectively for the special case of a body of constant mass $(dM/dt = 0)$. It is important to note that we *cannot* derive a general expression for Newton's second law for variable mass systems by treating the mass in $\mathbf{F} = d\mathbf{P}/dt = d(M\mathbf{v})/dt$ as a *variable*. For this leads to

$$\mathbf{F} = d(M\mathbf{v})/dt = M \, d\mathbf{v}/dt + \mathbf{v} \, dM/dt,$$

which is only a special case of the more general Eq. 9–20, namely, the case in which either (a) $dM/dt = 0$, a system of constant mass, or (b) $\mathbf{u} = 0$, a special choice of reference frame. We *can* use $\mathbf{F} = d\mathbf{P}/dt$ to analyze variable mass systems *only* if we apply it to an *entire system of constant mass* having parts among which there is an interchange of mass. This indeed is what we have done in deriving Eqs. 9–20. The importance of the momentum formulation $\mathbf{F} = d\mathbf{P}/dt$ in classical physics lies in the fact that it highlights momentum conservation and gives us a simple, physical way to treat complicated systems. Since the choice of what we will take as the system is ours to make, we can always choose a system of constant mass by defining our system broadly enough.

However, it is often convenient, as in rocket problems, to choose a system whose mass varies with time. In such cases we apply Newton's second law of Eqs. 9–20 in a form that is sometimes more convenient and interpretable more physically. The quantity $\mathbf{u} - (\mathbf{v} + \Delta \mathbf{v})$ in Eq. 9–19 is just $\mathbf{v}_{rel}$, the relative velocity of the ejected mass with respect to the main body. Therefore Eqs. 9–20 may be written as

$$M \frac{d\mathbf{v}}{dt} = \mathbf{F}_{\text{ext}} + (\mathbf{u} - \mathbf{v}) \frac{dM}{dt} \qquad (9\text{–}21a)$$

or

$$M \frac{d\mathbf{v}}{dt} = \mathbf{F}_{\text{ext}} + \mathbf{v}_{\text{rel}} \frac{dM}{dt}. \qquad (9\text{–}21b)$$

The last term in Eq. 9–21b, [$\mathbf{v}_{\text{rel}} (dM/dt)$], is the rate at which momentum is being transferred into (or out of) the system by the mass that the system has ejected (or collected). It can be interpreted as the force exerted *on* the system by the mass that leaves it (or joins it). For a rocket, this term is called the *thrust* and it is the rocket designer's aim to make it as large as possible. Inspection of Eq. 9–21 shows that this requires that the rocket eject as much mass per unit time as possible and that the speed of the ejected mass relative to the rocket be as high as possible. We can rewrite Eq. 9–21 as

$$M \frac{d\mathbf{v}}{dt} = \mathbf{F}_{\text{ext}} + \mathbf{F}_{\text{reaction}}$$

in which $\mathbf{F}_{\text{reaction}}$ ($= \mathbf{v}_{\text{rel}} \, dM/dt$) is the reaction force exerted on the system by the mass that leaves it.

▶ **Example 8.** A machine gun is mounted on a car on a horizontal frictionless surface as in Fig. 9–11a. The mass of the system (car + gun) at a particular instant is $M$. At that same instant the gun is firing bullets of mass $m$ whose velocity, in the reference frame shown, is $\mathbf{u}$. The velocity of the car in this same frame is $\mathbf{v}$ and the velocity of the bullets *with respect to the car* is $\mathbf{u} - \mathbf{v}$. The number of bullets fired per unit time is $n$. What is the acceleration of the car?

We select the car and gun as our system. Since its mass $M$ is variable, we apply Newton's second law in the form given in Eq. 9–21. Since no net external force acts on the system, we have $\mathbf{F}_{\text{ext}} = 0$ in that equation, yielding

$$M \frac{d\mathbf{v}}{dt} = \mathbf{v}_{\text{rel}} \frac{dM}{dt}.$$

Now $d\mathbf{v}/dt$ is $\mathbf{a}$, the acceleration of the system; $\mathbf{v}_{\text{rel}}$ is $\mathbf{u} - \mathbf{v}$, pointing to the left in Fig. 9–11a, and $dM/dt$ is $-mn$. Inserting these in the equation above yields

$$\mathbf{a} = \frac{d\mathbf{v}}{dt} = -\frac{\mathbf{v}_{\text{rel}}(mn)}{M}.$$

This shows that $\mathbf{a}$ points in the direction opposite to $\mathbf{v}_{\text{rel}}$, that is, $\mathbf{a}$ points to the right in Fig. 9–11a. If $v_{\text{rel}} = 500$ meters/sec, $m = 10$ gm, $n = 10/\text{sec}$, and $M = 200$ kg at some instant, then at that instant

$$a = \frac{(500 \text{ meters/sec})(10^{-2} \text{ kg})(10/\text{sec})}{200 \text{ kg}} = 0.25 \text{ meter/sec}^2.$$

The magnitude of the average "thrust" of the ejected bullets on the system (car + gun) at this instant is given by

$$F = v_{\text{rel}} n m = (500 \text{ meters/sec})(10/\text{sec})(10^{-2} \text{ kg})$$

$$= 50 \text{ nt.}$$

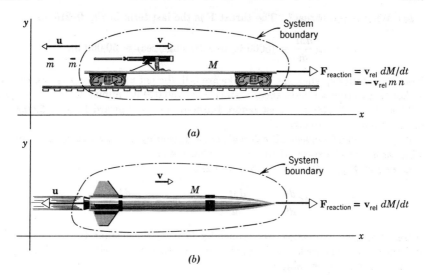

**Fig. 9–11**  (*a*) Example 8.   A machine gun is fixed to a car that rolls with negligible friction.   The gun fires bullets of mass $m$ at a rate (number per unit time) $n$, the velocity of the bullets with respect to the gun being $\mathbf{u} - \mathbf{v}$.   At the instant shown some bullets have already left the system.   The velocities indicated for the car and the bullets are those that would be measured by an observer in a reference frame fixed to the rails as shown.   The reaction force on the system is $\mathbf{F} = -mn\mathbf{v}_{rel} = (dM/dt)\mathbf{v}_{rel}$.   (*b*) A rocket moves through space with negligible external forces.   Gas particles are ejected from the exhaust, the particles having a velocity $\mathbf{u} - \mathbf{v}$ with respect to the rocket.   The rate at which mass is expelled at the exhaust is $-dM/dt$.   The reaction force on the rocket is $\mathbf{F} = (dM/dt)\mathbf{v}_{rel}$.   The velocities indicated for the rocket and exhaust gases are relative to the ground.

In Figure 9–11*b* we show the analagous situation for a rocket.   It is instructive to view this problem from the point of view of Newton's third law and the momentum principle.   Choose a fixed-mass system (rocket + gas) and attach a reference frame to its center of mass.   The rocket forces a jet of hot gases from its exhaust; this is the action force.   The jet of hot gases exerts a force on the rocket, propelling it forward.   This is the reaction force.   These forces are internal forces in the system (rocket + gas).   In the absence of external forces the total momentum of the system is constant (the center of mass, initially at rest, remains at rest).   The individual parts of the system (rocket and gases) may change their momentum, however; with respect to the center of mass frame, the hot gases acquire momentum in the backward direction and the rocket acquires an equal amount of momentum in the forward direction.

The student can analyze the system (bullets + car) in a similar way.

**Example 9.**   A rocket weighs 30,000 lb when fueled up on the launching pad. It is fired vertically upward and, at burnout, weighs 10,000 lb.   Gases are exhausted at the rate of 10 slugs/sec with a velocity of 5000 ft/sec, relative to the rocket (exhaust velocity), both quantities being assumed to be constant while the fuel is burning.

(a) What is the thrust?    The thrust $\mathbf{F}$ is the last term in Eq. 9–21b, or

$$F = v_{\text{rel}} \frac{dM}{dt} = (5000 \text{ ft/sec})(10 \text{ slugs/sec}) = 50{,}000 \text{ lb.}$$

Note that initially, when the fuel tanks are full, the net upward force acting on the rocket (neglecting air resistance) is the thrust (50,000 lb) minus the initial weight (30,000 lb) or 20,000 lb.    Just before burnout the net upward force is 50,000 lb minus 10,000 lb or 40,000 lb.

(b) If we could neglect *all external forces*, including gravity and air resistance, what would be the speed of the rocket at burnout?

If we put $\mathbf{F}_{\text{ext}} = 0$ in Eq. 9–21b, we have

$$M \frac{d\mathbf{v}}{dt} = \mathbf{v}_{\text{rel}} \frac{dM}{dt} \quad \text{or} \quad d\mathbf{v} = \mathbf{v}_{\text{rel}} \frac{dM}{M}.$$

Integrating this expression (see Appendix I) from the instant the velocity is $\mathbf{v}_0$ and the mass of the rocket is $M_0$ to the instant when the velocity is $\mathbf{v}$ and the mass of the rocket is $M$, we obtain

$$\int_{\mathbf{v}_0}^{\mathbf{v}} d\mathbf{v} = \mathbf{v}_{\text{rel}} \int_{M_0}^{M} \frac{dM}{M},$$

the exhaust velocity being assumed constant during this time.    This yields

$$\mathbf{v} - \mathbf{v}_0 = -\mathbf{v}_{\text{rel}} \ln (M_0/M) = -\mathbf{v}_{\text{rel}} \ln \left(1 + \frac{M_0 - M}{M}\right).$$

Hence the change in speed of the rocket in any interval of time depends only on the exhaust velocity (being opposite in direction from it) and on the fraction of mass exhausted during that time interval.

In our example, $v_0 = 0$ and $M_0/M = (30{,}000/10{,}000) = 3.0$, so that the speed of the rocket at burnout is

$$v = v_{\text{rel}} \ln (M_0/M) = (5000 \text{ ft/sec}) \ln 3.0 = 3800 \text{ miles/hr.}$$

If the external forces of gravity and air resistance were taken into account, the final speed would be smaller.*

Assuming that the rocket starts from rest ($v_0 = 0$) with an initial mass $M_0$ and reaches a final velocity $v_f$ at burnout when its mass is $M_f$, we can write the rocket equation above as

$$\frac{M_f}{M_0} = e^{-v_f/v_{\text{rel}}}$$

in which $v_{\text{rel}}$ is the exhaust velocity.

The classical rocket (or variable mass) equations imply that the speed of the rocket can increase to any value provided only that the rocket expels enough propellant so that the final remaining mass is sufficiently small.    However, we know from relativistic mechanics that a rocket cannot be accelerated to a speed equal to or greater than the speed of light.    Once the rocket's speed approaches the relativistic range the classical equations are no longer applicable.    One must take

---

* For an exact solution of the classical rocket problem see "Variable-Mass Dynamics" by J. L. Meriam, *Journal of Engineering Education*, December 1960.

into account the variation of inertial mass of a particle with speed and the relativistic velocity addition formula. The resulting equations apply to a relativistic rocket.*

**Example 10.** Sand drops from a stationary hopper at a rate $dM/dt$ onto a conveyor belt moving with velocity **v** in the reference frame of the laboratory, as in Fig. 9–12. What force is required to keep the belt moving at a speed $v$?

**Fig. 9–12** Example 10. Sand drops from a hopper at a rate $dM/dt$ onto a conveyer belt moving with velocity **v** in the reference frame of the laboratory. The force **F** required to keep the belt moving at constant velocity is **v** $dM/dt$. The hopper is at rest in the reference frame shown.

This is a clear-cut example of a force associated with change of mass alone, the velocity being constant. We take as our system the belt of varying mass so that Eq. 9–21 applies. We must put $dv/dt = 0$ in that equation because the velocity of the belt is constant. Furthermore, to an observer at rest on the belt, the falling sand (and the hopper) would appear to have a horizontal motion with speed $v$ in a direction opposite to that shown for the belt in the laboratory. Therefore $\mathbf{v}_{rel} = -\mathbf{v}$ in Eqs. 9–21. More formally, $\mathbf{v}_{rel} = \mathbf{u} - \mathbf{v}$; but $\mathbf{u} = 0$, so that $\mathbf{v}_{rel} = -\mathbf{v}$. Making these substitutions yields

$$0 = \mathbf{F}_{ext} - \mathbf{v}\,\frac{dM}{dt}$$

or

$$\mathbf{F}_{ext} = \mathbf{v}\,\frac{dM}{dt}.$$

In this example, $dM/dt$ is positive because the system is gaining mass with time. Hence, as expected, the necessary external force must point in the direction in which the belt moves. Note that, in the absence of friction, the mass of the belt itself does not enter the problem.

---

* See "The Equation of Motion for Relativistic Particles and Systems with a Variable Rest Mass," by Kalman B. Pomeranz, in *American Journal of Physics*, December 1964.

The power supplied by the external force is

$$P = \mathbf{F} \cdot \mathbf{v} = \mathbf{v} \cdot \mathbf{F} = \mathbf{v} \cdot (\mathbf{v}\, dM/dt) = v^2(dM/dt).$$

Since $v =$ a constant, we can write this as

$$P = \frac{d(Mv^2)}{dt} = 2\frac{d}{dt}\left(\frac{1}{2}Mv^2\right) = 2\frac{dK}{dt}.$$

This tells us that the power required to keep the belt moving is *twice* the rate at which the kinetic energy of the system is increasing; note that we need not consider the kinetic energy of the belt itself because—its speed being constant—its kinetic energy does not change. It is clear that mechanical energy is not conserved in this case. Where is the other half of the power going? In which of the previous examples did we have conservation of momentum without conservation of mechanical energy?

The student should be able to solve Example 10 alternatively by choosing a fixed-mass system and applying the momentum principle. ◀

## QUESTIONS

**1.** Must there necessarily be any mass at the center of mass of a system?

**2.** Does the center of mass of a solid body necessarily lie within the body? If not, give examples.

**3.** How is the center of mass concept related to the concept of geographic center of the country? To the population center of the country? What can you conclude from the fact that the geographic center differs from the population center?

**4.** A sculptor decides to portray a bird (Fig. 9–13). Luckily the final model is actually able to stand upright. The model is formed of a single sheet of metal of uniform thickness. Of the points shown, which is most likely to be the center of mass?

**Fig. 9–13**

**5.** If only an external force can change the state of motion of the center of mass of a body, how does it happen that the internal force of the brakes can bring a car to rest?

**6.** Can a body have energy without having momentum? Explain. Can a body have momentum without having energy? Explain.

**7.** A light and a heavy body have equal kinetic energies of translation. Which one has the larger momentum?

**8.** A bird is in a wire cage hanging from a spring balance. Is the reading of the balance when the bird is flying about greater than, less than, or the same as that when the bird sits in the cage?

**9.** Can a sailboat be propelled by air blown at the sails from a fan attached to the boat?

**10.** A man stands still on a large sheet of slick ice; in his hand he holds a lighted firecracker. He throws the firecracker into the air. Describe briefly, but as exactly as you can, the motion of the center of mass of the firecracker and the motion of the center of mass of the system consisting of man and firecracker. It will be most convenient to describe each motion during each of the following periods: (a) after he throws the firecracker, but before it explodes; (b) between the explosion and the first piece of firecracker hitting the ice; (c) between the first fragment hitting the ice and the last fragment landing; (d) during the time when all fragments have landed but none has reached the edge of the ice.

**11.** As stated in the text one cannot use the equation $\mathbf{F} = d(M\mathbf{v})/dt$ for a system of variable mass. To show this (a) put the equation in the equivalent form $(\mathbf{F} - M \, d\mathbf{v}/dt)/(dM/dt) = \mathbf{v}$ and (b) show that one side of this equation has the same value in all inertial frames, whereas the other side does not. Hence the equation cannot be generally valid. (c) Show that Eq. 9–20 leads to no such contradiction.

**12.** The final velocity of the final stage of a multistage rocket is much greater than the final velocity of a single-stage rocket of the same total weight and fuel supply. Explain this fact.

**13.** As a rocket expels burned fuel the location of the center of mass of the rocket (in a frame attached to the rocket) changes. Must one take this into account in an exact solution of the rocket problem?

**14.** Explain clearly the distinction between the origin of the varying mass of a classical system and that of a relativistic system.

**15.** Can you think of variable mass systems other than the examples given in the text?

## PROBLEMS

**1.** Show that the ratio of the distances of two particles from their center of mass is the inverse ratio of their masses.

**2.** Show that the center of mass of two particles is on the line joining them at a point whose distance from each particle is inversely proportional to the mass of that particle.

**3.** Experiments using the diffraction of electrons show that the distance between the centers of the carbon (C) and oxygen (O) atoms in the carbon monoxide gas molecule is $1.130 \times 10^{-10}$ meter. Locate the center of mass of a CO molecule relative to the carbon atom.

**4.** The mass of the moon is about 0.013 times the mass of the earth, and the distance from the center of the moon to the center of the earth is about 60 times the radius of the earth. How far is the center of mass of the earth-moon system from the center of the earth? Take the earth's radius to be 4000 miles.

**5.** In the ammonia ($NH_3$) molecule, the three hydrogen (H) atoms form an equilateral triangle, the distance between centers of the atoms being $1.628 \times 10^{-10}$ meter,

**Fig. 9—14**

so that the center of the triangle is $9.39 \times 10^{-11}$ meter from each hydrogen atom. The nitrogen (N) atom is at the apex of a pyramid, the three hydrogens constituting the base. (See Fig. 9-14.) The hydrogen-nitrogen distance is $1.014 \times 10^{-10}$ meter. Locate the center of mass relative to the nitrogen atom. (The nitrogen atom actually oscillates up and down through the base as indicated by the arrows and dotted lines. Assume a static molecule for this problem, however.)

**6.** Find the center of mass of a homogeneous semicircular plate. Let $a$ be the radius of the circle.

**7.** Two particles $P$ and $Q$ are initially at rest 1.0 meter apart. $P$ has a mass of 0.10 kg and $Q$ a mass of 0.30 kg. $P$ and $Q$ attract each other with a constant force of $1.0 \times 10^{-2}$ nt. No external forces act on the system. Describe the motion of the center of mass. At what distance from $P$'s original position do the particles collide?

**8.** Two bodies, each made up of weights from a set, are connected by a light cord which passes over a light, frictionless pulley with a diameter of 5.0 cm. The two bodies are at the same level. Each originally has a mass of 500 gm. (a) Locate their center of mass. (b) Twenty grams are transferred from one body to the other, but the bodies are prevented from moving. Locate the center of mass. (c) The two bodies are now released. Describe the motion of the center of mass and determine its acceleration.

**9.** What is the momentum of a 4000-lb car whose speed is 30 mph? At what speed would a 10-ton truck have the same momentum? The same kinetic energy?

**Fig. 9—15**

**10.** A 200-lb man standing on a surface of negligible friction kicks forward a 0.10-lb stone lying at his feet so that it acquires a speed of 10 ft/sec. What velocity does the man acquire as a result?

**11.** A dog, weighing 10.0 lb is standing on a flatboat so that he is 20 ft from the shore. He walks 8.0 ft on the boat toward shore and then halts. The boat weighs 40 lb, and one can assume there is no friction between it and the water. How far is he from the shore at the end of this time? (*Hint:* The center of mass of boat + dog does not move. Why?) The shoreline is also to the left in Fig. 9–15.

**12.** A cannon and a supply of cannon balls are inside a sealed railroad car as in Fig. 9–16. The cannon fires to the right, the car recoiling to the left. The cannon balls remain in the car after hitting the far wall. Show that no matter how the cannon balls are fired the railroad car cannot travel more than its length $L$, assuming it starts from rest.

**13.** A vessel at rest explodes, breaking into three pieces. Two pieces, having equal mass, fly off perpendicular to one another with the same speed of 30 meters/sec. The third piece has three times the mass of each other piece. What is the direction and magnitude of its velocity immediately after the explosion?

**Fig. 9–16**

**14.** A radioactive nucleus, initially at rest, decays by emitting an electron and a neutrino at right angles to one another. The momentum of the electron is $1.2 \times 10^{-22}$ kg-m/sec and that of the neutrino is $6.4 \times 10^{-23}$ kg-m/sec. (*a*) Find the direction and magnitude of the momentum of the recoiling nucleus. (*b*) The mass of the residual nucleus is $5.8 \times 10^{-26}$ kg. What is its kinetic energy of recoil?

**15.** A projectile is fired from a gun at an angle of 45° with the horizontal and with a muzzle speed of 1500 ft/sec. At the highest point in its flight the projectile explodes into two fragments of equal mass. One fragment, whose initial speed is zero, falls vertically. How far from the gun does the other fragment land, assuming a level terrain?

**16.** A body of mass 8.0 kg is traveling at 2.0 meters/sec under the influence of *no* external agency. At a certain instant an internal explosion occurs, splitting the body into two chunks of 4.0 kg mass each; 16 joules of translational kinetic energy are imparted to the two-chunk system by the explosion. Neither chunk leaves the line of the original motion. Determine the speed and direction of motion of each of the chunks after the explosion.

**17.** The last stage of a rocket is traveling at a speed of 17,000 miles/hr or 25,000 ft/sec. This last stage is made up of two parts which are clamped together, namely, a rocket case with a mass of 20 slugs and a passenger capsule with a mass of 10 slugs, including a chimpanzee. When the clamp is released, a compressed spring causes the two parts to separate with a relative speed of 3000 ft/sec. (*a*) What are the speeds of the two parts after they have separated? Assume that all velocities are along the same line. (*b*) Find the total kinetic energy of the two parts before and after they separate and account for the difference, if any.

**18.** A block of mass $m$ rests on a wedge of mass $M$ which, in turn, rests on a horizontal table, as shown in Fig. 9–17. All surfaces are frictionless. If the system starts at rest with point $P$ of the block a distance $h$ above the table, find the velocity of the wedge the instant point $P$ touches the table.

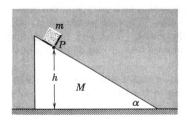

**Fig. 9–17**

**19.** A railroad flat car of weight $W$ can roll without friction along a straight horizontal track as shown. Initially a man of weight $w$ is standing on the car which is moving to the right with speed $v_0$. What is the change in velocity of the car if the man runs to the left (Fig. 9–18) so that his speed relative to the car is $v_{\text{rel}}$ just before he jumps off at the left end?

**Fig. 9–18**

**20.** Assume that the car in Problem 19 is initially at rest. It holds $n$ men each of weight $w$. If each man in succession runs with a relative velocity $v_{\text{rel}}$ and jumps off the end, do they impart to the car a greater velocity than if they all run and jump at the same time?

**21.** A machine gun fires 50-gm bullets at a speed of 1000 meters/sec. The gunner, holding the machine gun in his hands, can exert an average force of 180 nt against the gun. Determine the maximum number of bullets he can fire per minute.

**22.** A 6000-kg rocket is set for a vertical firing. If the exhaust speed is 1000 meters/ sec, how much gas must be ejected per second to supply the thrust needed $(a)$ to overcome the weight of the rocket, $(b)$ to give the rocket an initial upward acceleration of 19.6 meters/sec$^2$?

**23.** Show that the rocket speed is equal to the exhaust speed when the ratio $M_0/M$ is $e$ (about 2.7). Specify the coordinate system within which this result holds. Show also that the rocket speed is twice the exhaust speed when $M_0/M$ is $e^2$ (about 7.4).

**24.** A widely used rocket fuel is kerosene and liquid oxygen, capable of giving an exhaust velocity $v_{\text{rel}}$ of 8000 ft/sec (about 1.5 miles/sec). $(a)$ Neglect gravity and the weight of fuel tanks, pumps, etc., and find how many pounds of this fuel one needs for each pound of payload in order to get a rocket, starting from rest, to reach a velocity of 7.5 miles/sec (the velocity of escape from the earth is 7.0 miles/sec). $(b)$ In the Mariner probe to Mars the initial weight was about 200,000 lb and the payload about 500 lb, a "fuel" to payload ratio of 400 to 1. Starting a rocket from rest, what final velocity is achievable under these circumstances? $(c)$ The actual final rocket velocity was about 15 miles/sec, much greater than the value found in $(b)$. Explain this, considering the following factors: the external forces and weight neglected in $(a)$ must be taken into account; the rocket uses a number of stages; the initial rocket velocity is that of the earth's surface, in a reference frame attached to the sun.

**25.** A jet airplane is traveling 600 ft/sec. The engine takes in 2400 ft$^3$ of air having a mass of 4.8 slugs each second. The air is used to burn 0.20 slug of fuel each second. The energy is used to compress the products of combustion and to eject them at the rear of the plane at 1600 ft/sec relative to the plane. Find the thrust of the jet engine and the delivered horsepower.

**26.** A freight car, open at the top, weighing 10 tons, is coasting along a level track with negligible friction at 2.0 ft/sec when it begins to rain hard. The raindrops fall vertically with respect to the ground. What is the speed of the car when it has collected 0.50 ton of rain? What assumptions, if any, must you make to get your answer?

**27.** A freight car filled with sand has a hole so that sand leaks out through the bottom at a constant rate, $-dm/dt = \lambda$. A force **F** acts on the car in the direction of its motion. Call the instantaneous speed $v$ and write the equation of motion of the freight car.

**28.** A flexible rope of length $l$ and mass per unit length $\mu$ slides over the edge of a frictionless table. At time $t = 0$ let a length $y_0$ of it be hanging at rest over the edge and at time $t$ let a length $y$, moving with speed $dy/dt$, be over the edge. (a) Show that in terms of a variable mass problem $\mathbf{v}_{rel} = 0$, so that the equation of motion has the form $m \, d\mathbf{v}/dt = \mathbf{F}_{ext}$. (b) Show that the specific equation of motion is $l(d^2y/dt^2) = gy$. (c) Show that conservation of mechanical energy leads to $l(dy/dt)^2 - gy^2 = $ a constant, and that this is consistent with (b). (d) Show that $y = (y_0/2)(e^{\sqrt{g/l}\,t} + e^{-\sqrt{g/l}\,t})$ is a solution to the equation of motion [by substitution into (b)] and discuss the solution.

**29.** Consider a particle acted on by a force having the same direction as its velocity. (a) Using the relativistic relation $F = d(mv)/dt$ for a single particle, show that

$$F \, ds = mv \, dv + v^2 \, dm.$$

(b) Using the relativistic relation $v^2 = (1 - m_0^2/m^2)c^2$, show that

$$mv \, dv = \frac{m_0^2 c^2}{m^2} \, dm.$$

(c) Substitute the relations for $mv \, dv$ and $v^2$ into result (a) and show that

$$W = \int F \, ds = (m - m_0)c^2.$$

# Collisions

## 10–1  What is a Collision?

We learn much about atomic, nuclear, and elementary particles experimentally by observing collisions between them.  On a larger scale we can better interpret such things as the properties of gases in terms of particle collisions.  In this chapter we apply the principles of conservation of energy and conservation of momentum to the collisions of particles.

In a collision a relatively large force acts on each colliding particle for a relatively short time.  The basic idea of a "collision" is that the motion of the colliding particles (or of at least one of them) changes rather abruptly and that we can make a relatively clean separation of times that are "before the collision" and those that are "after the collision."

When a bat strikes a baseball for example, the beginning and the end of the collision can be determined fairly precisely.  The bat is in contact with the ball for an interval that is quite short in comparison to the time during which we are watching the ball.  During the collision the bat exerts a large force on the ball (Fig. 10–1).  This force varies with time in a complex way that we can measure only with difficulty.  Both the ball and the bat are deformed during the collision.  Forces that act for a time that is short compared to the time of observation of the system are called *impulsive* forces.

When an alpha particle ($He^4$) "collides" with a nucleus of gold ($Au^{197}$), the force acting between them may be the well-known repulsive electrostatic force associated with the charges on the particles.  The particles may not "touch," but we still may speak of a "collision" because a rela-

**Fig. 10–1** A high-speed flash photograph of a bat striking a baseball. Notice the deformation of the ball, indicating the enormous magnitude of the impulsive force at this instant. (Courtesy Harold E. Edgerton, Massachusetts Institute of Technology, Cambridge, Mass.)

tively strong force, acting for a time that is short in comparison to the time that the alpha particle is under observation, has a marked effect on the motion of the alpha particle.

When a proton ($H^1$ or p) with energy of, say, 25 Mev, "collides" with a nucleus of, say, a silver isotope (perhaps $Ag^{107}$), the particles may actually "touch," the predominant force then acting between them being, not the electrostatic repulsive force, but the strong, short-range, attractive nuclear force (see page 120). The proton may enter the silver nucleus, forming a compound structure. A short time later—the "collision interval" may be $10^{-18}$ sec—this compound structure may break up into two *different* particles, according to a scheme such as

$$p + Ag^{107} \rightarrow \alpha + Pd^{104},$$

in which $\alpha$ ($= He^4$) is an alpha particle. Thus we may broaden the concept of collision to include events (usually called *reactions*) in which the identities of the interacting particles change during the event. The conservation principles are applicable to all these examples

We may, if we wish, broaden our definition of "collision" even further to include the spontaneous decay of a single particle into two or more other particles. An example is the decay of the elementary particle called the *sigma particle* into two other particles, the *pion* and the *neutron* (see Appendix E) or

$$\Sigma^- \rightarrow \pi^- + n.$$

Although two bodies do not come in contact in this process (unless we consider it in reverse), it has many features in common with collisions: (1) there is a clean distinction between "before the event" and "after the event," and (2) the laws of conservation of momentum and energy permit us to learn much about such processes by studying the "before" and "after" situations, even though we may know little about the force laws that operate during the "event" itself.

In studying collisions in this chapter our aim will we this: given the initial motions of the colliding particles, what can we learn about their final motions from the principles of conservation of momentum and energy, assuming that we know nothing about the forces acting during the collision?

## 10–2 Impulse and Momentum

Let us assume that Fig. 10–2 shows the magnitude of the force exerted on a body during a collision. We assume that the force has a constant direction. The collision begins at time $t_i$ and ends at time $t_f$, the force being zero before and after collision. From Eq. 9–12 we can write the change in momentum $d\mathbf{p}$ of a body in a time $dt$ during which a force $\mathbf{F}$ acts on it as

$$d\mathbf{p} = \mathbf{F} \, dt. \qquad (10\text{–}1)$$

We can find the change in momentum of the body during a collision by integrating over the time of collision, that is,

$$\mathbf{p}_f - \mathbf{p}_i = \int_{\mathbf{p}_i}^{\mathbf{p}_f} d\mathbf{p} = \int_{t_i}^{t_f} \mathbf{F} \, dt \qquad (10\text{–}2)$$

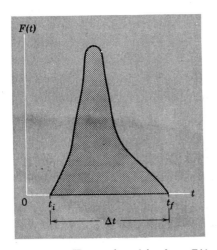

**Fig. 10–2** How an impulsive force $F(t)$ might vary with time during a collision starting at time $t_i$ and ending at $t_f$.

in which the subscripts $i$ ($= initial$) and $f$ ($= final$) refer to the times before and after the collision, respectively. The integral of a force over the time interval during which the force acts is called the *impulse* $\mathbf{J}$ of the force. Hence the change in momentum of a body acted on by an impulsive force is equal to the impulse. Both impulse and momentum are vectors and both have the same units and dimensions.

The impulsive force represented in Fig. 10–2 is assumed to have a constant direction.   The impulse of this force, $\int_{t_i}^{t_f} \mathbf{F}\, dt$, is represented in magnitude by the area under the force-time curve.*

## 10–3   Conservation of Momentum during Collisions

Consider now a collision between two particles, such as those of masses $m_1$ and $m_2$, shown in Fig. 10–3.   During the brief collision these particles exert large forces on one another.   At any instant $\mathbf{F}_1$ is the force exerted on particle 1 by particle 2 and $\mathbf{F}_2$ is the force exerted on particle 2 by particle 1.   By Newton's third law these forces at any instant are equal in magnitude but oppositely directed.

**Fig. 10–3** Two "particles" $m_1$ and $m_2$, in collision, experience equal and opposite forces along their line of centers, according to Newton's third law; $\mathbf{F}_2(t) \equiv -\mathbf{F}_1(t)$.

The change in momentum of particle 1 resulting from the collision is

$$\Delta \mathbf{p}_1 = \int_{t_i}^{t_f} \mathbf{F}_1\, dt = \overline{\mathbf{F}_1}\, \Delta t$$

in which $\overline{\mathbf{F}_1}$ is the average value of the force $\mathbf{F}_1$ during the time interval of the collision $\Delta t = t_f - t_i$.

The change in momentum of particle 2 resulting from the collision is

$$\Delta \mathbf{p}_2 = \int_{t_i}^{t_f} \mathbf{F}_2\, dt = \overline{\mathbf{F}_2}\, \Delta t$$

in which $\overline{\mathbf{F}_2}$ is the average value of the force $\mathbf{F}_2$ during the time interval of the collision $\Delta t = t_f - t_i$.

If no other forces act on the particles, then $\Delta \mathbf{p}_1$ and $\Delta \mathbf{p}_2$ give the total change in momentum for each particle.   But we have seen that at each instant $\mathbf{F}_1 = -\mathbf{F}_2$, so that $\overline{\mathbf{F}_1} = -\overline{\mathbf{F}_2}$, and therefore

$$\Delta \mathbf{p}_1 = -\Delta \mathbf{p}_2.$$

If we consider the two particles as an isolated system, the total momentum of the system is

$$\mathbf{P} = \mathbf{p}_1 + \mathbf{p}_2,$$

and the total *change* in momentum of the system as a result of the collision is zero, that is,

$$\Delta \mathbf{P} = \Delta \mathbf{p}_1 + \Delta \mathbf{p}_2 = 0.$$

---

* The impulse **J**, defined from Eq. 10–2, does not depend critically on the precise values of $t_i$ and $t_f$ as long as these times are far enough apart to include the crosshatched area of Fig. 10–2.   For reasons that will appear later we usually choose $t_i$ and $t_f$ with a separation that is *just large enough* to make a clean distinction between the "collision" and the "before and after intervals."

Hence, *if there are no external forces* the total momentum of the system is not changed by the collision. The impulsive forces acting during the collision are internal forces which have no effect on the total momentum of the system.

We have defined a collision as an interaction which occurs in a time $\Delta t$ that is negligible compared to the time during which we are observing the system. We can also characterize a collision as an event in which the external forces that may act on the system are negligible compared to the impulsive collision forces. When a bat strikes a baseball, a golf club strikes a golf ball, or one billiard ball strikes another, external forces act on the system. Gravity or friction exerts forces on these bodies, for example; these external forces may not be the same on each colliding body nor are they necessarily cancelled by other external forces. Even so it is quite safe to neglect these external forces during the collision and to assume momentum conservation provided, as is almost always true, that the external forces are negligible compared to the impulsive forces of collision. As a result the change in momentum of a particle during a collision

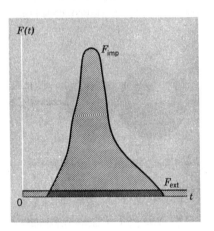

**Fig. 10–4** During a collision, the impulsive force $F_{imp}$ is generally much greater than any external forces $F_{ext}$, which may act on the system.

arising from an external force is negligible compared to the change in momentum of that particle arising from the impulsive collisional force (Fig. 10–4).

For example, when a bat strikes a baseball, the collision lasts only a small fraction of a second. Since the change in momentum is large and the time of collision is small, it follows from

$$\Delta \mathbf{p} = \bar{\mathbf{F}} \, \Delta t$$

that the average impulsive force $\bar{\mathbf{F}}$ is relatively large. Compared to this force, the external force of gravity is negligible. *During the collision* we can safely ignore this external force in determining the change in motion of the ball; the shorter the duration of the collision the more likely this is to be true.

In practice, therefore, *we can apply the principle of momentum conservation during collisions if the time of collision is small enough.* We can then say that the momentum of a system of particles just before the particles collide is equal to the momentum of the system just after the particles collide.

## 10–4    Collisions in One Dimension

We can always calculate the motions of bodies after collision from their motions before collision if we know the forces that act during the collision, and if we can solve the equations of motion. Often we do not know these forces. However, the principle of conservation of momentum must hold during the collision. We already know that the principle of conservation of total energy holds. Although we may not know the details of the interaction, we can use these principles in many cases to predict the results of the collision.

Collisions are usually classified according to whether or not *kinetic energy* is conserved in the collision. When kinetic energy is conserved, the collision is said to be *elastic*. Otherwise, the collision is said to be *inelastic*. Collisions between atomic, nuclear, and fundamental particles are sometimes elastic. These are, in fact, the only truly elastic collisions known. Collisions between gross bodies are always inelastic to some extent. We can often treat such collisions as approximately elastic, however, as, for example, collisions between ivory or glass balls. When two bodies stick together after collision, the collision is said to be *completely inelastic*. For example, the collision between a bullet and its target is completely inelastic when the bullet remains embedded in the target. The term completely inelastic does *not* mean that all the initial kinetic energy is lost; as we shall see, it means rather that the loss is as great as is consistent with momentum conservation.

Even if the forces of collision are not known, we can find the motions of the particles after collision from the motions before collision, provided the collision is completely inelastic, or, if the collision is elastic, provided the collision is a one-dimensional one. For a one-dimensional collision the relative motion after collision is along the same line as the relative motion before collision. We restrict ourselves to one-dimensional motion for the present.

Consider first an *elastic* one-dimensional collision. We can imagine two smooth nonrotating spheres moving initially along the line joining their centers, then colliding head-on and moving along the same straight line without rotation after collision (see Fig. 10–5). These bodies exert forces on each other during the collision that are along the initial line of motion, so that the final motion is also along this same line.

The masses of the spheres are $m_1$ and $m_2$, the (scalar) velocity components being $v_{1i}$ and $v_{2i}$ before collision and $v_{1f}$ and $v_{2f}$ after collision.* We take the positive direction of the momentum and velocity to be to the right. We assume, unless we specify otherwise, that the speeds of the colliding particles are low enough so that we need not use the relativistic

---

* The notation used is easy to interpret and to remember and reveals much information in a simple compact way. The number subscripts, such as 1 and 2, specify the particle and the letter subscripts, $i$ and $f$, indicate initial value (before the collision) and final value (after the collision), respectively.

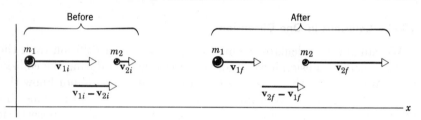

**Fig. 10–5** Two spheres before and after an elastic collision. The velocity, $v_{1i} - v_{2i}$, of $m_1$ relative to $m_2$ before collision is equal to the velocity, $v_{2f} - v_{1f}$, of $m_2$ relative to $m_1$ after collision.

expressions for momentum and kinetic energy. Then from conservation of momentum we obtain

$$m_1v_{1i} + m_2v_{2i} = m_1v_{1f} + m_2v_{2f}.$$

Because the collision is elastic, kinetic energy is conserved and we obtain

$$\tfrac{1}{2}m_1v_{1i}^2 + \tfrac{1}{2}m_2v_{2i}^2 = \tfrac{1}{2}m_1v_{1f}^2 + \tfrac{1}{2}m_2v_{2f}^2.$$

It is clear at once that, if we know the masses and the initial velocities, we can calculate the two final velocities $v_{1f}$ and $v_{2f}$ from these two equations.

The momentum equation can be written as

$$m_1(v_{1i} - v_{1f}) = m_2(v_{2f} - v_{2i}), \tag{10–3}$$

and the energy equation can be written as

$$m_1(v_{1i}^2 - v_{1f}^2) = m_2(v_{2f}^2 - v_{2i}^2). \tag{10–4}$$

Dividing Eq. 10–4 by Eq. 10–3, and assuming $v_{2f} \neq v_{2i}$ and $v_{1f} \neq v_{1i}$ (see Question 5), we obtain

$$v_{1i} + v_{1f} = v_{2f} + v_{2i}$$

and, after rearrangement,

$$v_{1i} - v_{2i} = v_{2f} - v_{1f} \tag{10–5}$$

This tells us that in an elastic one-dimensional collision, the relative velocity of approach before collision is equal to the relative velocity of separation after collision.

To find the velocity components $v_{1f}$ and $v_{2f}$ after collision from the velocity components $v_{1i}$ and $v_{2i}$ before collision, we can use any two of the three previous numbered equations. Thus from Eq. 10–5

$$v_{2f} = v_{1i} + v_{1f} - v_{2i}.$$

Inserting this into Eq. 10–3 and solving for $v_{1f}$, we find that

$$v_{1f} = \left(\frac{m_1 - m_2}{m_1 + m_2}\right)v_{1i} + \left(\frac{2m_2}{m_1 + m_2}\right)v_{2i}.$$

Likewise, inserting $v_{1f} = v_{2f} + v_{2i} - v_{1i}$ (from Eq. 10–5) into Eq. 10–3 and solving for $v_{2f}$, we obtain

$$v_{2f} = \left(\frac{2m_1}{m_1 + m_2}\right)v_{1i} + \left(\frac{m_2 - m_1}{m_1 + m_2}\right)v_{2i}.$$

There are several cases of special interest.  For example, when the colliding particles have the same mass, $m_1$ equals $m_2$ so that the two previous equations become simply

$$v_{1f} = v_{2i} \quad \text{and} \quad v_{2f} = v_{1i}.$$

That is, in a one-dimensional elastic collision of two particles of equal mass, the particles simply exchange velocities during collision.

Another case of interest is that in which one particle $m_2$ is initially at rest.  Then $v_{2i}$ equals zero and

$$v_{1f} = \left(\frac{m_1 - m_2}{m_1 + m_2}\right)v_{1i}, \qquad v_{2f} = \left(\frac{2m_1}{m_1 + m_2}\right)v_{1i}.$$

Of course, if $m_1 = m_2$ also, then $v_{1f} = 0$ and $v_{2f} = v_{1i}$ as we expect.  The first particle is "stopped cold" and the second one "takes off" with the velocity the first one originally had.  If, however, $m_2$ is very much greater than $m_1$, we obtain

$$v_{1f} \cong -v_{1i} \quad \text{and} \quad v_{2f} \cong 0.$$

That is, when a light particle collides with a very much more massive particle at rest, the velocity of the light particle is approximately reversed and the massive particle remains approximately at rest.  For example, suppose that we drop a ball vertically onto a horizontal surface attached to the earth.  This is in effect a collision between the ball and the earth.  If the collision is elastic, the ball will rebound with a reversed velocity and will reach the same height from which it fell.

If, finally, $m_2$ is very much smaller than $m_1$, we obtain

$$v_{1f} \cong v_{1i} \qquad v_{2f} \cong 2v_{1i}.$$

This means that the velocity of the massive incident particle is virtually unchanged by the collision with the light stationary particle, but that the light particle rebounds with approximately twice the velocity of the incident particle.  The motion of a bowling ball is hardly affected by collision with an inflated beach ball of the same size, but the beach ball bounces away quickly.

Neutrons produced in a reactor from the fission of uranium atoms move very fast and must be slowed down if they are to produce more fissions.  Assuming that they make elastic collisions with the nuclei at rest, what material should be picked to moderate the neutrons in the reactor?  We can answer this from the considerations just discussed.  If the stationary targets were massive nuclei, like lead, the neutrons would simply bounce back with practically the same speed they had initially.  If the stationary targets were very much lighter than the neutrons, like electrons, the neutrons would move on with practically the same velocity they had initially. However, if the stationary targets are particles of nearly the same mass, the neutrons will be brought almost to rest in a (head-on) collision with them. Hence, hydrogen, whose nucleus (proton) has nearly the same mass as a neutron, should be most effective. Other considerations affect the choice of a moderator for neutrons, but momentum and energy considerations alone limit the choice to the lighter elements.

If a collision is *inelastic* then, by definition, the kinetic energy is not conserved. The final kinetic energy may be less than the initial value, the difference being ultimately converted to heat or to potential energy of deformation in the collision, for example; or the final kinetic energy may exceed the initial value, as when potential energy is released in the collision. In any case, the conservation of momentum still holds, as does the conservation of *total* energy.

Let us consider finally a *completely inelastic* collision. The two particles stick together after collision, so that there will be a final common velocity $\mathbf{v}_f$. It is not necessary to restrict the discussion to one-dimensional motion. Using only the conservation of momentum principle, we find

$$m_1\mathbf{v}_{1i} + m_2\mathbf{v}_{2i} = (m_1 + m_2)\mathbf{v}_f. \qquad (10\text{-}6)$$

This determines $\mathbf{v}_f$ when $\mathbf{v}_{1i}$ and $\mathbf{v}_{2i}$ are known.

▶ **Example 1.** A baseball weighing 0.35 lb is struck by a bat while it is in horizontal flight with a speed of 90 ft/sec. After leaving the bat the ball travels with a speed of 110 ft/sec in a direction opposite to its original motion. Determine the impulse of the collision.

We cannot calculate the impulse from the definition $\mathbf{J} = \int \mathbf{F}\, dt$ because we do not know the force exerted on the ball as a function of time. However, we have seen (Eq. 10-2) that the change in momentum of a particle acted on by an impulsive force is equal to the impulse. Hence

$$\mathbf{J} = \text{change in momentum} = \mathbf{p}_f - \mathbf{p}_i$$

$$= m\mathbf{v}_f - m\mathbf{v}_i = \left(\frac{W}{g}\right)(\mathbf{v}_f - \mathbf{v}_i).$$

Assuming arbitrarily that the direction of $\mathbf{v}_i$ is positive, the impulse is then

$$J = \left(\frac{0.35 \text{ lb}}{32 \text{ ft/sec}_2}\right)(-110 \text{ ft/sec} - 90 \text{ ft/sec}) = -2.2 \text{ lb-sec}.$$

The minus sign shows that the direction of the impulse acting on the ball is opposite that of the original velocity of the ball.

We cannot determine the force of the collision from the data we are given. Actually, any force whose impulse is $-2.2$ lb-sec will produce the same change in momentum. For example, if the bat and ball were in contact for 0.0010 sec, the average force during this time would be

$$\bar{F} = \frac{\Delta p}{\Delta t} = \frac{-2.2 \text{ lb-sec}}{0.0010 \text{ sec}} = -2200 \text{ lb}.$$

For a shorter contact time the average force would be greater. The actual force would have a maximum value greater than this average value.

How far would gravity cause the baseball to fall during its collision time?

**Example 2.** (a) By what fraction is the kinetic energy of a neutron (mass $m_1$) decreased in a head-on elastic collision with an atomic nucleus (mass $m_2$) initially at rest?

The initial kinetic energy of the neutron $K_i$ is $\frac{1}{2}m_1 v_{1i}^2$. Its final kinetic energy $K_f$ is $\frac{1}{2}m_1 v_{1f}^2$. The fractional decrease in kinetic energy is

$$\frac{K_i - K_f}{K_i} = \frac{v_{1i}^2 - v_{1f}^2}{v_{1i}^2} = 1 - \frac{v_{1f}^2}{v_{1i}^2}.$$

But, for such a collision,

$$v_{1f} = \left(\frac{m_1 - m_2}{m_1 + m_2}\right) v_{1i},$$

so that

$$\frac{K_i - K_f}{K_i} = 1 - \left(\frac{m_1 - m_2}{m_1 + m_2}\right)^2 = \frac{4 m_1 m_2}{(m_1 + m_2)^2}.$$

(b) Find the fractional decrease in the kinetic energy of a neutron when it collides in this way with a lead nucleus, a carbon nucleus, and a hydrogen nucleus. The ratio of nuclear mass to neutron mass $(= m_2/m_1)$ is 206 for lead, 12 for carbon, and 1 for hydrogen.

For lead, $m_2 = 206 m_1$,

$$\frac{K_i - K_f}{K_i} = \frac{4 \times 206}{(207)^2} = 0.02 \quad \text{or} \quad 2\%.$$

For carbon, $m_2 = 12 m_1$,

$$\frac{K_i - K_f}{K_i} = \frac{4 \times 12}{(13)^2} = 0.28 \quad \text{or} \quad 28\%.$$

For hydrogen, $m_2 = m_1$,

$$\frac{K_i - K_f}{K_i} = \frac{4 \times 1}{(2)^2} = 1 \quad \text{or} \quad 100\%.$$

These results explain why paraffin, which is rich in hydrogen, is far more effective in slowing down neutrons than is lead.

**Example 3.** *The Ballistic Pendulum.* The ballistic pendulum is used to measure bullet speeds. The pendulum is a large wooden block of mass $M$ hanging vertically by two cords. A bullet of mass $m$, traveling with a horizontal speed $v_i$, strikes the pendulum and remains embedded in it (Fig. 10–6). If the collision time (the time required for the bullet to come to rest with respect to the block) is very small compared to the time of swing of the pendulum, the supporting cords remain approximately vertical during the collision. Therefore, no external horizontal force acts on the system (bullet + pendulum) during collision, and the horizontal component of momentum is conserved. The speed of the system after collision $v_f$ is much less than that of the bullet before collision. This final speed can be easily determined, so that the original speed of the bullet can be calculated from momentum conservation.

**Fig. 10–6** Example 3. A ballistic pendulum consisting of a large wooden block of mass $M$ suspended by cords. When a bullet of mass $m$ and velocity $v_i$ is fired into it, the block swings, rising a maximum distance $y$.

The initial momentum of the system is that of the bullet $mv_i$, and the momentum of the system just after collision is $(m + M)v_f$, so that

$$mv_i = (m + M)v_f.$$

After the collision is over, the pendulum and bullet swing up to a maximum height $y$, where the kinetic energy left after impact is converted into gravitational potential energy. Then, using the conservation of mechanical energy *for this part of the motion*, we obtain

$$\tfrac{1}{2}(m + M)v_f{}^2 = (m + M)gy.$$

Solving these two equations for $v_i$, we obtain

$$v_i = \frac{m + M}{m} \sqrt{2gy}.$$

Hence, we can find the initial speed of the bullet by measuring $m$, $M$, and $y$.

The kinetic energy of the bullet initially is $\tfrac{1}{2}mv_i{}^2$ and the kinetic energy of the system (bullet + pendulum) just after collision is $\tfrac{1}{2}(m + M)v_f{}^2$. The ratio is

$$\frac{\tfrac{1}{2}(m + M)v_f{}^2}{\tfrac{1}{2}mv_i{}^2} = \frac{m}{m + M}.$$

For example, if the bullet has a mass $m = 5$ gm and the block has a mass $M = 2000$ gm, only about one-fourth of 1% of the original kinetic energy remains; over 99% is converted to other forms of energy, such as heat. ◄

The velocity of the center of mass of two particles is not changed by their collision, for the collision does not change the total momentum of the system of two particles, only the distribution of momentum between the two particles. The momentum of the system can be written (Eq. 9–15) as $\mathbf{P} = (m_1 + m_2)\mathbf{v}_{cm}$. If no external forces act on the system, then $\mathbf{P}$ is constant before and after the collision, and the center of mass moves with uniform velocity throughout.

If we choose a reference frame attached to the center of mass, then in this center-of-mass reference frame, $\mathbf{v}_{cm} = 0$ and $\mathbf{P} = 0$. There is a great simplicity and symmetry in describing collisions with respect to the center of mass, and it is customary to do so in nuclear physics.  For whether collisions are elastic or inelastic, momentum is conserved, and in the center of mass reference frame the total momentum is zero.  These results hold in two and three dimensions as well as in one because momentum is a vector quantity.

As an example, consider a head-on elastic collision between two particles $m_1$ and $m_2$.  Let $m_2$ equal $3m_1$ and let $m_2$ be at rest, so that $v_{2i}$ equals zero in the laboratory reference frame.  The total momentum of the two particles is just that of the incident particle $m_1 v_{1i}$, so that

$$m_1 v_{1i} = (m_1 + m_2) v_{cm}$$

or

$$v_{cm} = \left( \frac{m_1}{m_1 + m_2} \right) v_{1i} = \tfrac{1}{4} v_{1i}.$$

After the collision, $m_1$ has a velocity $v_{1f} = -\tfrac{1}{2} v_{1i}$ and $m_2$ has a velocity $v_{2f} = \tfrac{1}{2} v_{1i}$. The total momentum of the two particles $(m_1 v_{1f} + m_2 v_{2f})$ is the same as before the collision, and the motion of the center of mass is unchanged (check this).   In Fig. 10–7a we show a series of "snapshots" of the collision taken at equal time intervals as seen in the laboratory reference frame.   In Fig. 10–7b we show the same situation as seen in the center-of-mass reference frame, where $v_{cm}$ is zero.   Notice the symmetry of the particles' motions when described in this way.   The particle coming from the left has a speed $\tfrac{3}{4} v_{1i}$ with respect to the center of mass (where $v_{1i}$ is the speed of $m_1$ in the laboratory frame) and recedes with this same speed. The particle coming from the right has a speed $\tfrac{1}{4} v_{1i}$ with respect to the center of mass and recedes with this same speed.

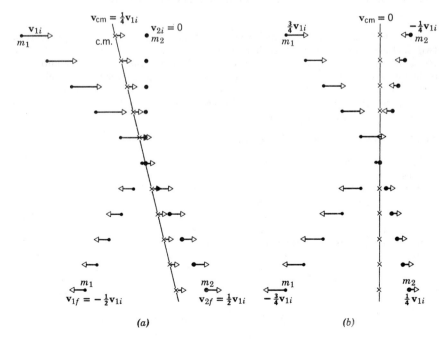

(a)    (b)

**Fig. 10–7**  (a) An elastic collision in the laboratory reference frame.  (b) The same elastic collision in the center-of-mass reference frame.

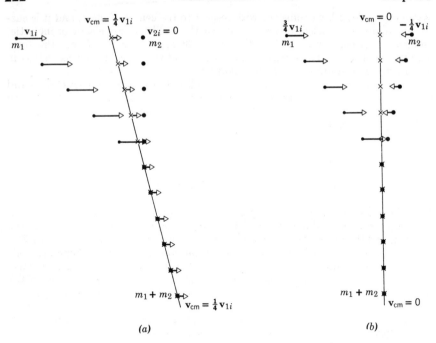

**Fig. 10–8** (a) A completely inelastic collision in the laboratory reference frame. (b) The same completely inelastic collision in the center-of-mass reference frame. In each case the motion before collision is the same as that of Fig. 10–7.

If the collision is completely inelastic, the motion after collision is simply that of two particles moving along together at the center of mass. In Figs. 10–8a and 10–8b we show how the collision of Fig. 10–7, now assumed to be completely inelastic, would be described in the laboratory and the center-of-mass reference frames, respectively. These figures are exactly like the previous ones until the collision occurs; after the collision, however, the motion of the center of mass describes that of the entire system.

## 10–5   The "True" Measure of a Force

The distinction between kinetic energy and momentum and the relationship of these concepts to force were not clearly understood until late in the eighteenth century. Scientists argued whether kinetic energy or momentum was the "true" measure of the effect of a force on a body. Descartes argued that when bodies interact, all that can happen is the transfer of momentum from one body to another, for the total momentum of the universe remains constant; hence the only "true" measure of a force is the change in momentum it produces in a given time. Leibnitz attacked this view and argued that the "true" measure of a force is the change it produces in kinetic energy (called by him *vis viva* or living force, taken to be twice what we now call kinetic energy).

In his treatise on mechanics (1743), D'Alembert dismissed the argument as being pointless and arising from a confusion of terminology. The cumulative effect of a force can be measured by its integrated effect over *time*, $\int F \, dt$, which produces a change in momentum, *or* by its integrated effect over *space*, $\int F \, dx$, which produces a change in kinetic energy. Both concepts are useful and valid, although different. Which one we use depends on what we are interested in or what is more convenient.   As our present study of collisions illustrates, we frequently use both concepts in the same problem.

A more modern view is to look for quantities of the motion that are invariant, rather than focusing on the concept of force.   The question as to whether the energy or the momentum is the "real" quantity of motion becomes pointless for there is no unique "quantity of motion."   Instead, *both* energy *and* momentum may be regarded as invariant quantities of the motion in that for an isolated system the total of each of these quantities, summed up over all parts of the system, remains constant with time.   There may be an exchange of energy, and of momentum, between different parts of an isolated system, but the total of each quantity is conserved.

## 10–6   Collisions in Two and Three Dimensions

In two or three dimensions (except for a completely inelastic collision) the conservation laws alone cannot tell us the motion of particles after a collision if we know the motion before the collision.   For example, for a two-dimensional elastic collision, which is the simplest case, we have four unknowns, namely the two components of velocity for each of two particles after collision; but we have only three known relations between them, one for the conservation of kinetic energy and a conservation of momentum relation for each of the two dimensions.   Hence we need more information than just the initial conditions.   When we do not know the actual forces of interaction, as is often the case, the additional information must be obtained from experiment.   It is simplest to specify the angle of recoil of one of the colliding particles.

Let us consider what happens when one particle is projected at a target particle which is at rest.   This case is not as restrictive as it may seem, for we can always pick our reference frame to be one in which the target particle is at rest before the collision.   Much experimental work in nuclear physics involves projecting nuclear particles at a target which is stationary in the laboratory reference frame.   In such collisions, because of momentum conservation, the motion is in a plane determined by the lines of recoil of the colliding particles.   The initial motion need not be along the line joining the centers of the two particles.   The force of interaction may be electromagnetic (in which we include "contact" forces; see page 120), gravitational, or nuclear.   The particles need not "touch"; strong forces, which act at relatively close distances of approach and for a time short compared to the observation time, deflect the particles from their initial courses.

A typical situation is shown in Fig. 10–9.   The distance $b$ between the initial line of motion and a line parallel to it through the center of the target particle is called the *impact parameter*.   This is a measure of the directness of the collision, $b = 0$, corresponding to a head-on collision. The direction of motion of the incident particle $m_1$ after collision makes an angle $\theta_1$ with the initial direction, and the target projectile $m_2$, initially at rest, moves in a direction after collision making an angle $\theta_2$ with the initial direction of the incident projectile.   Applying the conservation of momentum, which is a vector relation, we obtain two scalar equations; for

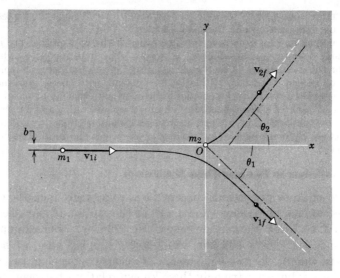

**Fig. 10–9** Two particles, $m_1$ and $m_2$, undergoing a collision. The open circles indicate their positions before collision, the shaded ones after collision. Initially $m_2$ is at rest. The impact parameter $b$ is the distance by which the collision misses being head-on.

the $x$-component of motion we have

$$m_1 v_{1i} = m_1 v_{1f} \cos \theta_1 + m_2 v_{2f} \cos \theta_2,$$

and for the $y$-component

$$0 = m_1 v_{1f} \sin \theta_1 - m_2 v_{2f} \sin \theta_2.$$

Let us now assume that the collision is *elastic*. Here the conservation of kinetic energy applies and we obtain a third equation,

$$\tfrac{1}{2} m_1 v_{1i}^2 = \tfrac{1}{2} m_1 v_{1f}^2 + \tfrac{1}{2} m_2 v_{2f}^2.$$

If we know the initial conditions ($m_1$, $m_2$, and $v_{1i}$), we are left with four unknowns ($v_{1f}$, $v_{2f}$, $\theta_1$, and $\theta_2$) but only three equations relating them. We can determine the motion after collision only if we specify a value for one of these quantities, such as $\theta_1$.

▶ **Example 4.** A gas molecule having a speed of 300 meters/sec collides elastically with another molecule of the same mass which is initially at rest. After the collision the first molecule moves at an angle of 30° to its initial direction. Find the speed of each molecule after collision and the angle made with the incident direction by the recoiling target molecule.

This example corresponds exactly to the situation just discussed, with $m_1 = m_2$, $v_{1i} = 300$ meters/sec, and $\theta_1 = 30°$. Setting $m_1$ equal to $m_2$, we have the relations

$$v_{1i} = v_{1f} \cos \theta_1 + v_{2f} \cos \theta_2,$$

$$v_{1f} \sin \theta_1 = v_{2f} \sin \theta_2,$$

and

$$v_{1i}^2 = v_{1f}^2 + v_{2f}^2.$$

We must solve for $v_{1f}$, $v_{2f}$, and $\theta_2$. To do this we square the first equation (rewriting it as $v_{1i} - v_{1f} \cos \theta_1 = v_{2f} \cos \theta_2$), and add this to the square of the second equation (noting that $\sin^2 \theta + \cos^2 \theta = 1$); we obtain

$$v_{1i}{}^2 + v_{1f}{}^2 - 2v_{1i}v_{1f} \cos \theta_1 = v_{2f}{}^2.$$

Combining this with the third equation, we obtain

$$2v_{1i}{}^2 = 2v_{1i}v_{1f} \cos \theta_1$$

or (since $v_{1i} \neq 0$)

$$v_{1f} = v_{1i} \cos \theta_1 = (300 \text{ meters/sec})(\cos 30°)$$

or

$$v_{1f} = 260 \text{ meters/sec}.$$

From the third equation

$$v_{2f}{}^2 = v_{1i}{}^2 - v_{1f}{}^2 = (300 \text{ meters/sec})^2 - (260 \text{ meters/sec})^2,$$

or

$$v_{2f} = 150 \text{ meters/sec}.$$

Finally, from the second equation

$$\sin \theta_2 = (v_{1f}/v_{2f}) \sin \theta_1$$

$$= (260/150)(\sin 30°) = 0.866$$

or

$$\theta_2 = 60°.$$

The two molecules move apart at right angles ($\theta_1 + \theta_2 = 90°$ in Fig. 10–9).

The student should be able to show that in an elastic collision between particles of equal mass, one of which is initially at rest, the recoiling particles always move off at right angles to one another. ◀

In Fig. 10–10, we show photographs of four elastic nuclear collisions that take place in a Wilson cloud chamber.* The tracks of the particles are made visible by the trail of droplets left in their wake. In each case the incident particle is an $\alpha$-particle ($He^4$) and the target nucleus is essentially at rest before collision. Notice that as the target mass increases, the angle between the recoiling particles increases (see Problem 26). In case (b) where the target is also an $\alpha$-particle, stereoscopic photos show that the recoiling particles move off at right angles; the angle is not quite a right angle in the figure because the particles do not lie in the plane of the figure.

Figure 10–11 shows a series of four successive elastic collisions between protons caused when a high energy proton enters a bubble chamber† filled

---

* In 1927, the English physicist, C. T. R. Wilson, received the Nobel prize for inventing the cloud chamber; his investigations started along an entirely different line, namely, an attempt to produce in the laboratory a certain atmospheric phenomenon observed on the mountain Ben Nevis in Scotland.

† In 1960, the American physicist, Donald Glaser, received the Nobel prize for inventing the bubble chamber; it is said that the concept occurred to him while watching bubbles form in a glass of beer.

with liquid hydrogen, which supplies the target protons. The tracks of the particles are made visible in this case by the trail of bubbles left in their wake. Since the interacting particles are of equal mass and the collisions are elastic, the particles recoil at right angles to each other; this is apparent when the tracks of Fig. 10–11a are viewed stereoscopically.

**Fig. 10–10** Photographs of trajectories of particles undergoing collisions in a cloud chamber, a device that makes these paths visible. The chamber contains saturated water vapor. If the vapor is slightly compressed and then allowed to expand quickly, the water vapor will condense in droplets along the trajectory. The incident particle in all four cases is a helium nucleus (He$^4$, or $\alpha$). In (a) the target is a hydrogen nucleus (H$^1$, or $p$). The other tracks are similar, except that in (b) the target is another He$^4$ nucleus, whereas in (c) and (d) the targets are fluorine and chlorine nuclei respectively. In general, the particles do not lie in the plane of the photograph. Stereoscopic photos are required for a complete analysis.

**Fig. 10–11**   (a) Four proton-proton collisions in a 10″-diameter bubble chamber.   The original high-energy proton entered from the upper right.   The spiral tracks are low energy electrons.   The other tracks passing through the chamber are mesons of various kinds.   This photo may be viewed stereoscopically using a device supplied with the explanatory booklet Introduction to the Detection of Nuclear Particles in a Bubble Chamber, Ealing Press, 1964 (courtesy Lawrence Radiation Laboratory).   Such stereoscopic viewing shows that the angle between the outgoing tracks in each case is 90°.   This is not apparent in the figure because the tracks do not lie in the plane of the figure.   (b) A schematic representation of the proton tracks in a.

## 10–7   Cross Section

Although we have introduced the concept of the impact parameter $b$ to describe collisions (see Fig. 10–9), it must be clear that, when we deal with particles of atomic or subatomic dimensions, we cannot define the track of the incident particle or the location of the target particle precisely enough.   In practice, as when we bombard a thin target foil with a beam of deuterons from a cyclotron, we must deal in a statistical way with a large number of collisions between deuterons and the nuclei in the target; the impact parameters for individual collisions cannot be determined.

The situation is much the same as if we were firing a machine gun at random (in the dark, say) at the side of a distant barn of area $A$ on which someone had hung a number of small dinner plates, each of area $\sigma$, in random (but not overlapping) positions.   If the number of plates is $q$ and if the rate at which bullets strike the barn is $R_0$, what is the rate $R$ at which plates are broken?   It is, on the basis of the random character of the events,

$$R = R_0(\sigma q/A), \qquad (10\text{–}7a)$$

where $\sigma q$ is the total area of all the plates.   We could, in fact, use this relation to measure $\sigma$, the geometrical area of a single plate.   Solving for $\sigma$ yields

$$\sigma = RA/R_0 q \qquad (10\text{–}7b)$$

which permits us to find $\sigma$ from measured values of $R$, $A$, $R_0$, and $q$. We may call $\sigma$ the *cross section* for the event consisting of the impact of a bullet on a plate.

Let us now consider a more restricted class of event, namely the impact of a bullet on a plate causing the plate to break into (say) exactly five pieces. The rate $R_5$ at which events of this kind occur is much less than the rate $R$ at which the events described above occur. We may assign a *cross section* $\sigma_5$ to these restricted events and may measure it, by analogy with Eq. 10–7, from

$$\sigma_5 = R_5 A / R_0 q. \tag{10–8}$$

We can consider other ways of breaking plates such as breaking into thirteen pieces, breaking so that one fragment has an area equal to half the plate or more, breaking so that one fragment flies vertically upward, etc. Each of these events can be assigned its own cross section $\sigma_x$ by measuring the rate $R_x$ at which the events occur. *None of these cross sections necessarily has anything to do with the geometrical area of the plate; all are measures of the probability of occurrence of the events to which they are assigned.* Cross sections are important because they are identified with single events and are independent of the details of particular experimental setups. In Eq. 10–8, for example, we would find the same value for $\sigma_5$ no matter how large the barn ($A$), how many plates ($q$), or how rapid the rate of fire of the machine gun ($R_0$); the measured value of $R_5$ would always be such as to yield the same measured value for $\sigma_5$.

Similarly, in nuclear physics we often bombard targets with nuclear projectiles, measure the rate at which events of a selected type occur, and assign a cross section to those events. For example, let us bombard a thin gold foil ($Au^{197}$) with deuterons ($H^2$, or $d$) whose energy is, say, 30 Mev. Many events can occur, among them (1) elastic scattering of the deuteron into the forward hemisphere, (2) elastic scattering of the deuteron into the backward hemisphere, (3) inelastic scattering of the deuteron between the angles of 30° and 60° with the direction of the incident beam, (4) the nuclear reaction $d + Au^{197} \rightarrow p + Au^{198}$, and (5) the nuclear reaction $d + Au^{197} \rightarrow n + Hg^{198}$, in which $n$ represents a neutron. Each of these events (and many others that could be written down) has its own cross section $\sigma_x$ which allows us to calculate the rate $R_x$ at which these events occur if we know the details of the experimental arrangement. The ultimate goal of all the experiments is to understand the nature of nuclear forces.

Let the area of the foil exposed to the beam be $A$ and the thickness of the foil be $x$. If there are $n$ target particles per unit volume in the foil, the total number of available target particles is $nAx$. If the *effective area* (that is, the cross section) for the event we are concerned with is $\sigma_x$, the total *effective area* of all the nuclei is $nAx\sigma_x$. If $R_0$ is the rate at which projectiles strike the target and $R_x$ is the rate at which the events in which we are interested occur, we have, because of the random nature of the

events (see Eq. 10-7a),

$$\frac{R_x}{R_0} = \frac{(nAx\sigma_x)}{A}$$

or

$$R_x = R_0 nx\sigma_x. \tag{10-9}$$

Thus we can measure $\sigma_x$ for the event by measuring $R_x$, $R_0$, $n$, and $x$ and substituting into Eq. 10-9. Cross sections are commonly expressed in *barns* or submultiples thereof; one barn $= 10^{-28}$ meter$^2$.

Cross sections almost always depend on the energy of the incident particle, often exhibiting sharp peaks as the energy is varied. This simply means that at certain rather precisely defined characteristic energies the reaction is much more likely to "go" than at others. In much the same way a steel plate will vibrate with large amplitude at a series of rather precisely defined characteristic frequencies. We shall study such "resonances" in Chapter 20 and elsewhere.

Figure 10-12 shows one of the thousands of cross section curves that have been measured for various atomic and nuclear process. Let a highly collimated beam of neutrons of kinetic energy $K$ fall on a thin foil of cadmium. The process to which the cross section $\sigma$ in Fig. 10-12 refers is any process (absorption, elastic scattering, or inelastic scattering) that

**Fig. 10-12** The cross section as a function of energy for processes that remove neutrons from a collimated beam as they pass through cadmium. Note that both scales are logarithmic.

results in the removal of a neutron from the collimated beam. The numbers above the various peaks show the particular isotope responsible for that peak; this can be learned from other experiments using foils made of the separated isotopes. The strong peak labeled "113" that occurs at 0.17 electron volts is caused by the reaction

$$Cd^{113} + n \rightarrow Cd^{114} + \gamma$$

in which $\gamma$ represents a gamma ray. This reaction, which has a peak cross section of 7600 barns, is responsible for the very large absorbing power of cadmium for slow neutrons. Note that both scales in Fig. 10–12 are logarithmic.

▶ **Example 5.** (a) About 1910, Geiger and Marsden, working under Lord Rutherford at Manchester University, performed a series of classic experiments that established the fact that atoms consisted of a small nucleus surrounded by a cloud of electrons rather than a sphere of distributed positive and negative charges, as Thomson had suggested earlier.

This experiment was in essence that shown in Fig. 10–13. Here $\alpha$-particles from a polonium source are allowed to strike a gold foil $4.0 \times 10^{-7}$ meter thick. It is found that although most of the $\alpha$-particles pass through the foil (forward scattering), about 1 in $6.17 \times 10^6$ are scattered backward, that is, are deflected through an angle greater than 90°. The number of gold atoms per unit volume in the foil is $5.9 \times 10^{28}$/meter³. What is the scattering cross section in barns for backward scattering (1 barn = $10^{-28}$ meter²)?

From

$$nx\sigma = \text{fraction scattered backward}$$

we have

$$(5.9 \times 10^{28}/\text{meter}^3)(4.0 \times 10^{-7} \text{ meter})\sigma = 1/(6.17 \times 10^6)$$

or

$$\sigma = 6.9 \times 10^{-28} \text{ meter}^2 = 6.9 \text{ barns.}$$

This is the cross section for backward scattering.

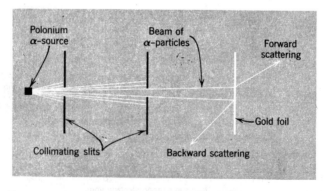

**Fig. 10–13** Example 5. $\alpha$-particles stream from a polonium source and a beam is formed by collimating slits. Some of the $\alpha$-particles are scattered backward by the gold foil target; the rest pass through the foil.

(b) Rutherford reasoned that the backward scattering could not be caused by electrons in the atom; the $\alpha$-particles are so much more massive than the electrons that they would hardly be deflected at all by them, let alone be scattered backward. He then suggested the nuclear model of the atom, attributing the scattering to collisions between $\alpha$-particles and the massive positive core of the atom, the nucleus.

Assuming that the cross section for backward scattering is approximately equal to the area offered by a gold nucleus for direct collisions, estimate the *effective* size of a gold nucleus.

If the *effective* radius of the gold nucleus is taken to be $r$, we have

$$\sigma = \pi r^2,$$

$$r^2 = \sigma/\pi = 6.9 \times 10^{-28} \text{ meter}^2/\pi,$$

or
$$r = 1.5 \times 10^{-14} \text{ meter}.$$

This is the approximate radius of a gold *nucleus* which compares with the value of about $1.5 \times 10^{-10}$ meter for the gold *atom*. Hence the massive nucleus is concentrated in a very small region of the atom (about 1 part in $10^{12}$ by volume). ◀

## 10–8   Reactions and Decay Processes

We stated in Section 10–1 that reactions and radioactive decay processes, for atoms, nuclei, and elementary particles, can be treated by the same methods used in collision studies, namely: We can apply the principles of conservation of linear momentum and energy to the (well-defined) periods "before the event" and "after the event." For these processes we must use the conservation of *total* energy because kinetic energy is *not* conserved. In this section we only consider examples in which the speeds of the particles are negligible with respect to the speed of light. This means that we may use the classical expressions for momentum and energy and need not use the relativistic expressions.

▶ **Example 6.** *Nuclear Reactions.* A thin film containing a fluorine ($F^{19}$) compound is bombarded by a beam of protons ($p$) which have been accelerated to an energy of 1.85 Mev (million electron volts; 1 Mev = $1.60 \times 10^{-13}$ joule) in a Van de Graaff accelerator. Some of the protons interact with the fluorine nuclei to produce the following nuclear reaction:

$$F^{19} + p \rightarrow O^{16} + \alpha$$

It is observed that the $\alpha$-particles (which are helium nuclei) that emerge at *right angles* to the incident proton beam (see Fig. 10–14) have speeds of $1.95 \times 10^7$ meters/sec. What can you learn about the reaction by applying the laws of conservation of linear momentum and of total energy? The masses involved are, to a precision good enough for our purposes,

$$m_p = 1.01 \text{ amu} \qquad m_O = 16.0 \text{ amu}$$

$$m_F = 19.0 \text{ amu} \qquad m_\alpha = 4.00 \text{ amu},$$

in which 1 amu (*atomic mass unit*) = $1.66 \times 10^{-27}$ kg.

The $x$- and $y$-components of linear momentum are conserved, which means that they have the same values before and after the reaction. In the laboratory refer-

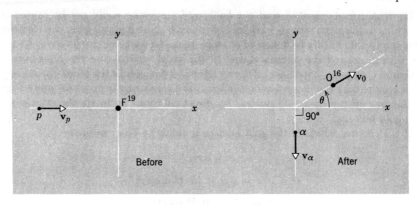

**Fig. 10–14**   The nuclear reaction $p + F^{19} \to \alpha + O^{16}$, showing the situation before and after the event in the laboratory reference frame.

ence frame of Fig. 10–14, then

$$m_p v_p = m_O v_O \cos \theta \qquad \text{(x-component)} \qquad (10\text{–}10)$$

and

$$0 = m_\alpha v_\alpha - m_O v_O \sin \theta \qquad \text{(y-component)} \qquad (10\text{–}11)$$

For the conservation of total energy we write

$$Q + \tfrac{1}{2} m_p v_p{}^2 = \tfrac{1}{2} m_O v_O{}^2 + \tfrac{1}{2} m_\alpha v_\alpha{}^2 \qquad (10\text{–}12)$$

in which it is clear that $Q$ is the amount by which the kinetic energy of the system after the reaction exceeds the kinetic energy of the system before the reaction. Note that we have assumed that the particles are moving slowly enough so that we may use the classical expression for kinetic energy ($\tfrac{1}{2} m v^2$) rather than the relativistic one ($m_0 c^2 \sqrt{1 - v^2/c^2}$).   If $Q$ is positive, kinetic energy must be generated by the reaction.

The energy represented by $Q$ can only come from differences in the rest energies of the particles before or after the reaction, according to Einstein's well-known relation $E = \Delta m c^2$ (see Section 8–9).   Thus (if $Q$ is positive) we expect that the rest mass of the system after the reaction would be slightly less than its rest mass before the reaction and that $Q$ would indeed be given by the Einstein relation

$$Q = \Delta m c^2$$

$$= [(m_p + m_F) - (m_\alpha + m_O)] c^2. \qquad (10\text{–}13)$$

Note that Eqs. 10–12 and 10–13 are independent relations for $Q$, being connected through Einstein's mass-energy relation.

The three conservation equations contain just three unknowns, $v_O$, $\theta$, and $Q$. To find $Q$ from them let us first eliminate $\theta$ between the first two equations by squaring and adding (recalling that $\cos^2 \theta + \sin^2 \theta = 1$).   We obtain

$$m_p{}^2 v_p{}^2 + m_\alpha{}^2 v_\alpha{}^2 = m_O{}^2 v_O{}^2.$$

We can now eliminate $v_O$ between this relation and Eq. 10–12.   The student can show that, after a little rearrangement, we obtain

$$Q = K_\alpha (1 + m_\alpha/m_O) - K_p (1 - m_p/m_O). \qquad (10\text{–}14)$$

From the data given we know that $K_p(= \frac{1}{2}m_p v_p{}^2) = 1.85$ Mev and

$$K_\alpha = \frac{1}{2}m_\alpha v_\alpha{}^2$$

$$= \frac{1}{2}(4.00 \text{ amu} \times 1.66 \times 10^{-27} \text{ kg/amu})(1.95 \times 10^7 \text{ meters/sec})^2$$

$$= (1.26 \times 10^{-12} \text{ joule})(1 \text{ Mev}/1.60 \times 10^{-13} \text{ joule})$$

$$= 7.88 \text{ Mev}.$$

We may now calculate $Q$ from Eq. 10–14 as

$$Q = (7.88 \text{ Mev})(1 + 4.00/16.0) - (1.85 \text{ Mev})(1 - 1.01/16.0) = 8.13 \text{ Mev}.$$

Thus, by using the principles of conservation of linear momentum and total energy, we can calculate $Q$ for the reaction without making any observations on the recoiling $O^{16}$ nucleus. If we want to know $v_O$ and $\theta$ for this nucleus we can easily calculate them from Eqs. 10–10 and 10–11.

The result $Q = 8.13$ Mev is an important bit of information about the reaction. From Eq. 10–13, which is a relation for $Q$ independent of Eq. 10–14, we can now calculate that the decrease in rest mass during the reaction is given by

$$\Delta m = Q/c^2$$

$$= (8.13 \text{ Mev} \times 1.60 \times 10^{-13} \text{ joule/Mev})/(3.00 \times 10^8 \text{ meters/sec})^2$$

$$= (1.44 \times 10^{-29} \text{ kg})(1 \text{ amu}/1.66 \times 10^{-27} \text{ kg})$$

$$= 0.00873 \text{ amu}.$$

We can verify this result by calculating $\Delta m \, [= (m_p + m_F) - (m_\alpha + m_O)]$ from very precise measurements of the four separate masses made in a mass spectrometer (see Problem 37). The excellent agreement that we get shows once again the essential validity of Einstein's mass-energy relationship. ◀

# QUESTIONS

**1.** Explain how conservation of momentum applies to a handball bouncing off a wall.

**2.** How can you reconcile the sailing of a sailboat into the wind with the conservation of momentum principle?

**3.** A sand glass is being weighed on a sensitive balance, first when sand is dropping in a steady stream from the upper to the lower part and then again after the upper part is empty. Are the two weights the same or not? Explain your answer.

**4.** The blades of a turbine are usually curved rather than flat in shape so that the fluid striking them follows a path resembling a u-turn. Convince yourself about the fluid's motion and explain the advantage of the curved shape over the flat one.

**5.** It is obvious from inspection of Eqs. 10–3 and 10–4 that a valid solution to the problem of finding the final velocities of two particles in a one-dimensional elastic collision is $v_{1f} = v_{1i}$ and $v_{2f} = v_{2i}$. What does this mean physically? Explain.

**6.** Consider a one-dimensional elastic collision between a given incoming body $A$ and a body $B$ initially at rest. How would you choose the mass of $B$, in comparison to the mass of $A$, in order that $B$ should recoil with $(a)$ the greatest speed, $(b)$ the greatest momentum, and $(c)$ the greatest kinetic energy?

**7.** In a two body collision *in the center-of-mass reference frame* the momenta of the particles are equal and opposite to one another both before and after the collision. Is the line of relative motion necessarily the same after collision as before? Under what conditions would the magnitudes of the velocities of the bodies increase? Decrease? Remain the same as a result of the collision?

**8.** When dealing with atoms, nuclei, or elementary particles, what does it mean to say that two such bodies "touch" during a collision?

**9.** When the forces of interaction between two particles have an infinite range, such as the mutual gravitational attraction between two bodies, can the cross section for "collision" be finite? Is it at all useful to regard this interaction as a collision?

**10.** Why does the computation of the radius of the gold nucleus in Example 5 give only an approximate answer?

**11.** Could we determine in principle the cross section for a collision by using only one bombarding particle and one target particle? In practice?

## PROBLEMS

**1.** A cue strikes a billiard ball, exerting an average force of 50 nt over a time of 10 milliseconds. If the ball has mass 0.20 kg, what speed does it have after impact?

**2.** A 1.0-kg ball drops vertically onto the floor with a speed of 25 meters/sec. It rebounds with an initial speed of 10 meters/second. (*a*) What impulse acts on the ball during contact? (*b*) If the ball is in contact for 0.020 sec, what is the average force exerted on the floor?

**3.** A croquet ball (mass 0.50 kg) is struck by a mallet, receiving the impulse shown in the graph (Fig. 10–15). What is the ball's velocity just after the force has become zero?

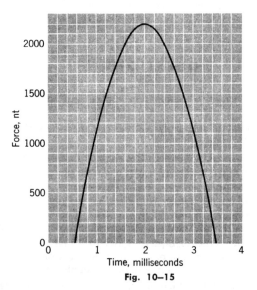

**Fig. 10–15**

**4.** A golfer hits a golf ball imparting to it an initial velocity of magnitude $5.0 \times 10^3$ cm/sec directed 30° above the horizontal. Assuming that the mass of the ball is 25 gm and the club and ball are in contact for 0.010 sec, find (*a*) the impulse imparted to the ball; (b) the impulse imparted to the club; (c) the average force exerted on the ball by the club; (d) the work done on the ball.

**5.** A ball of mass $m$ and speed $v$ strikes a wall perpendicularly and rebounds with undiminished speed. If the time of collision is $t$, what is the average force exerted by the ball on the wall?

**6.** A stream of water impinges on a stationary "dished" turbine blade, as shown in Fig. 10–16. The speed of the water is $u$, both before and after it strikes the curved surface of the blade, and the mass of water striking the blade per unit time is constant at the value $\mu$. Find the force exerted by the water on the blade.

**Fig. 10–16**

**7.** A 6.0-kg box sled is traveling across the ice at a speed of 9.0 meters/sec when a 12-kg package is dropped into it vertically. Describe the subsequent motion of the sled.

**8.** A body of 2.0 kg mass makes an elastic collision with another body at rest and afterwards continues to move in the original direction but with one-fourth of its original speed. What is the mass of the struck body?

**9.** A block of mass $m_1 = 100$ kg is at rest on a very long frictionless table, one end of which is terminated in a wall. Another block of mass $m_2$ is placed between the first block and the wall and set in motion to the left with constant speed $v_{2i}$, as in Fig. 10–17. Assuming that all collisions are completely elastic, find the value of $m_2$ for which both blocks move with the same velocity after $m_2$ has collided once with $m_1$ and once with the wall. The wall has infinite mass effectively.

**Fig. 10–17**

**10.** A bullet weighing $1.0 \times 10^{-2}$ lb is fired horizontally into a 4.0-lb wooden block at rest on a horizontal surface. The coefficient of kinetic friction between block and surface is 0.20. The bullet comes to rest in the block which moves 6.0 ft. Find the speed of the bullet.

**11.** A bullet of mass 10 gm strikes a ballistic pendulum of mass 2.0 kg. The center of mass of the pendulum rises a vertical distance of 12 cm. Assuming the bullet remains embedded in the pendulum, calculate its initial speed.

**12.** In a breech-loading automatic firearm of early vintage the reloading mechanism at the rear of the bore is activated when the breech-block, which recoils after the bullet is fired, compresses a spring by a predetermined amount $d$. (a) Show that the speed

$v$ of the bullet of mass $m$ must be at least $d \sqrt{kM/m}$ on firing, for automatic loading, where $k$ is the force constant of the spring and $M$ is the mass of the breech-block. (b) In what sense, if any, can this process be regarded as a collision?

**13.** A steel ball weighing 1.0 lb is fastened to a cord 27 in. long and is released when the cord is horizontal. At the bottom of its path the ball strikes a 5.0-lb steel block initially at rest on a frictionless surface (Fig. 10–18). The collision is elastic. Find the speed of the ball and the speed of the block just after the collision.

Fig. 10—18

Fig. 10—19

**14.** Two pendulums each of length $l$ are initially situated as in Fig. 10–19. The first pendulum is released and strikes the second. Assume that the collision is completely inelastic and neglect the mass of the strings and any frictional effects. How high does the center of mass rise after the collision?

**15.** A railroad freight car weighing 32 tons and traveling 5.0 ft/sec overtakes one weighing 24 tons traveling 3.0 ft/sec in the same direction. (a) Find the speed of the cars after collision and the loss of kinetic energy during collision if the cars couple together. (b) If the collision is elastic, the freight cars do not couple but separate after collision. What are their speeds?

**16.** An elevator is moving *up* at 6.0 ft/sec in a shaft. At the instant the elevator is 60 ft from the top, a ball is dropped from the top of the shaft. The ball rebounds elastically from the elevator roof. To what height can it rise relative to the top of the shaft? Do the same problem assuming the elevator is moving *down* at 6.0 ft/sec.

**17.** The two masses on the right of Fig. 10–20 are slightly separated and initially at rest; the left mass is incident with speed $v_0$. Assuming head-on elastic collisions, (a) if $M \leq m$, show that there are exactly two collisions and find all final velocities; (b) if $M > m$, show that there are three collisions and find all final velocities.

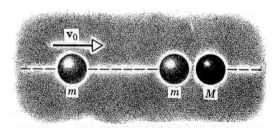

Fig. 10—20

**18.** A ball of mass $m$ is projected with speed $v_i$ into the barrel of a spring-gun of mass $M$ initially at rest on a frictionless surface; see Fig. 10–21. The mass $m$ sticks in the barrel at the point of maximum compression of the spring. No energy is lost in friction. What fraction of the initial kinetic energy of the ball is stored in the spring?

**19.** A block of mass $m_1 = 2.0$ kg slides along a frictionless table with a speed of 10 meters/sec. Directly in front of it, and moving in the same direction, is a block of mass $m_2 = 5.0$ kg moving at 3.0 meters/sec. A massless spring with a spring constant of $k = 1120$ nt/meter is attached to the backside of $m_2$ as shown in Fig. 10–22. When the blocks collide, what is the maximum compression of the spring? Assume that the spring does not bend and always obeys Hooke's law.

Fig. 10–21                           Fig. 10–22

**20.** A box is put on a scale which is adjusted to read zero when the box is empty. A stream of pebbles is then poured into the box from a height $h$ above its bottom at a rate of $\mu$ (pebbles per second). Each pebble has a mass $m$. If the collisions between the pebbles and box are completely inelastic, find the scale reading at time $t$ after the pebbles begin to fill the box. Determine a numerical answer when $\mu = 100$ sec$^{-1}$, $h = 25$ ft, $mg = 0.010$ lb, and $t = 10$ sec.

**21.** A scale is adjusted to read zero. Particles fall from a height of 9.0 ft before colliding with the balance pan on the scale; the collisions are elastic, i.e., the particles rebound upward with the same speed. If each particle has a mass of $\frac{1}{128}$ slug and collisions occur at the rate of 32 particles/sec, what is the scale reading in pounds?

**22.** An electron collides elastically with a hydrogen atom initially at rest. The initial and final motions are along the same straight line. What fraction of the electron's initial kinetic energy is transferred to the hydrogen atom? The mass of the hydrogen atom is 1840 times the mass of the electron.

**23.** An electron, mass $m$, collides head-on with an atom, mass $M$, initially at rest. As a result of the collision a characteristic amount of energy $E$ is stored internally in the atom. What is the minimum initial velocity $v_0$ that the electron must have? (Hint: Conservation principles lead to a quadratic equation for the final electron velocity $v$ and a quadratic equation for the final atom velocity $V$. The minimum value $v_0$ follows from the requirement that the radical in the solutions for $v$ and $V$ be real.)

**24.** (a) Show that in a one-dimensional elastic collision the speed of the center of mass of two particles, $m_1$ moving with initial speed $v_{1i}$ and $m_2$ moving with initial speed $v_{2i}$, is

$$v_{\text{cm}} = \left(\frac{m_1}{m_1 + m_2}\right)v_{1i} + \left(\frac{m_2}{m_1 + m_2}\right)v_{2i}$$

(b) Use the expressions obtained for $v_{1f}$ and $v_{2f}$, the particles' speeds after collision, to derive the same result for $v_{\text{cm}}$ *after* the collision.

**25.** Mass $m_1$ collides head-on with $m_2$, initially at rest, in a completely inelastic collision. (a) What is the kinetic energy of the system before collision? (b) What is the kinetic energy of the system after collision? (c) What fraction of the original kinetic energy was converted into heat? (d) Let $\mathbf{v}_{\text{cm}}$ be the velocity of the center of mass of the system. View the collision from a primed reference frame moving with the center of mass so that $v_{1i}' = v_{1i} - v_{cm}$, $v_{2i}' = -v_{cm}$. Repeat parts (a), (b), and (c), as seen by an observer in this reference frame. Is the mechanical energy converted to heat the same in each case? Explain.

**26.** Show that, in the case of an elastic collision between a particle of mass $m_1$ with a particle of mass $m_2$ initially at rest, (a) the maximum angle $\theta_m$ through which $m_1$ can be deflected by the collision is given by $\cos^2 \theta_m = 1 - m_2^2/m_1^2$, so that $0 \leq \theta_m \leq \pi/2$, when $m_1 > m_2$; (b) $\theta_1 + \theta_2 = \pi/2$, when $m_1 = m_2$; (c) $\theta_1$ can take on all values between 0 and $\pi$, when $m_1 < m_2$.

**27.** A billiard ball moving at a speed of 2.2 meters/sec strikes an identical stationary ball a glancing blow. After the collision one ball is found to be moving at a speed of 1.1 meters/sec in a direction making a 60° angle with the original line of motion. Find the velocity of the other ball. Can the collision be inelastic, given these data?

**28.** An $\alpha$-particle collides with an oxygen nucleus, initially at rest. The $\alpha$-particle is scattered at an angle of 64° from its initial direction of motion and the oxygen nucleus recoils at an angle of 51° on the other side of this initial direction. What is the ratio of the speeds of these particles? The mass of the oxygen nucleus is four times that of the $\alpha$-particle.

**29.** Two balls $A$ and $B$, having different but unknown masses, collide. $A$ is initially at rest when $B$ has a speed $v$. After collision $B$ has a speed $v/2$ and moves at right angles to its original motion. Find the direction in which ball $A$ moves after collision. Can you determine the speed of $A$ from the information given? Explain.

**30.** Two vehicles $A$ and $B$ are traveling west and south, respectively, toward the same intersection where they collide and lock together. Before the collision $A$ (total weight, 900 lb) is moving with a speed of 40 mph, and $B$ (total weight, 1200 lb) has a speed of 60 mph. Find the magnitude and direction of the velocity of the (interlocked) vehicles immediately after collision.

**31.** A deuteron is a nuclear particle made up of one proton and one neutron. Its mass is approximately $4 \times 10^{-24}$ gm. A deuteron, accelerated by a cyclotron to a speed of $10^9$ cm/sec, collides with another deuteron at rest. (a) If the two particles stick together to form a helium nucleus, find the velocity of the nucleus. (b) The helium nucleus then breaks up into a neutron with a mass of about $2 \times 10^{-24}$ gm and a helium isotope of mass $6 \times 10^{-24}$ gm. If the neutron is given off at right angles to the direction of the original velocity with a speed of $5 \times 10^8$ cm/sec, find the magnitude and direction of the velocity of the helium isotope.

**32.** In 1932 Chadwick in England demonstrated the existence and properties of the neutron (one of the fundamental particles making up the atom) with the device shown in Fig. 10–23. In an evacuated chamber, a sample of radioactive polonium decays to yield $\alpha$-rays (helium nuclei). These nuclei impinge on a block of beryllium inducing a process whereby neutrons are emitted. (The reaction is: He and Be combine to form radioactive carbon, which decays to stable carbon + neutrons.) The neutrons strike a film of paraffin ($CH_4$), releasing hydrogen nuclei which are detected in an ionization chamber. In other words, an elastic collision takes place in which the momentum of the neutron is partially transferred to the hydrogen nucleus.

(a) Find an expression for the maximum speed $v_H$ that the hydrogen nucleus (mass $m_H$) can achieve. Let the incoming neutrons have mass $m_n$ and speed $v_n$. (Hint: Will more energy be transferred in a head-on collision or in a glancing collision?)

(b) One of Chadwick's goals was to find the mass of his new particle. Inspection of expression (a) which contains this parameter, however, shows that two unknowns are present, $v_n$ and $m_n$ ($v_H$ is known; it can be measured with the ionization chamber). To eliminate the unknown $v_n$, he substituted a paracyanogen (CN) block for the paraffin. The neutrons then underwent elastic collisions with nitrogen nuclei instead of hydrogen nuclei. Of course, expression (a) still holds if $v_N$ is written for $v_H$ and $m_N$ for $m_H$.

Therefore if $v_H$ and $v_N$ are measured in separate experiments, $v_n$ can be eliminated between the two expressions for hydrogen and nitrogen to yield a value for $m_n$. Chadwick's values were

$$v_H = 3.3 \times 10^9 \text{ cm/sec},$$

$$v_N = 0.47 \times 10^9 \text{ cm/sec}.$$

What was his value for $m_n$? How does this compare with the established value $m_n = 1.00867$ amu? (Take $m_H = 1.0$ amu, $m_N = 14$ amu.)

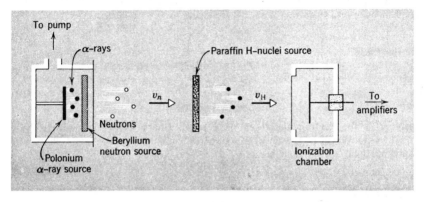

**Fig. 10–23**

**33.** A sphere of radius $r_1$ impinges on a sphere of radius $r_2$. What is the cross section for a contact collision?

**34.** A beam of fast neutrons impinges on a 5.0-mg sample of $Cu^{65}$, a stable isotope of copper. A possibility exists that the copper nucleus may capture a neutron to form $Cu^{66}$, which is radioactive and decays to $Zn^{66}$, which is again stable. If a study of the electron emission of the copper sample implies that $4.6 \times 10^{11}$ neutron captures occur each second, what is the neutron capture cross section in barns for this process? The intensity of the neutron beam is $1.1 \times 10^{18}$ neutrons/meter$^2$ sec.

**35.** A beam of slow neutrons strikes an aluminum foil $1.0 \times 10^{-5}$ meter thick. Some neutrons are captured by the aluminum which becomes radioactive and decays by emitting an electron ($\beta^-$) and forming silicon:

$$n + Al^{27} \rightarrow Al^{28} \rightarrow Si^{28} + \beta^-.$$

Suppose that the neutron flux is $3.0 \times 10^{16}$/meter$^2$ sec, and the neutron capture cross section is 0.23 barn. How many transmutations will occur each second?

**36.** In a thick foil there are a great many layers of target particles so that the number of projectile particles reaching a layer will depend on how many have been scattered out by previous layers. Let the number of particles reaching a layer at a depth $s$ be $N$ and the number lost by scattering from that layer be $-dN$; then show that

$$-\frac{dN}{N} = n\sigma \, ds$$

and

$$N = N_0 e^{-n\sigma s}$$

where $N_0$ is the number of particles incident on the face of the foil ($s = 0$).

**37.** The precise masses in the reaction

$$p + F^{19} \rightarrow \alpha + O^{16}$$

have been determined by mass spectrometer measurements and are

$$m_p = 1.00783 \quad \text{amu} \quad\quad m_\alpha = 4.00260 \quad\quad \text{amu}$$

$$m_F = 18.99840 \quad \text{amu} \quad\quad m_O = 15.99491 \quad\quad \text{amu}$$

Calculate the $Q$ of the reaction from these data and compare with the $Q$ calculated in Example 6 from reaction studies.

**38.** An elementary particle called $\Sigma^-$, at rest in a certain reference frame, decays spontaneously into two other particles according to

$$\Sigma^- \rightarrow \pi^- + n$$

The masses are

$$m_{\Sigma^-} = 2340.5 m_e$$

$$m_{\pi^-} = 273.2 m_e$$

$$m_n = 1838.65 m_e$$

where $m_e$ is the electron mass. (a) How much kinetic energy is generated in this process? (b) Which of the decay products ($\pi^-$ and $n$) gets the larger share of this kinetic energy? Of the momentum?

# Rotational Kinematics

## CHAPTER 11

## 11-1    Rotational Motion

So far we have dealt mostly with the translational motion of single particles or of rigid bodies, that is, of bodies whose parts all have a fixed relationship to each other.   No real body is truly rigid, but many bodies, such as molecules, steel beams, and planets, are rigid enough so that, in many problems, we can ignore the fact that they warp, bend, or vibrate.   As Fig. 3-1 shows, *a rigid body moves in pure translation if each particle of the body undergoes the same displacement as every other particle in any given time interval.*

In this chapter we are interested in *rotation*.   For the time being we again restrict ourselves to single particles and to rigid bodies, which means that we shall not consider such rotational motions as those of the solar system or of water in a spinning beaker.   We shall also deal only with rotation about axes that remain fixed in the reference frame in which we observe the rotation.

Figure 11-1 shows the rotational motion of a rigid body about a fixed axis, in this case the z-axis of our reference frame.   Let $P$ represent a particle in the rigid body, arbitrarily selected and described by the position vector **r**.   We then say that: *A rigid body moves in pure rotation if every particle of the body* (such as $P$ in Fig. 11-1) *moves in a circle, the centers of which are on a straight line called the axis of rotation* (the z-axis in Fig. 11-1). If we draw a perpendicular from any point in the body to the axis, each such line will sweep through the same angle in any given time interval as another such line.   Thus we can describe the pure rotation of a rigid body

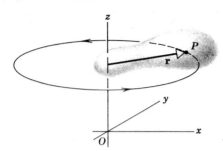

**Fig. 11–1** A rigid body rotating about the $z$-axis. Each point in the body, such as $P$, describes a circle about this axis.

by considering the motion of any one of the particles (such as $P$) that make it up. (We must rule out, however, particles that are on the axis of rotation. Why?)

The general motion of a rigid body is a combination of translation and rotation however, rather than one of pure rotation. We can locate a rigid body that is moving in pure translation by giving the three coordinates $x$, $y$, $z$ of any point in it (its center of mass, say) in a particular reference frame.

For a body that rotates as it moves translationally we need, in the most general case, three more coordinates, such as angles, to specify the orientation of the body with respect to the reference frame. Figure 11–2 (see also Fig. 9–1) shows a special case of rigid body motion combining translation and rotation. The figure is an extension of Fig. 3–1 in which the body now rotates as it moves translationally. To locate this body we must not only locate point $O$ in the body in the $xy$ reference frame but we must also say how the $x'y'$ reference frame, which is fixed in the body, is oriented with respect to the $xy$ frame.

As we saw in Chapter 9 we can describe the translational motion of any system of particles—whether rigid or not—whether rotating or not—by imagining that all of the mass $M$ of the body is concentrated at the center

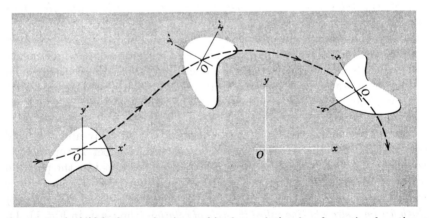

**Fig. 11–2** A rigid body moving in combined translational and rotational motion as seen from reference frame $x,y$. Notice that the reference frame fixed on the body ($x'$, $y'$) changes its orientation with respect to $x$, $y$ as the motion proceeds. Compare with Figs. 3–1 and 9–1. This figure represents a special case in that the translational motion occurs in two dimensions only (the $xy$ plane) and the rotational motion occurs about an axis that maintains a fixed direction (the $z'$-axis).

of mass and that $\mathbf{F}_{ext}$, the resultant of the external forces acting on the body, acts at this point. The acceleration of the center of mass is then given by Eq. 9–10 or $\mathbf{F}_{ext} = M\mathbf{a}_{cm}$. It is very helpful to be able to represent the translational motion of a rigid body by the motion of a single point—its center of mass; all that is left is to determine its rotational motion. We shall discuss such combined translational and rotational motions in the next chapter. This will be simpler to do after we have studied pure rotation about a fixed axis.

We now return, therefore, to the pure rotation of a rigid body about a fixed axis (Fig. 11–1). First, we must *describe* the rotational motion. We call this description rotational kinematics; we must define the variables of angular motion and relate them to each other, just as in particle kinematics we defined the variables of translational motion and related them to each other. The next part of our program is to relate the rotational motion of a body to the properties of the body and of its environment. This is rotational dynamics. In this chapter we study the kinematics of rotation. We develop the dynamics of rotation in the next chapter.

## 11–2  Rotational Kinematics—the Variables

In Fig. 11–1 let us pass a plane through $P$ at right angles to the axis of rotation. This plane, which cuts through the rotating body, contains the circle in which particle $P$ moves. Figure 11–3 shows this plane, as we look downward on it from above, along the $z$-axis in Fig. 11–1.

We can tell exactly where the entire rotating body is in our reference frame if we know the location of any single particle ($P$) of the body in this frame. Thus, for the kinematics of this problem, we need only consider the (two-dimensional) motion of a particle in a circle.

The angle $\theta$ in Fig. 11–3 is the angular position of particle $P$ with respect to the reference position. We arbitrarily choose the positive sense

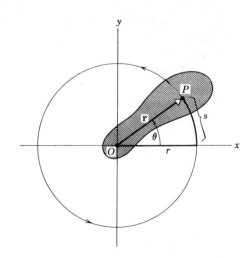

**Fig. 11–3**  A cross sectional view of the rigid body of Fig. 11–1, showing point $P$ and vector $\mathbf{r}$ of that figure. Point $P$, which is fixed in the rotating body, rotates counterclockwise about the origin in a circle of radius $r$.

of rotation in Fig. 11–3 to be counterclockwise, so that $\theta$ increases for counterclockwise rotation and decreases for clockwise rotation.

It is convenient to measure $\theta$ in radians* rather than in degrees. By definition $\theta$ is given in radians by the relation

$$\theta = s/r,$$

in which $s$ is the arc length shown in Fig. 11–3.

Let the body of Fig. 11–3 be rotating counterclockwise. At time $t_1$ the angular position of $P$ is $\theta_1$ and at a later time $t_2$ its angular position is $\theta_2$. This is shown in Fig. 11–4, which gives the positions of $P$ and of the position vector $\mathbf{r}$ at these times; the outline of the body itself has been omitted in that figure for simplicity. The *angular displacement* of $P$ will be $\theta_2 - \theta_1 = \Delta\theta$ during the time interval $t_2 - t_1 = \Delta t$. The *average angular speed* $\bar{\omega}$ of particle $P$ in this time interval is defined as

$$\bar{\omega} = \frac{\theta_2 - \theta_1}{t_2 - t_1} = \frac{\Delta\theta}{\Delta t}.$$

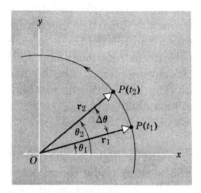

**Fig. 11–4** The reference line $r$ ($= OP$), fixed in the body of Figs. 11–1 and 11–3, is displaced through angle $\Delta\theta$ ($= \theta_2 - \theta_1$) in time $\Delta t$ ($= t_2 - t_1$).

The *instantaneous angular speed* $\omega$ is defined as the limit approached by this ratio as $\Delta t$ approaches zero:

$$\omega = \lim_{\Delta t \to 0} \frac{\Delta\theta}{\Delta t} = \frac{d\theta}{dt}. \quad (11\text{–}1)$$

For a rigid body all radial lines fixed in it perpendicular to the axis of rotation rotate through the same angle in the same time, so that the angular speed $\omega$ about this axis is the same for each particle in the body. Thus $\omega$ is characteristic of the body as a whole. Angular speed has the dimensions of an inverse time ($T^{-1}$); its units are commonly taken to be radians/sec or rev/sec.

If the angular speed of $P$ is not constant, then the particle has an angular acceleration. Let $\omega_1$ and $\omega_2$ be the instantaneous angular speeds at the times $t_1$ and $t_2$ respectively; then the *average angular acceleration* $\bar{\alpha}$ of the particle $P$ is defined as

$$\bar{\alpha} = \frac{\omega_2 - \omega_1}{t_2 - t_1} = \frac{\Delta\omega}{\Delta t}.$$

---

* The radian is a pure number, having no physical dimension since it is the ratio of two lengths. Since the circumference of a circle of radius $r$ is $2\pi r$, there are $2\pi$ radians in a complete circle, that is, $\theta = 2\pi r/r = 2\pi$. Therefore $2\pi$ radians $= 360°$, $\pi$ radians $= 180°$, and 1 radian $\cong 57.3°$.

The *instantaneous angular acceleration* is the limit of this ratio as $\Delta t$ approaches zero, or

$$\alpha = \lim_{\Delta t \to 0} \frac{\Delta \omega}{\Delta t} = \frac{d\omega}{dt}. \tag{11-2}$$

Because $\omega$ is the same for all particles in the rigid body, it follows from Eq. 11–2 that $\alpha$ must be the same for each particle and thus $\alpha$, like $\omega$, is a characteristic of the body as a whole. Angular acceleration has the dimensions of an inverse time squared $(T^{-2})$; its units are commonly taken to be radians/sec$^2$ or rev/sec$^2$.

The rotation of a particle (or a rigid body) *about a fixed axis* has a formal correspondence to the translational motion of a particle (or a rigid body) *along a fixed direction*. The kinematical variables are $\theta$, $\omega$, and $\alpha$ in the first case and $x$, $v$, and $a$ in the second. These quantities correspond in pairs: $\theta$ to $x$, $\omega$ to $v$, and $\alpha$ to $a$. Note that the angular quantities differ dimensionally from the corresponding linear quantities by a length factor. Note, too, that all six quantities may be treated as scalars in this special case. For example, a particle at any instant can be moving in one direction or the other along its straight-line motion, corresponding to a positive or a negative value for $v$; similarly a particle at any instant can be rotating in one direction or another about its fixed axis, corresponding to a positive or a negative value for $\omega$.

When, in translational motion, we remove the restriction that the motion be along a straight line and consider the general case of motion in three dimensions along a curved path, the linear variables $x$, $v$, and $a$ reveal themselves as the scalar components of the kinematic vectors $\mathbf{r}$, $\mathbf{v}$, and $\mathbf{a}$. In Section 11–4, we shall see to what extent the rotational kinematic variables reveal themselves as vectors when we remove the restriction of a fixed axis of rotation.

## 11–3   Rotation with Constant Angular Acceleration

For translational motion of a particle or a rigid body along a fixed direction, such as the $x$-axis, we have seen (in Chapter 3) that the simplest type of motion is that in which the acceleration $a$ is zero. The next simplest type corresponds to $a = $ a constant (other than zero); for this motion we derived the equations of Table 3–1, which connect the kinematic variables $x$, $v$, $a$, and $t$ in all possible combinations.

For the rotational motion of a particle or a rigid body around a fixed axis the simplest type of motion is that in which the angular acceleration $\alpha$ is zero (such as uniform circular motion). The next simplest type of motion, in which $\alpha = $ a constant (other than zero), corresponds exactly to linear motion with $a = $ a constant (other than zero). As before, we can derive four equations linking the four kinematic variables $\theta$, $\omega$, $\alpha$, and $t$ in all possible combinations. The student can either derive these angular equations by the methods used to derive the linear equations (see Example 2) or he may write them down at once by substituting corresponding angular quantities for the linear quantities in the linear equations.

We list both sets of equations in Table 11–1, having chosen $x_0 = 0$ and $\theta_0 = 0$ in these relations for simplicity. Here $\omega_0$ is the angular speed at the time $t = 0$. The student should check these equations dimensionally before verifying them. Both sets of equations hold not only for particles but also for rigid bodies.

### Table 11-1

MOTION WITH CONSTANT LINEAR OR ANGULAR ACCELERATION

| | Translational Motion (Fixed Direction) | Rotational Motion (Fixed Axis) | |
|---|---|---|---|
| (3–12) | $v = v_0 + at$ | $\omega = \omega_0 + \alpha t$ | (11–3) |
| (3–14) | $x = \dfrac{v_0 + v}{2} t$ | $\theta = \dfrac{\omega_0 + \omega}{2} t$ | (11–4) |
| (3–15) | $x = v_0 t + \frac{1}{2}at^2$ | $\theta = \omega_0 t + \frac{1}{2}\alpha t^2$ | (11–5) |
| (3–16) | $v^2 = v_0^2 + 2ax$ | $\omega^2 = \omega_0^2 + 2\alpha\theta$ | (11–6) |

For the angular quantities, we arbitrarily select one of the two possible directions of rotation about the fixed axis as the direction in which $\theta$ is increasing. From Eq. 11–1 ($\omega = d\theta/dt$) we see that if $\theta$ is increasing with time $\omega$ is positive. Similarly, from Eq. 11–2 ($\alpha = d\omega/dt$), we see that if $\omega$ is increasing with time $\alpha$ is positive. There are corresponding sign conventions for the linear quantities.

▶ **Example 1.** A grindstone has a constant angular acceleration $\alpha$ of 3.0 radians/sec². Starting from rest a line, such as $OP$ in Fig. 11–5, is horizontal. Find (a) the angular displacement of the line $OP$ (and hence of the grindstone) and (b) the angular speed of the grindstone 2.0 sec later.

(a) $\alpha$ and $t$ are given; we wish to find $\theta$. Hence, we use Eq. 11–5,

$$\theta = \omega_0 t + \frac{1}{2}\alpha t^2.$$

At $t = 0$, we have $\omega = \omega_0 = 0$ and $\alpha = 3.0$ radians/sec². Therefore, after 2.0 sec,

$$\theta = (0)(2.0 \text{ sec}) + \frac{1}{2}(3.0 \text{ radians/sec}^2)$$
$$(2.0 \text{ sec})^2 = 6.0 \text{ radians} = 0.96 \text{ rev.}$$

(b) $\alpha$ and $t$ are given; we wish to find $\omega$. Hence we use Eq. 11–3

$$\omega = \omega_0 + \alpha t,$$

and

$$\omega = 0 + (3.0 \text{ radians/sec}^2)$$
$$(2.0 \text{ sec}) = 6.0 \text{ radians/sec.}$$

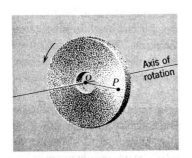

**Fig. 11–5** Example 1. The line $OP$ is attached to a grindstone rotating as shown about an axis through $O$ that is fixed in the reference frame of the observer.

Using Eq. 11–6 as a check, we have

$$\omega^2 = \omega_0{}^2 + 2\alpha\theta,$$

$$\omega^2 = 0 + (2)(3.0 \text{ radians/sec}^2)(6.0 \text{ radians}) = 36 \text{ radians}^2/\text{sec}^2,$$

$$\omega = 6.0 \text{ radians/sec}.$$

**Example 2.** Derive the equation $\omega = \omega_0 + \alpha t$ for constant angular acceleration.

(a) Starting from the definition of angular acceleration,

$$\alpha = \frac{d\omega}{dt},$$

we have

$$\alpha \, dt = d\omega$$

or

$$\int \alpha \, dt = \int d\omega.$$

But $\alpha$ is a constant, so that

$$\alpha \int dt = \int d\omega.$$

If at $t = 0$ we call the angular speed $\omega_0$, then

$$\alpha \int_0^t dt = \int_{\omega_0}^{\omega} d\omega$$

or

$$\alpha t = \omega - \omega_0$$

and

$$\omega = \omega_0 + \alpha t.$$

(b) We can also derive the result by making use of the fact that the average acceleration equals the instantaneous acceleration when the acceleration is constant. The average acceleration is

$$\bar{\alpha} = \frac{\omega - \omega_0}{t - t_0}.$$

For constant acceleration we have $\alpha = \bar{\alpha}$. Letting $t_0 = 0$, we obtain

$$\alpha = \frac{\omega - \omega_0}{t}$$

or

$$\omega = \omega_0 + \alpha t.$$

The student should compare this derivation with that of the corresponding linear relation $v = v_0 + at$ in Section 3–8. ◀

## 11–4   Rotational Quantities as Vectors

The linear displacement, velocity, and acceleration are vectors. The corresponding angular quantities *may* be vectors also, for in addition to a magnitude we must also specify a direction for them, namely the direction of the axis of rotation in space. Because we considered rotation only about a fixed axis, we were able to treat $\theta$, $\omega$, and $\alpha$ as scalar quantities. If

**Fig. 11–6** (a) A book rotated $\theta_1$ (90° as shown about a vertical axis) and then $\theta_2$ (90° as shown about a north-south axis) has a different final orientation than if rotated first through $\theta_2$ and then $\theta_1$. This property is called the noncommutivity of finite angles under addition: $\theta_1 + \theta_2 \neq \theta_2 + \theta_1$. (b) The middle group is the same except that the angular displacements are smaller, being 45°. Although the final orientations still differ, they are much nearer each other. (c) The lower group repeats the experiment for 20° displacements. We see here that $\theta_1 + \theta_2 \cong \theta_2 + \theta_1$. As $\theta_1$, $\theta_2 \to 0$, the final positions approach each other. Finite angles under addition tend to commute as the angles become very small. Infinitesimal angles *do* commute under addition, making it possible to treat them as vectors.

the direction of the axis changes, however, we can no longer avoid the question "are rotational quantities vectors?" We can find out only by seeing whether or not they obey the laws of vector addition.

Let us discuss first the angular displacement $\theta$. The magnitude of the angular displacement of a body is the angle through which the body turns. Angular displacements, however, are *not* vectors because they do *not* add like vectors. For example, give two successive rotations $\theta_1$ and $\theta_2$ to a book which initially lies flat on a table. Let rotation $\theta_1$ be a 90° clockwise turn about a vertical axis through the center of the book as we view it from above. Let $\theta_2$ be a 90° clockwise turn about a north-south axis through the center of the book as we view it looking north. In one case, apply operation $\theta_1$ first and then $\theta_2$. In the other case, apply operation $\theta_2$ first and then $\theta_1$. The student should try this for himself. Now, if angular displacements are vector quantities, they must add like vectors. In particular, they must obey the law of vector addition $\theta_1 + \theta_2 = \theta_2 + \theta_1$, which tells us that the order in which we add vectors does not affect their sum. This law fails for finite angular displacements (see exercise above and also Fig. 11–6a). Hence finite angular displacements are *not* vector quantities.

Suppose that instead of 90° rotations we had made 3° rotations. The result of $\theta_1 + \theta_2$ would still differ from the result of $\theta_2 + \theta_1$, but the difference would be much smaller. In fact, as the two angular displacements are made smaller, the difference between the two sums disappears rapidly (Fig. 11–6b,c). If the angular displacements are made infinitesimal, the order of addition no longer affects the result. Hence *infinitesimal angular displacements are vectors*.

Quantities defined in terms of infinitesimal angular displacements may themselves be vectors. For example, the angular velocity is $\omega = d\theta/dt$. Since $d\theta$ is a vector and $dt$ a scalar, the quotient is a vector. Therefore the angular velocity is a vector. In Fig. 11–7a, for example, we represent the

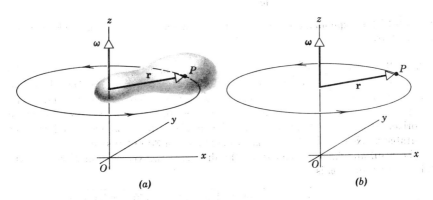

*(a)*                        *(b)*

**Fig. 11–7**   The angular velocity $\omega$ of (a) a rotating rigid body and (b) a rotating particle, about a fixed axis.

angular velocity **ω** of the rotating rigid body by an arrow drawn along the axis of rotation; in Fig. 11–7*b* we represent the rotation of a particle (such as *P* in Fig. 11–7*a*) about a fixed axis in just the same way. The length of the arrow is made proportional to the magnitude of the angular velocity. The sense of the rotation determines the direction in which the arrow points along the axis. By convention, if the fingers of the *right-hand* curl around the axis in the direction of rotation of the body, the extended thumb points along the direction of the angular velocity vector. For the rigid body of Fig. 11–1, therefore, the angular velocity vector will be in the positive *z*-direction. In Fig. 11–3, **ω** will be perpendicular to the page pointing up out of the page, corresponding to the counterclockwise rotation. The angular velocity of the turntable of a phonograph is a vector pointing down. Notice that nothing moves in the direction of the angular velocity vector. The vector represents the angular velocity of the rotational motion taking place in the plane perpendicular to it.

Angular acceleration is also a vector quantity. This follows from the definition **α** = *d***ω**/*dt*, in which *d***ω** is a vector and *dt* a scalar. Later we shall encounter other rotational quantities that are vectors, such as torque and angular momentum.

▶ **Example 3.** A disk spins on a horizontal shaft mounted in bearings, with an angular speed $\omega_1$ of 100 radians/sec as in Fig. 11–8*a*. The entire disk and shaft assembly are placed on a turntable rotating about a vertical axis at $\omega_2 = 30.0$ radians/sec, counterclockwise as we view it from above. Describe the rotation of the disk as seen by an observer in the room.

*(a)*

**Fig. 11–8** (*a*) A spinning disc on a rotating turntable. (*b*) The angular velocities add like vectors.

The disk is subject to two angular velocities simultaneously; we can describe its resultant motion by the vector sum of these vectors. The angular velocity **ω₁** associated with the shaft rotation has a magnitude of 100 radians/sec and occurs about an axis that is not fixed but, as seen by an observer in the room, rotates in a horizontal plane at 30 radians/sec. The angular velocity **ω₂** associated with the turntable is fixed vertically and has a magnitude of 30 radians/sec.

The resultant angular velocity of the disk **ω** is the vector sum of **ω₁** and **ω₂**. The magnitude of **ω** is

$$\omega = \sqrt{\omega_1{}^2 + \omega_2{}^2} = \sqrt{(100 \text{ radians/sec})^2 + (30.0 \text{ radians/sec})^2}$$

$$= 104 \text{ radians/sec.}$$

The direction of $\omega$ is not fixed in our observer's reference frame but rotates at the same angular rate as the turntable. The vector $\omega$ does not lie in the horizontal plane but points above it by an angle $\theta$ (see Fig. 11–8$b$), where

$$\theta = \tan^{-1} \omega_2/\omega_1 = \tan^{-1} (30.0 \text{ radians/sec})/(100 \text{ radians/sec})$$

$$= \tan^{-1} 0.300 = 16.7°$$

We can describe the motion of the disk as a simple rotation about this new axis (whose direction in our observer's reference frame is changing with time as described above) at an angular rate of 104 radians/sec. How would the situation change if the direction of rotation of the disk, or of the turntable, were changed?    ◀

## 11–5    Relation between Linear and Angular Kinematics for a Particle in Circular Motion—Scalar Form

In Sections 4–4 and 4–5 we discussed the linear velocity and acceleration of a particle moving in a circle. When a rigid body rotates about a fixed axis, every particle in the body moves in a circle. Hence we can describe the motion of such a particle either in linear variables or in angular variables. The relation between the linear and angular variables enables us to pass back and forth from one description to another and is very useful.

Consider a particle at $P$ in the rigid body, a distance $r$ from the axis through $O$. This particle moves in a circle of radius $r$ as the body rotates, as in Fig. 11–9$a$. The reference position is $Ox$. The particle moves through a distance $s$ along the arc when the body rotates through an angle $\theta$, such that

$$s = \theta r \qquad (11\text{–}7)$$

where $\theta$ is in radians.

Differentiating both sides of this equation with respect to the time, and

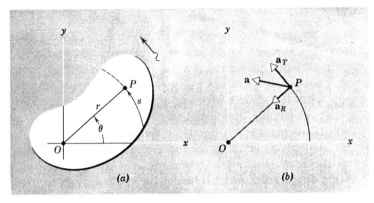

**Fig. 11–9**    (a) A rigid body rotates about a fixed axis through $O$ perpendicular to the page. The point $P$ sweeps out an arc $s$ which subtends an angle $\theta$.    (b) The acceleration $\mathbf{a}$ of point $P$ has components $\mathbf{a}_T$ (tangential) where $a_T = \alpha r$ and $\mathbf{a}_R$ (radial) where $a_R = v^2/r = \omega^2 r$ ($\omega$ = angular speed).

noting that $r$ is constant, we obtain

$$\frac{ds}{dt} = \frac{d\theta}{dt} r.$$

But $ds/dt$ is the linear speed of the particle at $P$ and $d\theta/dt$ is the angular speed $\omega$ of the rotating body so that

$$v = \omega r. \tag{11-8}$$

This is a relation between the *magnitudes* of the linear velocity and the angular velocity; the linear speed of a particle in circular motion is the product of the angular speed and the distance $r$ of the particle from the axis of rotation.

Differentiating Eq. 11–8 with respect to the time, we have

$$\frac{dv}{dt} = \frac{d\omega}{dt} r.$$

But $dv/dt$ is the magnitude of the *tangential* component of acceleration of the particle (see Section 4–5) and $d\omega/dt$ is the magnitude of the angular acceleration of the rotating body, so that

$$a_T = \alpha r. \tag{11-9}$$

Hence the magnitude of the tangential component of the linear acceleration of a particle in circular motion is the product of the magnitude of the angular acceleration and the distance $r$ of the particle from the axis of rotation.

We have seen that the *radial* component of acceleration is $v^2/r$ for a particle moving in a circle. This can be expressed in terms of angular speed by use of Eq. 11–8. We have

$$a_R = \frac{v^2}{r} = \omega^2 r. \tag{11-10}$$

The resultant acceleration of point $P$ is shown in Fig. 11–9b.

Equations 11–7 through 11–10 enable us to describe the motion of one point on a rigid body rotating about a fixed axis *either* in angular variables *or* in linear variables. We might ask why we need the angular variables when we are already familiar with the equivalent linear variables. The answer is that the angular description offers a distinct advantage over the linear description when various points on the same rotating body must be considered. Different points on the same rotating body do not have the same linear displacement, speed, or acceleration, but *all* points on a rigid body rotating about a fixed axis do have the same *angular* displacement, speed, or acceleration at any instant. By the use of angular variables we can describe the motion of the body as a whole in a simple way.

▶ **Example 4.** If the radius of the grindstone of Example 1 is 0.50 meter, calculate (a) the linear or tangential speed of a particle on the rim, (b) the tangential acceleration of a particle on the rim, and (c) the centripetal acceleration of a particle on the rim, at the end of 2.0 sec.

We have $\alpha = 3.0$ radians/sec$^2$, $\omega = 6.0$ radians/sec after 2.0 sec, and $r = 0.50$ meter. Then,

(a)
$$v = \omega r$$
$$= (6.0 \text{ radians/sec})(0.50 \text{ meter})$$
$$= 3.0 \text{ meter/sec} \quad \text{(linear speed)};$$

(b)
$$a_T = \alpha r$$
$$= (3.0 \text{ radians/sec}^2)(0.50 \text{ meter})$$
$$= 1.5 \text{ meters/sec}^2 \quad \text{(tangential acceleration)};$$

(c)
$$a_R = v^2/r = \omega^2 r$$
$$= (6.0 \text{ radians/sec})^2(0.50 \text{ meter})$$
$$= 18 \text{ meters/sec}^2 \quad \text{(centripetal acceleration)}.$$

(d) Are the results the same for a particle halfway in from the rim, that is, at $r = 0.25$ meter?

The *angular* variables are the same for this point as for a point on the rim. That is, once again

$$\alpha = 3.0 \text{ radians/sec}^2, \qquad \omega = 6.0 \text{ radians/sec}.$$

But now $r = 0.25$ meter, so that for this particle

$$v = 1.5 \text{ meters/sec}, \qquad a_T = 0.75 \text{ meter/sec}^2, \qquad a_R = 9.0 \text{ meters/sec}^2. \quad \blacktriangleleft$$

## 11–6   Relation between Linear and Angular Kinematics for a Particle in Circular Motion—Vector Form

The student should notice that the relations deduced in the previous section are relations between *scalar* quantities, both the linear and angular variables being expressed in scalar form. Let us now use vector methods, making an analysis essentially like that of Section 4–5 except that we now introduce the angular variables. This will illustrate, for a familiar case, the more general approach and prepare the way for situations in which vector methods are essential.

Figure 11–10a shows a particle $P$, rotating about a fixed axis through the origin, at times $t$ and $t + \Delta t$. The particle moves in a circle of constant radius $r$; beyond

(a)                   (b)                   (c)

**Fig. 11–10**   (a) The particle $P$ rotates through an angle $\Delta\theta$ in time $\Delta t$. The unit vectors, in polar coordinates, are shown at each point. (b) The change in $\mathbf{u}_r$; note that $\Delta\mathbf{u}_r$, as $\Delta\theta \to 0$, points in the direction of $\mathbf{u}_\theta$. (c) The change in $\mathbf{u}_\theta$; note that $\Delta\mathbf{u}_\theta$, as $\Delta\theta \to 0$, points in the direction of $-\mathbf{u}_r$.

this there are no restrictions on its motion and in general **ω** and **α** may have values that vary as the particle moves. We can express the restriction to a constant radius by

$$\mathbf{r} = \mathbf{u}_r r, \tag{11-11}$$

in which $\mathbf{u}_r$ is a unit vector in the direction of $\mathbf{r}$.

Differentiating Eq. 11–11, remembering that $r$ (but not $\mathbf{r}$ or $\mathbf{u}_r$, since their directions change) is a constant, we have

$$\frac{d\mathbf{r}}{dt} = \frac{d\mathbf{u}_r}{dt} r. \tag{11-12}$$

Now $d\mathbf{r}/dt$ is $\mathbf{v}$, the linear velocity of the particle. To evaluate $d\mathbf{u}_r/dt$, consider Fig. 11–10b, which shows the unit vector $\mathbf{u}_r$ for two different positions of $P$, corresponding to a rotation through a (small) angle $\Delta\theta$. Using the definition of angular measure in radians we obtain the *magnitude* of the (vector) change $\Delta\mathbf{u}_r$ in $\mathbf{u}_r$ from

$$\Delta u_r = (1)\,\Delta\theta,$$

in which the factor (1) reminds us that the two unit vectors in Fig. 11–10b have unit length. The above equation will be correct if $\Delta\theta$ is small enough so that we can neglect the difference between the chord and the arc in the small triangle in Fig. 11–10b. The change in $\mathbf{u}_r$ is a vector, $\Delta\mathbf{u}_r$, whose magnitude is given by the above equation; its *direction*, again assuming that $\Delta\theta$ is small enough, is given by the unit vector $\mathbf{u}_\theta$. This follows because, if $\Delta\mathbf{u}_r$ in Fig. 11–10b is translated to point $P$ in Fig. 11–10a, we see that, as $\Delta\theta \to 0$, it points in the direction of $\mathbf{u}_\theta$. Thus we find

$$\Delta\mathbf{u}_r \cong \mathbf{u}_r\,\Delta\theta.$$

Dividing by $\Delta t$ and allowing $\Delta t$ to approach zero, we have

$$\frac{d\mathbf{u}_r}{dt} = \mathbf{u}_\theta \frac{d\theta}{dt} = \mathbf{u}_\theta \omega. \tag{11-13}$$

Substituting these results into Eq. 11–12 yields, then,

$$\mathbf{v} = \mathbf{u}_\theta \omega r. \tag{11-14a}$$

The scalar relationship that corresponds to this is

$$v = \omega r \tag{11-14b}$$

and is one of the relationships, obtained before, connecting the linear speed $v$ of a particle in circular motion with its angular speed $\omega$.

To find the relation between linear and angular acceleration we differentiate Eq. 11–14a, remembering that $r$ is a constant although $\mathbf{u}_\theta$ and $\omega$ vary. We have

$$\frac{d\mathbf{v}}{dt} = \mathbf{u}_\theta \frac{d\omega}{dt} r + \omega \frac{d\mathbf{u}_\theta}{dt} r. \tag{11-15}$$

Now $d\mathbf{v}/dt = \mathbf{a}$, the linear acceleration of the particle and $d\omega/dt = \alpha$, its angular acceleration. From Fig. 11–10c the student, guided by the derivation of Eq. 11–13, should be able to prove that

$$\frac{d\mathbf{u}_\theta}{dt} = -\mathbf{u}_r \omega. \tag{11-16}$$

The minus sign comes in because when we translate $\Delta\mathbf{u}_\theta$ in Fig. 11–10c to point $P$, we see that, as $\Delta\theta \to 0$, it points radially inward, in the direction opposite to $\mathbf{u}_r$.

Making these substitutions into Eq. 11–15 yields

$$a = u_\theta \alpha r - u_r \omega^2 r. \qquad (11\text{–}17)$$

Thus, as we know from Section 4–5, **a** has a radial (or centripetal) component $a_R$ and a tangential component $a_T$. Their magnitudes, from Eq. 11–17, are

$$a_T = \alpha r \qquad (11\text{–}18a)$$

and (using Eq. 11–14b)

$$a_R = \omega^2 r = v^2/r. \qquad (11\text{–}18b)$$

This last is the familiar result derived in Section 4–4. In Supplementary Topic I we derive the relations between the linear and angular kinematic variables for a particle free to move in a plane but not restricted to circular motion. Equations 11–14a and 11–17 will prove to be special cases of the more general relationships derived there.

Equations 11–14a and 11–17 are relations between the linear kinematic variables in vector form and the angular kinematic variables in scalar form. We should be able to derive relationships in which *each* set of variables is expressed in vector form. Let us do so now. This will be especially useful in cases where the axis of rotation is not fixed.

Figure 11–11 shows the vectors **r**, **v**, $a_T$, $a_R$, **ω**, and **α** for the rotating particle of Fig. 11–7b. The angular quantities are on the axis of rotation, pointing in the direction given by the right-hand rule of page 25. We declare—and shall prove—that the relationships we seek are

$$\mathbf{v} = \boldsymbol{\omega} \times \mathbf{r} \qquad (11\text{–}19)$$

and

$$\mathbf{a} = \mathbf{a}_T + \mathbf{a}_R, \qquad (11\text{–}20a)$$

in which

$$\mathbf{a}_T = \boldsymbol{\alpha} \times \mathbf{r} \quad \text{and} \quad \mathbf{a}_R = \boldsymbol{\omega} \times \mathbf{v}$$
$$(11\text{–}20b)$$

**Fig. 11–11**  The directions of the vectors **r**, **v**, $a_T$, $a_R$, **ω** and **α** for a particle rotating in a circle about the $z$-axis.

In Section 2–4 (which the student should now reread) we defined the vector product of two vectors. If $\mathbf{c} = \mathbf{a} \times \mathbf{b}$, then the *magnitude* of **c** is $ab \sin \phi$, where $\phi$ is the angle between **a** and **b**. In applying this part of the definition to Eqs. 11–19 and 11–20 we note (see Fig. 11–11) that **ω** and **r**, **ω** and **v**, and **α** and **r** are each mutually perpendicular; thus the angle $\phi$ for each of these three pairs of vectors is 90°. In Eq. 11–19 we have, for magnitudes

$$v = \omega r \sin 90° = \omega r,$$

which is exactly Eq. 11–14b. In Eqs. 11–20b we have, for magnitudes

$$a_R = \omega v = \omega(\omega r) = \omega^2 r$$

and

$$a_T = \alpha r.$$

These relations agree with Eqs. 11–18b and a exactly.

It remains to be seen whether *directions* are correctly given by Eqs. 11–19 and 11–20b. For the vector product $\mathbf{c} = \mathbf{a} \times \mathbf{b}$, Fig. 2–12 shows that the direction of c is found by sweeping **a** into **b** through the (smaller) angle between them with the fingers of the right hand; the extended right thumb then points in the direction of **c**. The student can readily check that, in Fig. 11–11, the directions of the vectors **v**, $a_T$ and $a_R$ are indeed correctly given by Eqs. 11–19 and 11–20b.

## QUESTIONS

**1.** In Section 11–1 it was stated that, in general, six variables are required to locate a rigid body with respect to a particular reference frame. How many variables are required to locate the body of Fig. 11–2 with respect to the $x$-$y$ frame shown in that figure? If this number is not six, account for the difference.

**2.** An irregular body is free to rotate about its center of mass which is placed at the origin of a reference frame. How would you specify its orientation?

**3.** Could the angular quantities $\theta$, $\omega$, and $\alpha$ be expressed in terms of degrees instead of radians in the kinematical equations?

**4.** Explain why the radian measure of angle is equally satisfactory for all systems of units. Is the same true for degrees?

**5.** What is the angular speed of the second hand of a watch? Of the minute hand? Could you conveniently express the motion of these hands in terms of linear variables?

**6.** How could you express simply the relationship between the angular velocities of a pair of gears which are coupled?

**7.** A wheel is rotating about an axis through its center perpendicular to the plane of the wheel. Consider a point on the rim. When the wheel rotates with *constant angular velocity*, does the point have a radial acceleration? A tangential acceleration? When the wheel rotates with *constant angular acceleration*, does the point have a radial acceleration? A tangential acceleration? Do the magnitudes of these accelerations change?

**8.** Suppose you were asked to determine the equivalent distance traveled by a phonograph needle in playing, say, a 12-in., $33\frac{1}{3}$ rpm record. What information do you need? Discuss from the points of view of reference frames (a) fixed in the room, and (b) fixed on the rotating record.

**9.** (a) Describe the vector that would represent the angular velocity of the earth rotating about its axis. (b) Describe the vector that would represent the angular velocity of the earth rotating about the sun.

**10.** It is convenient to picture rotational vectors as lying along the axis of rotation. Is there any reason why they could not be pictured as merely parallel to the axis, but located anywhere? Recall that we are free to slide a displacement vector along its own direction or translate it sideways without changing its value.

**11.** In a centrifuge particles will tend to separate from the fluid in which they are suspended if their density (mass/volume) differs from that of the fluid. Discuss the dynamical principles upon which the operation of a centrifuge depends. View the situation from both an inertial (laboratory) frame and a noninertial (rotating) frame.

**12.*** A marksman stands at the center of a merry-go-round firing at a target fixed to a post on its outer perimeter. How, if at all, must the man take into account the (constant) angular velocity of the merry-go-round if he is to hit the target? What if the positions of marksman and target were reversed?

**13.*** A man on a merry-go-round rotating at constant angular velocity $\omega$ releases a cake of ice that he had been holding fixed to the merry-go-round at a radial distance $r_0$ from the center. Describe the motion of the ice in the reference frame of (a) a ground observer and (b) the man on the merry-go-round. Neglect frictional forces but describe all other forces.

---

* See Supplementary Topic I.

**14.*** A man on a rotating merry-go-round kicks a cake of ice outward along a radial line. What is its subsequent motion as seen by an observer (a) on the merry-go-round, and (b) on the ground? Assume that frictional forces may be neglected.

## PROBLEMS

**1.** A phonograph record on a turntable rotates at 33 rev/min. What is the linear speed of a point on the record at the needle at (a) the beginning and (b) the end of the recording? The distances of the needle from the turntable axis are $5\frac{7}{8}$ and $2\frac{7}{8}$ in., respectively, at these two positions.

**2.** A solar day is the time interval between two successive appearances of the sun overhead at a given longitude, that is, the time for one complete rotation of the earth relative to the sun. A sidereal day is the time for one complete rotation of the earth relative to the fixed stars, that is, the time interval between two successive overhead observations of a fixed direction in the heavens called the vernal equinox. (a) Show that there is exactly one less (mean) solar day in a year than there are (mean) sidereal days in a year. (b) If the (mean) solar day is exactly 24 hr, how long is a (mean) sidereal day?

**3.** One method of measuring the speed of light makes use of a rotating toothed wheel. A beam of light passes through a slot at the outside edge of the wheel, as in Fig. 11–12, travels to a distant mirror, and returns to the wheel just in time to pass through the next slot in the wheel. One such toothed wheel has a radius of 5.0 cm and 500 teeth at its edge. Measurements taken when the mirror was 500 meters from the wheel indicated a speed of light of $3.0 \times 10^5$ km/sec. (a) What was the (constant) angular speed of the wheel? (b) What was the linear speed of a point on its edge?

**Fig. 11–12**

**4.** The angular speed of an automobile engine is increased from 1200 rpm to 3000 rpm in 12 sec. (a) What is its angular acceleration, assuming it to be uniform? (b) How many revolutions does the engine make during this time?

**5.** A phonograph turntable rotating at 78 rev/min slows down and stops in 30 sec after the motor is turned off. (a) Find its (uniform) angular acceleration. (b) How many revolutions did it make in this time?

**6.** A wheel has a constant angular acceleration of 3.0 radians/sec². In a 4.0-sec interval it turns through an angle of 120 radians. Assuming the wheel started from rest, how long had it been in motion at the start of this 4.0-sec interval?

---

\* See Supplementary Topic I.

**7.** A heavy flywheel rotating on its axis is slowing down because of friction in its bearings. At the end of the first minute its angular velocity is 0.90 of its angular velocity $\omega_0$ at the start. Assuming constant frictional forces, find its angular velocity at the end of the second minute.

**8.** The angle turned through by the flywheel of a generator during a time interval $t$ is given by

$$\theta = at + bt^3 - ct^4,$$

where $a$, $b$, and $c$ are constants. What is the expression for its angular acceleration?

**9.** A body moves in the $x$–$y$ plane such that $x = R \cos \omega t$ and $y = R \sin \omega t$. Here $x$ and $y$ are the coordinates of the body, $t$ is the time, and $R$ and $\omega$ are constants. (a) Eliminate $t$ between these equations to find the equation of the curve in which the body moves. What is this curve? What is the meaning of the constant $\omega$? (b) Differentiate the equations for $x$ and $y$ with respect to the time to find the $x$ and $y$ components of the velocity of the body, $v_x$ and $v_y$. Combine $v_x$ and $v_y$ to find the magnitude and direction of **v**. Describe the motion of the body. (c) Differentiate $v_x$ and $v_y$ with respect to the time to obtain the magnitude and direction of the resultant acceleration.

**10.** A wheel rotates with an angular acceleration $\alpha$ given by

$$\alpha = 4at^3 - 3bt^2,$$

where $t$ is the time and $a$ and $b$ are constants. If the wheel has an initial angular speed $\omega_0$, write the equations for (a) the angular speed and (b) the angle turned through as functions of time.

**11.** The earth's orbit about the sun, although elliptical, is almost a circle. (a) Calculate the angular velocity of the earth (regarded as a particle) about the sun and its average linear speed in its orbit. (b) What is the centripetal acceleration of the earth with respect to the sun?

**12.** (a) What is the angular speed about the polar axis of a point on the earth's surface at a latitude of 45° N? What is the linear speed? (b) How do these compare with the similar values for a point at the equator?

**13.** What is the ratio of the centripetal acceleration, associated with the earth's rotation, of a point on the equator, to the centripetal acceleration of the earth itself, associated with its motion around the sun? Assume a circular orbit.

**14.** What is the centripetal acceleration of a point on the rim of a 12-in. record rotating at $33\frac{1}{3}$ rev/min?

**15.** An automobile traveling 60 miles/hr has wheels of 30-in. diameter. (a) What is the angular speed of the wheels about the axle? (b) If the wheels are brought to a stop uniformly in 30 turns, what is the angular acceleration? (c) How far does the car advance during this braking period?

**16.** (a) If an airplane propeller of radius 5.0 ft rotates at 2000 rpm and the airplane is propelled at a ground speed of 100 miles/hr, what is the speed of a point on the tip of the propeller? (b) What kind of path does this point traverse?

**17.** What is the angular speed of a car rounding a circular turn of radius 360 ft at 30 miles/hr?

**18.** A rigid body, starting at rest, rotates about a fixed axis with constant angular acceleration. (a) Express the radial acceleration and the tangential acceleration of a particle in the body in terms of the angular acceleration of the body. Let the particle be a distance $r$ from the axis. (b) If the resultant acceleration of the particle at some instant makes an angle of 60° with the tangential acceleration, what total angle has the body turned through to that instant?

**19.** Derive Eq. 11–20 by differentiation of Eq. 11–19.

**20.*** An insect of mass $8.0 \times 10^{-2}$ gm walks out with a constant speed of 1.6 cm/sec along a radial line marked on a phonograph turntable rotating at a constant angular velocity of $33\frac{1}{3}$ rev/min.    (a) Find the velocity and acceleration of the insect as seen by the ground observer when the insect is 12 cm from the axis of rotation.    (b) What must the minimum coefficient of friction be to allow the insect to get all the way to the edge of the turntable (radius = 16 cm) without slipping?    (c) In what way are the results of (a) and (b) changed if the turntable is given an angular acceleration that increases its angular velocity?

**21.*** A virus particle in solution in a centrifuge is, at a particular moment, at a distance of 6.5 cm from the axis of rotation and moving radially outward at a relatively constant speed.    The centrifuge is rotating at 55,000 rev/min.    Discuss the motion quantitatively, giving the magnitude of all forces and accelerations as viewed from a reference frame (a) rotating with the centrifuge tube and (b) fixed in the laboratory.

---

* See Supplementary Topic I.

# Rotational Dynamics I

## 12–1 Introduction

In Chapter 11 we considered the kinematics of rotation. In this chapter, following the pattern of our study of translational motion, we study the causes of rotation, a subject called *rotational dynamics*. Rotating systems are made up of particles and we have already learned how to apply the laws of classical mechanics to the motion of particles. For this reason rotational dynamics should contain no features that are fundamentally new. In the same way rotational kinematics contained no basic new features, the rotational parameters $\theta$, $\omega$, and $\alpha$ being related to corresponding translational parameters $x$, $v$, and $a$ for the particles that make up the rotating system. As in Chapter 11, however, it is very useful to recast the concepts of translational motion into a new form, especially chosen for its convenience in describing rotating systems.

We restricted our kinematical studies in Chapter 11 to a single but important special case, the rotation of a rigid body about an axis that is fixed in the reference frame in which we make our measurements. In studying rotational dynamics we start from a more fundamental point of view, that of a single particle viewed from an inertial reference frame. Later we shall generalize to systems of many particles, including the special case of a rigid body rotating about a fixed axis. In Chapter 13 we shall discuss the rotation of rigid bodies about axes that are *not* fixed in an inertial reference frame.

## 12–2 Torque Acting on a Particle

In translational motion we associate a *force* with the *linear acceleration* of a body. In rotational motion, what quantity shall we associate with the *angular acceleration* of a body? It cannot be simply force because, as experiment with a heavy revolving door teaches us, a given force (vector) can produce various angular accelerations of the door depending on where the force is applied and how it is directed; a force applied to the hinge line cannot produce any angular acceleration, whereas a force of given magnitude applied at right angles to the door at its outer edge produces a maximum acceleration.

We shall call the rotational analogue of force *torque* and shall now define it for the special case of a single particle observed from an inertial reference frame. Later we shall extend the torque concept to systems of particles (including rigid bodies) and shall show that torque is intimately associated with angular acceleration.

If a force **F** acts on a single particle at a point $P$ whose position with respect to the origin $O$ of the inertial reference frame is given by the displacement vector **r** (Fig. 12–1), the *torque* **τ** acting on the particle *with respect to the origin $O$* is defined as

$$\boldsymbol{\tau} = \mathbf{r} \times \mathbf{F}. \tag{12–1}$$

Torque is a vector quantity. Its magnitude is given by

$$\tau = rF \sin \theta, \tag{12–2a}$$

where $\theta$ is the angle between **r** and **F**; its direction is normal to the plane formed by **r** and **F**. The sense is given by the right-hand rule for the vector product of two vectors, namely, one swings **r** into **F** through the smaller angle between them with the curled fingers of the right hand; the direction of the extended thumb then gives the direction of **τ**.

Torque has the same dimensions as force times distance, or in terms of our assumed fundamental dimensions, $M$, $L$, $T$, it has the dimensions

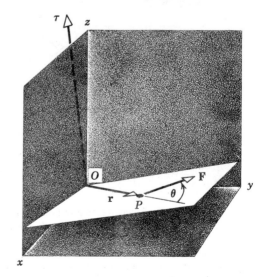

**Fig. 12–1** A force **F** is applied to a particle $P$, displaced **r** relative to the origin. The force vector makes an angle $\theta$ with the radius vector **r**. The torque **τ** about $O$ is shown. Its direction is perpendicular to the plane formed by **r** and **F** with the sense given by the right-hand rule.

$ML^2T^{-2}$. These are the same as the dimensions of work. However, torque and work are very different physical quantities. Torque is a vector and work is a scalar, for example. The unit of torque may be the nt-meter or lb-ft, among other possibilities.

Notice (Eq. 12–1) that the torque produced by a force depends not only on the magnitude and on the direction of the force but also on the point of application of the force relative to the origin, that is, on the vector **r**. In particular, when particle $P$ is at the origin, so that the line of action of **F** passes through the origin, **r** is zero and the torque **τ** about the origin is zero.

We can also write the magnitude of **τ** (Eq. 12–2a) either as

$$\tau = (r \sin \theta) F = Fr_{\perp}, \tag{12–2b}$$

or as

$$\tau = r(F \sin \theta) = rF_{\perp}, \tag{12–2c}$$

in which, as Fig. 12–2a shows, $r_{\perp}$ ($= r \sin \theta$) is the component of **r** at right angles to the line of action of **F**, and $F_{\perp}$ ($= F \sin \theta$) is the component of **F**

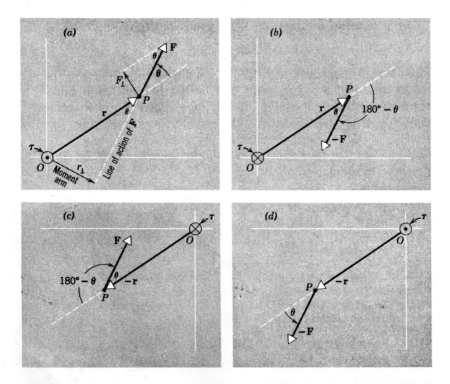

**Fig. 12–2** The plane shown is that defined by **r** and **F** in Fig. 12–1. (a) The magnitude of **τ** is given by $Fr_{\perp}$ (Eq. 12–2b) or by $rF_{\perp}$ (Eq. 12–2c). (b) Reversing **F** reverses the direction of **τ**. (c) Reversing **r** reverses the direction of **τ**. (d) Reversing **F** and **r** leaves the direction of **τ** unchanged. The directions of **τ** are represented by ⊙ (perpendicularly out of the figure, the symbol representing the tip of an arrow) and by ⊗ (perpendicularly into the figure, the symbol representing the tail of an arrow).

at right angles to **r**.   Torque is often called the *moment of force* and $r_\perp$ in Eq. 12–2*b* is called the *moment arm*.   Equation 12–2*c* shows that only the component of **F** perpendicular to **r** contributes to the torque.   In particular, when $\theta$ equals 0 or 180°, there is no perpendicular component $(F_\perp = F \sin \theta = 0)$; then the line of action of the force passes through the origin and the moment arm $r_\perp$ about the origin is also zero.   In this case both Eq. 12–2*b* and Eq. 12–2*c* show that the torque $\tau$ is zero.

If, as in Fig. 12–2*b*, we reverse the direction of **F**, the magnitude of $\tau$ remains unchanged but the direction of $\tau$ is reversed.   Similarly, if, as in Fig. 12–2*c*, we reverse **r**, thereby changing the point of application of **F**, the magnitude of $\tau$ remains unchanged but the direction of $\tau$ is again reversed.

If, as in Fig. 12–2*d*, we reverse *both* **r** and **F**, then both the magnitude and the direction of $\tau$ remain unchanged.   These results follow formally from the facts that: (1) $\sin \theta = \sin (180° - \theta)$, so that Eq. 12–2*a* for the magnitude of $\tau$ is unaffected; (2) reversing the direction of *one* vector in a vector product (either **r** *or* **F**) reverses the direction of the product; and (3) reversing the directions of *both* vectors in a vector product (both **r** *and* **F**) leaves the direction of the product unchanged.   The student should verify the directions of $\tau$ shown in Fig. 12–2, using the right-hand rule.

## 12–3   Angular Momentum of a Particle

We have found *linear momentum* to be useful in dealing with the translational motion of single particles or of systems of particles (including rigid bodies).   For example, linear momentum is conserved in collisions.   For a single particle the linear momentum is $\mathbf{p} = m\mathbf{v}$ (Eq. 9–11); for a system of particles it is $\mathbf{P} = M\mathbf{v}_{cm}$ (Eq. 9–15) in which $M$ is the total system mass and $\mathbf{v}_{cm}$ is the velocity of the center of mass.   In rotational motion, what is the analog of linear momentum?   We call it *angular momentum* and we define it below for the special case of a single particle.   Later we shall broaden the definition to include systems of particles and shall show that angular momentum, as we define it, is as useful a concept in rotational motion as linear momentum is in translational motion.

Consider a particle of mass $m$ and linear momentum **p** at a position **r** relative to the origin $O$ of an inertial reference frame (Fig. 12–3).   We define the *angular momentum* **l** of the particle *with respect to the origin $O$* to be

$$\mathbf{l} = \mathbf{r} \times \mathbf{p}. \tag{12–3}$$

Angular momentum is a vector.   Its magnitude is given by

$$l = rp \sin \theta, \tag{12–4a}$$

where $\theta$ is the angle between **r** and **p**; its direction is normal to the plane formed by **r** and **p**.   The sense is given by the right-hand rule, namely, one swings **r** into **p**, through the smaller angle between them, with the curled fingers of the right hand; the extended right thumb then points in the direction of **l**.

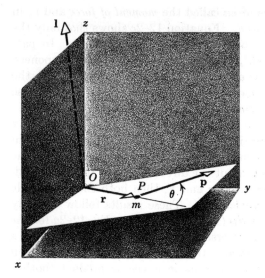

We can also write the magnitude of **l** either as

$$l = (r \sin \theta) p = p r_\perp, \qquad (12\text{–}4b)$$

or as

$$l = r(p \sin \theta) = r p_\perp, \qquad (12\text{–}4c)$$

in which $r_\perp$ ($= r \sin \theta$) is the component of **r** at right angles to the line of action of **p** and $p_\perp$ ($= p \sin \theta$) is the component of **p** at right angles to **r**. Angular momentum is often called *moment of* (linear) *momentum* and $r_\perp$ in Eq. 12–4b is often called the *moment arm*. Equation 12–4c shows that only the component of **p** perpendicular to **r** contributes to the angular momentum. When the angle $\theta$ between **r** and **p** is 0 or 180°, there is no perpendicular component ($p_\perp = p \sin \theta = 0$); then the line of action of **p** passes through the origin and $r_\perp$ is also zero. In this case both Eqs. 12–4b and 12–4c show that the angular momentum $l$ is zero.

We now derive an important relation between torque and angular momentum. We have seen that $\mathbf{F} = d(m\mathbf{v})/dt = d\mathbf{p}/dt$ for a particle. Let us take the vector product of **r** with both sides of this equation, obtaining

$$\mathbf{r} \times \mathbf{F} = \mathbf{r} \times \frac{d\mathbf{p}}{dt}.$$

But $\mathbf{r} \times \mathbf{F}$ is the torque, or moment of a force, about $O$. We can then write

$$\boldsymbol{\tau} = \mathbf{r} \times \frac{d\mathbf{p}}{dt}. \qquad (12\text{–}5)$$

Next we differentiate Eq. 12–3 and obtain

$$\frac{d\mathbf{l}}{dt} = \frac{d}{dt} (\mathbf{r} \times \mathbf{p}).$$

Now the derivative of a vector product is taken in the same way as the derivative of an ordinary product, except that we must not change the order of the terms. We have

$$\frac{d\mathbf{l}}{dt} = \frac{d\mathbf{r}}{dt} \times \mathbf{p} + \mathbf{r} \times \frac{d\mathbf{p}}{dt}.$$

But $d\mathbf{r}$ is the vector displacement of the particle in the time $dt$ so that $d\mathbf{r}/dt$ is the instantaneous velocity $\mathbf{v}$ of the particle. Also, $\mathbf{p}$ equals $m\mathbf{v}$, so that the equation can be rewritten as

$$\frac{d\mathbf{l}}{dt} = (\mathbf{v} \times m\mathbf{v}) + \mathbf{r} \times \frac{d\mathbf{p}}{dt}.$$

Now $\mathbf{v} \times m\mathbf{v} = 0$, because the vector product of two parallel vectors is zero. Therefore,

$$\frac{d\mathbf{l}}{dt} = \mathbf{r} \times \frac{d\mathbf{p}}{dt}. \qquad (12\text{–}6)$$

Inspection of Eqs. 12–5 and 12–6 shows that

$$\boldsymbol{\tau} = d\mathbf{l}/dt, \qquad (12\text{–}7)$$

which states that *the time rate of change of the angular momentum of a particle is equal to the torque acting on it.* This result is the rotational analog of Eq. 9–12, which stated that the time rate of change of the linear momentum of a particle is equal to the force acting on it, that is, that $\mathbf{F} = d\mathbf{p}/dt$.

Equation 12–7, like all vector equations, is equivalent to three scalar equations, namely

$$\tau_x = (dl/dt)_x \qquad \tau_y = (dl/dt)_y,$$
$$\tau_z = (dl/dt)_z. \qquad (12\text{–}8)$$

Hence, the $x$-component of the applied torque is given by the $x$-component of the change with time of the angular momentum. Similar results hold for the $y$- and $z$-directions.

▶ **Example 1.** A particle of mass $m$ is released from rest at point $a$ in Fig. 12–4, falling parallel to the (vertical) $y$-axis. (a) Find the torque acting on $m$ at any time $t$, with respect to origin $O$. (b) Find the angular momentum of $m$ at any time $t$, with respect to this same origin. (c) Show that the relation $\boldsymbol{\tau} = d\mathbf{l}/dt$ (Eq. 12–7) yields a correct result when applied to this familiar problem.

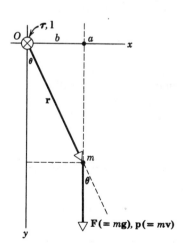

**Fig. 12–4** A particle of mass $m$ drops vertically from point $a$. The torque and the angular momentum about $O$ are directed perpendicularly into the figure, as shown by the symbol $\otimes$ at $O$.

(a) The torque is given by Eq. 12–1 or $\boldsymbol{\tau} = \mathbf{r} \times \mathbf{F}$, its magnitude being given by

$$\tau = rF \sin \theta.$$

In this example $r \sin \theta = b$ and $F = mg$ so that

$$\tau = mgb = \text{a constant.}$$

Note that the torque is simply the product of the force ($mg$) times the moment arm ($b$). The right-hand rule shows that $\boldsymbol{\tau}$ is directed perpendicularly into the figure.

(b) The angular momentum is given by Eq. 12–3 or $\mathbf{l} = \mathbf{r} \times \mathbf{p}$, its magnitude being given by

$$l = rp \sin \theta.$$

In this example $r \sin \theta = b$ and $p = mv = m(gt)$ so that

$$l = mgbt.$$

The right-hand rule shows that $\mathbf{l}$ is directed perpendicularly into the figure, which means that $\mathbf{l}$ and $\boldsymbol{\tau}$ are parallel vectors. The vector $\mathbf{l}$ changes with time in magnitude only, its direction always remaining the same in this case.

(c) Since $d\mathbf{l}$, the change in $\mathbf{l}$, and $\boldsymbol{\tau}$ are parallel we can replace the vector relation $\boldsymbol{\tau} = d\mathbf{l}/dt$ by the scalar relation

$$\tau = dl/dt.$$

Using the expressions for $\tau$ and $l$ from (a) and (b) above we have

$$mgb = \frac{d}{dt}(mgbt) = mgb,$$

which is an identity. Thus the relation $\boldsymbol{\tau} = d\mathbf{l}/dt$ yields correct results in this simple case. Indeed, if we cancel the constant $b$ out of the first two terms above and if we substitute for $gt$ the equivalent quantity $v$, we have

$$mg = \frac{d}{dt}(mv).$$

Since $mg = F$ and $mv = p$, this is the familiar result $F = dp/dt$. Thus, as we indicated earlier, relations such as $\boldsymbol{\tau} = d\mathbf{l}/dt$, though often vastly useful, are not new basic postulates of classical mechanics but are rather the reformulation of the Newtonian laws for rotational motion.

Note that the values of $\tau$ and $l$ depends on our choice of origin, that is, on $b$. In particular, if $b = 0$, then $\tau = 0$ and $l = 0$.    ◀

## 12–4    Systems of Particles

So far we have talked only about single particles. Let us now consider a system of many particles. To calculate the total angular momentum $\mathbf{L}$ of a system of particles about a given point, we must add vectorially the angular momenta of all the individual particles of the system about this same point. For a system containing $n$ particles we have, then,

$$\mathbf{L} = \mathbf{l}_1 + \mathbf{l}_2 + \cdots + \mathbf{l}_n = \sum_{i=1}^{i=n} \mathbf{l}_i,$$

in which the (vector) sum is taken over all particles in the system.

As time goes on, the total angular momentum $\mathbf{L}$ of the system about a fixed reference point (which we choose, as in our basic definition of $\mathbf{l}$ in Eq. 12–3, to be the origin of an inertial reference frame) may change. This change, $d\mathbf{L}/dt$, can arise from two sources: (1) torques exerted on the particles of the system by internal forces between the particles and (2) torques exerted on the particles of the system by external forces.

If Newton's third law holds in its so-called strong form, that is, if the forces between any two particles not only are equal and opposite but are also directed along the line joining the two particles, then the total internal torque is zero because the torque resulting from each internal action-reaction force pair is zero.

Hence the first source contributes nothing. For our reference point, therefore, only the second source remains, and we can write

$$\boldsymbol{\tau}_{\text{ext}} = d\mathbf{L}/dt, \tag{12–9}$$

where $\boldsymbol{\tau}_{\text{ext}}$ stands for the *sum* of *all* the *external* torques acting on the system. In words, *the time rate of change of the total angular momentum of a system of particles about the origin of an inertial reference frame is equal to the sum of the* external *torques acting on the system.* Later, for convenience, in situations in which no confusion is likely to arise, we shall drop the subscript on $\boldsymbol{\tau}_{\text{ext}}$.

Equation 12–9 is the generalization of Eq. 12–7 to many particles. When we have only one particle, there are no internal forces or torques. This relation (Eq. 12–9) holds whether the particles that make up the system are in motion relative to each other or whether they have fixed spatial relationships, as in a rigid body.

Equation 12–9 is the rotational analog of Eq. 9–17

$$\mathbf{F}_{\text{ext}} = d\mathbf{P}/dt \tag{9–17}$$

which tells us that for a system of particles (rigid body or not) the resultant external *force* acting on the system equals the time rate of change of the *linear momentum* of the system.

As we have derived it, Eq. 12–9 holds when $\boldsymbol{\tau}$ and $\mathbf{L}$ are measured with respect to the origin of an inertial reference frame. We may well ask whether it still holds if we measure these two vectors with respect to an arbitrary point (a particular particle, say) in the moving system. In general, such a point would move in a complicated way as the body or system of particles translated, tumbled, and changed its configuration and Eq. 12–9 would *not* apply to such a reference point. However, if the reference point is chosen to be the center of mass of the system, even though this point is not fixed in our reference frame, then Eq. 12–9 *does* hold.* This is another remarkable property of the center of mass. Thus we can separate the general motion of a system of particles into the trans-

---

*See Problem 8 of this chapter and Robert A. Becker, *Introduction to Theoretical Mechanics*, McGraw-Hill Book Co., 1954, Section 8–4.

lational motion of its center of mass (Eq. 9–17) and rotational motion about its center of mass (Eq. 12–9).

## 12–5   Kinetic Energy of Rotation and Rotational Inertia

We shall now confine our attention to an important special case of a system of particles, a rigid body. In a rigid body the particles in the system always maintain the same positions with respect to one another. In studying the rotation of a rigid body we shall consider first the special case, often encountered, in which the axis of rotation is fixed* in an inertial reference frame. Later we shall investigate more general systems and motions.

Let us now imagine a rigid body rotating with angular speed $\omega$ about an axis that is fixed in a particular inertial frame, as in Fig. 11–1. Each particle in such a rotating body has a certain amount of kinetic energy. A particle of mass $m$ at a distance $r$ from the axis of rotation moves in a circle of radius $r$ with an angular speed $\omega$ about this axis and has a linear speed $v = \omega r$. Its kinetic energy therefore is $\frac{1}{2}mv^2 = \frac{1}{2}mr^2\omega^2$. The total kinetic energy of the body is the sum of the kinetic energies of its particles.

If the body is rigid, as we assume in this section, $\omega$ is the same for all particles. The radius $r$ may be different for different particles. Hence the total kinetic energy $K$ of the rotating body can be written as

$$K = \tfrac{1}{2}(m_1 r_1{}^2 + m_2 r_2{}^2 + \cdots)\omega^2 = \tfrac{1}{2}(\Sigma\, m_i r_i{}^2)\omega^2.$$

The term $\Sigma\, m_i r_i{}^2$ is the sum of the products of the masses of the particles by the squares of their respective distances from the axis of rotation. If we denote this quantity by $I$, then

$$I = \Sigma\, m_i r_i{}^2 \tag{12–10}$$

is called the *rotational inertia*, or moment of inertia, of the body with respect to the particular axis of rotation. Note that *the rotational inertia of a body depends on the particular axis about which it is rotating* as well as on the shape of the body and the manner in which its mass is distributed. Rotational inertia has the dimensions $ML^2$ and is usually expressed in kg-m² or slug-ft².

In terms of rotational inertia we can now write the kinetic energy of the rotating rigid body as

$$K = \tfrac{1}{2}I\omega^2. \tag{12–11}$$

This is analogous to the expression for the kinetic energy of translation of a

---

* As stated in Section 12–4, we can separate the general motion of a system of particles into translational motion of its center of mass and rotational motion about its center of mass. Hence the considerations of this chapter apply also to rotations about an axis that is *not* fixed in an inertial reference frame, provided (1) the axis passes through the center of mass and (2) the moving axis always has the same direction in space, that is, the axis at one instant is parallel to the axis at any other instant. Although we shall often refer to a "fixed axis" in what follows we shall always mean to include this special case of a moving axis.

**Fig. 12–5** An experiment to show that $I_a < I_b < I_c$. The three lead bodies have the same mass $M$ but the mass is distributed differently about the axis of rotation.

body, $K = \frac{1}{2}Mv^2$. We have already seen that the angular speed $\omega$ is analogous to the linear speed $v$. Now we see that the rotational inertia $I$ is analogous to the mass, or the translational inertia $M$. Although the mass of a body does not depend on its location, the rotational inertia of a body does depend on the axis about which it is rotating.

We should understand that the rotational kinetic energy given by Eq. 12–11 is simply the sum of the ordinary translational kinetic energy of all the parts of the body and not a new kind of energy. Rotational kinetic energy is simply a convenient way of expressing the kinetic energy for a rotating rigid body.

Equations 12–10 and 12–11 show that the rotational energy of a body, for a given angular speed $\omega$, depends not only on the mass of the body but also on the way that mass is distributed around the axis of rotation. The experiment shown in Fig. 12–5 makes this convincing. The figure shows three identical aluminum shafts, to each of which is attached a body of mass $M$, made of lead. In $(a)$ the mass is very close to the shaft so that the quantities $r_i$ in Eq. 12–10 for the particles that make up the body are relatively small; in $(b)$ the particles are, on the average, farther from the shaft and in $(c)$, in which the body is a flywheel, they are still farther, corresponding to still larger values of $r_i$.

Now let us twist each handle until each shaft, starting from rest, is spinning at the same measured angular speed $\omega$. We know from experience that we shall need to do relatively little work on shaft $(a)$, somewhat more work on shaft $(b)$, and still more on shaft $(c)$. In fact, if we were not certain which body was attached to which shaft we could label the shafts with confidence using this technique. Since the work done on each shaft is equal to the kinetic energy $\frac{1}{2}I\omega^2$ imparted to each shaft, the experimental result, that $K_a < K_b < K_c$ when each shaft has the same angular speed $\omega$, leads to the conclusion that $I_a < I_b < I_c$. This is just what we expect from the defining equation for $I$ (Eq. 12–10). We shall see in Section 12–6 that just as the mass $M$, which we may call the translational inertia, is a measure of the resistance a body offers to a change in its translational motion, so $I$, the rotational inertia, is a measure of the resistance a body offers to a change in its rotational motion about a given axis.

▶ **Example 2.** Consider a body consisting of two spherical masses of 5.0 kg each connected by a light rigid rod 1.0 meter long (Fig. 12–6). Treat the spheres as point particles and neglect the mass of the rod. Determine the rotational inertia (or moment of inertia) of the body (*a*) about an axis normal to it through its center at $C$, and (*b*) about an axis normal to it through one sphere.

**Fig. 12–6** Example 2. Calculating the rotational inertia of a dumbell.

(*a*) If the axis is normal to the page through $C$, we have

$$I_C = \Sigma \, m_i r_i{}^2 = m_a r_a{}^2 + m_b r_b{}^2$$

$$= (5.0 \text{ kg})(0.50 \text{ meter})^2 + (5.0 \text{ kg})(0.50 \text{ meter})^2 = 2.5 \text{ kg-m}^2.$$

(*b*) If the axis is normal to the page through $A$ or $B$, we have

$$I_A = m_a r_a{}^2 + m_b r_b{}^2 = (5.0 \text{ kg})(0 \text{ meter})^2 + (5.0 \text{ kg})(1.0 \text{ meter})^2 = 5.0 \text{ kg-m}^2,$$

$$I_B = m_a r_a{}^2 + m_b r_b{}^2 = (5.0 \text{ kg})(1.0 \text{ meter})^2 + (5.0 \text{ kg})(0 \text{ meter})^2 = 5.0 \text{ kg-m}^2.$$

Hence the rotational inertia of this rigid dumbbell model is twice as great about an axis through an end as it is about an axis through the center. ◀

For a body that is not composed of discrete point masses but is instead a continuous distribution of matter, the summation in $I = \Sigma \, m_i r_i{}^2$ becomes an integration. We imagine the body to be subdivided into infinitesimal elements, each of mass $dm$. We let $r$ be the distance from such an element to the axis of rotation. Then the rotational inertia is obtained from

$$I = \int r^2 \, dm, \qquad (12\text{–}12)$$

where the integral is taken over the whole body. The procedure by which the summation $\Sigma$ of a discrete distribution is replaced by the integral $\int$ for a continuous distribution is the same as that discussed for the center of mass in Section 9–1.

For bodies of irregular shape the integrals may be hard to evaluate. For bodies of simple geometrical shape the integrals are relatively easy when an axis of symmetry is chosen as the axis of rotation.

Let us illustrate the procedure for an annular cylinder (or ring) about the cylinder axis (Fig. 12–7). The most convenient mass element is an infinitesimally thin cylindrical shell of radius $r$, thickness $dr$, and length $L$.

If the density of the material, that is, the mass per unit volume, is called $\rho$, then

$$dm = \rho\, dV,$$

where $dV$ is the volume of the cylindrical shell of mass $dm$. We have

$$dV = (2\pi r\, dr)L,$$

so that

$$dm = 2\pi L\rho r\, dr.$$

Then the rotational inertia about the cylinder axis is

$$I = \int r^2\, dm = 2\pi L \int_{R_1}^{R_2} \rho r^3\, dr.$$

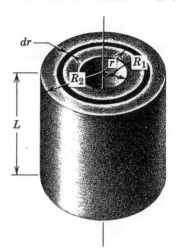

**Fig. 12–7**   Calculating the rotational inertia of an annular cylinder.

Here $R_1$ is the radius of the inner cylindrical wall and $R_2$ is the radius of the outer cylindrical wall.

If this body did not have a uniform constant density, we would have to know how $\rho$ depends on $r$ before we could carry out the integration. Let us assume for simplicity that the density is uniform. Then

$$I = 2\pi L\rho \int_{R_1}^{R_2} r^3\, dr = 2\pi L\rho\, \frac{R_2{}^4 - R_1{}^4}{4} = \rho\pi(R_2{}^2 - R_1{}^2)L\, \frac{R_2{}^2 + R_1{}^2}{2}.$$

The mass $M$ of the annular cylinder is the product of its density $\rho$ by its volume $\pi(R_2{}^2 - R_1{}^2)L$, or

$$M = \rho\pi(R_2{}^2 - R_1{}^2)L.$$

The rotational inertia of the *annular cylinder* (or ring) of mass $M$, inner radius $R_1$ and outer radius $R_2$, is therefore

$$I = \tfrac{1}{2}M(R_1{}^2 + R_2{}^2)$$

about the cylinder axis.

If the inner radius is zero, $R_1$ equals zero, and we have a solid cylinder (or disk). Then

$$I = \tfrac{1}{2}MR^2$$

about the cylinder axis, where $R$ is the radius of the solid cylinder of mass $M$.

A *hoop* can be thought of as a very thin-walled hollow cylinder. In that case

$$R_1 \cong R_2 \cong R,$$

and

$$I = MR^2$$

is the moment of a hoop of mass $M$ and radius $R$ about the cylinder axis.

## Table 12–1

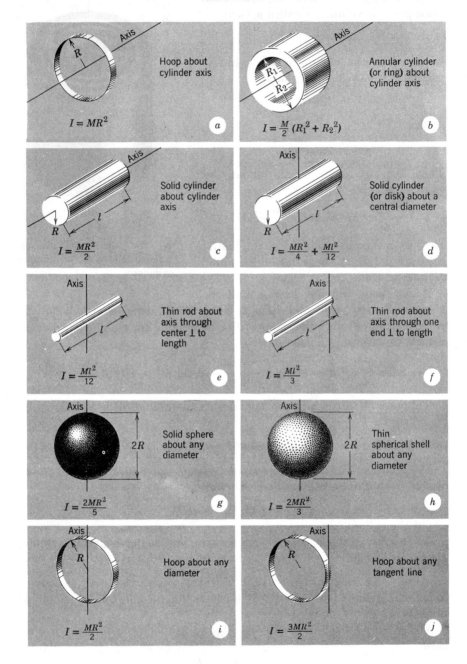

Hoop about cylinder axis

$$I = MR^2 \qquad a$$

Annular cylinder (or ring) about cylinder axis

$$I = \frac{M}{2}(R_1^2 + R_2^2) \qquad b$$

Solid cylinder about cylinder axis

$$I = \frac{MR^2}{2} \qquad c$$

Solid cylinder (or disk) about a central diameter

$$I = \frac{MR^2}{4} + \frac{Ml^2}{12} \qquad d$$

Thin rod about axis through center ⊥ to length

$$I = \frac{Ml^2}{12} \qquad e$$

Thin rod about axis through one end ⊥ to length

$$I = \frac{Ml^2}{3} \qquad f$$

Solid sphere about any diameter

$$I = \frac{2MR^2}{5} \qquad g$$

Thin spherical shell about any diameter

$$I = \frac{2MR^2}{3} \qquad h$$

Hoop about any diameter

$$I = \frac{MR^2}{2} \qquad i$$

Hoop about any tangent line

$$I = \frac{3MR^2}{2} \qquad j$$

This result for the thin hoop is obvious since every mass point in the hoop is the same distance $R$ from the central axis.   For the solid cylinder (or disk) having the *same mass* as the hoop, the rotational inertia (or moment of inertia) would naturally be less than that of the hoop, because most of the cylinder (or disk) is less than a distance $R$ from the axis.

The rotational inertias about certain axes of some common solids (of uniform density) are listed in Table 12–1.   Each of these results can be derived by integration in a manner similar to that of our illustration.   The total mass of the body is denoted by $M$ in each equation.

There is a simple and very useful relation between the rotational inertia $I$ of a body about any axis and its rotational inertia $I_{cm}$ with respect to a parallel axis *through the center of mass*.   If $M$ is the total mass of the body and $h$ the distance between the two axes, the relation is

$$I = I_{cm} + Mh^2. \qquad (12\text{–}13)$$

The proof of this relation (parallel-axis theorem) follows.   Let $C$ be the center of mass of the arbitrarily shaped body whose cross section is shown in Fig. 12–8.   The center of mass has coordinates $x_{cm}$ and $y_{cm}$.   We choose the $x$–$y$ plane to include $C$, so that $z_{cm}$ equals zero.   Consider an axis through $C$ at right angles to the plane of the paper and another axis parallel to it through $P$ at $(x_{cm} + a)$ and $(y_{cm} + b)$. The distance between the axes is $h = \sqrt{a^2 + b^2}$.   Then the square of the distance of a particle from the axis through $C$ is $x_i{}^2 + y_i{}^2$, where $x_i$ and $y_i$ measure the coordinates of a mass element $m_i$ relative to the axis through $C$.   The square of its distance from an axis through $P$ is $(x_i - a)^2 + (y_i - b)^2$.   Hence the rotational inertia about an axis through $P$ is

$$I = \Sigma\, m_i[(x_i - a)^2 + (y_i - b)^2]$$
$$= \Sigma\, m_i(x_i{}^2 + y_i{}^2) - 2a\, \Sigma\, m_i x_i - 2b\, \Sigma\, m_i y_i + (a^2 + b^2)\, \Sigma\, m_i.$$

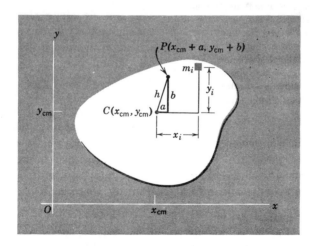

**Fig. 12–8**   Derivation of the parallel-axis theorem.   Knowing the rotational inertia about an axis through $C$, we can find its value about a parallel axis through $P$.

From the definition of center of mass,

$$\Sigma \, m_i x_i = \Sigma \, m_i y_i = 0,$$

so that the two middle terms are zero. The first term is simply the rotational inertia about an axis through the center of mass $I_{cm}$ and the last term is $Mh^2$ Hence it follows that $I = I_{cm} + Mh^2$.

With the aid of this formula several of the results of Table 12–1 can be deduced from previous results. For example, $(f)$ follows from $(e)$, and $(j)$ follows from $(i)$ with the aid of Eq. 12–13. The formula will prove to be especially useful in problems that combine rotational and translational motion.

## 12–6  Rotational Dynamics of a Rigid Body

In this section we continue to study the special case of a rigid body confined to rotate about an axis that is fixed* in an inertial reference frame.

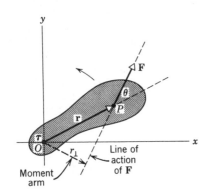

**Fig. 12–9** A force **F** acts on the particle $P$ in a rigid body, exerting a torque $\tau = \mathbf{r} \times \mathbf{F}$ on the body, with respect to an axis through $O$ at right angles to the plane of the figure. The moment arm $r_\perp$ is also shown, as is the torque $\tau$, which is a vector emerging perpendicularly from the page.

First we shall review the concept of torque as applied to such a rigid body; then we shall show how the torque is related to the angular acceleration of the body about this axis.

Suppose that we apply a torque $\tau$ to one of the particles in a rigid body. Since all the particles of a truly rigid body maintain a fixed spatial relationship to all the other particles that make up the body, the torque may be said to act on the rigid body as a whole. In general, the vector $\tau$ will not lie along the axis around which the body is free to rotate. We are not concerned in this section with the actual torques applied to the body but only with the components of these torques that lie along the axis.† Only these components can cause the body to rotate about this axis. Torque components perpendicular to the axis tend to turn the axis from its fixed position. We have specifically assumed, however, that the axis maintains a fixed direction. The body may, for example, be attached to a shaft that is held in a fixed position by bearings at each end; if an

---

* See the footnote on page 268.

† As for any other vector, we can speak of the vector component of a torque in any given direction, such as a given axis. For torque—and for other angular quantities—we also often speak of the component *around* a given direction or axis. The meaning is the same.

applied torque has a component at right angles to the shaft, tending to turn it, the bearings will automatically apply an equal and opposite counter-torque to the shaft, canceling the effect of this component.

In Fig. 12–9 (compare Fig. 11–3), we show a section through a rigid body that is free to rotate about the $z$-axis of an inertial reference frame. A force $\mathbf{F}$, taken for convenience to be in (or parallel to) the $x$-$y$ plane of the section, acts on a particle at point $P$ in the body, the position of $P$ with respect to the rotational axis (the $z$-axis) being defined by the vector $\mathbf{r}$. The torque acting on the particle at $P$ may be said to act on the rigid body as a whole and is given by Eq. 12–1, or

$$\boldsymbol{\tau} = \mathbf{r} \times \mathbf{F}.$$

Because we have chosen $\mathbf{r}$ and $\mathbf{F}$ to lie in a plane parallel to the $x$-$y$ plane, the torque $\boldsymbol{\tau}$ will point along the $z$-axis. The right-hand rule shows that it points perpendicularly *out of* the plane of Fig. 12–9. If $\mathbf{r}$ and $\mathbf{F}$ did *not* lie in the plane of the figure, $\boldsymbol{\tau}$ would not be parallel to the $z$-axis and we would concern ourselves here only with the component of $\boldsymbol{\tau}$ along this axis. The magnitude of $\boldsymbol{\tau}$ is given by Eq. 12–2 or

$$\tau = rF \sin \theta$$

which, as we have seen, can also be written as $\tau = rF_\perp$ or $\tau = Fr_\perp$.

▶ **Example 3.**    A wagon wheel is free to rotate about a horizontal axis through $O$. A force of 10 lb is applied to a spoke at the point $P$, 1.0 ft from the center. $OP$ makes an angle of 30° with the horizontal ($x$-axis) and the force is in the plane of the wheel making an angle of 45° with the horizontal ($x$-axis). What is the torque on the wheel?

The angle between the displacement vector $\mathbf{r}$ from $O$ to $P$ and the applied force $\mathbf{F}$ (Fig. 12–10) is $\theta$, where

$$\theta = 45° - 30° = 15°.$$

Then the magnitude of the torque is

$$\tau = rF \sin \theta$$

$$= (1.0 \text{ ft})(10 \text{ lb})(\sin 15°) = 2.6 \text{ lb-ft}.$$

It is clear that we can obtain this same result from $\tau = rF_\perp$ or $\tau = Fr_\perp$ as well (see Eqs. 12–2). The torque ($\boldsymbol{\tau} = \mathbf{r} \times \mathbf{F}$) is a vector pointing out ⊙ along the axis through $O$ having a magnitude 2.6 lb-ft.    ◀

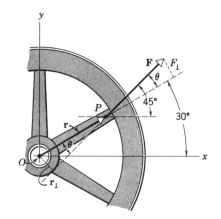

**Fig. 12–10**    Example 3.

We now investigate the relationship between the torque applied to the rigid body of Fig. 12–9 and the angular acceleration of this body. Let us observe the rigid body for an infinitesimal time $dt$, during which it will rotate through an infinitesimal angle $d\theta$. We have seen earlier that we can describe the rotation of a rigid body about a fixed axis by examining the motion of any single point fixed in the body, such as $P$ in Fig. 12–9. For convenience, then, we ignore the body itself in Fig. 12–11 and focus our attention on the representative point $P$ and on the vector $\mathbf{r}$ which locates point $P$ with respect to the axis of rotation.

During the time $dt$, the point $P$ will move an infinitesimal distance $ds$ along a circular path of radius $r$ as the body rotates through an infinitesimal angle $d\theta$, where

$$ds = r\, d\theta.$$

The work $dW$ done by this force during this small rotation is

$$dW = \mathbf{F} \cdot d\mathbf{s} = F \cos \phi\, ds$$
$$= (F \cos \phi)(r\, d\theta),$$

where $F \cos \phi$ is the component of $\mathbf{F}$ in the direction of $d\mathbf{s}$.

The term $(F \cos \phi)r$, however, is the magnitude of the instantaneous torque exerted by $\mathbf{F}$ on the rigid body about the axis perpendicular to the page through $O$, so that

$$dW = \tau\, d\theta. \qquad (12\text{–}14)$$

**Fig. 12–11** In time $dt$ point $P$ in the rigid body of Fig. 12–9 moves a distance $ds$ along the arc of a circle of radius $r$. The rigid body (not shown) and the vector $\mathbf{r}$ that locates point $P$ in it each rotate through an angle $d\theta$ during this interval.

This differential expression for the work done in rotation (about a fixed axis) is equivalent to the expression $dW = F\, dx$ for the work done in translation (along a straight line).

To obtain the rate at which work is done in rotational motion (about a fixed axis), we divide both sides of Eq. 12–14 by the infinitesimal time interval $dt$ during which the body is displaced through $d\theta$, obtaining

$$\frac{dW}{dt} = \tau \frac{d\theta}{dt}$$

or

$$P = \tau\omega,$$

giving the instantaneous power $P$. This last expression is the rotational analog of $P = Fv$ for translational motion (along a straight line).

If now a number of forces $\mathbf{F}_1$, $\mathbf{F}_2$, etc., are applied to the body in the plane normal to its axis of rotation, the work done by these forces on the body in a small rotation $d\theta$ will be

$$dW = F_1 \cos \phi_1 r_1\, d\theta + F_2 \cos \phi_2 r_2\, d\theta + \cdots,$$

$$= (\tau_1 + \tau_2 + \cdots)\, d\theta = \tau\, d\theta,$$

where $r_1\, d\theta$ equals $ds_1$, the displacement of the point at which $\mathbf{F}_1$ is applied, and $\phi_1$ is the angle between $\mathbf{F}_1$ and $d\mathbf{s}_1$, etc., and where $\tau$ is now the magnitude of the component of the *resultant* torque along the axis through $O$. In computing this sum each torque is considered positive or negative according to the sense in which it alone would tend to rotate the body about its axis. We can arbitrarily call the torque associated with a force positive if the effect of the force, acting alone, is to produce a counterclockwise rotation; then the torque is negative if the effect is to produce a clockwise rotation.

There is no internal motion of particles within a truly rigid body. The particles always maintain a fixed position relative to one another and move only with the body as a whole. Hence there can be no dissipation of energy within a truly rigid body. We can therefore equate the rate at which work is being done on the body to the rate at which its kinetic energy is increasing. The rate at which work is being done on the rigid body is

$$\frac{dW}{dt} = \tau \frac{d\theta}{dt} = \tau\omega. \tag{12–15}$$

The rate at which the kinetic energy of the rigid body is increasing is

$$\frac{d}{dt}\left(\tfrac{1}{2}I\omega^2\right).$$

But $I$ is constant because the body is rigid and the axis is fixed. Hence

$$\frac{d}{dt}\left(\tfrac{1}{2}I\omega^2\right) = \tfrac{1}{2}I\frac{d}{dt}\left(\omega^2\right) = I\omega\frac{d\omega}{dt} = I\omega\alpha. \tag{12–16}$$

Equating the right-hand members of Eqs. 12–15 and 12–16, we obtain

$$\tau\omega = I\alpha\omega,$$

or

$$\tau = I\alpha. \tag{12–17}$$

Equation 12–17 refers to the rotational motion of a rigid body about a fixed axis. The torque $\boldsymbol{\tau}$, the angular velocity $\boldsymbol{\omega}$, and the angular acceleration $\boldsymbol{\alpha}$ are all constrained to point along this axis, in one direction or the other. The equivalent translational case is that in which the force $\mathbf{F}$ acting on a body, its velocity $\mathbf{v}$, and its acceleration $\mathbf{a}$ all point along a given straight line, in one direction or the other.

The above six quantities are vectors, but when they are directed along a fixed line, they can have only two directions. By taking one of these directions as $+$ and the other as $-$, we can treat these vectors algebraically and deal with their magnitudes only. Thus, in deriving Eq. 12–17 ($\tau = I\alpha$), we have simply transformed Newton's second law ($F = Ma$), written in scalar form suitable to describe rectilinear motion, into rotational terms. This suggests that just as we associate a force with the linear acceleration of a body, so we may associate a torque with the angular acceleration of a body about a given axis. The rotational inertia $I$ is a measure of the resistance a body offers to having its rotational motion changed by a given torque just as the translational inertia, or mass, $M$ is a measure of the resistance a body offers to having its translational motion changed by a given force.

In Table 12–2 we compare the translational motion of a rigid body along a straight line with the rotational motion of a rigid body about a fixed axis.

**Table 12–2**

| Rectilinear Motion | | Rotation about a Fixed Axis | |
|---|---|---|---|
| Displacement | $x$ | Angular displacement | $\theta$ |
| Velocity | $v = \dfrac{dx}{dt}$ | Angular velocity | $\omega = \dfrac{d\theta}{dt}$ |
| Acceleration | $a = \dfrac{dv}{dt}$ | Angular acceleration | $\alpha = \dfrac{d\omega}{dt}$ |
| Mass | $M$ | Rotational inertia | $I$ |
| Force | $F = Ma$ | Torque | $\tau = I\alpha$ |
| Work | $W = \int F\,dx$ | Work | $W = \int \tau\,d\theta$ |
| Kinetic energy | $\frac{1}{2}Mv^2$ | Kinetic energy | $\frac{1}{2}I\omega^2$ |
| Power | $P = Fv$ | Power | $P = \tau\omega$ |
| Linear momentum | $Mv$ | Angular momentum | $I\omega$ |

The rotation of a rigid body about a fixed axis (to which $\tau = I\alpha$ applies) is not the most general kind of rotary motion in that the body may not be rigid and the axis may not be fixed in an inertial reference frame. In this general case Eq. 12–9, or $\tau_{\text{ext}} = d\mathbf{L}/dt$, applies. As we have already pointed out, this is equivalent to Newton's second law for the general translational motion of a system of particles, namely, Eq. 9–17, or $\mathbf{F}_{\text{ext}} = d\mathbf{P}/dt$.

In the rest of this chapter we confine ourselves to the rotations of rigid bodies about fixed axes. In Chapter 13 we shall consider some more general kinds of rotary motion.

▶ **Example 4.** A uniform disk of radius $R$ and mass $M$ is mounted on an axle supported in fixed frictionless bearings, as in Fig. 12–12. A light cord is wrapped around the rim of the wheel and a steady downward pull $\mathbf{T}$ is exerted on the cord. Find the angular acceleration of the wheel and the tangential acceleration of a point on the rim.

The torque about the central axis is $\tau = TR$, and the rotational inertia of the disk about its central axis is $I = \frac{1}{2}MR^2$. From

$$\tau = I\alpha,$$

we have

$$TR = (\tfrac{1}{2}MR^2)\alpha,$$

or

$$\alpha = \frac{2T}{MR}.$$

If the mass of the disk is taken to be $M = 0.20$ slug, its radius $R = 0.50$ ft, and the force $T = 1.0$ lb, then

$$\alpha = \frac{(2)(1.0\ \text{lb})}{(0.20\ \text{slug})(0.50\ \text{ft})}$$

$$= 20\ \text{radians/sec}^2.$$

The tangential acceleration of a point on the rim is given by

$$a = R\alpha = (20\ \text{radians/sec}^2)(0.50\ \text{ft})$$
$$= 10\ \text{ft/sec}^2.$$

**Example 5.** Suppose that we hang a body of mass $m$ from the cord in the previous problem. Find the angular acceleration of the disk and the tangential acceleration of a point on the rim in this case.

Now, let $T$ be the tension in the cord. Since the suspended body will accelerate downward, the magnitude of the downward pull of gravity on it, $mg$, must exceed the magnitude of the upward pull of the cord on it, $T$. The acceleration $a$ of the suspended body is the same as the tangential acceleration of a point on the rim of the disk. From Newton's second law

**Fig. 12–12** Example 4. A steady downward force **T** produces rotation of the disk. Example 5. Here **T** is supplied by the falling mass $m$.

$$mg - T = ma.$$

The resultant torque on the disk is $TR$ and its rotational inertia is $\frac{1}{2}MR^2$, so that from

$$\tau = I\alpha$$

we obtain

$$TR = \tfrac{1}{2}MR^2\alpha.$$

Using the relation $a = R\alpha$, we can write this last equation as

$$2T = Ma.$$

Solving the first and last equations simultaneously leads to

$$a = \left(\frac{2m}{M + 2m}\right)g,$$

and

$$T = \left(\frac{Mm}{M + 2m}\right)g.$$

If now we let the disk have a mass $M = 0.20$ slug and a radius $R = 0.50$ ft as before, and we let the suspended body weigh 1.0 lb, we obtain

$$a = \frac{2mg}{M + 2m} = \frac{(2)(1.0 \text{ lb})}{(0.20 \text{ slug}) + (2)(\frac{1}{32} \text{ slug})} = 7.6 \text{ ft/sec}^2,$$

$$\alpha = \frac{a}{R} = \frac{(7.6 \text{ ft/sec}^2)}{0.50 \text{ ft}} = 15 \text{ radians/sec}^2.$$

Notice that the accelerations are less for a suspended 1.0-lb body than they were for a steady 1.0-lb pull on the string (Example 4). This corresponds to the fact that the tension in the string supplying the torque is now less than 1.0 lb, namely

$$T = \frac{Mmg}{M + 2m} = \frac{(0.20 \text{ slug})(1.0 \text{ lb})}{(0.20 + 2.0/32) \text{ slug}} = 0.76 \text{ lb}.$$

The tension in the string must be less than the weight of the suspended body if the body is to accelerate downward.

**Example 6.** Assuming that the disk of Example 5 starts from rest, compute the work done by the applied torque on the disk in 2.1 sec. Compute also the increase in rotational kinetic energy of the disk.

Since the applied torque is constant, the resulting angular acceleration is constant. The total angular displacement in constant angular acceleration is obtained from Eq. 11–5,

$$\theta = \omega_0 t + \tfrac{1}{2}\alpha t^2,$$

in which

$$\omega_0 = 0, \qquad \alpha = 15 \text{ radians/sec}^2, \qquad t = 2.1 \text{ sec},$$

so that

$$\theta = 0 + (\tfrac{1}{2})(15 \text{ radians/sec}^2)(2.1 \text{ sec})^2 = 34 \text{ radians}.$$

For constant torque the work done in a finite angular displacement is

$$W = \tau(\theta_2 - \theta_1),$$

in which

$$\tau = TR = (0.76 \text{ lb})(0.50 \text{ ft}) = 0.38 \text{ lb-ft},$$

and

$$\theta_2 - \theta_1 = \theta = 34 \text{ radians}.$$

Therefore

$$W = (0.38 \text{ lb-ft})(34 \text{ radians}) = 13 \text{ ft-lb}.$$

This work must result in an increase in rotational kinetic energy of the disk. Starting from rest the disk acquires an angular speed $\omega$.

The rotational energy is $\tfrac{1}{2}I\omega^2 = \tfrac{1}{2}(\tfrac{1}{2}MR^2)\omega^2$. To obtain $\omega$ we use Eq. 11–3,

$$\omega = \omega_0 + \alpha t,$$

in which

$$\omega_0 = 0, \qquad t = 2.1 \text{ sec}, \qquad \alpha = 15 \text{ radians/sec}^2,$$

so that

$$\omega = 0 + (15 \text{ radians/sec}^2)(2.1 \text{ sec}) = 32 \text{ radians/sec}.$$

Then

$$\tfrac{1}{2}I\omega^2 = (\tfrac{1}{4})(0.20 \text{ slug})(0.50 \text{ ft})^2(32 \text{ radians/sec})^2 = 13 \text{ ft-lb},$$

as before. Hence the increase in kinetic energy of the disk is equal to the work done by the resultant force on the disk, as it must be.

**Example 7.** Show that the conservation of mechanical energy holds for the system of Example 5.

The resultant force acting on the system is the force of gravity on the suspended body. This is a conservative force. Viewing the system as a whole, we see that the suspended body loses potential energy $U$ as it descends,

$$U = mgy,$$

where $y$ is the vertical distance through which the block descends. At the same time the suspended body gains kinetic energy of translation and the disk gains kinetic energy of rotation. The total gain in kinetic energy is

$$\tfrac{1}{2}mv^2 + \tfrac{1}{2}I\omega^2,$$

where $v$ is the linear speed of the suspended mass. We must show then that

$$mgy = \tfrac{1}{2}mv^2 + \tfrac{1}{2}I\omega^2.$$

For the linear motion starting from rest we have $v^2 = 2ay$. From Example 5, we obtained $a = 2\,mg/(M + 2m)$. Hence

$$mgy = \frac{mgv^2}{2a} = \tfrac{1}{2}\,mv^2\left(\frac{g}{a}\right) = \tfrac{1}{2}\,mv^2\left(\frac{M + 2m}{2m}\right) = \tfrac{1}{4}\,(M + 2m)v^2.$$

We also know that $\omega = v/R$ and $I = \tfrac{1}{2}MR^2$. Substituting these relations into the right-hand side of the conservation equation, we obtain

$$\tfrac{1}{2}mv^2 + \tfrac{1}{2}I\omega^2 = \tfrac{1}{2}mv^2 + \tfrac{1}{2}(\tfrac{1}{2}MR^2)(v^2/R^2) = \tfrac{1}{4}(M + 2m)v^2.$$

The mechanical energy is therefore conserved.

**Example 8.** Derive the relation $L = I\omega$, shown in Table 12–2, for the angular momentum of a rigid body confined to rotate about a fixed axis.

Starting from the scalar relation $\tau = I\alpha$ and the definition of $\alpha$ $(= d\omega/dt)$, we may write

$$\tau = I\alpha = I(d\omega/dt) = d(I\omega)/dt,$$

in which the last step is justified by the fact that $I$ is a constant for a given rigid body and a specified (fixed) axis of rotation.

Next we use the vector relation $\boldsymbol{\tau}_{\text{ext}} = d\mathbf{L}/dt$ (Eq. 12–9) and write the corresponding relation for the *scalar components*, $\tau$ and $dL$, of $\boldsymbol{\tau}_{\text{ext}}$ and $d\mathbf{L}$ along the fixed axis of rotation, obtaining

$$\tau = dL/dt.$$

Simply by comparing the two equations above we obtain the relation sought. namely

$$L = I\omega. \tag{12–18}$$

Like Eq. 12–17 $(\tau = I\alpha)$, this is a scalar relation holding for the rotation of a rigid body about a fixed axis. $L$ is the component along that axis of the vector angular momentum $\mathbf{L}$ of the rigid body and $I$ must refer to that same axis.

Equation 12–18 is the rotational analog of the expression $P = Mv$ for the *linear* momentum of a rigid body of mass $M$ in pure translational motion with linear speed $v$. It gives the *angular* momentum about a fixed axis of a rigid body having rotational inertia $I$ and angular speed $\omega$ about that same axis. ◀

## 12–7    The Combined Translational and Rotational Motion of a Rigid Body

Up until now we have considered only bodies rotating about some fixed axis. If a body is rolling, however, it is rotating about an axis and also moving translationally. Therefore it would seem that the motion of rolling bodies must be treated as a combination of translational and rotational motion. It is also possible, however, to treat a rolling body as though its motion is one of pure rotation. We wish to illustrate the equivalence of the two approaches.

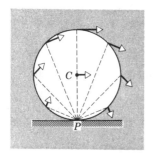

Consider, for example, a cylinder rolling along a level surface, as in Fig. 12–13. At any instant the bottom of the cylinder is at rest on the surface, since it does not slide. The axis normal to the diagram through the point of contact $P$ is called the *instantaneous axis of rotation*. At that instant the linear velocity of every particle of the cylinder is directed at right angles to the line joining the particle and $P$ and its magnitude is proportional to this distance. This is the same as saying that the cylinder is rotating about a fixed axis through $P$ with a certain angular speed $\omega$, *at that instant*. Hence, at a given instant the motion of the body is equivalent to a pure rotation. The total kinetic energy can, therefore, be written as

**Fig. 12–13** A rolling body may at any instant be thought of as rotating about a perpendicular axis through its point of contact $P$.

$$K = \tfrac{1}{2}I_P\omega^2, \tag{12–19}$$

where $I_P$ is the rotational inertia about the axis through $P$.

Let us now use the parallel axis theorem, which tells us that

$$I_P = I_{\text{cm}} + MR^2,$$

where $I_{\text{cm}}$ is the rotational inertia of the cylinder of mass $M$ and radius $R$ about a parallel axis through the center of mass. Equation 12–19 now becomes

$$K = \tfrac{1}{2}I_{\text{cm}}\omega^2 + \tfrac{1}{2}MR^2\omega^2. \tag{12–20}$$

The quantity $R\omega$ is the speed with which the center of mass of the cylinder is moving with respect to the fixed point $P$. Let $R\omega = v_{\text{cm}}$. Equation 12–20 then becomes

$$K = \tfrac{1}{2}I_{\text{cm}}\omega^2 + \tfrac{1}{2}Mv_{\text{cm}}^2. \tag{12–21}$$

Now notice that the speed of the center of mass with respect to $P$ is the same as the speed of $P$ with respect to the center of mass. Hence, the angular speed $\omega$ of the center of mass about $P$ as seen by someone at $P$ is the same as the angular speed of a particle at $P$ about $C$ as seen by someone at $C$ (moving along with the cylinder). This is equivalent to saying that any reference line in the cylinder turns through the same angle in a given time whether it is observed from a reference frame fixed with respect to the surface on which the cylinder is rolling or from a frame moving translationally with respect to this fixed frame. We can therefore interpret Eq. 12–21, which was derived on the basis of a pure rotational motion, in another way; that is, the first term, $\frac{1}{2}I_{cm}\omega^2$, is the kinetic energy the cylinder would have if it were merely rotating about an axis through its center of mass, without translational motion; and the second term, $\frac{1}{2}Mv_{cm}^2$, is the kinetic energy the cylinder would have if it were moving translationally with the speed of its center of mass, without rotating. Notice that there is now no reference at all to the instantaneous axis of rotation. In fact, Eq. 12–21 applies to any body that is moving and rotating about an axis perpendicular to its motion whether or not it is rolling on a surface.

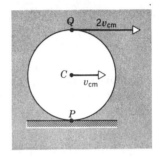

**Fig. 12–14** Since $Q$ and $C$ have the same angular velocity about $P$, therefore $Q$, being twice as far from $P$, moves with twice the linear velocity of $C$.

*The combined effects of translation of the center of mass and rotation about an axis through the center of mass are equivalent to a pure rotation with the same angular speed about an axis through the point of contact of a rolling body.*

To illustrate this result simply, let us consider the instantaneous speed of various points on the rolling cylinder. If the speed of the center of mass (as seen by an observer fixed with respect to the surface) is $v_{cm}$, the instantaneous angular speed about an axis through $P$ is $\omega = v_{cm}/R$. A point $Q$ at the top of the cylinder will therefore have a speed $\omega 2R = 2v_{cm}$ at that instant. The point of contact $P$ is instantaneously at rest. Hence, from the point of view of pure rotation about $P$, the situation is as shown in Fig. 12–14.

Now let us regard the rolling as a combination of translation of the center of mass and rotation about the cylinder axis through $C$. If we consider translation only, all points on the cylinder have the same speed $v_{cm}$ as the center of mass. This is shown in Fig. 12–15a. If we consider the rotation only, the center is at rest, whereas the point $Q$ at the top has a speed $+\omega R$ in the $x$-direction and the point $P$ at the bottom of the cylinder has a speed $-\omega R$ in the $-x$-direction. This is shown in Fig. 12–15b. Now let us combine these two results. Recalling that $\omega = v_{cm}/R$, we obtain

for the point $Q$     $v = v_{cm} + \omega R = v_{cm} + \dfrac{v_{cm}}{R}\,R = 2v_{cm},$

for the point $C$     $v = v_{cm} + 0 = v_{cm},$

for the point $P$     $v = v_{cm} - \omega R = v_{cm} - \dfrac{v_{cm}}{R}\,R = 0.$

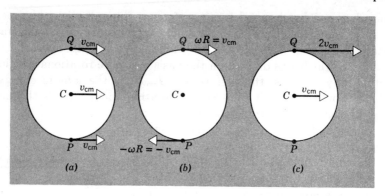

**Fig. 12–15**    (a) For pure translation, all points move with the same velocity.    (b) For pure rotation about $C$, opposite points move with opposite velocities.    (c) Combined rotation and translation is obtained by adding together corresponding vectors in (a) and (b).

This result, shown in Fig. 12–15c is exactly the same as that obtained from the purely rotational point of view, Fig. 12–14.

▶ **Example 9.**    Consider a solid cylinder of mass $M$ and radius $R$ rolling down an inclined plane without slipping. Find the speed of its center of mass when the cylinder reaches the bottom.

The situation is illustrated in Fig. 12–16. We can use the conservation of energy to solve this problem. The cylinder is initially at rest. In rolling down the incline the cylinder loses potential energy of an amount $Mgh$, where $h$ is the height of the incline. It gains kinetic energy equal to

$$\tfrac{1}{2}I_{cm}\omega^2 + \tfrac{1}{2}Mv^2,$$

where $v$ is the linear speed of the center of mass and $\omega$ is the angular speed about the center of mass at the bottom.

We have then the relation

$$Mgh = \tfrac{1}{2}I_{cm}\omega^2 + \tfrac{1}{2}Mv^2,$$

in which

$$I_{cm} = \tfrac{1}{2}MR^2 \quad \text{and} \quad \omega = \frac{v}{R}.$$

Hence

$$Mgh = \tfrac{1}{2}(\tfrac{1}{2}MR^2)\left(\frac{v}{R}\right)^2 + \tfrac{1}{2}Mv^2 = (\tfrac{1}{4} + \tfrac{1}{2})Mv^2,$$

$$v^2 = \tfrac{4}{3}gh \quad \text{or} \quad v = \sqrt{\tfrac{4}{3}gh}.$$

The speed of the center of mass would have been $v = \sqrt{2gh}$ if the cylinder had *slid* down a *frictionless* incline. The speed of the rolling cylinder is, therefore, less than the speed of the sliding cylinder, because for the rolling cylinder, part of the lost potential energy has been transformed into rotational kinetic energy, leaving less available for the translational part of the kinetic energy. Although the rolling cylinder arrives later at the bottom of the incline than an identical sliding cylinder started at the same time down a frictionless, but otherwise identical, incline, both

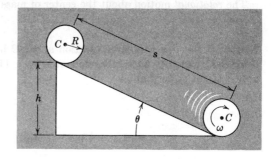

**Fig. 12–16** Example 9. A cylinder rolling down an incline.

arrive at the bottom with the same amount of energy; the rolling cylinder happens to be rotating as it moves, whereas the sliding one does not rotate as it moves.

Notice that static friction is needed to cause the cylinder to rotate. Remembering that friction is a dissipative force, how can you justify using the conservation of mechanical energy in this problem?

**Example 10.** The previous result was derived by use of energy methods. Solve the same problem using only dynamical methods.

The force diagram is shown in Fig. 12–17. $Mg$ is the weight of the cylinder acting vertically down through the center of mass,* $N$ is the normal force exerted by the incline on the cylinder, and $f$ is the force of static friction acting along the incline at the point of contact.

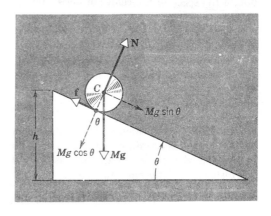

**Fig. 12–17** Example 10. Dynamic solution of the motion of a cylinder rolling down an incline.

The *translational* motion of a body is obtained by assuming that all the external forces act at its center of mass. Using Newton's second law, we obtain

$$N - Mg \cos \theta = 0 \qquad \text{for motion normal to the incline,}$$

and

$$Mg \sin \theta - f = Ma \qquad \text{for motion along the incline.}$$

---

* In drawing the vector diagram for this problem we tacitly assume that the total weight of the body can be thought of as acting at the center of mass. We saw in Section 9–2 that this is justified for analyzing the translational motion. However, later in the problem we use this result in analyzing the rotational motion as well. We shall justify this procedure in Section 14–3, where it is shown that the *weight* of a body can be considered to act at its center of mass for both translational *and* rotational motion.

The *rotational* motion about the center of mass follows from

$$\tau = I_{cm}\alpha.$$

Neither **N** nor $M\mathbf{g}$ can cause rotation about $C$ because their lines of action pass through $C$, and they have zero moment arms. The force of friction has a moment arm $R$ about $C$, so that

$$fR = I_{cm}\alpha.$$

But

$$I_{cm} = \tfrac{1}{2}MR^2 \quad \text{and} \quad \alpha = \frac{a}{R}$$

so that

$$f = I_{cm}\alpha/R = Ma/2.$$

Substituting this into the second translational equation, we find

$$a = \tfrac{2}{3}g \sin \theta.$$

That is, the acceleration of the center of mass for the rolling cylinder ($\tfrac{2}{3}g \sin \theta$) is less than the acceleration of the center of mass for the cylinder sliding down the incline ($g \sin \theta$).

This result holds at any instant, regardless of the position of the cylinder along the incline. The center of mass moves with constant linear acceleration. To obtain the speed of the center of mass, starting from rest, we use the relation

$$v^2 = 2as,$$

so that

$$v^2 = 2(\tfrac{2}{3}g \sin \theta)s = \tfrac{4}{3}g \frac{h}{s} s = \tfrac{4}{3}gh$$

or

$$v = \sqrt{\tfrac{4}{3}gh}.$$

This result is the same as that obtained before by the energy method. The energy method is certainly simpler and more direct. However, if we are interested in knowing what the forces are, such as **N** and **f**, we must use a dynamical method. This method determines the minimum force of static friction needed for rolling:

$$f = Ma/2 = (M/2)(\tfrac{2}{3}g \sin \theta) = \tfrac{1}{3}Mg \sin \theta.$$

What would happen if the force of static friction between the surfaces were less than this value?

**Example 11.** A sphere and a cylinder, having the same mass and radius, start from rest and roll down the same incline. Which body gets to the bottom first?
For a sphere $I_{cm}$ equals $\tfrac{2}{5}MR^2$. Using the dynamical method we obtain

$$Mg \sin \theta - f = Ma, \qquad \text{translation of cm,}$$

$$fR = I_{cm}\alpha = (\tfrac{2}{5}MR^2)(a/R), \qquad \text{rotation about cm,}$$

or

$$f = \tfrac{2}{5}Ma \quad \text{and} \quad a = \tfrac{5}{7}g \sin \theta, \quad \text{sphere.}$$

For the cylinder (Example 10)

$$a = \tfrac{2}{3}g \sin \theta, \qquad \text{cylinder.}$$

Hence the acceleration of the center of mass of the sphere is at all times greater than the acceleration of the center of mass of the cylinder. Since both bodies start from rest at the same instant, the sphere will reach the bottom first.

Which body has the greater rotational energy at the bottom? Which body has the greater translational energy at the bottom?

The student should note carefully that neither the mass nor the radius of the rolling object enters the previous results. How then would we expect the behavior of cylinders of different mass and radii to compare? How would we expect the behavior of spheres of different mass and radii to compare? How would the behavior of a cylinder and sphere having different masses and radii compare? ◄

## QUESTIONS

1. What are the dimensions of angular momentum? Can you find any significance in the fact that they are the same as those of energy multiplied by time?

2. Is the vector product of two vectors necessarily an axial vector?*

3. Can the mass of a body be considered as concentrated at its center of mass for purposes of computing its rotational inertia?

4. About what axis would a uniform cube have its minimum rotational inertia?

5. If two circular disks of the same weight and thickness are made from metals having different densities, which disk, if either, will have the larger rotational inertia about its central axis?

6. The rotational inertia of a body of rather complicated shape is to be determined. The shape makes a mathematical calculation from $\int r^2 \, dm$ exceedingly difficult. Suggest ways in which the rotational inertia could be measured *experimentally*.

7. Five solids are shown in cross section (Fig. 12–18). The cross sections have equal heights and maximum widths. The axes of rotation are perpendicular to the sections through the points shown. The solids have equal masses. Which one has the largest rotational inertia about a perpendicular axis through the center of mass? Which the smallest?

---

* See Supplementary Topic II.

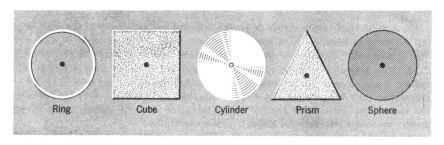

Ring    Cube    Cylinder    Prism    Sphere

Fig. 12–18

**8.** In Fig. 12–19*a* a meter stick, half of which is wood—the other half steel—is pivoted at the wooden end at *O* and a force is applied to the steel end at *a*. In Fig. 12–19*b* the stick is pivoted at the steel end at *O′* and the same force is applied at the wooden end at *a′*. Does one get the same angular acceleration in each case? Explain.

Fig. 12–19

**9.** A person can distinguish between a raw egg and a hard-boiled one by spinning each one on the table. Explain how.

**10.** Do the expressions for *a* and *T* in Example 5 give reasonable results for the special cases in which $g = 0$, $M = 0$, $M \to \infty$, $m = 0$, and $m \to \infty$?

**11.** The total momentum of a system of particles does not depend on the motions of the particles relative to the center of mass of the system. Can a similar statement be made about the total kinetic energy of a system of particles?

**12.** A cylindrical drum, pushed along by a board from an initial position shown in Fig. 12–20, rolls forward on the ground a distance $l/2$, equal to half the length of the board. There is no slipping at any contact. Where is the board then? How far has the man walked?

Fig. 12–20

**13.** A solid wooden sphere rolls down two different inclined planes of the same height but different inclines. Will it reach the bottom with the same speed in each case? Will it take longer to roll down one incline than the other? If so, which one and why?

**14.** Two heavy disks are connected by a short rod of much smaller radius. The system is placed on a narrow inclined plane so that the disks hang over the sides and the system rolls down on the rod without slipping (Fig. 12–21). Near the bottom of the incline the disks touch the horizontal table top and the system takes off with greatly increased translational speed. Explain carefully.

**15.** When a logger cuts down a tree he makes a cut on the side facing the direction in which he wants it to fall. Explain why. Would it be safe to stand directly behind the tree on the opposite side of the fall?

Fig. 12–21

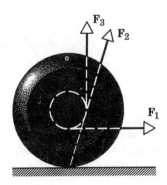

Fig. 12–22

16. A Yo-yo is resting on a horizontal table and is free to roll (Fig. 12–22). If the string is pulled by a horizontal force such as $F_1$, which way will the Yo-yo roll? What happens when the force $F_2$ is applied (its line of action passes through the point of contact of the Yo-yo and table)? If the string is pulled vertically with the force $F_3$, what happens?

17. State Newton's three laws of motion in words suitable for rotating bodies.

## PROBLEMS

1. (a) Given that $r = ix + jy + kz$ and $F = iF_x + jF_y + kF_z$ find the torque $\tau = r \times F$. (b) Show that if $r$ and $F$ lie in a given plane then $\tau$ has no component in that plane.

2. If we are given $r$, $p$, and $\theta$, we can calculate the angular momentum of a particle from Eq. 12–4a. Sometimes, however, we are given the components $(x,y,z)$ of $r$ and $(p_x,p_y,p_z)$ of $p$ instead. (a) Show that the components of $l$ along the $x$-, $y$-, and $z$-axes are then given by

$$l_x = yp_z - zp_y,$$

$$l_y = zp_x - xp_z,$$

$$l_z = xp_y - yp_x.$$

(b) Show that if the particle moves only in the $x$–$y$ plane, the resultant angular momentum vector has only a $z$-component.

3. (a) In Example 1, express $F$ and $r$ in terms of unit vectors and compute $\tau$. Do the same in Example 3. (b) In Example 1, express $p$ and $r$ in terms of unit vectors and compute $l$.

4. Show that the angular momentum about any point of a single particle moving with constant velocity remains constant throughout the motion.

5. Two particles, each of mass $m$ and speed $v$, travel in opposite directions along parallel lines separated by a distance $d$. Show that the vector angular momentum of this system of particles is the same about *any* point taken as origin.

6. In Fig. 12–23, show the line of action and the moment arm of each force about the origin $O$. Imagine these forces to be acting on a rigid body pivoted at $O$, all vectors shown being in the plane of the figure, and find the magnitude and the direction of the resultant torque on the body.

**Fig. 12–23**

7. Starting from Newton's third law, prove that the resultant internal torque on a system of particles is zero.

8. *Relation between the Resultant External Torque and the Angular Momentum of a System of Particles about the Center of Mass of the System.* Let $\mathbf{r}_{cm}$ be the position vector of the center of mass $C$ of a system of particles with respect to the origin $O$ of an inertial reference frame, and let $\mathbf{r}_i'$ be the position vector of the $i$th particle, of mass $m_i$, with respect to the center of mass $C$. Hence $\mathbf{r}_i = \mathbf{r}_{cm} + \mathbf{r}_i'$ (see Fig. 12–24). Now define the total angular momentum of the system of particles relative to the center of mass $C$ to be $\mathbf{L}' = \sum_i \mathbf{r}_i' \times \mathbf{p}_i'$, where $\mathbf{p}_i' = m_i\, d\mathbf{r}_i'/dt$.

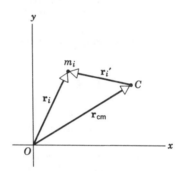

**Fig. 12–24**

(a) Show that $\mathbf{p}_i' = m_i\, d\mathbf{r}_i/dt - m_i\, d\mathbf{r}_{cm}/dt = \mathbf{p}_i - m_i\mathbf{v}_{cm}$. (b) Show next that $d\mathbf{L}'/dt = \sum_i \mathbf{r}_i' \times d\mathbf{p}_i'/dt$. (c) Combine the results of (a) and (b) and, using the definition of center of mass and Newton's third law, show that $\tau'_{ext} = d\mathbf{L}'/dt$, where $\tau'_{ext}$ is the sum of all the external torques acting on the system about its center of mass.

9. (a) Show that the sum of the rotational inertias of a plane laminar body about any two perpendicular axes in the plane of the body is equal to the rotational inertia of the body about an axis through their point of intersection perpendicular to the plane. (b) Apply this to a circular disk to find its rotational inertia about a diameter as axis.

10. (a) Prove that the rotational inertia of a thin rod of length $l$ about an axis through its center perpendicular to its length is $I = \frac{1}{12}Ml^2$. (See Table 12–1.) (b) Use the parallel-axis theorem to show that $I = \frac{1}{3}Ml^2$ when the axis of rotation is through one end perpendicular to the length of the rod.

11. Show that the rotational inertia of a rectangular plate of sides $a$ and $b$ about an axis perpendicular to the plate through its center is $\frac{1}{12}M(a^2 + b^2)$.

12. (a) Show that a solid cylinder of mass $M$ and radius $R$ is equivalent to a thin hoop of mass $M$ and radius $R/\sqrt{2}$, for rotation about a central axis. (b) The radial distance from a given axis at which the mass of a body could be concentrated without

altering the rotational inertia of the body about that axis is called the *radius of gyration*. Let $k$ represent radius of gyration and show that

$$k = \sqrt{I/M}.$$

This gives the radius of the "equivalent hoop" in the general case.

**13.** The oxygen molecule has a total mass of $5.30 \times 10^{-26}$ kg and a rotational inertia of $1.94 \times 10^{-46}$ kg-m$^2$ about an axis through the center perpendicular to the line joining atoms. Suppose that such a molecule in a gas has a mean speed of 500 meters/sec and that its rotational kinetic energy is two-thirds of its translational kinetic energy. Find its average angular velocity.

**14.** A hoop of radius 10 ft weighs 320 lb. It rolls along a horizontal floor so that its center of mass has a speed of 0.50 ft/sec. How much work has to be done to stop it?

**15.** Assume the earth to be a sphere of uniform density. (*a*) What is its rotational kinetic energy? Take the radius of the earth to be $6.4 \times 10^3$ km and the mass of the earth to be $6.0 \times 10^{24}$ kg. (*b*) Suppose this energy could be harnessed for man's use. For how long could the earth supply 1 kw of power to each of the $3.5 \times 10^9$ persons on earth?

**16.** A thin rod of length $l$ and mass $m$ is suspended freely at its end. It is pulled aside and swung about a horizontal axis, passing through its lowest position with an angular speed $\omega$. How high does its center of mass rise above its lowest position? Neglect friction and air resistance.

**17.** An automobile engine develops 100 hp when rotating at a speed of 1800 rev/min. What torque does it deliver?

**18.** A wheel of mass $M$ and radius of gyration $k$ (see Problem 12) spins on a fixed horizontal axle passing through its hub. The hub rubs the axle, of radius $a$, at only one point, the coefficient of friction being $\mu$. The wheel is given an initial angular velocity $\omega_0$. Assume uniform deceleration and find the time of rotation and the number of revolutions before the wheel comes to a stop.

**19.** A uniform steel rod of length 1.20 meters and mass 6.40 kg has attached to each end a small ball of mass 1.06 kg. The rod is constrained to rotate in a horizontal plane about a vertical axis through its midpoint. At a certain instant it is observed to be making 39.0 rev/sec. Because of axle friction it comes to rest 32.0 sec later. Compute, assuming a *constant* frictional torque, (*a*) the angular acceleration, (*b*) the retarding torque exerted by axle friction, (*c*) the total work done by the axle friction, and (*d*) the number of revolutions executed during the 32.0 sec. (*e*) Suppose, however, that the frictional torque is known *not* to be constant. Which, if any, of the quantities (*a*), (*b*), (*c*), or (*d*) can still be computed without requiring any additional information? If such exists, give its value.

**20.** In an Atwood's machine (Fig. 5–9) one block has a mass of 500 gm and the other a mass of 460 gm. The pulley, which is mounted in horizontal frictionless bearings, has a radius of 5.0 cm. When released from rest the heavier block is observed to fall 75 cm in 5.0 sec. Show how to determine the rotational inertia of the pulley from these data.

**21.** A 6.0-lb block is put on a plane inclined 30° to the horizontal and is attached by a cord parallel to the plane over a pulley at the top to a hanging block weighing 18 lb. The pulley weighs 2.0 lb and has a radius of 0.33 ft. The coefficient of kinetic friction between block and plane is 0.10. Find the acceleration of the hanging block and the tension in the cord on each side of the pulley. Assume the pulley to be a uniform disk.

**22.** Take the center of mass of a car to be 2.5 ft above the road and its width between wheels to be 4.5 ft. (*a*) If the car races around an unbanked curve having a radius of 100 ft without skidding, what is the largest speed possible without its overturning? (*b*) What minimum value would the coefficient of friction need to be at this speed?

**23.** A box 6 ft high by 4 ft wide by 3 ft deep containing a refrigerator sits in the back of a truck vertically. The weight of the refrigerator plus that of the box is 300 lb, and this is presumed to be uniformly distributed throughout the volume of the box. The box is tipped over by an acceleration of the truck. What was the minimum value that this acceleration must have had?

**24.** Show that a cylinder will slip on an inclined plane of inclination angle $\theta$ if the coefficient of static friction between plane and cylinder is less than $\frac{1}{3} \tan \theta$.

**25.** A sphere rolls up an inclined plane of inclination angle 30°. At the bottom of the incline the center of mass of the sphere has a translational speed of 16 ft/sec. (a) How far does the sphere travel up the plane? (b) How long does it take to return to the bottom?

**26.** A body of radius $R$ and mass $m$ is rolling horizontally without slipping with speed $v$. It then rolls up a hill to a maximum height $h$. If $h = 3v^2/4g$, (a) what is the body's rotational inertia? (b) What might the body be?

**27.** A small sphere rolls without slipping on the inside of a large hemisphere whose axis of symmetry is vertical. It starts at the top from rest. (a) What is its kinetic energy at the bottom? What fraction is rotational? What translational? (b) What normal force does the small sphere exert on the hemisphere at the bottom? Take the radius of the small sphere to be $r$, that of the hemisphere to be $R$, and let $m$ be the mass of the sphere.

**28.** A homogeneous sphere starts from rest at the upper end of the track shown in Fig. 12–25 and *rolls* without slipping until it rolls off the right-hand end. If $H = 204$ ft and $h = 64$ ft and the track is horizontal at the right-hand end, determine the distance to the right of point $A$ at which the ball strikes the horizontal base line.

**Fig. 12–25**

**Fig. 12–26**

**29.** A small solid marble of mass $m$ and radius $r$ *rolls* without slipping along the loop-the-loop track shown in Fig. 12–26. If it starts from rest at a height of $6R$ above the bottom ($R$ = radius of the circular part of the track), what is the force (horizontal and vertical components) acting on it at the point $Q$?

**30.** A Yo-yo of mass $M$ has a shaft of radius $r$ about which a string is wound. A child lets the Yo-yo unwind as he holds the loose end of the string in a fixed position. The Yo-yo accelerates down, reaches the bottom, and climbs back up, the string winding around the shaft in the opposite sense. Find the tension in the string during the descent and the ascent, assuming $r$ to be small enough to consider the string being vertical at all times. Let $I$ represent the rotational inertia of the Yo-yo about its central axis.

**31.** A uniform disk, of mass $M$ and radius $R$, lies on one side initially at rest on a frictionless horizontal surface. A constant force **F** is then applied tangentially at its perimeter by means of a string wrapped around its edge. Describe the subsequent (rotational and translational) motion of the disk.

**32.** A cylinder of length 1.0 ft and radius 1.0 in. weighs 6.0 lb. Two cords are wrapped around the cylinder, one near each end, and the cord ends are attached to hooks on the ceiling. The cylinder is held horizontally with the two cords exactly vertical and is then released (Fig. 12–27). Find the tension in the cords as they unwind, and determine the linear acceleration of the cylinder as it falls.

Fig. 12–27

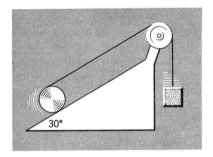

Fig. 12–28

**33.** A string is wrapped around a cylinder of mass $M$, radius $R$. The string is pulled vertically upward to prevent the center of mass from falling as the cylinder unwinds the string. (a) What is the tension in the string? (b) How much work has been done on the cylinder once it has reached an angular speed $\omega$? (c) What is the length of string unwound in this time?

**34.** A solid cylinder of weight 50 lb and radius 3 in. has a light thin tape wound around it. The tape passes over a light, smooth fixed pulley to a 10-lb body (Fig. 12–28). Find the tension in the tape and the linear acceleration of the cylinder up the incline, assuming no slipping.

**35.** A bowling ball is thrown down the alley in such a way that it slides with a speed $v_0$ initially without rolling. Prove that it will roll without any sliding when its speed falls to $\frac{5}{7}v_0$. The transition from pure sliding to pure rolling is gradual, so that both sliding *and* rolling take place during this interval. (*Hint:* Sliding ceases when the forward speed of the lowest point of the sphere is zero.)

**36.** A billiard ball is struck by a cue as in Fig. 12–29. The line of action of the applied impulse is horizontal and passes through the center of the ball. The initial velocity $v_0$ of

Fig. 12–29

the ball, its radius $R$, its mass $M$, and the coefficient of friction $\mu$ between the ball and the table are all known. How far will the ball move before it ceases to slip on the table?

**37.** A 10-ft-long ladder rests against a wall and makes an angle of 60° with the horizontal floor. If it starts to slip, where is the instantaneous axis of rotation?

**38.** (a) A tall chimney cracks near its base and falls over. Express the linear acceleration of the top of the chimney as a function of the angle $\theta$ made by the chimney with the vertical. Can this acceleration exceed $g$? (b) The chimney cracks up during the fall. Explain how this can happen.

**39.** A meter stick is held vertically with one end on the floor and is then allowed to fall. Find the speed of the other end when it hits the floor, assuming that the end on the floor does not slip.

# Rotational Dynamics II and the Conservation of Angular Momentum

## CHAPTER 13

### 13–1 Introduction

In Chapter 12 we discussed the dynamics of the rotational motion of a rigid body about an axis that was fixed in an inertial reference frame. We saw that the scalar relation $\tau = I\alpha$ (Eq. 12–17), in which only torque components along the axis of rotation were considered, were sufficient to solve dynamical problems in this special case.

In this chapter we shall first consider the rotation of a rigid body about an axis that is *not* fixed in an inertial reference frame. To solve dynamical problems in this more general case we shall use the general (vector) relation for rotational motion, namely,

$$\boldsymbol{\tau} = d\mathbf{L}/dt \qquad\qquad (12\text{–}9)$$

in which we have dropped the subscript on $\boldsymbol{\tau}_{\text{ext}}$ for convenience.

Later we shall consider once more the rotation of particles and rigid bodies about fixed axes. This time, however, we specifically examine the action of torques which have components at right angles to the axis. Our point of departure here will not be Eq. 12–17 ($\tau = I\alpha$) but again the more general Eq. 12–9 ($\boldsymbol{\tau} = d\mathbf{L}/dt$).

Finally we shall consider systems on which no external torques act and shall introduce the important principle of *conservation of angular momentum*.

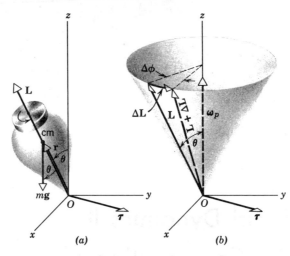

**Fig. 13–1** (a) A precessing top, showing the angular momentum **L**, the weight $m\mathbf{g}$ and the vector **r** which locates the center of mass. (b) The cone swept out by the precessing axis of the top. The angular velocity of precession is shown pointing vertically upward.

## 13–2   The Top

Figure 13–1a shows a top spinning about its axis of symmetry, the point of the top being fixed at the origin $O$ of an inertial reference frame. We know from experience that the axis of such a rapidly spinning top will move around the vertical axis, sweeping out a cone. This motion is called *precession*. Let us see if we can predict this motion from the principles of classical mechanics and, in particular, if we can calculate $\omega_p$, the angular speed of the precessional motion.

At the instant shown in Fig. 13–1a the top has an angular velocity **ω** about its own axis. It also has an angular momentum **L** about this same axis,* the axis making an angle $\theta$ with the vertical.

Two forces act on the top, an upward force on the pivot at $O$ and the pull of gravity, or weight, which acts downward at the center of mass. The upward force passes through $O$ and thus can exert no torque about that point because its moment arm is zero. The weight $m\mathbf{g}$, however, exerts a torque about $O$ given by

$$\boldsymbol{\tau} = \mathbf{r} \times \mathbf{F} = \mathbf{r} \times m\mathbf{g},$$

where **r** locates the center of mass with respect to the pivot. This equation

---

* The vector **ω** always points along the (fixed) axis of rotation of a spinning body but, in general, the vector **L** does not (see Section 13–3). For bodies with symmetry about the rotational axis, however, both **ω** and **L** point along this axis, assuming that the axis is fixed. We can assume that **ω** and **L** are coaxial for the spinning top of Fig. 13–1a if $\omega \gg \omega_p$, that is, if the precession rate is relatively slow so that the axis, although not fixed, changes direction only slowly.

requires that $\tau$ be perpendicular to the plane formed by $r$ and $mg$; application of the right-hand rule shows that its direction is as shown in Fig. 13-1$a$. Note that $\tau$, as well as $L$ and $r$, rotates about the axis at angular speed $\omega_p$ as the top precesses.

When a torque acts on a rigid body it changes the angular momentum of that body according to the fundamental relation (Eq. 12-9)

$$\tau = dL/dt. \qquad \text{(Eq. 12-9)}$$

Being a vector, $L$ can change in magnitude, in direction, or in both. Equation 12-9 shows that the *change* in $L$ (that is, $dL$) must point in the direction of $\tau$. Figure 13-1$a$ shows us that $\tau$ is *at right angles* to $L$; thus the change in $L$ brought about by the action of the torque must also be at right angles to $L$.

To examine the matter quantitatively let us observe the top for a time $\Delta t$. During this interval a change in $L$ of

$$\Delta L = \tau \, \Delta t$$

is predicted by Eq. 12-9 (if $\Delta t$ is small enough). This change $\Delta L$, which, like $\tau$, is at right angles to $L$, is displayed in Fig. 13-1$b$ where we see the cone swept out by the precessing axis of the top; the top itself is omitted here for clarity.

The angular momentum of the top at the end of the time interval $\Delta t$ is the vector sum of $L$ and $\Delta L$. Since $\Delta L$ is perpendicular to $L$ and is assumed to be very small in magnitude compared to it, the new angular momentum vector has the same *magnitude* as the old one but a different *direction*. Hence the head of the angular momentum vector swings around in a horizontal circle as time goes on (Fig. 13-1$b$). Since this vector always lies along the axis of rotation of the top, we have accounted qualitatively for the precession of the top.

The angular speed of precession $\omega_p$ follows from Fig. 13-1$b$ in which

$$\omega_p = \Delta\phi/\Delta t.$$

But, since $\Delta L \ll L$,

$$\Delta\phi \cong \Delta L/L \sin\theta = \tau \, \Delta t/L \sin\theta$$

or

$$\omega_p = \Delta\phi/\Delta t = \tau/L \sin\theta. \qquad (13\text{-}1)$$

Since (Fig. 13-1$a$)

$$\tau = rmg \sin(180° - \theta) = rmg \sin\theta$$

we have finally

$$\omega_p = mgr/L. \qquad (13\text{-}2a)$$

Notice that the precessional angular velocity is independent of $\theta$ and varies inversely as the magnitude of the angular momentum. If the angular momentum is large, the precessional angular velocity will be small.

We can express Eq. 13-2$a$ in vector form. We start by rewriting Eq. 13-1 as

$$\tau = \omega_p L \sin\theta.$$

Now $\omega_p$ is a vector pointing vertically upward in Fig. 13–1b, and $\theta$ in that figure is the angle between $\omega_p$ and **L**. We recognize the right side of the above equation as the magnitude of the vector product $\omega_p \times \mathbf{L}$ and we see that this equation gives the magnitude of $\tau$ in the vector relation

$$\tau = \omega_p \times \mathbf{L}. \qquad (13–2b)$$

This is the general vector expression relating the precessional angular velocity to $\tau$ and to **L**; the student should show that Eq. 13–2a may be derived readily from it. Application of right-hand rule to Fig. 13–1b shows that the order of factors on the right side of Eq. 13–2b is correct, that is, $\omega_p \times \mathbf{L}$ gives the correct direction as well as the correct magnitude for $\tau$.

▶ **Example 1.** A student holds a rim-loaded bicycle wheel, rotating at a relatively high angular speed $\omega$, with its shaft horizontal as in Fig. 13–2a. His physics instructor now asks him to turn the shaft rapidly (for a time $\Delta t$) so that the shaft points at a small angle $\Delta\theta$ above the horizontal as in Fig. 13–2b. He also asks the student to keep the shaft in a vertical plane at all times. What torques must the student exert on the shaft if he is to follow these instructions?

The student will be well aware from the strain in his wrists that he must exert a torque on the shaft simply to hold it in a horizontal position. This torque, which is needed to counteract the turning effect of the force of gravity that acts at the center of mass, is directed along a horizontal axis and emerges perpendicular out of the plane of Fig. 13–2. The student must supply this torque whether or not the wheel is rotating.

If now the student turns the shaft of the spinning wheel upward, he will find that the wheel will swerve around to his right, perhaps rather violently, so that he will have failed to keep the shaft in a vertical plane. If he is to keep the shaft in this plane while he is tilting it upward, he must exert a torque on the shaft (about an almost vertical axis) tending to turn it to his left to counteract this effect. Let us see why this is so.

In tilting the shaft one changes its angular momentum **L**, in time $\Delta t$, by an amount $\Delta$**L**, as Fig. 13–2b shows. During this interval, then, the student must exert an average torque on the wheel given from Eq. 12–9 as

$$\overline{\tau} = \Delta\mathbf{L}/\Delta t;$$

**Fig. 13–2** A student holds a heavy, rim-loaded, rapidly spinning bicycle wheel by the shaft and tilts the shaft upward from the horizontal through a small angle.

the magnitude of $\bar{\tau}$ is given by

$$\bar{\tau} = \Delta L / \Delta t = L \sin \Delta\theta / \Delta t.$$

This average torque $\bar{\tau}$ has the same direction as $\Delta L$, that is, it is approximately vertically upwards if the angle $\Delta\theta$ in Fig. 13–2b is not too large  We can see that such a torque would tend to turn the shaft to the left if the wheel was not rotating. This torque *must* be supplied by the student as he is tilting the shaft of the spinning wheel upward; if he fails to do so, the shaft will not remain in a vertical plane.

The student should experiment with such a spinning wheel, working out the relationships between the vectors $L$, $\Delta L$, and $\bar{\tau}$.  If one is not available he can experiment with a toy gyroscope, although this fails to give the kinesthetic appreciation of $\tau = dL/dt$ that is provided by a rim-loaded, rapidly spinning wheel.

There is an analogy between the experiment of Fig. 13–2 and another experiment in which the student is asked to swing a heavy weight (attached to a stout cord) around in a horizontal circle at constant speed.  In this latter experiment the student, during a time $\Delta t$, must change the direction of the *linear momentum* $P$ of the weight, leaving its magnitude unchanged.  To do so, he must supply a *force* that points at right angles to $P$ (in the direction of $\Delta P$), that is, radially inward.  In the experiment of Fig. 13–2 the student must, during a time $\Delta t$, change the direction of the *angular momentum* $L$ of the wheel, leaving its magnitude unchanged.  To do so he must supply a *torque* that points at right angles to $L$ (in the direction of $\Delta L$), that is, vertically upward.*

### 13–3  Angular Momentum and Angular Velocity

In this section it is our purpose to examine the relationship between the angular momentum and the angular velocity for particles and rigid bodies rotating about an axis fixed in an inertial reference frame.

First we consider a single particle of mass $m$ moving with speed $v$ in a circle about the $z$-axis of an inertial reference frame as in Fig. 13–3.  Its angular velocity $\omega$ lies on the $z$-axis and points upward.  Its angular momentum $l$ with respect to the origin $O$ of the reference frame is given by Eq. 12–3, or

$$l = r \times p,$$

where $r$ and $p$ ($= mv$) are shown in the figure.   The vector $l$ is perpendicular to the plane formed by $r$ and $p$, which means that $l$ is *not* parallel to $\omega$. Note that $l$ has a (vector) component $l_z$ which is parallel to $\omega$, but it has another (vector) component $l_\perp$ which is at right angles to $\omega$.  Note, too, that if we choose our origin to lie in the plane of the circulating particle, then $l$ *is* parallel to $\omega$; often, however, we do not find it convenient to make this choice.

The perhaps unexpected result that $l$ and $\omega$ are not parallel in this simple case may cause the student some concern.   However, this result is quite in accord with the general relationship $\tau = dl/dt$ for a torque acting on a single particle.   The vector $l$ is changing with time as the particle motion

---

* This analogy is explored by A. E. Benfield, *American Journal of Physics*, September 1958.   See also Problem 3.

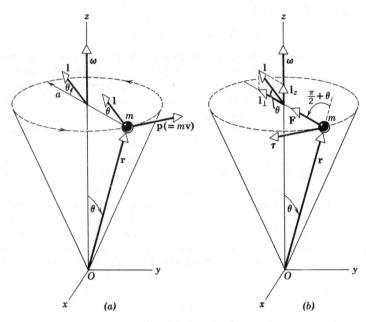

**Fig. 13–3**   (a) A particle of mass $m$ rotating with speed $v$ in a circle of radius $a$ about the $z$-axis of an inertial reference frame.   The angular momentum about $O$, $\mathbf{l}$ ($= \mathbf{r} \times \mathbf{p}$), is shown; for convenience, this vector is also shown translated to the center of the circle. (b) The same configuration, showing $\mathbf{l}$ and its components and also the centripetal force $\mathbf{F}$ and the torque $\tau$ about $O$.

proceeds, the change being entirely in direction and not in magnitude, just as it was for the precessing top in the preceding section.   Since the right side of the preceding relationship ($= d\mathbf{l}/dt$) has a nonzero value, the left side ($= \tau$) must also have a nonzero value; that is, a torque must act on the particle with respect to origin $O$.

There is indeed such a torque.   For if the particle moves in a circle, a centripetal force $\mathbf{F}$ must act on it, as in Fig. 13–3$b$.   We may imagine that $\mathbf{F}$ is provided by the tension in a light cord that ties the rotating particle to the $z$-axis.   The torque about $O$ is provided by $\mathbf{F}$ and is given by Eq. 12–1.

$$\tau = \mathbf{r} \times \mathbf{F}.$$

The torque $\tau$ is tangent to the circle (perpendicular to the plane formed by $\mathbf{r}$ and $\mathbf{F}$) and in the direction shown in Fig. 13–3$b$, as the student may verify from the right-hand rule.

▶ **Example 2.**   Show that the moving particle of Fig. 13–3 satisfies the relation $\tau = d\mathbf{l}/dt$ quantitatively.

The proof is along the same lines as that of Section 13–2 for the spinning top because, from a vector point of view, the two problems are identical.   In each case we have the precession of an angular momentum vector ($\mathbf{L}$ for the top and $\mathbf{l}$ for the particle of Fig. 13–3) about a vertical axis, at a rate which we called $\omega_p$

for the top and which we call $\omega$ for the particle. In each case we have a torque which is always at right angles to the plane formed by $\mathbf{L}$ (or $\mathbf{l}$) and $\boldsymbol{\omega}_p$ (or $\boldsymbol{\omega}$).

Thus, since the two problems are formally identical, it suffices to inquire whether the rotating particle of Fig. 13–3 obeys the vector equation for precession ($\boldsymbol{\tau} = \boldsymbol{\omega}_p \times \mathbf{L}$; Eq. 13–2b). This equation was derived for the precessing top directly from—and is directly equivalent to—the relation $\boldsymbol{\tau} = d\mathbf{L}/dt$ (Eq. 12–9). We can write the relation $\boldsymbol{\tau} = \boldsymbol{\omega}_p \times \mathbf{L}$ in terms of magnitudes as

$$\tau = \omega l \sin(90° - \theta) = \omega l \cos \theta, \tag{13–3}$$

in which we have substituted $\omega$ for $\omega_p$ and $l$ for $L$ and have noted in Fig. 13–3a that the angle between $\omega$ and $l$ is $90° - \theta$. For $\tau$ and $l$, again using the notation of Fig. 13–3a, we can write

$$\tau = Fr \sin(90° + \theta) = [m\omega^2(r \sin \theta)](r)(\cos \theta)$$

and

$$l = rp \sin 90° = r(mv) = (r)(m)[\omega(r \sin \theta)],$$

in which $r \sin \theta$ is the radius $a$ of the circle in which the particle moves, $(90° + \theta)$ is the angle between $\mathbf{r}$ and $\mathbf{F}$, and $90°$ is the angle between $\mathbf{r}$ and $\mathbf{p}$. Substituting these two expressions into Eq. 13–3 yields

$$m\omega^2 r^2 \sin \theta \cos \theta = \omega(m\omega r^2 \sin \theta) \cos \theta,$$

which is an identity. In terms of *magnitudes* we have proved our point. The student should refer to Fig. 13–3 and make certain that the *direction* of $\boldsymbol{\tau}$ is that of $d\mathbf{l}/dt$ (Eq. 12–7), or alternatively of $\boldsymbol{\omega} \times \mathbf{l}$ (Eq. 13–2b). ◀

Let us now investigate the relationship between $\mathbf{l}_z$ and $\boldsymbol{\omega}$ for the particle of Fig. 13–3. From Example 2 we have

$$l = mr^2\omega \sin \theta.$$

From Fig. 13–3b we see that

$$l_z = l \sin \theta = m\omega r^2 \sin^2 \theta.$$

Now $r \sin \theta = a$, the radius of the circle in which the particle moves. This leads to

$$l_z = ma^2\omega, \tag{13–4}$$

in which $ma^2$ is the rotational inertia $I$ of the particle with respect to the $z$-axis. Thus

$$l_z = I\omega, \tag{13–5}$$

which is to be compared with Eq. 12–18 ($L = I\omega$) for the rotation of a rigid body about a fixed axis. Note that the vector relation $\mathbf{l} = I\boldsymbol{\omega}$ is *not* correct in this case because $\mathbf{l}$ and $\boldsymbol{\omega}$ do not point in the same direction. However, $\mathbf{l}_z$ and $\boldsymbol{\omega}$ *do*, so that we could write Eq. 13–5 in vector form as $\mathbf{l}_z = I\boldsymbol{\omega}$.

Now let us add another particle of mass $m$ to the system of Fig. 13–3. In particular, let us add this particle in the same orbit, moving with the same speed, but always at a diametrically opposite point, on the other side of the axis of rotation. The angular momentum $\mathbf{l}_2$ with respect to $O$ for this second particle will have the same magnitude as that of $\mathbf{l}_1$ for the first

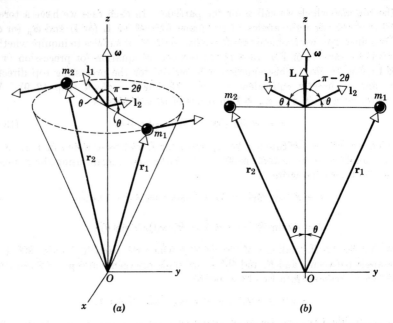

**Fig. 13–4** (a) Two particles of mass $m$ rotating as in Fig. 13–3 but maintaining diametrically opposite positions. (b) A cross section through the two particles, showing that the total angular momentum $\mathbf{L}$ ($= \mathbf{l}_1 + \mathbf{l}_2$) for the two-particle system points along the axis of rotation, in the same direction as $\boldsymbol{\omega}$.

particle and it will make the same angle ($90° - \theta$) with the $z$-axis, but it will have a different orientation around that axis. As Fig. 13–4a shows, $\mathbf{l}_2$ will lie in a plane formed by $\boldsymbol{\omega}$ and by $\mathbf{l}_1$ but will be on the opposite side of the $z$-axis from $\mathbf{l}_1$. The vectors $\mathbf{l}_1$ and $\mathbf{l}_2$ include an angle of $180° - 2\theta$.

The total angular momentum $\mathbf{L}$ of the system of two particles is the vector sum of the angular momenta of the separate particles, that is, $\mathbf{L} = \mathbf{l}_1 + \mathbf{l}_2$. The resultant vector $\mathbf{L}$, as Fig. 13–4b shows, points along the $z$-axis (in the direction of $\boldsymbol{\omega}$) and is constant in magnitude. Note that this statement is true no matter where the origin $O$ is located along the 'axis of rotation.

The fact that $\mathbf{L} =$ a constant (in both magnitude and direction), for this two-particle system, means that $d\mathbf{L}/dt = 0$, which in turn (Eq. 12–9) means that $\boldsymbol{\tau} = 0$ for this system. The student should convince himself (Fig. 13–3b will be helpful) that this is the case, the torques for the two particles about $O$ being equal in magnitude but oppositely directed so that the torque acting on the two-particle system is zero.

The fact that $\boldsymbol{\omega}$ and $\mathbf{L}$ point in the same direction in this problem but did not for the case of a single particle can be traced to the fact that, in the two-particle system, the particles have the same mass and are in diametrically opposite positions at the same distance from the rotation axis.

We can now extend our system to a rigid body, made up of many particles.   If the body is symmetric about the axis of rotation, by which we mean that for every mass element in the body there must be an identical mass element diametrically opposite the first element and at the same distance from the axis of rotation, then the body can be regarded as made up of sets of particle pairs of the kind we have been discussing.   Since **L** and **ω** are parallel for all such pairs, they are also parallel for rigid bodies that possess this kind of symmetry.   Note that, in Table 12–1, all the systems except $f$ and $j$ meet this criterion.

For such symmetrical rigid bodies **L** and **ω** are parallel and we can write Eq. 12–18 ($L = I\omega$) in vector form as

$$\mathbf{L} = I\boldsymbol{\omega}. \qquad (13\text{–}6)$$

The student must not forget, however, that, if **L** stands for the *total* angular momentum, then Eq. 13–6 applies *only* to bodies that have symmetry* about the (fixed) rotational axis.   If **L** stands for the vector component of angular momentum along the rotational axis (that is, for $\mathbf{L}_z$), then Eq. 13–6 is equivalent to Eq. 12–8 and holds for *any* rigid body, symmetrical or not, that is rotating about a fixed axis.

▶ **Example 3.**   Solve the problem of Example 5, Chapter 12, by direct application of Eq. 12–9 ($\tau = dL/dt$).

The system of Fig. 12–12, consisting of the wheel $M$ and the mass $m$ is acted on by two external forces, the downward pull of gravity $mg$ acting on mass $m$ and the upward force exerted by the bearings of the shaft of the cylinder, which we take as our origin.   The tension in the cord is an internal force and does not act from the outside on the system (wheel + weight).   Only the first of these external forces exerts a torque about the origin and its magnitude is $(mg)R$.

The angular momentum of the system about the origin at any instant is

$$L = I\omega + (mv)R,$$

in which $I\omega$ is the angular momentum of the (symmetrical) disk and $(mv)R$ is the angular momentum (= linear momentum × moment arm) of the falling mass about the origin.   Both these contributions to $L$ point in the same direction, namely, perpendicularly out of the plane of Fig. 12–12.

Applying $\tau = dL/dt$ (in scalar form) yields

$$(mg)R = \frac{d}{dt}(I\omega + mvR)$$

$$= I(d\omega/dt) + mR(dv/dt)$$

$$= I\alpha + mRa.$$

---

* We have oversimplified the symmetry requirement.   Every rigid body, no matter how irregular its shape, has three perpendicular axes through its center of mass, about each of which **L** and **ω** have the same direction, being related by $\mathbf{L} = I\boldsymbol{\omega}$.   These axes are called the *principal axes*.   The axis of a figure of revolution is always a principal axis, as are axes at right angles to it through the center of mass.   In general, however, **L** and **ω** point in different directions for axes that are not principal axes.   See Arnold Sommerfeld, *Mechanics*, Chapter IV, Academic Press, New York, (1964 paperback edition).

Since $a = \alpha R$ and $I = \frac{1}{2}MR^2$, this reduces to

$$mgR = (\tfrac{1}{2}MR^2)(a/R) + mRa$$

or

$$a = \frac{2\,mg}{M + 2m}.$$

**Example 4.** A simple example of an unsymmetrical rotating rigid body is a dumbbell-type rod whose bar makes an angle $\theta$ with the fixed axis of rotation passing through its center of mass. The rod rotates at a constant angular velocity $\omega$ about this axis, the vector $\boldsymbol{\omega}$ thus pointing along this axis, as shown in Fig.

Fig. 13–5

13–5. Experience tells us that such a system is "unbalanced" or "lop-sided," and if it were not securely fastened to the vertical shaft near $C$ it would break away from the shaft at high angular velocities. It would tend to move until the angle $\theta$ becomes 90°, in which limiting position the system would then be symmetrical about the shaft.

(a) Show qualitatively that in the unsymmetrical case shown in Fig. 13–5 L and $\boldsymbol{\omega}$ are not parallel.

Each particle of mass $m$ has an angular momentum with respect to $C$ given by $\mathbf{r} \times \mathbf{p}$ for that particle. At the instant shown the upper particle is moving into the page at right angles to it, and the lower particle is moving out of the page at right angles to it. The momentum vectors of the two masses are therefore equal but opposite, and so are their position vectors with respect to $C$. Hence, by application of the right-hand rule in $\mathbf{r} \times \mathbf{p}$, we find that $\mathbf{l}$ is the same for each particle and that their sum, the total angular momentum vector $\mathbf{L}$ of the dumbbell, is as shown in the figure, at right angles to the bar in the plane of the page. Hence $\mathbf{L}$ and $\boldsymbol{\omega}$ are *not* parallel at this instant. It is clear that as the dumbbell itself rotates, the angular momentum vector, while constant in magnitude, rotates around the fixed axis of rotation.

(b) The fact that $\mathbf{L}$ and $\boldsymbol{\omega}$ do not point in the same direction is perfectly consistent with the fundamental relation $\boldsymbol{\tau} = d\mathbf{L}/dt$. We have seen twice before (see Section 13–2 and Example 1) that an angular momentum vector of constant magnitude that rotates around a fixed axis must have associated with it a torque $\boldsymbol{\tau}$ that is at right angles to the plane formed by $\mathbf{L}$ and $\boldsymbol{\omega}$. At the instant shown in Fig. 13–5 this plane is the plane of the figure. Is there such a torque in this problem and if so, where does it come from?

There is indeed such a torque and it arises from the unbalanced sideways forces exerted by the bearings on the shaft and transmitted by the shaft to the dumbbell bar. At the instant shown in the figure the upper end of the dumbbell would tend to move outward to the right. The shaft would be pulled to the right against the upper bearing, which in turn exerts a force $\mathbf{F}$ on the shaft that points to the left. Similarly, the lower end of the dumbbell tends to move outwards to the left. The shaft would be pulled to the left against the lower bearing, which in turn exerts a force $-\mathbf{F}$ on the shaft that points to the right. The torque $\boldsymbol{\tau}$ about $C$ as a result of these forces points perpendicularly out of the page, at right angles to the plane formed by **L** and **ω**, and in the right direction to account for the rotary motion of **L** (the student should check this).

The forces **F** and −**F** lie in the plane of Fig. 13–5 at the instant shown. As the dumbbell rotates, these forces, and therefore the torque **τ**, rotate with it, so that **τ** always remains at right angles to the plane formed by **ω** and **L** (compare with Fig. 13–1). The rotating forces **F** and −**F** cause a "wobble" in the upper and lower bearings. The bearings and their supports must be made strong enough to provide these forces. For a symmetrical rotating body there is no bearing wobble and the shaft rotates smoothly.

Bearing wobble and internal strains can cause serious practical problems when objects, such as turbine rotors, are made to rotate at high speeds. Although designed to be symmetrical, such rotors, because of small errors of blade placement, etc., may be slightly unsymmetrical. They may be restored to symmetry by the addition or removal of metal at appropriate places; this is done by spinning the wheel in a special device such that bearing wobble can be measured quantitatively and the appropriate corrective measure computed and indicated automatically. We are all familiar with lead weights placed at strategic points on automobile tire rims to reduce wobble at high speeds due to unbalance.    ◀

### 13–4    Conservation of Angular Momentum

In Chapter 12, we found that the time rate of change of the total angular momentum of a system of particles about a point fixed in an inertial reference frame (or about the center of mass) is equal to the sum of the *external* torques acting on the system, that is,

$$\boldsymbol{\tau}_{\text{ext}} = d\mathbf{L}/dt. \tag{12–9}$$

Suppose now that $\boldsymbol{\tau}_{\text{ext}} = 0$; then $d\mathbf{L}/dt = 0$ so that $\mathbf{L} = $ a constant.

*When the resultant external torque acting on a system is zero, the total vector angular momentum of the system remains constant.* This is the *principle of the conservation of angular momentum.*

For a system of $n$ particles, the total angular momentum **L** about some point is

$$\mathbf{L} = \mathbf{l}_1 + \mathbf{l}_2 + \cdots + \mathbf{l}_n.$$

When the resultant external torque on the system is zero, we have

$$\mathbf{L} = \text{a constant} = \mathbf{L}_0, \tag{13–7}$$

where $\mathbf{L}_0$ is the constant total angular momentum vector. The angular momenta of the individual particles may change, but their vector sum $\mathbf{L}_0$ remains constant in the absence of a net external torque.

Angular momentum is a vector quantity so that Eq. 13–7 is equivalent to three scalar equations, one for each coordinate direction through the reference point. The conservation of angular momentum therefore supplies us with three conditions on the motion of a system to which it applies.

For a system consisting of a rigid body rotating about an axis (the $z$-axis, say) that is fixed in an inertial reference frame, we have

$$\mathbf{L}_z = I\boldsymbol{\omega}, \tag{13–6}$$

**Fig. 13–6** A diver leaves the diving board with arms and legs outstretched and with some initial angular velocity. Since no torques are exerted on him about his center of mass, $L\ (= I\omega)$ is constant while he is in the air. When he pulls his arms and legs in, since $I$ decreases, $\omega$ increases. When he again extends his limbs, his angular velocity drops back to its initial value. Notice the parabolic motion of his center of mass, common to all two-dimensional motion under the influence of gravity.

where $L_z$ is the component of the angular momentum along the rotation axis and $I$ is the rotational inertia for this same axis. It is possible for the rotational inertia $I$ of a rotating body to change by rearrangement of its parts. If no net external torque acts, then $L_z$ must remain constant and, if $I$ does change, there must be a compensating change in $\omega$. The principle of conservation of angular momentum in this case is expressed as

$$I\omega = I_0\omega_0 = \text{a constant.} \qquad (13\text{–}8)$$

Equation 13–8 holds not only for rotation about a fixed axis but also about an axis through the center of mass of the system that moves so that it always remains parallel to itself (see p. 268).

Acrobats, divers, ballet dancers, ice skaters, and others often use this principle. Because $I$ depends on the square of the distance of the parts of the body from the axis of rotation, a large variation is possible by extending or pulling in the limbs. Consider the diver in Fig. 13–6. Let us assume that as he leaves the diving board he has a certain angular speed $\omega_0$ about a horizontal axis through the center of mass, such that he would rotate through half a turn before he strikes water. If he wishes to make a one and one-half turn somersault instead, in the same time, he must triple his angular speed. Now there are no external forces acting on him except gravity, and gravity exerts no torque about his center of mass. His angular momentum therefore remains constant, and $I_0\omega_0 = I\omega$. Since

$\omega = 3\omega_0$, the diver must change his rotational inertia about the horizontal axis through the center of mass from the initial value $I_0$ to a value $I$, such that $I$ equals $\frac{1}{3}I_0$. This he does by pulling in his arms and legs toward the center of his body. The greater his initial angular speed and the more he can reduce his rotational inertia, the greater the number of revolutions he can make in a given time.

We should notice that the rotational kinetic energy of the diver is not constant. In fact, in our example, since

$$I\omega = I_0\omega_0$$

and

$$I < I_0,$$

it follows that

$$\tfrac{1}{2}I\omega^2 > \tfrac{1}{2}I_0\omega_0{}^2,$$

and the diver's rotational kinetic energy *increases*. This increase in energy is supplied by the diver, who does work when he pulls the parts of his body together.

In a similar way the ice skater and ballet dancer can increase or decrease the angular speed of a spin about a vertical axis. A cat manages to land on its feet after a fall by using the same principles, the tail serving as a useful, but unessential, extra appendage.

▶ **Example 5.** A small object of mass $m$ is attached to a light string which passes through a hollow tube. The tube is held by one hand and the string by the other. The object is set into rotation in a circle of radius $r_1$ with a speed $v_1$. The string is then pulled down, shortening the radius of the path to $r_2$ (Fig. 13–7). Find the new linear speed $v_2$ and the new angular speed $\omega_2$ of the object in terms of the initial values $v_1$ and $\omega_1$ and the two radii.

The downward pull on the string is transmitted as a radial force on the object. Such a force exerts a zero torque on the object about the center of rotation. Since no torque acts on the object about its axis of rotation, its angular momentum in that direction is constant. Hence

initial angular momentum
= final angular momentum,

$$mv_1r_1 = mv_2r_2,$$

and

$$v_2 = v_1\left(\frac{r_1}{r_2}\right).$$

Since $r_1 > r_2$, the object speeds up on being pulled in.

**Fig. 13–7** Example 5. A mass at the end of a cord moves in a circle of radius $r_1$ with angular speed $\omega_1$. The cord passes down through a tube. **F** supplies the centripetal force.

In terms of angular speed, since $v_1$ equals $\omega_1 r_1$ and $v_2$ equals $\omega_2 r_2$,

$$mr_1{}^2\omega_1 = mr_2{}^2\omega_2$$

and

$$\omega_2 = \left(\frac{r_1}{r_2}\right)^2 \omega_1,$$

so that there is an even greater increase in angular speed over the initial value (see Problem 23). What effect does the force of gravity (the object's weight) have on this analysis?

**Example 6.** A student sits on a stool that is free to rotate about a vertical axis. He holds his arms extended horizontally with an 8.0-lb weight in each hand. The instructor sets him rotating with an angular speed of 0.50 rev/sec. Assume that friction is negligible and exerts no torque about the vertical axis of rotation. Assume that the rotational inertia of the student remains constant at 4.0 slug-ft² as he pulls his hands to his sides and that the change in rotational inertia is due only to pulling the weights in. Take the original distance of the weights from the axis of rotation to be 3.0 ft and their final distance 0.50 ft. Find the final angular speed of the student.

The only external force is gravity acting through the center of mass, and that exerts no torque about the axis of rotation. Hence the angular momentum is conserved about this axis and

initial angular momentum = final angular momentum,

$$I_0\omega_0 = I\omega.$$

We have

$$I = I_{\text{student}} + I_{\text{weights}},$$

$$I_0 = 4.0 + 2\left(\frac{8.0}{32}\right)(3.0)^2 = 8.5 \text{ slug-ft}^2,$$

$$I = 4.0 + 2\left(\frac{8.0}{32}\right)\left(\frac{1}{2}\right)^2 = 4.1 \text{ slug-ft}^2,$$

$$\omega_0 = 0.50 \text{ rev/sec} = \pi \text{ radians/sec}.$$

Therefore

$$\omega = \frac{I_0}{I}\,\omega_0 = \frac{8.5}{4.1}\,\pi \text{ radians/sec} = 2.1\pi \text{ radians/sec} \cong 1.0 \text{ rev/sec}.$$

The final angular speed is approximately doubled.

If we had allowed for the decrease in $I$ caused by the arms being pulled in, the final angular speed would have been much greater.

What change would friction make? Is kinetic energy conserved as the student pulls in his arms and then puts them out again, assuming there is no friction? Explain.

**Example 7.** A classroom demonstration that illustrates the vector nature of the law of conservation of angular momentum is worth considering.

A student stands on a platform that can rotate only about a vertical axis. In his hand he holds the axle of a rim-loaded bicycle wheel with its axis vertical. The wheel is spinning about this vertical axis with an angular speed $\omega_0$, but the

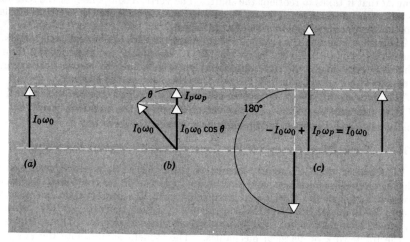

**Fig. 13–8** Example 7. (a) The initial angular momentum of the system is shown. In (b), the wheel has been tilted an angle $\theta$. Since no external torque in the vertical direction has been exerted on the system, the angular momentum in that direction must be conserved. The deficit, $(1 - \cos \theta)I_0\omega_0$, is made up by rotation of the student and platform. In (c), the wheel has been tilted 180°. The deficit is now $2I_0\omega_0$, which is now, as before, made up by the student and platform.

student and platform are at rest. The student tries to change the direction of rotation of the wheel. What happens?

Let us choose as the system the student plus platform plus wheel. The initial total angular momentum of this system is $I_0\boldsymbol{\omega}_0$, arising from the spinning wheel, $I_0$ being the rotational inertia of the wheel about its axis and $\boldsymbol{\omega}_0$ pointing vertically upward. Figure 13–8a shows the initial condition.

The student next turns the axis of the wheel through an angle $\theta$ from the vertical (to do this he must supply a torque; see Example 1. This torque, however, is *internal* to the system as we have defined it). Since there is no *external* component of torque on the system about the vertical axis, the vertical component of angular momentum of the system must be conserved. The wheel, however, is now spinning about an axis making an angle $\theta$ with the vertical so that it contributes a vertical component of angular momentum of only $I_0\omega_0 \cos \theta$ to the system. Hence the student and platform must supply the additional angular momentum about the vertical axes, and they begin to rotate about a vertical axis. This extra vertical angular momentum $I_p\omega_p$ when added to $I_0\omega_0 \cos \theta$ must equal the initial vertical angular momentum of the system $I_0\omega_0$. That is,

$$I_p\omega_p = I_0\omega_0(1 - \cos \theta).$$

This is shown in Fig. 13–8b. $I_p$ is the rotational inertia of student and platform with respect to the vertical axis, and $\omega_p$ is their angular speed about this axis.

If the student turns the wheel through an angle $\theta = 180°$, the student and platform acquire a vertical angular momentum of $2I_0\omega_0$. The total vertical angular momentum of the system is still being conserved at the initial value $I_0\omega_0$, as shown in Fig. 13–8c.

Consider now the angular momentum of the wheel alone. As the student turns the axis of the wheel through an angle $\theta$ he exerts a torque on it which lasts for the time $\Delta t$ that it takes to reorient the shaft. The vertical component of the reaction to this "torque-impulse" acts on the student and accounts for the vertical angular momentum acquired by him and the platform.

The wheel, held with its shaft fixed at an angle $\theta$ with the vertical axis, precesses about this axis just like the top of Fig. 13–1. As for the top, a horizontal torque, which always remains at right angles to the plane defined by the vertical axis and the axis of the wheel, must be provided, in this case by the student.

The precise analysis of the motion of this system depends only on the application of the equation $\tau = d\mathbf{L}/dt$ and the vector nature of the quantities involved. It will be left as an exercise for the interested student to work out.  ◀

### 13–5  Some Other Aspects of the Conservation of Angular Momentum

The conservation of angular momentum principle holds in atomic and nuclear physics as well as in celestial and macroscopic regions. Since Newtonian mechanics does not hold in the atomic and nuclear domain, this conservation law must be more fundamental than Newtonian principles. In our derivation of this principle we must have made more rigid assumptions than we needed to. This is true even in the framework of classical mechanics. The student should note the key role played by Newton's third law in our deduction of this conservation principle. This law was used to justify the assumption that the sum of the internal torques was zero. It was necessary to assert not only that the action and reaction forces were equal and opposite (the "weak" form of the third law) but also that these forces were directed along the line joining the two particles (the "strong" form of the third law). The strong form is known to be violated in some electromagnetic interactions. However, the assumption that the sum of the internal torques in a system of particles is zero can be proven on the basis of a much less stringent requirement than that the third law should hold.*

The law of conservation of angular momentum, as we have formulated it, holds for a system of bodies whenever the bodies can be treated as particles, that is, whenever effects due to the rotation of the individual bodies can be neglected. When the individual bodies have rotation, the conservation of angular momentum principle is still valid, providing we include the angular momentum associated with this rotation. However, the bodies then are no longer simple particles whose motion can be described by particle dynamics.

In atomic and nuclear physics we find that the "elementary particles" such as electrons, protons, mesons, and neutrons have angular momentum associated with an intrinsic spinning motion, as well as with orbital motion about some external point. When we use the law of conservation of total angular momentum we must include this *spin* angular momentum in the total. A fundamental aspect of atomic, molecular, and nuclear systems is that their angular momenta can take on only definite discrete values, rather than a continuum of values. Angular momentum is said to be *quantized*. Hence, angular momentum plays a central role in the description of the behavior of such systems (see Problems 4 and 6). These ideas will be developed in later chapters.

If we were to regard the sun, planets, and satellites as particles having no intrinsic spinning motion, the angular momentum of the solar system would turn out not to be constant. But these bodies do have intrinsic rotations; in fact, tidal forces convert some of the intrinsic spinning angular momentum into orbital angular momentum of the planets and satellites. When we use the law of conservation of the angular momentum, we must include this spin angular momentum in the total. The conservation of angular momentum plays a key role in the evaluation of theories of the origin of the solar system, the contraction of giant

---

* See E. Gerjuoy, *American Journal of Physics*, Vol. 17, 477 (1949).

stars, and other problems in astronomy.*    Some astronomical applications will be considered in Chapter 16.

The basis for this rather simple way of analyzing the total angular momentum of atomic or astronomical systems is a theorem (see Problem 10) that the *total* angular momentum L of any system with respect to the origin of an inertial reference frame may be computed by adding the angular momentum with respect to its center of mass (*spin* angular momentum) to the angular momentum arising from the motion of the center of mass with respect to the origin (*orbital* angular momentum).

The conservation laws of total energy and of linear momentum and angular momentum are fundamental to physics, being valid in all modern physical theories. We shall have occasion to use them many times in later chapters.

## 13-6    Rotational Dynamics—A Review

The subject of the rotary motions of particles and rigid bodies is reasonably complicated, so much so in fact that a completely general treatment is beyond our scope here.    It seems advisable to collect in one place all equations dealing with rotational dynamics and to comment on the conditions under which they can be used.    We do this in Table 13-1.

**Table 13–1**

### SUMMARY OF EQUATIONS FOR ROTARY MOTION

| Eq. No. | Equation | Remarks |
|---|---|---|

#### I. Defining Equations

| | | |
|---|---|---|
| 12–1 | $\boldsymbol{\tau} = \mathbf{r} \times \mathbf{F}$ | Torque on a particle about a point $O$, due to a resultant force $\mathbf{F}$ |
| | $\boldsymbol{\tau}_{ext} = \Sigma \boldsymbol{\tau}_i = \Sigma(\mathbf{r}_i \times \mathbf{F}_i)$ | Resultant external torque on a system of particles about a point $O$ |
| 12–3 | $\mathbf{l} = \mathbf{r} \times \mathbf{p}$ | Angular momentum of a particle about a point $O$ |
| | $\mathbf{L} = \Sigma \mathbf{l}_i = \Sigma(\mathbf{r}_i \times \mathbf{p}_i)$ | Resultant angular momentum of a system of particles about a point $O$ |

#### II. General Relations

| | | |
|---|---|---|
| 12–7 | $\boldsymbol{\tau} = d\mathbf{l}/dt$ | The law of motion for a single particle acted on by a torque. It is the rotational analog of $\mathbf{F} = d\mathbf{p}/dt$ (Eq. 9–12). Equation 12–7 holds only if $\boldsymbol{\tau}$ and $\mathbf{l}$ are measured with respect to any point $O$ fixed in an inertial reference frame |
| 12–9 | $\boldsymbol{\tau}_{ext} = d\mathbf{L}/dt$ | The law of motion for a system of particles acted on by a resultant external torque $\boldsymbol{\tau}_{ext}$. It is the rotational analog of $\mathbf{F} = d\mathbf{P}/dt$ (Eq. 9–7). Equation 12–9 holds only if $\boldsymbol{\tau}_{ext}$ and $\mathbf{L}$ are measured with respect to $(a)$ any point $O$ fixed in an inertial reference frame $or$ $(b)$ the center of mass of the system |

#### III. Special Case of a Rigid Body Rotating about an Axis Fixed in an Inertial Reference Frame (see footnote, p. 268)

| | | |
|---|---|---|
| 12–17 | $\tau = I\alpha$ | $\boldsymbol{\alpha}$ is constrained to lie along the axis; $I$ must also refer to this axis and $\tau$ must be the scalar component of $\boldsymbol{\tau}_{ext}$ directed along this same axis. It is the rotational analog of $F = Ma$ for rectilinear motion |
| 12–18 | $L = I\omega$ | $\boldsymbol{\omega}$ is constrained to lie along the axis; $I$ must also refer to this axis and $L$ must be the scalar component along this axis of the total angular momentum. If the rotation axis has special symmetry (that is, if it is a principal axis; see footnote, p. 303), then $\mathbf{L}$ and $\boldsymbol{\omega}$ are both axially directed. It is the rotational analog of $P = Mv$ for rectilinear motion |

## QUESTIONS

**1.** (a) In Example 1, why would merely turning the shaft up send the wheel to the student's right? (b) If the student is anchored to the floor of a large spaceship that is drifting in a region free from gravity, in what way, if any, would this affect his performance of the experiment?

**2.** If the top of Fig. 13–1 were not spinning, it would tip over. If its spin angular momentum is large compared to the change caused by the applied torque, the top precesses. What happens in between when the top spins slowly?

**3.** A famous physicist (R. W. Wood), who was fond of practical jokes, mounted a rapidly spinning flywheel in a suitcase which he gave to a porter with instructions to follow him. What happens when the porter is led quickly around a corner? Explain in terms of $\tau = d\mathbf{L}/dt$.

**4.** A single-engine airplane must be "trimmed" to fly level. (Trimming consists of raising one aileron and lowering the opposite one.) Why is this necessary? Is this necessary on a bi-engine plane under normal circumstances?

**5.** The propeller of an aircraft rotates clockwise as seen from the rear. When the pilot pulls upward out of a steep dive, he finds it necessary to apply left rudder at the bottom of the dive if he is to maintain his heading. Explain.

**6.** Describe, in terms of $\tau = d\mathbf{L}/dt$, the rotational dynamics of the wheels on a fast train going around a curve.

**7.** You are walking along a narrow railroad track and you start to lose your balance. If you start falling to the right, which way do you turn your body to regain balance? Explain.

**8.** In order to get a billiard ball to roll without sliding from the start the cue must hit the ball not at the center (that is, a height above the table equal to the ball's radius $R$) but exactly at a height $\frac{2}{5}R$ above the center. Explain.†

**9.** A cylinder rotates with angular speed $\omega$ about an axis through one end, as in Fig. 13–9. Choose an appropriate origin and show qualitatively the vectors $\mathbf{L}$ and $\boldsymbol{\omega}$. Are these vectors parallel? Do symmetry considerations enter here?

**10.** Explain, in terms of angular momentum and rotational inertia, exactly how one "pumps up" a swing.

**11.** Consider the motion of a football tumbling through the air. Is the angular momentum with respect to the center of mass of the football conserved in flight? Does the magnitude or the direction of the angular velocity change with respect either to axes fixed in space or in the body?

Bearing      Fixed axis

**Fig. 13–9**

**12.** In Chapter 1 the melting of the polar icecaps was cited as a possible cause of the variation in the earth's time of rotation. Explain.

**13.** Many great rivers flow toward the equator. What effect does the sediment they carry to the sea have on the rotation of the earth?

\* See, for example, *Frontiers of Astronomy*, by Fred Hoyle, Harper and Brothers, 1955.

† See Arnold Sommerfeld, *Mechanics, Volume I of Lectures on Theoretical Physics*, Academic Press, New York (1964 paperback edition), pp. 158–161, for a supplement on the mechanics of billiards.

**14.** A man turns on a rotating table with an angular speed $\omega$. He is holding two equal masses at arm's length. Without moving his arms, he drops the two masses. What change, if any, is there in his angular speed? Is the angular momentum conserved? Explain.

**Pan**

**Ice**

**Turntable**

$\omega$

**Fig. 13–10**

**15.** In Example 5, if the string is released suddenly back to where the object can travel in a circle of radius $r_1$, will the object return to its original speed? What happens if one repeatedly pulls down on and suddenly releases the string? Explain the behavior in terms of work-energy and torque-angular momentum considerations.

**16.** A circular turntable rotates at constant angular velocity about a vertical axis. There is no friction and no driving torque. A circular pan rests on the turntable and rotates with it; see Fig. 13–10. The bottom of the pan is covered with a layer of ice of uniform thickness, which is, of course, also rotating with the pan. The ice melts but none of the water escapes from the pan. Is the angular velocity now greater than, the same as, or less than the original velocity? Give reasons for your answer.

## PROBLEMS

**1.** A top is spinning 30 rev/sec about an axis making an angle of 30° with the vertical. Its mass is 0.50 kg and its rotational inertia is $5.0 \times 10^{-4}$ kg-m. The center of mass is 4.0 cm from the pivot point. If the spin is clockwise as seen from above, what is the magnitude and direction of the angular velocity of precession?

**2.** With center and spokes of negligible mass, a certain bicycle wheel has a thin rim of radius 1.14 ft and weight 8.36 lb; it can turn on its axle with negligible friction. A man holds the wheel above his head with the axis vertical while he stands on a turntable free to rotate without friction; the wheel rotates clockwise, as seen from above, with an angular speed 57.7 radians/sec, and the turntable is initially at rest. The rotational inertia of wheel-plus-man-plus-turntable about the common axis of rotation is 1.54 slug ft². (a) The man's hand suddenly stops the rotation of the wheel (relative to the turntable). Determine the resulting angular velocity (magnitude *and* direction) of the turntable. (b) The experiment is repeated with noticeable friction introduced into the axle of the wheel, which, starting from the same initial angular speed 57.7 radians/sec, *gradually* comes to rest (relative to the turntable) while the man holds the wheel as described above. (The turntable is still free to rotate without friction.) Describe what happens to the system, giving as much quantitative information as the data permit.

**3.** Start from Eq. 11–20b, $a_R = \omega \times v$, for a particle in circular motion and show that the force required for uniform circular motion is $F = \omega \times p$. Compare this to Eq. 13–2b, $\tau = \omega_p \times L$, and explain how the precessing spinning top can be regarded as a rotational analog to uniform circular motion.

**4.** (a) Assume that the electron moves in a circular orbit about the proton in a hydrogen atom. If the centripetal force on the electron is supplied by an electrical force $e^2/4\pi\epsilon_0 r^2$, where $e$ is the magnitude of the charge of an electron and of a proton, $r$ is the orbit radius, and $\epsilon_0$ is a constant, show that the radius of the orbit is

$$r = \frac{e^2}{4\pi\epsilon_0 m v^2},$$

where $m$ is the mass of the electron and $v$ is its speed.

(b) Assume now that the angular momentum of the electron about the nucleus can only have values that are integral multiples $n$ of $h/2\pi$, where $h$ is a constant called Planck's constant. Show that the only electronic orbits possible are those with a radius

$$r = \frac{nh}{2\pi mv}.$$

(c) Combine these results to eliminate $v$ and show that the only orbits consistent with both requirements have radii

$$r = \frac{n^2 \epsilon_0 h^2}{\pi me^2}.$$

Hence the allowed radii are proportional to the square of the integers $n = 1, 2, 3$, etc. When $n = 1$, $r$ is smallest and has the value $0.528 \times 10^{-10}$ meter.

5. Show that $\mathbf{L} = I\omega$ for the two-particle system of Fig. 13–4.

6. In 1913, Niels Bohr postulated that any mechanical rotating system with rotational inertia $I$ can have an angular momentum whose values can take on only integral multiples of a particular number $\hbar = 1.054 \times 10^{-34}$ joule-sec. (This number is $1/2\pi$ times Planck's constant $h$.) In other words,

$$L = I\omega = n\hbar,$$

where $n$ is any positive integer or zero. We say that $L$ is quantized, since it is no longer allowed to have any value whatsoever. (a) Show that this postulate restricts the kinetic energy the rotating system can have to a set of discrete values, that is, that the energy is quantized. (b) Consider the so-called *rigid rotator*, consisting of a mass $m$ constrained to rotate in a circle of radius $R$. With what angular speeds could the mass rotate if the postulate were correct? What values of kinetic energy may it assume? (c) Draw an energy-level diagram of some sort indicating how the spacing between the energy levels varies as $n$ increases. It might look something like Fig. 13–11. Certain low-energy diatomic molecules behave like a rigid rotator.

Fig. 13–11

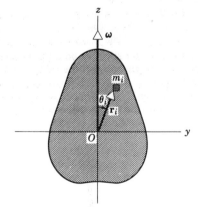

Fig. 13–12

7. Figure 13–12 shows a symmetrical rigid body rotating about a fixed axis. The origin of coordinates is fixed for convenience at the center of mass. Prove, by summing over the contributions made to the angular momentum by all of the mass elements $m_i$ into which the body is divided, that $\mathbf{L} = I\omega$, where $\mathbf{L}$ is the *total* angular momentum.

**8.** A cylinder rolls down an inclined plane of angle $\theta$. Show, by direct application of Eq. 12-9 ($\tau = d\mathbf{L}/dt$), that the acceleration of its center of mass is $\frac{2}{3}g \sin \theta$. Compare this method with that used in Example 10 of Chapter 12.

**9.** A thin rectangular sheet, of length $a$ and width $b$, rotates about one of its diagonals with constant angular speed $\omega$, the axis being fixed in an inertial reference frame. Find the direction and the magnitude of the angular momentum $\mathbf{L}$ with respect to an origin at the center of mass.

**10.** *Relation between the Total Angular Momentum of a System of Particles and the Orbital and Spin Angular Momenta.* The total angular momentum of a system of particles relative to the origin $O$ of an inertial reference frame is given by $\mathbf{L} = \Sigma \mathbf{r}_i \times \mathbf{p}_i$, where $\mathbf{r}_i$ and $\mathbf{p}_i$ are measured with respect to $O$.

(a) Use the relations $\mathbf{r}_i = \mathbf{r}_{cm} + \mathbf{r}_i'$ and $\mathbf{p}_i = m_i \mathbf{v}_{cm} + \mathbf{p}_i'$ of Problem 8, Chapter 12, to express $\mathbf{L}$ in terms of the positions $\mathbf{r}_i'$ and momenta $\mathbf{p}_i'$ relative to the center of mass $C$. (b) Use the definition of center of mass and the definition of angular momentum $\mathbf{L}'$ with respect to the center of mass (Problem 8, Chapter 12) to obtain $\mathbf{L} = \mathbf{L}' + \mathbf{r}_{cm} \times M\mathbf{v}_{cm}$. (c) Show how this result can be interpreted as regarding the total angular momentum to be the sum of spin angular momentum (angular momentum relative to the center of mass) and orbital angular momentum (angular momentum of the motion of the center of mass $C$ with respect to $O$ if all the system's mass were concentrated at $C$).

**11.** The moon revolves about the earth so we always see the same face of the moon. (a) How are the spin and orbital parts of the angular momentum of the moon with respect to the earth related? (b) By how much would its spin angular momentum have to change if we were to be able to see all the moon's surface during the course of a month?

**12.** Using data in the appendix, find (a) the angular momentum of the earth's spin about its own axis, (b) the angular momentum of the earth's orbital motion about the sun.

**13.** In a playground there is a small merry-go-round of radius 4.0 ft and mass 12.0 slugs. The radius of gyration (see Problem 12, Chapter 12) is 3.0 ft. A child of mass 3.0 slugs runs at a speed of 10 ft/sec tangent to the rim of the merry-go-round when it is at rest and then jumps on. Neglect friction and find the angular velocity of the merry-go-round and child.

**14.** The time integral of a torque is called the *angular impulse.* Starting from $\tau = d\mathbf{L}/dt$, show that the resultant angular impulse equals the change in angular momentum. This is the rotational analog of the linear impulse-momentum theorem.

**15.** A meter stick lies on a frictionless horizontal table. It has a mass $M$ and is free to move in any way on the table. A hockey puck $m$, moving as shown in Fig. 13–13, with speed $v$ collides elastically with the stick. (a) What quantities are conserved in the collision? (b) What must be the mass $m$ of the puck so that it remains at rest immediately after the collision?

**Fig. 13–13**

**Fig. 13–14**

**16.** A stick has a mass 0.30 slug and a length 4.0 ft. It is initially at rest on a friction-less horizontal plane and is struck perpendicularly by an impulsive force of impulse 3.0 lb-sec at a distance $l = 1.5$ ft from the center. Determine the subsequent motion.

**17.** A billiard ball, initially at rest, is given a sharp impulse by a cue. The cue is held horizontally a distance $h$ above the centerline as in Fig. 13–14. The ball leaves the cue with a speed $v_0$ and, because of its "forward english," eventually acquires a final speed of $\frac{9}{7}v_0$. Show that

$$h = \tfrac{4}{5}R,$$

where $R$ is the radius of the ball.

**18.** In the preceding problem, imagine $F$ to be applied below the centerline. Show that it is impossible, with this "reverse english," to reduce the forward speed to zero unless $h = R$. Show similarly that it is impossible to give the ball a backward velocity unless $F$ has a downward (vertical) component.

**19.** A wheel is rotating with an angular speed of 500 rev/min on a shaft whose rota-tional inertia is negligible. A second identical wheel, initially at rest, is suddenly coupled to the same shaft. What is the angular speed of the resultant combination of the shaft and the two wheels?

**20.** Two cylinders having radii $R_1$ and $R_2$ and rotational inertia $I_1$ and $I_2$, respec-tively, are supported by fixed axes perpendicular to the plane of Fig. 13–15. The large cylinder is initially rotating with angular velocity $\omega_0$. The small cylinder is moved to the right until it touches the large cylinder and is caused to rotate by the frictional force between the two. Eventually, slipping ceases, and the two cylinders rotate at constant rates in opposite directions. Find the final angular velocity $\omega_2$ of the small cylinder in terms of $I_1$, $I_2$, $R_1$, $R_2$, and $\omega_0$. Is total angular momentum conserved in this case?

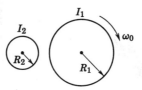

**Fig. 13–15**

**21.** The axis of the cylinder in Fig. 13–16 is fixed. The cylinder is initially at rest. The block of mass $M$ is initially moving to the right without friction with speed $v_1$. It passes over the cylinder to the dotted position. When it first makes contact with the cylinder, it slips on the cylinder, but the friction is large enough so that slipping ceases

**Fig. 13–16**

before $M$ loses contact with the cylinder. The cylinder has a radius $R$ and a rotational inertia $I$. Find the final speed $v_2$ in terms of $v_1$, $M$, $I$, and $R$. This can be done most easily by using the relation between impulse and change in momentum.

**22.** A man stands on a frictionless rotating platform which is rotating with a speed of 1.0 rev/sec; his arms are outstretched and he holds a weight in each hand. With his hands in this position the total rotational inertia of the man and platform is 6.0 kg-m$^2$. If by drawing in the weights the man decreases the rotational inertia to 2.0 kg-m$^2$, (a) what is the resulting angular speed of the platform? (b) By how much is the kinetic energy increased?

**23.** In Example 5 compare the kinetic energies of the object in two different orbits. Use the work-energy theorem to explain the difference quantitatively.

**24.** A cockroach, mass $m$, runs counterclockwise around the rim of a lazy-susan (a circular dish mounted on a vertical axle) of radius $R$ and rotational inertia $I$ with frictionless bearings. The cockroach's speed (relative to the earth) is $v$, whereas the lazy-susan turns clockwise with angular speed $\omega_0$. The cockroach finds a bread crumb on the rim and of course, stops. What is the angular speed of the lazy-susan after the cockroach stops? Is energy conserved?

**25.** A particle is projected horizontally along the interior of a smooth hemispherical bowl of radius $r$ which is kept at rest (Fig. 13-17). We wish to find the initial speed $v_0$ required for the particle to just reach the top of the bowl. Find $v_0$ as a function of $\theta_0$, the initial angular position of the particle. (*Hint:* Use conservation principles.)

**Fig. 13-17**

**Fig. 13-18**

**26.** A uniform flat disk of mass $M$ and radius $R$ rotates about a horizontal axis through its center with angular speed $\omega_0$. (a) What is its kinetic energy? Its angular momentum? (b) A chip of mass $m$ breaks off the edge of the disk at an instant such that the chip rises *vertically* above the point at which it broke off (Fig. 13-18). How high above the point does it rise before starting to fall? (c) What is the final angular speed of the broken disk? The final angular momentum and energy?

**27.** Two skaters, each of mass 50 kg, approach each other along parallel paths separated by 3.0 meters. They have equal and opposite velocities of 10 meters/sec. The first skater carries a long light pole, 3.0 meters long, and the second skater grabs the end of it as he passes. (Assume frictionless ice.) (a) Describe quantitatively the motion of the skaters after they are connected by the pole. (b) By pulling on the pole, the skaters reduce their distance apart to 1.0 meter. What is their motion then? (c) Compare the kinetic energy of the system in parts (a) and (b). Where does the change come from?

**28.** On a large horizontal frictionless circular track, radius $R$, lie two small masses $m$ and $M$, free to slide on the track. Between the two masses is squeezed a spring which, however, is *not fastened* to $m$ and $M$. The two masses are held together by a string.

(a) If the string breaks, the compressed spring (assumed massless) shoots off the two masses in opposite directions; the spring itself is left behind. The balls collide when they again meet on the track (Fig. 13–19). Where does this collision take place? (You might find it convenient to express the answer in terms of the angle $m$ or $M$ travels through.)    (b) If the potential energy initially stored in the spring was $U_0$, what is the time it takes after the string breaks for the collision to take place?    (c) Assuming the collision to be perfectly elastic and head-on, where will the balls again collide after the first collision?

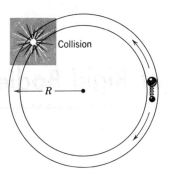

Fig. 13–19

# Equilibrium of Rigid Bodies

## CHAPTER 14

### 14–1  Rigid Bodies

The towers supporting a suspension bridge must be strong enough so that they do not collapse under the weight of the bridge and its traffic load; the landing gear of an aircraft must not collapse if the pilot makes a poor landing; the tines of a fork must not bend when we cut a tough steak. In all such problems the engineer is concerned that these presumed rigid structures do indeed remain rigid under the forces, and the associated torques, that act on them.

In such problems the engineer must ask two questions. (1) What forces and torques act on the presumed rigid body? (2) Considering its design and the materials used, will the body remain rigid under the action of these forces and torques? In this chapter we are concerned only with the first of these questions; the engineering student will deal at length with the second question in later courses.

### 14–2  The Equilibrium of a Rigid Body

We note that the presumed rigid bodies of the preceding section (that is, the bridge towers, the landing gear, and the fork) are in *mechanical equilibrium*. A rigid body is in mechanical equilibrium if, as viewed from an inertial reference frame, (1) the linear acceleration $a_{cm}$ of its center of mass is zero and (2) its angular acceleration $\alpha$ about any axis fixed in this reference frame is zero.

This definition does not require the body to be at rest with respect to the observer but only to be unaccelerated. Its center of mass, for example, may be moving with constant velocity $v_{cm}$ and the body may be rotating about a fixed axis with constant angular velocity $\omega$.  If the body is actually at rest (so that $v_{cm} = 0$ and $\omega = 0$), we often speak of *static equilibrium.* However, as we shall see, the restrictions imposed on the forces and torques are the same whether or not the equilibrium is static.  Furthermore, we can transform any case of (nonstatic) equilibrium to one of static equilibrium by choosing an appropriate new reference frame.

The translational motion of a rigid body of mass $M$ is governed by Eq. 9-10, or

$$\mathbf{F}_{ext} = M\mathbf{a}_{cm},$$

in which $\mathbf{F}_{ext}$ is the vector sum of all the external forces acting on the body. Because $\mathbf{a}_{cm}$ must be zero for equilibrium, the first condition of equilibrium (static or otherwise) is: *The vector sum of all the external forces acting on a body in equilibrium must be zero.*

We can write condition (1) as

$$\mathbf{F} = \mathbf{F}_1 + \mathbf{F}_2 + \cdots = 0, \qquad (14\text{-}1)$$

in which we have dropped the subscript on $\mathbf{F}_{ext}$ for convenience.  This vector equation leads to three scalar equations.

$$F_x = F_{1x} + F_{2x} + \cdots = 0,$$
$$F_y = F_{1y} + F_{2y} + \cdots = 0, \qquad (14\text{-}2)$$
$$F_z = F_{1z} + F_{2z} + \cdots = 0,$$

which state that the sum of the components of the forces along each of any three mutually perpendicular directions is zero.

The second requirement for equilibrium is that $\alpha = 0$ for any axis. Since the angular acceleration of a rigid body is associated with torque— recall that $\tau = I\alpha$ for a fixed axis—we can state this second condition of equilibrium (static or otherwise) as: *The vector sum of all the external torques acting on a body in equilibrium must be zero.*

We can write condition (2) as

$$\boldsymbol{\tau} = \boldsymbol{\tau}_1 + \boldsymbol{\tau}_2 + \cdots = 0. \qquad (14\text{-}3)$$

This vector equation leads to three scalar equations

$$\tau_x = \tau_{1x} + \tau_{2x} + \cdots = 0,$$
$$\tau_y = \tau_{1y} + \tau_{2y} + \cdots = 0, \qquad (14\text{-}4)$$
$$\tau_z = \tau_{1z} + \tau_{2z} + \cdots = 0,$$

which state that, at equilibrium, the sum of the components of the torques acting on a body, along each of any three mutually perpendicular directions, is zero.

The resultant torque $\boldsymbol{\tau}$ in Eq. 14-3, which must be zero for mechanical equilibrium, is defined with respect to a particular origin $O$.  The quantities $\tau_x$, $\tau_y$, and $\tau_z$ in Eq. 14-4 are the scalar components of $\boldsymbol{\tau}$ and refer to any set of three mutually perpendicular axes whose origin is at $O$, no matter how these axes are oriented in space. This follows because, if a vector is zero, its scalar components must be zero no matter how we orient the axes of the reference frame. The student may wonder whether the choice of an origin is essential. The answer—as we shall show below—is that it is not, because (for a body in translational equilibrium), if $\tau = 0$ for any single origin $O$ it is also zero for any other origin in the reference frame. The substance of this paragraph then is that condition 2 is satisfied for a body in translational equilibrium if we can show either that (a) $\tau = 0$ with respect to *any* one point (Eq. 14–3) or that (b) the torque components along *any* three mutually perpendicular axes are zero (Eq. 14–4).

Let us now assume that we have a rigid body in translational equilibrium, so that $\mathbf{F} = \mathbf{F}_1 + \mathbf{F}_2 + \cdots = 0$ (Eq. 14–1). We now wish to show that the torque about *any* point (such as $P$ in Fig. 14–1) will be zero if the torque about one particular point (such as $O$ in Fig. 14–1) is zero. The figure shows three of the $n$ forces, $\mathbf{F}_1$, $\mathbf{F}_2 \cdots \mathbf{F}_n$, applied at various points on a rigid body and pointing in various directions. The points of application with respect to $O$ are identified by displacement vectors, of which $\mathbf{r}_1$ is an example. The arbitrary point $P$ is identified by displacement vector $\mathbf{r}_P$; the vector $\mathbf{r}_1 - \mathbf{r}_P$ locates the point of application of $\mathbf{F}_1$ with respect to point $P$.

We can write for the resultant torque about $O$ (see Eq. 12–1)

$$\tau_O = \mathbf{r}_1 \times \mathbf{F}_1 + \mathbf{r}_2 \times \mathbf{F}_2 + \cdots + \mathbf{r}_n \times \mathbf{F}_n$$

and for the torque about $P$,

$$\tau_P = (\mathbf{r}_1 - \mathbf{r}_P) \times \mathbf{F}_1 + (\mathbf{r}_2 - \mathbf{r}_P) \times \mathbf{F}_2 + \cdots + (\mathbf{r}_n - \mathbf{r}_P) \times \mathbf{F}_n.$$

We can expand the latter equation as

$$\tau_P = [\mathbf{r}_1 \times \mathbf{F}_1 + \mathbf{r}_2 \times \mathbf{F}_2 + \cdots + \mathbf{r}_n \times \mathbf{F}_n] \\ - [\mathbf{r}_P \times (\mathbf{F}_1 + \mathbf{F}_2 + \cdots + \mathbf{F}_n)].$$

Now if, as we have assumed, the first condition of equilibrium is satisfied, then $\mathbf{F}_1 + \mathbf{F}_2 + \cdots + \mathbf{F}_n = 0$ and the second term above in the square brackets

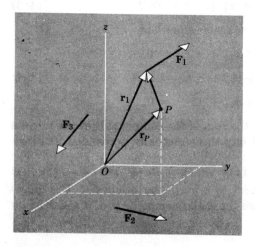

**Fig. 14–1** Three of the $n$ forces, $\mathbf{F}_1$, $\mathbf{F}_2$, $\mathbf{F}_3 \ldots \mathbf{F}_n$, that act on a rigid body, not shown. In the text we show that if $\tau = 0$ for point $O$ it also vanishes for any point such as $P$, assuming that the body is in translational equilibrium.

vanishes. The first term in the square brackets is simply $\tau_O$ (see above) so that, under these conditions

$$\tau_P = \tau_O.$$

Thus, for a body in translational equilibrium, if $\tau_O = 0$ then $\tau_P = 0$, where $P$ is an arbitrary point.

Hence we have *six independent conditions* on our forces for a body to be in equilibrium. These conditions are the six algebraic relations of Eqs. 14–2 and 14–4. These six conditions are a condition on each of the six degrees of freedom of a rigid body, three translational and three rotational.

Often we deal with problems in which all the forces lie in a plane. Then we have only three conditions on our forces: The sum of their components must be zero for each of any two perpendicular directions in the plane, and the sum of their torques about any one axis perpendicular to the plane must be zero. These conditions correspond to the three degrees of freedom for motion in a plane, two of translation and one of rotation.

We shall limit ourselves henceforth mostly to planar problems in order to simplify the calculations. This does not impose any fundamental restriction on the general principles. Also, as a matter of convenience, we shall consider only the case of static equilibrium, in which bodies are actually at rest.

## 14–3  Center of Gravity

One of the forces encountered in rigid-body motions is the force of gravity. Actually, for an extended body, this is not just one force but the resultant of a great many forces. Each particle in the body is acted on by a gravitational force. If the body of mass $M$ is imagined to be divided into a large number of particles, say $n$, the gravitational force exerted by the earth on the $i$th particle of mass $m_i$ is $m_i g$. This force is directed down toward the earth. If the acceleration due to gravity $\mathbf{g}$ is the same everywhere in a region, we say that a uniform gravitational field exists there; that is, $\mathbf{g}$ has the same magnitude and direction everywhere in that region. For a rigid body in a uniform gravitational field, $\mathbf{g}$ must be the same for each particle in the body and the weight forces on the particles must be parallel to one another. If we assume that the earth's gravitational field is uniform, we can show that all the individual weight forces acting on a body can be replaced by a single force $M\mathbf{g}$ acting down at the center of mass of the body. This is equivalent to showing that the individual weight forces, acting downward, can be counteracted in their accelerating effects by a single force $\mathbf{F}$ $(= -M\mathbf{g})$ acting upward, *provided this force $\mathbf{F}$ is applied at the center of mass of the body.*

Figure 14–2 shows two typical particles or mass elements $m_1$ and $m_2$, selected from the $n$ such elements into which the rigid body has been divided. An upward force $\mathbf{F}$ $(= -M\mathbf{g})$ is applied at a certain point $O$. It remains to show that the body is in mechanical equilibrium *if* (and only if) point $O$ is the center of mass. Condition 1 for equilibrium (Eq. 14–1) has already been satisfied by our choice of the magnitude and direction of

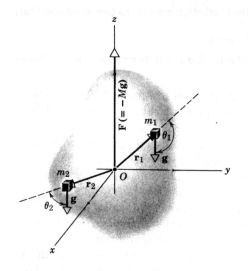

**F.**  That is,

$$\mathbf{F} + m_1\mathbf{g} + m_2\mathbf{g} + \cdots + m_n\mathbf{g} = 0,$$

or

$$\mathbf{F} = -(m_1 + m_2 + \cdots + m_n)\mathbf{g} = -M\mathbf{g},$$

which corresponds to our assumption.

It remains to prove that $\tau = 0$ for any single point in the body, such as $O$.  This is the second condition for equilibrium.  By choosing $O$ as our origin we insure that the torque of $\mathbf{F}$ about this point is zero, because the moment arm of $\mathbf{F}$ is zero for this point.  The torque about $O$ due to the gravitational pull on the mass elements is

$$\tau = \mathbf{r}_1 \times m_1\mathbf{g} + \mathbf{r}_2 \times m_2\mathbf{g} + \cdots + \mathbf{r}_n \times m_n\mathbf{g}$$

which (because $m_1$, $m_2$, etc., are scalars) we can write as

$$\tau = m_1\mathbf{r}_1 \times \mathbf{g} + m_2\mathbf{r}_2 \times \mathbf{g} + \cdots + m_n\mathbf{r}_n \times \mathbf{g}.$$

Since $\mathbf{g}$ is the same in each term, we can factor it out, obtaining

$$\tau = (m_1\mathbf{r}_1 + m_2\mathbf{r}_2 + \cdots + m_n\mathbf{r}_n) \times \mathbf{g}$$

$$= \left(\sum_1^n m_i\mathbf{r}_i\right) \times \mathbf{g},$$

in which the sum is taken over all the mass elements that make up the body.

Now *if* point $O$ is the center of mass of the body, the sum above is zero. This follows from the definition of the center of mass (see Eq. 9–5b and the discussion following it).  We conclude then that *if* (and only if) point $O$ is the center of mass, then $\tau = 0$ and the second condition for mechanical equilibrium is satisfied.

Thus the gravitational forces acting on the individual mass elements that make up a rigid body are equivalent in their translational and rotational effects to a single force equal to $M\mathbf{g}$, the total weight of the body, acting at the center of mass. We can obtain the same result if the body is continuous and divided into an infinite number of particles. The student should be able to do this by the methods of integral calculus (see Section 9–1). The point of application of the equivalent resultant gravitational force is often called the *center of gravity*.

The coincidence of the center of gravity and the center of mass came about because of the assumption that the earth's gravitational field was uniform. Actually this assumption is not strictly true, for the magnitude of $\mathbf{g}$ changes with distance from the center of the earth and furthermore the direction of $\mathbf{g}$ is radially in toward the center of the earth from any point (Chapter 16). To see the effect this has, let us consider a uniform stick many miles long inclined to the vertical in the earth's gravitational field, as in Fig. 14–3. The center of gravity of a body is the point at which the equivalent resultant gravitational force on it acts. This point must be the same as the point at which a single oppositely directed force is applied for the body to be kept in equilibrium. If the field were uniform, a single upward force of magnitude $Mg$ at the center of mass would keep the stick in translational and rotational equilibrium. But the field is not uniform, and the value of $g$ at $m_1$ is less than the value of $g$ at $m_n$. The point at which a single force must be applied to keep the body in equilibrium is therefore at a point $P$ some distance below the center of mass. Furthermore, if the orientation

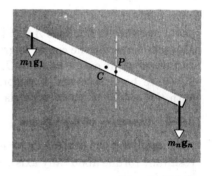

**Fig. 14–3**  The center of mass $C$ and center of gravity $P$ in reality do not coincide, since the earth's gravitational field is not uniform.

of the body is changed, the position of the point $P$, required for application of an equilibrium force, changes. Hence center of gravity really has little usefulness in such a case. Not only does it not coincide with the center of mass, but its position changes with respect to the body as the body is moved.

Because almost all problems in mechanics involve objects having dimensions small compared to the distances over which $\mathbf{g}$ changes appreciably, we can assume that $\mathbf{g}$ is uniform over the body. The center of mass and the center of gravity can then be taken as the same point. In fact, we can use this coincidence to determine experimentally the center of mass in irregularly shaped objects. For example, let us locate the center of mass of a thin plate of irregular shape, as in Fig. 14–4. We suspend the body by a cord from some point $A$ on its edge. When the body is at rest, the center of gravity must lie directly under the point of support somewhere on the line $Aa$, for only then can the torque resulting from the cord and the weight add to zero. We next suspend the body from another point $B$ on its edge. Again, the center of gravity must lie somewhere on $Bb$. The only

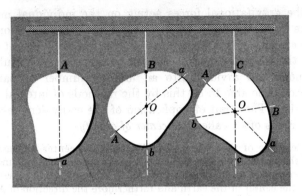

**Fig. 14–4** Since the center of mass $O$ always hangs directly below the point of suspension, hanging a plate from two different points determines $O$.

point common to the lines $Aa$ and $Bb$ is $O$, the point of intersection, so that this point must be the center of gravity. If now we suspend the body from any other point on its edge, as $C$, the vertical line $Cc$ will pass through $O$. Since we have assumed a uniform field, the center of gravity coincides with the center of mass, which is therefore located at $O$.

### 14–4 Examples of Equilibrium

In applying the conditions for equilibrium (zero resultant force and zero resultant torque about any axis), we can clarify and simplify the procedure in many ways.

First, we draw an imaginary boundary around the system under consideration. This assures that we see clearly just what body or system of bodies it is to which we are applying the laws of equilibrium. This process is called isolating the system.

Second, we draw vectors representing the magnitude, direction, and point of application of all *external* forces. An external force is one that acts from outside the boundary which was drawn earlier. Examples of external forces often encountered are gravitational forces and forces transmitted by strings, wires, rods, and beams which cross the boundary. A question sometimes arises about the direction of a force. In this case make an imaginary cut through the member transmitting the force at the point where it crosses the boundary. If the ends of this cut tend to pull apart, the force acts outward. If you are in doubt, choose the direction arbitrarily. A negative value for a force in the solution means that the force acts in the direction opposite to that assumed. Note that only external forces acting on the system need be considered; all internal forces cancel one another in pairs.

Third, we choose a convenient reference frame along whose axes we resolve the external forces before applying the first condition of equilibrium (Eq. 14–2). The object here is to simplify the calculations. The preferable reference frame is usually obvious.

Fourth, we choose a convenient reference frame along whose axes we resolve the external torques before applying the second condition of equilibrium (Eq. 14-4). The object again is to simplify calculations and we may use different reference frames in applying the two conditions for static equilibrium if this proves to be convenient. Suppose that an axis passes through the point at which two forces concur and is at right angles to the plane formed by these forces; these forces will automatically have no torque component along (or about) this axis. The torque components resulting from all external forces must be zero about any axis for equilibrium. Internal torques will cancel in pairs and need not be considered.

▶ **Example 1.**   (a) A uniform steel meter bar rests on two scales at its ends (Fig. 14-5). The bar weighs 4.0 lb. Find the readings on the scales.

Our system is the bar. The forces acting on the bar are $W$, the gravitational force acting down at the center of gravity, and $F_1$ and $F_2$, the forces exerted upward on the bar at its ends by the scales. These are shown in Fig. 14-5a. By Newton's third law, the force exerted by a scale on the bar is equal and opposite to that exerted by the bar on the scale. Therefore, to obtain the readings on the scales, we must determine the magnitudes of $F_1$ and $F_2$.

For translational equilibrium (Eq. 14-1) the condition is

$$\mathbf{F}_1 + \mathbf{F}_2 + \mathbf{W} = 0.$$

All forces act vertically, so that if we choose the $y$-axis to be vertical, no other axes need be considered. Then we get the scalar equation

$$F_1 + F_2 - 4.0 \text{ lb} = 0.$$

For rotational equilibrium, the component of the resultant torque on the bar must be zero about *any* axis. We have seen that it is enough to show that the torque components are zero for any set of three mutually perpendicular axes. These components are certainly zero for any two perpendicular axes that lie in the plane of Fig. 14-5a (Why?). It remains to require that the resultant torque is zero about any one axis at right angles to the plane of the figure. Let us choose an axis through the center of gravity. Then, taking clockwise rotation as positive and counterclockwise rotation as negative, the condition for rotational equilibrium

(a)                                             (b)

**Fig. 14-5**   (a) Example 1a.  A uniform steel bar rests on two spring scales.   (b) Example 1b.  A weight is suspended a quarter of the way from one end.

(Eq. 14–4) is

$$F_1\left(\frac{l}{2}\right) - F_2\left(\frac{l}{2}\right) + W(0) = 0,$$

or

$$F_1 - F_2 = 0.$$

Combining the two equations, we obtain

$$F_1 + F_2 = 2F_1 = 2F_2 = 4.0 \text{ lb},$$

$$F_1 = F_2 = 2.0 \text{ lb}.$$

Each scale reads 2.0 lb, as we might have expected.

If we had chosen an axis through one end of the bar, we would have obtained the same result. For example, taking torques about an axis through the right end, we obtain

$$F_1(l) - W\left(\frac{l}{2}\right) + F_2(0) = 0,$$

or

$$F_1 = \frac{W}{2} = \frac{4.0 \text{ lb}}{2} = 2.0 \text{ lb}.$$

Combining this with $F_1 + F_2 = 4.0$ lb, we obtain $F_2 = 2.0$ lb, as before.

(b) Suppose that a 6.0-lb block is placed at the 25-cm mark on the meter bar. What do the scales read now?

The external forces acting on the bar are shown in Fig. 14–5b, where w is the force exerted on the bar by the block. The first condition for equilibrium is

$$F_1 + F_2 - W - w = 0.$$

With $W = 4.0$ lb and $w = 6.0$ lb, we obtain

$$F_1 + F_2 = 10 \text{ lb}.$$

If we take an axis through the left end of the bar, the second condition for equilibrium is

$$w\left(\frac{l}{4}\right) + W\left(\frac{l}{2}\right) - F_2(l) = 0.$$

With $W = 4.0$ lb and $w = 6.0$ lb, we obtain

$$F_2 = 3.5 \text{ lb}.$$

Putting this result into the first equation, we obtain

$$F_1 + 3.5 \text{ lb} = 10 \text{ lb},$$

$$F_1 = 6.5 \text{ lb}.$$

The left-hand scale reads 6.5 lb and the right-hand scale reads 3.5 lb at equilibrium.

Why do we obtain only two conditions on the forces in this problem rather than the three conditions expected for problems in which all forces lie in the same plane?

**Example 2.** (a) A 60-ft ladder weighing 100 lb rests against a wall at a point 48 ft above the ground. The center of gravity of the ladder is one-third the way up. A 160-lb man climbs halfway up the ladder. Assuming that the wall is frictionless, find the forces exerted by the system on the ground and the wall.

The forces acting on the ladder are shown in Fig. 14–6. **W** is the weight of the man standing on the ladder, and **w** is the weight of the ladder itself. A force $\mathbf{F_1}$ is exerted by the ground on the ladder. $\mathbf{F_{1v}}$ is the vertical component and $\mathbf{F_{1h}}$ is the horizontal component of this force (due to friction). The wall, being frictionless, can exert only a force normal to its surface, called $\mathbf{F_2}$. We are given the following data:

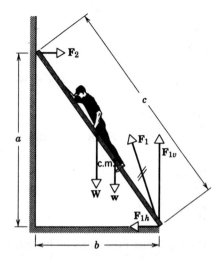

**Fig. 14–6**   Example 2.

$$W = 160 \text{ lb}, \quad w = 100 \text{ lb},$$
$$a = 48 \text{ ft}, \quad c = 60 \text{ ft}.$$

From the geometry we conclude that $b = 36$ ft. The line of action of **W** intersects the ground at a distance $b/2$ from the wall and the line of action of **w** intersects the ground at a distance $2b/3$ from the wall.

We choose the $x$-axis to be along the ground and the $y$-axis along the wall. Then, the conditions on the forces for translational equilibrium (Eq. 14–2) are

$$F_2 - F_{1h} = 0,$$
$$F_{1v} - W - w = 0.$$

For rotational equilibrium (Eq. 14–4) choose an axis through the point of contact with the ground and obtain

$$F_2(a) - W\left(\frac{b}{2}\right) - w\left(\frac{b}{3}\right) = 0.$$

Using the data given, we obtain

$$F_2(48 \text{ ft}) - (160 \text{ lb})(18 \text{ ft}) - (100 \text{ lb})(12 \text{ ft}) = 0,$$
$$F_2 = 85 \text{ lb},$$
$$F_{1h} = F_2 = 85 \text{ lb},$$
$$F_{1v} = 160 \text{ lb} + 100 \text{ lb} = 260 \text{ lb}.$$

By Newton's third law the forces exerted by the ground and the wall on the ladder are equal but opposite to the forces exerted by the ladder on the ground and the wall, respectively. Therefore, the normal force on the wall is 85 lb, and the force on the ground has components of 260 lb down and 85 lb to the right.

(b) If the coefficient of static friction between the ground and the ladder is $\mu_s = 0.40$, how high up the ladder can the man go before it starts to slip?

Let $x$ be the fraction of the total length of the ladder the man can climb before slipping begins. Then our equilibrium conditions are

$$F_2 - F_{1h} = 0,$$

$$F_{1v} - W - w = 0,$$

and

$$F_2 a - Wbx - w\left(\frac{b}{3}\right) = 0.$$

Now we obtain

$$F_2(48 \text{ ft}) = (160 \text{ lb})(36 \text{ ft})x + (100 \text{ lb})(12 \text{ ft}),$$

$$F_2 = (120x + 25) \text{ lb}.$$

Hence

$$F_{1h} = (120x + 25) \text{ lb},$$

and, as before,

$$F_{1v} = 260 \text{ lb}.$$

The maximum force of static friction is given by

$$F_{1h} = \mu_s F_{1v} = (0.40)(260 \text{ lb}) = 104 \text{ lb}.$$

Therefore,

$$F_{1h} = (120x + 25) \text{ lb} = 104 \text{ lb}$$

and

$$x = \tfrac{79}{120},$$

so that the man can climb up the ladder

$$60x \text{ ft} = 39.5 \text{ ft}$$

before slipping begins.

In this example the ladder is treated as a one-dimensional object, with only one point of contact at the wall and ground. The student should reflect on how this limits consideration of the less artificial case of two contact points at each end.

The reason for assuming that the wall is frictionless is discussed later. Can you guess what it is?

**Example 3.** A uniform beam is hinged at the wall. A wire connected to the wall a distance $d$ above the hinge is attached to the other end of the beam. The beam makes an angle of 30° with the horizontal when a weight $w$ is hung from a string fastened to the end of the beam. If the beam has a weight $W$ and a length $l$, find the tension in the wire and the forces exerted by the hinge on the beam.

The situation is depicted in Fig. 14–7, in which all the forces acting on the beam are shown. The wire pulling on the beam makes some angle $\alpha$ with the horizontal so that the tension **T** in the wire has horizontal and vertical components $T_h$ and $T_v$, respectively, as shown. The force **F** exerted by the hinge on the beam also has horizontal and vertical components $F_h$ and $F_v$, respectively. **W** is the weight of the beam, acting at its center of gravity, and **w** is the tension in the string that transmits the weight of the suspended body to the beam.

**Fig. 14–7**   Example 3.

Choosing our axes to be horizontal and vertical, we obtain for translational equilibrium

$$F_v + T_v - W - w = 0,$$

and

$$F_h - T_h = 0.$$

Choosing an axis through the point of intersection of **T** and **w** (Why?), we obtain for rotational equilibrium

$$F_v(l \cos 30°) - F_h(l \sin 30°) - \frac{W(l \cos 30°)}{2} = 0$$

Our unknowns are $T_h$, $T_v$, $F_h$, and $F_v$. Let us assign the following values to the other quantities:

$$W = 300 \text{ lb}, \quad w = 200 \text{ lb}, \quad l = 10 \text{ ft}, \quad d = 6.0 \text{ ft}.$$

Therefore

(1) $$F_v + T_v = 500 \text{ lb},$$

(2) $$F_h = T_h,$$

and

$$F_v(10)(0.866) = F_h(5.0) + (300)(5.0)(0.866),$$

or

(3) $$F_v = F_h(5.0/8.66) + 150 \text{ lb}.$$

Recall that we have four unknowns, namely $F_v$, $F_h$, $T_v$, and $T_h$. We need another relation between these quantities if we are to solve the problem. This relation follows from the fact that $T_v$ and $T_h$ must add to give a resultant vector **T** directed along the wire. The wire cannot supply or support a force transverse to its orientation. (Notice that this is not true for the beam, however.) Hence our fourth relation is

$$T_v = T_h \tan \alpha,$$

where $\tan \alpha = (d - l \sin 30°)/ l \cos 30° = 1.0/8.66$, so that

(4) $$T_v = T_h/8.66.$$

Combining (1) and (4) we obtain

$$F_v = 500 \text{ lb} - T_h/8.66.$$

Combining (2) and (3), we obtain

$$F_v = T_h(5.0/8.66) + 150 \text{ lb}.$$

Solving these equations simultaneously, we obtain

$$T_h = 505 \text{ lb},$$

and

$$F_v = 442 \text{ lb}.$$

From (2) we obtain

$$F_h = 505 \text{ lb}.$$

From (1) we obtain

$$T_v = 58 \text{ lb}.$$

The tension in the wire will then be

$$T = \sqrt{T_h{}^2 + T_v{}^2} = 509 \text{ lb},$$

and the hinge will exert a horizontal force of 505 lb and a vertical force of 442 lb on the beam.     ◀

In the preceding examples we have been careful to limit the number of unknown forces to the number of independent equations relating the forces. When all the forces act in a plane, we can have only three independent equations of equilibrium, one for rotational equilibrium about any axis normal to the plane and two others for translational equilibrium in the plane. However, we often have more than three unknown forces. For example, in the ladder problem of Example 2a, if we drop the artificial assumption of a frictionless wall, we have four unknown scalar quantities, namely, the horizontal and vertical components of the force acting on the ladder at the wall and the horizontal and vertical components of the force acting on the ladder at the ground. Since we have only three scalar equations, these forces cannot be determined. For any value assigned to one unknown force, the other three forces can be determined. But if we have no basis for assigning any particular value to an unknown force, there are an infinite number of solutions possible mathematically. We must therefore find another independent relation between the unknown forces if we hope to solve the problem uniquely.

Another simple example of such underdetermined structures is the automobile. In this case we wish to determine the forces exerted by the ground on each of the four tires when the car is at rest on a horizontal surface. If we assume that these forces are normal to the ground, we have four unknown scalar quantities. All other forces, such as the weight of the car and passengers, act normal to the ground. Therefore we have only three independent equations giving the equilibrium conditions, one for translational equilibrium in the single direction of all the forces and two for rotational equilibrium about the two axes perpendicular to each other in a horizontal plane. Again the solution of the problem is indeterminate, mathematically. A four-legged table with all its legs in contact with the floor is a similar example.

Of course, since there is actually a unique solution to any real physical problem, we must find a physical basis for the additional independent relation between the forces that enable us to solve the problem. The difficulty is removed when we realize that structures are never perfectly rigid, as we have tacitly assumed throughout. Actually our structures will be somewhat deformed. For example, the automobile tires and the ground will be deformed, as will the ladder and wall. The laws of elasticity and the elastic properties of the structure determine the nature of the deformation and will provide the necessary additional relation between the four forces. A complete analysis therefore requires not only the laws of rigid body mechanics but also the laws of elasticity. In courses in civil and mechanical engineering, many such problems are encountered and analyzed in this way. We shall not consider the matter further here.

## 14–5   Stable, Unstable, and Neutral Equilibrium of Rigid Bodies in a Gravitational Field

In Chapter 8 we saw that the gravitational force is a conservative force. For conservative forces we can define a potential energy function $U(x,y,z)$, where $U$ is related to $\mathbf{F}$ by

$$F_x = -\partial U/\partial x, \qquad F_y = -\partial U/\partial y, \qquad F_z = -\partial U/\partial z.$$

At points where $\partial U/\partial x$ is zero, a particle subject to this conservative force will be in translational equilibrium in the $x$-direction, for then $F_x$ equals zero. Likewise, at points where $\partial U/\partial y$ or $\partial U/\partial z$ are zero, a particle will be in translational equilibrium in the $y$- and $z$-directions, respectively. The derivative of $U$ at a point will be zero when $U$ has an extreme value (maximum or minimum) at that point or when $U$ is constant with respect to the variable coordinate.

When $U$ is a minimum, the particle is in *stable* equilibrium; any displacement from this position will result in a restoring force tending to return the particle to the equilibrium position. Another way of stating this is to say that if a body is in stable equilibrium, work must be done on it by an external agent to change its position. This results in an increase in its potential energy.

When $U$ is a maximum, the particle is in *unstable* equilibrium; any displacement from this position will result in a force tending to push the particle farther from the equilibrium position. In this case no work must be done on the particle by an external agent to change its position; the work done in displacing the body is supplied internally by the conservative force, resulting in a decrease in potential energy.

When $U$ is constant, the particle is in *neutral* equilibrium. In this case a particle can be displaced slightly without experiencing either a repelling or restoring force.

Notice that a particle can be in equilibrium with respect to one coordinate without necessarily being in equilibrium with respect to another coordinate, as for example a freely falling ball. Furthermore, a particle may be in stable equilibrium with respect to one coordinate and in unstable equilibrium with respect to another coordinate, as for example a particle at a saddle point (Fig. 14–8).

All these remarks apply to particles, that is, to translational motion. Suppose now we treat a rigid body. We must consider rotational equilibrium as well as translational equilibrium. The problem of a rigid body in a gravitational field is

**Fig. 14–8**  A gravitational potential surface, which may be thought of as a real surface. A particle placed at $A$, $B$ or $C$ remains at rest; a plane tangent to any of these points is horizontal.  We say that a particle here is *in equilibrium*.  At $A$, a particle, if slightly displaced, tends to return to $A$.  $A$ represents a point of *stable equilibrium*.  At $B$, a particle, if slightly displaced, tends to increase its displacement.  Thus $B$ represents a point of *unstable equilibrium*.  At $C$, the particle, if slightly displaced in the direction $aa'$, will tend to return to $C$, but if it is displaced in direction $bb'$, it will tend to increase its displacement.  $C$ is called a *saddle point* since a saddle has somewhat this shape. Neutral equilibrium, experienced by a particle anywhere on a plane horizontal surface, is not illustrated.

particularly simple, however, because *all the gravitational forces on the particles of the rigid body can be considered to act at one point, both for translational and rotational purposes.*  We can replace this entire rigid body, for purposes of equilibrium under gravitational forces, by a single particle having the equivalent mass at the center of gravity.

For example, consider a cube at rest on one side on a horizontal table.  The center of gravity is shown at the center of the central cross section of the cube in Fig. 14–9a.  Let us supply a force to the cube so as to rotate it without its slipping about an axis along an edge.  Notice that the center of gravity is raised and that work is done on the cube, which increases its potential energy.  If the force is removed, the cube tends to return to its original position, its increased potential energy being converted into kinetic energy as it falls back.  This initial position is, therefore, one of *stable* equilibrium.  In terms of a particle of equivalent mass at the center of gravity, this process is described by the dotted line which indicates the path taken by the center of gravity during this motion.  The particle is seen to have a minimum potential energy in the position of stable equilibrium, as required.  We can conclude that the rigid body will be in stable equilibrium if the application of any force can raise the center of gravity of the body but not lower it.

If the cube is rotated until it balances on an edge, as in Fig. 14–9b, then once again the cube is in equilibrium.  This equilibrium position is seen to be unstable. The application of even the slightest horizontal force will cause the cube to fall away from this position with a decrease of potential energy.  The particle of equivalent mass at the center of gravity follows the dotted path shown.  At the position of unstable equilibrium this particle has a maximum potential energy, as required.  We can conclude that the rigid body will be in unstable equilibrium if

**Fig. 14–9** Equilibrium of an extended body. (a) A cube resting on one side is in *stable equilibrium* since its center of gravity C is raised if the cube is tipped by a horizontal force **F**. (b) A cube resting on one edge is in *unstable equilibrium* since C falls if the cube is tipped by **F**. (c) A sphere or cylinder is in *neutral equilibrium* since C neither rises nor falls when **F** is applied. Compare these criteria for equilibrium with those given in Fig. 14–8. How are the criteria in the two figures related?

the application of any horizontal force tends to lower the center of gravity of the body.

The neutral equilibrium of a rigid body is illustrated by a sphere on a horizontal table (Fig. 14–9c). If the sphere is subjected to any horizontal force, the center of gravity is neither raised nor lowered but moves along the horizontal dotted line. The potential energy of the sphere is constant during the displacement, as is that of the particle of equivalent mass at the center of gravity. The system has no tendency to move in any direction when the applied force is removed. A rigid body will be in neutral equilibrium if the application of any horizontal force neither raises nor lowers the center of gravity of the body.

Under what circumstances would a *suspended* rigid body be in stable equilibrium? When would a *suspended* rigid body be in unstable equilibrium, and when would it be in neutral equilibrium?

## QUESTIONS

**1.** Are Eqs. 14–1 and 14–3 both necessary and sufficient conditions for mechanical equilibrium? For static equilibrium?

**2.** A wheel rotating at constant angular velocity ω about a fixed axis is in mechanical equilibrium because no net external force or torque acts on it. However, the particles that make up the wheel undergo a centripetal acceleration **a** directed toward the axis. Since **a** $\neq$ 0 how can the wheel be said to be in equilibrium?

**3.** Give several examples of a body which is not in equilibrium, even though the resultant of all the forces acting on it is zero.

**4.** If a body is not in translational equilibrium, will the torque about any point be zero if the torque about some particular point is zero?

**5.** Which is more likely to break in use, a hammock stretched tightly between two trees or one that sags quite a bit? Prove your answer.

**6.** A ladder is at rest with its upper end against a wall and the lower end on the ground. Is it more likely to slip when a man stands on it at the bottom or at the top? Explain.

**7.** In Example 2, if the wall were rough, would the empirical laws of friction supply us with the extra condition needed to determine the extra (vertical) force exerted by the wall on the ladder?

**8.** In Example 3, why isn't it necessary to consider friction at the hinge?

**9.** A picture hangs from a wall by two wires. What orientation should the wires have to be under minimum tension? Explain how equilibrium is possible with any number of orientations and tensions, even though the picture has a definite mass.

**10.** Show how to use a spring balance to weigh objects well beyond the maximum reading of the balance.

**11.** Do the center of mass and the center of gravity coincide for a building? For a lake? Under what conditions does the difference between the center of mass and the center of gravity of a body become significant?

**12.** If a rigid body is thrown into the air without spinning, it does not spin during its flight, provided air resistance can be neglected. What does this simple result imply about the location of the center of gravity?

**13.** A uniform block, in the shape of a rectangular parallelepiped of sides in the ratio 1:2:3, lies on a horizontal surface. In which position, that is, on which of its three different faces, can it be said to be most stable, if any?

**14.** A virus particle in a rotating liquid-filled centrifuge tube is in uniform circular motion (that is, in *accelerated* motion) as viewed by an observer in the laboratory. An observer rotating with the centrifuge, however, would declare the particle to be *unaccelerated*. Explain how the virus particle can be in equilibrium for this second observer but not for the first.

**15.** In Chapter 5 we *defined* force in terms of acceleration from the relation $\mathbf{F} = m\mathbf{a}$. For a body in equilibrium, however, there are no accelerations. How, then, can we give meaning to the forces acting on such a body?

## PROBLEMS

**1.** What force $F$ applied horizontally at the axle of the wheel is necessary to raise the wheel over an obstacle of height $h$? Take $r$ as the radius of the wheel and $W$ as its weight (Fig. 14–10).

**Fig. 14–10**

**2.** A beam is carried by three men, one man at one end and the other two supporting the beam between them on a crosspiece so placed that the load is equally divided among the three men. Find where the crosspiece is placed. Neglect the mass of the crosspiece.

**3.** A meter stick balances on a knife edge at the 50.0-cm mark. When two nickels are stacked over the 12.0-cm mark, the loaded stick is found to balance at the 45.5-cm mark. A nickel has a mass of 5.0 gm. What is the mass of the meter stick? Try this technique sometimes and check your answer experimentally.

**4.** Prove that when only three forces act on a body in equilibrium, they must be coplanar, and their lines of action must meet at a point or at infinity.

**5.** A circular section of radius $r$ is cut out of a uniform disk of radius $R$, the center of the hole being $R/2$ from the center of the original disk. Locate the center of gravity of the resulting body.

**6.** In Fig. 14–11 a man is trying to get his car out of the mud on the shoulder of a road. He ties one end of a rope tightly around the front bumper and the other end tightly around a telephone pole 60 ft away. He then pushes sideways on the rope at its midpoint with a force of 125 lb, displacing the center of the rope 1.0 ft from its previous position and the car almost moves. What force does the rope exert on the car? (The rope stretches somewhat under the tension.)

Fig. 14–11

**7.** A homogeneous sphere of radius $r$ and weight $\mathbf{W}$ *slides* along the floor under the action of a constant *horizontal* force $\mathbf{P}$ applied to a string, as shown in Fig. 14–12. (a) Show that, if $\mu$ is the coefficient of friction between sphere and floor, the height $h$ is given by $h = r(1 - \mu W/P)$. (b) Show that the sphere is not in translational equilibrium under these circumstances. Is there any point about which the sphere is in rotational equilibrium? (c) Can one get the sphere to be in both rotational *and* translational equilibrium by a different choice of $h$? . . . By a different direction for $\mathbf{P}$? Explain.

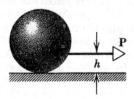

Fig. 14–12

**8.** A thin horizontal bar $AB$ of negligible weight and length $l$ is pinned to a vertical wall at $A$ and supported at $B$ by a thin wire $BC$ that makes an angle $\theta$ with the horizontal. A weight $P$ can be moved anywhere along the bar as defined by the distance $x$ from the wall (Fig. 14–13). (a) Find the tensile force $T$ in the thin wire as a function of $x$. (b) Find the horizontal and vertical components of the force exerted on the bar by the pin at $A$.

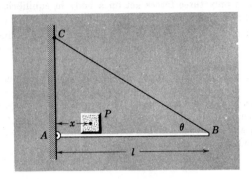

**Fig. 14–13**

**9.** A *non*uniform bar of weight $\mathbf{W}$ is suspended at rest in a horizontal position by two light ropes as shown in Fig. 14–14; the angle one rope makes with the vertical is $\theta = 36.9°$; the other makes the angle $\phi = 53.1°$ with the vertical. If the length $l$ of the bar is 20.0 ft, compute the distance $x$ from the left-hand end to the center of gravity.

**Fig. 14–14**

**10.** A well-known problem is the following (see, for example, *Scientific American*, November 1964, p. 128): Uniform bricks are placed one upon another in such a manner as to have the maximum offset. This is accomplished by having the center of gravity of the top brick directly above the edge of the brick below it, the center of gravity of the two top bricks combined directly above the edge of the third brick from the top, etc. (a) Justify this criterion for maximum offset. (b) Show that, if the process is continued downward, one can obtain as large an offset as he wants. (Martin Gardner, in the article referred to above, states: "With 52 playing cards, the first placed so that its end is flush with a table edge, the maximum overhang is a little more than $2\frac{1}{4}$ card lengths . . . .") (c) Suppose now, instead, one piles up uniform bricks so that the end of one brick is offset from the one below it by a constant fraction, $1/n$, of a brick length $l$. How many bricks, $N$, can one use in this process before the pile will fall over? Check the plausibility of your answer for $n = 1$, $n = 2$, $n = \infty$.

**11.** Four bricks, each of length $l$, are put on top of one another (see Fig. 14–15) in such a way that part of each extends beyond the one beneath it. Show that the *largest* equilibrium extensions are (a) top brick overhanging the one below by $l/2$, (b) second brick from top overhanging the one below by $l/4$, and (c) third brick from top overhanging the bottom one by $l/6$.

**Fig. 14–15**

**12.** A door 7.0 ft high and 3.0 ft wide weighs 60 lb.   A hinge 1.0 ft from the top and another 1.0 ft from the bottom each support half the door's weight.   Assume that the center of gravity is at the geometrical center of the door and determine the force exerted by each hinge on the door.

**13.** An automobile weighing 3000 lb has a wheel base of 120 in.   Its center of gravity is located 70 in. behind the front axle.   Determine the force exerted on each of the front wheels (assumed the same) and the force exerted on each of the back wheels (assumed the same) by the level ground.

**14.** A balance is made up of a rigid rod free to rotate about a point not at the center of the rod.   It is balanced by unequal weights placed in the pans at each end of the rod. When an unknown mass $m$ is placed in the left-hand pan, it is balanced by a mass $m_1$ placed in the right-hand pan, and similarly when the mass $m$ is placed in the right-hand pan, it is balanced by a mass $m_2$ in the left-hand pan.   Show that

$$m = \sqrt{m_1 m_2},$$

and state any assumptions you make in doing this.

**15.** In the stepladder shown in Fig. 14–16, $AC$ and $CE$ are 8.0 ft long and hinged at $C$. $BD$ is a tie rod 2.5 ft long, halfway up.   A man weighing 192 lb climbs 6.0 ft along the ladder.   Assuming that the floor is frictionless and neglecting the weight of the ladder, find the tension in the tie rod and the forces exerted on the ladder by the floor.   (Hint: it will help to isolate parts of the ladder in applying the equilibrium conditions.)

**Fig. 14–16**

**16.** A 100-lb plank, of length $l$ = 20 ft, rests on the ground and on a frictionless roller at the top of a wall of height $h$ = 10 ft (see Fig. 14–17). The center of gravity of the plank is at its center. The plank remains in equilibrium for any value of $\theta \geq 70°$, but slips if $\theta < 70°$. (a) Draw a diagram showing all forces acting on the plank. (b) Find the coefficient of friction between the plank and the ground.

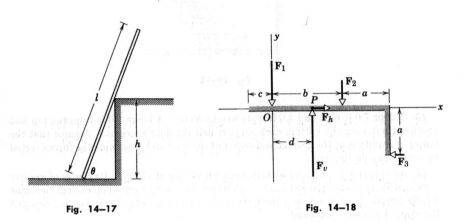

Fig. 14–17          Fig. 14–18

**17.** Forces $\mathbf{F_1}$, $\mathbf{F_2}$, and $\mathbf{F_3}$ act on the structure of Fig. 14–18 as shown. We wish to put the structure in equilibrium by applying a force, at a point such as $P$, whose vector components are $\mathbf{F_h}$ and $\mathbf{F_v}$. We are given that $a$ = 2.0 ft, $b$ = 3.0 ft, $c$ = 1.0 ft, $F_1$ = 20 lb, $F_2$ = 10 lb, and $F_3$ = 5.0 lb. Find $F_h$, $F_v$, and $d$.

**18.** By means of a turnbuckle $G$, a tensile force $\mathbf{T}$ is produced in bar $AB$ of the square frame $ABCD$, as in Fig. 14–19. Determine the forces produced in the other bars. The diagonals $AC$ and $BD$ pass each other freely at $E$. Show how symmetry considerations can lead to considerable simplification in this and similar problems.

Fig. 14–19

**19.** A flexible chain of weight $W$ hangs between two fixed points, $A$ and $B$, at the same level, as shown in Fig. 14–20. Find (a) the vector force exerted by the chain on each end point and (b) the tension in the chain at the lowest point.

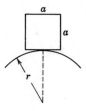

**Fig. 14–20**                    **Fig. 14–21**

**20.** A bowl having a radius of curvature $r$ rests on a horizontal table. Show that the bowl will be in stable equilibrium about the center point at its bottom only if the center of mass of the material piled up in the bowl is not as high as $r$.

**21.** A cube of uniform density and edge $a$ is balanced on a cylindrical surface of radius $r$ as shown in Fig. 14–21. Show that the criterion for stable equilibrium of the cube, assuming that friction is sufficient to prevent slipping, is $r > a/2$.

# Oscillations

## 15–1    Oscillations

Any motion that repeats itself in equal intervals of time is called *periodic motion*. As we shall see, the displacement of a particle in periodic motion can always be expressed in terms of sines and cosines. Because the term harmonic is applied to expressions containing these functions, periodic motion is often called *harmonic motion*.

If a particle in periodic motion moves back and forth over the same path, we call the motion *oscillatory* or *vibratory*. The world is full of oscillatory motions. Some examples are the oscillations of the balance wheel of a watch, a violin string, a mass attached to a spring, atoms in molecules or in a solid lattice, and air molecules as a sound wave passes by.

Many oscillating bodies do not move back and forth between precisely fixed limits because frictional forces dissipate the energy of motion. Thus a violin string soon stops vibrating and a pendulum stops swinging. We call such motions *damped* harmonic motions. Although we cannot eliminate friction from the periodic motions of gross objects, we can often cancel out its damping effect by feeding energy into the oscillating system so as to compensate for the energy dissipated by friction. The main spring of a watch and the falling weight in a pendulum clock supply external energy in this way, so that the oscillating system, that is, the balance wheel or the pendulum, moves as if it were undamped.

Not only mechanical systems can oscillate. Radio waves, microwaves, and visible light are oscillating magnetic and electric field vectors. Thus a tuned circuit in a radio and a closed metal cavity in which microwave energy is introduced can oscillate electromagnetically.   The analogy is close, being based on the fact that *mechanical and electromagnetic oscillations are described by the same basic mathematical equations.*   We will make the most of this analogy in later chapters.

The *period* $T$ of a harmonic motion is the time required to complete one round trip of the motion, that is, one complete oscillation or *cycle.*   The *frequency* of the motion $\nu$ is the number of oscillations (or cycles) per unit of time.   The frequency is therefore the reciprocal of the period, or

$$\nu = 1/T. \tag{15–1}$$

The mks unit of frequency is the cycle per second, or *hertz.*\*   The position at which no net force acts on the oscillating particle is called its *equilibrium* position.   The *displacement* (linear or angular) is the distance (linear or angular) of the oscillating particle from its equilibrium position at any instant.

Let us focus attention on a particle oscillating back and forth along a straight line between fixed limits.   Its displacement **x** changes periodically in both magnitude and direction.   Its velocity **v** and acceleration **a** also vary periodically in magnitude and direction and, in view of the relation **F** = $m$**a**, so does the force **F** acting on the particle.

Forces associated with harmonic motion are the most general kinds of forces that we have discussed so far.   In the earlier chapters we dealt only with constant forces (and accelerations).   Later, when we considered forces that are not constant but instead vary with time, we examined a force (and thus an acceleration) that varied in direction although its magnitude was constant (the centripetal force of Section 6–3), and a force (and thus an acceleration) which varied in magnitude although its direction was constant (the impulsive force of Section 10–1).   Here, in harmonic motion, the force, and the acceleration, vary both in direction *and* magnitude.

In terms of energy, we can say that a particle undergoing harmonic motion passes back and forth through a point (its equilibrium position) at which its potential energy is a minimum.   A swinging pendulum is a good example, its potential energy being a minimum at the bottom of the swing, that is, at the equilibrium position.   Figure 15–1$a$ shows a particle oscillating between the limits $x_1$ and $x_2$, $O$ being the equilibrium position. Figure 15–1$b$ shows the corresponding potential energy curve, which has a minimum value at that position.   The force acting on the particle at any position is derivable from the potential energy function; it is given by Eq. 8–7,

$$F = -dU/dx, \tag{8–7}$$

and is displayed in Fig. 15–1$c$.   The force is zero at the equilibrium position $O$, points to the right (that is, has a positive value) when the particle

---

\* This frequency unit is named after Heinrich Hertz (1857–1894) whose research in electromagnetism was universally recognized as providing the experimental confirmation of the electromagnetic waves predicted by Maxwell.

is to the left of $O$, and points to the left (that is, has a negative value) when the particle is to the right of $O$. The force is *a restoring force* because it always acts to accelerate the particle in the direction of its equilibrium position. Hence in harmonic motion the position of equilibrium is always one of *stable* equilibrium.

(a)

(b)

Fig. 15–1   (a) A particle of mass $m$ oscillates harmonically between points $x_1$ and $x_2$, $O$ being the equilibrium position. (b) The potential energy of the particle as a function of position. The force acting on the particle at position $x$ is given by $F = -dU/dx$. (c) The force acting on the particle as a function of position $x$; note that the force is directed toward the equilibrium position.

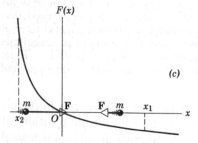

(c)

The total mechanical energy $E$ for an oscillating particle is the sum of its kinetic energy and its potential energy, or

$$E = K + U \qquad (15\text{-}2)$$

in which $E$ remains constant if no nonconservative forces, such as the force of friction, are acting. Figure 15–2 shows $E$ for the motion of Fig. 15–1. Note how Eq. 15–2 is satisfied for the particle in the typical position shown. The particle cannot move outside the limits $x_1$ and $x_2$ because, in these regions, $U$ exceeds $E$. This, as Eq. 15–2 shows, would require the kinetic energy to be negative, an impossibility.

For a given environment, that is, for a given function $U(x)$, an oscillating particle can have various total energies, depending on how it is set into motion initially. Thus the total energy may be $E'$, rather than $E$, in which case the limits of oscillation would be $x_1'$ and $x_2'$, as Fig. 15-2 shows, rather than $x_1$ and $x_2$.

### 15-2  The Simple Harmonic Oscillator

Let us consider an oscillating particle (Fig. 15-3a) moving back and forth about an equilibrium position through a potential that varies as

$$U(x) = \tfrac{1}{2}kx^2 \qquad (15\text{-}3)$$

in which $k$ is a constant; see Fig. 15-3b. The force acting on the particle is given by Eq. 8-7, or

$$F(x) = -dU/dx = -d(\tfrac{1}{2}kx^2)/$$
$$dx = -kx; \quad (15\text{-}4)$$

**Fig. 15-2** The total mechanical energy $E$ for the motion of Fig. 15-1 is shown. If the total mechanical energy of the oscillating particle is reduced to $E'$, the limits of oscillation are reduced to $x_1'$ and $x_2'$ respectively.

see Fig. 15-3c. Such an oscillating particle is called a *simple harmonic oscillator* and its motion is called *simple harmonic motion*. In such motion, as Eq. 15-3 shows, the potential energy curve varies as the square of the displacement, and, as Eq. 15-4 shows, the force acting on the particle is proportional to the displacement but is opposite to it in direction. In simple harmonic motion the limits of oscillation are equally spaced about the equilibrium position. This is not true for the more general motion of

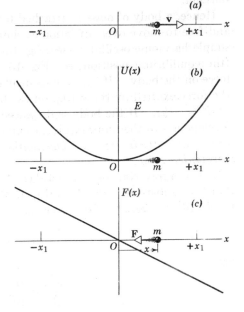

**Fig. 15-3** (a) A particle of mass $m$ oscillates with simple harmonic motion between points $+x_1$ and $-x_1$, $O$ being the equilibrium position. (b) The potential energy and the total mechanical energy. (c) The force acting on the particle. The student should compare this figure carefully with Fig. 15-1, which illustrates the general case of harmonic motion.

**Fig. 15-4** A simple harmonic oscillator. The force exerted by the spring is shown in each case. The block slides on a frictionless horizontal table.

Fig. 15-1 which, although harmonic, is not simple harmonic. The magnitude of the maximum displacement, that is, the quantity $x_1$ in Fig. 15-3, always taken as positive, is called the *amplitude* of the simple harmonic motion.

The student will have recognized Eq. 15-3 $[U(x) = \frac{1}{2}kx^2]$ as the expression for the potential energy of an "ideal" spring, compressed or extended by a distance $x$; see Section 8-4. In this same section an ideal spring was defined as one in which the force exerted by the stretched or compressed spring is. given by $F(x) = -kx$ (see Eq. 15-4), $k$ being called the *force constant*.

Hence, a body of mass $m$ attached to an ideal spring of force constant $k$ and free to move over a frictionless horizontal surface is an example of a simple harmonic oscillator (see Fig. 15-4). Note that there is a position (the.equilibrium position; see Fig. 15-4b) in which the spring exerts no force on the body. If the body is displaced to the right (as in Fig. 15-4a), the force exerted by the spring on the body points to the left and is given by $F = -kx$. If the body is displaced to the left (as in Fig. 15-4c), the force points to the right and is also given by $F = -kx$. In each case the force is a *restoring* force. The motion of the oscillating mass is *simple harmonic motion*.

Let us apply Newton's second law, $F = ma$, to the motion of Fig. 15-4. For $F$ we substitute $-kx$ (from Eq. 15-4) and for the acceleration $a$ we put in $d^2x/dt^2$ ($= dv/dt$). This gives us

$$-kx = m\frac{d^2x}{dt^2}$$

or

$$\frac{d^2x}{dt^2} + \frac{k}{m}x = 0. \tag{15-5}$$

This equation involves derivatives and is, therefore, called a *differential equation*. To solve this equation means to determine how the displacement $x$ of the particle must depend on the time $t$ in order that the equation be satisfied. When we know how $x$ depends on time, we know the motion of the particle; thus, Eq. 15-5 is called the *equation of motion* of a simple harmonic oscillator. We shall solve this equation and describe the motion in detail in the next section.

The simple harmonic oscillator problem is important for two reasons. First, most problems involving mechanical vibrations reduce to that of the simple harmonic oscillator at small amplitudes of vibration, or to a combination of such vibrations. This is equivalent to saying that if we consider a small enough portion of the restoring force curve of Fig. 15-1c (around the origin), it becomes arbitrarily close to a straight line which, as Fig. 15-3c shows, is characteristic of simple harmonic motion. Or, in other words, the potential energy curve of Fig. 15-1b for general oscillatory motion reduces to that of Fig. 15-3b for simple harmonic oscillation when the amplitude of vibration is made sufficiently small about the equilibrium position $O$.

Second, as we have indicated, equations like Eq. 15-5 turn up in many physical problems in acoustics, in optics, in mechanics, in electrical circuits, and even in atomic physics. The simple harmonic oscillator exhibits features common to many physical systems.

Equation 15-4 $(F = -kx)$ is an empirical relation known as *Hooke's law*. It is a special case of a more general relation, dealing with the deformation of elastic bodies, discovered by Robert Hooke (1635-1703).* It is obeyed by springs and other elastic bodies provided the deformation is not too great. If the solid is deformed beyond a certain point, called its *elastic limit*, it will not return to its original shape when the applied force is removed (Fig. 15-5). It turns out that Hooke's law holds almost up to the elastic limit for many common materials. The range of applied forces over which Hooke's law is valid is called the "proportional region." Beyond the elastic limit, the force can no longer be specified by a potential energy function, because the force then depends on many factors including the speed of deformation and the previous history of the solid.

Notice that the restoring force and potential energy function of the simple harmonic oscillator are the same as that of a solid deformed in one dimension in the proportional region. If the deformed solid is released, it will vibrate, just as the simple harmonic oscillator does. Therefore, as long as the amplitude of the vibration is small enough, that is, as long as the deformation remains in the proportional region, mechanical vibrations behave exactly like simple harmonic oscillators. It is easy to generalize

---

* Robert Hooke expressed his law in the Latin words *Ut tensio sic vis* ["the (ex)tension is proportional to the force"]. Although he discovered this law in 1660, he did not publish it until sixteen years later and then only in the form of the cryptogram *c e i i i n o s s s t t u v*. Hooke may have been motivated by a desire to establish priority without revealing information to other investigators.

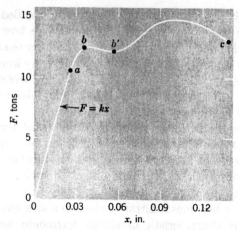

**Fig. 15–5** Typical graph of applied force $F$ versus resulting elongation of an aluminum bar under tension. The sample was a foot long and a square inch in cross section. Notice that we may write $F = kx$ only for the portion $Oa$, since beyond this point the slope is no longer constant but varies in a complicated way with $x$. At some point such as $b$ (the *elastic limit*) the sample does not return to its original length when the applied force is removed. Between $b$ and $b'$ the elongation increases, even though the force is held constant; the material flows like a viscous fluid. At $c$, the sample can be stretched no farther; any increase in elongation results in the sample's breaking in two. The applied force is equal in magnitude to the restoring force so that no minus sign appears in the relation $F = kx$.

this discussion to show that any problem involving mechanical vibrations of small amplitude in three dimensions reduces to a combination of simple harmonic oscillators.

The vibrating string or membrane, sound vibrations, the vibrations of atoms in solids, and electrical or acoustical oscillations in a cavity can all be described in a form which is identical mathematically to a system of harmonic oscillators. The analogy enables us to solve problems in one area by using the techniques developed in other areas.

### 15–3  Simple Harmonic Motion

Let us now solve the equation of motion of the simple harmonic oscillator,

$$\frac{d^2x}{dt^2} + \frac{k}{m}\,x = 0. \tag{15–6}$$

Recall that any system of mass $m$ upon which a force $F = -kx$ acts will be governed by this equation. In the case of a spring, the proportionality constant $k$ is the force constant of the spring determined by the stiffness of the spring. In other oscillating systems the proportionality constant $k$ may be related to other physical features of the system, as we shall see later. We can use the oscillating spring as our prototype.

Equation 15–6 is a differential equation. It gives a relation between a function of the time $x(t)$ and its second time derivative $d^2x/dt^2$. To find the position of the particle as a function of the time, we must find a function $x(t)$ which satisfies this relation.

We can rewrite Eq. 15-6 as

$$\frac{d^2x}{dt^2} = -\frac{k}{m}x. \tag{15-7}$$

Equation 15-7 then requires that $x(t)$ be some function whose second derivative is the negative of the function itself, except for a constant factor $k/m$. We know from the calculus, however, that the sine function or the cosine function has this property.* For example,

$$\frac{d}{dt}\cos t = -\sin t \quad \text{and} \quad \frac{d^2}{dt^2}\cos t = -\frac{d}{dt}\sin t = -\cos t.$$

This property is not affected if we multiply the cosine function by a constant $A$. We can allow for the fact that the sine function will do as well, and for the fact that Eq. 15-7 contains a constant factor, by writing as a tentative solution of Eq. 15-7,

$$x = A\cos(\omega t + \delta). \tag{15-8}$$

Here since

$$\cos(\omega t + \delta) = \cos\delta\cos\omega t - \sin\delta\sin\omega t = a\cos\omega t + b\sin\omega t,$$

the constant $\delta$ allows for any combination of sine and cosine solutions. Hence, with the (as yet) unknown constants $A$, $\omega$, and $\delta$, we have written as general a solution to Eq. 15-7 as we can. In order to determine these constants such that Eq. 15-8 is actually the solution of Eq. 15-7, we differentiate Eq. 15-8 twice with respect to the time. We have

$$\frac{dx}{dt} = -\omega A\sin(\omega t + \delta)$$

and

$$\frac{d^2x}{dt^2} = -\omega^2 A\cos(\omega t + \delta).$$

Putting this into Eq. 15-7, we obtain

$$-\omega^2 A\cos(\omega t + \delta) = -\frac{k}{m}A\cos(\omega t + \delta).$$

Therefore, if we choose the constant $\omega$ such that

$$\omega^2 = \frac{k}{m}, \tag{15-9}$$

then

$$x = A\cos(\omega t + \delta)$$

is in fact a solution of the equation of a simple harmonic oscillator.

---

* Harmonic motion is not only periodic but also bounded. Only the sine and cosine functions (or combinations of them) have both these properties.

The constants $A$ and $\delta$ are still undetermined and, therefore, still completely arbitrary. This means that any choice of $A$ and $\delta$ whatsoever will satisfy Eq. 15–7, so that a large variety of motions is possible for the oscillator. Actually, this is characteristic of a differential equation of motion, for such an equation does not describe just one single motion but a group or family of possible motions which have some features in common but differ in other ways. In this case $\omega$ is common to all the allowed motions, but $A$ and $\delta$ may differ among them. We shall see later that $A$ and $\delta$ are determined for a particular harmonic motion by how the motion starts.

Let us find the *physical* significance of the constant $\omega$. If the time $t$ in Eq. 15–8 is increased by $2\pi/\omega$, the function becomes

$$x = A \cos [\omega(t + 2\pi/\omega) + \delta],$$
$$= A \cos (\omega t + 2\pi + \delta),$$
$$= A \cos (\omega t + \delta).$$

That is, the function merely repeats itself after a time $2\pi/\omega$. Therefore, $2\pi/\omega$ is the *period* of the motion $T$. Since $\omega^2 = k/m$, we have

$$T = \frac{2\pi}{\omega} = 2\pi \sqrt{\frac{m}{k}}. \tag{15–10}$$

Hence, all motions given by Eq. 15–7 have the same period of oscillation, and this is determined only by the mass $m$ of the vibrating particle and the force constant $k$. The *frequency* $\nu$ of the oscillator is the number of complete vibrations per unit time and is given by

$$\nu = \frac{1}{T} = \frac{\omega}{2\pi} = \frac{1}{2\pi} \sqrt{\frac{k}{m}}. \tag{15–11}$$

Hence, $$\omega = 2\pi\nu = \frac{2\pi}{T}. \tag{15–12}$$

The quantity $\omega$ is called the *angular frequency;* it differs from the frequency $\nu$ by a factor $2\pi$. It has the dimension of reciprocal time (the same as angular speed) and its unit is the radian/sec. In Section 15–6 we shall give a geometric meaning to this angular frequency.

The constant $A$ has a simple physical meaning. The cosine function takes on values from $-1$ to $1$. The *displacement* $x$ from the central equilibrium position $x = 0$, therefore, has a maximum value of $A$. Hence, $A$ ($= x_{max}$) is the *amplitude* of the motion. Since $A$ is not fixed by our differential equation, motions of various amplitudes are possible, but all have the same frequency and period. *The frequency of a simple harmonic motion is independent of the amplitude of the motion.*

The quantity $(\omega t + \delta)$ is called the *phase* of the motion. The constant $\delta$ is called the *phase constant.* Two motions may have the same amplitude and frequency but differ in phase. If $\delta = -\pi/2$, for example,

$$x = A \cos (\omega t + \delta) = A \cos (\omega t - 90°)$$
$$= A \sin \omega t$$

so that the displacement is zero at the time $t = 0$. When $\delta = 0$, the displacement $x = A \cos \omega t$ is a maximum at the time $t = 0$. Other initial displacements correspond to other phase constants.

The amplitude $A$ and the phase constant $\delta$ of the oscillation are determined by the initial position and speed of the particle. These two initial conditions will specify $A$ and $\delta$ exactly.* Once the motion has started, however, the particle will continue to oscillate with a constant amplitude and phase constant at a fixed frequency, unless other forces disturb the system.

In Fig. 15-6 we plot the displacement $x$ versus the time $t$ for several simple harmonic motions. Three comparisons are made. In Fig. 15-6a,

---

\* A phase constant may be increased by any integral multiple of $2\pi$, or of 360°, and it will still describe the motion equally well.

**Fig. 15-6** Several solutions of the simple harmonic oscillator equation. (a) Both solutions have the same amplitude and period but differ in phase by 45°. (b) Both have the same period and phase constant but differ in amplitude by a factor of 2. (c) Both have the same phase constant and amplitude but differ in period by a factor of 2.

**Fig. 15-7** The relations between displacement, velocity, and acceleration in simple harmonic motion. The phase constant $\delta$ is zero in this particular case since the displacement is maximum at $t = 0$; see Eq. 15-8.

I and II have the same amplitude and frequency but differ in phase by $\delta = \pi/4$ or 45°.    In Fig. 15–6b, I and III have the same frequency and phase constant but differ in amplitude by a factor of 2.    In Fig. 15–6c, I and IV have the same amplitude and phase constant but differ in frequency by a factor $\frac{1}{2}$ or in period by a factor 2.    The student should study these curves carefully to become familiar with the terminology used in simple harmonic motion.

Another distinctive feature of simple harmonic motion is the relation between the displacement, the velocity, and the acceleration of the oscillating particle.    Let us compare these quantities for curve I of Fig. 15–6, which is typical.    In Fig. 15–7 we plot separately the displacement $x$ versus the time $t$, the velocity $v = dx/dt$ versus the time $t$, and the acceleration $a = d^2x/dt^2$ versus the time $t$.    The equations of these curves are

$$x = A \cos (\omega t + \delta),$$

$$v = \frac{dx}{dt} = -\omega A \sin (\omega t + \delta), \qquad (15\text{–}13)$$

$$a = \frac{dv}{dt} = -\omega^2 A \cos (\omega t + \delta).$$

**Fig. 15–8**  The force acting on, and the acceleration, velocity and displacement of a mass $m$ undergoing simple harmonic motion.  Compare carefully with Fig. 15–7.

For the case plotted we have taken $\delta = 0$. The units and scale of displacement, velocity, and acceleration are omitted for simplicity of comparison. Notice that the maximum displacement is $A$, the maximum speed is $\omega A$, and the maximum acceleration is $\omega^2 A$.

When the displacement is a maximum in either direction, the speed is zero because the velocity must now change its direction. The acceleration at this instant, like the restoring force, has a maximum value but is directed opposite to the displacement. When the displacement is zero, the speed of the particle is a maximum and the acceleration is zero, corresponding to a zero restoring force. The speed increases as the particle moves toward the equilibrium position and then decreases as it moves out to the maximum displacement, just as for a pendulum bob.

In Fig. 15–8 we show the instantaneous values of x, v, and a at four instants in the motion of a particle oscillating at the end of a spring.

## 15–4   Energy Considerations in Simple Harmonic Motion

Equation 15–2 tells us that for harmonic motion, including simple harmonic motion, in which no dissipative forces act the total mechanical energy $E$ $(= K + U)$ is conserved. We can now study this in more detail for the special case of simple harmonic motion, for which the displacement is given by

$$x = A \cos (\omega t + \delta). \qquad (15\text{–}8)$$

The potential energy $U$ at any instant is given by

$$U = \tfrac{1}{2} kx^2$$

$$= \tfrac{1}{2} kA^2 \cos^2 (\omega t + \delta) \qquad (15\text{–}14)$$

The potential energy has a maximum value of $\tfrac{1}{2}kA^2$. During the motion the potential energy varies between zero and this maximum value, as the curves in Fig. 15–9a and 15–9b show.

The kinetic energy $K$ at any instant is $\tfrac{1}{2}mv^2$. Using the relations

$$v = dx/dt = -\omega A \sin (\omega t + \delta)$$

and $$\omega^2 = k/m,$$

we obtain $$K = \tfrac{1}{2}mv^2,$$

$$= \tfrac{1}{2}m\omega^2 A^2 \sin^2 (\omega t + \delta),$$

$$= \tfrac{1}{2}kA^2 \sin^2 (\omega t + \delta). \qquad (15\text{–}15)$$

The kinetic energy, therefore, has a maximum value of $\tfrac{1}{2}kA^2$ or $\tfrac{1}{2}m(\omega A)^2$, in agreement with the maximum speed $\omega A$ noted earlier. During the motion the kinetic energy varies between zero and this maximum value, as shown by the curves in Fig. 15–9a and 15–9b.

The total mechanical energy is the sum of the kinetic and the potential energy. Using Eqs. 15–14 and 15–15 we obtain

$$E = K + U = \tfrac{1}{2}kA^2 \sin^2 (\omega t + \delta) + \tfrac{1}{2}kA^2 \cos^2 (\omega t + \delta) = \tfrac{1}{2}kA^2. \qquad (15\text{–}16)$$

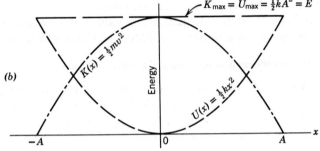

**Fig. 15–9** Energies of a simple harmonic oscillator. (a) Potential energy (— — — —), kinetic energy (— · —), and total energy (— —) plotted as a function of time. (b) Potential, kinetic, and total energy plotted as a function of displacement from the equilibrium position. Compare with Fig. 8–4.

We see that the total mechanical energy is constant, as we expect, and has the value $\frac{1}{2}kA^2$. At the maximum displacement the kinetic energy is zero, but the potential energy has the value $\frac{1}{2}kA^2$. At the equilibrium position the potential energy is zero, but the kinetic energy has the value $\frac{1}{2}kA^2$. At other positions the kinetic and potential energies each contribute energy whose sum is always $\frac{1}{2}kA^2$. This constant total energy is shown in Fig. 15–9a and 15–9b. *The total energy of a particle executing simple harmonic motion is proportional to the square of the amplitude of the motion.* It is clear from Fig. 15–9a that the *average* kinetic energy for the motion during one period is exactly equal to the *average* potential energy and that each of these average quantities is $\frac{1}{4}kA^2$.

Equation 15-16 can be written quite generally as

$$K + U = \tfrac{1}{2}mv^2 + \tfrac{1}{2}kx^2 = \tfrac{1}{2}kA^2. \tag{15–17}$$

From this relation we obtain $v^2 = (k/m)(A^2 - x^2)$ or

$$v = \frac{dx}{dt} = \pm \sqrt{\frac{k}{m}}\,(A^2 - x^2). \tag{15–18}$$

This relation shows clearly that the speed is a maximum at the equilibrium position $x = 0$ and zero at the maximum displacement $x = A$. In fact, we can start from the conservation of energy principle, Eq. 15–17 (in which $\frac{1}{2}kA^2 = E$), and by integration of Eq. 15–18 obtain the displacement as a function of time. The result is identical with Eq. 15–8 which we deduced from the differential equation of the motion, Eq. 15–6. (See Problem 18.) The effect of dissipative forces will be discussed in Section 15–9.

▶ **Example 1.** The horizontal spring of Fig. 15–4 is found to be stretched 3.0 in. from its equilibrium position when a force of 0.75 lb acts on it. Then a 1.5-lb body is attached to the end of the spring and is pulled 4.0 in. along a horizontal frictionless table from the equilibrium position. The body is then released and executes simple harmonic motion.

(a) What is the force constant of the spring?

A force of 0.75 lb *on* the spring produces a displacement of 0.25 ft. Hence,

$$k = F/x = 0.75 \text{ lb}/0.25 \text{ ft} = 3.0 \text{ lb/ft}.$$

Why didn't we use $k = -F/x$ here?

(b) What is the force exerted by the spring on the 1.5-lb body just before it is released?

The spring is stretched 4.0 in. or $\frac{1}{3}$ ft. Hence, the force exerted *by* the spring is

$$F = -kx = -(3.0 \text{ lb/ft})(\tfrac{1}{3} \text{ ft}) = -1.0 \text{ lb}.$$

The minus sign indicates that the force is directed opposite to the displacement.

(c) What is the period of oscillation after release?

$$T = 2\pi \sqrt{\frac{m}{k}} = 2\pi \sqrt{\frac{1.5/32}{3.0}} \text{ sec} = \frac{\pi}{4} \text{ sec} = 0.79 \text{ sec}.$$

This corresponds to a frequency $\nu (= 1/T)$ of 1.3 cycles/sec and to an angular frequency $\omega (= 2\pi\nu)$ of 8.0 rad/sec.

(d) What is the amplitude of the motion?

The maximum displacement corresponds to zero kinetic energy and a maximum potential energy. This is the initial condition before release, so that the amplitude is the initial displacement of 4.0 in. Hence, $A = \frac{1}{3}$ ft.

(e) What is the maximum speed of the vibrating body?

From Eq. 15–13, $v_{max} = \omega A = (2\pi/T)A$,

$$v_{max} = \left(\frac{2\pi}{\pi/4} \text{ sec}^{-1}\right)(\tfrac{1}{3} \text{ ft}) = 2.7 \text{ ft/sec}.$$

The maximum speed occurs at the equilibrium position, where $x = 0$. This value is achieved twice in each period, the velocity being $-2.7$ ft/sec when the body passes through $x = 0$ first after release and $+2.7$ ft/sec when the body passes through $x = 0$ on the return trip.

(f) What is the maximum acceleration of the body?

From Eq. 15–13, $a_{max} = \omega^2 A = (k/m)A$,

$$a_{max} = \left(\frac{3.0}{1.5/32}\right)\left(\frac{1}{3}\right) \text{ ft/sec}^2 = 21 \text{ ft/sec}^2.$$

The maximum acceleration occurs at the ends of the path where $x = \pm A$ and $v = 0$. Hence, $a = -21$ ft/sec$^2$ at $x = +A$ and $a = +21$ ft/sec$^2$ at $x = -A$, the acceleration and displacement being oppositely directed.

(*g*) Compute the velocity, the acceleration, and the kinetic and potential energies of the body when it has moved in halfway from its initial position toward the center of motion.

At this point, $x = \dfrac{A}{2} = \tfrac{1}{6}$ ft,

so that from Eq. 15–18,

$$v = -\frac{2\pi}{T}\sqrt{A^2 - x^2}$$

$$= -\frac{2\pi}{\pi/4}\sqrt{\left(\frac{1}{3}\right)^2 - \left(\frac{1}{6}\right)^2}\ \text{ft/sec} = -\frac{4}{\sqrt{3}}\ \text{ft/sec} = -2.3\ \text{ft/sec},$$

$$a = -\frac{k}{m}x = \frac{-3.0}{1.5/32}\left(\frac{1}{6}\right)\ \text{ft/sec}^2 = -11\ \text{ft/sec}^2,$$

$$K = \tfrac{1}{2}mv^2 = \left(\frac{1}{2}\right)\left(\frac{1.5}{32}\right)\left(\frac{4}{\sqrt{3}}\right)^2\ \text{ft-lb} = \tfrac{1}{8}\ \text{ft-lb},$$

$$U = \tfrac{1}{2}kx^2 = \left(\frac{1}{2}\right)(3)\left(\frac{1}{6}\right)^2\ \text{ft-lb} = \tfrac{1}{24}\ \text{ft-lb}.$$

(*h*) Compute the total energy of the oscillating system.

Since the total energy is conserved, we can compute it at any stage of the motion. Using previous results, we obtain

$$E = K + U = \tfrac{1}{8} + \tfrac{1}{24} = \tfrac{1}{6}\ \text{ft-lb}, \quad \text{(particle at } x = A/2)$$

$$E = U_{\max} = \tfrac{1}{2}kx_{\max}{}^2 = \left(\frac{1}{2}\right)(3)\left(\frac{1}{3}\right)^2\ \text{ft-lb} = \tfrac{1}{6}\ \text{ft-lb}, \quad \text{(particle at } x = A)$$

$$E = K_{\max} = \tfrac{1}{2}mv_{\max}{}^2 = \left(\frac{1}{2}\right)\left(\frac{1.5}{32}\right)\left(\frac{8}{3}\right)^2\ \text{ft-lb} = \tfrac{1}{6}\ \text{ft-lb}, \quad \text{(particle at } x = 0)$$

(*i*) What is the displacement of the body as a function of time?

In general, we have

$$x = A \cos(\omega t + \delta).$$

We have already found that $A = \tfrac{1}{3}$ ft. We must now determine $\omega$ and $\delta$. We obtain

$$\omega = \frac{2\pi}{T} = \frac{2\pi}{\pi/4} = 8\ \text{radians/sec},$$

so that, with our particular units,

$$x = \tfrac{1}{3}\cos(8t + \delta).$$

At the time $t = 0$, $x = \tfrac{1}{3}$ ft, so that at that instant

$$x = \tfrac{1}{3}\cos\delta = \tfrac{1}{3}$$

or

$$\delta = 0 \text{ radian.}$$

Therefore, with $A = \tfrac{1}{3}$ ft, $\omega = 8$ radians/sec, and $\delta = 0$ radian, we obtain

$$x = \tfrac{1}{3}\cos 8t.$$

This describes the motion of the body, where $x$ is in feet, $t$ is in seconds, and the angle $8t$ is in radians.    ◄

## 15-5  Applications of Simple Harmonic Motion

A few physical systems that move with simple harmonic motion are considered here. We will discuss others from time to time throughout the text.

**The Simple Pendulum.** A simple pendulum is an idealized body consisting of a point mass, suspended by a light inextensible cord. When pulled to one side of its equilibrium position and released, the pendulum swings in a vertical plane under the influence of gravity. The motion is periodic and oscillatory. We wish to determine the period of the motion.

Figure 15-10 shows a pendulum of length $l$, particle mass $m$, making an angle $\theta$ with the vertical. The forces acting on $m$ are $m\mathbf{g}$, the gravitational force, and $\mathbf{T}$, the tension in the cord. Choose axes tangent to the circle of motion and along the radius. Resolve $m\mathbf{g}$ into a radial component of magnitude $mg \cos \theta$, and a tangential component of magnitude $mg \sin \theta$. The radial components of the forces supply the necessary centripetal acceleration to keep the particle moving on a circular arc. The tangential component is the restoring force acting on $m$ tending to return it to the equilibrium position. Hence, the restoring force is

**Fig. 15-10** The forces acting on a simple pendulum are the tension **T** in the string and the weight $m\mathbf{g}$ of mass $m$. The magnitudes of the radial and tangential components of $m\mathbf{g}$ are labeled.

$$F = -mg \sin \theta.$$

Notice that the restoring force is not proportional to the angular displacement $\theta$ but to $\sin \theta$ instead. The resulting motion is, therefore, not simple harmonic. However, *if the angle $\theta$ is small*, $\sin \theta$ is very nearly equal to $\theta$ in radians.* The displacement along the arc is $x = l\theta$, and for small angles

---

* For example,

|  |  | Difference, % |
|---|---|---|
| $\theta = 0° = 0.0000$ radian | $\sin \theta = 0.0000$ | 0 |
| $\theta = 2° = 0.0349$ radian | $\sin \theta = 0.0349$ | 0.00 |
| $\theta = 5° = 0.0873$ radian | $\sin \theta = 0.0872$ | 0.11 |
| $\theta = 10° = 0.1745$ radian | $\sin \theta = 0.1736$ | 0.51 |
| $\theta = 15° = 0.2618$ radian | $\sin \theta = 0.2588$ | 1.14 |

this is nearly straight-line motion. Hence, assuming

$$\sin \theta \cong \theta,$$

we obtain $\qquad F = -mg\theta = -mg\dfrac{x}{l} = -\dfrac{mg}{l}x.$

For *small displacements*, therefore, the restoring force is proportional to the displacement and is oppositely directed. This is exactly the criterion for simple harmonic motion. The constant $mg/l$ represents the constant $k$ in $F = -kx$. Check the dimensions of $k$ and $mg/l$. The period of a simple pendulum when its amplitude is small is

$$T = 2\pi \sqrt{\frac{m}{k}} = 2\pi \sqrt{\frac{m}{mg/l}} \quad \text{or} \quad T = 2\pi \sqrt{\frac{l}{g}}. \qquad (15\text{–}19)$$

Notice that the period is independent of the mass of the suspended particle.

When the amplitude of the oscillation is not small, the general equation for the period can be shown to be

$$T = 2\pi \sqrt{\frac{l}{g}\left(1 + \frac{1}{2^2} \cdot \sin^2 \frac{\theta_m}{2} + \frac{1}{2^2} \cdot \frac{3^2}{4^2} \cdot \sin^4 \frac{\theta_m}{2} + \cdots\right)}. \qquad (15\text{–}20)$$

Here $\theta_m$ is the maximum angular displacement and the succeeding terms become smaller and smaller. The period can then be computed to any desired degree of accuracy by taking enough terms in the infinite series. When $\theta_m = 15°$, corresponding to a total to-and-fro angular displacement of 30°, the true period differs from that given by Eq. 15–19 by less than 0.5%.

Because the period of a simple pendulum is practically independent of the amplitude, the pendulum is useful as a timekeeper. As damping forces reduce the amplitude of swing, the period remains very nearly unchanged. In a pendulum clock energy is supplied automatically by an escapement mechanism to compensate for frictional loss. The pendulum clock with escapement was invented by Christian Huygens (1629–1695).

The simple pendulum also provides a convenient method for measuring the value of $g$, the acceleration due to gravity. We need not perform a free-fall experiment here, but instead we merely measure $l$ and $T$.

**The Torsional Pendulum.** In Fig. 15–11 we show a disk suspended by a wire attached to the center of mass of the disk. The wire is securely fixed to a solid support and to the disk. At the equilibrium position of the disk a radial line is drawn from its center to $P$, as shown. If the disk is rotated in a horizontal plane to the radial position $Q$, the wire will be twisted. The twisted wire will exert a torque on the disk tending to return it to the position $P$. This is a restoring torque. For small twists the restoring torque is found to be proportional to the amount of twist, or the angular displacement (Hooke's law), so that

$$\tau = -\kappa\theta. \qquad (15\text{–}21)$$

Here $\kappa$ is a constant that depends on the properties of the wire and is called the *torsional* constant. The minus sign shows that the torque is directed opposite to the angular displacement $\theta$. Equation 15–21 is the condition for *angular simple harmonic motion.*

The equation of motion for such a system is

$$\tau = I\alpha = I\frac{d^2\theta}{dt^2},$$

so that, on using Eq. 15–21, we obtain

$$-\kappa\theta = I\frac{d^2\theta}{dt^2}$$

or $$\frac{d^2\theta}{dt^2} = -\frac{\kappa}{I}\theta \qquad (15\text{–}22)$$

**Fig. 15–11** The torsional pendulum. The line drawn from the center to $P$ oscillates between $Q$ and $R$, sweeping out an angle $2\theta_m$ where $\theta_m$ is the (angular) amplitude of the motion.

Notice the similarity between Eq. 15–22 for simple angular harmonic motion and Eq. 15–7 for simple linear harmonic motion. In fact, the equations are identical mathematically. We have simply substituted angular displacement $\theta$ for linear displacement $x$, rotational inertia $I$ for mass $m$, and torsional constant $\kappa$ for force constant $k$. The solution of Eq. 15–22 is, therefore, a simple harmonic oscillation in the angle coordinate $\theta$, namely

$$\theta = \theta_m \cos(\omega t + \delta). \qquad (15\text{–}23)$$

Here, $\theta_m$ is the maximum angular displacement, that is, the amplitude of the angular oscillation. In Fig. 15–11 the disk oscillates about the equilibrium position $\theta = 0$ (line $OP$), the total angular range being $2\theta_m$ (from $OQ$ to $OR$).

The period of the oscillation by analogy with Eq. 15–10 is

$$T = 2\pi\sqrt{\frac{I}{\kappa}}. \qquad (15\text{–}24)$$

If $\kappa$ is known and $T$ is measured, the rotational inertia $I$ about the axis of rotation of any oscillating rigid body can be determined. If $I$ is known and $T$ is measured, the torsional constant $\kappa$ of any sample of wire can be determined.

Many laboratory instruments involve torsional oscillations, notably the galvanometer. The Cavendish balance is a torsional pendulum (Chapter 16). The balance wheel of a watch is another example of angular harmonic motion, the restoring torque here being supplied by a spiral hairspring.

▶ **Example 2.** A thin rod of mass 0.10 kg and length 0.10 meter is suspended by a wire which passes through its center and is perpendicular to its length. The wire is twisted and the rod set oscillating. The period is found to be 2.0 sec.

When a flat body in the shape of an equilateral triangle is suspended similarly through its center of mass, the period is found to be 6.0 sec. Find the rotational inertia of the triangle about this axis.

The rotational inertia of the rod is $Ml^2/12$ (see Table 12–1). Hence

$$I_{\text{rod}} = \frac{(0.10 \text{ kg})(0.10 \text{ meter})^2}{12} = 8.3 \times 10^{-5} \text{ kg-m}^2.$$

From Eq. 15–24,

$$\frac{T_{\text{rod}}}{T_{\text{triangle}}} = \left(\frac{I_{\text{rod}}}{I_{\text{triangle}}}\right)^{\frac{1}{2}} \quad \text{or} \quad I_{\text{triangle}} = I_{\text{rod}}\left(\frac{T_t}{T_r}\right)^2,$$

so that

$$I_{\text{triangle}} = (8.3 \times 10^{-5} \text{ kg-m}^2)\left(\frac{6.0 \text{ sec}}{2.0 \text{ sec}}\right)^2 = 7.5 \times 10^{-4} \text{ kg-m}^2.$$

Does the amplitude of the oscillation affect the period in these cases? ◀

**The Physical Pendulum.** Any rigid body mounted so that it can swing in a vertical plane about some axis passing through it is called a physical pendulum. This is a generalization of the simple pendulum in which a weightless cord holds a single particle. Actually all real pendulums are physical pendulums.

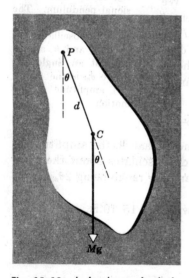

In Fig. 15–12 a body of irregular shape is pivoted about a horizontal frictionless axis through $P$ and displaced from the equilibrium position by an angle $\theta$. The equilibrium position is that in which the center of mass of the body, $C$, lies vertically below $P$. The distance from pivot to center of mass is $d$, the rotational inertia of the body about an axis through the pivot is $I$, and the mass of the body is $M$. The restoring torque for an angular displacement $\theta$ is

**Fig. 15–12** A laminar physical pendulum, with center of mass $C$, is pivoted at $P$ and displaced an angle $\theta$ from its equilibrium position (when $C$ hangs directly below $P$). Its weight $M\mathbf{g}$ supplies a restoring torque.

$$\tau = -Mgd \sin \theta$$

and is due to the tangential component of the force of gravity. Since $\tau$ is proportional to $\sin \theta$, rather than $\theta$, the condition for simple angular harmonic motion does not, in general, hold here. For small angular displacements, however, the relation $\sin \theta \cong \theta$ is, as before, an excellent approximation, so that for *small amplitudes,*

$$\tau = -Mg d \theta$$

or

$$\tau = -\kappa\theta,$$

where

$$\kappa = Mgd.$$

But

$$\tau = I\frac{d^2\theta}{dt^2} = I\alpha,$$

so that

$$\frac{d^2\theta}{dt^2} = \frac{\tau}{I} = -\frac{\kappa}{I}\theta.$$

Hence, the period of a physical pendulum oscillating with small amplitude is

$$T = 2\pi\sqrt{\frac{I}{\kappa}} = 2\pi\sqrt{\frac{I}{Mgd}}. \tag{15-25}$$

At larger amplitudes the physical pendulum still has a harmonic motion, but not a simple harmonic one.

Notice that this treatment applies to a laminar object of any shape and that the pivot can be located anywhere.  As a special case consider a point mass $m$ suspended at the end of a weightless string of length $l$.  Here

$$I = ml^2, \qquad M = m, \qquad d = l,$$

so that

$$T = 2\pi\sqrt{\frac{I}{Mgd}} = 2\pi\sqrt{\frac{l}{g}},$$

which is the period of a simple pendulum with small amplitude.  The physical pendulum is used for accurate determinations of $g$.

Equation 15–25 can be solved for the rotational inertia $I$, giving

$$I = \frac{T^2 Mgd}{4\pi^2}. \tag{15-26}$$

The quantities on the right are all directly measurable.  The center of mass can be determined by suspension as was shown in Fig. 14–4.  Hence, the rotational inertia about an axis of rotation not through the center of mass of a body of any shape can be determined by suspending the body as a physical pendulum from that axis.

▶ **Example 3.**  Find the length of a simple pendulum whose period is equal to that of a particular physical pendulum.

Equating the period of a simple pendulum to that of a physical pendulum, we obtain

$$T = 2\pi\sqrt{\frac{l}{g}} = 2\pi\sqrt{\frac{I}{Mgd}}$$

or

$$l = \frac{I}{Md}. \tag{15-27}$$

Hence, as far as its period of oscillation is concerned, the mass of a physical pendulum may be considered to be concentrated at a point whose distance from the pivot is $l = I/Md$.  This point is called the *center of oscillation* of the physical pendulum.  Notice that it depends on the location of the pivot for any given body.

**Example 4.**  A disk is pivoted at its rim (Fig. 15–13).  Find its period for small oscillations and the length of the equivalent simple pendulum.

The rotational inertia of a disk about an axis through its center is $\frac{1}{2}Mr^2$, where $r$ is the radius and $M$ is the mass of the disk. The rotational inertia about the pivot at the rim is

$$I = \tfrac{1}{2}Mr^2 + Mr^2 = \tfrac{3}{2}Mr^2.$$

The period then, with $d = r$, is

$$T = 2\pi \sqrt{\frac{I}{Mgr}} = 2\pi \sqrt{\frac{3}{2}\frac{Mr^2}{Mgr}} = 2\pi \sqrt{\frac{3}{2}\frac{r}{g}},$$

independent of the mass of the disk.

The simple pendulum having the same period has a length

$$l = \frac{I}{Mr} = \tfrac{3}{2}r$$

or three-fourths the diameter of the disk. The center of oscillation of the disk pivoted at $P$ is, therefore, at $O$, a distance $\frac{3}{2}r$ below the point of support. Is any particular mass required of the equivalent simple pendulum?

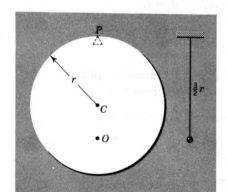

If we pivot the disk at a point midway between the rim and the center, as at $O$, we find that $I = \frac{3}{4}Mr^2$ and $d = \frac{1}{2}r$. The period $T$ is

$$T = 2\pi \sqrt{\tfrac{3}{2}r/g}$$

just as before. This illustrates a general property of the center of oscillation $O$ and the point of support $P$, namely, if the pendulum is pivoted about a new axis through $O$, its period is unchanged and $P$ becomes the new center of oscillation.

If the disk were pivoted at the center, what would be its period of oscillation?

**Fig. 15–13** Example 4. A physical pendulum consisting of a disk pivoted at the edge ($P$), along with a simple pendulum having the same period. $O$ is the center of oscillation.

**Example 5.** The period of a disk of radius 4.00 in. executing small oscillations about a pivot at its rim is measured to be 0.784 sec. Find the value of $g$, the acceleration due to gravity at that location.

From $T = 2\pi \sqrt{\tfrac{3}{2}r/g}$, we obtain

$$g = \frac{6\pi^2 r}{T^2}.$$

With $T = 0.784$ sec and $r = \frac{1}{3}$ ft, we obtain

$$g = \frac{6\pi^2 \cdot \frac{1}{3}}{(0.784)^2} \text{ ft/sec}^2 = 32.1 \text{ ft/sec}^2.$$

## 15-6    Relation between Simple Harmonic Motion and Uniform Circular Motion

Let us consider the relation between simple harmonic motion along a straight line and uniform circular motion. This relation is useful in describing many features of simple harmonic motion. It also gives a simple geometric meaning to the angular frequency $\omega$ and the phase constant $\delta$. Uniform circular motion is also an example of a combination of simple harmonic motions, a phenomenon we deal with rather often in wave motion.

In Fig. 15–14 $Q$ is the point moving around a circle of radius $A$ with a constant angular speed of $\omega$, expressed, say, in radians/sec. $P$ is the perpendicular projection of $Q$ on the horizontal diameter, along the $x$-axis. Let us call $Q$ the *reference point* and the circle on which it moves the *reference circle*. As the reference point revolves, the projected point $P$ moves back and forth along the horizontal diameter. The $x$-component of $Q$'s

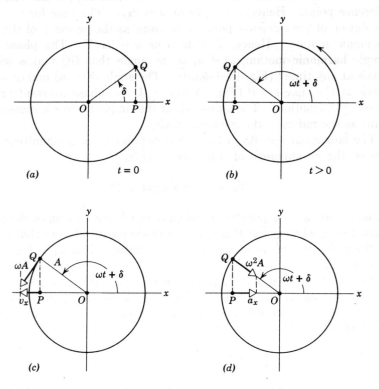

**Fig. 15–14**   The relation of simple harmonic motion to uniform circular motion. $Q$ moves in uniform circular motion and $P$ in simple harmonic motion. $Q$ has angular speed $\omega$, $P$ angular frequency $\omega$. (a, b) The $x$-component of $Q$'s displacement is always equal to $P$'s displacement. (c) The $x$-component of $Q$'s velocity is always equal to $P$'s velocity. (d) The $x$-component of $Q$'s acceleration is always equal to $P$'s acceleration.

displacement is always the same as the displacement of $P$; the $x$-component of the velocity of $Q$ is always the same as the velocity of $P$; and the $x$-component of the acceleration of $Q$ is always the same as the acceleration of $P$.

Let the angle between the radius $OQ$ and the $x$-axis at the time $t = 0$ be called $\delta$. At any later time $t$, the angle between $OQ$ and the $x$-axis is $(\omega t + \delta)$, the point $Q$ moving with constant angular speed. The $x$-coordinate of $Q$ at any time is, therefore,

$$x = A \cos (\omega t + \delta). \tag{15-28}$$

Hence, the projected point $P$ moves with simple harmonic motion along the $x$-axis. Therefore, *simple harmonic motion can be described as the projection along a diameter of uniform circular motion.*

The angular frequency $\omega$ of simple harmonic motion is the same as the angular speed of the reference point. The frequency of the simple harmonic motion is the same as the number of revolutions per unit time of the reference point. Hence, $\nu = \omega/2\pi$ or $\omega = 2\pi\nu$. The time for a complete revolution of the reference point is the same as the period $T$ of the simple harmonic motion. Hence, $T = 2\pi/\omega$ or $\omega = 2\pi/T$. The phase of the simple harmonic motion, $\omega t + \delta$, is the angle that $OQ$ makes with the $x$-axis at any time $t$ (Fig. 15–14*b,c,d*). The angle that $OQ$ makes with the $x$-axis at the time $t = 0$ (Fig. 15–14*a*) is $\delta$, the phase constant or initial phase of the motion. The amplitude of the simple harmonic motion is the same as the radius of the reference circle.

The tangential velocity of the reference point $Q$ has a magnitude of $\omega A$. Hence, the $x$-component of this velocity (Fig. 15–14*c*) is

$$v_x = -\omega A \sin (\omega t + \delta).$$

This relation gives a negative $v_x$ when $Q$ and $P$ are moving to the left and a positive $v_x$ when $Q$ and $P$ are moving to the right. Notice that $v_x$ is zero at the end points of the simple harmonic motion, where $\omega t + \delta$ is zero and $\pi$, as required.

The acceleration of point $Q$ in uniform circular motion is directed radially inward and has a magnitude of $\omega^2 A$. The acceleration of the projected point $P$ is the $x$-component of the acceleration of the reference point $Q$ (Fig. 15–14*d*). Hence,

$$a_x = -\omega^2 A \cos (\omega t + \delta)$$

gives the acceleration of the point executing simple harmonic motion. Notice that $a_x$ is zero at the midpoints of the simple harmonic motion, where $\omega t + \delta = \pi/2$ or $3\pi/2$, as required.

These results are all identical with those of simple harmonic motion along the $x$-axis; see Eqs. 15–13.

If we had taken the perpendicular projection of the reference point onto the $y$-axis, instead, we would have obtained for the motion of the $y$-projected point

$$y = A \sin (\omega t + \delta).$$ (15-29)

This is again a simple harmonic motion. It differs only in phase from Eq. 15-28, for if we replace $\delta$ by $\delta - \pi/2$, then $\cos (\omega t + \delta)$ becomes $\sin (\omega t + \delta)$. It is clear that the projection of uniform circular motion along *any* diameter gives a simple harmonic motion.

Conversely, uniform circular motion can be described as a combination of two simple harmonic motions. It is that combination of two simple harmonic motions, occurring along perpendicular lines, which have the same amplitude and frequency but differ in phase by 90°. When one component is at the maximum displacement, the other component is at the equilibrium point. If we combine these components (Eqs. 15-28 and 15-29), we obtain at once the relation

$$r = \sqrt{x^2 + y^2} = A.$$

By writing the relations for $v_y$ and $a_y$ (the student should do this) and combining corresponding quantities, we obtain also the relations

$$v = \sqrt{v_x{}^2 + v_y{}^2} = \omega A,$$

$$a = \sqrt{a_x{}^2 + a_y{}^2} = \omega^2 A.$$

These relations correspond respectively to the magnitudes of the displacement, the velocity, and the acceleration in uniform circular motion.

It will be possible for us to analyze many complicated motions as combinations of individual simple harmonic motions. Circular motion is a particularly simple combination. In the next section we shall consider other combinations of simple harmonic motions.

**Example. 6.**  In Example 1 we considered a body executing a horizontal simple harmonic motion. The equation of that motion (units?) was

$$x = \tfrac{1}{3} \cos 8t.$$

This motion can also be represented as the projection of uniform circular motion along a horizontal diameter.

(*a*) Give the properties of the corresponding uniform circular motion.

The $x$-component of the circular motion is given by

$$x = A \cos (\omega t + \delta).$$

Therefore, the reference circle must have a radius $A = \tfrac{1}{3}$ ft, the initial phase or phase constant must be $\delta = 0$, and the angular velocity must be $\omega = 8$ radians/sec, in order to obtain the equation $x = \tfrac{1}{3} \cos 8t$ for the horizontal projection.

(*b*) From the motion of the reference point determine the time required for the body to come halfway in toward the center of motion from its initial position.

As the body moves halfway in, the reference point moves through an angle of

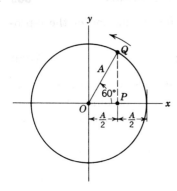

$\omega t = 60°$ (Fig. 15–15). The angular velocity is constant at 8 radians/sec so that the time required to move through 60° is

$$t = \frac{60°}{\omega} = \frac{\pi/3 \text{ radians}}{8 \text{ radians/sec}} = \frac{\pi}{24} \text{ sec} = 0.13 \text{ sec.}$$

The time may also be computed directly from the equation of motion. Thus,

$$x = \tfrac{1}{3} \cos 8t \quad \text{and} \quad x = \frac{A}{2} = \tfrac{1}{6},$$

Hence

**Fig. 15–15** Example 6. The particles $Q$ and $P$ of Fig. 15–14 are shown for $\omega t = 60°$. Since $\omega$ is known, $t$ may be found.

$$\tfrac{1}{6} = \tfrac{1}{3} \cos 8t \quad \text{or} \quad 8t = \cos^{-1}(\tfrac{1}{2}) = \frac{\pi}{3}.$$

Therefore,

$$t = \frac{\pi}{24} \text{ sec} = 0.13 \text{ sec.} \quad \blacktriangleleft$$

## 15–7  Combinations of Harmonic Motions

Often two linear simple harmonic motions *at right angles* are combined. The resulting motion is the sum of two independent oscillations. Consider first the case in which the *frequencies* of the vibrations *are the same*, such as

$$x = A_x \cos (\omega t + \delta),$$
$$y = A_y \cos (\omega t + \alpha). \tag{15–30}$$

The $x$- and $y$-motions have different amplitudes and different phase constants, however.

If the phase constants are the same so that $\delta = \alpha$, the resulting motion is a straight line. This can be shown analytically, for when we eliminate $t$ from the equations

$$x = A_x \cos (\omega t + \delta) \qquad y = A_y \cos (\omega t + \delta),$$

we obtain $\qquad y = (A_y/A_x)x.$

This is the equation of a straight line, whose slope is $A_y/A_x$. In Fig. 15–16a and b we show the resultant motion for two cases, $A_y/A_x = 1$ and $A_y/A_x = 2$. In these cases both the $x$- and $y$-displacements reach a maximum at the same time and reach a minimum at the same time. They are in phase.

If the phase constants are different, the resulting motion will not be a straight line. For example, if the phase constants differ by $\pi/2$, the maximum $x$-displacement occurs when the $y$-displacement is zero and vice versa. When the amplitudes are equal, the resulting motion is circular; when the amplitudes are unequal, the resulting motion is elliptical. Two cases, $A_y/A_x = 1$ and $A_y/A_x = 2$, are shown in Fig. 15–16c and d, for $\delta = \alpha + \pi/2$. The cases $A_y/A_x = 1$ and $A_y/A_x = 2$, for $\delta = \alpha - \pi/4$, are shown in Fig. 15–15e and f.

All possible combinations of two simple harmonic motions at right angles having the same frequency correspond to *elliptical* paths, the circle and straight line being special cases of an ellipse. This can be shown analytically by combining Eqs. 15–30 and eliminating the time; the student can show that the resulting equation is that of an ellipse. The shape of the ellipse depends only on the ratio of the amplitudes, $A_y/A_x$, and the *difference* in phase between the two oscillations, $\delta - \alpha$. The actual motion can

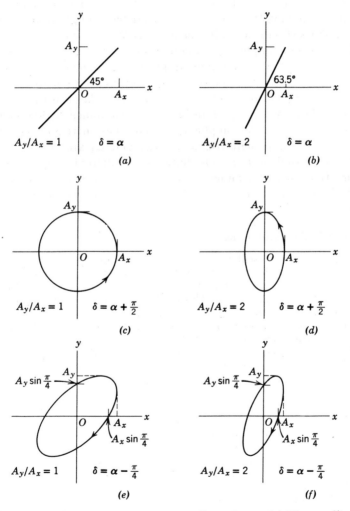

**Fig. 15–16** Simple harmonic motions in two dimensions. (a) The amplitudes of $x$ and $y$ (namely $A_x$ and $A_y$) are the same, as are their phase constants. (b) $y$'s amplitude is twice $x$'s, but their phase constants are the same. (c) Their amplitudes are equal, but $x$ leads $y$ in phase by 90°. (d) Same as (c) except that $y$'s amplitude is twice $x$'s. (e) Equal amplitudes, but $x$ lags $y$ in phase by 45°. (f) Same as (e) except that $y$'s amplitude is twice $x$'s.

be either clockwise or counterclockwise, depending on which component leads in phase.

A simple way to produce such patterns is by means of an oscilloscope. In this, electrons are deflected by each of two electric fields at right angles to one another. The field strengths alternate sinusoidally with the same frequency, but their phases and amplitudes can be varied. In this way the electrons can be made to trace out the various patterns discussed above on a fluorescent screen. We can also produce these patterns mechanically by means of a pendulum swinging with small amplitude but not confined to one vertical plane. Such combinations of two simple harmonic motions at right angles having the same frequency are particularly important in the study of polarized light and alternating current circuits.

Combinations of simple harmonic motions of the same frequency in the *same direction*, but with different amplitudes and phases, are of special interest in the study of diffraction and interference of light, sound, and electromagnetic radiation. This will be discussed later in the text.

If two oscillations of *different frequencies* are combined at right angles, the resulting motion is more complicated. The motion is not even periodic unless the two component frequencies $\omega_1$ and $\omega_2$ are the ratio of two integers (see Problem 35). Oscillations of different frequencies in the same direction may also be combined. The treatment of this motion is particularly important in the case of sound vibrations and will be discussed in Chapter 20.

### 15–8  Two-Body Oscillations

The simple harmonic oscillator of Fig. 15–4 is a mass $m$ coupled by a spring of force constant $k$ to a solid wall. The wall is rigidly connected to the earth, so that this system is really a two-body system, connected by a spring, one of the bodies being effectively of infinite mass. This solid support remains at rest in an inertial reference frame so that the change in length of the spring is equal to the displacement of the mass $m$; the other end of the spring does not move. In this case we defined the potential energy $U(x)$ of the oscillating system of Fig. 15–4 to be a function of the displacement $x$ of the mass $m$ alone (see Figs. 15–3, 9). This again is equivalent to assuming that one end of the spring is connected to an infinite mass so that the extension of the spring is determined by the motion of mass $m$ alone.

Often in nature we find two-body oscillating systems in which we *cannot* take the mass of one of the bodies to be infinite and we must consider the motions of both bodies in an appropriate inertial reference frame. Examples are diatomic molecules such as $H_2$, CO, HCl, etc., which can oscillate along their axis of symmetry. The coupling between the atoms that make up these molecules is electromagnetic, but we may imagine them, for our purpose, to be connected by a tiny, massless spring.

The surprising thing about two-body oscillators is that, by redefining terms slightly and by introducing a new concept (that of *reduced mass*), we can describe the oscillations by exactly the same equations that we have already derived for the (effectively) one-body system of Fig. 15-4. Let us prove this.

Figure 15–17a shows two bodies $m_1$ and $m_2$ connected by a (massless) spring of force constant $k$; the system is free to oscillate on a frictionless horizontal surface. We locate the ends of the spring by the coordinates $x_1(t)$ and $x_2(t)$, as shown. The length of the spring at any instant is $x_1 - x_2$. If its normal, unstressed length is $l$, then the *change* in length of the spring, $x(t)$, is given by

$$x = (x_1 - x_2) - l. \qquad (15\text{–}31)$$

If $x$ is positive, the spring is stretched, if $x = 0$, the spring has its normal length, and if $x$ is negative, it is compressed.

In Fig. 15–17$a$ we assume, for concreteness, that the spring is stretched, so that $x > 0$. We show also the force **F** exerted by the spring on $m_2$ and the force $-$**F** exerted on $m_2$. These two forces are equal and opposite, as the figure shows, and have the common magnitude $F = kx$.

If we apply Newton's second law, $F = ma$, to masses $m_1$ and $m_2$ we obtain

$$m_1 \frac{d^2x_1}{dt^2} = -kx$$

and

$$m_2 \frac{d^2x_2}{dt^2} = +kx.$$

Let us now multiply the first equation by $m_2$ and the second equation by $m_1$ and subtract. We obtain

$$m_1 m_2 \frac{d^2x_1}{dt^2} - m_1 m_2 \frac{d^2x_2}{dt^2} = -m_2 kx - m_1 kx,$$

which we can write as

$$\frac{m_1 m_2}{m_1 + m_2} \frac{d^2}{dt^2} (x_1 - x_2) = -kx. \qquad (15\text{–}32)$$

Let us call the quantity $m_1 m_2/(m_1 + m_2)$, which has the dimensions of mass, the *reduced mass* of the system and give it the symbol $\mu$; that is,

$$\mu = \frac{m_1 m_2}{m_1 + m_2}. \qquad (15\text{–}33)$$

Because $l$ is a constant, $d^2(x_1 - x_2)/dt^2 = d^2x/dt$ and Eq. 15–32 now can be written as

$$\frac{d^2x}{dt^2} + \frac{k}{\mu} x = 0. \qquad (15\text{–}34)$$

This is identical in form to Eq. 15–5 which we developed for the single-body oscillation of Fig. 15–4. The differences are that (1) $x$ in Eq. 15–34 is the *relative* displacement of the two blocks from their equilibrium positions (see Eq. 15–31) rather than the displacement of a single block from its equilibrium position, and (2) $\mu$ is the *reduced mass* of the pair of blocks rather than the mass of a single block.

**Fig. 15–17**  ($a$) Two bodies of masses $m_1$ and $m_2$ connected by a (massless) spring whose unstressed length is $l$. ($b$) A single body of mass $\mu$ (the reduced mass) connected by an identical spring to a rigid wall.

Note from Eq. 15–33, which we can write either as

$$\mu = m_1 \frac{m_2}{m_1 + m_2} = m_2 \frac{m_1}{m_1 + m_2}$$

or as

$$\frac{1}{\mu} = \frac{1}{m_1} + \frac{1}{m_2}.$$

that (for finite masses) $\mu$ is always *smaller* than $m_1$ or $m_2$; hence the name *reduced mass*. Equation 15–34 leads, by way of the derivation that follows Eq. 15–6, to

$$\nu = \frac{1}{2\pi} \sqrt{\frac{k}{\mu}} \quad \text{or} \quad T = 2\pi \sqrt{\frac{\mu}{k}} \tag{15-35}$$

for the frequency and period of oscillation of the system of Fig. 15–17a. It is clear that this system has the same frequency and period as a single block of mass $\mu$, connected by a similar spring to a rigid wall, as in Fig 15–17b. Hence, the two-body oscillation of Fig. 15–17a is equivalent to the one-body oscillation of Fig. 15–17b. One particle moves relative to the other particle as though the other particle were fixed and the mass of the moving one were reduced to $\mu$. The reduced mass concept is applied widely in physics, especially in quantum and solid-state physics.

We can solve Eq. 15–34, as in Section 15–3, to yield these relations:

$$x = A \cos (\omega t + \delta),$$

$$v = dx/dt = -\omega A \sin (\omega t + \delta),$$

and

$$a = dv/dt = -\omega^2 A \cos (\omega t + \delta).$$

They are identical with Eqs. 15–13 except that here $x$, $v$, and $a$ are the *relative* displacement, velocity, and acceleration, respectively, of the two blocks. Thus

$$x = (x_1 - x_2) - l,$$

$$v = dx/dt = v_1 - v_2, \tag{15-36}$$

and

$$a = dv/dt = a_1 - a_2,$$

in which the subscripts refer to the two blocks.

The potential energy of a two-body, simple harmonic oscillator is given by $U(x) = \frac{1}{2}kx^2$ which shows clearly, because $x$ depends on the positions of both blocks (see Eq. 15–36), that the potential energy is a characteristic of the system as a whole.

Many actual two-body oscillators, although harmonic, are not simple harmonic; their potential energy curves, like that of Fig. 8–7a which refers to a diatomic molecule, are not parabolic. Even such oscillators, however, behave like simple harmonic oscillators for small enough amplitudes of oscillation about the equilibrium position. Note, too, that $x$ in Fig. 8–7a has a different meaning than we have assigned to it in this chapter; it is the actual separation, rather than (see Eq. 15–36) the difference between the actual separation and the equilibrium separation. Thus in Fig. 8–7a the stable equilibrium position corresponds, not to $x = 0$ as in Fig. 15–2, but to $x = \sqrt[6]{2a/b}$. This change is only a change in the origin of the $x$-axis of the potential energy curve and has no fundamental significance.

## 15–9 Damped Harmonic Motion

Up to this point we have assumed that no frictional forces act on the oscillator. If this assumption held strictly, a pendulum or a weight on a spring would oscillate indefinitely. Actually, the amplitude of the oscillation gradually decreases to zero as a result of friction. The motion is said to be damped by friction and is called *damped harmonic motion*. Often the friction arises from air resistance or internal forces. The magnitude of the frictional force usually depends on the speed. In most cases of interest the frictional force is proportional to the velocity of the body but directed opposite to it. An example of a damped oscillator is shown in Fig. 15–18.

The equation of motion of the damped simple harmonic oscillator is given by the second law of motion, $F = ma$, in which $F$ is the sum of the restoring force $-kx$ and the damping force $-b\,dx/dt$. Here $b$ is a positive constant. We obtain

$$F = ma,$$

or

$$-kx - b\frac{dx}{dt} = m\frac{d^2x}{dt^2}$$

or

$$m\frac{d^2x}{dt^2} + b\frac{dx}{dt} + kx = 0. \qquad (15\text{–}37)$$

If $b$ is small, the solution of this differential equation (given without proof)* is

$$x = Ae^{-bt/2m}\cos(\omega' t + \delta), \qquad (15\text{–}38)$$

where

$$\omega' = 2\pi\nu' = \sqrt{\frac{k}{m} - \left(\frac{b}{2m}\right)^2}. \qquad (15\text{–}39)$$

In Fig. 15–19 we plot the displacement $x$ as a function of the time $t$ for oscillatory motion with small damping.

We can interpret the solution as follows. First, the frequency is smaller and the period is longer when friction is present. Friction slows down the motion, as might be expected  If no friction were present, $b$ would equal zero and $\omega'$ would equal $\sqrt{k/m}$ or $\omega$, which is the angular frequency of undamped motion. When friction is present, $\omega'$ is less than $\omega$, as shown by Eq. 15–39. Second, the amplitude of the motion gradually decreases to zero. The time interval $\tau$ during which the amplitude drops to $1/e$ of its initial value is called the *mean lifetime* of the oscillation. The amplitude factor is $Ae^{-bt/2m}$, so that $\tau = 2m/b$. Once again, if there were no friction present, $b$ would equal zero

**Fig. 15–18** A damped harmonic oscillator. A disk is attached to the mass and immersed in a fluid which exerts a damping force $-b\,dx/dt$. The elastic restoring force is $-kx$.

and the amplitude would have the constant value $A$ as time went on; the lifetime would be infinite.

If the force of friction is great enough, $b$ becomes so large that Eq. 15–38 is no longer a valid solution of the equation of motion.† Then the motion will not be periodic at all. The body merely returns to its equilibrium position when released from its initial displacement $A$.

In damped harmonic motion the energy of the oscillator is gradually dissipated by friction and falls to zero in time.

---

* See, for example, H. W. Reddick and F. H. Miller, *Advanced Mathematics for Engineers*, third edition, John Wiley and Sons, 1955, pp. 76–78.

† *Ibid.*, pp. 80–83.

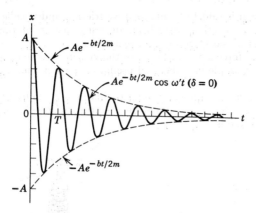

**Fig. 15–19** Damped harmonic motion plotted versus time. The motion is oscillatory with everdecreasing amplitude. The amplitude (– – –) is seen to start with value $A$ and decay exponentially to zero as $t \to \infty$.

## 15–10  Forced Oscillations and Resonance

Thus far we have discussed only the natural oscillations of a body, that is, the oscillations that occur when the body is displaced and then released. For a mass attached to a spring the natural frequency is

$$\omega = 2\pi\nu = \sqrt{\frac{k}{m}}$$

in the absence of friction and

$$\omega' = 2\pi\nu' = \sqrt{\frac{k}{m} - \left(\frac{b}{2m}\right)^2},$$

in the presence of a small frictional force $bv$.

A different situation arises, however, when the body is subject to an oscillatory external force. As examples, a bridge vibrates under the influence of marching soldiers, the housing of a motor vibrates owing to periodic impulses from an irregularity in the shaft, and a tuning fork vibrates when exposed to the periodic force of a sound wave. The oscillations that result are called *forced* oscillations. These forced oscillations have the frequency of the *external force* and not the natural frequency of the body. However, the response of the body depends on the relation between the forced and the natural frequency. A succession of small impulses applied at the proper frequency can produce an oscillation of large amplitude. A child using a swing learns that by pumping at proper time intervals he can make the swing move with a large amplitude. The problem of forced oscillations is a very general one. Its solution is useful in acoustic systems, alternating current circuits, and atomic physics as well as in mechanics.

The equation of motion of a forced oscillator follows from the second law of motion. In addition to the restoring force $-kx$ and the damping force $-b\,dx/dt$, we have also the applied oscillating external force. For simplicity let this external force be given by $F_m \cos \omega'' t$. Here $F_m$ is the maximum value of the external force and $\omega''$ ($= 2\pi\nu''$) is its angular frequency. We can imagine such a force applied directly to the suspended mass of Fig. 15–18, if we wish, for concreteness.

From
$$F = ma,$$

we obtain
$$-kx - b\frac{dx}{dt} + F_m \cos \omega'' t = m\frac{d^2x}{dt^2}$$

or
$$m\frac{d^2x}{dt^2} + b\frac{dx}{dt} + kx = F_m \cos \omega'' t. \qquad (15\text{–}40)$$

The solution of this equation (given without proof)* is

$$x = \frac{F_m}{G} \sin (\omega'' t - \delta),$$     (15-41)

where     $$G = \sqrt{m^2(\omega''^2 - \omega^2)^2 + b^2\omega''^2},$$     (15-42)

and     $$\delta = \cos^{-1} \frac{b\omega''}{G}.$$     (15-43)

Let us consider the resulting motion in a qualitative way.

Notice (Eq. 15-41) that the system vibrates with the frequency of the driving force, $\omega''$, rather than with its natural frequency $\omega$, and that the motion is undamped harmonic motion.

The simplest case is that in which there is no damping, which means that $b = 0$ in Eq. 15-42. The factor $G$, which has the value $|m(\omega''^2 - \omega^2)|$ for $b = 0$, is large when the frequency of the driving force $\omega''$ is very different from the natural undamped frequency of the system $\omega$. This means that the amplitude of the resultant motion, $F_m/G$, is small. As the driving frequency approaches the natural frequency, that is, as $\omega'' \to \omega$, we see that $G \to 0$ and the amplitude $F_m/G \to \infty$. Actually some damping is always present so that the amplitude of oscillation, although it may become large, remains finite in practice.

For actual, damped oscillators (for which $b \neq 0$ in Eq. 15-42), there is a characteristic value of the driving frequency $\omega''$ at which the amplitude of oscillation is a maximum. This condition is called *resonance*† and the value of $\omega''$ at which resonance occurs is called the *resonant frequency*. The smaller the damping in a given system the closer is the resonant frequency to the natural undamped frequency $\omega$. Frequently the damping is small enough so that the resonant frequency can be taken to equal the natural undamped frequency $\omega$ with small error. Likewise, for small damping, the natural undamped frequency $\omega$ ($= \sqrt{k/m}$) can be taken to equal the natural damped frequency $\omega'$ (see Eq. 15-39) with small error.

In Fig. 15-20 we have drawn five curves giving the amplitude of the forced vibrations as a function of the ratio of the driving frequency $\omega''$ to the undamped natural frequency $\omega$. Each of the five curves corresponds to a different value of the damping constant $b$. Curve (a) shows the amplitude when $b = 0$, that is, when there is no damping. In this case, as we have seen, the amplitude becomes infinite at $\omega'' = \omega$ because energy is being fed into the system continuously by the applied force and none of it is dissipated. In practice, some friction is always present, so the amplitude reaches a large, but finite, value. Of course, when the amplitude gets so large that Hooke's law no longer holds and the elastic limit is exceeded, the system is no longer governed by Eq. 15-40. Often the system breaks, as in the Tacoma Bridge disaster (Fig. 15-21). Curves (b) and (c) give the amplitude of forced vibration for two cases of increasing damping.

The displacement caused by a constant force $F_m$ applied to a system with a force constant $k$ is simply $F_m/k$. Notice (Fig. 15-20) that the amplitude of the forced vibrations is rather large compared to this static displacement. A column of soldiers marching in step across a bridge can set it vibrating with a destructively

---

* *Ibid.*, pp. 80-83.

† Resonance, defined here to occur at the frequency at which the forced oscillations have their maximum amplitude, may be defined in other ways as, for example, at the frequency at which maximum power is transferred from the driving unit to the oscillating system or at which the speed of the oscillating mass is a maximum. The definitions are not equivalent; we will discuss the matter further when we deal with forced electrical oscillations; see Problem 42.

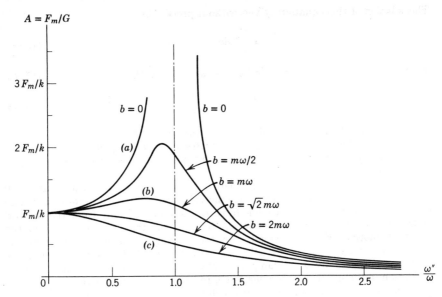

**Fig. 15–20** The amplitude of a driven damped simple harmonic oscillator is plotted versus the ratio of the driving frequency $\omega''$ to the undamped natural frequency $\omega$. Curves for five different degrees of damping are shown; curve (a) shows no damping and curve (c) high damping. We notice that the resonant peak moves nearer and nearer the vertical line at $\omega''/\omega = 1$ as $b$ becomes smaller and smaller.

**Fig. 15–21** On July 1, 1940, the Tacoma Narrows Bridge at Puget Sound, Washington, was completed and opened to traffic. Just four months later a mild gale set the bridge oscillating until the main span broke up, ripping loose from the cables and crashing into the water below. The wind produced a fluctuating resultant force in resonance with a natural frequency of the structure. This caused a steady increase in amplitude until the bridge was destroyed. Many other bridges were later redesigned to make them aerodynamically stable.

large amplitude if the frequency of their steps happens to be some natural frequency of the bridge. This is the reason why soldiers break step when crossing a bridge. Resonance considerations are very important in many electrical, acoustic, and atomic devices, as we shall see later.

# QUESTIONS

**1.** Give some examples of motions that are approximately simple harmonic. Why are motions that are exactly simple harmonic rare?

**2.** A spring has a force constant $k$, and a mass $m$ is suspended from it. The spring is cut in half and the same mass is suspended from one of the halves. Is the frequency of vibration the same before and after the spring is cut? How are the frequencies related?

**3.** An unstressed spring has a force constant $k$. It is stretched by a weight hung from it to an equilibrium length well within the elastic limit. Does the spring have the same force constant $k$ for displacements from this new equilibrium position?

**4.** Any real spring has mass. If this mass is taken into account, explain qualitatively how this will change our expressions for the period of oscillation of a spring-and-mass system (see Problem 40).

**5.** Suppose we have a block of unknown mass and a spring of unknown force constant. Show how we can predict the period of oscillation of this block-spring system simply by measuring the extension of the spring produced by attaching the block to it.

**6.** Can one have an oscillator which even for smaller amplitudes is not simple harmonic? That is, can one have a nonlinear restoring force in an oscillator even at arbitrarily small amplitudes?

**7.** Could we ever construct a simple pendulum?

**8.** Could standards of mass, length, and time be based on properties of a pendulum? Explain.

**9.** Show that as the amplitude $\theta_m$ in Eq. 15-20 approaches 180° the period approaches infinity. Is this reasonable?

**10.** Predict by qualitative arguments whether a pendulum oscillating with large amplitude will have a period longer or shorter than the period for oscillations with small amplitude. (Consider extreme cases.)

**11.** How is the period of a pendulum affected when its point of suspension is (a) moved horizontally with acceleration $a$; (b) moved vertically upward with acceleration $a$; (c) moved vertically downward with acceleration $a < g$. Which case, if any, applies to a pendulum mounted on a cart rolling down an inclined plane?

**12.** Why was an axis through the center of mass excluded in using Eq. 15-26 to determine $I$? Does this equation apply to such an axis? How can you determine $I$ for such an axis using physical pendulum methods?

**13.** A hollow sphere is filled with water through a small hole in it. It is hung by a long thread and, as the water slowly flows out of the hole at the bottom, one finds that the period of oscillation first increases and then decreases. Explain.

**14.** Two pendula, each consisting of a disk attached to a light bar, are identical except for the coupling between disk and bar. In one the bar is rigidly mounted to the disk; in the other ball-bearings are used so that the disk would be free to spin about the end of the bar, for example. Both pendula are hung, pulled aside to the same height, and released. Which has the greater period? Explain.

**15.** How can a pendulum be used so as to trace out a sinusoidal curve?

**16.** What component simple harmonic motions would give a figure 8 as the resultant motion?

**17.** Is there a connection between the $F$ vs. $x$ relation at the molecular level and the macroscopic relation between $F$ and $x$ in a spring?

**18.** Why are damping devices often used on machinery? Give an example.

**19.** Give some examples of common phenomena in which resonance plays an important role.

**20.** The lunar ocean tide is much more important than the solar ocean tide (see Question 13 of Chapter 16, for example). The opposite is true for tides in the earth's atmosphere, however. Explain this, using resonance ideas, given the fact that the atmosphere has a natural period of oscillation of nearly 12 hours.

## PROBLEMS

**1.** A 4.0-kg block extends a spring 16 cm from its unstretched position. The block is removed and a 0.50-kg body is hung from the same spring. If the spring is then stretched and released, what is its period of motion?

**2.** A 2.0-kg mass hangs from a spring. A 300-gm body hung below the mass stretches the spring 2.0 cm farther. If the 300-gm body is removed and the mass set into oscillation, find the period of motion.

**3.** A small body of mass 0.10 kg is undergoing simple harmonic motion of amplitude 1.0 meter and period 0.20 sec. (a) What is the maximum value of the force acting on it? (b) If the oscillations are produced by a spring, what is the force constant of the spring?

**4.** A body oscillates with simple harmonic motion according to the equation

$$x = 6.0 \cos\left(3\pi t + \frac{\pi}{3}\right) \text{ meters.}$$

What is (a) the displacement, (b) the velocity, and (c) the acceleration at the time $t = 2$ sec. Find also (d) the phase, (e) the frequency $\nu$, and (f) the period of the motion.

**5.** A particle executes linear harmonic motion about the point $x = 0$; at $t = 0$ it has displacement $x = 0.37$ cm and zero velocity. If the frequency of the motion is 0.25/ sec, determine (a) the period, (b) the angular frequency, (c) the amplitude, (d) the displacement at time $t$ (arbitrary), (e) the velocity at time $t$ (arbitrary), (f) the maximum speed, (g) the maximum acceleration, (h) the displacement at $t = 3.0$ sec, and (i) the velocity at $t = 3.0$ sec.

**6.** Two particles execute simple harmonic motion of the same amplitude and frequency along the same straight line. They pass one another when going in opposite directions each time their displacement is half their amplitude. What is the phase difference between them?

**7.** A block is on a horizontal surface which is moving horizontally with a simple harmonic motion of frequency two oscillations per second. The coefficient of static friction between block and plane is 0.50. How great can the amplitude be if the block does not slip along the surface?

**8.** A block is on a piston which is moving vertically with a simple harmonic motion of period 1.0 sec. (a) At what amplitude of motion will the block and piston separate? (b) If the piston has an amplitude of 5.0 cm, what is the maximum frequency for which the block and piston will be in contact continuously?

**9.** A uniform spring whose unstressed length is $l$ has a force constant $k$. The spring is cut into two pieces of unstressed lengths $l_1$ and $l_2$, where $l_1 = nl_2$ and $n$ is an integer. What are the corresponding force constants $k_1$ and $k_2$ in terms of $n$ and $k$? Check your result for $n = 1$ and $n = \infty$.

**10.** Two springs are joined and connected to a mass $m$ as shown in Fig. 15–22. The surfaces are frictionless. If the springs separately have force constants $k_1$ and $k_2$, show that the frequency of oscillation of $m$ is

$$f = \frac{1}{2\pi} \sqrt{\frac{k_1 k_2}{(k_1 + k_2)m}}.$$

(The electrical analog of this system is a parallel connection of two capacitors.)

Fig. 15–22

Fig. 15–23

11. The springs are now attached to $m$ and to fixed supports as shown in Fig. 15–23. Show that the frequency of oscillation in this case is

$$f = \frac{1}{2\pi} \sqrt{\frac{k_1 + k_2}{m}}.$$

(The electrical analog of this system is a series combination of two capacitors.)

12. The vibration frequencies of atoms in solids at normal temperatures are of the order $10^{13}$/sec. Imagine the atoms to be connected to one another by springs. Suppose that a single silver atom vibrates with this frequency and that all the other atoms are at rest. Then compute the force constant of a single spring. One mole of silver has a mass of 108 gm and contains $6.02 \times 10^{23}$ atoms.

13. The end of one of the prongs of a tuning fork which executes simple harmonic motion of frequency 1000 per second has an amplitude of 0.40 mm. Neglect damping and find (a) the maximum acceleration and maximum speed of the end of the prong, and (b) the speed and acceleration of the end of the prong when it has a displacement 0.20 mm.

14. A spring of force constant 19.6 nt/meter hangs vertically. A body of mass 0.20 kg is attached to its free end and then released. Assume that the spring was unstretched before the body was released and find how far below the initial position the body descends. Find also the frequency and amplitude of the resulting simple harmonic motion.

15. An 8.0-lb block is suspended from a spring with a force constant of 3.0 lb/in. A bullet weighing 0.10 lb is fired into the block from below with a velocity of 500 ft/sec and comes to rest in the block. (a) Find the amplitude of the resulting simple harmonic motion. (b) What fraction of the original kinetic energy of the bullet is stored in the harmonic oscillator? Is energy lost in this process? Explain your answer.

16. An automobile can be considered to be mounted on a spring as far as vertical oscillations are concerned. The springs of a certain car are adjusted so that the vibrations have a frequency of 3.0 per second. What is the spring's force constant if the car weighs 3200 lb? What will the vibration frequency be if five passengers, averaging 160 lb each, ride in the car?

17. The scale of a spring balance reading from 0 to 32 lb is 4.0 in. long. A package suspended from the balance is found to oscillate vertically with a frequency of 2.0 oscillations per second. How much does the package weigh?

**18.** Start from Eq. 15–17 for the conservation of energy (with $\frac{1}{2}kA^2 = E$) and obtain the displacement as a function of the time by integration of Eq. 15–18. Compare with Eq. 15–18.

**19.** When the displacement is one-half the amplitude, what fraction of the total energy is kinetic and what fraction is potential in simple harmonic motion? At what displacement is the energy half kinetic and half potential?

**20.** (a) Prove that in simple harmonic motion the average potential energy equals the average kinetic energy when the average is taken with respect to time over one period of the motion, and that each average equals $\frac{1}{4}kA^2$. (See Fig. 15–9a.) (b) Prove that when the average is taken with respect to position over one cycle, the average potential energy equals $\frac{1}{3}kA^2$ and the average kinetic energy equals $\frac{1}{6}kA^2$. (See Fig. 15–9b.) (c) Explain physically why the two results above (a and b) are different.

**21.** (a) Show that the general relations for the period and frequency of any simple harmonic motion are

$$T = 2\pi \sqrt{-\frac{x}{a}} \quad \text{and} \quad \nu = \frac{1}{2\pi} \sqrt{-\frac{a}{x}}.$$

(b) Show that the general relations for the period and frequency of any simple angular harmonic motion are

$$T = 2\pi \sqrt{-\frac{\theta}{\alpha}} \quad \text{and} \quad \nu = \frac{1}{2\pi} \sqrt{-\frac{\alpha}{\theta}}.$$

**22.** *Vertical Spring in a Uniform Gravitational Field.* Consider a massless spring of force constant $k$ in a uniform gravitational field. Attach a mass $m$ to the spring. (a) Show that if $x = 0$ marks the slack position of the spring, the static equilibrium position is given by $x = mg/k$ (see Fig. 15–24). (b) Show that the equation of motion of the mass-spring system is

$$m\frac{d^2x}{dt^2} + kx = mg$$

and that the solution for the displacement as a function of time is $x = A \cos(\omega t + \delta) + mg/k$, where $\omega = \sqrt{k/m}$ as before. (c) Show, therefore, that the system has the same $\omega$, $v$, $a$, $\nu$, and $T$ in a uniform gravitational field as in the absence of such a field, with the one change that the equilibrium position has been displaced by $mg/k$. (d) Now consider the energy of the system, $\frac{1}{2}mv^2 + \frac{1}{2}kx^2 + mg(h - x) = $ constant, and show that time differentiation leads to the equation of motion of part (b). (e) Show that when mass falls from $x = 0$ to the static equilibrium position, $x = mg/k$, the loss in gravitational potential energy goes half into a gain in elastic potential energy and half into a gain in kinetic energy. (f) Finally, consider the system in motion at the static equilibrium position. Compute separately the change in gravitational potential energy and in elastic potential energy when the mass moves *up* through a displacement $A$, and when the mass moves *down* through a displacement $A$. Show that the *total* change in potential energy is the same in each case, namely $\frac{1}{2}kA^2$.

**Fig. 15–24**

In view of the results (c) and (f), one can simply ignore the uniform gravitational field in the analysis merely by shifting the reference position from $x = 0$ to $x_0 = x - mg/k = 0$. The new potential energy curve $[U(x_0) = \frac{1}{2}kx_0^2 + \text{constant}]$ has the same parabolic slope as the potential energy curve in the absence of a gravitational field $[U(x) = \frac{1}{2}kx^2]$.

**23.** A simple pendulum of length 1.00 meter makes 100 complete oscillations in 204 sec at a certain location. What is the value of the acceleration of gravity at this point?

**24.** What is the length of a simple pendulum whose period is exactly 1 sec at a point where $g = 32.2$ ft/sec$^2$?

**25.** Show that the maximum tension in the string of a simple pendulum, when the amplitude $\theta_m$ is small, is $mg(1 + \theta_m^2)$. At what position of the pendulum is the tension a maximum?

**26.** (a) What is the frequency of a simple pendulum 2.0 meters long? (b) Assuming small amplitudes, what would its frequency be in an elevator accelerating upward at a rate of 2.0 meters/sec$^2$? (c) What would its frequency be in free fall?

**27.** A simple pendulum of length $l$ and mass $m$ is suspended in a car that is traveling with a constant speed $v$ around a circle of radius $R$. If the pendulum undergoes small oscillations about its equilibrium position, what will its frequency of oscillation be?

**28.** What is the period of a pendulum formed by pivoting a meter stick so that it is free to rotate about a horizontal axis passing through its end? Through the 75-cm mark? Through the 60-cm mark?

**29.** Show that if a uniform stick of length $l$ is mounted so as to rotate about a horizontal axis perpendicular to the stick and at a distance $d$ from the center of mass, the period has a *minimum* value when $d = l/\sqrt{12} = 0.289l$.

**30.** A disk 1.0 meter in diameter is cut from a metal sheet. The disk is made to swing as a pendulum by drilling a small hole in it and mounting it on a nail driven into a wall. Let $l$ be the distance from the nail to the center of the plate. (a) For what value or values of $l$ will the period be 1.7 sec? (b) Suppose you want the period to be as small as possible. What value of $l$ would you use?

**31.** A circular hoop of radius 2.0 ft and weight 8.0 lb is suspended on a horizontal nail. (a) What is its frequency of oscillation for small displacements from equilibrium? (b) What is the length of the equivalent simple pendulum?

**32.** A solid sphere of mass 2.0 kg and diameter 0.30 meter is suspended on a wire. Find the period of angular oscillation for small displacements if the torque required to twist the wire is $6.0 \times 10^{-3}$ nt-m/radian.

**33.** The balance wheel of a watch vibrates with an angular amplitude of $\pi$ radians and a period of 0.50 sec. Find (a) the maximum angular speed of the wheel, (b) the angular speed of the wheel when its displacement is $\pi/2$ radians, and (c) the angular acceleration of the wheel when its displacement is $\pi/4$ radians.

**34.** Electrons in an oscilloscope are deflected by two mutually perpendicular electric fields in such a way that at any time $t$ the displacement is given by

$$x = A \cos \omega t, \qquad y = A \cos (\omega t + \alpha).$$

(a) Describe the path of the electrons and determine its equation when $\alpha = 0°$. (b) When $\alpha = 30°$. (c) When $\alpha = 90°$.

**35.** *Lissajous Figures.* When oscillations at right angles are combined, the frequencies for the motion of the particle in the $x$- and $y$-directions need not be equal, so that in the general case Eqs. 15–30 become

$$x = A_x \cos (\omega_x t + \delta) \qquad \text{and} \qquad y = A_y \cos (\omega_y t + \alpha).$$

The path of the particle is no longer an ellipse but is called a *Lissajous curve*, after Jules Antoine Lissajous (1822–1880) who first demonstrated such curves in 1857. (a) If

$\omega_x/\omega_y$ is a rational number, so that the angular frequencies $\omega_x$ and $\omega_y$ are "commensurable," then the curve is closed and the motion repeats itself at regular intervals of time. Assume $A_x = A_y$ and $\delta = \alpha$ and draw the Lissajous curve for $\omega_x/\omega_y = \frac{1}{2}$, $\frac{1}{3}$, and $\frac{2}{3}$. (b) Let $\omega_x/\omega_y$ be a rational number, either $\frac{1}{2}$, $\frac{1}{3}$, or $\frac{2}{3}$ say, and show that the shape of the Lissajous curve depends upon the phase difference $\alpha - \delta$. Draw curves for $\alpha - \delta = 0$, $\pi/4$, and $\pi/2$ radians. (c) If $\omega_x/\omega_y$ is not a rational number, then the curve is "open." Convince yourself that after a long time the curve will have passed through every point lying in the rectangle bounded by $x = \pm A_x$ and $y = \pm A_y$, the particle never passing twice through a given point with the same velocity.

**36.** (a) Show that when $m_2 \to \infty$ in Eq. 15–33, $\mu \to m_1$. (b) Show that the effect of a noninfinite wall $(m_2 < \infty)$ on the oscillations of a mass $m_1$ at the end of a spring attached to the wall is to reduce the period, or increase the frequency, of oscillation compared to (a). (c) Show that when $m_2 = m_1$ the effect is as though the spring were cut in half, each mass oscillating independently about the center of mass at the middle.

**37.** (a) What is the reduced mass of each of the following diatomic molecules: $O_2$, HCl and CO? Express your answers in atomic mass units, the mass of a hydrogen atom being approximately 1.00 amu. (b) An HCl molecule is known to vibrate at a fundamental frequency of $\nu = 8.7 \times 10^{13}$ cycles/sec. What is the effective "force constant" $k$ for the coupling forces between the atoms? In terms of your experience with ordinary springs, would you say that this "molecular spring" is relatively stiff or not?

**38.** The spring in Fig. 15–17a has a force constant $k = 250$ nt/m. Let $m_1 = 1.0$ kg and $m_2 = 3.0$ kg. (a) What is the oscillation frequency of the two-body system? (b) What is the ratio $K_1/K_2$ of the kinetic energies of the bodies?

**39.** Show that the kinetic energy of the two-body oscillator of Fig. 15–17a is given by $K = \frac{1}{2}\mu v^2$, where $\mu$ is the reduced mass and $v$ ($= v_1 - v_2$) is the relative velocity. It may help to note that linear momentum is conserved while the system oscillates.

**40.** If the mass of a spring $m_s$ is not negligible but is small compared to the mass $m$ of the object suspended from it, the period of motion is $T = 2\pi \sqrt{(m + m_s/3)/k}$. Derive this result. (*Hint:* The condition $m_s \ll m$ is equivalent to the assumption that the spring stretches uniformly along its length.)

**41.** (a) Attach a solid cylinder to a horizontal massless spring so that it can *roll without slipping* along a horizontal surface, as in Fig. 15–25. The force constant $k$ of the spring is 3.0 nt/meter. If the system is released from rest at a position in which the spring is stretched by 0.25 meter, find the translational kinetic energy and the rotational kinetic energy of the cylinder as it passes through the equilibrium position. (b) Show that under these conditions the center of mass of the cylinder executes simple harmonic motion with a period

**Fig. 15–25**

$$T = 2\pi \sqrt{3M/2k}.$$

**42.** Starting from Eq. 15–41, find the velocity $v$ ($= dx/dt$), in forced oscillatory motion. Show that the velocity amplitude is $v_m = F_m/[(m\omega'' - k/\omega'')^2 + b^2]^{\frac{1}{2}}$.

The equations of Section 15–10 are identical in form with those representing an electrical circuit containing a resistance $R$, an inductance $L$, and a capacitance $C$ in series with an alternating emf $V = V_m \cos \omega''t$. Hence, $b$, $m$, $k$, and $F_m$ are analogous to $R$, $L$, $1/C$, and $V_m$, respectively, and $x$ and $v$ are analogous to electric charge $q$ and current $i$, respectively. In the electrical case the current amplitude $i_m$, analogous to the velocity amplitude $v_m$ above, is used to describe the quality of the resonance.

**43.** Two equal masses $m$ and three identical springs of force constant $k$ are arranged as shown in Fig. 15–26.   (a) Let $x_1$, $x_2$ represent the displacement of each mass from its

**Fig. 15–26**

equilibrium position and show that

$$m \frac{d^2 x_1}{dt^2} = k(x_2 - 2x_1)$$

and

$$m \frac{d^2 x_2}{dt^2} = k(x_1 - 2x_2).$$

(b) Find the frequencies of vibration for the system by assuming a solution of the form $x_1 = A_1 \sin \omega t$ and $x_2 = A_2 \sin \omega t$.

# Gravitation

---

## 16–1   Historical Introduction

Until the seventeenth century the tendency of a body to fall toward the earth, that is, its weight, was regarded as an inherent property of all bodies needing no further explanation.   That the weight of a body should be regarded as a force of attraction between the earth and that body was an idea that occurred to Newton and some of his contemporaries, notably Robert Hooke.

The laws governing celestial motions were regarded as quite different from those governing the motions of bodies on the earth.   The motion of the heavenly bodies, particularly the planets and the sun, was a subject of much active interest at this time.   This subject was discussed by students of natural philosophy at Cambridge in 1664.   In 1665, the plague broke out.   School was suspended and the students were sent home.   One of them was Isaac Newton, then a 23-year-old "scholar of the college."

At home in Woolsthorpe, Newton continued to think about these questions.   Apparently he was inspired as he saw an apple fall to the earth from a tree.*   It occurred to him that the same force of gravitation which attracts the apple to the earth might also attract the moon to the earth. Newton thought that the centripetal acceleration of the moon in its orbit and the downward acceleration of a body on the earth might have the same

---

* In a biography of Newton written in 1752 by his friend Stukeley, the author writes of having tea with Newton in a garden under some apple trees, when Newton said that the setting was the same as when he got the idea of gravitation.   "It was occasioned by the fall of an apple, as he sat in a contemplative mood . . . ," writes Stukeley.

origin (Fig. 16–1). The very idea that celestial motions and terrestrial motions were subject to similar laws was a break with tradition.

The acceleration of the moon toward the earth can be computed from its period of revolution and the radius of its orbit. We obtain $0.0089 \text{ ft/sec}^2$ (see Example 4, Chapter 4). This value is about 3600 times smaller than $g$, the acceleration due to gravity on the surface of the earth. Newton sought to account for this difference by assuming that the acceleration of a falling body is inversely proportional to the square of its distance from the earth.

The question of what we mean by "distance from the earth" arises immediately. Newton regarded every particle of the earth as contributing to the gravitational attraction it had on other bodies. The distance and direction of particles of the earth from some object are different for each particle. Newton made the daring assumption that the earth could be treated for such purposes as if all the mass were concentrated at its center.

We could treat the earth as a particle with respect to the sun, for example. It is not obvious at all, however, that we could safely treat the earth as a particle with respect to an apple located only a few feet above its surface. On this assumption, however, a falling body near the earth's surface is a distance of one earth radius from the effective center of attraction of the earth, or 4000 miles. The moon is about 240,000 miles away. The inverse square of the ratio of these distances is $(4000/240{,}000)^2 = 1/3600$, in agreement with the ratio of the accelerations of the moon and apple.

It is believed that Newton made these calculations in 1666. To quote him,

And in the same year (1666) I began to think of gravity extending to the orb of the moon. . . . I deduced that the forces which keep the planets in their Orbs must [be] reciprocally as the squares of their distances from the centers about which they revolve: and thereby compared the force requisite to keep the Moon in

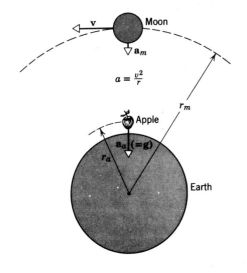

**Fig. 16–1** Both the moon and the apple are accelerated toward the center of the earth. The difference in their motions arises because the moon has a tangential velocity **v** whereas the apple does not.

her Orb with the force of gravity at the surface of the earth and found them answer pretty nearly.

His results were not published until 1687, however, when his *Principia Mathematica* appeared. The reason is thought to be that he was not satisfied at first that he could prove his basic assumption about the earth's acting as a mass particle for objects outside it.* Before he could solve this problem exactly, Newton had to invent the calculus. His proof will be given in Section 16–6.

The *force* on the moon and on the apple depends on the mass of the moon and the mass of the apple, respectively, as well as on that of the earth. Hence, Newton assumed that the gravitational force depended on the masses of the attracting bodies as well as inversely on the square of their distance of separation. He then generalized his concept of gravitational attraction into a law of universal gravitation. He thought that all bodies, no matter where they were located, exerted forces of gravitational attraction upon one another. In order to discover the exact nature of this attractive force, he had to consider bodies of various different masses at significantly different distances from one another. He could not change the distance between the center of the earth and a body on the earth very appreciably, however. It was for this reason that he first compared the motion of the moon and a body on earth. The force between different macroscopic bodies on the earth was so small that it was not detected in Newton's time. Newton apparently realized that this force was small and easily masked by frictional or other forces. Hence, he focused his attention on the motion of the planets in an attempt to confirm his ideas.

The earliest scientific attempts to understand the solar system were made by the Greeks. A detailed description of the conclusions of Greek astronomy was given by Ptolemy (second century). His system is known as the Ptolemaic, or geocentric, theory. It assumes that the earth is stationary at the center of the universe, with the sun, moon, planets, and stars all revolving about the earth in complex orbits. This theory was accepted for almost fifteen centuries and greatly influenced philosophy and literature as well as science. However, the theory was quite complex and could not quantitatively account for an increasing number of observations. In the sixteenth century Copernicus suggested that a simpler description of celestial motions could be given by assuming that the sun was at rest at the center of the universe. In the Copernican or heliocentric theory, the earth was a planet rotating on its axis and revolving about the sun, and the other planets had similar motions (Fig. 16–2).

The growing controversy over the two theories stimulated astronomers

---

* Some students of history believe that he merely wished to avoid controversy. The publication of his *Theory of Light and Colors* had involved him in bitter arguments. Newton was a shy and introspective man. Bertrand Russell writes of Newton, "If he had encountered the sort of opposition with which Galileo had to contend, it is probable that he would never have published a line." It was Halley, a devoted friend with a great interest in celestial mechanics, who persuaded Newton to publish the *Principia*.

**Fig. 16–2** (*a*) The Copernican view of the solar system. The planets move in concentric orbits with the sun at the center. (*b*) The Ptolemaic view of the solar system. Each planet undergoes two simultaneous circular motions. For example, Mars travels about an epicycle while the center of the epicycle travels along a deferent. The earth is at the center of the system. Only the moon and sun have no epicycles.

to obtain more accurate observational data. Such data were compiled by Tycho Brahe (1546–1601), who was the last great astronomer to make observations without the use of a telescope.* His data on planetary motions were analyzed and interpreted for about twenty years by Johannes Kepler (1571–1630), who had been Brahe's assistant. Kepler found important regularities in the motion of the planets. These regularities are known as *Kepler's three laws of planetary motion.*

1. All planets move in elliptical orbits having the sun as one focus (the law of orbits).

2. A line joining any planet to the sun sweeps out equal areas in equal times (the law of areas).

3. The square of the period of any planet about the sun is proportional to the cube of the planet's mean distance from the sun (the law of periods).

Kepler's laws lent strong support to the Copernican theory. They showed the great simplicity with which planetary motions could be described when the sun was taken as the reference body. However, these

---

* The first scientifically useful telescope was built in 1609 by Galileo. With it he discovered the moons of Jupiter and the phases of Venus. Galileo was a strong advocate of the Copernican theory and used his observations to argue in its behalf. Newton, incidentally, invented a telescope, the reflecting type.

laws were empirical; they simply described the observed motion of the planets without any theoretical interpretation.   Kepler had no concept of force as a cause of such regularities.   In fact, the concept of force was not yet clearly formulated.   It was, therefore, a great triumph for Newton's ideas that he could *derive* Kepler's laws from his laws of motion and his law of gravitation.   Newton's law of gravitation in this case required each planet to be attracted toward the sun with a force proportional to the mass of the planet and inversely proportional to the square of its distance from the sun.

In this way Newton was able to account for the motion of the planets in the solar system and of bodies falling near the surface of the earth with one common concept.   He thereby synthesized into one theory the previously separate sciences of terrestrial mechanics and celestial mechanics.   The real scientific significance of Copernicus' work lies in the fact that the heliocentric theory opened the way for this synthesis.*   Subsequently, on the assumption that the earth rotates and revolves about the sun, it became possible to explain such diverse phenomena as the daily and the annual apparent motion of the stars, the flattening of the earth from a spherical shape, the behavior of the tradewinds, and many other things that could not have been tied together so simply in a geocentric theory.

It is instructive to review the development of our understanding of the motions of the bodies in the solar system in terms of the program of classical mechanics that we outlined in Chapter 5; see page 80.   Historically, there were four "breakthroughs."

1. Copernicus pointed out that the sun and not the earth is the central body of the solar system.   In today's language he gave us a reference frame (the sun) much more suitable than the one previously used (the earth) for describing the motions of the solar system.   Among other advantages, the Copernican frame, fixed with respect to the sun but not rotating with it, is essentially an *inertial* reference frame; the reference frame fixed to the revolving earth on which we live cannot be so considered for problems involving planetary motions.

2. Brahe made accurate measurements of the motions of the planets as viewed from the earth.   He provided the necessary observational data that made further progress possible.

3. Kepler, studying Brahe's data, deduced from it the three simple empirical laws of planetary motion that we have discussed above.   Adopting Copernicus' reference frame, he displayed the kinematic information about planetary motions in simple form.

4. Newton discovered the laws of motion for mechanical systems in general as well as the particular force law that applies to the motions of the planets, namely the law of universal gravitation.

Thus, over a span of about 200 years, we see emerging (1) the appropriate reference frame, (2) accurate kinematical information, (3) the empirical laws of planetary motion, and (4) the general laws of classical mechanics and the force law appropriate to planetary motion.

---

* Newton would have been the first to insist that his work was the culmination of the work of others.   He once said in a letter to Robert Hooke, "If I have seen further [than others] it is by standing upon the shoulders of Giants."   Among these giants we must certainly include Galileo and Kepler.

## 16–2   The Law of Universal Gravitation

*The force between any two particles having masses $m_1$ and $m_2$ separated by a distance $r$ is an attraction acting along the line joining the particles and has the magnitude*

$$F = G \frac{m_1 m_2}{r^2}, \qquad (16\text{–}1)$$

*where $G$ is a universal constant having the same value for all pairs of particles.* This is Newton's law of universal gravitation. It is important to stress at once many features of this law in order that we understand it clearly.

First, the gravitational forces between two particles are an action-reaction pair. The first particle exerts a force on the second particle that is directed toward the first particle along the line joining the two. Likewise, the second particle exerts a force on the first particle that is directed toward the second particle along the line joining the two. These forces are equal in magnitude but oppositely directed.

The universal constant $G$ must not be confused with the **g** which is the acceleration of a body arising from the earth's gravitational pull on it. The constant $G$ has the dimensions $L^3/MT^2$ and is a scalar; **g** has the dimensions $L/T^2$, is a vector, and is neither universal nor constant.

Notice that Newton's law of universal gravitation is not a defining equation for any of the physical quantities (force, mass, or length) contained in it. According to our program for classical mechanics in Chapter 5, force is defined from Newton's second law, $F = ma$. The essence of this law, however, is the assumption that the force on a particle, so defined, can be related in a simple way to measurable properties of the particle and of its environment, that is, the existence of simple force laws is assumed. The law of universal gravitation is such a simple law. The constant $G$ must be found from experiment. Once $G$ is determined for a given pair of bodies, we can use that value in the law of gravitation to determine the gravitational forces between any other pair of bodies.

Notice also that Eq. 16–1 expresses the force between mass *particles.* If we want to determine the force between extended bodies, as for example the earth and the moon, we must regard each body as decomposed into particles. Then the interaction between all particles must be computed. Integral calculus makes such a calculation possible. Newton's motive in developing the calculus arose in part from a desire to solve such problems. In general, it is incorrect to assume that all the mass of a body can be concentrated at its center of mass for gravitational purposes. This assumption is correct for uniform spheres, however, a result that we shall use often and shall prove in Section 16–6.

Implicit in the law of universal gravitation is the idea that the gravitational force between two particles is independent of the presence of other bodies or the properties of the intervening space. The correctness of this idea depends on the correctness of the deductions using it and has so far

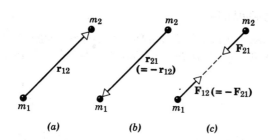

been borne out. This fact has been used by some to rule out the possible existence of "gravity screens."

We can express the law of universal gravitation in vector form. Let the displacement vector $\mathbf{r}_{12}$ point *from* the particle of mass $m_1$ *to* the particle of mass $m_2$, as Fig. 16–3*a* shows. The gravitational force $\mathbf{F}_{21}$, exerted *on* $m_2$ *by* $m_1$, is given in direction and magnitude by the vector relation

$$\mathbf{F}_{21} = -G\,\frac{m_1 m_2}{r_{12}{}^3}\,\mathbf{r}_{12} \qquad (16\text{--}2a)$$

in which $r_{12}$ is the magnitude of $\mathbf{r}_{12}$. The minus sign in Eq. 16–2a shows that $\mathbf{F}_{21}$ points in a direction opposite to $\mathbf{r}_{12}$; that is, the gravitational force is *attractive*, $m_2$ feeling a force directed toward $m_1$ (see Fig. 16–3). That Eq. 16–2a is indeed an inverse square law can be seen by writing it as $\mathbf{F}_{21} = -(Gm_1m_2/r_{12}{}^2)(\mathbf{r}_{12}/r_{12})$; here the displacement vector divided by its own magnitude, $\mathbf{r}_{12}/r_{12}$, is simply a unit vector $\mathbf{u}_r$ in the direction of the displacement. If we express the relation in scalar form by equating the magnitudes of each side, a factor $r_{12}$ in the numerator cancels one of the factors of $r_{12}{}^3$ in the denominator and the inverse square relation of Eq. 16–1 results.

The force exerted *on* $m_1$ *by* $m_2$ is clearly

$$\mathbf{F}_{12} = -G\,\frac{m_2 m_1}{r_{21}{}^3}\,\mathbf{r}_{21}. \qquad (16\text{--}2b)$$

Note, in Eqs. 16–2, that $\mathbf{r}_{21} = -\mathbf{r}_{12}$ (see Fig. 16–3a,b) so that, as we expect, $\mathbf{F}_{12} = -\mathbf{F}_{21}$ (see Fig. 16–3c); that is, the gravitational forces acting on the two bodies form an action-reaction pair.

## 16–3　The Constant of Universal Gravitation, G

To determine the value of $G$ it is necessary to measure the force of attraction between two known masses. The first accurate measurement was made by Lord Cavendish in 1798. Significant improvements were made by Poynting and Boys in the nineteenth century. The present accepted value of $G$ was obtained by P. R. Heyl and P. Chizanowski at the U. S. National Bureau of Standards in 1942. This value is

$$G = 6.673 \times 10^{-11}\,\text{nt-m}^2/\text{kg}^2,$$

accurate to within $0.003 \times 10^{-11}$ nt-m$^2$/kg$^2$. In the British engineering system this value is $3.436 \times 10^{-8}$ lb-ft$^2$/slug$^2$.

The constant $G$ can be determined by the maximum deflection method illustrated in Fig. 16–4. Two small balls, each of mass $m$, are attached to the ends of a light rod.  This rigid "dumbbell" is suspended, with its axis horizontal, by a fine vertical fiber.  Two large balls each of mass $M$ are placed near the ends of the dumbbell on opposite sides.  When the large masses are in the positions $A$ and $B$, the small masses are attracted, by the law of gravitation, and a torque is exerted on the dumbbell rotating it counterclockwise, as viewed from above.  When the large masses are in the positions $A'$ and $B'$, the dumbbell rotates clockwise.  The fiber opposes these torques as it is twisted.  The angle $\theta$ through which the fiber is twisted when the balls are moved from one position to the other is measured by observing the deflection of a beam of light reflected from the small mirror attached to it.  If the masses and their distances of separation and the torsional constant of the fiber are known, we can calculate $G$ from the measured angle of twist.  The force of attraction is very small so that the fiber must have an extremely small torsion constant if we are to obtain a detectable twist.  In Example 1 at the end of this section some data are given from which $G$ can be calculated.

The masses in the Cavendish balance of Fig. 16–4 are, of course, not particles but extended objects.  Since they are uniform spheres, however, they act gravitationally as though all their mass were concentrated at their centers (Section 16–6).

Because $G$ is so small, the gravitational forces between bodies on the earth's surface are extremely small and can be neglected for ordinary pur-

**Fig. 16–4**  The Cavendish balance, used for experimental verification of Newton's law of universal gravitation.  Masses $m,m$ are suspended from a fiber.  Masses $M,M$ can rotate on a stationary support.  An image of the lamp filament is reflected by the mirror attached to $m,m$ onto the scale so that any rotation of $m,m$ can be measured.

poses. For example, two spherical objects each having a mass of 100 kg (about 220-lb weight) and separated by 1.0 meter at their centers attract each other with a force

$$F = \frac{Gm_1m_2}{r^2} = \frac{(6.67 \times 10^{-11}) \times (100) \times (100)}{(1.0)^2} \text{ nt}$$

$$= 6.7 \times 10^{-7} \text{ nt}$$

or about $1.5 \times 10^{-7}$ lb! The Cavendish experiment must be a very delicate one indeed.

The large gravitational force which the earth exerts on all bodies near its surface is due to the extremely large mass of the earth. In fact, we can determine the mass of the earth from the law of universal gravitation and the value of $G$ calculated from the Cavendish experiment. For this reason Cavendish is said to have been the first person to "weigh" the earth. Consider the earth, mass $M_e$, and an object on its surface of mass $m$. The force of attraction is given both by

$$F = mg$$

and

$$F = \frac{GmM_e}{R_e^2}.$$

Here $R_e$ is the radius of the earth, which is the separation of the two bodies, and $g$ is the acceleration due to gravity at the earth's surface. Combining these equations we obtain

$$M_e = \frac{g R_e^2}{G} = \frac{(9.80 \text{ meters/sec}^2)(6.37 \times 10^6 \text{ meters})^2}{6.67 \times 10^{-11} \text{ nt-m}^2/\text{kg}^2} = 5.97 \times 10^{24} \text{ kg}$$

or                        $6.6 \times 10^{21}$ tons       "weight."

If we were to divide the total mass of the earth by its total volume, we would obtain the average density of the earth. This turns out to be 5.5 gm/cm$^3$, or about 5.5 times the density of water. The average density of the rock on the earth's surface is much less than this value. We conclude that the interior of the earth contains material of density greater than 5.5 gm/cm$^3$. From the Cavendish experiment we have obtained information about the nature of the earth's core' (See Question 5 and Problem 35.)

▶ **Example 1.** Let the small spheres of Fig. 16–4 each have a mass of 10.0 gm and let the light rod be 50.0 cm long. The period of torsional oscillation of this system is found to be 769 sec. Then two large fixed spheres each of mass 10.0 kg are placed near each suspended sphere so as to produce the maximum torsion. The angular deflection of the suspended rod is then $3.96 \times 10^{-3}$ radian and the distance between centers of the large and small spheres is 10.0 cm. Calculate the universal constant of gravitation $G$ from these data.

The period of torsional oscillation is given by Eq. 15–24,

$$T = 2\pi \sqrt{\frac{I}{\kappa}}.$$

For the rigid dumbbell, if we neglect the contribution of the light rod,

$$I = \Sigma\, mr^2 = (10.0 \text{ gm})(25.0 \text{ cm})^2 + (10.0 \text{ gm})(25.0 \text{ cm})^2$$

or $$I = 1.25 \times 10^{-3} \text{ kg-m}^2.$$

With $T = 769$ sec, we can obtain the torsional constant $\kappa$ as

$$\kappa = \frac{4\pi^2 I}{T^2} = \frac{(4\pi^2)(1.25 \times 10^{-3} \text{ kg-m}^2)}{(769 \text{ sec})^2} = 8.34 \times 10^{-8} \text{ kg-m}^2/\text{sec}^2.$$

The relation between the applied torque and the angle of twist is $\tau = \kappa\theta$. We now know $\kappa$ and the value of $\theta$ at maximum deflection.

The torque arises from the gravitational forces exerted by the large spheres on the small ones. This torque will be a maximum for a given separation when the line joining the centers of these spheres is at right angles to the rod. The force on *each* small sphere is

$$F = \frac{GMm}{r^2},$$

and the moment arm for each force is half the length of the rod $(l/2)$. Then,

$$\text{torque} = \text{force} \times \text{moment arm}$$

or $$\tau = 2\,\frac{GMm}{r^2}\,\frac{l}{2}.$$

Combining this with $$\tau = \kappa\theta,$$

we obtain

$$G = \frac{\kappa\theta r^2}{Mml} = \frac{(8.34 \times 10^{-8} \text{ kg-m}^2/\text{sec}^2)(3.96 \times 10^{-3} \text{ radian})(0.100 \text{ meter})^2}{(10.0 \text{ kg})(0.0100 \text{ kg})(0.500 \text{ meter})}$$

$$= 6.63 \times 10^{-11} \text{ nt-m}^2/\text{kg}^2.$$

Notice that this result is about 1 % lower than the accepted value. What have we neglected in this calculation that might account for this difference?     ◄

## 16–4    Inertial and Gravitational Mass

The gravitational force on a body is proportional to its mass, as Eq. 16–1 shows. This proportionality between gravitational force and mass is the reason we ordinarily consider the theory of gravitation to be a branch of mechanics, whereas theories of other kinds of force (electromagnetic, nuclear, etc.) may not be.

An important consequence of this proportionality is that we can measure a mass by measuring the gravitational force on it. This can be done by using a spring balance or by comparing the gravitational force on one mass with that on a standard mass, as in a balance; in other words, we can determine the mass of a body by weighing it. This gives us a more practical and more convenient method of measuring mass than is given by our original definition of mass (Section 5–4).

The question arises whether these two methods really measure the same property. The word mass has been used in two quite different experimental situations. For example, if we try to push a block that is at rest on a horizontal frictionless surface, we notice that it requires some effort to move it. The block seems to be inert and tends to stay at rest, or if it is moving it tends to keep moving. Gravity does not enter here at all. It would take the same effort to accelerate the block in gravity-free space. It is the mass of the block which makes it necessary to exert a force to change its motion. This is the mass occurring in $\mathbf{F} = m\mathbf{a}$ in our original experiments in dynamics. We call this mass $m$ the *inertial mass*. Now there is a different situation which involves the mass of the block. For example, it requires effort just to hold the block up in the air at rest above the earth. If we do not support it, the block will fall to the earth with accelerated motion. The force required to hold up the block is equal in magnitude to the force of gravitational attraction between it and the earth. Here inertia plays no role whatever; the property of material bodies, that they are attracted to other objects such as the earth, does play a role. The force is given by

$$F = G\frac{m'M_e}{R_e{}^2},$$

where $m'$ is the *gravitational mass* of the block. *Are the gravitational mass $m'$ and the inertial mass $m$ of the block really the same?* Let us look more carefully at this.

Consider two particles $A$ and $B$ of gravitational masses $m_A'$ and $m_B'$ acted on by a third particle $C$ of gravitational mass $m_C'$. Let the third particle be an equal distance $r$ from the other two. Then, the gravitational force exerted on $A$ by $C$ is

$$F_{AC} = G\frac{m_A'm_C'}{r^2},$$

and the gravitational force exerted on $B$ by $C$ is

$$F_{BC} = G\frac{m_B'm_C'}{r^2}.$$

The ratio of the gravitational forces on $A$ and $B$ is the ratio of their gravitational masses; that is,

$$\frac{F_{AC}}{F_{BC}} = \frac{m_A'}{m_B'}.$$

Now suppose that the third body $C$ is the earth. Then $F_{AC}$ and $F_{BC}$ are what we have called the *weights* of bodies $A$ and $B$. Hence,

$$\frac{W_A}{W_B} = \frac{m_A'}{m_B'}.$$

Therefore, the law of universal gravitation contains within it the result that the weights of various bodies, at the same place on the earth, are exactly proportional to their *gravitational masses*.

Now suppose we measure the inertial masses $m_A$ and $m_B$ of the particles $A$ and $B$ by dynamical experiments, perhaps using a spring as in Section 5–4. Having done this, we then let these particles fall to the earth from a given place and measure their accelerations. We find experimentally that objects of different *inertial masses* all fall with the same acceleration $g$ arising from the earth's gravitational pull. But the earth's gravitational pulls on these bodies are their weights, so that using the second law of motion we obtain

$$W_A = m_A g,$$

$$W_B = m_B g,$$

or

$$\frac{W_A}{W_B} = \frac{m_A}{m_B}.$$

In other words, the weights of bodies at the same place on the earth are exactly proportional to their *inertial masses* as well. Hence, inertial mass and gravitational mass are at least proportional to one another. In fact, they appear to be identical.

Newton devised an experiment to test directly the apparent equivalence of inertial and gravitational mass. If we go back (Section 15–5) and look up the derivation of the period of a simple pendulum, we find that the period (for small angles) was given by

$$T = 2\pi \sqrt{\frac{ml}{m'g}},$$

where $m$ in the numerator refers to the inertial mass of the pendulum bob and $m'$ in the denominator is the gravitational mass of the pendulum bob, such that $m'g$ gives the gravitational pull on the bob. Only if we assume that $m$ equals $m'$, as we did there implicitly, do we obtain the expression

$$T = 2\pi \sqrt{\frac{l}{g}},$$

for the period. Newton made a pendulum bob in the form of a thin shell. Into this hollow bob he put different substances, being careful always to have the same *weight* of substance as determined by a balance. Hence, in all cases the force on the pendulum was the same at the same angle. Because the external shape of the bob was always the same, even the air resistance on the moving pendulum was the same. As one substance replaced another inside the bob, any difference in acceleration could only be due to a difference in the *inertial* mass. Such a difference would show up by a change in the period of the pendulum. But in all cases Newton found the period of the pendulum to be the same, always given by $T = 2\pi \sqrt{l/g}$. Hence, he concluded that $m = m'$ and that inertial and gravitational masses are equivalent.

In 1909, Eötvös devised an apparatus which could detect a difference of 5 parts in $10^9$ in gravitational force. He found that equal inertial masses always experienced equal gravitational forces within the accuracy of his apparatus. A refined version of the Eötvös experiment was reported in 1964 by R. H. Dicke and his collaborators, who improved the accuracy of the original experiment by a factor of several hundred.[*]

In classical physics the equivalence of gravitational and inertial mass was looked upon as a remarkable accident having no deep significance. But in modern physics this equivalence is regarded as a clue leading to a deeper understanding of gravitation (see Sec 16–13). This was, in fact, an important clue leading to the development of the general theory of relativity.

## 16–5   Variations in Acceleration Due to Gravity

Up to this point we have taken the acceleration due to gravity $g$ as a constant. From Newton's law of gravitation, however, it is apparent that

---

[*] See "The Eötvös Experiment," by R. H. Dicke, *Scientific American*, December 1961, for an elegant review of this subject.

$g$ will vary with altitude, that is, with distance from the center of the earth. We have already pointed this out specifically in the moon-apple discussion. Let us compute the change in $g$ that occurs as we proceed outward from the earth's surface. From Eq. 16–1,

$$F = G\frac{m_1 m_2}{r^2},$$

we obtain, on differentiating with respect to $r$,

$$dF = -2\frac{Gm_1 m_2}{r^3}\, dr.$$

Combining these two equations, we obtain

$$\frac{dF}{F} = -2\frac{dr}{r}.$$

Therefore, the fractional change in $F$ is twice the fractional change in $r$. The minus sign indicates that the force decreases as the separation distance increases. If we let $m_1$ be the earth's mass and $m_2$ the object's mass, the gravitational force on the object attributable to the earth is

$$F = m_2 g$$

directed toward the earth. If we differentiate this expression, we obtain

$$dF = m_2\, dg,$$

and on dividing this equation by the previous one we find that

$$\frac{dF}{F} = \frac{dg}{g} = -2\frac{dr}{r}. \tag{16–3}$$

For example, in going up 10 miles from the earth's surface, $r$ changes from about 4000 miles to 4010 miles, a relative increase of 1/400. Therefore,* $g$ must change by about $-1/200$ over this distance, or from about 980 cm/sec$^2$ to about 975 cm/sec$^2$. Hence, $g$ is really very nearly constant near the earth's surface at a given latitude. At higher altitudes, such as those for a typical satellite orbit or for the moon's orbit, $g$ drops appreciably, as Table 16–1 shows.

Measurements of **g** are an essential source of information about the shape of the earth. To define the problem more closely we usually consider not the earth itself but an imaginary closed surface called the *geoid*. Over the oceans the geoid is defined to coincide with mean sea level, whereas over the continents it is defined as a continuation of this level; in principle the position of the geoid can be found by digging small sea-level canals across the continents and noting the mean water

---

* Equation 16–3 is a differential expression and is exact. The corresponding expression obtained when $dr$ is replaced by a finite change $\Delta r$ is a good approximation, provided that $\Delta r/r$ is very small.

**Table 16–1**

VARIATION OF $g$ WITH ALTITUDE AT 45° LATITUDE

| Altitude, meters | $g$, meters/sec$^2$ | Altitude, meters | $g$, meters/sec$^2$ |
|---|---|---|---|
| 0 | 9.806 | 32,000 | 9.71 |
| 1,000 | 9.803 | 100,000 | 9.60 |
| 4,000 | 9.794 | 500,000 | 8.53 |
| 8,000 | 9.782 | 1,000,000[1] | 7.41 |
| 16,000 | 9.757 | 380,000,000[2] | 0.00271 |

[1] Typical satellite orbit altitude (= 620 miles).
[2] Radius of moon's orbit (= 240,000 miles).

level.   The geoid is a surface of constant gravitational potential; at any point the direction of a plumb line is at right angles to it.

The ancient Greeks believed the earth to be round and one of them, Eratosthenes (c 276–194 BC), measured the radius of the earth on the assumption that it is a sphere.   He obtained a value of 7400 km, which is to be compared with the modern value of 6371 km.   This basic information about the shape of the earth was gradually forgotten and was not rediscovered until the great voyages of exploration of the fifteenth century.

Later it was learned by measurement that, to a good second approximation, the geoid is not a sphere but is an ellipsoid of revolution, flattened along the earth's rotational axis and bulging at the equator.   The equatorial radius, in fact, exceeds the polar radius by 21 km.   This flattening is caused by centrifugal effects in the rotating, plastic earth.   The geoidic surface is not exactly ellipsoidal, lying outside the ellipsoid of closest fit under mountain masses and inside it over the oceans.

The fact that the equator is farther from the center of the earth than are the poles means that there should be a steady increase in the measured value of $g$ as one goes from the equator (latitude 0°) to either pole (latitude 90°).   This is shown in Table 16–2.   As Example 2 shows, however, about half of this variation can be accounted for by another effect, namely, the change in the effective value of $g$ caused by the earth's rotation.   If the earth were rotating fast enough, for example,

**Table 16–2**

VARIATION OF $g$ WITH LATITUDE AT SEA LEVEL

| Latitude | $g$, meters/sec$^2$ | Latitude | $g$, meters/sec$^2$ |
|---|---|---|---|
| 0° | 9.78039 | 50° | 9.81071 |
| 10° | 9.78195 | 60° | 9.81918 |
| 20° | 9.78641 | 70° | 9.82608 |
| 30° | 9.79329 | 80° | 9.83059 |
| 40° | 9.80171 | 90° | 9.83217 |

*(a)*                                *(b)*

Path of $m$

W

F

$R_e$

North Pole

**Fig. 16–5**  Example 2.  Effect of the earth's rotation on the weight of a body as measured by a spring balance.

objects on its surface at the equator would seem to be weightless, which means that the effective value of $g = (W/m)$ would be zero.  For all rotational speeds less than this critical value, $g$ has a definite nonzero value which is, however, less than the value it would have at the same point on a nonrotating earth.

In 1959, it was observed that the orbit of the Vanguard artificial earth satellite, calculated using values of **g** based on an ellipsoidal geoid, did not agree exactly with the observed orbit.  It was concluded that the geoid is best approximated not by an ellipsoid of revolution but by a slightly pear-shaped figure, the small end of the "pear" being in the northern hemisphere and extending about 15 meters above the reference ellipsoid.  The motion of a satellite is governed at all times by the value of **g** at its position.  Thus an artificial earth satellite forms a useful probe to explore the values of **g** near the surface of the earth and from this to deduce information about the shape of the geoid.  These studies* are continuing as of this date.

▶  **Example 2.**  *Effect on g of the rotation of the earth.*  Figure 16–5 is a schematic view of the earth looking down on the North Pole.  In it we show an enlarged view of a body of mass $m$ hanging from a spring balance at the equator.  The forces on this body are the upward pull of the spring balance $w$, which is the apparent weight of the body, and the downward pull of the earth's gravitational attraction $F = GmM_e/R_e^2$.  This body is not in equilibrium because it experiences a centripetal acceleration $a_R$ as it rotates with the earth.  There must, therefore, be a net force acting on the body toward the center of the earth.  Consequently,

---

* See, for example, "Satellite Orbits and Their Geophysical Implications," by D. G. King-Hele, *Contemporary Physics*, April 1961.

the force $F$ of gravitational attraction (the true weight of the body) must exceed the upward pull of the balance $w$ (the apparent weight of the body).

From the second law of motion we obtain

$$F - w = ma_R,$$

$$\frac{GM_e m}{R_e^2} - mg = ma_R,$$

$$g = \frac{GM_e}{R_e^2} - a_R \qquad \text{at the equator.}$$

At the poles $a_R = 0$ so that

$$g = \frac{GM_e}{R_e^2} \qquad \text{at the poles.}$$

This is the value of $g$ we would obtain anywhere (assuming a spherical earth) were the rotation of the earth to be neglected.

Actually the centripetal acceleration is not directed in toward the center of the earth other than at the equator. It is directed perpendicularly in toward the earth's axis of rotation at any given latitude. The detailed analysis is, therefore, really a two-dimensional one. However, the extreme case is at the equator. There

$$a_R = \omega^2 R_e = \left(\frac{2\pi}{T}\right)^2 R_e = \frac{4\pi^2 R_e}{T^2},$$

in which $\omega$ is the angular speed of the earth's rotation, $T$ is the period, and $R_e$ is the radius of the earth. Using the values

$$R_e = 6.37 \times 10^6 \text{ meters,}$$

$$T = 8.64 \times 10^4 \text{ sec,}$$

we obtain $\qquad a_R = 0.0336 \text{ meter/sec}^2.$

Referring to Table 16–2, we see that this effect is enough to account for more than half the difference between the observed values of $g$ at low and high latitudes. ◀

## 16–6   Gravitational Effect of a Spherical Distribution of Mass

We have already used the fact that a large sphere attracts particles outside it, just as though the mass of the sphere were concentrated at its center. Let us now prove this result.

Consider a uniformly dense spherical shell whose thickness $t$ is small compared to its radius $r$ (Fig. 16–6). We seek the gravitational force it exerts on an external particle $P$ of mass $m$.

We assume that each particle of the shell exerts on $P$ a force which is proportional to the mass of the small part, inversely proportional to the square of the distance between that part of the shell and $P$, and directed along the line joining them. We must then obtain the resultant force on $P$ attributable to all parts of the spherical shell.

The small part of the shell at $A$ attracts $m$ with a force $\mathbf{F}_1$. A small part of equal mass at $B$, equally far from $m$ but diametrically opposite $A$, attracts $m$ with a force $\mathbf{F}_2$. The resultant of these two forces on $m$ is $\mathbf{F}_1 + \mathbf{F}_2$. Notice,

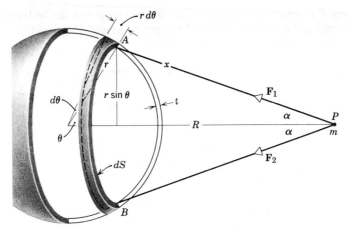

**Fig. 16–6**   Gravitational attraction of a section $dS$ of a spherical shell of matter on a particle of mass $m$.

however, that the vertical components of these two forces cancel one another and that the horizontal components, $F_1 \cos \alpha$ and $F_2 \cos \alpha$, are equal. By dividing the spherical shell into pairs of particles like these, we can see at once that all transverse forces on $m$ cancel in pairs. A small mass in the upper hemisphere exerts a force having an upward component on $m$ that will annul the downward component of force exerted on $m$ by an equal symmetrically located mass in the lower hemisphere of the shell. To find the resultant force on $m$ arising from the shell, we need consider only horizontal components.

Let us take as our element of mass of the shell a circular strip labeled $dS$ in the figure. Its length is $2\pi(r \sin \theta)$, its width is $r \, d\theta$, and its thickness is $t$. Hence, it has a volume

$$dV = 2\pi t r^2 \sin \theta \, d\theta.$$

Let us call the density $\rho$, so that the mass within the strip is

$$dM = \rho \, dV = 2\pi t \rho r^2 \sin \theta \, d\theta.$$

The force exerted by $dM$ on the particle of mass $m$ at $P$ is horizontal and has the value

$$dF = G \frac{m \, dM}{x^2} \cos \alpha$$

$$= 2\pi G t \rho m r^2 \frac{\sin \theta \, d\theta}{x^2} \cos \alpha.$$

(16–4)

The variables $x$, $\alpha$, and $\theta$ are related. From the figure we see that

$$\cos \alpha = \frac{R - r \cos \theta}{x}.$$

(16–5)

Since, by the law of cosines,

$$x^2 = R^2 + r^2 - 2Rr \cos \theta,$$

(16–6)

we have

$$r \cos \theta = \frac{R^2 + r^2 - x^2}{2R}.$$

(16–7)

On differentiating Eq. 16–6, we obtain

$$2x\,dx = 2Rr\sin\theta\,d\theta$$

or
$$\sin\theta\,d\theta = \frac{x}{Rr}\,dx. \tag{16–8}$$

We now put Eq. 16–7 into Eq. 16–5 and then put Eqs. 16–5 and 16–8 into Eq. 16–4. As a result we eliminate $\theta$ and $\alpha$ and obtain

$$dF = \frac{\pi Gt\rho mr}{R^2}\left(\frac{R^2 - r^2}{x^2} + 1\right)dx.$$

This is the force exerted by the circular strip $dS$ on the particle $m$.

We must now consider every element of mass in the shell and sum up over all the circular strips in the entire shell. This operation is an integration over the shell with respect to the variable $x$. But $x$ ranges from a minimum value of $R - r$ to a maximum value $R + r$.

Since
$$\int_{R-r}^{R+r}\left(\frac{R^2 - r^2}{x^2} + 1\right)dx = 4r,$$

we obtain the resultant force

$$F = \int_{R-r}^{R+r} dF = G\frac{(4\pi r^2\rho t)m}{R^2} = G\frac{Mm}{R^2}, \tag{16–9}$$

where
$$M = (4\pi r^2 t\rho)$$

is the total mass of the shell. This is exactly the same result we would obtain for the force between *particles* of mass $M$ and $m$ separated a distance $R$. We have proved, therefore, that *a uniformly dense spherical shell attracts an external mass point as if all its mass were concentrated at its center.*

A solid sphere can be regarded as composed of a large number of concentric shells. If each spherical shell has a uniform density, even though different shells may have different densities, the same result applies to the solid sphere. Hence, a body like the earth, the moon, or the sun, to the extent that they are such spheres, may be regarded gravitationally as point particles to bodies outside them.

Notice that our proof applies only to spheres and then only when the density is constant over the sphere or a function of radius alone.

An interesting result of some significance is the force exerted by a spherical shell on a particle *inside* it. This force is *zero*. To prove this we refer to Fig. 16–7, where $m$ is shown inside the shell. Notice that $R$ is now smaller than $r$. The limits of our integration over $x$ are now $r - R$ to $R + r$. But

$$\int_{r-R}^{R+r}\left(\frac{R^2 - r^2}{x^2} + 1\right)dx = 0,$$

so that $F = 0$.

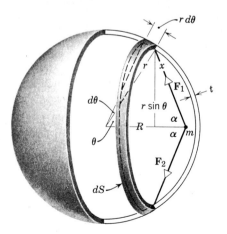

**Fig. 16–7** Gravitational attraction of a section $dS$ of a spherical shell of matter on a particle of mass $m$. Here the particle is inside the shell.

This last result, although not obvious, is plausible because the mass elements of the shell on opposite sides of $m$ now exert forces of opposite directions on $m$ inside. The total annulment depends on the fact that the force varies precisely as an inverse square of the separation distance of two particles. (See Problem 10.) Important consequences of this result will be discussed in the chapters on electricity. There we shall see that the electrical force between charged particles also depends inversely on the square of the distance between them. A consequence of interest in gravitation is that the gravitational force exerted by the earth on a particle decreases as the particle goes deeper into the earth, *assuming a constant density for the earth*, for the portions of matter in shells external to the position of the particle exert no force on it, the force becoming zero at the center of the earth.

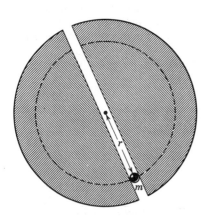

Hence, $g$ would be a maximum at the earth's surface and decrease both outward and inward from that point *if the earth had constant density*. Can you imagine a spherically symmetric distribution of the earth's mass which would not give this result? (See Problem 35.)

▶ **Example 3.** Suppose a tunnel could be dug through the earth from one side to the other along a diameter, as shown in Fig. 16–8.

(a) Show that the motion of a particle dropped into the tunnel is simple harmonic motion. Neglect all frictional forces and assume that the earth has a uniform density.

The gravitational attraction of the earth for the particle at a distance $r$ from the center of the earth arises entirely from that portion of matter of the earth in shells internal to the position of the particle. The external shells exert no force on the particle. Let us assume that the earth's density is uniform at the value $\rho$. Then the mass inside a sphere of radius $r$ is

**Fig. 16–8** Example 3. Particle moving in a tunnel through the earth.

$$M' = \rho V' = \rho \frac{4\pi r^3}{3}.$$

This mass can be treated as though it were concentrated at the center of the earth for gravitational purposes. Hence, the force on the particle of mass $m$ is

$$F = \frac{-GM'm}{r^2}.$$

The minus sign is used to indicate that the force is attractive and directed toward the center of the earth.

Substituting for $M'$, we obtain

$$F = -G\frac{(\rho 4\pi r^3)m}{3r^2} = -\left(G\rho\frac{4\pi m}{3}\right)r = -kr.$$

Here $G\rho 4\pi m/3$ is a constant, which we have called $k$. The force is, therefore, proportional to the displacement $r$ but oppositely directed. This is exactly the criterion for simple harmonic motion.

(b) If mail were delivered through this chute, how much time would elapse between deposit at one end and delivery at the other end?

The period of this simple harmonic motion is

$$T = 2\pi \sqrt{\frac{m}{k}} = 2\pi \sqrt{\frac{3m}{G\rho 4\pi m}} = \sqrt{\frac{3\pi}{G\rho}}.$$

Let us take $\rho = 5.51 \times 10^3$ kg/meter$^3$ and $G = 6.67 \times 10^{-11}$ nt-m$^2$/kg$^2$. This gives

$$T = \sqrt{\frac{3\pi}{G\rho}} = \sqrt{\frac{3\pi}{(6.67 \times 10^{-11})(5.51 \times 10^3)}} \; \text{sec} = 5050 \; \text{sec} = 84.2 \; \text{min}.$$

The time for delivery is one-half period, or about 42 min. Notice that this time is independent of the mass of the mail.

The earth does not really have a uniform density. Suppose $\rho$ were some function of $r$, rather than a constant. What effect would this have on our problem? ◄

## 16–7   The Motions of Planets and Satellites

The motions of bodies in the solar system can be deduced from the laws of motion and the law of universal gravitation. As Kepler pointed out (see page 385), all planets move in elliptical orbits, the sun being at one focus. We can learn a lot about planetary motion by considering the special case of circular orbits. We shall neglect the forces between planets, considering only the interaction between the sun and a given planet. These considerations apply equally well to the motion of a satellite (natural or artificial) about a planet.

Consider two spherical bodies of masses $M$ and $m$ moving in circular orbits under the influence of each other's gravitational attraction. The center of mass of this system of two bodies lies along the line joining them at a point $C$ such that $mr = MR$ (Fig. 16–9). If there are no external forces acting on this sys-

**Fig. 16–9** Two bodies moving in circular orbits under the influence of each other's gravitational attraction. They both have the same angular velocity $\omega$.

tem, the center of mass has no acceleration. In this case we choose $C$ to be the origin of our reference frame. The large body of mass $M$ moves in an orbit of constant radius $R$ and the small body of mass $m$ in an orbit of constant radius $r$, both having the same angular velocity $\omega$. In order for this to happen, the gravitational force acting on each body must provide the necessary centripetal acceleration. Since these gravitational forces are simply an action-reaction pair, the centripetal forces must be equal but oppositely directed. That is, $m\omega^2 r$ (the magnitude of the centripetal force exerted by $M$ on $m$) must equal $M\omega^2 R$ (the magnitude of the centripetal force exerted by $m$ on $M$). That this is so follows at once, for $mr = MR$ so that $m\omega^2 r = M\omega^2 R$. The specific requirement, then, is that the gravitational force on either body must equal the centripetal force needed to keep it moving in its circular orbit, that is,

$$\frac{GMm}{(R+r)^2} = m\omega^2 r. \tag{16-10}$$

If one body has a much greater mass than the other, as in the case of the sun and a planet, its distance from the center of mass is much smaller than that of the other body. Let us therefore assume that $R$ is negligible compared to $r$. Equation 16–10 then becomes

$$GM_s = \omega^2 r^3,$$

where $M_s$ is the mass of the sun. If we express the angular velocity in terms of the period of the revolution, $\omega = 2\pi/T$, we obtain

$$GM_s = \frac{4\pi^2 r^3}{T^2}. \tag{16-11}$$

This is a basic equation of planetary motion; it holds also for elliptical orbits if we define $r$ to be the semi-major axis of the ellipse. Let us consider some of its consequences.

One immediate consequence of Eq. 16–11 is that it predicts Kepler's third law of planetary motion in the special case of circular orbits. For we can express Eq. 16–11 as

$$T^2 = \frac{4\pi^2}{GM_s} r^3.$$

Notice that the mass of the planet is not involved in this expression. Here, $4\pi^2/GM_s$ is a constant, the same for all planets.

When the period $T$ and radius $r$ of revolution are known for any planet, Eq. 16–11 can be used to determine the mass of the sun. For example, the earth's period is

$$T = 365 \text{ days} = 3.15 \times 10^7 \text{ sec},$$

and its orbital radius is

$$r = 93 \text{ million miles} = 1.5 \times 10^{11} \text{ meters}.$$

Hence,

$$M_s = \frac{4\pi^2 r^3}{GT^2} = \frac{(4\pi^2)(1.5 \times 10^{11} \text{ meters})^3}{(6.67 \times 10^{-11} \text{ nt-m}^2/\text{kg}^2)(3.15 \times 10^7 \text{ sec})^2} \cong 2.0 \times 10^{30} \text{ kg}.$$

The mass of the sun is thus about 300,000 times the mass of the earth.  The error made in neglecting $R$ compared to $r$ is seen to be trivial, for

$$R = \frac{m}{M} r = \frac{1}{300,000} r \cong 300 \text{ miles}; \qquad \frac{R}{r} 100\% \cong \frac{1}{3000} \text{ of } 1\%.$$

In a similar manner we can determine the mass of the earth from the period and radius of the moon's orbit about the earth.  (See Problem 22.)

If we know the mass of the sun $M_s$ and the period of revolution $T$ of any planet about it, we can determine the radius of the planet's orbit $r$ from Eq. 16–11.  Since the period is easily obtained from astronomical observations, this method of determining a planet's distance from the sun is fairly reliable.

Equation 16–11 holds also for the motion of artificial satellites about the earth; we need only substitute the mass of the earth $M_e$ for $M_s$ in that equation.

Kepler's second law of planetary motion (see page 385) must, of course, hold for circular orbits.  In such orbits both $\omega$ and $r$ are constant so that equal areas are swept out in equal times by the line joining a planet and the sun.  For the exact elliptical orbits, however, or for any orbit in general, both $r$ and $\omega$ will vary.  Let us consider this case.

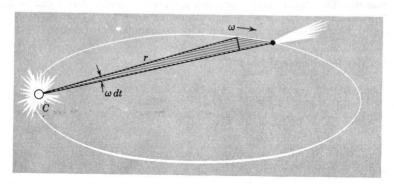

**Fig. 16–10**  A comet moving along an elliptical path with the sun $C$ at the focus of the ellipse.  In time $dt$ the comet sweeps out an angle $d\theta = \omega dt$.

Figure 16–10 shows a particle revolving about $C$ along some arbitrary path.  The area swept out by the radius vector in a very short time interval $\Delta t$ is shown shaded in the figure.  This area, neglecting the small triangular region at the end, is one-half the base times the altitude or approximately $\frac{1}{2}(r\omega \, \Delta t) \cdot r$.  This expression becomes more exact in the limit as $\Delta t \to 0$, the small triangle going to zero more rapidly than the large one.  The rate at which area is being swept out instantaneously is therefore

$$\lim_{\Delta t \to 0} \frac{\frac{1}{2}(r\omega \, \Delta t)(r)}{\Delta t} = \frac{1}{2}\omega r^2.$$

But $m\omega r^2$ is simply the angular momentum of the particle about $C$. Hence, Kepler's second law, which requires that the rate of sweeping out of area $\frac{1}{2}\omega r^2$ be constant, is entirely equivalent to the statement that *the angular momentum of any planet about the sun remains constant.* The angular momentum of the particle about $C$ cannot be changed by a force on it directed toward $C$. Kepler's second law would, therefore, be valid for any *central force*, that is, any force directed toward the sun. The exact nature of this force—how it depends on distance of separation or other properties of the bodies—is not revealed by this law.

It is Kepler's first law that requires the gravitational force to depend exactly on the inverse square of the distance between two bodies, that is, on $1/r^2$. Only such a force, it turns out, can yield planetary orbits which are elliptical with the sun at one focus.

Newton's laws of motion and his law of universal gravitation are in almost complete agreement with astronomical observations.* In our calculation we considered the motion of a planet about the sun as a "two-body" problem. However, we saw that the motion of the sun could be neglected while retaining a high degree of accuracy because of the large ratio of solar mass to planetary mass. This reduced the problem to that of motion of one body about a center of force. If we had required greater accuracy, we would have had to include the sun's motion in our problem (see Problem 39). In fact, for an exact treatment we would have to take into account the effect of other planets and satellites on the motion of sun and planet. This "many-body" problem is quite formidable, but it can be solved by approximation methods to a high degree of accuracy. The results of such calculations are in excellent agreement with astronomical observations.

### 16-8  The Gravitational Field

A basic fact of gravitation is that two masses exert forces on one another. We can think of this as a direct interaction between the two mass particles, if we wish. This point of view is called *action-at-a-distance*, the particles interacting even though they are not in contact. Another point of view is the *field* concept which regards a mass particle as modifying the space around it in some way and setting up a *gravitational field*. This field then acts on any other mass particle in it, exerting the force of gravitational attraction on it. The field, therefore, plays an intermediate role in our thinking about the forces between mass particles. According to this view we have two separate parts to our problem. First, we must determine the field established by a given distribution of mass particles; and secondly, we must calculate the force that this field exerts on another mass particle placed in it.

For example, consider the earth as an isolated mass. If a body is now brought in the vicinity of the earth, a force is exerted on it. This force has a definite direction and magnitude at each point in space. The direction is

---

* The major axis of the elliptical orbit of Mercury rotates slightly more than that predicted by Newtonian mechanics when the perturbing influence of other planets is included. This effect is accounted for in the general theory of relativity.

radially in toward the center of the earth and the magnitude is $mg$. We can, therefore, associate with each point near the earth a vector **g** which is the acceleration that a body would experience if it were released at this point. We call **g** the *gravitational field strength* at the point in question. Since

$$\mathbf{g} = \frac{\mathbf{F}}{m}, \tag{16–12}$$

we may define gravitational field strength at any point as the gravitational force per unit mass at that point. We calculate the force from the field simply by multiplying **g** by the mass $m$ of the particle placed at any point.

The gravitational field is an example of a *vector field*, each point in this field having a vector associated with it. There are also scalar fields, such as the temperature field in a heat-conducting solid. The gravitational field arising from a fixed distribution of matter is also an example of a *stationary field*, because the value of the field at a given point does not change with time.

The field concept is particularly useful for understanding electromagnetic forces between moving electric charges. It has distinct advantages, both conceptually and in practice, over the action-at-a-distance concept. The field concept was not used in Newton's day. It was developed much later by Faraday for electromagnetism and only then applied to gravitation. Subsequently, this point of view was adopted for gravitation in the general theory of relativity. The chief purpose of introducing it here is to give the student an early familiarity with a concept that proves to be important in the development of physical theory.

▶ **Example 4.** In Chapter 15 we derived the formula for the period of a simple pendulum, $T = 2\pi \sqrt{l/g}$. Keeping in mind that the earth's gravitational field is not uniform over large distances, as was assumed for small distances, what is the longest period a simple pendulum could have in the vicinity of the earth's surface?

The formula $T = 2\pi \sqrt{l/g}$, although not applicable when $g$ varies over the pendulum's path, suggests that we increase the length of the pendulum. Let us make the length infinite. The pendulum bob would then travel along the arc of a circle of infinite radius, that is, along a straight line, as shown in Fig. 16–11. The direction of the earth's gravitational field is everywhere radially in toward the center of the earth, so that its direction changes along the arc. Let us assume that the bob of mass $m$ has an amplitude that is small compared to the radius of the earth. Then the bob is always a distance $R_e$, the earth's radius, from the center of the earth, to a good approximation. Then the force $F$ on $m$ is

$$F = \frac{GM_e m}{R_e^2} = mg,$$

where $M_e$ is the mass of the earth. This force is directed toward the earth's center as shown. The component of this vector force along $x$, the line of motion of the bob, is

$$F_x = F \cos \theta = -F \frac{x}{R_e} = -\frac{GM_e m}{R_e^3} x,$$

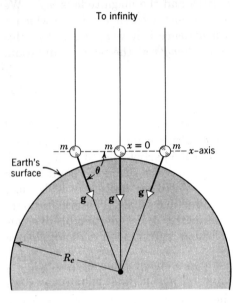

**Fig. 16–11** Example 4. A simple pendulum suspended at infinity.

where the minus sign indicates that the force is directed opposite to the displacement from $x = 0$. We can write this as

$$F_x = -kx,$$

where $k = GM_e m/R_e^3$, a constant.

The formula for the period of a simple harmonic oscillator is $T = 2\pi \sqrt{m/k}$. Hence,

$$T = 2\pi \sqrt{\frac{m}{k}} = 2\pi \sqrt{\frac{m}{GM_e m/R_e^3}} = 2\pi \sqrt{\frac{R_e}{GM_e/R_e^2}} = 2\pi \sqrt{\frac{R_e}{g}},$$

because $g$ at the earth's surface equals $GM_e/R_e^2$. Putting in $R_e = 6.37 \times 10^6$ meters and $g = 9.80$ meters/sec$^2$, we obtain $T = 84.3$ min as the longest period of a simple pendulum in the vicinity of the earth's surface. (See Problem 14.) ◄

### 16–9 Gravitational Potential Energy

In Chapter 8 we discussed the gravitational potential energy of a particle (mass $m$) and the earth (mass $M$). We considered only the special case in which the particle remains close to the earth so that we could assume the gravitational force acting on the particle to be constant for all positions of the particle. In this section we remove that restriction and consider particle-earth separations that may be appreciably greater than the earth's radius.

Equation 8–5$b$, which we may write as,

$$\Delta U = U_b - U_a = -W_{ab}, \qquad (8\text{–}5b)$$

defines the change $\Delta U$ in the potential energy of any system, in which a conservative force (gravity, say) acts, as the system changes from configuration $a$ to configuration $b$. $W_{ab}$ is the work done by that conservative force as the system changes.

The potential energy of the system in any arbitrary configuration $b$ is (see Eq. 8–5$b$)

$$U_b = -W_{ab} + U_a. \tag{16-13}$$

To give a value to $U_b$ we must (arbitrarily) choose configuration $a$ to be some agreed-upon reference configuration and we must assign to $U_a$ some (arbitrarily) agreed-upon value, usually zero.

In Chapter 8 we chose as a reference configuration for the earth-particle system that in which the particle is resting on the surface of the earth and we assigned to this configuration the potential energy $U_a = 0$. When the particle is at a height $y$ above the surface of the earth, the potential energy $U (= U_b)$ is given from Eq. 16–13 as

$$U = -W_{ab} + 0 = -(-mg)(y) = mgy.$$

The conservative force in question, gravity, points down and has the value $(-mg)$; the displacement of the particle $(+y)$ points up from the reference level; hence the difference in sign for these quantities.

For the more general case, in which the restriction $y \ll R$ (in which $R$ is the radius of the earth) is not imposed, we find it convenient to select a different reference configuration, namely that in which the particle and the earth are infinitely far apart. We assign the value zero to the potential energy of the system in this configuration. Thus the zero-potential-energy configuration is also the zero-force configuration. We made a similar choice when we defined the zero-energy configuration of a spring to be its normal unstressed state, for which the restoring force is zero.

When the particle of mass $m$ is a distance $r$ from the center of the earth, the system potential energy is given by Eq. 16–13 as

$$U(r) = -W_{\infty r} + 0 \tag{16-14}$$

in which $W_{\infty r}$ is the work done by the conservative force (gravity) on the particle as the particle moves in from infinity to a distance $r$ from the center of the earth. For simplicity we assume for the present that the particle moves toward the earth along a radial line. The gravitational force $F(r)$ acting on the particle (assuming $r \geqslant R$) will then be $-GMm/r^2$, the minus sign indicating an attractive force, that is, a force that pulls the particle toward the earth. We may then find $U(r)$ from Eq. 16–14 as

$$U(r) = -W_{\infty r}$$

$$= -\int_{\infty}^{r} F(r)\, dr$$

$$= -\int_{\infty}^{r} \left(-\frac{GMm}{r^2}\right) dr = -\frac{GMm}{r}\Big|_{\infty}^{r}$$

$$= -\frac{GMm}{r}. \tag{16-15}$$

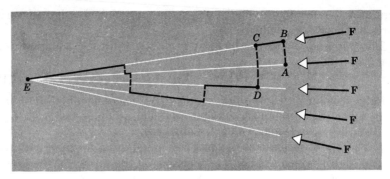

**Fig. 16–12**   Work done in taking a mass from $A$ to $E$ is independent of the path.

The minus sign indicates that the potential energy is negative at any finite distance; that is, the potential energy is zero at infinity and decreases as the separation distance decreases. This corresponds to the fact that the gravitational force exerted on the particle by the earth is attractive. As the particle moves in from infinity, the work $W_{\infty r}$ done by this force on the particle is positive, which means, from Eq. 16–14, that $U(r)$ is negative.

Equation 16–15 holds no matter what path is followed by the particle in moving in from infinity to radius $r$. We can show this by breaking up any arbitrary path into infinitesimal steplike portions, which are drawn alternately along the radius and perpendicular to it (Fig. 16–12). No work is done along perpendicular segments, like $AB$, because along them the force is perpendicular to the displacement. But the work done along the radial parts of the path, such as $BC$, adds up to the work done in going directly along a radial path, such as $AE$. The work done in moving the particle between two points in a gravitational field is, therefore, independent of the actual path connecting these points. Hence, the gravitational force is a *conservative* force.

Equation 16–15 shows that the potential energy of the particles $M$ and $m$ is a characteristic of the system $M + m$. The potential energy is a property of the *system* of bodies, rather than of either body alone. The potential energy changes whether $M$ or $m$ is displaced; each is in the gravitational field of the other. Nor does it make any sense to assign part of the potential energy to $M$ and part of it to $m$. Often, however, we *do* speak of the potential energy of a body $m$ (planet or stone, say) in the gravitational field of a much more massive body $M$ (sun or earth, respectively). The justification for speaking as though the potential energy belongs to the planet or to the stone alone is this: When the potential energy of a system of two bodies changes into kinetic energy, the lighter body gets most of the kinetic energy. The sun is so much more massive than a planet that the sun receives hardly any of the kinetic energy; and the same is true for the earth in the earth-stone system.

We can derive the gravitational force from the potential energy. The relation for spherically symmetric potential energy functions is $F = -dU/dr$; see Eq. 8–7. This relation is the converse of Eq. 16–15. From it we obtain

$$F = -\frac{dU}{dr} = -\frac{d}{dr}\left(-\frac{GMm}{r}\right) = -\frac{GMm}{r^2}. \qquad (16\text{–}16)$$

The minus sign here shows that the force is an attractive one, directed inward along a radius opposite to the radial displacement vector.

We can, if we wish, associate a scalar field with gravitation. We first define the *gravitational potential V* as the *gravitational potential energy per unit mass* of a body in a gravitational field. Then,

$$V = \frac{U(r)}{m} = -\frac{GM}{r} \qquad (16\text{–}17)$$

Associated with every point in the space around a mass $M$ we then have a number, the gravitational potential. This gives us a *scalar field*, potential being a scalar quantity. To determine the force exerted by this field on a mass particle $m$ placed in it, we simply compute $-dV/dr$ at the point in question and multiply by $m$. The force has a magnitude $-m\,dV/dr$ and a direction radially in toward the center of force $M$.

▶ **Example 5.** *Escape velocity.* We can readily find the gravitational potential energy of a particle of mass $m$ at the surface of the earth as (Eq. 16–15) $U(R) = -GM_em/R_e$. The amount of work required to move a body from the surface of the earth to infinity is $GM_em/R_e$, or about $6.0 \times 10^7$ joules/kg. If we could give a projectile more than this energy at the surface of the earth, then, neglecting the resistance of the earth's atmosphere, it would escape from the earth never to return. As it proceeds outward its kinetic energy decreases and its potential energy increases, but its speed is never reduced to zero. The critical initial speed, called the escape speed $v_0$, such that the projectile does not return, is given by

$$\tfrac{1}{2}mv_0{}^2 = \frac{GM_em}{R_e}$$

or

$$v_0 = \sqrt{2\frac{GM_e}{R_e}} = 7.0 \text{ miles/sec } (25{,}000 \text{ miles/hr}) = 11.2 \text{ km/sec}$$

Should a projectile be given this initial speed, it would escape from the earth. For initial speeds less than this the projectile will return. Its kinetic energy becomes zero at some finite distance from the earth and the projectile falls back to earth.*    ◀

The lighter molecules in the earth's upper atmosphere can attain high enough speeds by thermal agitation to escape into outer space. Hydrogen gas, which must have been present in the earth's atmosphere a long time ago, has now disappeared from it. Helium gas escapes at a steady rate, much of it resupplied by radioactive decay from the earth's crust. The escape speed for the sun is much too great to

---

* We have ignored the forces exerted on the projectile by bodies other than the earth. At sufficiently great distances from the earth we must take into account the gravitational forces arising from the moon, the planets, the sun etc., so that we can no longer use the simple "two-body" result. A projectile can escape from the earth by being "captured" by another astronomical body, for example, in such "many-body" cases.

allow hydrogen to escape from its atmosphere. On the other hand, the speed of escape on the moon is so small that it can hardly keep any atmosphere at all. (See Problem 23).

## 16–10 Potential Energy for Many-Particle Systems

If two particles are separated by a distance $r$, their potential energy is given from Eq. 16–14 as

$$U(r) = -W_{\infty r} \qquad (16\text{–}14)$$

in which $W_{\infty r}$ is the work done *by the gravitational force* as the particles move from an infinite separation to separation $r$. We now give another interpretation to $U(r)$.

Let us balance out the gravitational force by an *external force* applied by some external agent and let us arrange it so that, at all times, this external force is equal and opposite to the gravitational force for each particle. The work done by the *external* force as the particles move from an infinite separation to separation $r$ is not $W_{\infty r}$ but $-W_{\infty r}$; this follows because the displacements are the same but the forces are equal and opposite. Thus we may interpret Eq. 16–14 as follows: *The potential energy of a system of particles is equal to the work that must be done by an external agent to assemble the system, starting from the standard reference configuration.*

Thus, if you lift a stone of mass $m$ a distance of $y$ above the earth's surface, you are the external agent (separating earth and stone) and the work you do in "assembling the system" is $+mgy$, which is also the potential energy. Similarly, the work done *by an external agent* as a body of mass $m$ moves in from infinity to a distance $r$ from the earth is *negative* because the agent must exert a restraining force on the body; this is in agreement with Eq. 16–14.

These considerations hold for systems that contain more than two particles. Consider three bodies of masses $m_1$, $m_2$, and $m_3$. Let them initially be infinitely far from one another. The problem is to compute the work done by an external agent to bring them into the positions shown in Fig. 16–13. Let us first bring $m_2$ in toward $m_1$ from an infinite separation to the separation $\mathbf{r}_{12}$. The work done against the gravitational force exerted by $m_1$ on $m_2$ is $-Gm_1m_2/r_{12}$. Now let us bring $m_3$ in from infinity to the separation $\mathbf{r}_{13}$ from $m$ and $\mathbf{r}_{23}$ from $m_2$. The work done against the gravitational force exerted by $m_1$ on $m_3$ is $-Gm_1m_3/r_{13}$ and that against the gravitational force exerted by $m_2$ on $m_3$ is $-Gm_2m_3/r_{23}$. The total work done in assembling this system is the total potential energy of the system

$$-\left(\frac{Gm_1m_2}{r_{12}} + \frac{Gm_1m_3}{r_{13}} + \frac{Gm_2m_3}{r_{23}}\right)$$

Notice that no vector operations are needed in this procedure.

No matter how we assemble the system, that is, regardless of which bodies are moved or which paths are taken, we always find this same amount of work required to being the bodies into the configuration of Fig. 16–13 from an initial infinite separation. The potential energy must, therefore, be associated with the system rather than with any one or two bodies. If we wanted to separate the system into three isolated masses once again, we would have to supply an amount of energy

$$+ \left( \frac{Gm_1m_2}{r_{12}} + \frac{Gm_1m_3}{r_{13}} + \frac{Gm_2m_3}{r_{23}} \right)$$

This energy may be regarded as a sort of binding energy holding the mass particles together in the configuration shown.

Just as we can associate elastic potential energy with the compressed or stretched configuration of a spring holding a mass particle, so we can associate gravitational potential energy with the configuration of a system of mass particles held together by gravitational forces. Similarly, if we want to think of the elastic potential energy of a particle as being stored in the spring, so we can think of the gravitational potential energy as being stored in the gravitational field of the system of particles. A change in either configuration results in a change of potential energy.

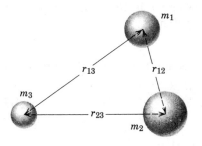

**Fig. 16–13**   Three masses $m_1$, $m_2$, and $m_3$ brought together from infinity.

These concepts occur again when we meet forces of electric or magnetic origin, or, in fact, of nuclear origin. Their application is rather broad in physics. The advantage of the energy method over the dynamical method is derived from the fact that the energy method uses scalar quantities and scalar operations rather than vector quantities and vector operations. When the actual forces are not known, as is often the case in nuclear physics, the energy method is essential.

▶ **Example 6.**   What is the binding energy of the earth-sun system?   Neglect the presence of other planets or satellites.

For simplicity assume that the earth's orbit about the sun is circular at a radius $r_{es}$.   The work done against the gravitational force to bring the earth and sun from an infinite separation to a separation $r_{es}$ is

$$-G \frac{M_s M_e}{r_{es}} \cong -5.0 \times 10^{33} \text{ joules,}$$

where we take $M_s \cong 330,000 M_e$, $M_e = 6.0 \times 10^{24}$ kg, $r_{es} = 150 \times 10^9$ meters. The minus sign indicates that the force is attractive, so that work is done by the gravitational force.   It would take an equivalent amount of work by an outside agent to separate these bodies completely from rest.   Because the kinetic energy of the earth in its orbit is half the magnitude of the potential energy of the earth-sun system, only half of this work is needed to break up the system, so that the effective binding energy, assuming that the earth-sun-system is at rest after breakup, is about $2.5 \times 10^{33}$ joules.

What effect does the presence of the moon and other planets have on the energy binding the earth to the solar system?                                                    ◀

## 16–11   Energy Considerations in the Motions of Planets and Satellites

Consider again the motion of a body of mass $m$ (planet or satellite, say) about a massive body of mass $M$ (sun or earth, say). We shall consider $M$ to be at rest in an inertial reference frame with the body $m$ moving about it in a circular orbit. The potential energy of the system is

$$U(r) = -\frac{GMm}{r},$$

where $r$ is the radius of the circular orbit. The kinetic energy of the system is

$$K = \tfrac{1}{2}m\omega^2 r^2$$

the sun being at rest. From the equation preceding Eq. 16–11 we obtain

$$\omega^2 r^2 = \frac{GM}{r},$$

so that
$$K = \frac{1}{2}\frac{GMm}{r}.$$

The total energy is

$$E = K + U = \frac{1}{2}\frac{GMm}{r} - \frac{GMm}{r} = -\frac{GMm}{2r}. \tag{16–18}$$

This energy is constant and is negative. Now the kinetic energy can never be negative, but from Eq. 16–18 we see that it must go to zero as the separation goes to infinity. The potential energy is always negative, except for its zero value at infinite separation. The meaning of the total negative energy, then, is that the system is a closed one, the planet $m$ always being bound to the attracting solar center $M$ and never escaping from it (Fig. 16–14).

Even when we consider elliptical orbits, in which $r$ and $\omega$ vary, the total energy is negative. It is also constant, corresponding to the fact that gravitational forces are conservative. Hence, both the total energy and the total angular momentum are constant in planetary motion. These quantities are often called *constants of the motion*. We obtain the actual orbit of a planet with respect to the sun by starting with these conservation relations and eliminating the time variable by use of the laws of dynamics and gravitation. The result is that planetary orbits are elliptical.

In the earlier theories of the atom, as in the Bohr theory of the hydrogen

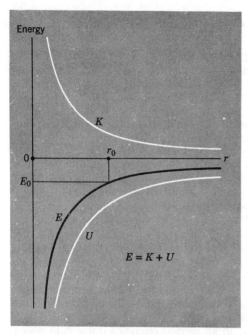

**Fig. 16–14** Kinetic energy $K$, potential energy $U$, and total energy $E = U + K$ of a body in circular planetary motion. A planet with total energy $E_0 < 0$ will remain in an orbit of radius $r_0$. The farther the planet is from the sun, the greater (that is, less negative) its (constant) total energy $E$. To escape from the center of force and still have kinetic energy at infinity, it would need positive total energy.

atom, these identical mechanical relations are used in describing the motion of an electron about an attracting nuclear center. These same relations are used for open orbits (total energy positive) as in the experiments of Rutherford on the scattering of charged nuclear particles. Central forces, and particularly inverse square forces, are encountered often in physical systems.

### 16–12   The Earth as an Inertial Reference Frame

In describing the experiments which were fundamental to our definitions of force and mass, we had to assume some reference frame relative to which accelerations could be measured. If the reference frame itself were erratically accelerated, we would not observe any regularity in our measured accelerations. As a matter of fact, our laboratory experiments are performed in a reference frame which is fixed to the earth. We have already discussed the effect that the rotation of the earth about its own axis has on our measurements. What effect does the motion of the earth as a whole about the sun, or some other cosmic body, have?

The acceleration of the earth with respect to the sun is $\omega^2 r$ or about $6 \times 10^{-3}$ meter/sec$^2$. It would seem at first that this acceleration, small as it is, might prove disturbing in experiments involving small forces. That this is not the case, however, follows from the universality of the law of gravitation. Not only the earth but also the masses we use in our laboratory apparatus are accelerated toward the sun at practically the same rate.

Let us compute the error made in neglecting the earth's orbital acceleration. The acceleration of the earth toward the sun is $k/r^2$ where $r$ is the distance from the center of the sun and the center of the earth and $k$ is $GM_s$. Consider now a body on that side of the earth most distant from the sun. We can imagine that we are weighing it on a spring scale, for example. Then, the part of its acceleration toward the sun which is due to the gravitational attraction of the sun itself is

$$\frac{k}{(r + r_0)^2} = \frac{k}{r^2}\left(1 - \frac{2r_0}{r} + \cdots + \text{much smaller terms}\right),$$

where $r_0$ is the radius of the earth. The *difference* between the acceleration of the earth due to the sun's attraction (that is, $k/r^2$) and the acceleration of the apparatus due to the sun's attraction (the expression above) would be less than $(k/r^2)(2r_0/r)$. But $2r_0/r$ is about $10^{-4}$. The difference, then, would be less than $10^{-4}$ of the earth's acceleration, or less than $10^{-6}$ meter/sec$^2$. The relative acceleration of the body and the earth due to the sun's attraction is about one-tenmillionth as strong as the gravitational acceleration of the body due to the earth. The moon has a similar effect of comparable magnitude on the body. Hence, only if we were measuring to one part in a million would we need to consider seriously the accelerating nature of a reference frame attached to the earth. For almost all practical purposes the earth is good enough as an inertial reference frame.

### 16–13 The Principle of Equivalence

Consider two reference frames: (1) a nonaccelerating (inertial) reference frame $S$ in which there is a uniform gravitational field and (2) a reference frame $S'$ which is accelerating uniformly with respect to an inertial frame but in which there is no gravitational field. In his general theory of relativity, Albert Einstein showed that two such frames are exactly equivalent physically. That is, experiments carried out under the same conditions in these two frames should give the same results. This is the *principle of equivalence*.

Suppose that a space ship is at rest in an inertial reference frame $S$ in which there is a uniform gravitational field, say at the surface of the earth. Inside the spaceship objects, such as an apple, which are released will fall with an acceleration, say $\mathbf{g}$, in the gravitational field; objects which are at rest—such as an astronaut sitting on the floor or a package on a spring scale attached to the ceiling—will experience a force, exerted by the floor or the spring respectively, opposing their weight.

Now suppose that the rockets are turned on and that the spaceship proceeds to a region of outer space where there is no gravitational field. Let the acceleration of the spaceship, our new frame $S'$, be $\mathbf{a} = -\mathbf{g}$ with respect to the inertial reference frame $S$; that is, the ship is accelerating away from the earth beyond the region where the earth's field (or any other gravitational field) is appreciable. The conditions in the spaceship will now be similar to those in a spaceship at rest on the surface of the earth. Inside the ship, if the astronaut releases an apple, it will accelerate downward relative to the spaceship with an acceleration $\mathbf{g}$. In fact, since all bodies that are free of any forces move with uniform velocity relative to the inertial frame $S$, all such bodies appear to fall with the *same* acceleration $\mathbf{g}$ with respect to the spaceship, $S'$. Furthermore, objects which are at rest relative to the spaceship—such as an astronaut sitting on the floor or a package on a spring scale attached to the ceiling—will experience forces indistinguishable from the forces which balanced their weight in the case when the spaceship was at rest in a gravitational field in $S$.

Indeed, if the astronaut did not know that rockets were accelerating his ship from $S$, he would be justified in concluding that he was in a gravitational field—a field whose pull accelerated the falling apple in $S'$ and whose pull required that a balancing force be applied to the package (the tension in the spring) and to the spaceman (the normal force of the floor) to keep them at rest in $S'$. The astronaut simply could not tell the difference, from observations in his own frame, between a situation in which his ship was accelerating relative to an inertial frame in a region having no gravitational field and a situation in which the spaceship was unaccelerated in an inertial frame in which a uniform gravitational field existed. The two situations are exactly equivalent. Einstein pointed out that, from the principle of equivalence, it follows that one cannot speak of the absolute acceleration of a reference frame, only a relative one, just as it followed from the special theory of relativity that one cannot speak of the absolute velocity of a reference frame, only a relative one. It also follows from the principle of equivalence that inertial mass and gravitational mass are equal. For all bodies which are free of any forces will move with uniform velocity relative to an inertial reference frame no matter what their inertial masses are, and they should, therefore, all have the same acceleration relative to an accelerated reference frame. Hence, from the principle of equivalence of $S$ and $S'$, all bodies should fall with the same acceleration in a homogeneous gravitational field.

From the discussion so far we see that a uniform gravitational field can be imitated by a "field of acceleration." Indeed, a uniform gravitational field can be "transformed away" by transforming to a reference frame accelerating in the direction of the field with an acceleration equal in magnitude to that due to the field. In this new frame a particle whose motion was originally subject to a gravitational field is now a free particle. For example, in an artificial earth satellite an apple released by an astronaut will not fall relative to the satellite and the astronaut himself will be free of the forces which countered the pull of gravity before launching, so that he feels weightless. In general, however, gravitational fields, such as that of the earth, are not uniform through all space, so that one cannot replace the gravitational fields throughout space simply by transforming to a single reference frame accelerating with respect to the source of the field. One would need a different accelerated frame at each point in space to imitate the entire gravitational field.

## QUESTIONS

1. If the force of gravity acts on all bodies in proportion to their masses, why doesn't a heavy body fall faster than a light body?

2. Modern observational astronomy and navigation procedures make use of the geocentric (or Ptolemaic) point of view (by using the rotating "celestial sphere"). Is this wrong? If not, then what criterion determines the system (the Copernican or Ptolemaic) we use? When would we use the heliocentric (or Copernican) system?

3. How does the weight of a body vary en route from the earth to the moon? Would its mass change?

4. Would we have more sugar to the pound at the pole or the equator?

5. Does the concentration of the earth's mass near its center change the variation of $g$ with height compared with a homogeneous sphere? How?

6. Because the earth bulges near the equator, the source of the Mississippi River, although high above sea level, is nearer to the center of the earth than is its mouth. How can the river flow "uphill"?

7. The earth is an oblate spheroid because of the "flattening" effect of the earth's rotation. Is a degree of latitude larger or smaller near either pole than near the equator? Why?

8. Why can we learn more about the shape of the earth by studying the motion of an artificial satellite than by studying the motion of the moon?

9. How can one determine the mass of the moon?

10. One clock is based on an oscillating spring, the other on a pendulum. Both are taken to Mars. Will they keep the same time there that they kept on Earth? Will they agree with each other? Explain. Mars has a mass 0.1 that of Earth and a radius half as great.

**11.** From Kepler's second law and observations of the sun's motion as seen from the earth, we can conclude that the earth is closer to the sun during winter in the Northern hemisphere than during summer. Explain.

**12.** Does the law of universal gravitation require the planets of our solar system to have the actual orbits observed? Would planets of another star, similar to our Sun, have the same orbits? Suggest factors that might have determined the special orbits observed.

**13.** The gravitational force exerted by the sun on the Moon is greater than (about twice as great as) the gravitational force exerted by the earth on the moon. Why then doesn't the moon escape from the earth (during a solar eclipse, for example)?

**14.** Explain why the following reasoning is wrong. "The sun attracts all bodies on the earth. At midnight, when the sun is directly below, it pulls on an object in the same direction as the pull on the earth on that object; at noon, when the sun is directly above, it pulls on an object in a direction opposite to the pull of the earth. Hence, all objects should be heavier at midnight (or night) than they are at noon (or day)."

**15.** The gravitational attraction of the sun and the moon on the earth produces tides. The sun's tidal effect is about half as great as that of the moon's. The direct pull of the sun on the earth, however, is about 175 times that of the moon. Why is it then that the moon causes the larger tides?

**16.** If lunar tides slow down the rotation of the earth (owing to friction), the angular momentum of the earth decreases. What happens to the motion of the moon as a consequence of the conservation of angular momentum? Does the sun (and solar tides) play a role here?

**17.** Would you expect the total energy of the solar system to be constant? The total angular momentum? Explain your answers.

**18.** Does a rocket really need the escape speed of 25,000 miles/hr initially to escape from the earth?

**19.** Objects at rest on the earth's surface move in circular paths with a period of 24 hr. Are they "in orbit" in the sense that an earth satellite is in orbit? Why not? What would the length of the "day" have to be to put such objects in true orbit?

**20.** Neglecting air friction and technical difficulties, can a satellite be put into an orbit by being fired from a huge cannon at the earth's surface? Explain.

**21.** Can a satellite move in a stable orbit in a plane not passing through the earth's center? Explain.

**22.** As measured by an observer on earth would there be any difference in the periods of two satellites, each in a circular orbit near the earth in an equatorial plane, but one moving eastward and the other westward?

**23.** After Sputnik I was put into orbit we were told that it would not return to earth but would burn up in its *descent*. Considering the fact that it did not burn up in its *ascent*, how is this possible?

**24.** Show that a satellite may speed down; that is, show that if frictional forces cause a satellite to lose total energy, it will move into an orbit closer to the earth and may have increased kinetic energy.

**25.** An artificial satellite is in a circular orbit about the earth. How will its orbit change if one of its rockets is momentarily fired (*a*) toward the earth, (*b*) away from the earth, (*c*) in a forward direction, (*d*) in a backward direction, (*e*) at right angles to the plane of the orbit?

**26.** Inside a space ship what difficulties would you encounter in walking? In jumping? In drinking?

**27.** If a planet of given density were made larger, its force of attraction for an object on its surface would increase because of the planet's greater mass but would decrease because of the greater distance from the object to the center of the planet. Which effect predominates?

28. Consider a hollow spherical shell. How does the gravitational potential inside compare with that on the surface? What is the gravitational field strength inside?

29. A stone is dropped along the center of a deep vertical mine shaft. Assume no air resistance but consider the earth's rotation. Will the stone continue along the center of the shaft? If not, describe its motion.

30. Can one regard gravity as a "fictitious" force arising from the acceleration of one's reference frame relative to an inertial reference frame, rather than a "real" force?

## PROBLEMS

1. At what altitude above the earth's surface would the acceleration of gravity be about 16 ft/sec²?

2. The distinction between mass and weight drew attention when Jean Richer in 1672 took a pendulum clock from Paris to Cayenne, French Guiana, for use in astronomical observations and found that it lost 2.5 min each day. It was already known from Huygens' work that the period of a pendulum of given length was proportional to $1/\sqrt{g}$. If $g = 980.9$ cm/sec² in Paris, what is $g$ in Cayenne?

3. What is the period of a "seconds pendulum" (period = 2 sec on earth) on the surface of the moon?

4. How far from the earth must a body be along a line toward the sun so that the sun's gravitational pull balances the earth's? The sun is $9.3 \times 10^7$ miles away and its mass is $3.24 \times 10^5 M_e$.

5. A body is suspended on a spring balance in a ship sailing along the equator with a speed $v$. Show that the scale reading will be very close to $W_0(1 \pm 2\omega v/g)$, where $\omega$ is the angular speed of the earth and $W_0$ is the scale reading when the ship is at rest. Explain the plus or minus.

6. A scientist is making a precise measurement of $g$ at a certain point in the Indian Ocean (on the equator) by timing the swings of a pendulum of accurately known construction. To provide a stable base the measurements are conducted in a submerged submarine. It is observed that slightly different result for $g$ is obtained when the submarine is moving eastward through the point than when it is moving westward, the speed in each case being 10 miles/hr. Account for this difference and calculate the effect, in parts per million, that it has on the value of $g$.

7. Masses, assumed equal, hang from strings of different lengths on a balance at the surface of the earth, as shown in Fig. 16–15. If the strings have negligible mass and differ in length by $h$, (a) show that the error in weighing, $W' - W$, is given by $W' - W = 8\pi G\rho mh/3$ and (b) find the difference in length which will give an error of one part in a million. Take mass of each body to be $m$ and the density of the earth, $\rho$, to be 5.5 gm/cm³.

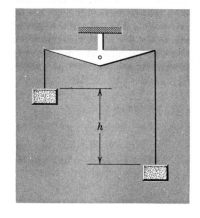

**Fig. 16–15**

8. With what speed would mail pass through the center of the earth if it were delivered by the chute of Example 3?

9. (a) Show that in a chute dug through the earth along any chord line, rather than along a diameter, the motion of an object will be simple harmonic. (b) Find the period

of the motion. (c) Will the object attain the same speed along the chord line as it does along a diameter?

**10.** Consider a mass particle at a point $P$ anywhere inside a spherical shell of matter. Assume the shell is of uniform thickness and density. Construct a narrow double cone with apex at $P$ intercepting areas $A_1$ and $A_2$ on the shell (Fig. 16–16). (a) Show that the resultant gravitational force exerted on the particle at $P$ by the intercepted mass elements is zero. (b) Show then that the resultant gravitational force of the entire shell on an internal particle is zero everywhere.

Fig. 16–16

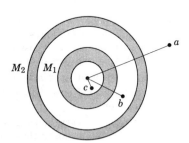

Fig. 16–17

**11.** Two concentric spherical shells of uniform density of mass $M_1$ and $M_2$ are situated as shown in Fig. 16–17. Find the force on a particle of mass $m$ when (a) the particle is located at $r = a$, (b) the particle is located at $r = b$, and (c) the particle is located at $r = c$. The distance $r$ is measured from the center of the shells.

**12.** The following problem is from the 1946 "Olympic" examination of Moscow State University (see Fig. 16–18): A spherical hollow is made in a lead sphere of radius $R$, such that its surface touches the outside surface of the lead sphere and passes through its center. The mass of the sphere before hollowing was $M$. With what force, according to the law of universal gravitation, will the lead sphere attract a small sphere of mass $m$, which lies at a distance $d$ from the center of the lead sphere on the straight line connecting the centers of the spheres and of the hollow?

Fig. 16–18

**13.** (a) With what horizontal speed must a satellite be projected at 100 miles above the surface of the earth so that it will have a circular orbit about the earth? Take the earth's radius as 4000 miles. (b) What will be the period of rotation?

**14.** Use qualitative arguments to explain why the following four periods are equal (all are 84 min): (a) time of revolution of a satellite just above the earth's surface; (b) period of oscillation of mail in a tunnel through the earth; (c) period of simple pendulum having a length equal to the earth's radius in a uniform field 9.8 nt/kg; (d) period of an infinite simple pendulum in the earth's real gravitational field.

**15.** A projectile is fired vertically from the earth's surface with an initial speed of 10 km/sec. Neglecting atmospheric retardation, how far above the surface of the earth would it go? Take the earth's radius as 6400 km.

**16.** Does it take more energy to get a satellite up to 1000 miles above the earth than to put it in orbit there? 2000 miles? 3000 miles? Take the earth's radius to be 4000 miles.

**17.** Two earth satellites, $A$ and $B$, each of mass $m$, are to be launched into (nearly) circular orbits about the earth's center. Satellite $A$ is to orbit at an altitude of 4000 miles. Satellite $B$ is to orbit at an altitude of 12,000 miles. The radius of the earth $R_e$ is 4000 miles (Fig. 16–19). (a) What is the ratio of the potential energy of satellite $B$ to that of satellite $A$, in orbit? (Explain the result in terms of the work required to get each satellite from its orbit to infinity.) (b) What is the ratio of the kinetic energy of satellite $B$ to that of satellite $A$, in orbit? (c) Which satellite has the greater total energy if each has a mass of 1.0 slug? By how much?

**Fig. 16–19**

**18.** (a) Can a satellite be sent out to a distance where it will revolve about the earth with an angular velocity equal to that at which the earth rotates, so that it remains always above the same point on the earth? (b) Must the plane of its orbit be an equatorial plane? (c) What would be the radius of such an orbit?

**19.** Consider two satellites $A$ and $B$ of equal mass $m$, moving in the same circular orbit of radius $r$ around the earth $E$ but in *opposite* senses of rotation and therefore on a collision course (see Fig. 16–20). (a) In terms of $G$, $M_e$, $m$, and $r$, find the total mechan-

**Fig. 16–20**

ical energy $E_A + E_B$ of the two-satellite-plus-earth system before collision. (b) If the collision is completely inelasti: so that wreckage remains as one piece of tangled material (mass $= 2m$), find the total mechanical energy immediately after collision. (c) Describe the subsequent motion of the wreckage.

**20.** A satellite travels initially in an approximately circular orbit 400 miles above the surface of the earth; its mass is 217 kg. (a) Determine its speed. (b) Determine its period. For various reasons the satellite loses mechanical energy at the (average) rate of $1.42 \times 10^5$ joules per complete orbital revolution. Adopting the reasonable approximation that the trajectory is a "circle of slowly diminishing radius," (c) determine the distance from the *surface* of the earth, the speed, and the period of the satellite at the end of its 1500th orbital revolution. (d) What is the average retarding force? (e) Is angular momentum conserved?

**21.** The mean distance of Mars from the sun is 1.524 times that of Earth from the sun. Find the number of years required for Mars to make one revolution about the sun.

**22.** Determine the mass of the earth from the period $T$ and the radius $r$ of the moon's orbit about the earth; $T = 27.3$ days and $r = 2.39 \times 10^5$ miles.

**23.** (a) Show that to escape from the atmosphere of a planet a necessary condition for a molecule is that it have a speed such that $v^2 > 2GM/r$, where $M$ is the mass of the planet and $r$ is the distance of the molecule from the center of the planet. (b) Determine the escape speed from the earth for an atmospheric particle 1000 km above the earth's surface. (c) Do the same for the moon and the sun.

**24.** Mars has a mean diameter of 4200 miles, Earth one of 7900 miles. The mass of Mars is $0.11 M_e$. (a) How does the mean density of Mars compare with that of Earth? (b) What is the value of $g$ on Mars? (c) What is the escape velocity on Mars?

**25.** A pair of stars rotates about a common center of mass. One of the stars has a mass $M$ which is twice as large as the mass $m$ of the other, that is, $M = 2m$. Their centers are a distance $d$ apart, $d$ being large compared to the size of either star. (a) Derive an expression for the period of rotation of the stars about their common center of mass in terms of $d$, $m$, and $G$. (b) Compare the angular momenta of the two stars about their common center of mass by calculating the ratio $L_m/L_M$. (c) Compare the kinetic energies of the two stars by calculating the ratio $K_m/K_M$.

**26.** In a double star, two stars of mass $3 \times 10^{30}$ kg each rotate about their common center of mass, $10^{11}$ meters away. (a) What is their common angular speed? (b) Suppose that a meteorite passes through this center of mass moving at right angles to the line joining the stars. What must its speed be if it is to escape from the gravitational field of the double star?

**27.** Three identical bodies of mass $M$ are located at the vertices of an equilateral triangle with side $L$. At what speed must they move if they all revolve under the influence of one another's gravity in a circular orbit circumscribing the triangle while still preserving the equilateral triangle?

**28.** Two particles of mass $m$ and $M$ are initially at rest an infinite distance apart. Show that at any instant their relative velocity of approach attributable to gravitational attraction is $\sqrt{2G(M + m)/d}$, where $d$ is their separation at that instant.

**29.** A particle of mass $m$ is subject to an attractive central force of magnitude $k/r^2$, $k$ being a constant. If at the instant when the particle is at an extreme position in its closed orbit, at a distance $a$ from the center of force, its speed is $\sqrt{k/2ma}$, find the other extreme position.

**30.** What is the percentage change in the acceleration of the earth toward the sun from a total eclipse of the sun to the point where the moon is on a side of the earth directly opposite the sun?

**31.** An 800-kg mass and a 600-kg mass are separated by 0.25 meter. (a) What is the gravitational field strength due to these masses at a point 0.20 meter from the 800-kg mass and 0.15 meter from the 600-kg mass? (b) What is the gravitational potential at this point due to these same masses?

**32.** Masses of 200 and 800 gm are 12 cm apart. (a) Find the gravitational force on a unit mass at a point on the line joining the masses 4.0 cm from the 200-gm mass. (b) Find the potential energy per unit mass at that point. (c) How much work is needed to move this unit mass to a point 4.0 cm from the 800-gm mass along the line of centers?

**33.** (a) Write an expression for the potential energy of a body of mass $m$ in the gravitational field of the earth and moon. Let $M_e$ be the earth's mass, $M_\mu$ the moon's mass (where $M_e = 81M_\mu$), $R$ the distance from the earth's center, and $r$ the distance from the moon's center. The distance between earth and moon is about 240,000 miles. (b) At what point or points will the gravitational field strength attributable to the earth and moon be zero? (c) What will the potential energy and field strength be for $m$ when it is on the earth's surface? The moon's surface? Are these answers unique?

**34.** A sphere of matter, radius $a$, has a concentric cavity, radius $b$, as shown in cross section in Fig. 16–21. (a) Sketch the gravitational force $F$ exerted by the sphere on a

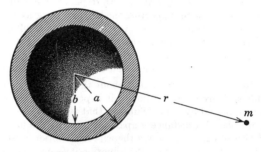

**Fig. 16–21**

particle of mass $m$, located a distance $r$ from the center of the sphere, as a function of $r$ in the range $0 \leq r \leq \infty$. Consider points $r = 0$, $b$, $a$, and $\infty$ in particular. (b) Sketch the corresponding curve for the potential energy $U(r)$ of the system. (c) From these graphs, how would you obtain graphs of the gravitational field strength and the gravitational potential due to the sphere?

**35.** The variation of $g$ in the earth's interior is given in the accompanying table. The earth's radius is 6400 km.

| Depth, km | $g$, meters/sec$^2$ | Depth, km | $g$, meters/sec$^2$ |
|---|---|---|---|
| 0 | 9.82 | 1400 | 9.88 |
| 33 | 9.85 | 1600 | 9.86 |
| 100 | 9.89 | 1800 | 9.85 |
| 200 | 9.92 | 2000 | 9.86 |
| 300 | 9.95 | 2200 | 9.90 |
| 413 | 9.98 | 2400 | 9.98 |
| 600 | 10.01 | 2600 | 10.09 |
| 800 | 9.99 | 2800 | 10.26 |
| 1000 | 9.95 | 2900 | 10.37 |
| 1200 | 9.91 | 4000 | 8.00 |

Within the earth's central core (below 2900 km) the values of $g$ diminish monotonically (not linearly) from 10.37 meters/sec$^2$ to zero. The actual variation of $g$ below 4000 km is uncertain. (a) Plot qualitatively $g$ versus $r$ (where $r$ *is the distance from the earth's center*) from 0 to 6400 km. (b) Explain carefully how the earth's density must vary as we proceed from its surface to its center in order to account for this variation of $g$. (c) Take $\rho = 1$ at the surface (its average value is actually 3.0 gm/cm$^3$), and plot qualitatively $\rho$ versus $r$. Assume throughout that $\rho$ and $g$ are spherically symmetrical.

**36.** In addition to acceleration toward the earth's axis of rotation and toward the sun, a frame of reference attached to the earth is accelerated toward the center of the galaxy. Take the period of the sun's rotation about the galactic center to be 2.5 × 10$^8$ yr and its distance from the center to be 2.4 × 10$^{20}$ meters and compare these three accelerations for a point on the equator.

**37.** *Foucault Pendulum.* A pendulum whose upper end is attached so as to allow the pendulum to swing freely in any direction can be used to repeat an experiment first shown publicly by Foucault in Paris in 1851. If the pendulum is set oscillating, the plane of oscillation slowly rotates with respect to a line drawn on the floor, even though the tension in the wire supporting the bob and the gravitational pull of the earth on the bob lie in a vertical plane. (a) Show that this is a result of the fact that the earth is not an inertial reference frame. (b) Show that for a Foucault pendulum at a latitude angle $\theta$, the period of rotation of the plane is $(24/\sin \theta)$ hr. (c) Explain in simple terms the result at $\theta = 90°$ (the poles) and $\theta = 0°$ (the equator).

**38.** Physicists have speculated about the possible existence of bodies with negative mass; for such hypothetical bodies it is postulated that $m$ in the formulas of physics should be replaced by $-m$. Suppose that two particles, of mass $+m$ and $-m$ respectively, are placed a distance $d$ apart. Show (a) the force acting on each and (b) the acceleration of each. Describe the expected motion, assuming that both particles are initially at rest, and show that this motion does not violate the laws of conservation of linear momentum or of mechanical energy. Such negative-mass particles have not been found.

**39.** (a) Show that the two-body problem of Section 16–7 can be simplified to a one-body problem by use of the reduced mass concept of Section 15–8. That is, show that if we use $\mu = mM/(m + M)$ instead of $m$, we may solve for the motion of $m$ relative to $M$ exactly as though $M$ were the origin of our inertial reference frame. (b) Show that the assumption made in Section 16–7 that $R$ is negligibly small compared to $r$ is equivalent to assuming that the reduced mass $\mu$ is equal to $m$. (c) Compare $\mu$ for the earth-sun system with the earth's mass; compare $\mu$ for the moon-earth system with the moon's mass. (d) If we were to use the reduced mass $\mu$ of the two-body system instead of $m$, how would this affect the equations of Section 16–7?

# Fluid Statics

## CHAPTER 17

## 17–1 Fluids

It is customary to classify matter, viewed macroscopically, into solids
and fluids. A *fluid* is a substance that can *flow*. Hence the term fluid
includes liquids and gases. Such classifications are not always clearcut.
Some fluids, such as glass or pitch, flow so slowly that they behave like
solids for the time intervals that we usually work with them. Plasma,
which is highly ionized gas, does not fit easily into any of these categories;
it is often called a "fourth state of matter" to distinguish it from the solid,
the liquid, and the gaseous state. Even the distinction between a liquid
and a gas is not clearcut because, by changing the pressure and temperature properly, it is possible to change a liquid (water, say) into a gas
(steam, say) without the appearance of a meniscus and without boiling; the
density and viscosity change in a continuous manner throughout the
process.* In this text, however, we will define a fluid as it is ordinarily
understood, and we will be interested only in those properties of fluids
connected with their ability to flow. Therefore, the same basic laws control the static and dynamic behavior of both liquids and gases in spite of
the differences between them that we observe at ordinary pressures.

For solids, which have a definite size and shape, we formulated the
mechanics of rigid bodies, modified by the laws of elasticity for bodies that
cannot be considered perfectly rigid. Since fluids change their shape
readiーy and, in the case of gases, have a volume equal to that of the container in which they are confined, we must develop new techniques for

---

* Pressures higher than the so-called critical point pressure must be employed to do
this; for $H_2O$ the critical point pressure is 218 atmospheres.

solving problems in fluid mechanics.   Our applications of mechanics to continuous media, both solids and fluids, are based on Newton's laws of motion combined with the appropriate force laws.   For fluids, as for solids, however, we find it convenient to develop special formulations of these basic laws.

### 17–2   Pressure and Density

There is a difference in the way a surface force acts on a fluid and on a solid.   For a solid there are no restrictions on the direction of such a force, but for a fluid at rest the surface force must always be directed at right angles to the surface.   For a fluid at rest cannot sustain a tangential force; the fluid layers would simply slide over one another when subjected to such a force.   Indeed, it is the inability of fluids to resist such tangential forces (or shearing stresses) that gives them their characteristic ability to change their shape or to flow.

It is convenient, therefore, to describe the force acting on a fluid by specifying the *pressure p*, which is defined as the magnitude of the *normal* force per unit surface area.   Pressure is transmitted to solid boundaries or across arbitrary sections of fluid *at right angles* to these boundaries or sections at every point.   Pressure is a scalar quantity.   Some common units of pressure are lb/in.$^2$, nt/meter$^2$, dynes/cm$^2$, bars (1 bar $= 10^6$ dynes/cm$^2$), atmospheres (1 atm $= 14.7$ lb/in.$^2$) and mm-Hg (760 mm-Hg $=$ 1 atm).

A fluid under pressure exerts a force on any surface in contact with it. Consider a closed surface containing a fluid (Fig. 17–1).   An element of the surface can be represented by a vector $\Delta\mathbf{S}$ whose magnitude gives the area of the element and whose direction is taken to be the outward normal to the surface of the element.   Then the force $\Delta\mathbf{F}$ exerted by the fluid against this surface element is

$$\Delta\mathbf{F} = p\,\Delta\mathbf{S}.$$

Since $\Delta\mathbf{F}$ and $\Delta\mathbf{S}$ have the same direction, the pressure $p$ can be written as

$$p = \frac{\Delta F}{\Delta S}.$$

**Fig. 17–1**   An element of surface $\Delta S$ can be represented by a vector $\Delta\mathbf{S}$, equal to its area in magnitude and normal to it in direction.

The pressure so defined may depend on the size of the element of area $\Delta S$ that we choose. To avoid this difficulty we refine our definition of pressure by taking a small element of surface containing a point in question and considering this quotient as the element shrinks to the point. Then the pressure at the point is given as

$$p = \lim_{\Delta S \to 0} \frac{\Delta F}{\Delta S}.$$

The pressure may vary from point to point on the surface.

The density $\rho$ of a homogeneous fluid (its mass divided by its volume) may depend on many factors, such as its temperature and the pressure to which it is subjected. For liquids the density varies very little over wide ranges in pressure and temperature, and we can safely treat it as a constant for our present purposes; see entries under *Water* in Table 17–1. The density of a gas, however, is very sensitive to changes in temperature and pressure; see entries under *Air* in Table 17–1. This table shows the range of densities that occur in nature.

**Table 17–1**

DENSITIES OF SOME MATERIALS AND OBJECTS IN KG/METER$^3$

| | |
|---|---|
| Interstellar space | $10^{-18} \times 10^{-21}$ |
| Best laboratory vacuum | $\sim 10^{-16}$ |
| Hydrogen: at 0° C and 1.0 atm | $9.0 \quad \times 10^{-2}$ |
| Air:   at 0° C and 1.0 atm | 1.3 |
|    at 100°C and 1.0 atm | 0.95 |
|    at 0° C and 50 atm | 6.5 |
| Styrofoam | $\sim 1 \quad \times 10^2$ |
| Ice | $0.92 \times 10^3$ |
| Water: at 0° C and 1.0 atm | $1.000 \times 10^3$ |
|    at 100° C and 1.0 atm | $0.958 \times 10^3$ |
|    at 0° C and 50 atm | $1.002 \times 10^3$ |
| Aluminum | $2.7 \quad \times 10^3$ |
| Mercury | $1.36 \times 10^4$ |
| Platinum | $2.14 \times 10^4$ |
| The earth: average density | $5.52 \times 10^3$ |
|    density of core | $9.5 \quad \times 10^3$ |
|    density of crust | $2.8 \quad \times 10^3$ |
| The sun:   average density | $1.4 \quad \times 10^3$ |
|    density at center | $\sim 1.6 \quad \times 10^5$ |
| White dwarf stars (central densities) | $10^8 - 10^{15}$ |
| A uranium nucleus | $\sim 10^{17}$ |

**17–3   The Variation of Pressure in a Fluid at Rest**

If a fluid is in equilibrium, every portion of the fluid is in equilibrium. Let us consider a small element of fluid volume submerged within the body

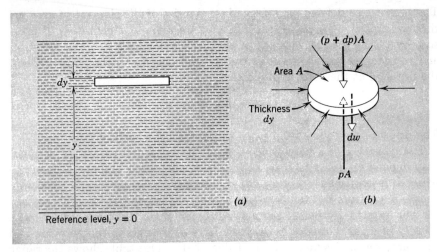

**Fig. 17-2**     (a) A small volume element of fluid at rest.     (b) The forces on the element.

of the fluid. Let this element have the shape of a thin disk and be a distance $y$ above some reference level, as shown in Fig. 17–2$a$. The thickness of the disk is $dy$ and each face has an area $A$. The mass of this element is $\rho A \, dy$ and its weight is $\rho g A \, dy$. The forces exerted on the element by the surrounding fluid are perpendicular to its surface at each point (Fig. 17–2$b$).

The resultant horizontal force is zero, for the element has no horizontal acceleration. The horizontal forces are due only to the pressure of the fluid, and by symmetry the pressure must be the same at all points within a horizontal plane at $y$.

The fluid element is also unaccelerated in the vertical direction, so that the resultant vertical force on it must be zero. However, the vertical forces are due not only to the pressure of the fluid on its faces but also to the weight of the element. If we let $p$ be the pressure on the lower face and $p + dp$ the pressure on its upper face, the upward force is $pA$ (exerted on the lower face) and the downward force is $(p + dp)A$ (exerted on the upper face) plus the weight of the element $dw$. Hence, for vertical equilibrium

$$pA = (p + dp)A + dw$$

$$= (p + dp)A + \rho g A \, dy,$$

and $$\frac{dp}{dy} = -\rho g. \tag{17-1}$$

This equation tells us how the pressure varies with elevation above some reference level in a fluid in static equilibrium. As the elevation increases ($dy$ positive), the pressure decreases ($dp$ negative). The cause of this pressure variation is the weight per unit cross-sectional area of the layers of fluid lying between the points whose pressure difference is being measured.

The quantity $\rho g$ is often called the *weight density* of the fluid; it is the weight per unit volume of the fluid. For water, for example, the weight density is 62.4 lb/ft$^3$.

If $p_1$ is the pressure at elevation $y_1$ and $p_2$ the pressure at elevation $y_2$ above some reference level, integration of Eq. 17–1 gives

$$\int_{p_1}^{p_2} dp = -\int_{y_1}^{y_2} \rho g \, dy$$

or

$$p_2 - p_1 = -\int_{y_1}^{y_2} \rho g \, dy. \qquad (17\text{--}2)$$

For liquids $\rho$ is practically constant because liquids are nearly incompressible; and differences in level are rarely so great that any change in $g$ need be considered. Hence, taking $\rho$ and $g$ as constants, we obtain

$$p_2 - p_1 = -\rho g(y_2 - y_1) \qquad (17\text{--}3)$$

for a homogeneous liquid.

If a liquid has a free surface, this is the natural level from which to measure distances. To change our reference level to the top surface, we take $y_2$ to be the elevation of the surface, at which point the pressure $p_2$ acting on the fluid is usually that exerted by the earth's atmosphere $p_0$. We take $y_1$ to be at any level and we represent the pressure there as $p$. Then,

**Fig. 17–3**    A liquid whose top surface is open to the atmosphere.

$$p_0 - p = -\rho g(y_2 - y_1).$$

But $y_2 - y_1$ is the depth $h$ below the surface at which the pressure is $p$ (see Fig. 17–3), so that

$$p = p_0 + \rho g h. \qquad (17\text{--}4)$$

This shows clearly that the pressure is the same at all points at the same depth.

For gases $\rho$ is comparatively small and the difference in pressure at two points is usually negligible (see Eq. 17–3). Thus, in a vessel containing a gas the pressure can be taken as the same everywhere. However, this is not the case if $y_2 - y_1$ is very great. The pressure of the air varies greatly as we ascend to great heights in the atmosphere. In fact, in such cases the density $\rho$ varies with altitude and $\rho$ must be known as a function of $y$ before we can integrate Eq. 17–2.

▶ **Example 1.**   We can get a reasonable idea of the variation of pressure with altitude in the earth's atmosphere if we assume that the density $\rho$ is proportional to the pressure. This would be very nearly true if the temperature of the air remained the same at all altitudes. Using this assumption, and also assuming that the variation of $g$ with altitude is negligible, find the pressure $p$ at an altitude $y$ above sea level.

From Eq. 17–1 we have

$$\frac{dp}{dy} = -\rho g.$$

Since $\rho$ is proportional to $p$, we have

$$\frac{\rho}{\rho_0} = \frac{p}{p_0},$$

where $\rho_0$ and $p_0$ are the known values of density and pressure at sea level. Then,

$$\frac{dp}{dy} = -g\rho_0 \frac{p}{p_0},$$

so that

$$\frac{dp}{p} = -\frac{g\rho_0}{p_0} dy.$$

Integrating this from the value $p_0$ at the point $y = 0$ (sea level) to the value $p$ at the point $y$ (above sea level), we obtain

$$\ln \frac{p}{p_0} = -\frac{g\rho_0}{p_0} y$$

**Fig. 17–4** Example 1. Variation of pressure with altitude in air and with depth in water. Note that the pressure scales are different for altitude and depth. The solid line for air is calculated on the assumption that the air has a constant temperature and that $g$ does not change with altitude. The dashed line (the U.S. Standard Atmosphere—1962) is a more refined calculation in which these assumptions are not made.

or

$$p = p_0 e^{-g(\rho_0/p_0)y}.$$

However,

$$g = 9.80 \text{ meters/sec}^2, \qquad \rho_0 = 1.20 \text{ kg/meters}^2 \text{ (at 20°C)},$$

$$p_0 = 1.01 \times 10^5 \text{ nt/meter}^2,$$

so that

$$g\,\frac{\rho_0}{p_0} = 1.16 \times 10^{-4} \text{ meter}^{-1} = 0.116 \text{ km}^{-1}.$$

Hence,

$$p = p_0 e^{-ay}.$$

where $a = 0.116 \text{ km}^{-1}$.

We have seen that because liquids are almost imcompressible the lower layers are not noticeably compressed by the weight of the upper layers superimposed on them and the density $\rho$ is practically constant at all levels. For gases at uniform temperature the density $\rho$ of any layer is proportional to the pressure $p$ at that layer. The variation of pressure with distance above the bottom of the fluid for a gas is different from that for a liquid. Figure 17–4 shows the pressure distribution in water and in air.   ◀

Equation 17–3 gives the relation between the pressures at any two points in a fluid, regardless of the shape of the containing vessel. For no matter what the shape of the containing vessel, two points in the fluid can be connected by a path made up of vertical and horizontal steps. For example, consider points $A$ and $B$ in the homogeneous liquid contained in the U-tube of Fig. 17–5a. Along the zigzag path from $A$ to $B$ there is a difference in pressure $\rho g y'$ for each vertical segment of length $y'$, whereas along each horizontal segment there is no change in pressure. Hence, the difference in pressure $p_B - p_A$ is $\rho g$ times the algebraic sum of the vertical segments from $A$ to $B$, or $\rho g(y_2 - y_1)$.

If the U-tube contains different imiscible liquids, say a dense liquid in the right tube and a less dense one in the left tube, as shown in Fig. 17–5b,

**Fig. 17–5** (a) The difference in pressure between two points $A$ and $B$ in a homogeneous liquid depends only on their difference in elevation $y_2 - y_1$. (b) Two points $A$ and $B$ at the same elevation can be at different pressures if the densities there differ.

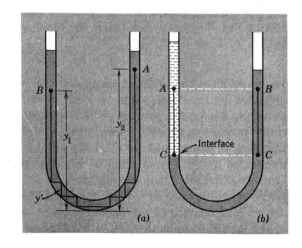

(a)     (b)

the pressure can be different at the same level on different sides. In the figure the liquid surface is higher in the left tube than in the right. The pressure at $A$ will be greater than at $B$. The pressure at $C$ is the same on both sides, but the pressure falls less from $C$ to $A$ than from $C$ to $B$, for a column of liquid of unit cross-sectional area connecting $A$ and $C$ will weigh less than a corresponding column connecting $B$ and $C$.

▶   **Example 2.** A U-tube is partly filled with water. Another liquid, which does not mix with water, is poured into one side until it stands a distance $d$ above the water level on the other side, which has meanwhile risen a distance $l$ (Fig. 17–6). Find the density of the liquid relative to that of water.

In Fig. 17–6 points $C$ are at the same pressure. Hence, the pressure drop from $C$ to each surface is the same, for each surface is at atmospheric pressure.

The pressure drop on the water side is $\rho_w g 2l$; the $2l$ comes from the fact that the water column has risen a distance $l$ on one side and fallen a distance $l$ on the other side, from its initial position. The pressure drop on the other side is $\rho g(d + 2l)$, where $\rho$ is the density of the unknown liquid. Hence,

$$\rho_w g 2l = \rho g(d + 2l)$$

and

$$\frac{\rho}{\rho_w} = \frac{2l}{(2l + d)}.$$

**Fig. 17–6**   Example 2.

The ratio of the density of a substance to the density of water is called the *relative density* (or the *specific gravity*) of that substance. ◀

## 17–4   Pascal's Principle and Archimedes' Principle

Figure 17–7 shows a liquid in a cylinder that is fitted with a piston to which we may apply an external pressure $p_0$. The pressure $p$ at any arbitrary point $P$ a distance $h$ below the upper surface of the liquid is given by Eq. 17–4, or

$$p = p_0 + \rho g h.$$

Let us increase the external pressure by an arbitrary amount $\Delta p_0$ (which need not be small compared to $p_0$). Since liquids are virtually incompressible, the density $\rho$ in the preceding equations remains essentially constant during the process. The equation shows that, to this extent, the change in pressure $\Delta p$ at the arbitrary point $P$ is equal to $\Delta p_0$. This result was stated by the French scientist Blaise Pascal (1623–1662) and is called *Pascal's principle*. It is usually given as follows: Pressure applied to an enclosed fluid is transmitted undiminished to every portion of the fluid and the walls of the containing vessel. This result is a necessary consequence of the laws of fluid mechanics, rather than an independent principle.

Although we often assume liquids to be incompressible, they are, in fact, slightly compressible. This means that a change of pressure applied to one portion of a liquid propagates through the liquid as a wave at the speed of sound in that liquid. Once the disturbance has died out and equilibrium is established, it is found that Pascal's principle is valid. The principle holds for gases with slight complications of interpretation caused by the large volume changes that may occur when the pressure on a confined gas is changed.

Archimedes' principle is also a necessary consequence of the laws of fluid statics. When a body is wholly or partly immersed in a fluid (either a liquid or a gas) at rest, the fluid exerts pressure on every part of the body's surface in contact with the fluid. The pressure is greater on the parts immersed more deeply. The resultant of all the forces is an upward force called the *buoyancy* of the immersed body. We can determine the magnitude and direction of this resultant force quite simply as follows.

The pressure on each part of the surface of the body certainly does not depend on the material the body is made of. Let us suppose, then, that the body, or as much of it as is immersed, is replaced by fluid like the surroundings. This fluid will experience the pressures that acted on the immersed body (Fig. 17–8) and will be at rest. Hence, the resultant upward force on it will equal its weight and will act vertically upward through its center of gravity. From this follows *Archimedes' principle*, namely, that a body wholly or partly immersed in a fluid is buoyed up with a force equal to the weight of the fluid displaced by the body. We have seen that the force acts vertically up through the center of gravity of the fluid before its displacement. The corresponding point in the immersed body is called its *center of buoyancy*.

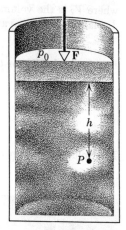

**Fig. 17–7**  A fluid in a cylinder fitted with a movable piston. The pressure at any point $P$ is due not only to the weight of the fluid above the level of $P$ but also to the force exerted by the piston.

▶  **Example 3.**  What fraction of the total volume of an iceberg is exposed?  The density of ice is $\rho_i = 0.92$ gm/cm$^3$ and that of sea water is $\rho_w = 1.03$ gm/cm$^3$.  The weight of the iceberg is

$$W_i = \rho_i V_i g,$$

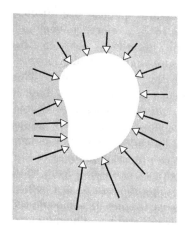

**Fig. 17–8**  Archimedes' principle.

where $V_i$ is the volume of the iceberg; the weight of the volume $V_w$ of sea water displaced is the buoyant force

$$B = \rho_w V_w g.$$

But $B$ equals $W_i$, for the iceberg is in equilibrium, so that

$$\rho_w V_w g = \rho_i V_i g,$$

and
$$\frac{V_w}{V_i} = \frac{\rho_i}{\rho_w} = \frac{0.92}{1.03} = 89\%.$$

The volume of water displaced $V_w$ is the volume of the submerged portion of the iceberg, so that 11% of the iceberg is exposed. ◀

### 17–5 Measurement of Pressure

Evangelista Torricelli (1608–1647) devised a method for measuring the pressure of the atmosphere by his invention of the mercury barometer in 1643. The mercury barometer is a long glass tube that has been filled with mercury and then inverted in a dish of mercury, as in Fig. 17–9. The space above the mercury column contains only mercury vapor whose pressure is so small at ordinary temperatures that it can be neglected. It is easily shown (see Eq. 17–3) that the atmospheric pressure $p_0$ is

$$p_0 = \rho g h.$$

Most pressure gauges use atmospheric pressure as a reference level and measure the difference between the actual pressure and atmospheric pressure, called the *gauge pressure*. The actual pressure at a point in a fluid is called the *absolute pressure*. Gauge

**Fig. 17–9** The Torricelli barometer.

pressure is given either above or below atmospheric pressure. A gauge that reads pressures below atmospheric is usually called a vacuum gauge.

The pressure of the atmosphere at any point is numerically equal to the weight of a column of air of unit cross-sectional area extending from that point to the top of the atmosphere. The atmospheric pressure at a point, therefore, decreases with altitude. There are variations in atmospheric pressure from day to day since the atmosphere is not static. The mercury column in the barometer will have a height of about 76 cm at sea level, varying with the atmospheric pressure. A pressure equivalent to that exerted by exactly 76 cm of mercury at 0°C under standard gravity, $g = 32.174$ ft/sec$^2$ = 980.665 cm/sec$^2$, is called *one atmosphere* (1 atm). The density of mercury at this temperature is 13.5950 gm/cm$^3$. Hence, one atmosphere is equivalent to

$$1 \text{ atm} = (13.5950 \text{ gm/cm}^3)(980.665 \text{ cm/sec}^2)(76.00 \text{ cm})$$

$$= 1.013 \times 10^5 \text{ nt/meter}^2$$

$$= 2116 \text{ lb/ft}^2$$

$$= 14.70 \text{ lb/in.}^2$$

Often pressures are specified by giving the height of mercury column, at 0°C under standard gravity, which exerts the same pressure. This is the origin of the expression "centimeters of mercury (cm-Hg)" or "inches of mercury (in-Hg)" pressure. Pressure is the ratio of force to area, however, and not a length.

Torricelli was Galileo's successor as professor of mathematics at the Accademia in Florence. He described his experiments with the mercury barometer in two letters of 1644 to his friend M. A. Ricci in Rome. In them he says that the aim of his investigation was "not simply to produce a vacuum, but to make an instrument which shows the mutations of the air, now heavier and dense, and now lighter and thin." On hearing of the Italian experiments, Blaise Pascal, in France, reasoned that if the mercury column was held up simply by the pressure of the air, the column ought to be shorter at a high altitude. He tried it on a church steeple in Paris, but desiring more decisive results, he wrote to his brother-in-law to try the experiment on the Puy de Dôme, a high mountain in Auvergne. There was a difference of 3 inches in the height of the mercury, "which ravished us with admiration and astonishment." Pascal himself constructed a barometer using red wine and a glass tube 46 feet long.

The chief significance of these experiments at the time was the realization it brought that an evacuated space could be created. Aristotle believed that a vacuum could not exist, and as late a writer as Descartes held the same view. For two thousand years philosophers spoke of the horror that nature had for empty space—the *horror vacui*. Because of this horror nature was said to prevent the formation of a vacuum by laying hold of anything nearby and with it instantly filling up any vacuated space. Hence, the mercury or wine should fill up the inverted tube because "nature abhorred a vacuum." The experiments of Torricelli and Pascal showed that there were limitations to nature's ability to prevent a vacuum. They created a sensation at the time. The goal of producing a vacuum became more of a practical reality through the development of pumps by Otto von Guericke in Germany around 1650 and by Robert Boyle in England around 1660. Even though these pumps were relatively crude, they did provide a tool for experimentation. With a pump and a glass jar, an experimental space could be provided in which to study the properties of heat, light, sound, and later electricity and magnetism, are affected by an increasingly rarefied atmosphere. Although even today we cannot completely remove every trace of gas from a closed vessel, these seventeenth-century experimenters freed science from the bugaboo of *horror vacui* and spurred efforts to create highly evacuated systems.

Except for the telescope, no scientific discovery of the seventeenth century excited wonder and curiosity to a greater degree than did the experiments with the barometer and the air pump.

$p_2 = p_0$

$h = y_2 - y_1$

$y_2$

$p_1 = p$

To tank

$y_1$

**Fig. 17–10**  The open-tube manometer, as used to measure the pressure in a tank.

The open-tube manometer (Fig. 17–10) measures gauge pressure. It consists of a U-shaped tube containing a liquid, one end of the tube being open to the atmosphere and the other end being connected to the system (tank) whose pressure $p$ we want to measure. From Eq. 17–4 we obtain

$$p - p_0 = \rho gh.$$

Thus the gauge pressure, $p - p_0$, is proportional to the difference in height of the liquid columns in the U-tube. If the vessel contains gas under high pressure, a dense liquid like mercury is used in the tube; water can be used when low gas pressures are involved.

▶ **Example 4.**  An open-tube mercury manometer (Fig. 17–10) is connected to a gas tank. The mercury is 39.0 cm higher on the right side than on the left when a barometer nearby reads 75.0 cm-Hg. What is the absolute pressure of the gas? Express the answer in cm-Hg, atm, and lb/in.$^2$.

The gas pressure is the pressure at the top of the left mercury column. This is the same as the pressure at the same horizontal level in the right column. The pressure at this level is the atmospheric pressure (75.0 cm-Hg) plus the pressure exerted by the extra 39.0-cm column of Hg, or (assuming standard values of mercury density and gravity) a total of 114 cm-Hg. Therefore, the absolute pressure of the gas is

$$114 \text{ cm-Hg} = \tfrac{114}{76} \text{ atm} = 1.50 \text{ atm} = (1.50)(14.7) \text{ lb/in.}^2$$

$$= 22.1 \text{ lb/in.}^2.$$

What is the gauge pressure of the gas?    ◀

## QUESTIONS

**1.**  (a) Two bodies (for example, balls) have the same shape and size but one is denser than the other. Assuming the air resistance to be the same on each, show that when they are released simultaneously from the same height the heavier body will get to the ground first.  (b) Two bodies (for example, raindrops) have the same shape and density but one is larger than the other. Assuming the air resistance to be proportional to the body's speed through the air, which body will fall faster?

**2.**  Water is poured to the same level in each of the three vessels shown, all of the same base area (Fig. 17–11). If the pressure is the same at the bottom of each vessel, the force experienced by the base of each vessel is the same. Why then do the three vessels have different weights when put on a scale? This apparently contradictory result is commonly known as the "hydrostatic paradox."

**Fig. 17–11**

**3.** Can a mountain climber climb high enough so that the atmospheric pressure is reduced to one-half of its sea-level value?

**4.** (a) An ice cube is floating in a glass of water. When the ice melts, will the water level rise? Explain. (b) If the ice cube contains a piece of lead, the water level will fall when the ice melts. Explain.

**5.** Does Archimedes' law hold in a vessel in free fall? In a satellite moving in a circular orbit? Explain.

**6.** A spherical bob made of cork floats half submerged in a pot of tea at rest on the earth. Will the cork float or sink aboard a spaceship coasting in free space? On the surface of Jupiter?

**7.** Two bodies of equal weight and volume and having the same shape, except that one has an opening at the bottom and the other is sealed, are immersed to the same depth in water. Is less work required to immerse one than the other? If so, which one and why?

**8.** A ball floats on the surface of water in a container exposed to the atmosphere. Will the ball remain immersed at its former depth or will it sink or rise somewhat if (a) the container is covered and the air is removed, (b) the container is covered and the air is compressed?

**9.** Explain why an inflated balloon will rise to a definite height once it starts to rise, whereas a submarine will always sink to the bottom of the ocean once it starts to sink, if no changes are made. How then can a submarine stay at a definite level under the water?

**10.** A soft plastic bag weighs the same when empty as when filled with air at atmospheric pressure. Why? Would the weights be the same if measured in a vacuum?

**11.** A leaky tramp steamer that is barely able to float in the North Sea steams up the Thames estuary toward the London docks. It sinks before it arrives. Why?

**12.** Is it true that a floating object will only be in stable equilibrium if its center of buoyancy lies above its center of gravity? Illustrate with examples.

**13.** Very öften a sinking ship will turn over as it becomes immersed in water. Why?

**14.** A barge filled with scrap iron is in a canal lock. If the iron is thrown overboard, what happens to the water level in the lock?

**15.** A bucket of water is suspended from a spring balance. Does the balance reading change when a piece of iron suspended from a string is immersed in the water? When a piece of cork is put in the water?

**16.** Explain why a uniform wooden stick which will float horizontally if it is not loaded will float vertically if enough weight is added to one end. See Problem 8.

**17.** A solid cylinder is placed in a container in contact with the base. When liquid is poured into the container, none of it goes beneath the solid, which remains closely in contact with the base. Is there a buoyant force on the solid? Explain.

**18.** Estimate with some care the buoyant force exerted by the atmosphere on you.

**19.** An open-tube manometer has one tube twice the diameter of the other. Explain how this would affect the operation of the manometer. Does it matter which end is connected to the chamber whose pressure is to be measured?

**20.** An open bucket of water is on a smooth plane inclined at an angle $\alpha$ to the horizontal. Find the equilibrium inclination to the horizontal of the free surface of the water when (a) the bucket is held at rest, $a = 0$ and $v = 0$; (b) the bucket is allowed to slide down at constant speed, $a = 0$, $v = $ constant; (c) the bucket slides down without restraint, $a = $ constant. If the plane is curved so that $a \neq $ constant, what will happen?

**21.** If a U-tube containing water is rotated about a vertical axis through the center of one limb, the water level will fall in one limb and rise in the other compared to the rest position. Explain carefully. See Problem 22.

**22.** Explain how it can be that pressure is a scalar quantity when forces, which are vectors, can be produced by the action of pressures.

## PROBLEMS

**1.** (a) Find the pressure, in lb/in.$^2$, 500 ft below the surface of the ocean. The relative density of sea water is 1.03. (b) Find the pressure in the atmosphere 10 miles above sea level.

**2.** A simple U-tube contains mercury. When 13.6 cm of water is poured into the right arm, how high does the mercury rise in the left arm from its initial level?

**3.** In 1654 Otto von Guericke, burgomeister of Magdeburg and inventor of the air pump, gave a demonstration before the Imperial Diet in which two teams of eight horses could not pull apart two evacuated brass hemispheres. (a) Show that the force $F$ required to pull apart the hemispheres is $F = \pi R^2 P$ where $R$ is the (outside) radius of the hemispheres and $P$ is the difference in pressure outside and inside the sphere (Fig. 17–12). (b) Taking $R$ equal to 1 ft and the inside pressure as 0.1 atm, what force would the team of horses have had to exert to pull apart the hemispheres? (c) Why were two teams of horses used? Would not one team prove the point just as well?

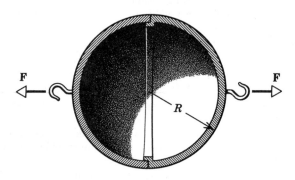

**Fig. 17–12**

**4.** The height at which the pressure in the atmosphere is just $1/e$ that at sea level is called the *scale height* of the atmosphere at sea level.  (a) Show that the scale height $H$ at sea level is also the height of an atmosphere that has the same density everywhere as at sea level and that will exert the same pressure at sea level as the actual infinite atmosphere does.  (b) Show that the scale height at sea level is 8.6 km.

**5.** Water stands at a depth $D$ behind the vertical upstream face of a dam, as shown in Fig. 17-13.  Let $W$ be the width of the dam.  (a) Find the resultant force exerted on

**Fig. 17–13**

the dam by the water and the torque exerted about $O$ by this force.  (b) What is the line of action of the equivalent resultant force?

**6.** A swimming pool has the dimensions 80 ft $\times$ 30 ft $\times$ 8.0 ft.  When it is filled with water, what is the force on the bottom?  On the ends?  On the sides?

**7.** A U-tube is filled with a single homogeneous liquid.  The liquid is temporarily depressed in one side by a piston.  The piston is removed and the level of the liquid in each side oscillates.  Show that the period of oscillation is $\pi \sqrt{2L/g}$ where $L$ is the total length of the liquid in the tube.

**8.** A cylindrical wooden rod is loaded with lead at one end so that it floats upright in water as in Fig. 17–14. The length of the submerged portion is $l = 8.0$ ft.  The rod is set into vertical oscillation.  (a) Show that the oscillation is simple harmonic.  (b) Find the period in seconds of the oscillation.  Neglect the fact that the water has a damping effect on the motion.

**Fig. 17–14**

**9.** Two identical cylindrical vessels with their bases at the same level each contain a liquid of density $\rho$. The area of either base is $A$, but in one vessel the liquid height is $h_1$ and in the other $h_2$.  Find the work done by gravity in equalizing the levels when the two vessels are connected.

**10.** The surface of contact of two fluids of different densities that are at rest and do not mix is horizontal.  Prove this general result (a) from the fact that the potential energy of a system must be a minimum in stable equilibrium; (b) from the fact that at any two points in a horizontal plane in either fluid the pressures are equal.

**11.** A piston of small cross-sectional area $a$ is used in the hydraulic press to exert a small force $f$ on the enclosed liquid.  A connecting pipe leads to a larger piston of cross-sectional area $A$ (Fig. 17–15). (a) What force $F$ will the larger piston sustain? (b) If the small piston has a diameter of 1.5 in. and the large piston one of 21 in., what weight on the small piston will support 2.0 tons on the large piston?

**Fig. 17–15**

12. What is the minimum area of a block of ice 1.0 ft thick floating on water that will hold up an automobile weighing 2500 lb? Does it matter where the car is placed on the block of ice?

13. An iron casting weighs 60 lb in air and 40 lb in water. What is the volume of cavities in the casting?

14. A hollow spherical iron shell floats almost completely submerged in water. If the outer diameter is 2.0 ft and the relative density of iron is 7.8, find the inner diameter.

15. A block of wood floats in water with two-thirds of its volume submerged. In oil it has 0.90 of its volume submerged. Find the density of the wood and the oil.

16. A block of wood weighs 8.0 lb and has a relative density of 0.60. It is to be loaded with lead so that it will float in water with 0.90 of its volume immersed. What weight of lead is needed (a) if the lead is on top of the wood? (b) if the lead is attached below the wood?

17. A cube floating on mercury has one-fourth of its volume submerged. If enough water is added to cover the cube, what fraction of its volume will remain immersed in mercury? Does the answer depend on the shape of the body?

18. A long uniform wooden bar with square cross section floats on water. Show that (a) if the relative density of the wood is 0.50, the bar will float with all four faces making an angle of 45° with the water surface but (b) if the relative density of the wood is 0.20 or 0.80, the bar will float with two faces parallel to the water surface. (*Hint:* The bar floats in the equilibrium position for which the potential energy is a minimum.)

19. Assume the density of brass weights to be 8.0 gm/cm$^3$ and that of air to be 0.0012 gm/cm$^3$. What per cent error arises from neglecting the buoyancy of air in weighing an object of mass $m$ gm and relative density $\rho$ on a beam balance?

20. (a) Consider a container of fluid subject to a *vertical upward* acceleration $a$. Show that the pressure variation with depth in the fluid is given by

$$p = \rho h(g + a),$$

where $h$ is the depth and $\rho$ is the density. (b) Show also that if the fluid as a whole undergoes a *vertical downward* acceleration $a$, the pressure at a depth $h$ is given by

$$p = \rho h(g - a).$$

(c) What is the state of affairs in free fall?

21. (a) Consider the horizontal acceleration of a mass of liquid in an open tank. Acceleration of this kind causes the liquid surface to drop at the front of the tank and to rise at the rear. Show that the liquid surface slopes at an angle $\theta$ with the horizontal, where $\tan \theta = a/g$, $a$ being the horizontal acceleration. (b) How does the pressure vary with depth?

22. (a) A fluid mass is rotating at constant angular velocity $\omega$ about the central vertical axis of a cylindrical container. Show that the variation of pressure in the radial direction is given by

$$\frac{dp}{dr} = \rho\omega^2 r.$$

(b) Take $p = p_c$ at the axis of rotation ($r = 0$) and show that the pressure $p$ at any point $r$ is

$$p = p_c + \tfrac{1}{2}\rho\omega^2 r^2.$$

(c) Show that the liquid surface is of paraboloidal form (Fig. 17–16); that is, a vertical cross section of the surface is the curve $y = \omega^2 r^2/2g$. (d) Show that the variation of pressure with depth is $dp = \rho g \, dh$.

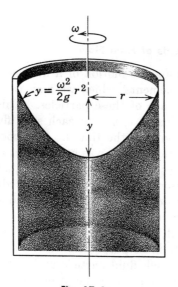

Fig. 17–16

# Fluid Dynamics

## CHAPTER 18

## 18-1 General Concepts of Fluid Flow

One way of describing the motion of a fluid is to divide the fluid into infinitesimal volume elements, which we may call fluid particles, and to follow the motion of each of these particles. This is a formidable task. We would give coordinates $x$, $y$, $z$ to each such fluid particle and would specify these as functions of the time $t$. The coordinates $x$, $y$, $z$ at the time $t$ of the fluid particle which was at $x_0$, $y_0$, $z_0$ at the time $t_0$ would be determined by functions $x(x_0,y_0,z_0,t_0,t)$, $y(x_0,y_0,z_0,t_0,t)$, $z(x_0,y_0,z_0,t_0,t)$, which then describe the motion of the fluid. This procedure is a direct generalization of the concepts of particle mechanics and was first developed by Joseph Louis Lagrange (1736–1813).

There is a treatment, developed by Leonhard Euler (1707–1783), which is more convenient for most purposes. In it we give up the attempt to specify the history of each fluid particle and instead specify the density and the velocity of the fluid at each point in space at each instant of time. This is the method we shall follow here. We describe the motion of the fluid by specifying the density $\rho(x,y,z,t)$ and the velocity $\mathbf{v}(x,y,z,t)$ at the point $(x,y,z)$ at the time $t$. We thus focus our attention on what is happening at a particular point in space at a particular time, rather than on what is happening to a particular fluid particle. Any quantity used in describing the state of the fluid, for example the pressure $p$, will have a definite value at each point in space and at each instant of time. Although this description of fluid motion focuses attention on a point in space rather than on a fluid particle, we cannot avoid following the fluid particles themselves, at least for short time intervals $dt$. For it is the particles, after all, and not the space points, to which the laws of mechanics apply.

In order to understand the nature of the simplifications we shall make, let us consider first some general characteristics of fluid flow.

Fluid flow can be *steady* or *nonsteady*. When the fluid velocity **v** at any given point is constant in time, the fluid motion is said to be steady. That is, at any given point in a steady flow the velocity of each passing fluid particle is always the same. At some other point a particle may travel with a different velocity, but every other particle which passes this second point behaves there just as this particle did when it passed this point. These conditions can be achieved at low flow speeds; a gently flowing stream is an example. In nonsteady flow, as in a tidal bore, the velocities **v** *are* a function of the time. In the case of turbulent flow, such as rapids or a waterfall, the velocities vary erratically from point to point as well as from time to time.

Fluid flow can be *rotational* or *irrotational*. If the element of fluid at each point has no net angular velocity about that point, the fluid flow is irrotational. We can imagine a small paddle wheel immersed in the moving fluid (Fig. 18–1). If the wheel moves without rotating, the motion is irrotational; otherwise it is rotational. Irrotational flow is important chiefly because it yields fairly simple mathematical problems.

**Fig. 18–1** A small paddle wheel placed in a flowing liquid rotates in rotational flow and does not rotate in irrotational flow.

Angular momentum will play no role here and **v** is relatively simple. Rotational flow includes vortex motion, such as whirlpools or eddies, and motion in which the velocity vector varies in the transverse direction.

Fluid flow can be *compressible* or *incompressible*. Liquids can usually be considered as flowing incompressibly. But even a highly compressible gas may sometimes undergo unimportant changes in density. Its flow is then practically incompressible. In flight at speeds much lower than the speed of sound in air (described by subsonic aerodynamics), the motion of the air relative to the wings is one of nearly incompressible flow. In such cases the density $\rho$ is a constant, independent of $x$, $y$, $z$, and $t$, and the mathematical treatment of fluid flow is thereby greatly simplified.

Finally, fluid flow can be *viscous* or *nonviscous*. Viscosity in fluid motion is the analog of friction in the motion of solids. In many cases, such as in lubrication problems, it is extremely important. Sometimes, however, it is negligible. Viscosity introduces tangential forces between layers of fluid in relative motion and results in dissipation of mechanical energy.

We shall confine our discussion of fluid dynamics for the most part to *steady, irrotational, incompressible, nonviscous* flow. The mathematical simplifications resulting should be obvious. We run the danger, however, of making so many simplifying assumptions that we are no longer talking about a meaningfully real fluid.* Furthermore, it is sometimes difficult to decide whether a given property of a fluid—its viscosity, say—can be neglected in a particular situation. In spite of all this the restricted analysis that we are going to give has wide application in practice, as we shall see.

## 18–2 Streamlines

In steady flow the velocity **v** at a given point is constant in time. Consider the point $P$ (Fig. 18–2) within the fluid. Since **v** at $P$ does not change in time, every particle arriving at $P$ will pass on with the same speed in the same direction. The same is true about the points $Q$ and $R$. Hence, if we trace out the path of the particle, as is done in the figure, that curve will be the path of every particle arriving at $P$. This curve is called a *streamline*. A streamline is parallel to the velocity of the fluid particles at every point. No two streamlines can ever cross one another, for if they did, an oncoming fluid particle could go either one way or the other, and the flow could not be steady. In steady flow the pattern of streamlines in a flow is stationary with time.†

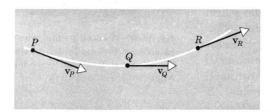

**Fig. 18–2** A particle passing through points $P$, $Q$, and $R$ traces out a streamline, assuming steady flow. Any other particle passing through $P$ must be traveling along the same streamline in steady flow.

In principle we can draw a streamline through every point in the fluid. Let us assume steady flow and select a finite number of streamlines to form a bundle, like the streamline pattern of Fig. 18–3. This tubular region is called a *tube of flow*. The boundary of such a tube consists of streamlines and is always parallel to the velocity of the fluid particles. Hence, *no fluid can cross the boundaries of a tube of flow* and the tube behaves somewhat like a pipe of the same shape. The fluid that enters at one end must leave at the other.

---

* Richard Feynman has pointed out that the late John von Neuman called this idealized fluid "dry water."

† The family of streamlines in a fluid is so drawn that, at any point in the fluid, the direction of the instantaneous velocity **v** for the fluid particle at that point is tangent to the streamline at that point. In nonsteady flow the pattern of streamlines in the fluid changes as time goes on and the path of an individual fluid particle through the fluid does not coincide with a streamline of a given instant. The streamline and the line of motion of the particle touch each other at the point, locating the particle at the instant in question. The path or line of motion and the streamline coincide only for steady flow.

**Fig. 18–3**   A tube of flow made up of a bundle of streamlines.

## 18–3   The Equation of Continuity

In Fig. 18–4 we have drawn a thin tube of flow.  The velocity of the fluid inside, although parallel to the tube at any point, may have different magnitudes at different points.  Let the speed be $v_1$ for fluid particles at $P$ and $v_2$ for fluid particles at $Q$.  Let $A_1$ and $A_2$ be the cross-sectional areas of the tubes perpendicular to the streamlines at the points $P$ and $Q$, respectively.  In the time interval $\Delta t$ a fluid element travels approximately the distance $v\,\Delta t$.  Then the mass of fluid $\Delta m_1$ crossing $A_1$ in the time interval $\Delta t$ is approximately

$$\Delta m_1 = \rho_1 A_1 v_1\,\Delta t$$

or the *mass flux* $\Delta m_1 / \Delta t$ is approximately $\rho_1 A_1 v_1$.  We must take $\Delta t$ small enough so that in this time interval neither $v$ nor $A$ varies appreciably over the distance the fluid travels.  In the limit as $\Delta t \to 0$, we obtain the precise definitions:

$$\text{mass flux at } P = \rho_1 A_1 v_1, \quad \text{and}$$

$$\text{mass flux at } Q = \rho_2 A_2 v_2,$$

where $\rho_1$ and $\rho_2$ are the fluid densities at $P$ and $Q$ respectively.  Since no fluid can leave through the walls of the tube and there are no "sources" or "sinks" wherein fluid can be created or destroyed in the tube, the mass crossing each section of the tube per unit time must be the same.  In par-

**Fig. 18–4**   A tube of flow used in proving the equation of continuity.

ticular, the mass flux at $P$ must equal that at $Q$:

$$\rho_1 A_1 v_1 = \rho_2 A_2 v_2,$$

or $\qquad\qquad\qquad \rho A v = \text{constant}.$ $\qquad\qquad\qquad$ (18-1)

This result (Eq. 18-1) expresses the law of conservation of mass in fluid dynamics.

Would you expect Eq. 18-1 to hold when the flow is viscous? When it is rotational?

In the more general case in which sources or sinks are present and in which the density varies with time as well as position, mass must still be conserved and we can write down (without proof) an *equation of continuity* that expresses this fact. It is

$$\frac{\partial(\rho v_x)}{\partial x} + \frac{\partial(\rho v_y)}{\partial y} + \frac{\partial(\rho v_z)}{\partial z} + \frac{\partial \rho}{\partial t} = S \qquad\qquad (18\text{-}2)$$

in which $v_x$, $v_y$, and $v_z$ are the velocity components of the fluid; like the density $\rho$ they vary both with position and with time.*

Let us consider a small volume element in such a fluid. It can be shown that:

1. The sum of the first three terms of Eq. 18-2 gives the net outflow, per unit volume, of mass from the volume element.

2. The fourth term gives the rate, per unit volume, at which mass is accumulating within the volume element.

3. The last term, $S$, gives the rate, per unit volume, at which mass is being introduced into volume element from a "source" (if $S$ is positive) or is disappearing from the volume element into a "sink" (if $S$ is negative).

It is clear that, with these interpretations of its terms, Eq. 18-2 is a statement of the conservation of mass for fluid flow. Is this equation dimensionally correct? If $S = 0$ in Eq. 18-2, there are no sources or sinks. If the sum of the first three terms is negative there is a net *inflow* of mass to the volume element. Thus the mass contained in the element must increase with time as fluid "piles up." This is in agreement with Eq. 18-2 because, for the conditions stated, $\partial\rho/\partial t$ must be positive, which means that the density of the fluid (and thus the mass of the fluid) in the volume element is increasing as time goes on.

If the fluid is incompressible, as we shall henceforth assume, then $\rho_1 = \rho_2$ and Eq. 18-1 takes on the simpler form

$$A_1 v_1 = A_2 v_2.$$

or $\qquad\qquad\qquad A v = \text{constant}$ $\qquad\qquad\qquad$ (18-3)

The product $Av$ gives the *volume flux* or flow rate, as it is often called. Notice that it predicts that in steady incompressible flow the speed of flow varies inversely with the cross-sectional area, being larger in narrower parts of the tube. The fact that the product $Av$ remains constant along

---

* Because these four quantities are functions of more than one variable we have written the derivatives in Eq. 18-2 as partial derivatives. See, for example, *Physical Mechanics*, Section 12.3, by R. B. Lindsay, D. Van Nostrand Company, 1961, for a derivation of Eq. 18-2.

a tube of flow allows us to interpret the streamline picture somewhat.   In a narrow part of the tube the streamlines must crowd closer together than in a wide part.   Hence, as the distance between streamlines decreases, the fluid speed must increase.   Therefore, we conclude that widely spaced streamlines indicate regions of low speed, and closely spaced streamlines indicate regions of high speed.

We can obtain another interesting result by applying the second law of motion to the flow of fluid between $P$ and $Q$ (Fig. 18-4).   A fluid particle at $P$ with speed $v_1$ must be decelerated in the forward direction in acquiring the smaller forward speed $v_2$ at $Q$.   Hence the fluid is decelerated in going from $P$ to $Q$.   The deceleration can come about from a difference in pressure acting on the fluid particle flowing from $P$ to $Q$ or from the action of gravity.   In a horizontal tube of flow the gravitational force does not change.   Hence we can conclude that in steady horizontal flow the pressure is greatest where the speed is least.

Were you ever in a crowd when it started to push its way through a small opened door?   Outside in the back of the crowd the cross-sectional area was large, the pressure was great, but the speed of advance rather small. Through the door of small cross section the pressure was relieved and the speed of advance gratifyingly increased.   This particular "human fluid" is compressible and viscous, of course, and the flow is sometimes turbulent and rotational.

### 18-4  Bernoulli's Equation

Bernoulli's equation is a fundamental relation in fluid mechanics.   Like all equations in fluid mechanics it is not a new principle but is derivable from the basic laws of Newtonian mechanics.   We will find it convenient to derive it from the work-energy theorem (see Section 7-4), for it is essentially a statement of the work-energy theorem for fluid flow.

Consider the nonviscous, steady, incompressible flow of a fluid through the pipeline or tube of flow in Fig. 18-5.   The portion of pipe shown in the figure has a uniform cross section $A_1$ at the left.   It is horizontal there at an elevation $y_1$ above some reference level.   It gradually widens and rises and at the right has a uniform cross section $A_2$.   It is horizontal there at an elevation $y_2$.   Let us concentrate our attention on the portion of fluid represented by both cross-shading and horizontal shading and call this fluid the "system."   Consider then the motion of the system from the position shown in (a) to that in (b).   At all points in the narrow part of the pipe the pressure is $p_1$ and the speed $v_1$; at all points in the wide portion the pressure is $p_2$ and the speed $v_2$.

The work-energy theorem (see Eq. 7-14) states: *The work done by the resultant force acting on a system is equal to the change in kinetic energy of the system.*   In Fig. 18-5 the forces that do work on the system, assuming that we can neglect viscous forces, are the pressure forces $p_1A_1$ and $p_2A_2$ that act on the left- and right-hand ends of the system, respectively, and the force of gravity.   As fluid flows through the pipe the net effect, as a

**Fig. 18–5** A portion of fluid (cross-shading *and* horizontal shading) moves through a section of pipeline from the position shown in (*a*) to that shown in (*b*).

comparison of Figs. 18–5*a* and *b* shows, is to raise an amount of fluid represented by the crosshatched area in Fig. 18–5*a* to the position shown in Fig. 18–5*b*. The amount of fluid represented by the horizontal shading is unchanged by the flow.

We can find the work $W$ done on the system by the resultant force as follows:

1. The work done on the system by the pressure force $p_1 A_1$ is $p_1 A_1 \, \Delta l_1$.

2. The work done on the system by the pressure force $p_2 A_2$ is $-p_2 A_2 \, \Delta l_2$. Note that it is negative, which means that positive work is done *by* the system.

3. The work done on the system by gravity is associated with lifting the crosshatched fluid from height $y_1$ to height $y_2$ and is $-mg(y_2 - y_1)$ in which $m$ is the mass of fluid in either crosshatched area. It too is negative because work is done by the system *against* the gravitational force.

The work $W$ done *on* the system by the *resultant* force is found by adding these three terms, or

$$W = p_1 A_1 \, \Delta l_1 - p_2 A_2 \, \Delta l_2 - mg(y_2 - y_1).$$

Now $A_1 \, \Delta l_1 (= A_2 \, \Delta l_2)$ is the volume of the crosshatched fluid element, which we can write as $m/\rho$, in which $\rho$ is the (constant) fluid density.

Recall that the two fluid elements have the same mass, so that in setting $A_1 \Delta l_1 = A_2 \Delta l_2$ we have assumed the fluid to be incompressible. With this assumption we have

$$W = (p_1 - p_2)(m/\rho) - mg(y_2 - y_1). \qquad (18\text{--}4a)$$

The change in kinetic energy of the fluid element is

$$\Delta K = \tfrac{1}{2}mv_2{}^2 - \tfrac{1}{2}mv_1{}^2. \qquad (18\text{--}4b)$$

From the work-energy theorem (Eq. 7–14) we then have

$$W = \Delta K$$

or $\qquad (p_1 - p_2)(m/\rho) - mg(y_2 - y_1) = \tfrac{1}{2}mv_2{}^2 - \tfrac{1}{2}mv_1{}^2, \qquad (18\text{--}5a)$

which can be rearranged to read

$$p_1 + \tfrac{1}{2}\rho v_1{}^2 + \rho g y_1 = p_2 + \tfrac{1}{2}\rho v_2{}^2 + \rho g y_2. \qquad (18\text{--}5b)$$

Since the subscripts 1 and 2 refer to *any* two locations along the pipeline, we can drop the subscripts and write

$$p + \tfrac{1}{2}\rho v^2 + \rho g y = \text{constant}. \qquad (18\text{--}6)$$

Equation 18–6 is called *Bernoulli's equation* for steady, nonviscous, incompressible flow. It was first presented by Daniel Bernoulli (1700–1782) in his *Hydrodynamica* in 1738.

Bernoulli's equation is strictly applicable only to steady flow, the quantities involved being evaluated along a streamline. In our figure the streamline used is along the axis of the pipeline. If the flow is irrotational, however, it can be shown (see Problem 21 for a special case) that the constant in Eq. 18–6 is the same for *all* streamlines.

In a nonviscous incompressible fluid we cannot change the temperature of the fluid by mechanical means. Hence, Bernoulli's equation, as stated above, refers to isothermal (constant temperature) processes. It is possible, however, to change the temperature of a nonviscous *compressible* fluid by mechanical means. We can generalize this equation to include a compressible fluid by adding to the left of Eq. 18–6 a term $u$, which represents the *internal energy* per unit volume of the fluid. This term (and the pressure $p$) will have a value that depends on the temperature.

If the flow is viscous, forces of a frictional nature act on the fluid so that some of the work done that appeared as a change in kinetic energy in the nonviscous case appears now as heat energy in the fluid. We must then write Eq. 18–5a as

$$(p_1 - p_2)(m/\rho) - mg(y_2 - y_1) = \tfrac{1}{2}mv_2{}^2 - \tfrac{1}{2}mv_1{}^2 + Q$$

where $Q$ represents the heat energy generated in the viscous flow from point 1 to point 2. In practice, Bernoulli's equation can be modified accordingly by use of empirical corrections for conversion of mechanical energy to heat energy. However, if the pipe is smooth and the diameter is large compared to the length, and if the fluid flows slowly and has a small viscosity, the heat generated is negligible.

Just as the statics of a particle is a special case of particle dynamics, so fluid statics is a special case of fluid dynamics. It should come as no surprise, therefore, that the law of pressure change with height in a fluid at rest is included in Bernoulli's equation as a special case. For let the fluid be at rest; then $v_1 = v_2 = 0$ and Eq. 18–5$b$ becomes

$$p_1 + \rho g y_1 = p_2 + \rho g y_2$$

or $$p_2 - p_1 = -\rho g(y_2 - y_1),$$

which is the same as Eq. 17–3.

In Eq. 18–6 all terms have the dimension of a pressure (check this). The pressure $p + \rho g h$, which would be present even if there were no flow ($v = 0$), is called the *static pressure;* the term $\frac{1}{2}\rho v^2$ is called the *dynamic pressure.*

## 18–5   Applications of Bernoulli's Equation and the Equation of Continuity

Bernoulli's equation can be used to determine fluid speeds by means of pressure measurements. The principle generally used in such measuring devices is the following: The equation of continuity requires that the speed of the fluid at a constriction increase; Bernoulli's equation then shows that the pressure must fall there. That is, for a horizontal pipe $\frac{1}{2}\rho v^2 + p$ equals a constant; if $v$ increases and the fluid is incompressible, $p$ must decrease. This result was also deduced from dynamic considerations in Section 18–3.

### 1. The Venturi meter

This (Fig. 18–6) is a gauge put in a flow pipe to measure the flow speed of a liquid. A liquid of density $\rho$ flows through a pipe of cross-sectional area $A$. At the throat the area is reduced to $a$ and a manometer tube is attached, as shown. Let the manometer liquid, such as mercury, have a density $\rho'$. By applying Bernoulli's equation and the equation of continuity at points 1 and 2, the student can show that the speed of flow at

**Fig. 18–6** The Venturi meter, used to measure the speed of flow of a fluid.

$A$ is

$$v = a \sqrt{\frac{2(\rho' - \rho)gh}{\rho(A^2 - a^2)}}.$$

If we want the volume flux or flow rate $R$, which is the volume of liquid transported past any point per second, we simply compute

$$R = vA.$$

### 2. The Pitot tube

This device (Fig. 18–7) is used to measure the flow speed of a gas.   Consider the gas, say air, flowing past the openings at $a$.   These openings are parallel to the direction of flow and are set far enough back so that the velocity and pressure outside the openings have the free-stream values. The pressure in the left arm of the manometer, which is connected to these openings, is then the static pressure in the gas stream, $p_a$. The opening of the right arm of the manometer is at right angles to the stream.   The velocity is reduced to zero at $b$ and the gas is stagnant at that point.   The pressure at $b$ is the full ram pressure, $p_b$.   Applying Bernoulli's equation to points $a$ and $b$, we obtain

$$p_a + \tfrac{1}{2}\rho v^2 = p_b,$$

**Fig. 18–7**   Cross-sectional diagram of a Pitot tube.

where, as shown in the figure, $p_b$ is greater than $p_a$.   If $h$ is the difference in height of the liquid in the manometer arms and $\rho'$ is the density of the manometer liquid, then

$$p_a + \rho'gh = p_b.$$

Comparing these two equations, we find

$$\tfrac{1}{2}\rho v^2 = \rho'gh$$

or

$$v = \sqrt{\frac{2gh\rho'}{\rho}},$$

which gives the gas speed.   This device can be calibrated to read $v$ directly and is then known as an air-speed indicator.

### 3. Dynamic Lift

Dynamic lift is the force that acts on a body, such as an airplane wing, a hydrofoil, or a spinning baseball, by virtue of its motion through a fluid.

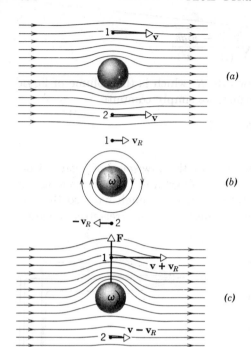

(a)

(b)

(c)

**Fig. 18–8** (a) Streamlines for air moving past a (nonrotating) baseball. The velocity **v** is shown for typical corresponding points 1 and 2. (b) Streamlines for airflow around a rotating baseball, showing the velocities $v_R$ and $-v_R$ at points 1 and 2 respectively. (c) the superposition of (a) and (b). The velocities at points 1 and 2 are shown along with the dynamic lift **F**.

We must distinguish it from *static lift*, which is the buoyant force that acts on an object, such as a balloon, in accord with Archimedes' principle.

Figure 18–8a shows the streamlines around a (nonspinning) baseball as it moves through the air. For convenience, we examine the situation from a reference frame in which the baseball is at rest and the air moves past it; this reference frame can be realized in practice by mounting a baseball in a wind tunnel. From the symmetry of the streamlines it is clear that the velocity of the air is the same at corresponding points above and below the ball, such as 1 and 2 in Fig. 18–8a. From Bernoulli's equation we then deduce that the pressures at such corresponding points are equal and that the air exerts no upward or downward force on the ball by virtue of its motion; the dynamic lift is zero.

In a separate experiment let us spin a resting baseball about an axis that is perpendicular to the plane of Fig. 18–8b. Since the ball is not perfectly smooth, it drags some air around with it, the streamlines associated with this motion being shown in the figure.

Finally, let us combine both motions by throwing a baseball and spinning it at the same time. Figure 18–8c shows the resulting streamlines from a reference frame in which the center of mass of the ball is at rest. These streamlines represent a distribution of velocities found by adding (vectorially) at every point the velocities in Figs. 18–8a and b. The velocities at point 1 add numerically while those at point 2 subtract. Thus the speed at point 1 in Fig. 18–8c is *greater* than the speed at point 2 as, indeed, the crowding of the streamlines suggests. From Bernoulli's principle, then, the pressure at point 1 is *less* than the pressure at point 2, so that there is a net upward force (a dynamic lift) on the spinning baseball.   Such forces on actual spinning baseballs and tennis balls are well known in practice.*

   When dynamic lift on an object occurs it is always associated with an unsymmetrical set of streamlines relatively close together on one side and relatively far apart on the other, like those of Fig. 18–8c, that correspond, as Fig. 18–8b shows, to circulation of fluid around the object.   For the spinning baseball the circulation is obtained by actually spinning the object; in other cases of dynamic lift, of which the airplane wing is a good example, streamline patterns that contain the necessary circulation are obtained by properly shaping the object and properly orienting it in the moving fluid.   Figure 18–9 shows streamlines around an airplane wing.   As required, they are closer together above the wing than they are below so that (compare Fig. 18–8c) Bernoulli's principle predicts the observed upward dynamic lift.

**Fig. 18–9**  Streamlines about an airfoil.

## 4. Thrust on a Rocket

   As our final example let us compute the thrust on a rocket produced by the escape of its exhaust gases.   Consider a chamber (Fig. 18–10) of cross-sectional area $A$ filled with a gas of density $\rho$ at a pressure $p$.   Let there be a small orifice of cross-sectional area $A_0$ at the bottom of the chamber.   We wish to find the speed $v_0$ with which the gas escapes through the orifice.   Let us write Bernoulli's equation (Eq. 18–5b) as

$$p_1 - p_2 = \rho g(y_2 - y_1) + \tfrac{1}{2}\rho(v_2{}^2 - v_1{}^2).$$

For a gas the density is so small that we can neglect the variation in pressure with height in a chamber (see Section 17–3).   Hence, if $p$ represents the pressure $p_1$ in the chamber and $p_0$ represents the atmospheric pressure

---

* See *The Flettner Ship*, an article by Albert Einstein in his book *Essays in Science*, Philosophical Library, New York.   The Flettner ship, like a sailboat, derives its motive power from the wind.   Instead of a sail it has a large cylinder that is caused to rotate about a vertical axis by a small motor.   The resulting dynamic "lift" (in this case, horizontal) propels the vessel.

$p_2$ just outside the orifice, we have

$$p - p_0 = \tfrac{1}{2}\rho(v_0{}^2 - v^2)$$

or                    $$v_0{}^2 = \frac{2(p - p_0)}{\rho} + v^2, \qquad (18\text{–}7)$$

where $v$ is the speed of the flowing gas inside the chamber and $v_0$ is the *speed of efflux* of the gas through the orifice. Although a gas is compressible and the flow may become turbulent, we can treat the flow as steady and incompressible for pressure and efflux speeds that are not too high.

Now let us assume continuity of mass flow (in a rocket engine this is achieved when the mass of escaping gas equals the mass of gas created by burning the fuel), so that (for an assumed constant density)

$$Av = A_0 v_0.$$

If the orifice is very small so that $A_0 \ll A$, then $v_0 \gg v$, and we can neglect $v^2$ compared to $v_0{}^2$ in Eq. 18–7. Hence, the speed of efflux is

**Fig. 18–10** Fluid streaming out of a chamber.

$$v_0 = \sqrt{\frac{2(p - p_0)}{\rho}}. \qquad (18\text{–}8)$$

If our chamber is the exhaust chamber of a rocket, the thrust on the rocket (Section 9–7) is $v_0\, dM/dt$. But the mass of gas flowing out in time $dt$ is $dM = \rho A_0 v_0\, dt$, so that

$$v_0 \frac{dM}{dt} = v_0 \rho A_0 v_0 = \rho A_0 v_0{}^2,$$

and from Eq. 18–8 the thrust is

$$2A_0(p - p_0). \qquad (18\text{–}9)$$

## 18–6    Conservation of Momentum in Fluid Mechanics

In Newtonian particle mechanics the derivation of the laws of conservation of linear momentum and angular momentum makes explicit use of Newton's third law of motion. The internal forces and torques in a mechanical system cancel one another because of this third law, leaving only the external forces and torques to contribute to the momenta. In the case of a fluid the internal forces are represented by the pressure within the fluid. But the very concept of pressure itself contains Newton's third law implicitly. The force produced by pressure exerted in one direction across any surface element is equal and opposite to the force exerted in the opposite direction across the same surface element. Also, each of these two forces is applied at the same place, namely at the surface element. Both forces must have the same line of action. Hence, in the equations for the time rate of change of linear momentum or of angular momentum of a fluid, the internal pressures will cancel out. We can conclude then that the time rate of change of the total linear momentum in a volume $V$ of moving fluid is equal to the total *external force* acting on it. Likewise, the time rate of change of the total angular momentum in a volume $V$ of moving fluid is equal to the total *external torque* acting on it. The conservation laws of linear and angular momentum follow.

## 18–7  Fields of Flow

In the chapter on gravitation we saw how to summarize the physical state of affairs near masses by use of a field. Each point in the field can be regarded as having a vector associated with it, namely **g**, the gravitational force per unit mass at that point. Or, alternately, we can associate a scalar quantity with each point in space, namely the gravitational potential $V$. We can then draw a surface, called an equipotential surface, through all points that have the same potential. We draw several such surfaces, the potential on one differing by a constant amount from that on the next one, etc. The gravitational force at any point is then directed along a line passing through this point perpendicular to these surfaces, and its magnitude is determined from the rate of change of potential with distance in this direction, as indicated by the spacing and orientation of the equipotential surfaces. By drawing in lines of force we can picture vividly how space is affected by the presence of mass.

Likewise, in fluid dynamics we can summarize the physical state of affairs within a moving fluid by means of a field of flow. In general, the field of flow is a *vector* field. We associate a vector quantity with each point in space, namely the flow velocity **v** at that point. For a steady flow the field of flow is stationary. Of course, even in this case a particular fluid particle may still have a variable velocity as it moves from point to point in the field. The field gives the properties of the space from which we deduce the behavior of particles in that space. If the flow is irrotational, as well as steady, we call it *potential flow*. Then the flow velocity **v** can be related to a velocity potential $\psi$, just as in gravitation **g** can be related to the gravitational potential $V$. If we draw in surfaces of equal velocity potential, as we drew in surfaces of equal gravitational potential, we can deduce **v** from the equipotential flow surfaces just as **g** is deduced from the equipotential gravitational surfaces. Hence, a field for potential flow is analogous to a conservative force field.

A flowing fluid mass can always be divided into tubes of flow. When the flow is steady, the tubes remain unchanged in shape and the fluid that is at one instant in a tube remains inside this tube thereafter. We have seen that the flow velocity inside a tube of flow is parallel to the tube and has a magnitude inversely proportional to the area of the cross section (Eq. 18–1). Let us assign such cross sections to the tubes that the constant of proportionality is the same for all of them; if possible we take this constant to be unity. That is, the volume flux is the same for all tubes, namely unit flux. Then the magnitude of the flow velocity can be

**Fig. 18–11** Streamlines (horizontal) and surfaces of equal velocity potential (vertical) for a homogeneous field of flow.

determined from the areas of the cross sections of the tubes of flow.  There is another procedure equivalent to this which consists of setting up a unit area perpendicular to the direction of flow and drawing through it just as many streamlines as the number of units of magnitude of the velocity at that point.

Let us consider some examples of fields of flow.  For drawing purposes we consider only *two-dimensional* examples.  In these the flow velocity is the same at all points on a line perpendicular to the plane at any point.

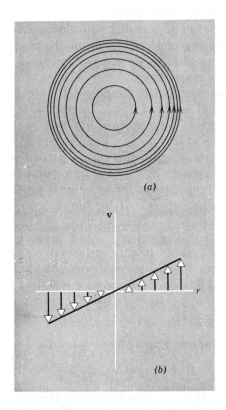

**Fig. 18–12**  (*a*) Uniform rotational field of flow.  (*b*) Variation of fluid velocity from the center.

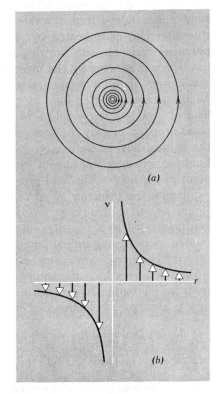

**Fig. 18–13**  (*a*) Vortical field of flow.  (*b*) Variation of fluid velocity from the center.

In Fig. 18–11 we have drawn a *homogeneous field of flow*. Here all the stream-lines are parallel and the flow velocity **v** is the same at all points. We have seen that there are two equivalent ways of deriving the relative magnitudes of the flow velocities from such fields of flow: (a) from the widths of the tubes of flow and (b) from the distances between lines of equal velocity potential. The latter method applies to steady irrotational flow only. For such flows we draw in the lines of equal velocity potential as dashed lines.

In Fig. 18–12 we show the field for a *uniform rotation* (see Problem 22, Chapter 17). Here $v$ is proportional to $r$. In Fig. 18–13 we draw the field of flow of a *vortex*. In this case $v$ is proportional to $1/r$ (see Problem 19). Notice that both uniform rotation and vortex motion are represented by circular streamlines but are entirely different kinds of flow. Obviously, the *shapes* of the streamlines give only limited information; their spacing is needed too.

Figure 18–14 represents the field of flow for a *source*. All streamlines are directed radially outward. The source is a line through the center perpendicular to the paper emitting a mass per unit time $Q$. The field of flow around a linear *sink* is the same as the source except for the sign of the flow, which is directed radially inward.

For a linear source and linear sink which have the same strengths, $Q$ and $-Q$, and are slightly separated, we obtain the combined field called *linear dipole flow*, shown in Fig. 18–15.

As we shall see later the electrostatic field, the magnetic field, and the field of flow for an electric current are also vector fields. In this connection, the homo-

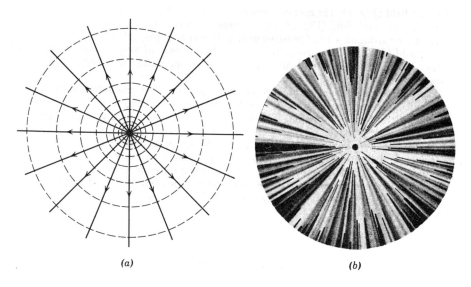

(a)    (b)

**Fig. 18–14**   (a) Flow from a linear point source.   (b) Fluid flow map of the same. The map in this figure is made by allowing water to flow between a horizontal layer of plate glass and a horizontal layer of plaster. In (b) the water comes up through a hole in the center of the plaster and flows out toward the edges. The direction of the flow is made visible by sprinkling the plaster with potassium permanganate crystals which dissolve and color the water a deep red. (The fluid flow map was made and photographed by Professor A. D. Moore at the University of Michigan, and is taken from *Introduction to Electric Fields*, by W. E. Rogers, McGraw-Hill Book Co., 1954.)

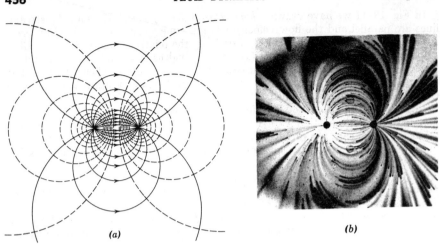

**Fig. 18-15** (*a*) Linear dipole flow. The source is on the left, the sink on the right. (*b*) A fluid flow map of the same. (The fluid flow map was made and photographed by Professor A. D. Moore at the University of Michigan, and is taken from *Introduction to Electric Fields*, by W. E. Rogers, McGraw-Hill Book Co., 1954.)

geneous field (Fig. 18-11) corresponds to the electric field of a plane capacitor, the source field or sink field (Fig. 18-14) correspond to the electric field of a cylindrical capacitor or straight wire of positive or negative charge respectively, and the linear dipole field (Fig. 18-15) corresponds to the electric field of two oppositely charged wires. In all these the field of flow is potential flow and the electric fields are conservative.

The homogeneous field of Fig. 18-11 also represents the magnetic field inside a solenoid. The vortex field of Fig. 18-13 represents the magnetic field around a straight current-carrying wire. This last is an example of a field that is rotational (about the vortex axis).

Because of these analogies between fluid and electromagnetic fields, we can often determine a field of flow, which is impossible to calculate by present mathematical methods, by experimental measurements on appropriate electrical devices.

As we have seen throughout this chapter, the basic field ideas and conservation principles find application in many areas of physics. We shall encounter them many times again.

## QUESTIONS

1. Can you assign a coefficient of static friction between two surfaces, one of which is a fluid surface?

2. Describe the forces acting on an element of fluid as it flows through a pipe of nonuniform cross section.

3. The height of the liquid in the standpipes indicates that the pressure drops along the channel, even though the channel has a uniform cross section and the flowing liquid is incompressible (Fig. 18-16). Explain.

**Fig. 18–16**

**4.** It is found that liquid will flow faster and more smoothly from a sealed can when two holes are punctured in the can than when one hole is made. Explain.

**5.** In a lecture demonstration a ping-pong ball is kept in midair by a vertical jet of air. Is the equilibrium stable, unstable, or neutral? Explain.

**6.** (a) Explain how a pitcher can make a baseball curve to his right or left. Justify your answer by drawing a diagram of the streamlines and applying Bernoulli's equation. (b) Why is it easier to throw a curve with a tennis ball than with a baseball?

**7.** Two rowboats moving parallel to one another in the same direction are pulled toward one another. Two automobiles moving parallel are also pulled together. Explain such phenomena on the basis of Bernoulli's equation.

**8.** Can the action of a parachute in retarding free fall be explained by Bernoulli's equation?

**9.** Liquid is flowing inside a horizontal pipe which has a constriction along its length. Vertical tube manometers are attached at both the wide portion and the narrow portion of the pipe. If a stopcock at the exit end is closed, will the liquid in the manometer tubes rise or fall? Explain.

**10.** Can you explain why water flows in a continuous stream down a vertical pipe, whereas it breaks into drops when falling freely?

**11.** Can you explain why an object falling from a great height reaches a steady terminal speed?

**12.** On take off would it be better for an airplane to move into the wind or with the wind? On landing . . . ?

**13.** Does the difference in pressure between the lower and upper surfaces of an airplane wing depend on the altitude of the moving plane? Explain.

**14.** The accumulation of ice on an airplane wing may change its shape in such a way that its lift is greatly reduced. Explain.

**15.** How is an airplane able to fly upside down?

**16.** Why does the factor "2" appear in Eq. 18–9, rather than "1"? One might naively expect that the thrust would simply be the pressure difference times the area, that is, $A_0(p - p_0)$.

**17.** The destructive effect of a tornado (twister) is greater near the center of the disturbance than near the edge. Explain.

**18.** When a stopper is pulled from a filled basin, the water drains out while circulating like a small whirlpool. The angular velocity of a fluid element about a vertical axis through the orifice appears to be greatest near the orifice. Explain.

**19.** Use the criterion of the paddle wheel (Fig. 18–1) to determine which flow fields (Figs. 18–11 through 18–15) are rotational.

**20.** In steady flow the velocity vector **v** at any point is constant. Can there then be accelerated motion of the fluid particles? Discuss.

**21.** How can we justify applying Bernoulli's equation to the spinning baseball of Fig. 18-8c? Points 1 and 2 are not on the same streamline.

## PROBLEMS

**1.** A garden hose having an internal diameter of 0.75 in. is connected to a lawn sprinkler that consists merely of an enclosure with 24 holes, each 0.050 in. in diameter. If the water in the hose has a speed of 3.0 ft/sec, at what speed does it leave the sprinkler holes?

**2.** Models of torpedoes are sometimes tested in a pipe of flowing water, much as a wind tunnel is used to test model airplanes. Consider a circular pipe of internal diameter 10 in. and a torpedo model, aligned along the axis of the pipe, with a diameter of 2.0 in. The torpedo is to be tested with water flowing past it at 8.0 ft/sec. (a) With what speed must the water flow in the unconstricted part of the pipe? (b) What will the pressure difference be between the constricted and unconstricted parts of the pipe?

**3.** How much work is done by pressure in forcing 50 ft³ of water through a 0.50-in. pipe if the difference in pressure at the two ends of the pipe is 15 lb/in.²?

**4.** Water falls from a height of 60 ft at the rate of 500 ft³/min and drives a water turbine. What is the maximum power that can be developed by this turbine?

**5.** By applying Bernoulli's equation and the equation of continuity to points 1 and 2 of Fig. 18–6, show that the speed of flow at the entrance is

$$v = a \sqrt{\frac{2(\rho' - \rho)gh}{\rho(A^2 - a^2)}}.$$

**6.** A Venturi meter has a pipe diameter of 10 in. and a throat diameter of 5.0 in. If the water pressure in the pipe is 8.0 lb/in.² and in the throat is 6.0 lb/in.², determine the rate of flow of water in ft³/sec (volume flux).

**7.** Consider the Venturi tube of Fig. 18–6 without the manometer. Let $A$ equal $5a$. Suppose the pressure at $A$ is 2.0 atm. Compute the values of $v$ at $A$ and $v'$ at $a$ that would make the pressure $p'$ at $a$ equal to zero. Compute the corresponding volume flow rate if the diameter at $A$ is 5.0 cm. The phenomenon at $a$ when $p'$ falls to nearly zero is known as *cavitation*. The water vaporizes into small bubbles.

**8.** In a horizontal oil pipeline of constant cross-sectional area the pressure decrease between two points 1000 ft apart is 5 lb/in.². What is the energy loss per cubic foot of oil per unit distance?

**9.** Figure 18–17 shows liquid discharging from an orifice in a large tank at a distance $h$ below the water level. (a) Apply Bernoulli's equation to a streamline connecting points 1, 2, and 3, and show that the speed of efflux is

$$v = \sqrt{2gh}.$$

This is known as Torricelli's law. (b) If the orifice were curved directly upward, how high would the liquid stream rise? (c) How would viscosity or turbulence affect the analysis?

**10.** Suppose that two tanks, each with a large opening at the top, contain different liquids. A small hole is made in the side of each tank at the same depth $h$ below the liquid surface, but one hole has twice the cross-sectional area of the other. (a) What is the ratio of the densities of the fluids if it is observed that the mass flux is the same for

**Fig. 18–17**

each hole? (*b*) How do the flow rates (volume flux) from each hole compare? (*c*) Could the flow rates be made equal? How?

11. A tank is filled with water to a height $H$. A hole is punched in one of the walls at a depth $h$ below the water surface (Fig. 18–18). (*a*) Find the distance $x$ from the foot of the wall at which the stream strikes the floor. (*b*) Could a hole be punched at another depth so that this second stream would have the same range? If so, at what depth?

**Fig. 18–18**

12. The upper surface of water in a standpipe is a height $H$ above level ground. At what depth $h$ should a small hole be put to make the emerging horizontal water stream strike the ground at the maximum distance from the base of the standpipe? What is this maximum distance?

13. Calculate the speed of efflux of a liquid from an opening in a tank, taking into account the velocity of the top surface of the liquid, as follows. (*a*) Show, from Bernoulli's equation, that

$$v_0{}^2 = \frac{2gh}{1 - v^2/v_0{}^2}$$

where $v$ is the speed of the top surface. (*b*) Then consider the flow as one big tube of flow and obtain $v/v_0$ from the equation of continuity, so that

$$v_0 = \sqrt{2gh/[1 - (A_0/A)^2]}$$

where $A$ is the tube cross section at the top and $A_0$ is the tube cross section at the opening. (*c*) Then show that if the hole is small compared to the area of the surface,

$$v_0 \cong \sqrt{2gh}\,[1 + \tfrac{1}{2}(A_0/A)^2].$$

14. A Pitot tube is mounted on an airplane wing to determine the speed of the plane relative to the air. The tube contains alcohol and indicates a level difference of 4.9 in. What is the plane's speed in miles/hr relative to the air?

15. Air streams horizontally past an airplane wing of area 36 ft$^2$ weighing 540 lb. The speed over the top surface is 200 ft/sec and 150 ft/sec under the bottom surface. What is the lift on the wing? The net force on it?

16. If the speed of flow past the lower surface of a wing is 350 ft/sec, what speed of flow over the upper surface will give a lift of 20 lb/ft$^2$?

**17.** (a) Consider the stagnant air at the front edge of a wing and the air rushing over the wing surface at a speed $v$. Find the greatest value possible for $v$ in streamline flow, assuming air is incompressible and using Bernoulli's equation. Take the density of air to be $1.2 \times 10^{-3}$ gm/cm$^3$. (b) How does this compare with the speed of sound of 770 miles/hr? Can you explain the difference? Why should there be any connection between these quantities?

**18.** A hollow tube has a disk $DD$ attached to its end. When air is blown through the tube, the disk attracts the card $CC$. Let the area of the card be $A$ and let $v$ be the average airspeed between $CC$ and $DD$ (Fig. 18–19); calculate the resultant upward force on $CC$. Neglect the card's weight.

**Fig. 18–19**

**19.** Before Newton proposed his theory of gravitation, a model of planetary motion proposed by René Descartes was widely accepted. In Descartes' model the planets were caught in and dragged along by a whirlpool of ether particles centered around the sun. Newton showed that this vortex scheme contradicted observations, for: (a) The speed of an ether particle in the vortex varies inversely as its distance from the sun. (b) The period of revolution of such a particle varies directly as the square of its distance from the sun. (c) This result contradicts Kepler's third law. Prove (a), (b), and (c).

**20.** Consider a uniform U-tube with a diaphragm at the bottom and filled with a liquid to different heights in each arm (see Fig. 18–20). Now imagine that the diaphragm is punctured so that the liquid flows from left to right. (a) Show that application of Bernoulli's principle to points 1 and 3 leads to a contradiction. (b) Explain why Bernoulli's principle is not applicable here. (*Hint:* Is the flow steady?)

**Fig. 18–20**

**21.** Show that the constant in Bernoulli's equation (Eq. 18–6) is the same for *all* streamlines in the case of the steady, irrotational flow of Fig. 18–11.

**22.** (a) Consider a stream of fluid of density $\rho$ with speed $v_1$ passing *abruptly* from a cylindrical pipe of cross-sectional area $a_1$ into a wider cylindrical pipe of cross-sectional area $a_2$ (see Fig. 18–21). The jet will mix with the surrounding fluid and, after the mixing, will flow on almost uniformly with an average speed $v_2$. Without referring to

**Fig. 18–21**

the details of the mixing, use momentum ideas to show that the increase in pressure due to the mixing is approximately

$$p_2 - p_1 = \rho v_2(v_1 - v_2).$$

(b) Show from Bernoulli's principle that in a *gradually* widening pipe we would get

$$p_2 - p_1 = \tfrac{1}{2}\rho(v_1{}^2 - v_2{}^2)$$

and explain the loss of pressure [the difference is $\tfrac{1}{2}\rho(v_1 - v_2)^2$] due to the abrupt enlargement of the pipe. Can you draw an analogy with elastic and inelastic collisions in particle mechanics?

**23.** A force field is conservative if $\oint \mathbf{F} \cdot d\mathbf{s} = 0$. The circle on the integration sign means that the integration is to be taken along a closed curve (a round trip) in the field. A flow is a potential flow (hence irrotational) if $\oint \mathbf{v} \cdot d\mathbf{s} = 0$ for every closed path in the field.

Using this criterion, show that the fields of Figs. 18–11 and 18–14 are fields of potential flow.

**24.** The so-called Poiseuille field of flow is shown in Fig. 18–22. The spacing of the streamlines indicates that although the motion is rectilinear, there is a velocity gradient in the transverse direction. Show that such a flow is rotational.

**Fig. 18–22**

**25.** In flows that are sharply curved centrifugal effects are appreciable. Consider an element of fluid which is moving with speed $v$ along a streamline of a curved flow in a horizontal plane (Fig. 18–23).

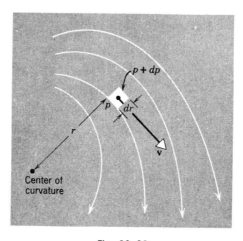

**Fig. 18–23**

(a) Show that $dp/dr = \rho v^2/r$, so that the pressure increases by an amount $\rho v^2/r$ per unit distance perpendicular to the streamline as we go from the concave to the convex side of the streamline.

(b) Then use Bernoulli's equation and this result to show that $vr$ equals a constant, so that speeds increase toward the center of curvature. Hence, streamlines that are uniformly spaced in a straight pipe will be crowded toward the inner wall of a curved passage and widely spaced toward the outer wall. This problem should be compared to Problem 17–22 in which the curved motion is produced by rotating a container. There the speed varied directly with $r$, but here it varies inversely.

(c) Show that this flow is irrotational.

# Waves in Elastic Media

## CHAPTER 19

### 19–1 Mechanical Waves

Wave motion appears in almost every branch of physics. We are all familiar with water waves. There are also sound waves, as well as light waves, radio waves, and other electromagnetic waves. One formulation of the mechanics of atoms and subatomic particles is called wave mechanics. Clearly the properties and behavior of waves are very important in physics.

In this chapter and the next we confine our attention to waves in deformable or elastic media. These waves, among which ordinary sound waves in air are one example, might be called *mechanical waves*. They originate in the displacement of some portion of an elastic medium from its normal position, causing it to oscillate about an equilibrium position. Because of the elastic properties of the medium, the disturbance is transmitted from one layer to the next. This disturbance, or wave, consequently progresses through the medium. Note that the medium itself does not move as a whole along with the wave motion; the various parts of the medium oscillate only in limited paths. For example, in water waves small floating objects like corks show that the actual motion of various parts of the water is slightly up and down and back and forth. Yet the water waves move steadily along the water. As they reach floating objects they set them in motion, thus transferring energy to them.* Energy can be transmitted over considerable distances by wave motion. The energy in the waves is the kinetic and potential energy of the matter, but the transmission of the

---

* See "Ocean Waves," by Willard Bascom, *Scientific American*, August 1957.

energy comes about by its being passed along from one part of the matter to the next, not by any long-range motion of the matter itself. Mechanical waves are characterized by the transport of energy through matter by the motion of a disturbance in that matter without any corresponding bulk motion of the matter itself.

It is necessary to have a material medium to transmit mechanical waves. We do not need such a medium, however, to transmit electromagnetic waves, light passing freely, for example, through the near vacuum of space from the stars. The properties of the medium that determine the speed of a wave through that medium, as we will see in Section 19–5, are its inertia and its elasticity. All material media, including, say, air, water and steel, possess these properties and can transmit mechanical waves. It is the elasticity that gives rise to the restoring forces on any part of the medium displaced from its equilibrium position; it is the inertia that tells us how this displaced portion of the medium will respond to these restoring forces. Together these two factors determine the wave speed.

## 19–2  Types of Waves

In listing water waves, light waves, and sound waves as examples of wave motion, we are classifying waves according to their broad physical properties. Waves can be classified in other ways.

We can distinguish different kinds of waves by considering how the motions of the particles of matter are related to the direction of propagation of the waves themselves. If the motions of the matter particles conveying the wave are perpendicular to the direction of propagation of the wave itself, we then have a *transverse* wave. For example, when a vertical string under tension is set oscillating back and forth at one end, a transverse wave travels down the string; the disturbance moves along the string but the string particles vibrate at right angles to the direction of propagation of the disturbance (Fig. 19–1a).

Light waves are not mechanical waves. The disturbance that travels along is not a motion of matter but an electromagnetic field (Chapter 40). But because the electric and magnetic fields are perpendicular to the direction of propagation, light waves are also transverse waves.

If, however, the motion of the particles conveying a mechanical wave is back and forth along the direction of propagation, we then have a *longitudinal wave*. For example, when a vertical spring under tension is set oscillating up and down at one end, a longitudinal wave travels along the spring; the coils vibrate back and forth in the direction in which the disturbance travels along the spring (Fig. 19–1b). Sound waves in a gas are longitudinal waves. We shall discuss them in greater detail in Chapter 20.

Some waves are neither purely longitudinal nor purely transverse. For example, in waves on the surface of water the particles of water move both up and down and back and forth, tracing out elliptical paths as the water waves move by.

Waves can also be classified as one-, two-, and three-dimensional waves,

(a)

(b)

**Fig. 19–1**   (a) In a transverse wave the particles of the medium (string) vibrate at right angles to the direction in which the wave itself is propagated.  (b) In a longitudinal wave the particles of the medium (spring) vibrate in the same direction as that in which the wave itself is propagated.

according to the number of dimensions in which they propagate energy. Waves moving along the string or the spring of Fig. 19–1 are one-dimensional. Surface waves or ripples on water, caused by dropping a pebble into a quiet pond, are two-dimensional. Sound waves and light waves which emanate radially from a small source are three-dimensional.

Waves may be classified further according to the behavior of a particle of the matter conveying the wave during the course of time the wave propagates. For example, we can produce a *pulse* or a *single wave* traveling down a taut rope by applying a single sidewise movement at its end. Each particle remains at rest until the pulse reaches it, then it moves during a short time, and then it again remains at rest. If we continue to move the end of the rope back and forth (Fig. 19–1a), we produce a *train of waves* traveling along the rope. If our motion is periodic, we produce a *periodic train of waves* in which each particle of the rope has a periodic motion. The simplest special case of a periodic wave is a *simple harmonic wave* which gives each particle a simple harmonic motion.

Consider a three-dimensional pulse. We can draw a surface through all points undergoing a similar disturbance at a given instant. As time goes on, this surface moves along showing how the pulse propagates. We can draw similar surfaces for subsequent pulses. For a periodic wave we can generalize the idea by drawing in surfaces, all of whose points are in the same phase of motion. These surfaces are called *wavefronts*. If the medium is homogeneous and isotropic, the direction of propagation is always at right angles to the wavefront. A line normal to the wavefronts, indicating the direction of motion of the waves, is called a *ray*.

Wavefronts can have many shapes. If the disturbances are propagated in a single direction, the waves are called *plane waves*. At a given instant conditions are the same everywhere on any plane perpendicular to the direction of propagation. The wavefronts are plane and the rays are parallel straight lines (Fig. 19–2a). Another simple case is that of *spherical waves*. Here the disturbance is propagated out in all directions from a

**Fig. 9–2**   (a) A plane wave. The planes represent wavefronts spaced a wavelength apart, and the arrows represent rays. (b) A spherical wave. The rays are radial and the wavefronts, spaced a wavelength apart, form spherical shells. Far out from the source, however, small portions of the wavefronts become nearly plane.

point source of waves. The wavefronts are spheres and the rays are radial lines leaving the point source in all directions (Fig. 19–2b). Far from the source the spherical wavefronts have very small curvature, and over a limited region they can often be regarded as plane. Of course, there are many other possible shapes for wavefronts.

We shall refer to all these wave types as we progress through the wave phenomena of physics. In this chapter we often use the transverse wave in a string to illustrate the general properties of waves. In the next chapter we shall see the consequences of these properties for sound, a longitudinal mechanical wave. Later in the text we will discuss the properties of nonmechanical waves such as light and matter waves.

## 19–3 Traveling Waves

Let us consider a long string stretched in the $x$-direction along which a transverse wave is traveling. At some instant of time, say $t = 0$, the shape of the string can be represented by

$$y = f(x) \qquad t = 0, \tag{19–1}$$

where $y$ is the transverse displacement of the string at the position $x$. In Fig. 19–3a we show a possible waveform (a pulse) on the string at $t = 0$. Experiment shows that as time goes on such a wave travels along the string without changing its form, provided internal frictional losses are small enough. At some time $t$ later the wave has traveled a distance $vt$ to the right, where $v$ is magnitude of the wave velocity, assumed constant. The equation of the curve at the time $t$ is therefore

$$y = f(x - vt) \qquad t = t. \tag{19–2}$$

This gives us the same waveform about the point $x = vt$ at time $t$ as we had about $x = 0$ at the time $t = 0$ (Fig. 19–3b). Equation 19–2 is the

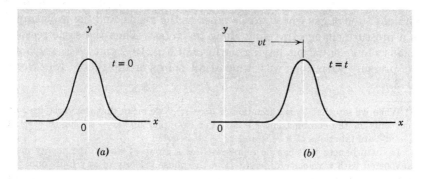

**Fig. 19–3** (a) The shape of a string (in this case a pulse) at $t = 0$. (b) At a later time $t$ the pulse has traveled to the right a distance $x = vt$.

general equation representing a wave of *any* shape *traveling to the right.* To describe a particular shape we must specify exactly what the function $f$ is.*

Let us look more carefully at this equation. If we wish to follow a particular part (or phase) of the wave as times goes on, then in the equation we look at a particular value of $y$ (say, the top of the pulse just described). Mathematically this means we look at how $x$ changes with $t$ when $(x - vt)$ has some particular fixed value. We see at once that as $t$ increases $x$ must increase in order to keep $(x - vt)$ fixed. Hence, Eq. 19–2 does in fact represent a wave traveling to the right (increasing $x$ as time goes on). If we wished to represent a wave *traveling to the left*, we would write

$$y = f(x + vt), \tag{19-3}$$

for here the position $x$ of some fixed phase $(x + vt)$ of the wave decreases as time goes on. The velocity of a particular phase of the wave is easily obtained. For a particular phase of a wave traveling to the right we require that

$$x - vt = \text{constant.}$$

Then differentiation with respect to time gives

$$\frac{dx}{dt} - v = 0 \quad \text{or} \quad \frac{dx}{dt} = v, \tag{19-4}$$

so that $v$ is really the *phase velocity* of the wave. For a wave traveling to the left we obtain $-v$, in the same way, as its phase velocity.†

The general equation of a wave can be interpreted further. Note that for any fixed value of the time $t$ the equation gives $y$ as a function of $x$. This defines a curve, and this curve represents the actual shape of the string at this chosen time. It gives us a snapshot of the wave at this time. Suppose, on the other hand, we wish to focus our attention on one point of the string, that is, a fixed value of $x$. Then the equation gives us $y$ as a function of the time $t$. This describes how the transverse position of this point on the string changes with time.

The argument just presented holds for longitudinal waves as well as for transverse waves. The analogous longitudinal example is that of a long straight tube of gas whose axis is taken as the $x$-axis, and the wave or pulse is a pressure change traveling along the tube. Then the same reasoning leads us to an equation, having the form of Eqs. 19–2 and 19–3, which gives the pressure variations with time at all points of the tube. (See Section 20–3.)

---

* When we say that "$y$ is a function of $(x - vt)$," we mean that the variables $x$ and $t$ occur only in the combination $x - vt$. For example, $\sin k(x - vt)$, $\log (x - vt)$, and $(x - vt)^3$ are functions of $x - vt$, but $x^2 - vt^2$ is not.

† In disturbances that can be represented as a group of waves, the energy may be transported with a velocity different from the phase velocity of any individual wave. This group velocity will be considered in Chapter 39 in connection with electromagnetic waves. Until then whenever we use the term wave velocity we mean the phase velocity of the wave.

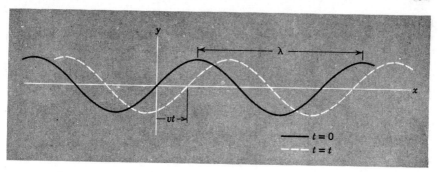

**Fig. 19–4**   At $t = 0$, the string has a shape $y = y_m \sin 2\pi x/\lambda$ (solid line). At a later time $t$ the sine wave has moved to the right a distance $x = vt$, and the string has a shape given by $y = y_m \sin 2\pi(x - vt)/\lambda$.

Let us now consider a particular waveform, whose importance will soon become clear. Suppose that at the time $t = 0$ we have a wavetrain along the string given by

$$y = y_m \sin \frac{2\pi}{\lambda} x. \tag{19–5}$$

The wave shape is a sine curve (Fig. 19–4). The maximum displacement $y_m$ is the *amplitude* of the sine curve. The value of the transverse displacement $y$ is the same at $x$ as it is at $x + \lambda$, $x + 2\lambda$, etc. The symbol $\lambda$ is called the *wavelength* of the wavetrain and represents the distance between two adjacent points in the wave having the same phase. As times goes on let the wave travel to the right with a phase velocity $v$. Hence, the equation of the wave at the time $t$ is

$$y = y_m \sin \frac{2\pi}{\lambda} (x - vt). \tag{19–6}$$

Notice that this has the form required for a traveling wave (Eq. 19–2).

The *period* $T$ is the time required for the wave to travel a distance of one wavelength $\lambda$, so that

$$\lambda = vT. \tag{19–7}$$

Putting this relation into the equation of the wave, we obtain

$$y = y_m \sin 2\pi \left( \frac{x}{\lambda} - \frac{t}{T} \right). \tag{19–8}$$

From this form it is clear that $y$, at any given time, has the same value at $x + \lambda$, $x + 2\lambda$, etc., as it does at $x$, and that $y$, at any given position, has the same value at the time $t + T$, $t + 2T$, etc., as it does at the time $t$.

To reduce Eq. 19–8 to a more compact form, we define two quantities, the *wave number* $k$ and the *angular frequency* $\omega$ (see Eq. 15–12). They are given by

$$k = \frac{2\pi}{\lambda} \quad \text{and} \quad \omega = \frac{2\pi}{T}. \tag{19-9}$$

In terms of these quantities, the equation of a sine wave traveling to the right is

$$y = y_m \sin (kx - \omega t). \tag{19-10a}$$

For a sine wave traveling to the left, we have

$$y = y_m \sin (kx + \omega t). \tag{19-10b}$$

Comparing Eqs. 19–7 and 19–9, we see that the phase velocity $v$ of the wave is given by

$$v = \frac{\lambda}{T} = \frac{\omega}{k}. \tag{19-11}$$

In the traveling waves of Eqs. 19–10a and 19–10b we have assumed that the displacement $y$ is zero at the position $x = 0$ at the time $t = 0$. This, of course, need not be the case. The general expression for a sinusoidal wave-train traveling to the right is

$$y = y_m \sin (kx - \omega t - \phi),$$

where $\phi$ is called the phase constant. For example, if $\phi = -90°$, the displacement $y$ at $x = 0$ and $t = 0$ is $y_m$. This particular example is

$$y = y_m \cos (kx - \omega t),$$

for the cosine function is displaced by 90° from the sine function.

If we fix our attention on a given point of the string, say $x = \pi/k$, the displacement $y$ at that point can be written* as

$$y = y_m \sin (\omega t + \phi).$$

This is similar to Eq. 15–29 for simple harmonic motion. Hence, any particular element of the string undergoes simple harmonic motion about its equilibrium position as this wavetrain travels along the string.

## 19–4   The Superposition Principle

It is an experimental fact that for many kinds of waves *two or more waves can traverse the same space independently of one another*. The fact that waves act independently of one another means that the displacement of any particle at a given time is simply the sum of the displacements that the individual waves alone would give it. This process of vector addition of the displacements of a particle is called *superposition*. For example, radio waves of many frequencies pass through a radio antenna; the electric currents set up in the antenna by the superposed action of all these waves are very complex. Nevertheless, we can still tune to a particular station,

---

* Using the fact that sin $(\pi - \theta) = \sin \theta$.

the signal that we receive from it being in principle the same as that which we would receive if all other stations were to stop broadcasting. Likewise, in sound we can listen to notes played by individual instruments in an orchestra, even though the sound wave reaching our ears from the full orchestra is very complex.

For waves in deformable media the superposition principle holds whenever the mathematical relation between the deformation and the restoring force is one of simple proportionality. Such a relation is expressed mathematically by a linear equation. For electromagnetic waves the superposition principle holds because the mathematical relations between the electric and magnetic fields are linear.

The superposition principle seems so obvious that it is worthwhile to point out that it does not always hold. Superposition fails when the equations governing wave motion are not linear. Physically this happens when the wave disturbance is relatively large and the ordinary linear laws of mechanical action no longer hold. For example, beyond the elastic limit Hooke's law no longer holds and the linear relation $F = -kx$ can no longer be used.

As for sound, violent explosions create shock waves. Although shock waves are longitudinal elastic waves in air, they behave differently from ordinary sound waves. The equation governing their propagation is quadratic, and superposition does not hold. With two very loud notes the ear hears something more than just the two individual notes. Those familiar with high-fidelity apparatus will know that "intermodulation distortion" between two tones arises when the system fails to combine the tones linearly, and that this distortion is more apparent when the amplitude of the tones is high. A more obvious physical example is water waves. Ripples cannot travel independently across breakers as they can across gentle swells.

The importance of the superposition principle physically is that, where it holds, it makes it possible to analyze a complicated wave motion as a combination of simple waves. In fact, as was shown by the French mathematician J. Fourier (1768–1830), all that we need to build up the most general form of periodic wave are simple harmonic waves.* Fourier showed that any periodic motion of a particle can be represented as a combination of simple harmonic motions. For example, if $y(t)$ represents the motion of a source of waves having a period $T$, we can analyze $y(t)$ as follows:

$$y(t) = A_0 + A_1 \sin \omega t + A_2 \sin 2\omega t + A_3 \sin 3\omega t + \cdots$$
$$+ B_1 \cos \omega t + B_2 \cos 2\omega t + B_3 \cos 3\omega t + \cdots$$

where $\omega = 2\pi/T$. This expression is called a Fourier series. The $A$'s and $B$'s are constants which have definite values for any particular periodic motion $y(t)$. (See Fig. 19–5, for example.) If the motion is not periodic, as a pulse, the sum is replaced by an integral, the so-called Fourier integral. Hence, any motion of a source of waves can be represented in terms of simple harmonic motions. Since the motion of the source creates the

---

* See, for example, Thomas, *Calculus and Analytic Geometry*, Addison-Wesley, second edition, 1953, pp. 596–599.

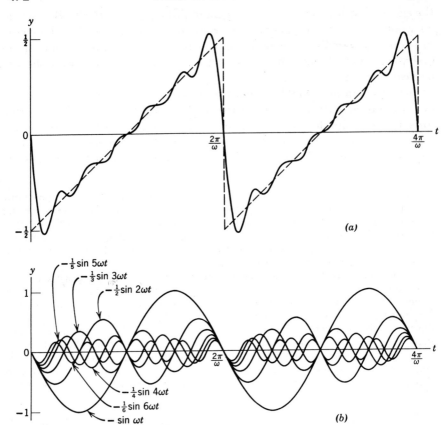

**Fig. 19–5** (a) The dashed line is a sawtooth "wave" commonly encountered in electronics. It can be written $y(t) = (\omega/2\pi)t - \frac{1}{2}$ for $0 < t < 2\pi/\omega$, as $y(t) = (\omega/2\pi)t - \frac{3}{2}$ for $2\pi/\omega < t < 4\pi/\omega$, etc. The Fourier series for this function is $y(t) = -\sin \omega t - \frac{1}{2}\sin 2\omega t - \frac{1}{3}\sin 3\omega t - \ldots$ The solid line is the sum of the first six terms of this series and can be seen to approximate the sawtooth quite closely, except for overshooting near the discontinuities. As more terms of the series are included, the approximation becomes better and better. (b) Here are shown the first six terms of the Fourier series which, when added together, yield the solid curve in (a).

waves, it should come as no surprise that the waves themselves can be analyzed as combinations of simple harmonic waves. Herein lies the importance of simple harmonic motion and simple harmonic waves.

### 19–5  Wave Speed

Given the characteristics of the medium it should be possible to calculate the wave speed from the basic principles of Newtonian mechanics. In this section we continue to focus our attention on transverse waves in a string and in Supplementary Topic III we show how to calculate the speed of such waves in the most general way. Here we consider two other approaches— a treatment based on dimensional analysis and a somewhat less general mechanical analysis in which we compute the speed of a transverse pulse along a stretched string.

We stated in Section 19–1 that the wave speed for a medium depends on the elasticity of the medium and on its inertia. For a stretched string the elasticity is measured by the tension $F$ in the string; the greater the tension the greater will be the elastic restoring force on an element of the string that is pulled sideways. The inertia characteristic is measured by $\mu$, the mass per unit length of the string. Assuming, then, that the wave speed $v$ depends only on $F$ and $\mu$, we can use dimensional analysis to find how $v$ depends on these quantities. In terms of mass $M$, length $L$, and time $T$, the dimensions of $F$ are $MLT^{-2}$ and the dimensions of $\mu$ are $ML^{-1}$. The only way these dimensions can be combined to get a velocity (which has the dimensions $LT^{-1}$) is to take the square root of $F/\mu$. That is, $F/\mu$ has the dimensions $L^2 T^{-2}$ and $\sqrt{F/\mu}$ has the dimensions $LT^{-1}$ of a velocity. Dimensional analysis cannot account for any dimensionless quantities, so that the result

$$v = \sqrt{\frac{F}{\mu}} \qquad (19\text{–}12)$$

may or may not be complete. The most we can say is that the wave speed is equal to a dimensionless constant times $\sqrt{F/\mu}$. The value of the constant can be obtained from a mechanical analysis of the problem or from experiment. These methods show that the constant is equal to unity and that Eq. 19–12 is correct as it stands.

Now let us *derive* the velocity of a pulse in a stretched string by a mechanical analysis. In Fig. 19–6 we show a wave pulse proceeding from right to left in the string with a speed $v$. We can imagine the entire string to be moved from left to right with this same speed so that the wave pulse remains fixed in space, whereas the particles composing the string successively pass through the pulse. This simply means that, instead of taking our reference frame to be the walls between which the string is stretched, we choose a reference frame which is in uniform motion with respect to that one. Because Newton's laws involve only accelerations, which are the same in both frames, we can use them in either frame. We just happen to choose a more convenient frame.

We consider a small section of the pulse of length $\Delta l$ to form an arc of a circle of radius $R$, as shown in the diagram. If $\mu$ is the mass per unit length of the string, the so-called linear density, then $\mu \, \Delta l$ is the mass of this element. The tension $F$ in the string is a tangential pull at each end of this small segment of the string. The horizontal components cancel and the vertical components are each equal to

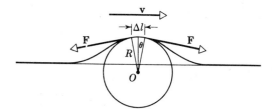

**Fig. 19–6** Derivation of wave speed by considering the forces on a section of string of length $\Delta l$.

$F \sin \theta$. Hence, the total vertical force is $2F \sin \theta$. Since $\theta$ is small, we can take $\sin \theta \cong \theta$ and

$$2F \sin \theta = 2F\theta = 2F \frac{(\Delta l/2)}{R} = F \frac{\Delta l}{R}.$$

This gives the force supplying the centripetal acceleration of the string particles directed toward $O$. Now the centripetal force acting on a mass $\mu \, \Delta l$ moving in a circle of radius $R$ with speed $v$ is $\mu \, \Delta l \, v^2/R$; see Section 6–3. Notice that the tangential velocity $v$ of this mass element along the top of the arc is horizontal and is the same as the pulse phase velocity. Combining the equivalent expressions just given we obtain

$$F \frac{\Delta l}{R} = \frac{\mu \, \Delta l \, v^2}{R}$$

or

$$v = \sqrt{\frac{F}{\mu}}.$$

If the amplitude of the pulse were very large compared to the length of the string, we would not have been able to use the approximation $\sin \theta \cong \theta$. Furthermore, the tension $F$ in the string would be changed by the presence of the pulse, whereas we assumed $F$ to be unchanged from the original tension in the stretched string. Therefore, our result, like superposition, holds only for relatively small transverse displacements of the string—which case, however, is widely applicable in practice. Notice also that the wave speed is independent of the shape of the wave, for no particular assumption about the actual shape of the pulse was used in the proof.

The frequency of a wave is naturally determined by the frequency of the source. The speed with which the wave travels through a medium is determined by the properties of the medium, as illustrated before. Once the frequency $\nu$ and speed $v$ of the wave are determined, the wavelength $\lambda$ is fixed. In fact, from Eq. 19–7 and the relation, $\nu = 1/T$, we have

$$\lambda = \frac{v}{\nu}. \tag{19–13}$$

▶ **Example 1.** A transverse sinusoidal wave is generated at one end of a long horizontal string by a bar which moves the end up and down through a distance of $\frac{1}{2}$ ft. The motion is continuous and is repeated regularly twice each second.

(a) If the string has a linear density of 0.0050 slug/ft and is kept under a tension of 2.0 lb, find the speed, amplitude, frequency, and wavelength of the wave motion.

The end moves $\frac{1}{4}$ ft away from the equilibrium position, first above it, then below it, for a total displacement of $\frac{1}{2}$ ft. Therefore, the amplitude $y_m$ is $\frac{1}{4}$ ft.

The entire motion is repeated twice each second so that the frequency is 2.0 vibrations per second.

The wave speed is given by $v = \sqrt{F/\mu}$. But $F = 2.0$ lb and $\mu = 0.0050$ slug/ft, so that

$$v = \sqrt{\frac{2.0 \text{ lb}}{0.0050 \text{ slug/ft}}} = 20 \text{ ft/sec.}$$

The wavelength is given by $\lambda = v/\nu$, so that

$$\lambda = \frac{20 \text{ ft/sec}}{2.0 \text{ vib/sec}} = 10 \text{ ft.}$$

(b) Assuming the wave moves from left to right and that, at $t = 0$, the end of the string described by $x = 0$ is in its equilibrium position $y = 0$, write the equation of the wave.

The general expression for a transverse sinusoidal wave moving from left to right is

$$y = y_m \sin (kx - \omega t - \phi).$$

Requiring that $y = 0$ for the conditions $x = 0$ and $t = 0$ yields

$$0 = y_m \sin (-\phi),$$

which means that the phase constant $\phi$ must be zero.* Hence for this wave

$$y = y_m \sin (kx - \omega t),$$

and with the values just found,

$$y_m = \tfrac{1}{4} \text{ ft} = 0.25 \text{ ft},$$

$$\lambda = 10 \text{ ft} \quad \text{or} \quad k = \frac{2\pi}{\lambda} = \frac{\pi}{5} \text{ ft}^{-1},$$

$$v = 20 \text{ ft/sec} \quad \text{or} \quad \omega = vk = 4\pi \text{ sec}^{-1},$$

we obtain as the equation for the wave

$$y = 0.25 \sin (0.2\pi x - 4\pi t),$$

where $x$ and $y$ are in feet and $t$ is in seconds.

**Example 2.** As this wave passes along the string, each particle of the string moves up and down at right angles to the direction of the wave motion. Find the velocity and acceleration of a particle 10 ft from the end.

The general form of this wave is

$$y = y_m \sin (kx - \omega t) = y_m \sin k(x - vt).$$

The $v$ in this equation is the constant horizontal velocity of the wavetrain. What we are after now is the velocity of a particle in the string through which this wave moves; this particle velocity is neither horizontal nor constant. In fact, each particle moves vertically, that is, in the $y$-direction. In order to determine the particle velocity, which we shall designate by the symbol $u$, let us fix our attention on a particle at a particular position $x$—that is, $x$ is now a constant in this equation—and ask how the particle displacement $y$ changes with time. With $x$ constant we obtain

$$u = \frac{\partial y}{\partial t} = -y_m \omega \cos (kx - \omega t),$$

in which the *partial derivative* notation $\partial y / \partial t$ reminds us that although in general $y$ is a function of both $x$ and $t$, we here assume that $x$ remains constant so that $t$ becomes the only variable. The acceleration $a$ of the particle at this (constant)

---

* It could also be $\pi$, $2\pi$, $3\pi$, etc., but these values for $\phi$ will not change our final results, as the student should show.

value of $x$ is

$$a = \frac{\partial^2 y}{\partial t^2} = \frac{\partial u}{\partial t} = -y_m \omega^2 \sin{(kx - \omega t)} = -\omega^2 y.$$

This shows that for each particle through which this transverse sinusoidal wave passes we have precisely SHM (simple harmonic motion), for the acceleration $a$ is proportional to the displacement $y$, but oppositely directed.

For a particle at $x = 10$ ft with the wave of Example 1, in which

$$y_m = 0.25 \text{ ft}, \qquad k = \frac{\pi}{5} \text{ ft}^{-1}, \qquad \omega = 4\pi \text{ sec}^{-1},$$

we obtain $\qquad\qquad u = -y_m \omega \cos{(kx - \omega t)}$

or $\quad u = -(0.25) \left[ 4\pi \cos{\left( \frac{10\pi}{5} - 4\pi t \right)} \right] = -\pi \cos{(2\pi - 4\pi t)},$

and $\qquad\qquad a = -\omega^2 y$

or $\quad a = -(4\pi)^2 0.25 \sin{(0.2\pi x - 4\pi t)} = -4\pi^2 \sin{(2\pi - 4\pi t)},$

where $t$ is expressed in seconds $u$ in ft/sec and $a$ in ft/sec$^2$.

Can you describe the motion of this particle at the time $t = 4$ sec?  ◀

## 19–6  Power and Intensity in Wave Motion

In Fig. 19-7 we draw an element of the stretched string at some position $x$ and at a particular time $t$. The *transverse* component of the tension in the string exerted *by* the element to the left of $x$ *on* the element of the right of $x$ is

$$F_{\text{trans}} = -F \frac{\partial y}{\partial x}.$$

$\mathbf{F}$ is the tension in the string; $\partial y / \partial x$ gives the tangent of the angle made by the direction of $\mathbf{F}$ with the horizontal at the time $t$ in question and, because we assume small displacements, this can be taken equal also to the sine of the angle. The transverse force is in the direction of increasing $y$; in the figure the slope is negative, so the transverse force is positive. The transverse velocity of the particle at $x$ is $\partial y / \partial t$, which may be positive or negative. The power being expended by

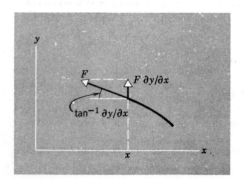

**Fig. 19–7** The transverse component of the tension in the string at each point $x$ is $F\ (\partial y / \partial x)$.

the force at $x$, or the energy passing through the position $x$ per unit time in the positive $x$-direction (see Section 7–6), is

$$P = \left(-F \frac{\partial y}{\partial x}\right) \frac{\partial y}{\partial t}.$$

Suppose that the wave on the string is the simple sine wave

$$y = y_m \sin (kx - \omega t).$$

Then the magnitude of the slope at $x$ is

$$\frac{\partial y}{\partial x} = k y_m \cos (kx - \omega t), \qquad [t = \text{constant}]$$

and the transverse force is

$$-F \frac{\partial y}{\partial x} = -F k y_m \cos (kx - \omega t).$$

The transverse velocity of a particle of the string at $x$ is

$$u = \frac{\partial y}{\partial t} = -\omega y_m \cos (kx - \omega t), \qquad [x = \text{constant}].$$

Hence, the power transmitted through $x$ is

$$P = (-F k y_m)(-\omega y_m) \cos^2 (kx - \omega t),$$
$$= y_m^2 k \omega F \cos^2 (kx - \omega t).$$

Notice that the power or rate of flow of energy is not constant. The power is not constant because the power input oscillates. As the energy is passed along the string, it is stored in each element of string as a combination of kinetic energy of motion and potential energy of deformation. The situation is much like that in an alternating current circuit; there energy is stored both in the inductor and in the capacitor and the power input oscillates. For a string the power is absorbed by internal friction and viscous effects and appears as heat; in the circuit the power is expended in the resistor and appears as heat. The power input to the string or the circuit is often taken to be the *average* over one period of motion. The average power delivered is

$$\bar{P} = \frac{1}{T} \int_t^{t+T} P \, dt,$$

where $T$ is the period. Using the fact that the average value of $\sin^2 x$ or $\cos^2 x$ over one cycle is $\frac{1}{2}$, we obtain for the string

$$\bar{P} = \frac{1}{2} y_m^2 k \omega F = 2\pi^2 y_m^2 \nu^2 \frac{F}{v},$$

a result which does not depend on $x$ or $t$. For the string, however, $v = \sqrt{F/\mu}$, so that

$$\bar{P} = 2\pi^2 y_m^2 \nu^2 \mu v.$$

The fact that the rate of transfer of energy depends on the square of the wave amplitude and square of the wave frequency is true in general, holding for all types of waves.

The student should confirm the fact that, if we had picked a wave traveling in the negative $x$-direction, we would have obtained the negative of this result. That is, the wave delivers power in the direction of wave propagation.

In a three-dimensional wave, such as a light wave or a sound wave from a point source, it is more significant to speak of the *intensity* of the wave. Intensity is defined as the power transmitted across a unit area normal to the direction in which the wave is traveling. Just as with power in the wave in a string, the intensity of a space wave is always proportional to the square of the amplitude.

As a wave progresses through space, its energy may be absorbed. For example, in a viscous medium, such as syrup or lead, mechanical waves would rapidly decay in amplitude and disappear, owing to absorption of energy by internal friction. In most cases of interest to us, however, absorption will be negligible. Throughout this chapter we have assumed that there is no loss of energy in a given wave, no matter how far it travels.

▶ **Example 3.** Spherical waves travel from a source of waves whose power output is $P$; see Fig. 19–8. Find how the wave intensity depends on the distance from the source. We assume that the medium is isotropic and that the source radiates uniformly in all directions, that is, that its emission is spherically symmetrical.

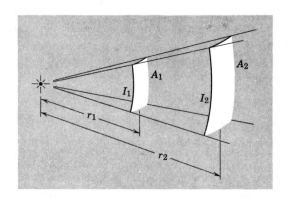

**Fig. 19–8** Example 3.

The intensity of a 3-dimensional wave is the power transmitted across a unit area normal to the direction of propagation. As the wavefront expands from a distance $r_1$ from the source at the center to a distance $r_2$, its surface area increases from $4\pi r_1^2$ to $4\pi r_2^2$. If there is no absorption of energy, the total energy transported per second by the wave remains constant at the value $P$, so that

$$P = 4\pi r_1^2 I_1 = 4\pi r_2^2 I_2,$$

where $I_1$ and $I_2$ are the wave intensities at $r_1$ and $r_2$ respectively. Hence,

$$\frac{I_1}{I_2} = \frac{r_2^2}{r_1^2}$$

and the wave intensity varies inversely as the square of its distance from the source. Since the intensity is proportional to the square of the amplitude, the amplitude of the wave must vary inversely as the distance from the source. ◀

### 19–7 Interference of Waves

*Interference* refers to the physical effects of superimposing two or more wave trains. Let us consider two waves of equal frequency and amplitude traveling with the same speed in the same direction ($+x$) but with a phase difference $\phi$ between them. The equations of the two waves will be

$$y_1 = y_m \sin (kx - \omega t - \phi) \qquad (19\text{-}14)$$

and $\qquad y_2 = y_m \sin (kx - \omega t). \qquad (19\text{-}15)$

We can rewrite the first equation in two equivalent forms

$$y_1 = y_m \sin \left[ k \left( x - \frac{\phi}{k} \right) - \omega t \right] \qquad (19\text{-}14a)$$

or $\qquad y_1 = y_m \sin \left[ kx - \omega \left( t + \frac{\phi}{\omega} \right) \right]. \qquad (19\text{-}14b)$

Equations 19-14a and 19-15 suggest that if we take a "snapshot" of the two waves at any time $t$, we will find them displaced from one another along the $x$-axis by the constant distance $\phi/k$. Equations 19-14b and 19-15 suggest that if we station ourselves at any position $x$ the two waves will give rise to two simple harmonic motions having a constant time difference $\phi/\omega$. This gives some insight into the meaning of the phase difference $\phi$.

Now let us find the resultant wave, which, on the assumption that superposition occurs, is the sum of Eqs. 19-14 and 19-15 or

$$y = y_1 + y_2 = y_m[\sin (kx - \omega t - \phi) + \sin (kx - \omega t)].$$

From the trigonometric equation for the sum of the sines of two angles

$$\sin B + \sin C = 2 \sin \tfrac{1}{2}(B + C) \cos \tfrac{1}{2}(C - B), \qquad (19\text{-}16)$$

we obtain $\qquad y = y_m \left[ 2 \sin \left( kx - \omega t - \frac{\phi}{2} \right) \cos \frac{\phi}{2} \right],$

$$= \left( 2y_m \cos \frac{\phi}{2} \right) \sin \left( kx - \omega t - \frac{\phi}{2} \right). \qquad (19\text{-}17)$$

This resultant wave corresponds to a new wave having the same frequency but with an amplitude $2y_m \cos (\phi/2)$. If $\phi$ is *very small* (compared to 180°), the resultant amplitude will be nearly $2y_m$. That is, when $\phi$ is very small, $\cos (\phi/2) \cong \cos 0° = 1$. When $\phi$ is *zero*, the two waves have the same phase everywhere. The crest of one corresponds to the crest of the other and likewise for the troughs. The waves are then said to interfere constructively. The resultant amplitude is just twice that of either wave alone. If $\phi$ is *near* 180°, on the other hand, the resultant amplitude will be *nearly* zero. That is, when $\phi \cong 180°$, $\cos (\phi/2) \cong \cos 90° = 0$. When $\phi$ is *exactly* 180°, the crest of one wave corresponds exactly to the trough of the other. The waves are then said to interfere destructively. The resultant amplitude is zero.

In Fig. 19-9a we show the superposition of two wavetrains almost in phase ($\phi$ small) and in Fig. 19-9b the superposition of two wavetrains almost 180° out of phase ($\phi \cong 180°$). Notice that in these figures the

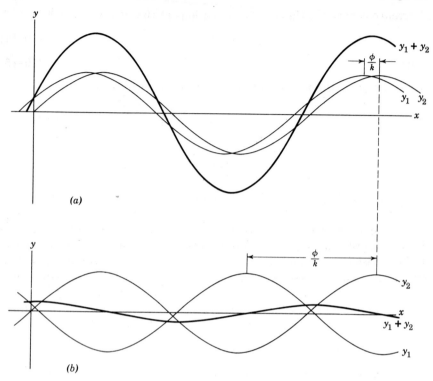

(a)

(b)

**Fig. 19–9**  (a) The superposition of two waves of equal frequency and amplitude that are almost in phase results in a wave of almost twice the amplitude of either component.  (b) The superposition of two waves of equal frequency and amplitude and almost 180° out of phase results in a wave whose amplitude is nearly zero.  Note that in both the resultant frequency is unchanged.  (The drawings correspond to the instant $t = 0$.)

algebraic sum of the ordinates of the thin (component) curves at any value of $x$ equals the ordinate of the thick (resultant) curve.  The sum of two waves can, therefore, have different values, depending on their phase relations.

The resultant wave will be a sine wave, even when the amplitudes of the component sine waves are unequal.  Figure 19–10, for example, illustrates the addition of two sine waves of the same frequency and velocity but different amplitudes.  The resultant amplitude depends on the phase difference, which is taken as zero in this figure.  The result for other phase differences could be obtained by shifting one of the component waves sideways with respect to the other and would give a smaller resultant amplitude.  The smallest resultant amplitude would be the difference in the amplitudes of the components, obtained when the phases differ by 180°.  However, the resultant is always a sine wave.  The addition of any number of sine waves having the same frequency and velocity gives a

**Fig. 19–10** The addition of two waves of same frequency and phase but differing amplitudes (light lines) yields a third wave of the same frequency and phase (heavy line).

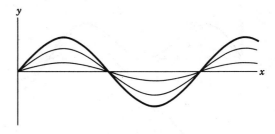

similar result.   The resultant waveform will always have a constant amplitude because the component waves (and their resultant) all move with the same velocity and maintain the same relative position.   The actual state of affairs can be pictured by having all the waves in Figs. 19–9 and 19–10 move toward the right with the same speed.

In practice, interference effects are obtained from wavetrains which originate in the same source (or in sources having a fixed phase relationship to one another) but which follow different paths to the point of interference. The phase difference $\phi$ between the waves arriving at a point can be calculated by finding the difference between the paths traversed by them from the source to the point of interference.   The path difference is $\phi/k$ or $(\phi/2\pi)\lambda$.   When the path difference is 0, $\lambda$, $2\lambda$, $3\lambda$, etc., so that $\phi = 0$, $2\pi$, $4\pi$, etc., the two waves interfere constructively.   For path differences of $\frac{1}{2}\lambda$, $\frac{3}{2}\lambda$, $\frac{5}{2}\lambda$, etc., $\phi$ is $\pi$, $3\pi$, $5\pi$, etc., and the waves interfere destructively. We shall return to these matters later in more detail.

## 19–8   Complex Waves

The waves we have considered so far have been of the simple harmonic type, in which the displacements at any time are represented by a sine curve.   We have seen that superposition of any number of such waves having the same frequency and velocity, but arbitrary amplitudes and phases, still gives rise to a resultant wave of this simple type.   If, however, we superimpose waves that have *different frequencies*, the resulting wave is *complex*.   In a complex wave the motion of a particle is no longer simple harmonic motion, and the wave shape is no longer a sine curve.   In this section we consider only the qualitative aspects of complex waves. The analytical treatment of such waves will be given when we encounter physical situations described by them.   We will look at the results of adding graphically two or more waves traveling with the same speed in the same direction but having various relative frequencies, amplitudes, and phases.

In Figs. 19–11a and 19–11b we add two waves having the same amplitude but having frequencies in the ratio 3 to 1; the phase relation is changed from a to b and we see how changing the phase relation may produce a resultant of very different form.   If these represent sound waves, our eardrums will vibrate in a way represented by the resultant in each case, but we will hear and interpret these as the two original frequencies, regardless of their phase relation.   If the resultant waves represent visible light, our eyes will receive the same sensation of a mixture of two colors, regardless of the phase relation of the components.

In Fig. 19–12 three waves of different frequencies, and amplitudes are added. The resultant complex wave is quite different from a simple periodic wave and, in this respect resembles waveforms normally generated by musical instruments.   In Fig. 19–13 a wave of very high frequency is added to one of very low frequency.

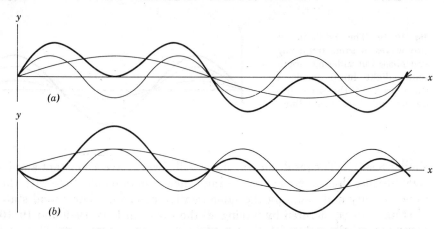

**Fig. 19–11**   The addition of two waves with frequency ratio 3:1 (light lines) yields a wave whose shape (heavy line) depends on the phase relationship of the components. Compare (a) and (b).

**Fig. 19–12**   The addition of three waves (top) of differing frequencies yields a complex waveform (bottom).

**Fig. 19–13**   The addition (heavy line) of two waves of widely differing frequency (light lines).

**Fig. 19–14** The addition (bottom) of two waves with nearly the same frequency (top), illustrating the phenomenon of beats. (see Chapter 20.)

Each component frequency is clearly discernible in the resultant. In Fig. 19–14 two waves of nearly the same frequency are added. The resultant wave consists of groups which, in the case of sound, produce the familiar phenomenon of beats (Section 20–6).

In all of these figures the resultant wave is obtained under the assumption that the principle of superposition holds, by simply adding the displacements caused by the individual waves at every point. Because all the component waves travel with the same velocity, the resultant waveform moves with this same velocity and the wave shape is unchanged.

The cathode-ray oscilloscope (Chapter 27) gives the simplest way of observing how complex waves can be synthesized and analyzed in terms of simple harmonic waves.

## 19–9 Standing Waves

In a one-dimensional body of finite size, such as a taut string held by two clamps a distance $l$ apart, traveling waves in the string are reflected from the boundaries of the body, that is, from the clamps. Each such reflection gives rise to a wave traveling in the string in the opposite direction. The reflected waves add to the incident waves according to the principle of superposition.

Consider two wavetrains of the same frequency, speed, and amplitude which are traveling in *opposite directions* along a string. Two such waves may be represented by the equations

$$y_1 = y_m \sin (kx - \omega t),$$

$$y_2 = y_m \sin (kx + \omega t).$$

Hence, the resultant may be written as

$$y = y_1 + y_2 = y_m \sin (kx - \omega t) + y_m \sin (kx + \omega t) \quad (19\text{–}18a)$$

or, making use of the trigonometric relation of Eq. 19–16, as

$$y = 2y_m \sin kx \cos \omega t. \quad (19\text{–}18b)$$

Equation 19–18b is the equation of a *standing* wave.* Notice that a

---

* Standing waves may also be produced in finite bodies of two or three dimensions; see Sections 20–5 and 38–5 respectively for examples.

particle at any particular point $x$ executes simple harmonic motion as time goes on, and that all particles vibrate with the same frequency. In a traveling wave each particle of the string vibrates with the same amplitude. *Characteristic of a standing wave, however, is the fact that the amplitude is not the same for different particles but varies with the location $x$ of the particle.* * In fact, the amplitude, $2y_m \sin kx$, has a *maximum* value of $2y_m$ at positions where

$$kx = \frac{\pi}{2}, \frac{3\pi}{2}, \frac{5\pi}{2}, \text{etc.}$$

or

$$x = \frac{\lambda}{4}, \frac{3\lambda}{4}, \frac{5\lambda}{4}, \text{etc.}$$

These points are called *antinodes* and are spaced one-half wavelength apart. The amplitude has a *minimum* value of zero at positions where

$$kx = \pi, 2\pi, 3\pi, \text{etc.}$$

or

$$x = \frac{\lambda}{2}, \lambda, \frac{3\lambda}{2}, 2\lambda, \text{etc.}$$

These points are called *nodes* and are spaced one-half wavelength apart. The separation between a node and an adjacent antinode is one-quarter wavelength.

It is clear that energy is not transported along the string to the right or to the left, for energy cannot flow past the nodal points in the string which are permanently at rest. Hence, the energy remains "standing" in the string, although it alternates between vibrational kinetic energy and elastic potential energy. We call the motion a wave motion because we can think of it as a superposition of waves traveling in opposite directions (Eq. 19–18a). We can equally well regard the motion as an oscillation of the string as a whole (Eq. 19–18b), each particle oscillating with SHM of angular frequency $\omega$ and with an amplitude that depends on its location. Each small part of the string has inertia and elasticity, and the string as a whole can be thought of as a collection of coupled oscillators. Hence, the vibrating string is the same in principle† as a spring-mass system, except that a spring-mass system has only one natural frequency, and a vibrating string has a large number of natural frequencies (Section 19–10).

In Fig. 19–15, in (a), (b), (c), and (d), we show a standing wave pattern separately at intervals of one-quarter of a period in the lower figures, 3. The traveling waves, one moving in the positive $x$-direction and the other moving in the negative $x$-direction, whose superposition can be considered

---

* The combining waves moving in opposite directions along the string will still produce standing waves even if their amplitudes are unequal. We consider only the equal-amplitude case here; see Problem 25, however.

† For a general discussion see "On the Teaching of 'Standing Waves,' " J. Rekveld, *American Journal of Physics*, March 1958, p. 159.

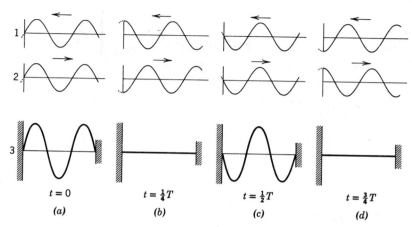

**Fig. 19-15** Standing waves as the superposition of left- and right-going waves; 1 and 2 are the components, 3 the resultant.

to give rise to the standing wave, are shown for the same quarter-period intervals in the upper figures 2 and 1. Standing waves can also be produced with electromagnetic waves and with sound waves.

In Fig. 19-16 we show how the energy associated with the oscillating string shifts back and forth between kinetic energy of motion $K$ and potential energy of deformation $U$ during one cycle. The student should compare this with Fig. 8-4, which shows the same thing for a mass-spring oscillator. Oscillating strings often vibrate so rapidly that the eye perceives only a blur whose shape is that of the envelope of the motion; see Fig. 19-17.

The superposition of an incident wave and a reflected wave, being the sum of two waves traveling in opposite directions, will give rise to a standing wave. We shall now consider the process of reflection of a wave more closely. Suppose a pulse travels down a stretched string which is fixed at one end, as shown in Fig. 19-18a. When the pulse arrives at that end, it exerts an upward force on the support. The support is rigid, however, and does not move. By Newton's third law the support exerts an equal but oppositely directed force on the string. This reaction force generates a pulse at the support, which travels back along the string in a direction opposite to that of the incident pulse. We say that the incident pulse has been *reflected* at the fixed end point of the string. Notice that the reflected pulse returns with its transverse displacement reversed. If a wavetrain is incident on the fixed end point, a reflected wavetrain is generated at that point in the same way. The displacement of any point along the string is the sum of the displacements caused by the incident and reflected wave. Since the end point is fixed, these two waves must always interfere destructively at that point so as to give zero displacement there. Hence, the reflected wave is always 180° out of phase with the incident wave at a fixed

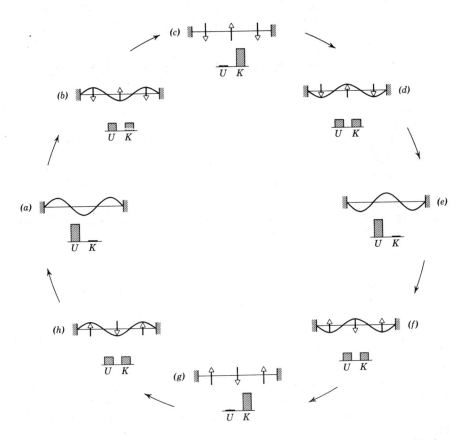

**Fig. 19–16** A standing wave in a stretched string, showing one cycle of oscillation. At (a) the string is momentarily at rest and the energy of the system is all potential energy of elastic deformation associated with the transverse displacement of the string. (b) An eighth-cycle later the displacement is reduced and the string is in motion. The two arrows show the velocities of the string particles at the positions shown. $K$ and $U$ have the same value. (c) The string is not displaced, but its particles have their maximum speeds; the energy is all kinetic. The motion continues until the initial condition (a) is reached after which the cycle continues to repeat itself.

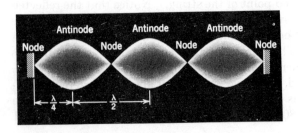

**Fig. 19–17** The envelope of a standing wave, corresponding to a time exposure of the motion, and showing the patterns of nodes and antinodes.

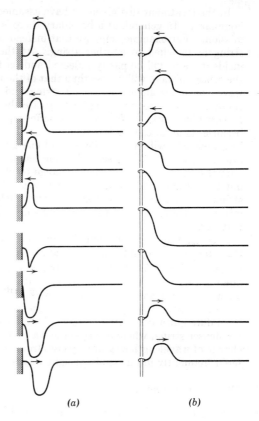

**Fig. 19–18** (*a*) Reflection of a pulse at the fixed end of a string. The drawings are spaced uniformly in time. The phase is changed by 180° on reflection. (*b*) Reflection of a pulse at an end free to move in a transverse direction. (The string is attached to a ring which slides vertically without friction.) The phase is unchanged on reflection.

(*a*)                          (*b*)

boundary. We say that *on reflection from a fixed end a wave undergoes a phase change of 180°*.

Let us now consider the reflection of a pulse at a free end of a stretched string, that is, at an end that is free to move transversely. This can be achieved by attaching the end to a very light ring free to slide without friction along a transverse rod, or (see later) to a long and very much lighter string. When the pulse arrives at the free end, it exerts a force on the element of string there. This element is accelerated and its inertia carries it past the equilibrium point; it "overshoots" and exerts a reaction force on the string. This generates a pulse which travels back along the string in a direction opposite to that of the incident pulse. Once again we get reflection, but now at a free end. The free end will obviously suffer the maximum displacement of the particles on the string; an incident and a reflected wavetrain must interfere constructively at that point if we are to have a maximum there. Hence, the reflected wave is always in phase with the incident wave at that point (see Fig. 19–18*b*). We say that *at a free end a wave is reflected without change of phase.*

Hence, when we have a standing wave in a string, there will be a node at a fixed end and an antinode at a free end. These ideas will be applied to sound waves and electromagnetic waves in subsequent chapters.

In the treatment just given we have assumed that there is total reflection at the boundary. In general, at a boundary there is partial reflection and partial transmission. For example, suppose that instead of being attached to a rigid wall the string is attached to another string. At the boundary joining the strings the incident wave will be partly reflected and partly transmitted. The amplitude of the reflected wave will be less than that of the incident wave because a transmitted wave continues along the second string and carries away some of the incident energy. If the second string has a greater linear density than the first, the wave reflected back into the first will still suffer a phase shift of 180° on reflection. But because its amplitude is less than the incident wave, the boundary point will not be a node and will move. Thus a net energy transfer occurs along the first string into the second. If the second string has a smaller linear density than the first, partial reflection occurs without change of phase, but once again energy is transmitted to the second string. In practice the best way to realize a "free end" for a string is to attach it to a long and very much lighter string. The energy transmitted is negligible, and the second string serves to maintain the tension in the first one.

It is of interest to note that the transmitted wave travels with a different speed than the incident and reflected waves. The wave speed is determined by the relation $v = \sqrt{F/\mu}$; the tension is the same in both strings, but their densities are different. Hence, the wave travels more slowly in the denser string. The frequency of the transmitted wave is the same as that of the incident and reflected waves. Waves having the same frequency but traveling with different speeds have different wavelengths. Hence, from the relation $\lambda = v/\nu$ we conclude that in the denser string, where $v$ is less, the wavelength is shorter. This phenomenon of change of wavelength as a wave passes from one medium to another will be encountered frequently in our study of light waves.

## 19–10  Resonance

In general, whenever a system capable of oscillating is acted on by a periodic series of impulses having a frequency equal or nearly equal to one of the natural frequencies of oscillation of the system, the system is set into oscillation with a relatively large amplitude. This phenomenon is called *resonance* (see Section 15–10) and the system is said to resonate with the applied impulses.

Consider a string fixed at both ends. Oscillations or standing waves can be established in the string. The only requirement we have to satisfy is that the end points be nodes. There may be any number of nodes in between or none at all, so that the wavelength associated with the standing waves can take on many different values. The distance between adjacent nodes is $\lambda/2$, so that in a string of length $l$ there must be exactly an integral number $n$ of half wavelengths, $\lambda/2$. That is,

$$\frac{n\lambda}{2} = l$$

or
$$\lambda = \frac{2l}{n}, \qquad n = 1, 2, 3, \cdots .$$

But $\lambda = v/\nu$ and $v = \sqrt{F/\mu}$, so that the natural frequencies of oscillation of the system are

$$\nu = \frac{n}{2l} \sqrt{\frac{F}{\mu}}, \quad n = 1, 2, 3, \cdots . \tag{19–19}$$

If the string is set vibrating and left to itself, the oscillations gradually die out. The motion is damped by dissipation of energy through the elastic supports at the ends and by the resistance of the air to the motion. We can pump energy into the system by applying a driving force. If the driving frequency is near that of any natural frequency of the string, the string will vibrate at that frequency with a large amplitude. Because the string has a large number of natural frequencies, resonance can occur at many different frequencies. A mass-spring system, by contrast, has only one resonant frequency. The difference is associated with the fact that in the mass-spring system the inertia characteristic is concentrated ("lumped") in one part of the system—the mass—and the elastic characteristic is concentrated in a separate part of the system—the spring. We say that this system has *lumped elements*.

A stretched string, on the other hand, is said to have *distributed elements* because every element of the string has both inertia and elastic characteristics. In the mass-spring system, there is only one way to exchange energy between kinetic and potential forms as the system oscillates; energy in kinetic form must be associated with the moving mass and energy in potential form must be associated with the deformed spring. In the stretched string, however, masslike (inertia) and springlike (elasticity) elements are distributed uniformly along the string. There are many possible ways, rather than a single way, of exchanging energy between kinetic and potential forms as the system oscillates, corresponding to the sequence of allowed values for $n$ in Eq. 19–19.

Resonance in a string is often demonstrated by attaching a string to a fixed end, by means of a weight attached to it over a pulley, and connecting the other end to a vibrator, as shown in Fig. 19–19. The transverse oscillations of the vibrator set up a traveling wave in the string which is reflected back from the fixed end. The frequency of the waves is that of the vibrator, and the wavelength is determined by $\lambda = v/\nu$. The fixed end $P$

**Fig. 19–19** Standing waves in a driven string when the natural and driving frequencies are very nearly equal.

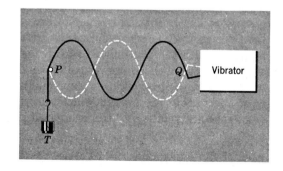

is a node, but the end $Q$ vibrates and is not. If we now vary the tension in the string by changing the hanging weight, for example, we can change the wavelength. Changing the tension changes the wave velocity, and the wavelength changes in proportion to the velocity, the frequency being constant. Whenever the wavelength becomes nearly equal to $2l/n$, where $l$ is the length of the string, we obtain standing waves of great amplitude. The string now vibrates in one of its natural modes and resonates with the vibrator. The vibrator does work on the string to maintain these oscillations against the losses due to damping. The amplitude builds up only to the point at which the vibrator expends all its energy input against damping losses. The point $Q$ is almost a node because the amplitude of the vibrator is small compared to that of the string.

Hence, with damping, the resonant frequency is almost, but not quite, a natural frequency of the string. One end point is a node, the other almost a node. In between there are points that are almost nodes, points at which the amplitude is very small. These points cannot be true nodes, for energy must flow along the string past them from the vibrator. This situation is analogous to the resonance condition for a damped harmonic oscillator with driving force, discussed in Section 15–10. There, too, the resonant frequency was almost the same as the natural frequency of the system, and the amplitude was large but not infinite. If no damping were present, the resonant frequency would be exactly a natural frequency. Then the amplitude would build up to infinity as the energy is pumped in. In practice, the system would cease to obey Hooke's law, or the small-oscillations condition, as the amplitude becomes large and the system would break. This happens even with damping, when the damping is small or the driving force is large (as in the Tacoma Bridge disaster, Fig. 15–21).

If the frequency of the vibrator is much different from a natural frequency of the system, as given by Eq. 19–19, the wave reflected at $P$ on returning to $Q$ may be much out of phase with the vibrator, and it can do work on the vibrator. That is, the string can give up some energy to the vibrator just as well as receive energy from it. The "standing" wave pattern is not fixed in form but wiggles about. On the average the amplitude is small and not much different from that of the vibrator. This situation is analogous to the erratic motion of a swing being pushed periodically with a frequency other than its natural one. The displacement of the swing is rather small.

Hence, the string absorbs peak energy from the vibrator at resonance. Tuning a radio is an analogous process. By tuning a dial the natural frequency of an alternating current in the receiving circuit is made equal to the frequency of the waves broadcast by the station desired. The circuit resonates with the transmitted signals and absorbs peak energy from the signal. We shall encounter resonance conditions again in sound, in electromagnetism, in optics, and in atomic and nuclear physics. In these areas, as in mechanics, the system will absorb peak energy from the source at resonance and relatively little energy off resonance.

▶ **Example 4.** In a demonstration with the apparatus just described, the vibrator has a frequency $\nu = 20$ cycles/sec, and the string has a linear density

$\mu = 1.56 \times 10^{-4}$ slug/ft and a length $l = 24$ ft.   The tension $F$ is varied by pulling down on the end of the string over the pulley.   If the demonstrator wants to show resonance, starting with one loop and then with two, three, and four loops, what force must he exert on the string?

At resonance,

$$\nu = \frac{n}{2l}\sqrt{\frac{F}{\mu}}.$$

Hence, the tension $F$ is given by

$$F = \frac{4l^2\nu^2\mu}{n^2}.$$

For one loop, $n = 1$, so that

$$F_1 = 4l^2\nu^2\mu = 4(24 \text{ ft})^2(20 \text{ sec}^{-1})^2(1.56 \times 10^{-4} \text{ slug/ft}) = 144 \text{ lb}.$$

For two loops, $n = 2$, and

$$F_2 = \frac{4l^2\nu^2\mu}{4} = \frac{F_1}{4} = 36 \text{ lb}.$$

Likewise, for three and four loops

$$F_3 = \frac{F_1}{(3)^2} = 16 \text{ lb},$$

$$F_4 = \frac{F_1}{(4)^2} = 9 \text{ lb}.$$

Hence, the demonstrator gradually relaxes the tension to obtain resonance with an increasing number of loops.   Although the resonant frequency is always the same under these circumstances, the speed of propagation and the wavelength at resonance decrease proportionately.

Taking damping into account, are the tensions given exactly correct?

If the tension were kept fixed, giving a definite wave speed, would we obtain more than one resonance condition by varying the frequency of the vibrator.   ◀

## QUESTIONS

**1.** How could you prove experimentally that energy is associated with a wave?

**2.** Energy can be transferred by particles as well as by waves.   How can we distinguish experimentally between these methods of energy transfer?

**3.** Can a wave motion be generated in which the particles of the medium vibrate with angular simple harmonic motion?   If so, explain how and describe the wave.

**4.** Are torsional waves transverse or longitudinal?   Can they be considered as a superposition of two waves, which are either transverse or longitudinal?

**5.** How can one create plane waves?   Spherical waves?

**6.** The following functions in which $A$ is a constant are of the form $f(x \pm vt)$:

$$y = A(x - vt), \qquad y = A(x + vt)^2,$$
$$y = A\sqrt{x - vt}, \qquad y = A\ln(x + vt).$$

Explain why these functions are not useful in wave motion.

7. How do the amplitude and the intensity of surface water waves vary with the distance from the source?

8. The inverse square law does not apply exactly to the decrease in intensity of sounds with distance. Why not?

9. When two waves interfere, does one alter the progress of the other?

10. When waves interfere, is there a loss of energy? Explain your answer.

11. Why don't we observe interference effects between the light beams emitted from two flashlights or between the sound waves emitted by two violins.

12. If two waves differ only in amplitude and are propagated in opposite directions through a medium, will they produce standing waves? Is energy transported? Are there any nodes? (See Problem 25.)

13. The partial reflection of wave energy by discontinuities in the path of transmission is usually wasteful and can be minimized by insertion of "impedance matching" devices between the sections of the path bordering on the discontinuity. For example, a megaphone helps match the air column of mouth and throat to the air outside the mouth. Give other examples and explain qualitatively how such devices minimize reflection losses (see Problem 25).

14. Is an oscillation a wave? Explain.

15. Consider the standing waves in a string to be a superposition of traveling waves and explain, using superposition ideas, why there are no true nodes in the resonating string of Fig. 19–19, even at the "fixed" end. (*Hint:* Consider damping effects.)

16. In the discussion of transverse waves in a string we have dealt only with displacements in a single plane, the $x$-$y$ plane. If all displacements lie in one plane the wave is said to be *plane polarized*. Can there be displacements in a plane other than the single plane dealt with? If so, can two differently plane-polarized waves be combined? What appearance would such a combined wave have?

17. A wave transmits energy. Does it transfer momentum? Can it transfer angular momentum? (See Question 16.)

## PROBLEMS

1. Show that $y = y_m \sin (kx - \omega t)$ may be written in the alternative forms

$$y = y_m \sin k(x - vt), \qquad y = y_m \sin 2\pi \left( \frac{x}{\lambda} - vt \right),$$

$$y = y_m \sin \omega \left( \frac{x}{v} - t \right), \qquad y = y_m \sin 2\pi \left( \frac{x}{\lambda} - \frac{t}{T} \right).$$

2. The speed of electromagnetic waves in vacuum is $3 \times 10^8$ meters/sec. (a) Wavelengths in the visible part of the spectrum (light) range from about $4 \times 10^{-7}$ meter in the violet to about $7 \times 10^{-7}$ in the red. What is the range of frequencies of light waves? (b) The range of frequencies for shortwave radio (for example, FM radio and VHF television) is 1.5 megacycles/sec to 300 megacycles/sec. What is the corresponding wavelength range? (c) X-rays are also electromagnetic. Their wavelength range extends from about $5 \times 10^{-9}$ meter to $1.0 \times 10^{-11}$ meter. What is the frequency range for X-rays?

3. The equation of a transverse wave traveling in a rope is given by

$$y = 10 \sin \pi(0.01x - 2.00t),$$

where $y$ and $x$ are expressed in centimeters and $t$ in seconds. (a) Find the amplitude, frequency, velocity, and wavelength of the wave. (b) Find the maximum transverse speed of a particle in the rope.

**4.** Write the equation for a wave traveling in the negative direction along the $x$-axis and having an amplitude 0.010 meter, a frequency 550 vib/sec, and a speed 330 meters/ sec.

**5.** A wave of frequency 500 cycles/sec has a phase velocity of 350 meters/sec. (a) How far apart are two points $60°$ out of phase? (b) What is the phase difference between two displacements at a certain point at times $10^{-3}$ sec apart?

**6.** (a) A continuous sinusoidal longitudinal wave is sent along a coil spring from a vibrating source attached to it. The frequency of the source is 25 vib/sec, and the distance between successive rarefactions in the spring is 24 cm. Find the wave speed. (b) If the maximum longitudinal displacement of a particle in the spring is 3.0 cm and the wave moves in the $-x$ direction, write the equation for the wave. Let the source be at $x = 0$ and the displacement at $x = 0$ and $t = 0$ be zero.

**7.** What is the speed of a transverse wave in a rope of length 2.0 meters and mass 0.060 kg under a tension of 500 nt?

**8.** Prove that the slope of a string at any point $x$ is numerically equal to the ratio of the particle speed to the wave speed at that point.

**9.** A uniform circular hoop of string is rotating clockwise in the absence of gravity (see Fig. 19–20). The tangential speed is $v_0$. Find the speed of waves traveling on this string. (*Hint:* The answer is independent of the radius of the circle and the mass per unit length of the string!)

**10.** (a) From Example 2 show that the *maximum* speed of a particle in a string through which a sinusoidal wave is passing is $u = y_m\omega$. (b) In Example 2 we saw that the particles in the string oscillate with simple harmonic motion. The mechanical energy of each particle is the sum of its potential and kinetic energies and is always equal to the *maximum* value of its kinetic energy. Consider an element of string of mass $\mu \, \Delta x$ and show that the energy *per unit length* of the string is given by ·

**Fig. 19–20**

$$E_l = 2\pi^2\mu\nu^2 y_m{}^2.$$

(c) Show finally that the average power or average rate of transfer of energy is the product of the energy per unit length and the wave speed. (d) Do these results hold only for a sinusoidal wave?

**11.** Spherical waves are emitted from a 1.0-watt source in an isotropic nonabsorbing medium. What is the wave intensity 1.0 meter from the source?

**12.** (a) Show that the intensity $I$ (the energy crossing unit area per unit time) is the product of the energy per unit volume $e$ and the speed of propagation $v$ of a wave disturbance. (b) Radio waves travel at a speed of $3.0 \times 10^8$ meters/sec. Find the energy density in a radio wave 300 miles from a 50,000-watt source, assuming the waves to be spherical and the propagation to be isotropic.

**13.** A line source emits a cylindrical expanding wave. Assuming the medium absorbs no energy, find how the amplitude and intensity of the wave depend on the distance from the source.

**14.** Determine the amplitude of the resultant motion when two sinusoidal motions having the same frequency and traveling in the same direction are combined, if their amplitudes are 3.0 cm and 4.0 cm and they differ in phase by $\pi/2$ radians.

**15.** A source $S$ and a detector $D$ of high-frequency waves are a distance $d$ apart on the ground. The direct wave from $S$ is found to be in phase at $D$ with the wave from $S$

that is reflected from a horizontal layer at an altitude $H$ (Fig. 19–21). The incident and reflected rays make the same angle with the reflecting layer. When the layer rises a distance $h$, no signal is detected at $D$. Neglect absorption in the atmosphere and find the relation between $d$, $h$, $H$, and the wavelength $\lambda$ of the waves.

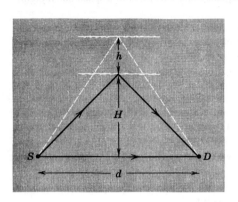

**Fig. 19–21**

**16.** Three component sinusoidal waves have the same period, but their amplitudes are in the ratio 1, 1/2, and 1/3 and their phase angles are 0, $\pi/2$, and $\pi$ respectively. Plot the resultant waveform and discuss its nature.

**17.** Four component sine waves have frequencies in the ratio 1, 2, 3, and 4 and amplitudes in the ratio 1, 1/2, 1/3, and 1/4, respectively. The first and third components are 180° out of phase with the second and fourth components. Plot the resultant waveform and discuss its nature.

**18.** A string vibrates according to the equation

$$y = 5 \sin \frac{\pi x}{3} \cos 40\pi t,$$

where $x$ and $y$ are in centimeters and $t$ is in seconds. (a) What are the amplitude and velocity of the component waves whose superposition can give rise to this vibration? (b) What is the distance between nodes? (c) What is the velocity of a particle of the string at the position $x = 1.5$ cm when $t = \frac{9}{8}$ sec?

**19.** Two pulses are traveling along a string in opposite direction, as shown in Fig. 19–22. (a) If the wave velocity is 2.0 cm/sec and the pulses are 6.0 cm apart, sketch the patterns after 0.5, 1.0, 1.5, 2.0, 2.5 sec. (b) What has happened to the energy at $t = 1.5$ sec?

**Fig. 19–22**

**20.** Two transverse sinusoidal waves travel in opposite directions along a string. Each has an amplitude of 3.0 cm and a wavelength of 6.0 cm. The speed of a transverse wave in the string is 0.50 cm/sec. Plot the shape of the string at each of the following times: $t = 0$ (arbitrary), $t = 1.5$, $t = 3.0$, $t = 6.0$, $t = 7.5$, and $t = 9.0$ sec.

**21.** The equation of a transverse wave traveling in a rope is given by

$$y = 60 \cos \frac{\pi}{2} (0.0050x - 8.0t - 0.57),$$

in which $x$ and $y$ are expressed in centimeters and $t$ in seconds. Write down the equation of a wave that, when added to the given one, would produce standing waves on the rope.

**22.** In a laboratory experiment on standing waves a string 3.0 ft long is attached to the prong of an electrically driven tuning fork which vibrates perpendicular to the length of the string at a frequency of 60 vib/sec. The weight of the string is 0.096 lb. (a) What tension must the string be under (weights are attached to the other end) if it is to vibrate in four loops? (b) What would happen if the tuning fork is turned so as to vibrate parallel to the length of the string?

**23.** A wave travels out uniformly in all directions from a point source. Justify the following expression for the displacement $y$ of the medium at any distance $r$ from the source:

$$y = \frac{Y}{r} \sin k(r - vt).$$

Consider the speed, direction of propagation, periodicity, and intensity of the wave. What are the dimensions of the constant $Y$?

**24.** Consider two point sources $S_1$ and $S_2$ in Fig. 19–23 which emit waves of the same frequency and amplitude. The waves start in the same phase, and this phase relation at the sources is maintained throughout time. Consider points $P$ at which $r_1$ is nearly

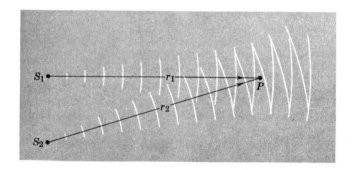

**Fig. 19–23**

equal to $r_2$. (a) Show that the superposition of these two waves gives a wave whose amplitude varies with the position $P$ approximately according to

$$\frac{2Y}{r} \cos \frac{k}{2} (r_1 - r_2),$$

in which $r = (r_1 + r_2)/2$. (b) Then show that total annulment occurs when $r_1 - r_2 = (n + \frac{1}{2})\lambda$, $n$ being any integer, and that total re-enforcement occurs when $r_1 - r_2 = n\lambda$.

The locus of points whose difference in distance from two fixed points is a constant is a hyperbola, the fixed points being the foci. Hence each value of $n$ gives a hyperbolic line of constructive interference and a hyperbolic line of destructive interference. At points at which $r_1$ and $r_2$ are not approximately equal (as near the sources), the amplitudes of the waves from $S_1$ and $S_2$ differ and the annulments are only partial.

**25.** If an incident traveling wave is only partially reflected from a boundary, the resulting superposition of two waves having different amplitudes and traveling in opposite directions gives a standing wave pattern of waves whose envelope is shown in Fig. 19–24. The standing wave ratio (SWR) is defined as $(A_i + A_r)/(A_i - A_r) = A_{max}/A_{min}$. (a) Show that for 100% reflection SWR $= \infty$ and that for no reflection SWR $= 1$. (b) Show that a measurement of the SWR just before the boundary reveals

**Fig. 19–24**

the per cent reflection occurring at the boundary according to the formula

$$\% \text{ reflection} = [(\text{SWR} - 1)^2/(\text{SWR} + 1)^2] \times 100.$$

**26.** Two strings of linear density $\mu_1$ and $\mu_2$ are knotted together at $x = 0$ and stretched to a tension $F$. A wave $y = A \sin k_1(x - v_1 t)$ in the string of density $\mu_1$ reaches the junction between the two strings, at which it is partly transmitted into the string of density $\mu_2$ and partly reflected. Call these waves $B \sin k_2(x - v_2 t)$ and $C \sin k_1(x + v_1 t)$, respectively. (a) Assuming that $k_2 v_2 = k_1 v_1 = \omega$ and that the displacement of the knot arising from the incident and reflected waves is the same as that arising from the transmitted wave, show that $A = B + C$. (b) If it is assumed that both strings near the knot have the same slope (why?), i.e., that $dy/dx$ in string 1 $= dy/dx$ in string 2, show that

$$C = A \frac{(k_2 - k_1)}{(k_2 + k_1)}$$

$$= A \frac{v_1 - v_2}{v_1 + v_2}.$$

Under what conditions is $C$ negative?

# Sound Waves

## CHAPTER 20

### 20–1 Audible, Ultrasonic, and Infrasonic Waves

Sound waves are longitudinal mechanical waves. They can be propagated in solids, liquids, and gases. The material particles transmitting such a wave oscillate in the direction of propagation of the wave itself. There is a large range of frequencies within which longitudinal mechanical waves can be generated, sound waves being confined to the frequency range which can stimulate the human ear and brain to the sensation of hearing. This range is from about 20 cycles/sec to about 20,000 cycles/sec and is called the *audible* range. A longitudinal mechanical wave whose frequency is below the audible range is called an *infrasonic* wave, and one whose frequency is above the audible range is called an *ultrasonic* wave.

Infrasonic waves of interest are usually generated by large sources, earthquake waves being an example.* The high frequencies associated with ultrasonic waves may be produced by elastic vibrations of a quartz crystal induced by resonance with an applied alternating electric field (piezoelectric effect). It is possible to produce ultrasonic frequencies as high as $6 \times 10^8$ cycles/sec in this way; the corresponding wavelength in air is about $5 \times 10^{-5}$ cm, the same as the length of visible light waves.

Audible waves originate in vibrating strings (violin, human vocal cords), vibrating air columns (organ, clarinet), and vibrating plates and membranes (xylophone, loudspeaker, drum). All of these vibrating elements alternately compress the surrounding air on a forward movement and rarefy it on a backward movement. The air transmits these disturbances

---

* See "Long Earthquake Waves," by Jack Oliver, *Scientific American*, March 1959.

outward from the source as a wave. Upon entering the ear, these waves produce the sensation of sound. Waveforms which are approximately periodic or consist of a small number of approximately periodic components give rise to a pleasant sensation (if the intensity is not too high), as, for example, musical sounds. Sound whose waveform is nonperiodic is heard as noise. Noise can be represented as a superposition of periodic waves, but the number of components is very large.

In this chapter we deal with the properties of longitudinal mechanical waves, using sound waves as the prototype.

### 20–2 Propagation and Speed of Longitudinal Waves

Sound waves, if unimpeded, will spread out in all directions from a source. It is simpler to deal with one-dimensional propagation, however, than with three-dimensional propagation, so that we consider first the transmission of longitudinal waves in a tube.

Figure 20–1 shows a piston at one end of a long tube filled with a compressible medium. The vertical lines divide the compressional (fluid) medium into thin "slices," each of which contains the same mass of fluid. Where the lines are relatively close together the fluid pressure and density are greater than they are in the normal undisturbed fluid, and conversely. We shall treat the fluid as a continuous medium and ignore for the time being the fact that it is made up of molecules that are in continual random motion.

If we push the piston of Fig. 20–1 forward, the fluid in front of it is compressed, the fluid pressure and density rising above their normal undisturbed values. The compressed fluid moves forward, compressing the fluid layers next to it, and a compressional pulse travels down the tube. If we then withdraw the piston, the fluid in front of it expands, its pressure and density falling below their normal undisturbed values; a pulse of rarefaction travels down the tube. These pulses are similar to transverse pulses traveling along a string, except that the oscillating fluid elements are

**Fig. 20–1** Sound waves generated in a tube by an oscillating piston. The vertical lines divide the compressible medium in the tube into layers of equal mass.

displaced along the direction of propagation (longitudinal) instead of at right angles to this direction (transverse). If the piston oscillates back and forth, a continuous train of compressions and rarefactions will travel along the tube (Fig. 20–1). As for transverse waves in a string (see Section 19–5) we should be able, using Newton's laws of motion, to express the speed of propagation of this longitudinal wave in terms of an elastic and an inertial property of the medium. We now do so.

For the moment, let us assume that the tube is very long so that we can ignore reflections from the other end. As for the string of Fig. 19–6, we will consider not an extended wave but a single (compressional) pulse that we might generate by giving the piston in Fig. 20–1 a short, rapid, inward stroke.

Figure 20–2 shows such a pulse (labeled "compressional zone") traveling at speed $v$ along the tube from left to right. For simplicity we have assumed this pulse to have sharply defined leading and trailing edges and to have a uniform fluid pressure and density in its interior. When we analyzed the motion of a transverse pulse in a string, we found it convenient to choose a reference frame in which the pulse remained stationary; we will do this here also. In Fig. 20–2, then, the com-pressional zone remains stationary in our reference frame while the fluid moves through it from right to left with speed $v$, as shown.

Let us follow the motion of the element of fluid contained between the vertical lines at $P$ in Fig. 20–2. This element moves forward at speed $v$ until it strikes the compressional zone. While it is entering this zone it encounters a difference of pressure $\Delta p$ between its leading and its trailing edges. The element is compressed and *decelerated*, moving with a lower speed $v + \Delta v$ within the zone, the quantity $\Delta v$ being negative. The element eventually emerges from the left face of the zone where it expands to its original volume and the pressure differential $\Delta p$ acts to *accelerate* it to its original speed $v$. The figure shows the element at point $R$, having passed through the compressional zone and moving again with speed $v$, as at $P$.

Let us apply Newton's laws to the fluid element while it is entering the com-pressional zone. The resultant force acting during entry points to the right in Fig. 20–2 and has magnitude

$$F = (p + \Delta p)A - pA = \Delta pA$$

in which $A$ is the cross-sectional area of the tube.

The length of the element outside the compressional zone (at $P$, say) is $v \Delta t$, where $\Delta t$ is the time required for the element to move past any given point. The volume of the element is thus $vA \Delta t$ and its mass is $\rho_0 vA \Delta t$, where $\rho_0$ is the density of the fluid outside the compressional zone. The deceleration $a$ experienced by the

**Fig. 20–2** A compressional pulse travels along a gas-filled tube. In a reference frame in which the undisturbed gas is at rest the pulse moves from left to right with speed $v$. We view the pulse, however, from a reference frame in which the pulse is stationary; in such a frame the gas outside the pulse streams through the tube from right to left with speed $v$, as shown. Note that $\Delta v$ is negative.

element as it enters the zone is $-\Delta v/\Delta t$; because $\Delta v$ is inherently negative, $a$ is positive, which means that, like the force $\Delta pA$ in Fig. 20–2, it points to the right. Thus Newton's second law

$$F = ma$$

yields

$$\Delta pA = (\rho_0 vA \, \Delta t) \frac{-\Delta v}{\Delta t},$$

which we may write as

$$\rho_0 v^2 = \frac{-\Delta p}{\Delta v/v}.$$

Now the fluid that would occupy a volume $V = Av \, \Delta t$ at $P$ is compressed by an amount $A(\Delta v) \Delta t = \Delta V$ on entering the compressional zone. Hence,

$$\frac{\Delta V}{V} = \frac{A \, \Delta v \, \Delta t}{Av \, \Delta t} = \frac{\Delta v}{v}$$

and we obtain

$$\rho_0 v^2 = \frac{-\Delta p}{\Delta V/V}.$$

The ratio of the change in pressure on a body, $\Delta p$, to the fractional change in volume resulting, $-\Delta V/V$, is called the *bulk modulus of elasticity* $B$ of the body. That is, $B = -V \Delta p/\Delta V$. $B$ is positive because an increase in pressure causes a decrease in volume. In terms of $B$, the speed of the longitudinal pulse in the medium of Fig. 20–2 is

$$v = \sqrt{B/\rho_0}. \qquad (20\text{--}1)$$

A more extended analysis than given above shows that Eq. 20–1 applies not only to rectangular pulses of the type displayed in Fig. 20–2 but also

### Table 20–1

SPEED OF SOUND

| Medium | Tempera-ture, °C | Speed | |
| --- | --- | --- | --- |
| | | Meters/sec | Ft/sec |
| Air | 0 | 331.3 | 1,087 |
| Hydrogen | 0 | 1,286 | 4,220 |
| Oxygen | 0 | 317.2 | 1,041 |
| Water | 15 | 1,450 | 4,760 |
| Lead | 20 | 1,230 | 4,030 |
| Aluminum | 20 | 5,100 | 16,700 |
| Copper | 20 | 3,560 | 11,700 |
| Iron | 20 | 5,130 | 16,800 |
| Extreme values | | | |
| Granite | | 6,000 | 19,700 |
| Vulcanized rubber | 0 | 54 | 177 |

to pulses of any shape and to extended wave trains. Notice that the speed of the wave is determined by the properties of the medium through which it propagates, and that an elastic property $B$ and an inertial property $\rho_0$ are involved. Table 20-1 gives the speed of longitudinal (sound) waves in various media.

If the medium is a gas, such as air, it is possible to express $B$ in terms of the undisturbed gas pressure $p_0$. For a sound wave in a gas we obtain

$$v = \sqrt{\gamma p_0/\rho_0},$$

where $\gamma$ is a constant called the ratio of specific heats for the gas (Chapter 23).

If the medium is a solid, for a thin rod the bulk modulus is replaced by a stretch modulus (called Young's modulus). If the solid is extended, we must allow for the fact that, unlike a fluid, a solid offers elastic resistance to tangential or shearing forces and the speed of longitudinal waves will depend on the shear modulus as well as the bulk modulus.

### 20-3  Traveling Longitudinal Waves

Consider again the continuous train of compressions and rarefactions traveling down the tube of Fig. 20-1. As the wave advances along the tube, each small volume element of fluid oscillates about its equilibrium position. The displacement is to the right or left along the $x$-direction of propagation of the wave. For convenience let us represent the displacement of any such volume element (or layer of elements that move in the same way) from its equilibrium position at $x$ by the letter $y$. It is to be understood that the displacement $y$ is *along the direction of propagation* for a longitudinal wave, whereas for a transverse wave the displacement $y$ is *at right angles to the direction of propagation*. Then the equation of a longitudinal wave traveling to the right may be written as

$$y = f(x - vt).$$

For the particular case of a simple harmonic oscillation we may have

$$y = y_m \cos \frac{2\pi}{\lambda} (x - vt).$$

In this equation $v$ is the speed of the longitudinal wave, $y_m$ is its amplitude, and $\lambda$ is its wavelength; $y$ gives the displacement of a particle at time $t$ from its equilibrium position at $x$. As before, we may write this more compactly as

$$y = y_m \cos (kx - \omega t). \qquad (20-2)$$

It is usually more convenient to deal with pressure variations in a sound wave than with the actual displacements of the particles conveying the wave. Let us therefore write the equation of the wave in terms of the pressure variation rather than in terms of the displacement.

From the relation

$$B = -\frac{\Delta p}{\Delta V/V},$$

we have
$$\Delta p = -B\frac{\Delta V}{V}.$$

Just as we let $y$ represent the displacement from the equilibrium position $x$, so we now let $p$ represent the *change* from the undisturbed pressure $p_0$. Then $p$ replaces $\Delta p$, and

$$p = -B\frac{\Delta V}{V}.$$

If a layer of fluid at pressure $p_0$ has a thickness $\Delta x$ and cross-sectional area $A$, its volume is $V = A\,\Delta x$. When the pressure changes, its volume will change by $A\,\Delta y$, where $\Delta y$ is the amount by which the thickness of the layer changes during compression or rarefaction. Hence,

$$p = -B\frac{\Delta V}{V} = -B\frac{A\,\Delta y}{A\,\Delta x}.$$

As we let $\Delta x \to 0$ so as to shrink the fluid layer to infinitesimal thickness, we obtain

$$p = -B\frac{\partial y}{\partial x}. \tag{20-3}$$

We have used partial derivative notation because (see Eq. 20–2) $y$ is a function of both $x$ and $t$ and we take the latter quantity as constant in this discussion. If the particle displacement is simple harmonic, then, from Eq. 20–2, we obtain

$$\frac{\partial y}{\partial x} = -ky_m \sin(kx - \omega t),$$

and from Eq. 20–3
$$p = Bky_m \sin(kx - \omega t). \tag{20-4}$$

Hence, the pressure variation at each position $x$ is also simple harmonic. Since $v = \sqrt{B/\rho_0}$, we can write Eq. 20–4 more conveniently as

$$p = [k\rho_0 v^2 y_m]\sin(kx - \omega t).$$

Recall that $p$ represents the change from standard pressure $p_0$. The term in brackets represents the maximum change in pressure and is called the *pressure amplitude*. If we denote this by $P$, then

$$p = P\sin(kx - \omega t), \tag{20-5}$$

where
$$P = k\rho_0 v^2 y_m. \tag{20-6}$$

Hence, a sound wave may be considered either as a displacement wave or as a pressure wave. If the former is written as a cosine function, the latter will be a sine function and vice versa. The displacement wave is thus 90° out of phase with the pressure wave. That is, when the displacement from equilibrium at a point is a maximum or a minimum, the excess pressure there is zero; when the displacement at a point is zero, the excess or deficiency of pressure there is a maximum. Equation 20–6 gives the relation between the pressure amplitude (maximum variation of pressure from equilibrium) and the displacement amplitude (maximum variation of position from equilibrium). The student should check the dimensions of each side of Eq. 20–6 for consistency. What units may the pressure amplitude have?

The intensity of a wave is proportional to the square of the displacement amplitude of the wave; see Section 19–6. We have just shown that for sound waves the pressure amplitude is proportional to the displacement amplitude. Hence, the intensity of a sound wave is proportional to the square of the pressure amplitude. In fact, when the intensity is expressed in terms of the pressure amplitude, the frequency does not appear explicitly in the expression (see Problem 9). Hence, by measuring pressure changes, the intensities of sounds having *different* frequencies can be compared directly. For this reason instruments that measure pressure changes are preferred to those that measure displacement amplitude. As we shall see in Example 1, the displacement amplitudes would be difficult to measure in any case.

▶ **Example 1.** (a) The maximum pressure variation $P$ that the ear can tolerate in loud sounds is about 28 nt/meter². Normal atmospheric pressure is about 100,000 nt/meter². Find the corresponding maximum displacement for a sound wave in air having a frequency of 1000 cycles/sec.

From Eq. 20–6 we have

$$y_m = \frac{P}{k\rho_0 v^2}.$$

From Table 20–1, $v = 331$ meters/sec so that

$$k = \frac{2\pi}{\lambda} = \frac{2\pi\nu}{v} = \frac{2\pi \times 10^3}{331} \text{ meter}^{-1} = 19 \text{ meter}^{-1}.$$

The density of air $\rho_0$ is 1.22 kg/meter³. Hence, for $P = 28$ nt/meter² we obtain

$$y_m = \frac{28}{(19)(1.22)(331)^2} \text{ meter} = 1.1 \times 10^{-5} \text{ meter}.$$

The displacement amplitudes for the *loudest* sounds are about $10^{-5}$ meter, a very small value indeed.

(b) In the faintest sound that can be heard at 1000 cycles/sec the pressure amplitude is about $2.0 \times 10^{-5}$ nt/meter². Find the corresponding displacement amplitude.

From $y_m = P/k\rho_0 v^2$, using these values for $k$, $v$, and $\rho_0$, we obtain, with $P = 2.0 \times 10^{-5}$ nt/meter²,

$$y_m \cong 8 \times 10^{-12} \text{ meter} \cong 10^{-11} \text{ meter}.$$

This is smaller than the radius of an atom, which is about $10^{-10}$ meter! How can it be that the ear responds to such a small displacement?    ◀

In our analysis we have ignored the molecular structure of matter and treated the fluid is a continuous medium. In gases, however, the spaces between molecules are large compared to the diameters of the molecules. The molecules move about at random. The oscillations produced by a sound wave passing through are superimposed on this random thermal motion. An impulse given to one molecule is passed on to another molecule only after the first one has moved through the empty space between them and collided with the second. From this brief discussion, would you ever expect the speed of sound to exceed the average molecular speed in a fluid?

### 20–4   Standing Longitudinal Waves

Longitudinal waves traveling along a tube are reflected at the ends of the tube, just as transverse waves in a string are reflected at its ends. Interference between the waves traveling in opposite directions gives rise to standing longitudinal waves.

If the end of the tube is closed, the reflected wave is 180° out of phase with the incident wave. This result is a necessary consequence of the fact that the displacement of the small volume elements at a closed end must always be zero. Hence, a closed end is a displacement *node*. If the end of the tube is open, the fluid elements there are free to move. However, the nature of the reflection there depends on whether the tube is wide or narrow compared to the wavelength. If the tube is narrow compared to the wavelength, as in most musical instruments, the reflected wave has nearly the same phase as the incident wave. Then the open end is almost a displacement *antinode*. The exact antinode is usually somewhere near the opening, but the effective length of the air columns of a wind instrument, for example, is not as definite as the length of a string fixed at both ends.

Standing longitudinal waves in a gas column can be dramatically demonstrated by means of the apparatus shown in Fig. 20–3. A source of longitudinal waves, such as the speaker of an audio oscillator at $S$, sets up vibrations in a flexible diaphragm at one end of the tube. Gas fills the tube from the inlet and passes slowly out through regularly spaced small openings along the top. The escaping gas is lit, giving a series of flames. When a frequency is found at which the gas column is in resonance, the amplitude of the standing longitudinal waves becomes rather large and we can see a wavelike variation in the height and width of the gas flames along the tube. The interval between nodes or antinodes is clearly visible. By varying

**Fig. 20–3** Flames show the presence of standing waves in a tube filled with illuminating gas. *A* and *N* refer to *displacement* antinodes and nodes, respectively.

the frequency we can pass from one resonance condition to another. The natural modes of oscillation of the gas column are determined by the effective length of the column and the wave speed. The wavelength $\lambda$ at resonance can be taken to be twice the distance between adjacent nodes (or antinodes), and knowing the frequency $\nu$ of the source at resonance, we can determine the wave speed in the gas under these conditions from $v = \nu\lambda$. In practice there are more flexible and accurate ways to measure the speed of sound in gases. (See Problem 17 and Example 2.)

In Fig. 20–3 the nodes and antinodes, $N$ and $A$, refer to the particle *displacements* in the standing wave. At a displacement node, the pressure variations (above and below the average) are a maximum. Hence, a displacement node corresponds to a pressure antinode. At a displacement antinode the pressure remains constant with time. Hence, a displacement antinode corresponds to a pressure node.

This can be understood physically by realizing that two small volume elements of gas on opposite sides of a displacement node are vibrating in *opposite phase*. Hence, when they approach each other, the pressure at this node is a maximum, and when they recede from each other, the pressure at this node is a minimum. Two small elements of gas which are on opposite sides of a displacement antinode vibrate *in phase* and therefore give rise to no pressure variations at the antinode.

## 20–5    Vibrating Systems and Sources of Sound

If a string fixed at both ends is bowed, transverse vibrations travel along the string; these disturbances are reflected at the fixed ends, and a standing wave pattern is formed. The natural modes of vibration of the string are excited and these vibrations give rise to longitudinal waves in the surrounding air which transmits them to our ears as a musical sound.

We have seen (Section 19–10) that a string of length $l$, fixed at both ends, can resonate at frequencies given by

$$\nu_n = \frac{n}{2l} v = \frac{n}{2l} \sqrt{\frac{F}{\mu}}, \qquad n = 1, 2, 3, \ldots \qquad (20\text{–}7)$$

Here $v$ is the speed of the transverse waves in the string whose superposition can be thought of as giving rise to the vibrations; the speed $v \, (= \sqrt{F/\mu})$ is the same for all frequencies. At any one of these frequencies the string will contain a whole number $n$ of loops between its ends, and the condition that the ends be nodes is met (Fig. 20–4).

The lowest frequency, $\sqrt{F/\mu}/2l$, is called the *fundamental* frequency $\nu_1$ and the others are called *overtones*. Overtones whose frequencies are integral multiples of the fundamental are said to form a harmonic series. The fundamental is the first harmonic. The frequency $2\nu_1$ is the first overtone or the second harmonic, the frequency $3\nu_1$ is the second overtone or the third harmonic, and so on.

If the string is initially distorted so that its shape is the same as *any one*

$$\nu_1 = \frac{1}{2}\frac{v}{l} \qquad\qquad \lambda_1 = 2l$$

$$\nu_2 = \frac{v}{l} \qquad\qquad \lambda_2 = l$$

$$\nu_3 = \frac{3}{2}\frac{v}{l} \qquad\qquad \lambda_3 = \frac{2}{3}l$$

$$\nu_4 = 2\frac{v}{l} \qquad\qquad \lambda_4 = \frac{1}{2}l$$

**Fig. 20–4** The first four modes of vibration of a string fixed at both ends. Note that $\nu_n\lambda_n = v = \sqrt{F/\mu}$.

of the possible harmonics, it will vibrate at the frequency of that particular harmonic, when released. The initial conditions usually arise from striking or bowing the string, however, and in such cases not only the fundamental but many of the overtones are present in the resulting vibration. We have a superposition of several natural modes of oscillation. The actual displacement is the sum of the several harmonics with various amplitudes; see Fig. 19–12. The impulses that are sent through the air to the ear and brain give rise to one net effect which is characteristic of the particular stringed instrument. The quality of the sound of a particular note (fundamental frequency) played by an instrument is determined by the number of overtones present and their respective intensities. Figure 20–5 shows the sound spectra and corresponding waveforms for the violin and piano.*

An organ pipe is a simple example of sound originating in a vibrating air column. If both ends of a pipe are open and a stream of air is directed against an edge, standing longitudinal waves can be set up in the tube.

---

\* See "The Physics of the Piano" by E. Donnell Blackham in *Scientific American*, December 1965.

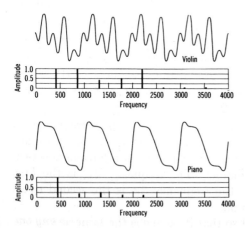

**Fig. 20–5** Waveform and sound spectrum for two stringed instruments, the violin and the piano. The fundamental frequency in both cases is 440 cycles/sec (concert A). In each diagram we show only four cycles of the wave. The sound spectrum shows the relative amplitude of the various harmonic components of the wave. Notice the presence of loud higher harmonics (especially the fifth) in the violin spectrum.

The air column will then resonate at its natural frequencies of vibration, given by

$$\nu_n = \frac{n}{2l}\, v, \qquad n = 1, 2, 3, \ldots$$

Here $v$ is the speed of the longitudinal waves in the column whose superposition can be thought of as giving rise to the vibrations, and $n$ is the number of half wavelengths in the length $l$ of the column. As with the bowed string, the fundamental and overtones are excited at the same time.

In an open pipe the fundamental frequency corresponds (approximately) to a displacement antinode at each end and a displacement node in the middle, as shown in Fig. 20–6a. The succeeding drawings of Fig. 20–6a show three of the overtones, the second, third, and fourth harmonics. Hence, in an open pipe the fundamental frequency is $v/2l$ and *all* harmonics are present.

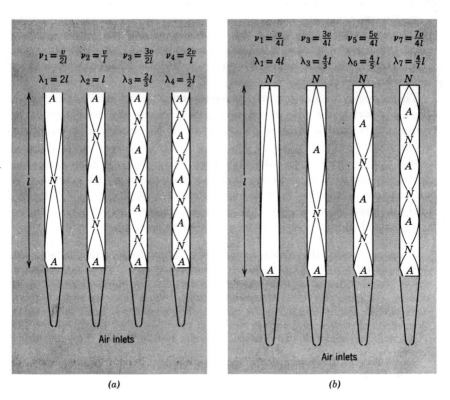

(a)                                                        (b)

**Fig. 20–6**   (a) The first four modes of an open organ pipe. The distance from the center line of the pipe to the light lines drawn inside the pipe shows the displacement amplitude at each place.   $N$ and $A$ mark the locations of the displacement nodes and antinodes.   Note that *both* ends of the pipe are open.   (b) The first four modes of vibration of a closed organ pipe.   Notice that the even-numbered harmonics are absent and the upper end of the pipe is closed.

In a closed pipe the closed end is a displacement node. Figure 20–6b shows the modes of vibration of a closed pipe. The fundamental frequency is $v/4l$ (approximately), which is one-half that of an open pipe of the same length. The only overtones present are those that give a displacement node at the closed end and an antinode (approximately) at the open end. Hence, as is shown in Fig. 20–6b, the second, fourth, etc., harmonics are missing. In a closed pipe the fundamental frequency is $v/4l$, and only the *odd* harmonics are present. The quality of the sounds from an open pipe is therefore different from that from a closed pipe.

Vibrating rods, plates, and stretched membranes also give rise to sound waves. Consider a stretched flexible membrane, such as a drumhead. If it is struck a blow, a two-dimensional pulse travels outward from the struck point and is reflected again and again at the boundary of the membrane. If some point of the membrane is forced to vibrate periodically, continuous trains of waves travel out along the membrane. Just as in the one-dimensional case of the string, so here too standing waves can be set up in the two-dimensional membrane. Each of these standing waves has a certain frequency natural to (or characteristic of) the membrane. Again the lowest frequency is called the fundamental and the others are overtones. Generally, a number of overtones are present along with the fundamental when the membrane is vibrating. These vibrations may excite sound waves of the same frequency.

The nodes of a vibrating membrane are lines rather than points (as in a vibrating string) or planes (as in a pipe). Since the boundary of the membrane is fixed, it must be a nodal line. For a circular membrane fixed at its edge, possible modes of vibration along with their nodal lines are shown in Fig. 20–7. The natural frequency of each mode is given in terms of the fundamental $\nu_1$. Notice that the frequencies of the overtones are *not* harmonics, that is, they are not integral multiples of $\nu_1$. Vibrating rods also have a nonharmonic set of natural frequencies. Rods and plates have limited use as musical instruments for this reason.

In general, we find that all elastic bodies will vibrate freely with a definite set of frequencies for a given set of boundary or end conditions. These frequencies are called proper frequencies, characteristic frequencies, or *eigenfrequencies** of the system. In general, the eigenfrequencies do *not* form a harmonic series, although some of them may be related as the ratio of whole numbers. In all these cases we have standing waves, and certain regions of the bodies stay at rest all the time. These nodes are curves in two-dimensional bodies and surfaces in three-dimensional bodies.

Recall that for a vibrating string the equation describing a standing wave (see Eq. 19–18b) is of the type

$$y = 2y_m \cos 2\pi \nu t \sin \frac{2\pi x}{\lambda}.$$

This holds for a string fixed at both ends ($y = 0$ at $x = 0$ and $x = n\lambda/2$). The

---

* *Eigen*—from the German—meaning *own, individual, characteristic.*

**Fig. 20–7**   (a) The first six modes of vibration of a circular drumhead clamped around its periphery. The lines represent nodes, the circumference being a node in every case. The + and − signs represent opposite displacements; at an instant when the + areas are raised, the − areas will be depressed. Note that the frequency of each mode is not an integral multiple of the fundamental $\nu_1$ as is the case for strings and tubes. (b) A sketch of a drum-head vibrating in mode $\nu_6$. The displacement shown here is exaggerated for clarity.

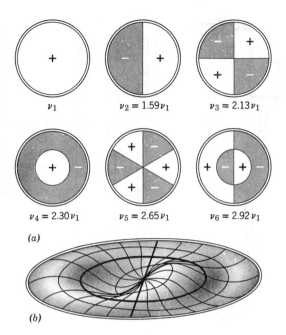

$\nu_1$     $\nu_2 = 1.59\nu_1$     $\nu_3 = 2.13\nu_1$

$\nu_4 = 2.30\nu_1$     $\nu_5 = 2.65\nu_1$     $\nu_6 = 2.92\nu_1$

(a)

(b)

picture of the string at any time is determined by the equation

$$y = C \sin \frac{2\pi x}{\lambda} = C \sin \frac{n\pi x}{l} \qquad (t = \text{constant}),$$

where $C$ is a constant "scale factor," whose value varies with time; $l$ is the length of the string, and $n$ is an integer specifying the mode of vibration (the harmonic). This function $\sin 2\pi x/\lambda$ fixes the position of the nodes and is called the proper function, characteristic function, or *eigenfunction* of the string.

Likewise, the nodes of *any* vibrating elastic body are fixed by certain functions of position which are called the eigenfunctions of the problem. In general, these functions are *not* sinusoidal functions but are functions that become zero for certain values of the coordinates. The determination of these functions and the corresponding values of the eigenfrequencies is an important problem in atomic, nuclear, and solid-state physics. They characterize the behavior of such systems. It is in quantum mechanics that the procedure has been successfully worked out for microscopic systems. However, the results bear a striking analogy to the results of classical vibration and wave theory, as applied to macroscopic systems.

▶ **Example 2.**   Figure 20–8 shows a simple apparatus that can be used to measure the speed of sound in air by resonance methods. A vibrating tuning fork of frequency $\nu$ is held near the open end of a tube. The tube is partly filled with water. The length of the air column can be varied by changing the water level. It is found that the sound intensity is a maximum when the water level is gradually lowered from the top of the tube a distance $a$. Thereafter, the intensity reaches a maximum again at distances $s$, $2s$, $3s$, etc., below the level at $a$. Find the speed of sound in air.

The sound intensity reaches a maximum when the air column resonates with the tuning fork. The air column acts like a tube closed at one end. The standing wave pattern consists of a node at the water surface and an antinode near the

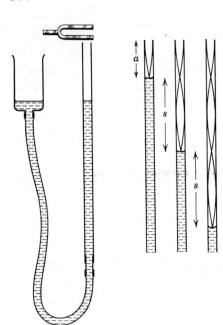

**Fig. 20–8** Example 2. Measuring the speed of sound in air. The water level in the tube can be adjusted by raising or lowering the reservoir on the left which is connected to the tube by a rubber hose.

open end. Since the frequency of the source is fixed and the speed of sound in the air column has a definite value, resonance occurs at one specific wavelength,

$$\lambda = \frac{v}{\nu}.$$

The distance $s$ between successive resonance positions is therefore the distance between adjacent nodes. (See Fig. 20–8.) Hence,

$$s = \frac{\lambda}{2} \quad \text{or} \quad \lambda = 2s.$$

Combining equations we find

$$2s = \frac{v}{\nu} \quad \text{or} \quad v = 2s\nu.$$

In an experiment with a fork of frequency $\nu = 1080$ cycles/sec, $s$ is found to be 15.3 cm. Hence,

$$\lambda = 2s = 30.6 \text{ cm}$$

and $\qquad v = \nu\lambda = (1080)(0.306)$ meters/sec $= 330$ meters/sec.

What significance does the distance $a$ have? Could gases other than air be used conveniently in this apparatus? ◀

## 20–6 Beats

When two wavetrains of the same frequency travel along the same line in opposite directions, standing waves are formed in accord with the principle of superposition. We may characterize these waves by drawing a plot of the amplitude of oscillation as a function of distance, as in Fig. 20–4. This illustrates a type of interference that we can call *interference in space*.

The same principle of superposition leads us to another type of interference, which we can call *interference in time*. It occurs when two wavetrains of slightly *different frequency* travel through the same region. With sound such a condition exists when, for example, two adjacent piano keys are struck simultaneously.

Consider some one point in space through which the waves are passing. In Fig. 20–9a we plot the displacements produced at such a point by the two waves separately as a function of time. For simplicity we have assumed that the two waves have equal amplitude, although this is not necessary. The resultant vibration at that point as a function of time is the sum of the individual vibrations and is plotted in Fig. 20–9b. We see that the *amplitude* of the resultant wave at the given point is not constant but *varies in time*. In the case of sound the varying amplitude gives rise to variations in loudness which are called *beats*. Two strings may be tuned to the same frequency by tightening one of them while sounding both until the beats disappear.

Let us represent the displacement at the point produced by one wave as

$$y_1 = y_m \cos 2\pi\nu_1 t,$$

and the displacement at the point produced by the other wave of equal amplitude as

$$y_2 = y_m \cos 2\pi\nu_2 t.$$

By the superposition principle, the resultant displacement is

$$y = y_1 + y_2 = y_m(\cos 2\pi\nu_1 t + \cos 2\pi\nu_2 t),$$

and since
$$\cos a + \cos b = 2 \cos \frac{a - b}{2} \cos \frac{a + b}{2},$$

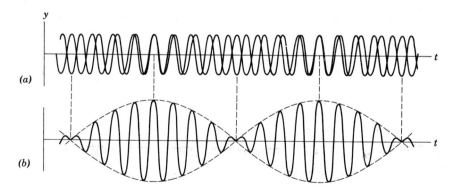

**Fig. 20–9** The beat phenomenon. Two waves of slightly different frequencies, shown in (a), combine in (b) to give a wave whose amplitude (dashed line) varies periodically with time. Compare with Fig. 19-14, which shows the same phenomenon displayed as a function of distance.

this can be written as

$$y = \left[ 2y_m \cos 2\pi \left( \frac{\nu_1 - \nu_2}{2} \right) t \right] \cos 2\pi \left( \frac{\nu_1 + \nu_2}{2} \right) t. \qquad (20\text{--}8)$$

The resulting vibration may then be considered to have a frequency

$$\bar{\nu} = \frac{\nu_1 + \nu_2}{2},$$

which is the average frequency of the two waves, and an amplitude given by the expression in brackets. Hence, the amplitude itself varies with time with a frequency

$$\nu_{\text{amp}} = \frac{\nu_1 - \nu_2}{2}.$$

If $\nu_1$ and $\nu_2$ are nearly equal, this term is small and the amplitude fluctuates slowly. This phenomenon is a form of amplitude modulation which has a counterpart (side bands) in AM radio receivers.

A beat, that is, a maximum of amplitude, will occur whenever

$$\cos 2\pi \left( \frac{\nu_1 - \nu_2}{2} \right) t$$

equals 1 or $-1$. Since *each* of these values occurs once in each cycle (see Fig. 19–14), the number of beats per second is *twice* the frequency $\nu_{\text{amp}}$ or $\nu_1 - \nu_2$. Hence, the number of beats per second equals the difference of the frequencies of the component waves. Beats between two tones can be detected by the ear up to a frequency of about seven per second. At higher frequencies individual beats cannot be distinguished in the sound produced.

## 20–7  The Doppler Effect

When a listener is in motion toward a stationary source of sound, the pitch (frequency) of the sound heard is higher than when he is at rest. If the listener is in motion away from the stationary source, he hears a lower pitch than when he is at rest. We obtain similar results when the source is in motion toward or away from a stationary listener. The pitch of the whistle of the locomotive is higher when the source is approaching the hearer than when it has passed and is receding.

Christian Johann Doppler (1803–1853), an Austrian, in a paper of 1842, called attention to the fact that the color of a luminous body, just as the pitch of a sounding body, must be changed by relative motion of the body and the observer. This *Doppler effect*, as it is called, applies to waves in general. Let us apply it now to sound waves. We consider only the special case in which the source and observer move along the line joining them.

Let us consider a reference frame at rest in the medium through which the sound travels. Figure 20–10 shows a source of sound $S$ at rest in this

**Fig. 20–10**  The Doppler effect due to motion of the observer (ear).   The source is at rest.

frame and an observer $O$ (note the ear) moving *toward* the source at a speed $v_o$.   The circles represent wavefronts, spaced one wavelength apart, traveling through the medium.   If the observer were at rest in the medium he would receive $vt/\lambda$ waves in time $t$, where $v$ is the speed of sound in the medium and $\lambda$ is the wavelength.   Because of his motion toward the source, however, he receives $v_o t/\lambda$ *additional* waves in this same time $t$. The frequency $\nu'$ that he hears is the number of waves received per unit time or

$$\nu' = \frac{vt/\lambda + v_o t/\lambda}{t} = \frac{v + v_o}{\lambda} = \frac{v + v_o}{v/\nu}.$$

That is,

$$\nu' = \nu \frac{v + v_o}{v} = \nu \left(1 + \frac{v_o}{v}\right). \qquad (20\text{–}9a)$$

The frequency $\nu'$ heard by the observer is the ordinary frequency $\nu$ heard at rest plus the increase $\nu(v_o/v)$ arising from the motion of the observer. When the observer is in motion *away* from the stationary source, there is a *decrease* in frequency $\nu(v_o/v)$ corresponding to the waves that do not reach the observer each unit of time because of his receding motion.   Then

$$\nu' = \nu \left(\frac{v - v_o}{v}\right) = \nu \left(1 - \frac{v_o}{v}\right). \qquad (20\text{–}9b)$$

**Fig. 20–11**  The Doppler effect due to motion of the source.  The observer is at rest. Wavefront 1 was emitted by the source when it was at $S_1$, wavefront 2 was emitted when it was at $S_2$, etc.  At the instant the "snapshot" was taken, the source was at $S$.

Hence, the general relation holding when the *source is at rest* with respect to the medium but the *observer is moving* through it is

$$\nu' = \nu \left( \frac{v \pm v_o}{v} \right), \qquad (20\text{–}9)$$

where the *plus* sign holds for motion *toward* the source and the *minus* sign holds for motion *away* from the source.  Notice that the cause of the change here is the fact that the observer intercepts more or fewer waves each second because of his motion through the medium.

When the *source* is in motion *toward* a stationary observer, the effect is a shortening of the wavelength (see Fig. 20–11), for the source is following after the approaching waves and the crests therefore come closer together. If the frequency of the source is $\nu$ and its speed is $v_s$, then during each vibration it travels a distance $v_s/\nu$ and each wavelength is shortened by this amount.   Hence, the wavelength of the sound arriving at the observer is not $\lambda = v/\nu$ but $\lambda' = v/\nu - v_s/\nu$.   Therefore, the frequency of the sound heard by the observer is *increased*, being

$$\nu' = \frac{v}{\lambda'} = \frac{v}{(v - v_s)/\nu} = \nu \left( \frac{v}{v - v_s} \right). \qquad (20\text{–}10a)$$

If the source moves *away* from the observer, the wavelength emitted is $v_s/v$ greater than $\lambda$, so that the observer hears a *decreased* frequency, namely

$$\nu' = \frac{v}{(v + v_s)/\nu} = \nu\left(\frac{v}{v + v_s}\right). \qquad (20\text{-}10b)$$

Hence, the general relation holding when the *observer is at rest* with respect to the medium but the *source is moving* through it is

$$\nu' = \nu\left(\frac{v}{v \mp v_s}\right), \qquad (20\text{-}10)$$

where the *minus* sign holds for motion *toward* the observer and the *plus* sign holds for motion *away* from the observer. Notice that the cause of the change here is the fact that the motion of the source through the medium shortens or increases the wavelength transmitted through the medium.

If both source *and* observer move through the transmitting medium, the student should be able to show that the observer hears a frequency

$$\nu' = \nu\left(\frac{v \pm v_o}{v \mp v_s}\right). \qquad (20\text{-}11)$$

where the upper signs (+ numerator, − denominator) correspond to the source and observer moving along the line joining the two in the direction *toward* the other, and the lower signs in the direction *away* from the other. Notice that Eq. 20-11 reduces to Eq. 20-9 when $v_s = 0$ and to Eq. 20-10 when $v_o = 0$, as it must.

If a vibrating tuning fork on its resonating box is moved rapidly toward a wall, the observer will hear two notes of different frequency. One is the note heard directly from the receding fork and is lowered in pitch by the motion. The other note is due to the waves reflected from the wall, and this is raised in pitch. The superposition of these two wave trains produces beats.

The Doppler effect is important in light. The speed of light is so great that only astronomical or atomic sources, which have high velocities compared to terrestrial macroscopic sources, show pronounced Doppler effects. The astronomical effect consists of a shift in the wavelength observed from light emitted by elements on moving astronomical bodies compared to the wavelength observed from these same elements on earth. (See Chapter 40.) An easily observed consequence of the Doppler effect is the broadening (or spread in frequency) of the radiation emitted from hot gases. This broadening results from the fact that the emitting atoms or molecules move in all directions and with varying speeds relative to the observing instruments, so that a spread of frequencies is detected.

There are differences, however, in the Doppler effect formula for light and for sound. In sound it is not just the relative motion of source and observer that determines the frequency change. In fact, as we have seen, even when the relative motion is the same ($v_o$ in Eq. 20-9a equals $v_s$ in Eq. 20-10a), we obtain different quantitative results, depending on whether the source or the observer is moving. This difference occurs because $v_o$ and $v_s$ are measured relative to the medium in which the sound wave is propagated and because this medium determines the wave speed. Light, however, does not require a material medium for its transmission, and the speed of light relative to the source or the observer is always the same value $c$, regardless of the motion of these bodies relative to each other. This is a basic postulate of the special theory of relativity. Hence, for light only the relative motion of source and observer can lead to physical changes, there being no material medium to use as a reference frame. Although the Doppler formula for light (Chapter 40) differs from that for sound, the effects are qualitatively the same. We can apply Eq. 20–10 to light as a good approximation if $v_s$ is taken to mean the *relative* velocity of source and observer and if $v_s$ is very small compared to the velocity of light.

▶ **Example 3.** Show that Eqs. 20–9 and 20–10 become practically identical when the speed of the sources and the observer are small compared to the speed of sound in the medium.

Let $v_o = v_s = u$. That is, let $u$ represent the speed of observer *or* source. Then Eq. 20–9 becomes

$$\nu' = \nu\left(1 \pm \frac{u}{v}\right).$$

We must show then that Eq. 20–10,

$$\nu' = \nu\left(\frac{v}{v \mp u}\right),$$

reduces to the previous form when $u/v \ll 1$.

We can rewrite Eq. 20–10 as

$$\nu' = \nu\left(\frac{1}{1 \mp u/v}\right).$$

Now by the binomial expansion

$$\left(\frac{1}{1 \mp u/v}\right) = \left(1 \mp \frac{u}{v}\right)^{-1} = 1 \pm \frac{u}{v} + \left(\frac{u}{v}\right)^2 \pm \cdots$$

But if $u/v$ is sufficiently small compared to unity that we may neglect $(u/v)^2$ and higher powers, then

$$\left(\frac{1}{1 \mp u/v}\right) \cong 1 \pm \frac{u}{v},$$

and Eq. 20–10 becomes      $\nu' \cong \nu\left(1 \pm \dfrac{u}{v}\right),$

the same as Eq. 20–9.

As a numerical example take $u = 73.0$ miles/hr. The speed of sound in air is about 730 miles/hr. Then if the source has a speed $v_s = u = 73.0$ miles/hr toward the stationary observer, the frequency heard by the observer is Eq. 20–10,

$$\nu' = \nu\left(\frac{v}{v - v_s}\right) = \nu\left(\frac{730}{730 - 73.0}\right)$$

or          $\dfrac{\nu'}{\nu} = 1.11.$

If the observer has a speed $v_o = u = 73.0$ miles/hr toward the stationary source, the frequency heard by the observer is Eq. 20-9,

$$\nu' = \nu \left( \frac{v + v_o}{v} \right) = \nu \left( \frac{730 + 73.0}{730} \right)$$

or

$$\frac{\nu'}{\nu} = 1.10.$$

Hence, when $u/v = 73.0/730 = 1/10$, the percentage difference in the frequency heard between that for the moving observer and that for the moving source, the relative motion being the same, is only 1%.          ◀

When $v_o$ or $v_s$ becomes comparable in magnitude to $v$, the formulas just given for the Doppler effect must be modified. The modification is required because the linear relation between restoring force and displacement assumed up until now no longer holds in the medium. The speed of wave propagation is no longer the normal phase velocity, and the wave shapes change in time. Components of the motion at right angles to the line joining source and observer also contribute to the Doppler effect at these high speeds. When $v_o$ or $v_s$ exceeds $v$, the Doppler formula clearly has no meaning.

There are many instances in which the source moves through a medium at a speed greater than the phase velocity of the wave in that medium. In such cases the wavefront takes the shape of a cone with the moving body at its apex. Some examples are the bow wave from a speedboat on the water and the "shock wave" from an airplane or projectile moving through the air at a speed greater than the

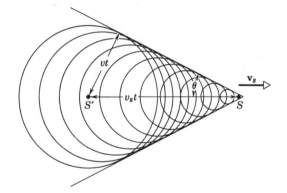

**Fig. 20-12** Above, right, a group of wavefronts associated with a projectile moving with supersonic speed. The wavefronts are spherical and their envelope is a cone. The student should see the relation between this figure and the previous one. Below, right, a spark photograph of a projectile undergoing this motion. (U.S. Navy Photograph.)

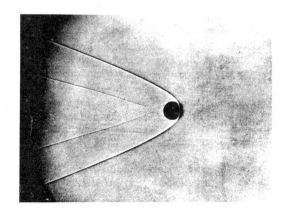

velocity of sound in that medium (supersonic speeds). The Cerenkov radiation consists of light waves emitted by charged particles which move through a medium with a speed greater than the phase velocity of light in that medium.*

In Fig. 20–12 we show the present positions of the spherical waves which originated at various positions of the source during its motion. The radius of each sphere at this time is the product of the wave speed $v$ and the time $t$ which has elapsed since the source was at its center. The envelope of these waves is a cone whose surface makes an angle $\theta$ with the direction of motion of the source. From the figure we obtain the result

$$\sin \theta = \frac{v}{v_s}.$$

For water waves the cone reduces to a pair of intersecting lines. In aerodynamics the ratio $v_s/v$ is called the Mach number.

## QUESTIONS

**1.** List some sources of infrasonic waves. Of ultrasonic waves.

**2.** What experimental evidence is there for assuming that the speed of sound is the same for all wavelengths?

**3.** What quantity, if any, for transverse waves in a string corresponds to the pressure amplitude for longitudinal waves in a tube?

**4.** A bell is rung for a short time in a school. After a while its sound is inaudible. Trace the sound waves and the energy they transfer from the time of emission until they become inaudible.

**5.** How can we experimentally locate the positions of nodes and antinodes in a string? In an air column? On a vibrating surface?

**6.** Explain how a stringed instrument is "tuned."

**7.** Discuss the factors that determine the range of frequencies in your voice and the quality of your voice.

**8.** The bugle has no valves. How then can we sound different notes on it? To what notes is the bugler limited? Why?

**9.** Would a plucked violin string oscillate for a longer or shorter time if the violin had no sounding board? Explain.

**10.** Two ships with steam whistles of the same pitch sound off in the harbor. Would you expect this to produce an interference pattern with regions of high and low intensity?

**11.** Suppose that, in the Doppler effect for sound, the source and receiver are at rest in some reference frame but the transmitting medium is moving with respect to this frame. Will there be a change in wavelength, or in frequency, received?

**12.** Is there a Doppler effect for sound when the observer or the source moves at right angles to the line joining them? How then can we determine the Doppler effect when the motion has a component at right angles to this line?

**13.** A satellite emits radio waves of constant frequency. These waves are picked up on the ground and made to beat against some standard frequency. The beat frequency is then sent through a loudspeaker and one "hears" the satellite signals. Describe how the sound changes as the satellite approaches, passes overhead, and recedes from the detector on the ground.

---

* See "Cerenkov Radiation: its Origin, Properties and Applications," by J. V. Jelley in *Contemporary Physics*, October 1961.

**14.** Two identical tuning forks emit notes of the same frequency. Explain how you might hear beats between them.

**15.** Transverse waves in a string can be polarized (see, for example, Question 16 of Chapter 19). Can sound waves be polarized?

## PROBLEMS

**1.** The lowest pitch detectable as sound by the average human ear consists of about 20 vib/sec and the highest of about 20,000 vib/sec. What is the wavelength of each in air?

**2.** A sound wave has a frequency of 440 vib/sec. What is the wavelength of this sound in air? In water?

**3.** Bats emit ultrasonic waves. The shortest wavelength emitted in air by a bat is about 0.13 in. What is the highest frequency a bat can emit?

**4.** (a) A loudspeaker has a diameter of 6.0 in. At what frequency will the wavelength of the sound it emits in air be equal to its diameter? Be ten times its diameter? Be one-tenth its diameter? (b) Make the same calculations for a speaker of diameter 12.0 in. If the wavelength is large compared to the diameter of the speaker, the sound waves spread out almost uniformly in all directions from the speaker, but when the wavelength is small compared to the diameter of the speaker, the wave energy is propagated mostly in the forward direction.

**5.** A rule for finding your distance from a lightning flash is to count seconds from the time you see the flash until you hear the thunder and then divide the count by five. The result is supposed to give the distance in miles. Explain this rule and determine the per cent error in it at standard conditions.

**6.** A stone is dropped into a well. The sound of the splash is heard at a time $t$ later. What is the depth $d$ of the well? Find $d$ when $t = 3.0$ sec.

**7.** (a) The speed of sound in a certain metal is $V$. One end of a pipe of that metal of length $l$ is struck a blow. A listener at the other end hears two sounds, one from the wave that has traveled along the pipe and the other from the wave that has traveled through the air. If $v$ is the speed of sound in air, what time interval $t$ elapses between the two sounds? (b) Suppose $t = 1.4$ sec and the metal is iron. Find the length $l$.

**8.** The pressure in a traveling sound wave is given by the equation

$$p = 1.5 \sin \pi(x - 330t),$$

where $x$ is in meters, $t$ in seconds, and $p$ in nt/meter$^2$. Find the pressure amplitude, frequency, wavelength, and speed of the wave.

**9.** Show that the intensity of a sound wave (a) when expressed in terms of the pressure amplitude $P$, is given by

$$I = \frac{P^2}{2\rho_0 v},$$

where $v$ is the speed of the wave and $\rho_0$ is the standard density of air, and, (b) when expressed in terms of the displacement amplitude $y_m$, is given by

$$I = 2\pi^2 \rho_0 v y_m^2 \nu^2,$$

where $\nu$ is the frequency of the wave.

**10.** (a) If two sound waves, one in air and one in water, are equal in intensity, what is the ratio of the pressure amplitude of the wave in water to that of the wave in air? (b) If the pressure amplitudes are equal instead, what is the ratio of the intensities of the waves?

**11.** A note of frequency 300 vib/sec has an intensity of 1.0 microwatt/meter$^2$. What is the amplitude of the air vibrations caused by this sound?

**12.** Two waves give rise to pressure variations at a certain point in space given by

$$p_1 = P \sin 2\pi \nu t,$$

$$p_2 = P \sin 2\pi(\nu t - \phi).$$

What is the amplitude of the resultant wave at this point when $\phi = 0$, $\phi = \frac{1}{4}$, $\phi = \frac{1}{6}$, $\phi = \frac{1}{8}$?

**13.** In Fig. 20–13 we show an acoustic interferometer, used to demonstrate the interference of sound waves. $S$ is a diaphragm that vibrates under the influence of an

**Fig. 20–13**

electromagnet. $D$ is a sound detector, such as the ear or a microphone. Path $SBD$ can be varied in length, but path $SAD$ is fixed.

The interferometer contains air, and it is found that the sound intensity has a minimum value of 100 units at one position of $B$ and continuously climbs to a maximum value of 900 units at a second position 1.65 cm from the first. Find (a) the frequency of the sound emitted from the source, and (b) the relative amplitudes of the two waves arriving at the detector. (c) How can it happen that these waves have different amplitudes, considering that they originate at the same source?

**14.** Two loudspeakers, $S_1$ and $S_2$, each emit sound of frequency 200 vib/sec uniformly in all directions. $S_1$ has an acoustic output of $1.2 \times 10^{-3}$ watt and $S_2$ one o 1.8 $\times 10^{-3}$ watt. $S_1$ and $S_2$ vibrate in phase. Consider a point $P$ which is 4.0 meters from $S_1$ and 3.0 meters from $S_2$. (a) How are the phases of the two waves arriving at $P$ related? (b) What is the intensity of sound at $P$ with both $S_1$ and $S_2$ on? (c) What is the intensity of sound at $P$ if $S_1$ is turned off ($S_2$ on)? (d) What is the intensity of sound at $P$ if $S_2$ is turned off ($S_1$ on)?

**Fig. 20–14**

**15.** A spherical sound source is placed at $P_1$ near a reflecting wall $AB$ and a microphone is located at point $P_2$, as shown in Fig. 20–14. The frequency of the sound source $P_1$ is variable. Find two different frequencies for which the sound intensity, as observed at $P_2$, will be a maximum. The speed of sound in air is 1100 ft/sec.

**16.** The water level in a vertical glass tube 1.0 meter long can be adjusted to any position in the tube. A tuning fork vibrating at 660 vib/sec is held just over the open top end of the tube. At what positions of the water level will there be resonance?

**17.** In Fig. 20–15 a rod $R$ is clamped at its center and a disk $D$ at its end projects into a glass tube, which has cork filings spread over its interior. A plunger $P$ is provided at the other end of the tube. The rod is set into longitudinal vibration and the plunger is moved until the filings form a pattern of nodes and antinodes (the filings form well-defined ridges at the antinodes). If we know the frequency $\nu$ of the longitudinal vibrations in the rod, a measurement of the average distance $d$ between successive antinodes

**Fig. 20–15**

determines the speed of sound $v$ in the gas in the tube. Show that

$$v = 2\nu d.$$

This is Kundt's method for determining the speed of sound in various gases.

**18.** A tube 1.0 meter long is closed at one end. A stretched wire is placed near the open end. The wire is 0.30 meter long and has a mass of 0.010 kg. It is held fixed at both ends and vibrates in its fundamental mode. It sets the air column in the tube into vibration at its fundamental frequency by resonance. Find (a) the frequency of oscillation of the air column and (b) the tension in the wire.

**19.** A tube can act like an acoustic filter, discriminating against the passage through it of sound of frequencies different from the natural frequencies of the tube. The muffler of an automobile is an example. (a) Explain how such a filter works. (b) How can we determine the cut-off frequency, below which frequency sound is not transmitted?

**20.** An open organ pipe has a fundamental frequency of 300 vib/sec. The first overtone of a closed organ pipe has the same frequency as the first overtone of the open pipe. How long is each pipe?

**21.** $S$ in Fig. 20–16 is a small loudspeaker driven by an audio oscillator and amplifier, adjustable in frequency from 1000 to 2000 cycles/sec only. $D$ is a piece of cylindrical sheet-metal pipe 18.0 in. long. If the velocity of sound in air is 1130 ft/sec at the existing temperature, at what frequencies will resonance occur when the frequency emitted by the speaker is varied from 1000 to 2000 cycles/sec? Sketch the displacement modes for each. Neglect end effects.

**Fig. 20–16**

**22.** A certain violin string is 50 cm long between its fixed points and has a mass of 2.0 gm. The string sounds an $A$ note (440 vib/sec) when played without fingering. Where must one put one's finger to play a $C$ (528 vib/sec)?

**23.** The strings of a cello have a length $L$. By what length $l$ must they be shortened by fingering to change the pitch by a frequency ratio $r$? Find $l$, if $L = 0.80$ meter and $r = 6/5, \ldots, r = 3/2$.

**24.** If a violin string is tuned to a certain note, by how much must the tension in the string be increased if it is to emit a note of double the original frequency (that is, a note one octave higher in pitch).

**25.** An aluminum wire of length $l_1 = 60.0$ cm and of cross-sectional area $1.00 \times 10^{-2}$ cm$^2$ is connected to a steel wire of the same cross-sectional area. The compound wire, loaded with a block $m$ of mass 10.0 kg, is arranged as shown in Fig. 20–17, so that the distance $l_2$ from the joint to the supporting pulley is 86.6 cm. Transverse waves are set up in the wire by using an external source of variable frequency. (a) Find the lowest frequency of excitation for which standing waves are observed such that the joint in the wire is a node. (b) What is the total number of nodes observed at this frequency, excluding the two at the ends of the wire? The density of aluminum is 2.60 gm/cm$^3$, and that of steel is 7.80 gm/cm$^3$.

**Fig. 20–17**

**26.** Two identical piano wires have a fundamental frequency of 600 vib/sec when kept under the same tension. What fractional increase in the tension of one wire will lead to the occurrence of six beats per second when both wires vibrate simultaneously?

**27.** A tuning fork of unknown frequency makes three beats per second with a standard fork of frequency 384 vib/sec. The beat frequency decreases when a small piece of wax is put on a prong of the first fork. What is the frequency of this fork?

**28.** Microwaves, which travel with the speed of light, are reflected from a distant airplane approaching the wave source. It is found that when the reflected waves are beat against the waves radiating from the source the beat frequency is 990 cycles/sec. If the microwaves are 0.10 meter in wavelength, what is the approach speed of the airplane?

**29.** Could you go through a red light fast enough to have it appear green? Would you get a ticket for speeding? Take $\lambda = 6200 \times 10^{-8}$ cm for red light, $\lambda = 5400 \times 10^{-8}$ cm for green light, and $c = 3 \times 10^{10}$ cm/sec as the speed of light.

**30.** A whistle of frequency 540 vib/sec rotates in a circle of radius 2.0 ft at an angular speed of 15 radians/sec. What is the lowest and the highest frequency heard by a listener a long distance away at rest with respect to the center of the circle?

**31.** A siren emitting a sound of frequency 1000 vib/sec moves away from you toward a cliff at a speed of 10 meters/sec. (a) What is the frequency of the sound you hear coming directly from the siren? (b) What is the frequency of the sound you hear reflected off the cliff? (c) What beat frequency would you hear? Take the speed of sound in air as 330 meters/sec.

**32.** Trooper $B$ is chasing speeder $A$ along a straight stretch of road. Both are moving at a top speed of about 100 miles/hr, which is about 150 ft/sec. Trooper $B$, failing to catch up, sounds his siren again. Take the speed of sound in air to be 1100 ft/sec and the frequency of the source to be 500 cycles/sec. Demonstrate clearly whether there will be a Doppler shift in the frequency heard by speeder $A$ and, if there is, what the frequency change is.

**33.** A source of sound waves of frequency 1080 vib/sec moves to the right with a speed of 108 ft/sec relative to the ground. To its right is a reflecting surface moving to the left with a speed of 216 ft/sec relative to the ground. Take the speed of sound in air to be 1080 ft/sec and find (a) the wavelength of the sound emitted in air by the source, (b) the number of waves per second arriving at the reflecting surface, (c) the speed of the reflected waves, (d) the wavelength of the reflected waves.

**34.** A bullet is fired with a speed of 2200 ft/sec. Find the angle made by the shock wave with the line of motion of the bullet.

**35.** A jet plane passes overhead at a height of 5000 meters and a speed of Mach 1.5 (that is, 1.5 times the speed of sound). (a) Find the angle made by the shock wave with the line of motion of the jet. (b) How long after the jet has passed directly overhead will the shock wave reach the ground?

**36.** The speed of light in water is about three-fourths the speed of light in vacuum. A beam of high-speed electrons from a betatron emits Cerenkov radiation in water, the wavefront being a cone of angle 60°. Find the speed of the electrons in the water.

**37.** Calculate the speed of the projectile illustrated in the photograph in Fig. 20–12. Assume the speed of sound in the medium through which the projectile is traveling to be 380 meters/sec.

# Temperature

## CHAPTER 21

### 21–1  Macroscopic and Microscopic Descriptions

In analyzing physical situations we usually focus our attention on some portion of matter which we separate, in our minds, from the environment external to it.   We call such a portion the *system*.   Everything outside the system which has a direct bearing on its behavior we call the *environment*. We then seek to determine the behavior of the system by finding how it interacts with its environment.   For example, a ball can be the system and the environment can be the air and the earth.   In free fall we seek to find how the air and the earth affect the motion of the ball.   Or the gas in a container can be the system, and a movable piston and a Bunsen burner can be the environment.   We seek to find how the behavior of the gas is affected by the action of the piston and burner.   In all such cases we must choose suitable observable quantities to describe the behavior of the system.   We classify these quantities, which are gross properties of the system measured by laboratory operations, as *macroscopic*.   For processes in which heat is involved the laws relating the appropriate macroscopic quantities (which include pressure, volume, temperature, internal energy, and entropy, among others) form the basis for the science of *thermodynamics*.   Many of the macroscopic quantities (pressure, volume, and temperature, for example) are directly associated with our sense perceptions.   We can also adopt a *microscopic* point of view.   Here we consider quantities that describe the atoms and molecules that make up the system, their speeds, energies, masses, angular momenta, behavior during collisions, etc.   These quantities, or mathematical formulations based on them, form the basis for the science of *statistical mechanics*. The microscopic properties are not directly associated with our sense perceptions.

For any system the macroscopic and the microscopic quantities must be, related because they are simply different ways of describing the same situation. In particular, we should be able to express the former in terms of the latter. The pressure of a gas, viewed macroscopically, is measured operationally using a manometer (Fig. 17–10). Viewed microscopically it is related to the average rate per unit area at which the molecules of the gas deliver momentum to the manometer fluid as they strike its surface. In Section 23–4 we will make this microscopic definition of pressure quantitative. Similarly (see Section 23–5), the temperature of a gas may be related to the average kinetic energy of translation of the molecules.

If the macroscopic quantities can be expressed in terms of the microscopic quantities, we should be able to express the laws of thermodynamics quantitatively in the language of statistical mechanics. We can indeed do this. In the words of R. C. Tolman:

> The explanation of the complete science of thermodynamics in terms of the more abstract science of statistical mechanics is one of the greatest achievements of physics. In addition, the more fundamental character of statistical mechanical considerations makes it possible to supplement the ordinary principles of thermodynamics to an important extent.

We begin our examination of heat phenomena in this chapter with a study of temperature. As we progress we shall try to gain a deeper understanding of these phenomena by interweaving the microscopic and the macroscopic description—statistical mechanics and thermodynamics. The interweaving of the microscopic and the macroscopic points of view is characteristic of modern physics.

## 21–2 Thermal Equilibrium—The Zeroth Law of Thermodynamics

The sense of touch is the simplest way to distinguish hot bodies from cold bodies. By touch we can arrange bodies in the order of their hotness, deciding that $A$ is hotter than $B$, $B$ than $C$, etc. We speak of this as our *temperature* sense. This is a very subjective procedure for determining the temperature of a body and certainly not very useful for purposes of science. A simple experiment, suggested in 1690 by John Locke, shows the unreliability of this method. Let a person immerse his hands, one in hot water, the other in cold. Then let him put both hands in water of intermediate hotness. This will seem cooler to the first hand and warmer to the second hand. Our judgment of temperature can be rather misleading. Further, the range of our temperature sense is limited. What we need is an objective, numerical, measure of temperature.

To begin with, we should try to understand the meaning of temperature. Let an object $A$ which feels cold to the hand and an identical object $B$ which feels hot be placed in contact with each other. After a sufficient length of time, $A$ and $B$ give rise to the same temperature sensation.

Then $A$ and $B$ are said to be in *thermal equilibrium* with each other. We can generalize the expression "two bodies are in thermal equilibrium" to mean that the two bodies are in states such that, if the two *were* connected, the combined systems would be in thermal equilibrium. The logical and operational test for thermal equilibrium is to use a third or test body, such as a thermometer. This is summarized in a postulate often called *the zeroth law of thermodynamics: If A and B are in thermal equilibrium with a third body C (the "thermometer"), then A and B are in thermal equilibrium with each other.*

This discussion expresses the idea that the temperature of a system is a property which eventually attains the same value as that of other systems when all these systems are put in contact. This concept agrees with the everyday idea of temperature as the measure of the hotness or coldness of a system, because as far as our temperature sense can be trusted, the hotness of all objects becomes the same after they have been in contact long enough. The idea contained in the zeroth law, although simple, is not obvious. For example, Jones and Smith each know Green, but they may or may not know each other. Two pieces of iron attract a magnet but they may or may not attract each other.

A more formal, but perhaps more fundamental phrasing of the zeroth law is: *There exists a scalar quantity called* temperature, *which is a property of all thermodynamic systems (in equilibrium states), such that temperature equality is a necessary and sufficient condition for thermal equilibrium.* This statement* justifies our use of temperature as a thermodynamic variable; the formulation given above is the corollary of this new statement. Speaking loosely, the essence of the zeroth law is: *there exists a useful quantity called "temperature."*

## 21–3 Measuring Temperature

There are many measurable physical properties that vary as our physiological perception of temperature varies. Among these are the volume of a liquid, the length of a rod, the electrical resistance of a wire, the pressure of a gas kept at constant volume, the volume of a gas kept at constant pressure, and the color of a lamp filament. Any of these properties can be used in the construction of a thermometer—that is, in the setting up of a particular "private" temperature scale. Such a temperature scale is established by choosing a particular thermometric substance and a particular thermometric property of this substance. We then define the temperature scale by an *assumed* continuous monotonic relation between the chosen thermometric property of our substance and the temperature as measured on our (private) scale. For example, the thermometric substance may be a liquid in a glass capillary tube and the thermometric property can be the length of the liquid column; or the thermometric substance may be a gas kept in a container at constant volume and the thermometric property can be the pressure of the gas; and so forth. *We must realize that each choice of thermometric substance and property—along with the assumed rela-*

---

* See J. S. Thomsen, *American Journal of Physics*, 30, 294, 1962.

tion between property and temperature—leads to an individual temperature scale whose measurements need not necessarily agree with measurements made on any other independently defined temperature scale.

This apparent chaos in the definition of temperature is removed by universal agreement, within the scientific community, on the use of a particular thermometric substance, a particular thermometric property, and a particular functional relation between measurements of that property and a universally accepted temperature scale. A private temperature scale defined in any other way can then always be calibrated against the universal scale. We describe such a universal scale in Section 21-5 and an equivalent one in Section 25-6.

Suppose that we have chosen a thermometric substance. Let us represent by $X$ the thermometric property that we wish to use in setting up a temperature scale. We arbitrarily choose the following linear function of the property $X$ as the temperature $T$ which the appropriate thermometer, and any system in thermal equilibrium with it, has:

$$T(X) = aX. \tag{21-1}$$

In this expression $a$ is a constant which we must still evaluate. By choosing this linear form for $T(X)$ we have fixed it so that *equal temperature differences*, or temperature intervals, *correspond to equal changes in $X$*. This means, for example, that every time the mercury column in the mercury-in-glass thermometer changes in length by one unit, the temperature changes by a definite fixed amount, no matter what the starting temperature. It also follows that two temperatures, measured with the same thermometer, are in the same ratio as their corresponding $X$'s, that is

$$\frac{T(X_1)}{T(X_2)} = \frac{X_1}{X_2}.$$

To determine the constant $a$, and hence to calibrate the thermometer, we specify a *standard fixed point* at which all thermometers must give the same reading for temperature $T$. This fixed point is chosen to be that at which ice, liquid water, and water vapor coexist in equilibrium and is called the *triple point of water*. This state can be achieved only at a definite pressure and is unique (Fig. 21-1). The water vapor pressure at the triple point is 4.58 mm-Hg. The temperature at this standard fixed point is arbitrarily* set at 273.16 degrees Kelvin and is abbreviated as 273.16° K. The Kelvin degree is a unit temperature interval.

If we indicate values at the triple point by the subscript $tr$, then, for any thermometer,

$$\frac{T(X)}{T(X_{tr})} = \frac{X}{X_{tr}},$$

---

* Adopted in 1954 at the Tenth General Conference on Weights and Measures in Paris.

Water vapor

Water

Ice

Sealed cell

Thermometer well

Water-ice mixture

Vacuum flask

**Fig. 21–1** The National Bureau of Standards triple-point cell. It contains pure water and is sealed after all air has been removed. It is then immersed in a water-ice bath. The system is at the triple point when ice, water, and vapor are all present, and in equilibrium, inside the cell. The thermometer to be calibrated is immersed in the central well.

where, for *all* thermometers,

$$T(X_{tr}) = 273.16° \text{ K},$$

so that

$$T(X) = 273.16° \text{ K} \frac{X}{X_{tr}}. \tag{21–2}$$

Hence, when the thermometric property has the value $X$, the temperature $T$, on the particular private scale selected, is given in °K by $T(X)$, when the value of $X$ and $X_{tr}$ are inserted on the right-hand side of this equation.

We can now apply Eq. 21–2 to several thermometers. For a liquid-in glass thermometer $X$ is $L$, the length of the liquid column, and Eq. 21–2 yields

$$T(L) = 273.16° \text{ K} \frac{L}{L_{tr}}.$$

For a gas at constant pressure, $X$ is $V$, the volume of the gas, and

$$T(V) = 273.16° \text{ K} \frac{V}{V_{tr}} \qquad (\text{constant } P).$$

For a gas at constant volume, $X$ is $P$, the gas pressure, and

$$T(P) = 273.16° \text{ K} \frac{P}{P_{tr}} \qquad (\text{constant } V).$$

For a platinum resistance thermometer, $X$ is $R$, the electrical resistance, and

$$T(R) = 273.16° \text{ K } \frac{R}{R_{tr}},$$

and likewise for other thermometric substances and thermometric properties.

▶ **Example 1.** A certain platinum resistance thermometer has a resistance $R$ of 90.35 ohms when its bulb is placed in a triple-point cell like that of Fig. 21–1. What temperature is defined by Eq. 21–2 if the bulb is placed in an environment such that its resistance is 96.28 ohms?

From Eq. 21–2,

$$T(X) = 273.16° \text{ K } \frac{X}{X_{tr}}$$

$$= (273.16° \text{ K}) \left( \frac{96.28}{90.35} \right) = 280.6° \text{ K.}$$

Note that this temperature is on a private scale, defined by applying Eq. 21–2 to a particular device, the platinum resistance thermometer.    ◀

The question now arises whether the value we obtain for the temperature of a system depends on the choice of the thermometer we use to measure it. We have insured by definition that all the different kinds of thermometers will agree at the standard fixed point, but what happens at other points? We can imagine a series of tests in which the temperature of a given system is measured simultaneously with many different thermometers. Results of such tests show that the thermometers all read differently. Even when different thermometers of the same kind are used, such as constant-volume gas thermometers using different gases, we obtain different temperature readings for a given system in a given state.

Hence, to obtain a definite temperature scale, we must select one particular kind of thermometer as the standard. The choice will be made, not on the basis of experimental convenience, but by inquiring whether the temperature scale defined by a particular thermometer proves to be a useful quantity in the formulation of the laws of physics. The smallest variation in readings is found among different constant-volume gas thermometers, which suggests that we choose a gas as the standard thermometric substance. It turns out that as the amount of gas used in such a thermometer, and therefore its pressure, is reduced, the variation in readings between gas thermometers using different kinds of gas is reduced also. Hence, there seems to be something fundamental about the behavior of a constant-volume thermometer containing a gas at low pressure.

## 21–4   The Constant Volume Gas Thermometer

If the volume of a gas is kept constant, its pressure depends on the temperature and increases steadily with rising temperature. The constant-volume gas thermometer uses the pressure at constant volume as the thermometric property.

The thermometer is shown diagrammatically in Fig. 21–2. It consists of a bulb of glass, porcelain, quartz, platinum or platinum-iridium (depending on the temperature range over which it is to be used), connected by a capillary tube to a mercury manometer. The bulb containing some gas is put into the bath or environment whose temperature is to be measured; by raising or lowering the mercury reservoir the mercury in the left branch of the U-tube can be made to coincide with a fixed reference mark, thus keeping the confined gas at a constant volume. Then we read the height of the mercury in the right branch. The pressure of the confined gas is the difference of the heights of the mercury columns (times $\rho g$) plus the atmospheric pressure, as indicated by the barometer. In practice the apparatus is very elaborate and we must make many corrections, for example, (1) to allow for the small volume change owing to slight contraction or expansion of the bulb and (2) to allow for the fact that not all the confined gas (such as that in the capillary) has been immersed in the bath. Assume that all corrections have been made, and let $P$ be the corrected value of the pressure at the temperature of the bath. Then the temperature is given provisionally (see below) by

**Fig. 21–2**  A representation of a constant-volume gas thermometer. As long as the mercury in the left manometer tube remains at the same position on the scale (zero) the volume of the confined gas will be constant. The meniscus can always be brought to the zero position by raising or lowering reservoir $R$.

$$T(P) = 273.16° \text{ K } \frac{P}{P_{tr}} \qquad \text{(constant } V\text{)}. \qquad (21\text{--}3)$$

The constant-volume thermometer, used as described below, is the thermometer which serves to establish the temperature scale used universally in scientific work today.

### 21–5  Ideal Gas Temperature Scale

Let a certain amount of gas be put into the bulb of a constant-volume gas thermometer so that when the bulb is surrounded by water at the triple point the pressure $P_{tr}$ is equal to a definite value, say 80 cm-Hg. Now surround the bulb with steam condensing at 1-atm pressure and, with the volume kept constant at its previous value, measure the gas pressure $P_s$, the pressure at the steam point, in this case, $P_{s80}$. Then calculate the temperature provisionally from $T(P_{s80}) = 273.16°$ K $(P_{s80}/80$ cm-Hg$)$. Next remove some of the gas so that $P_{tr}$ has a smaller value, say 40 cm-Hg. Then measure the new value of $P_s$ and calculate another provisional temperature from $T(P_{s40}) = 273.16°$ K $(P_{s40}/40$ cm-Hg$)$. Continue this same procedure, reducing the amount of gas in the bulb again, and at this new lower value of $P_{tr}$ calculating the temperature at the steam point $T(P_s)$. If we plot the values $T(P_s)$ against $P_{tr}$ and have enough data, we can extrapolate the resulting curve to the intersection with the axis where $P_{tr} = 0$.

In Fig. 21–3, we plot curves obtained from such a procedure for constant-volume thermometers of some different gases. These curves show that the temperature readings of a constant-volume gas thermometer depend on the gas used at ordinary values of the reference pressure. However, as

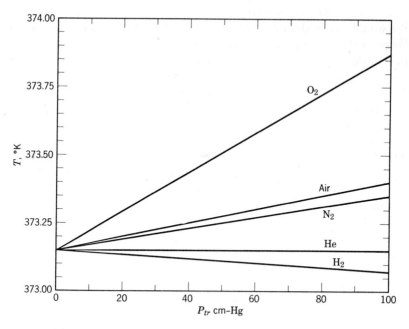

**Fig. 21–3**   The readings of a constant-volume gas thermometer for the temperature $T$ of condensing steam as a function of $P_{tr}$, when different gases are used. As the amount of gas in the thermometer is reduced its pressure $P_{tr}$ at the triple point decreases. Note that at a particular $P_{tr}$ the values of $T$ given by different gas thermometers differ. The discrepancy is small but measurable, being about 0.2 per cent in the most extreme cases shown ($O_2$ and $H_2$ at 100 cm-Hg). Helium gives nearly the same $T$ at all pressures (the curve is almost horizontal) so that its behaviour is the most similar to that of an ideal gas over the entire range shown.

the reference pressure is decreased, the temperature readings of constant-volume gas thermometers using different gases approach the same value. Therefore, *the extrapolated value of the temperature depends only on the general properties of gases and not on any particular gas.* We therefore define an *ideal gas temperature scale* by the relation

$$T = 273.16° \text{ K} \lim_{P_{tr} \to 0} \left( \frac{P}{P_{tr}} \right) \quad \text{(constant } V\text{)}. \quad (21\text{–}4)$$

Our standard thermometer is therefore chosen to be a constant-volume gas thermometer using a temperature scale defined by Eq. 21–4.

Although our temperature scale is independent of the properties of any one particular gas, it does depend on the properties of gases in general (that is, on the properties of an ideal gas). Therefore, to measure a temperature, a gas must be used at that temperature. The lowest temperature that can be measured with any gas thermometer is about 1° K. To obtain this temperature we must use low-pressure helium, for helium becomes a liquid at a temperature lower than any other gas. Therefore we cannot give experimental meaning to temperatures below about 1° K, by means of a gas thermometer.

We would like to define a temperature scale in a way that is *independent of the properties of any particular substance.* We will show in Section 25–6 that the *absolute thermodynamic temperature scale*, called the Kelvin scale, is such a scale. We will show also that *the ideal gas scale and the Kelvin scale are identical in the range of temperatures in which a gas thermometer may be used.* For this reason we can write °K after an ideal gas temperature, as we have already done.

We will also show in Section 25–6 that the Kelvin scale has an *absolute zero* of 0° K and that temperatures below this do not exist. The absolute zero of temperature has defied all attempts to reach it experimentally, although it is possible to come arbitrarily close.* The existence of the absolute zero is inferred by extrapolation. The student should not think of absolute zero as a state of zero energy and no motion. The conception that all molecular action would cease at absolute zero is incorrect. This notion assumes that the purely macroscopic concept of temperature is strictly connected to the microscopic concept of molecular motion. When we try to make such a connection, we find in fact that as we approach absolute zero the kinetic energy of the molecules approaches a finite value, the so-called zero-point energy. The molecular energy is a minimum, but not zero, at absolute zero.

---

* It is possible to prepare systems that have *negative Kelvin temperatures.* Surprisingly enough, such temperatures are *not* reached by passing through 0° K but by proceeding through infinite temperatures. That is, negative temperatures are not 'colder' than absolute zero but instead are 'hotter' than infinite temperatures. See *Science by Degrees*, by Castle, Emmerich, Heikes, Miller, and Rayne, published by Walker and Company, New York, 1965. The absolute zero remains experimentally unattainable.

## Table 21–1

### SOME TEMPERATURES* (°K)

| | |
|---|---|
| Carbon thermonuclear reaction | $5 \times 10^8$ |
| Helium thermonuclear reaction | $10^8$ |
| Solar interior | $10^7$ |
| Solar corona | $10^6$ |
| Shock wave in air at Mach 20 | $2.5 \times 10^4$ |
| Luminous nebulae | $10^4$ |
| Solar surface | $6 \times 10^3$ |
| Tungsten melts | $3.6 \times 10^3$ |
| Lead melts | $6.0 \times 10^2$ |
| Water freezes | $2.7 \times 10^2$ |
| Oxygen boils (1 atm) | $9.0 \times 10^1$ |
| Hydrogen boils (1 atm) | $2.0 \times 10^1$ |
| Helium (He$^4$) boils at 1 atm | $4.2$ |
| He$^3$ boils at attainable low pressure | $3.0 \times 10^{-1}$ |
| Adiabatic demagnetization of paramagnetic salts | $10^{-3}$ |
| Adiabatic demagnetization of nuclei | $10^{-6}$ |

\* See *Scientific American*, September 1954; special issue on heat.

In Table 21–1 we list the temperatures, on the Kelvin scale, of various bodies and processes.

### 21–6   The Celsius and Fahrenheit Scales

Two temperature scales in common use are the Celsius* and the Fahrenheit scales. These are defined in terms of the Kelvin scale, which is the fundamental temperature scale in science.

The Celsius temperature scale uses a degree (the unit of temperature) which has the same magnitude as the degree on the Kelvin scale. If we let $t$ represent the Celsius temperature, then

$$T_C = T - 273.15° \qquad (21–5)$$

relates the Celsius temperature $t$ (°C) and the Kelvin temperature $T$ (°K). We see that the triple point of water ( = 273.16° K by definition) corresponds to 0.01° C. By experiment the temperature at which ice and air-saturated water are in equilibrium at atmospheric pressure—the so-called ice point—proves to be 0.00° C and the temperature at which steam and liquid water are in equilibrium at 1-atm pressure—the so-called steam point—proves to be 100.00° C.

The Fahrenheit scale, in common use in English-speaking countries (except in England itself, which adopted the Celsius scale for commercial

---

\* This scale, based on a scale invented by a Swede named Celsius in 1742, was called the "centigrade" scale until 1948, when the Ninth General Conference on Weights and Measures decided that the name should be changed.

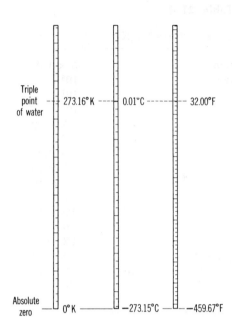

**Fig. 21–4** The Kelvin, Celsius, and Fahrenheit temperature scales.

and civil use in 1964) is not used in scientific work. The relationship between the Fahrenheit and Celsius scales is defined to be

$$T_C = 32° \text{ F} + \tfrac{9}{5}T_F.$$

From this relation we can conclude that the ice point (0.00° C) equals 32.0° F, that the steam point (100.0° C) equals 212.0° F, and that one Fahrenheit degree is exactly $\frac{5}{9}$ as large as one Celsius degree. In Fig. 21–4 we compare the Kelvin, Celsius, and Fahrenheit scales.

### 21–7 The International Practical Temperature Scale

Let us now summarize the ideas of the last few sections. The standard fixed point in thermometry is the triple point of water which is arbitrarily assigned a value 273.16° K. The constant-volume gas thermometer is the standard thermometer. The extrapolated gas scale is used to define the ideal gas temperature from $T = 273.16° \text{ K} \lim_{P_{tr} \to 0} (P/P_{tr})$. This scale is identical with the (absolute thermodynamic) Kelvin scale in the range in which a gas thermometer can be used.

By using the standard thermometer in this way, we can experimentally determine other reference points for temperature measurements, called fixed points. We list the basic fixed points adopted for experimental reference in Table 21–2. The temperatures can be expressed on the Celsius scale, with the use of Eq. 21–5, once the Kelvin temperature is determined.

Determining ideal gas temperatures is a painstaking job. It would not make sense to use this procedure to determine temperatures for all work.

## Table 21-2

FIXED POINTS ON THE INTERNATIONAL PRACTICAL TEMPERATURE SCALE
(1960)*

| | | Temperature | |
| Substance | Designation | °C | °K |
|---|---|---|---|
| Oxygen | Normal boiling point | −182.97 | 90.18 |
| Water | Triple point | 0.01 | 273.16 |
| Water | Normal boiling point | 100.00 | 373.15 |
| Sulfur† | Normal boiling point | 444.60 | 717.75 |
| Silver | Normal boiling point | 960.80 | 1233.95 |
| Gold | Normal boiling point | 1063.00 | 1336.15 |

* All temperatures assumed exact for the purposes of establishing the scale.
† The normal melting point of zinc (419.505° C) may be substituted.

Hence, an International Practical Temperature Scale (IPTS) was adopted in 1927 (revised in 1948 and again in 1954 and 1960) to provide a scale that can be used easily for practical purposes, such as for calibration of industrial or scientific instruments. This scale consists of a set of recipes for providing in practice the best possible approximations to the Kelvin scale. A set of fixed points, the basic points in Table 21-2, is adopted, and a set of instruments is specified to be used in interpolating between these fixed points and in extrapolating beyond the highest fixed point. Formulas are specified for correcting the basic temperatures according to the barometer reading. The IPTS departs from the Kelvin scale at temperatures between the fixed points, but the difference is usually negligible. The IPTS has become the legal standard in nearly all countries.

### 21-8 Temperature Expansion

Common effects of temperature changes are changes in size and changes of state of materials. Let us consider changes of sizes which occur without changes of state. Consider a simple model of a crystalline solid. The atoms are held together in a regular array by forces of electrical origin. The forces between atoms are like those that would be exerted by a set of springs connecting the atoms, so that we can visualize the solid body as a microscopic bedspring (Fig. 21-5). These "springs" are quite stiff (Problem 38, Chapter 15), and there are about $10^{22}$ of them per cubic centimeter. At any temperature the atoms of the solid are vibrating. The amplitude of vibration is about $10^{-9}$ cm and the frequency about $10^{13}$/sec.

When the temperature is increased the average distance between atoms increases. This leads to an expansion of the whole solid body as the temperature is increased. The change in *any* linear dimension of the solid, such as its length, width, or thickness, is called a linear expansion. If the

**Fig. 21-5** A solid behaves in many ways as if it is a microscopic "bedspring" in which the molecules are held together by elastic forces.

length of this linear dimension is $l$, the change in length, arising from a change in temperature $\Delta T$, is $\Delta l$. We find from experiment that, if $\Delta T$ is small enough, this change in length $\Delta l$ is proportional to the temperature change $\Delta T$ and to the original length $l$. Hence, we can write

$$\Delta l = \alpha l \, \Delta T, \qquad (21\text{-}6)$$

where $\alpha$, called the *coefficient of linear expansion*, has different values for different materials. Rewriting this formula we obtain

$$\alpha = \frac{1}{l} \frac{\Delta l}{\Delta T},$$

so that $\alpha$ has the meaning of a fractional change in length per degree temperature change.

Strictly speaking, the value of $\alpha$ depends on the actual temperature and the reference temperature chosen to determine $l$ (see Problem 15). However, its variation is usually negligible compared to the accuracy with which engineering measurements need to be made. We can safely take it as a constant for a given material, independent of the temperature. In Table 21-3 we list the experimental values for the average coefficient of linear expansion of several common solids. For all the substances listed, the change in size consists of an expansion as the temperature rises, for $\bar{\alpha}$ is positive. The order of magnitude of the expansion is about 1 millimeter per meter length per 100 Celsius degrees.*

▶ **Example 2.** A steel metric scale is to be ruled so that the millimeter intervals are accurate to within about $5 \times 10^{-5}$ mm at a certain temperature. What is the maximum temperature variation allowable during the ruling? From Eq. 21-6,

$$\Delta l = \alpha l \, \Delta T,$$

we have

$$5 \times 10^{-5} \text{ mm} = (11 \times 10^{-6}/\text{C}°)(1.0 \text{ mm}) \, \Delta T$$

in which we have used $\bar{\alpha}$ for steel, taken from Table 21-3. This yields $\Delta T \cong 5$ C°. The temperature maintained during the ruling process must be maintained when the scale is being used and it must be held constant to within about 5 C°.

Note (see Table 21-3) that if the alloy invar is used instead of steel, then for the

---

* One Celsius degree (1 C°) is a temperature *interval* ($\Delta T$) of one unit measured on a Celsius scale. One degree Celsius (1° C) is a specific temperature reading ($T$) on that scale.

same required tolerance one can permit a temperature variation of about 75 C°; or for the same temperature variation ($\Delta T = 5$ C°) the tolerance achieved would be more than an order of magnitude better.    ◄

**Table 21-3**

SOME VALUES* of $\bar{\alpha}$

| Substance | $\bar{\alpha}$ (per C°) | Substance | $\bar{\alpha}$ (per C°) |
|---|---|---|---|
| Aluminum | 23 $\times 10^{-6}$ | Hard rubber | 80 $\times 10^{-6}$ |
| Brass | 19 $\times 10^{-6}$ | Ice | 51 $\times 10^{-6}$ |
| Copper | 17 $\times 10^{-6}$ | Invar | 0.7 $\times 10^{-6}$ |
| Glass (ordinary) | 9 $\times 10^{-6}$ | Lead | 29 $\times 10^{-6}$ |
| Glass (pyrex) | 3.2 $\times 10^{-6}$ | Steel | 11 $\times 10^{-6}$ |

* For the range 0° C to 100° C; except −10° C to 0° C for ice.

On the microscopic level thermal expansion of a solid suggests an increase in the average separation between the atoms in the solid. The potential energy curve for two adjacent atoms in a crystalline solid as a function of their internuclear separation is an asymmetric curve like that of Fig. 21-6. As the atoms move close together, their separation decreasing from the equilibrium value $r_0$, strong repulsive forces come into play and the potential curve rises steeply ($F = -dU/dr$); as the atoms move farther apart, their separation increasing from the equilibrium value, somewhat weaker attractive forces take over and the potential curve rises more slowly. At a given vibrational energy the separation of the atoms will

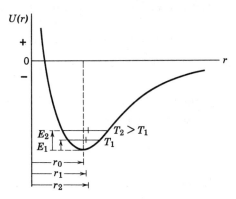

**Fig. 21-6** Potential energy curve for two adjacent atoms in a crystalline solid as a function of internuclear separation. The equilibrium separation is $r_0$. Because the curve is asymmetric the average separation ($r_1, r_2$) increases as the temperature ($T_1, T_2$), and hence the vibrational energy ($E_1, E_2$), increases.

change periodically from a minimum to a maximum value, the average separation being greater than the equilibrium separation because of the asymmetric nature of the potential energy curve. At still higher vibrational energy the average separation will be even greater. The effect is enhanced by the fact that in taking a time average of the motion one must allow for the longer time spent at extreme separations (lower vibrational speeds). Because the vibrational energy increases as the temperature rises, the average separation between atoms increases with temperature and the solid as a whole expands.

Note that if the potential energy curve were symmetric about the equilibrium separation, then no matter how large the amplitude of the vibration becomes the average separation would correspond to the equilibrium separation. Hence, thermal expansion is a direct consequence of the deviation from symmetry (that is, the asymmetry) of the potential energy curve characteristic of solids.

Some crystalline solids, in certain temperature regions, may contract as the temperature rises. The above analysis remains valid if one assumes that only compressional (i.e. longitudinal) modes of vibration exist or that these modes predominate. However, solids may vibrate in shear-like (i.e. transverse) modes as well and these modes of vibration will allow the solid to contract as the temperature rises, the average separation of the planes of atoms decreasing. For certain types of crystalline structure and in certain temperature regions these transverse modes of vibration may predominate over the longitudinal ones, giving a net negative coefficient of thermal expansion.

It should be emphasized that the microscopic models presented here are over-simplifications of a complex phenomenon which can be treated with greater care with the use of thermodynamics and quantum theory.

For many solids, called *isotropic*, the per cent change in length for a given temperature change is the same for all lines in the solid. The expansion is quite analogous to a photographic enlargement, except that a solid is three-dimensional. Thus, if you have a flat plate with a hole punched in it, $\Delta l/l$ ($= \alpha \Delta T$) for a given $\Delta T$ is the same for the length, the thickness, the face diagonal, the body diagonal, and the hole diameter. Every line, whether straight or curved, lengthens in the ratio $\alpha$ per degree temperature rise. If you scratch your name on the plate, the line representing your name has the same fractional change in length as any other line. The analogy to a photographic enlargement is shown in Fig. 21–7.

With these ideas in mind, the student should be able to show (see Problems 16 and 17) that to a high degree of accuracy the fractional change in area $A$ per degree temperature change for an isotropic solid is $2\alpha$, that is,

$$\Delta A = 2\alpha A \ \Delta T,$$

and the fractional change in volume $V$ per degree temperature change for an isotropic solid is $3\alpha$, that is,

$$\Delta V = 3\alpha V \ \Delta T.$$

Because the shape of a fluid is not definite, only the change in volume with temperature is significant. Gases respond strongly to temperature or pressure changes, whereas the change in volume of liquids with changes in temperature or pressure is very small. If we let $\beta$ represent the coefficient of volume expansion for a liquid, that is,

$$\beta = \frac{1}{V} \frac{\Delta V}{\Delta T},$$

we find that $\beta$ is relatively independent of the temperature. Liquids typi-

**Fig. 21–7**  The same steel rule at two different temperatures.  On expansion every dimension is increased by the same proportion: the scale, the numbers, the hole, and the thickness are all increased by the same factor.  (The expansion shown, from (a) to (b), is obviously exaggerated, for it would correspond to an imaginary temperature rise of about 100,000 C°!)

cally expand with increasing temperature, their volume expansion being generally about ten times greater than that of solids.

However, the most common liquid, water, does not behave like other liquids.  In Fig. 21–8 we show the expansion curve for water.  Notice that above 4° C water expands as the temperature rises, although not linearly. As the temperature is lowered from 4 to 0° C, however, water expands instead of contracting.  Such an expansion with decreasing temperature is not observed in any other common liquid; it is observed in rubberlike substances and in certain crystalline solids over limited temperature intervals.  The density of water is a maximum at 4° C, where its value* is 1000 kg/meter$^3$ or 1.000 gm/cm$^3$.  At all other temperatures its density is less.  This behavior of water is the reason why lakes freeze first at their upper surface.

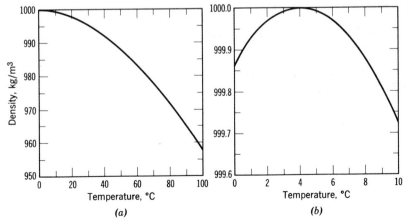

**Fig. 21–8**  (a) The variation with temperature of density of water under atmospheric pressure.  (b) The variation between 0 and 10°C in more detail.

## QUESTIONS

**1.** Is temperature a microscopic or macroscopic concept?

**2.** Does our "temperature sense" have a built-in sense of direction; that is, does hotter necessarily mean higher temperature, or is this just an arbitrary convention? Celsius, by the way, originally chose the steam point as 0° C and the ice point as 100° C.

**3.** How would you suggest measuring the temperature of (a) the sun, (b) the earth's upper atmosphere, (c) an insect, (d) the moon, (e) the ocean floor, and (f) liquid helium?

**4.** Is one gas any better than another for purposes of a standard constant-volume gas thermometer? What properties are desirable in a gas for such purposes?

**5.** State some objections to using water-in-glass as a thermometer. Is mercury-in-glass an improvement?

**6.** Can you explain why the column of mercury first descends and then rises when a mercury-in-glass thermometer is put in a flame?

**7.** What are the dimensions of $\alpha$, the coefficient of linear expansion? Does the value of $\alpha$ depend on the unit of length used? When F° are used instead of C° as a unit of temperature change, does the numerical value of $\alpha$ change? If so, how?

**8.** A metal ball can pass through a metal ring. When the ball is heated, however, it gets stuck in the ring. What would happen if the ring, rather than the ball, were heated?

**9.** A bimetallic strip, consisting of two different metal strips riveted together, is used as a control element in the common thermostat. Explain how it works.

**10.** Explain how the period of a pendulum clock can be kept constant with temperature by attaching tubes of mercury to the bottom of the pendulum. (See Problem 13).

**11.** Explain why some rubberlike substances contract with rising temperature. (See Question 21, Chapter 25.)

**12.** Explain why the apparent expansion of a liquid in a bulb does not give the true expansion of the liquid.

**13.** Does the change in volume of a body when its temperature is raised depend on whether the body has cavities inside, other things being equal? Consider a solid sphere and a hollow sphere, for example.

**14.** What difficulties would arise if you defined temperature in terms of the density of water?

**15.** Explain why lakes freeze first at the surface.

---

\* It is to this value of *unit* maximum density of water that the relative sizes of the kilogram and meter were originally supposed to correspond. Accurate measurements show, however, that the international standards of mass and length do not correspond exactly to this value. The maximum density of water is actually 999.973 kg/meter³ at 3.98° C.

## PROBLEMS

**1.** If the ideal gas temperature at the steam point is 373.15° K, what is the limiting value of the ratio of the pressures of a gas at the steam point and at the triple point of water when the gas is kept at constant volume?

**2.** Let $p_{tr}$ be the pressure in the bulb of a constant-volume gas thermometer when the bulb is at the triple-point temperature of 273.16° K and $p$ the pressure when the bulb is at room temperature. Given three constant-volume gas thermometers: For No. 1 the gas is oxygen and $p_{tr} = 20$ cm-Hg; for No. 2 the gas is also oxygen but $p_{tr} = 40$ cm-Hg; for No. 3 the gas is hydrogen and $p_{tr} = 30$ cm-Hg. The measured values of $p$ for the three thermometers are $p_1$, $p_2$, and $p_3$. (a) An approximate value of the room temperature $T$ can be obtained with each of the thermometers using

$$T_1 = 273.16° \text{ K} \frac{p_1}{20 \text{ cm-Hg}}; \quad T_2 = 273.16° \text{ K} \frac{p_2}{40 \text{ cm-Hg}}; \quad T_3 = 273.16° \text{ K} \frac{p_3}{30 \text{ cm-Hg}}.$$

Mark "true" or "false" each of the following statements: (1) With the method described, all three thermometers will give the same value of $T$. (2) The two oxygen thermometers will agree with each other but not with the hydrogen thermometer. (3) Each of the three will give a different value of $T$. (b) In the event that there is disagreement among the three thermometers, explain how you would change the method of using them to cause all three to give the same value of $T$.

**3.** It is an everyday observation that hot and cold objects cool down or warm up to the temperature of their surroundings. If the temperature difference $\Delta T$ between an object and its surroundings is not too great, the rate of cooling or warming is approximately proportional to the temperature difference between the object and its surroundings; that is,

$$\frac{d \Delta T}{dt} = -K \Delta T,$$

where $K$ is a constant. The minus sign appears because $\Delta T$ *decreases* with time if $\Delta T$ is positive and vice versa. This is known as *Newton's law of cooling*. (a) On what factors does $K$ depend? What are its dimensions? (b) If at some instant the temperature difference is $\Delta T_0$, show that it is

$$\Delta T = \Delta T_0 e^{-Kt}$$

at a time $t$ later.

**4.** A mercury-in-glass thermometer is placed in boiling water for a few minutes and then removed. The temperature readings at various times after removal are as follows:

| $t$, sec | $T$, °C | $t$, sec | $T$, °C | $t$, sec | $T$, °C | $t$, sec | $T$, °C |
|---|---|---|---|---|---|---|---|
| 0 | 98.4 | 25 | 65.1 | 100 | 50.3 | 700 | 26.5 |
| 5 | 76.1 | 30 | 63.9 | 150 | 43.7 | 1000 | 26.1 |
| 10 | 71.1 | 40 | 61.6 | 200 | 38.8 | 1400 | 26.0 |
| 15 | 67.7 | 50 | 59.4 | 300 | 32.7 | 2000 | 26.0 |
| 20 | 66.4 | 70 | 55.4 | 500 | 27.8 | 3000 | 26.0 |

Plot $K$ as a function of time, assuming Newton's law of cooling to apply (see Problem 3). How constant is the "constant" $K$? What might give rise to the observed variations of $K$ with time?

**5.** At what temperature do the Fahrenheit and Celsius scales give the same reading? The Fahrenheit and the Kelvin scales?

**6.** (a) The temperature of the surface of the sun is about 6000° K. Express this on the Fahrenheit scale. (b) Express normal human body temperature, 98.6° F, on the Celsius scale. (c) Excluding Hawaii and Alaska, the highest recorded temperature in the United States is 134° F at Death Valley, California, and the lowest is −70° F at Rogers Pass, Montana. Express these extremes on the Celsius scale. (d) Express the normal boiling point of oxygen, −183° C, on the Fahrenheit scale. (e) At what Celsius temperature would you find a room to be uncomfortably warm?

**7.** In the interval between 0 and 660° C, a platinum resistance thermometer of definite specifications is used for interpolating temperatures on the International Practical Temperature Scale. The temperature $t$ is given by a formula for the variation of resistance with temperature:

$$R = R_0(1 + At + Bt^2).$$

$R_0$, $A$, and $B$ are constants determined by measurements at the ice point, the steam point, and the sulphur point. (a) If $R$ equals 10.000 ohms at the ice point, 13.946 ohms at the steam point, and 24.817 ohms at the sulphur point, find $R_0$, $A$, and $B$. (b) Plot $R$ versus $t$ in the temperature range from 0 to 660° C.

**8.** (a) Show that if the lengths of two rods of different solids are inversely proportional to their respective coefficients of linear expansion at some initial temperature, the difference in length between them will be constant at all temperatures. (b) What should be the lengths of a steel and a brass rod at 0° C so that at all temperatures their difference in length is 0.30 meter?

**9.** A circular hole in an aluminum plate is 1.000 in. in diameter at 0° C. What is its diameter when the temperature of the plate is raised to 100° C?

**10.** The Pyrex glass mirror in the telescope at Palomar Observatory has a diameter of 200 in. The temperature ranges from −10 to 50° C on Mount Palomar. Determine the maximum change in the diameter of the mirror.

**11.** A clock pendulum made of invar has a period of 0.500 sec at 20° C. If the clock is used in a climate where the temperature averages 30° C, what correction (approximately) is necessary at the end of 30 days to the time given by the clock?

**12.** The distance between the towers at the ends of the main span of the Golden Gate Bridge at San Francisco is 4200 ft. The sag of the cable halfway between the towers at 50° F is 470 ft. Take $\bar{\alpha} = 6.5 \times 10^{-6}/\text{F}°$ for the cable and compute the change in length of the cable between the towers and the change in sag midway between for a temperature change from −20 to 110° F. Assume no bending of the towers.

**13.** A glass tube nearly filled with mercury is attached to the bottom of an iron pendulum rod 100 cm long. How high must the mercury be in the glass tube so that the center of mass of this pendulum will not rise or fall with changes in temperature?

**14.** A steel rod is 3.000 cm in diameter at 25° C. A brass ring has an interior diameter of 2.992 cm at 25° C. At what common temperature will the ring just slide onto the rod?

**15.** Show that if $\alpha$ is treated as a variable, dependent on the temperature $T$, then

$$L = L_0 \left[ 1 + \int_{T_0}^{T} \alpha(T)\, dT \right]$$

where $L_0$ is the length at a reference temperature $T_0$.

**16.** The area $A$ of a rectangular plate is $ab$. Its coefficient of linear expansion is $\alpha$. After a temperature rise $\Delta T$, side $a$ is longer by $\Delta a$ and side $b$ is longer by $\Delta b$. Show that if we neglect the small area $\Delta a \cdot \Delta b$, shown cross-hatched and greatly exaggerated in size in Fig. 21–9, then $\Delta A = 2\alpha A \, \Delta T$.

**Fig. 21–9**

**17.** Prove that, if we neglect extremely small quantities, the change in volume of a solid on expansion through a temperature rise $\Delta T$ is given by $\Delta V = 3\alpha V \, \Delta T$ where $\alpha$ is the coefficient of linear expansion.

**18.** When the temperature of a "copper" penny is raised by 100° C, its diameter increases by 0.18%. To two significant figures give the per cent increase in the (a) area of a face, (b) thickness, (c) volume, and (d) mass of the penny. (e) What is the coefficient of linear expansion?

**19.** Find the change in volume of an aluminum sphere of 10.0-cm radius when it is heated from 0.00 to 100° C.

**20.** Consider a mercury-in-glass thermometer. Assume that the cross-section of the capillary is constant at $A_0$, and that $V_0$ is the volume of the bulb of mercury at 0.00° C. If the mercury just fills the bulb at 0.00° C, show that the length of the mercury column in the capillary at a temperature $t°$ C is

$$l = \frac{V_0}{A_0} \, (\beta - 3\alpha)t,$$

that is, proportional to the temperature, where $\beta$ is the volume coefficient of expansion of mercury and $\alpha$ is the linear coefficient of expansion of glass.

**21.** Density is mass per unit volume. If the volume $V$ is temperature dependent, so is the density $\rho$. Show that the change in density $\Delta\rho$ with change in temperature $\Delta T$ is given by

$$\Delta\rho = -\beta\rho \, \Delta T$$

where $\beta$ is the volume coefficient of expansion. Explain the minus sign.

**22.** (a) Prove that the change in rotational inertia $I$ with temperature of a solid object is given by $\Delta I = 2\alpha I \, \Delta T$. (b) Prove that the change in period $t$ of a physical pendulum with temperature is given by $\Delta t = \frac{1}{2}\alpha t \, \Delta T$.

**23.** Consider a uniform solid brass cylinder of mass $M = 0.50$ kg and radius $R = 0.030$ meter. The cylinder is placed in frictionless bearings and set to rotate about its cylinder axis with an angular velocity $\omega = 60$ radians/sec. (a) What is the angular momentum of the cylinder and how much work is required to reach this rate of rotation, starting from rest? (b) After the cylinder has reached the state of rotation just described we heat it, without mechanical contact, from room temperature (20° C) to 100° C. Take the mean coefficient of linear expansion of brass to be $\bar{\alpha} = 2.0 \times$

$10^{-5}/C°$.  Find the fractional changes, if any, in the angular velocity, the angular momentum, and the kinetic energy of rotation of the cylinder.   Explain.

**24.** Show that when the temperature of a liquid in a barometer changes by $\Delta T$, and the pressure is constant, the height $h$ changes by $\Delta h = \beta h \, \Delta T$ where $\beta$ is the coefficient of volume expansion.

**25.** Two vertical glass tubes filled with a liquid are connected at their lower ends by a horizontal capillary tube.   One tube is surrounded by a bath containing ice and water

**Fig. 21–10**

in equilibrium (0.0° C), the other by a hot-water bath ($t$).   The difference in height of the liquids in the two columns is $\Delta h$, and $h_0$ is the height of the column at 0.0° C.   Show how this apparatus (Fig. 21–10), first used in 1816 by Dulong and Petit, can be used to measure the true coefficient of volume expansion $\beta$ of a liquid (rather than the differential expansion between glass and liquid).   Determine $\beta$ if $t = 16.0°$ C, $h_0 = 126$ cm, and $\Delta h = 1.50$ cm.

# Heat and the First Law of Thermodynamics

## CHAPTER 22

## 22–1    Heat, a Form of Energy

When two systems at different temperatures are placed together, the final temperature reached by both systems is somewhere between the two starting temperatures. This is a common observation. Man has long sought for a deeper understanding of such phenomena. Up to the beginning of the nineteenth century, they were explained by postulating that a material substance, *caloric*, existed in every body. It was believed that a body at high temperature contained more caloric than one at a low temperature. When the two bodies were put together, the body rich in caloric lost some to the other until both bodies reached the same temperature. The caloric theory was able to describe many processes, such as heat conduction or the mixing of substances in a calorimeter, in a satisfactory way. However, the concept of heat as a *substance*, whose total amount remained constant, eventually could not stand the test of experiment. Nevertheless, we still describe many common temperature changes as the transfer of "something" from one body at a higher temperature to one at the lower, and this "something" we call heat. A useful but nonoperational definition, is: *heat is that which is transferred between a system and its surroundings as a result of temperature differences only.*

Eventually it became generally understood that heat is a form of energy rather than a substance. The first conclusive evidence that heat could not be a substance was given by Benjamin Thompson (1753–1814), an American who later became Count Rumford of Bavaria.  In a paper read before the Royal Society* in 1798 he wrote:

I . . . am persuaded, that a habit of keeping the eyes open to everything that is going on in the ordinary course of the business of life has oftener led, as it were by accident, or in the playful excursions of the imagination . . . to useful doubts and sensible schemes for investigation and improvement, than all the more intense meditations of philosophers, in the hours expressly set apart for study.  It was by accident that I was led to make the Experiments of which I am about to give an account.

Rumford made his discovery while supervising the boring of cannon for the Bavarian government.  To prevent overheating, the bore of the cannon was kept full of water.  The water was replenished as it boiled away during the boring process.  It was accepted that caloric had to be supplied to water to boil it.  The continuous production of caloric was explained by assuming that when a substance was more finely subdivided, as in boring, its capacity for retaining caloric became smaller, and that the caloric released in this way was what caused the water to boil.  Rumford observed in specific experiments, however, that the water boiled away even when his boring tools became so dull that they were no longer cutting or subdividing matter.

He wrote after ruling out by experiment all possible caloric interpretations,

. . . in reasoning on this subject, we must not forget to consider that most remarkable circumstance, that the source of Heat generated by friction, in these Experiments, appeared evidently to be *inexhaustible* . . . it appears to me to be extremely difficult, if not quite impossible, to form any distinct idea of any thing capable of being excited and communicated in the manner the Heat was excited and communicated in these Experiments, except it be *MOTION*.

Here we have the germ of the idea that the mechanical work expended in the boring process was responsible for the creation of heat.  The idea was not clearly put until much later, by others.  Instead of the continuous disappearance of mechanical energy and the continuous creation of heat, neither obeying any conservation principle, the whole process is now viewed as a transformation of energy from one form to another, the total energy being conserved.

Although the concept of energy and its conservation seems self-evident today, it was a novel idea as late as the 1850's and had eluded such men as Galileo and Newton.  Throughout the subsequent history of physics this conservation idea led men to new discoveries.  Its early history was remarkable in many ways.  Several thinkers arrived at this great concept at about the same time; at first, all of them either met with a cold reception or were ignored.  The principle of the conservation of energy

---

* Rumford, an American, was founder of the Royal Institution in London.  On the other hand, the Smithsonian Institution in Washington owes its origin to an Englishman.

was established independently by Julius von Mayer (1814–1878) in Germany, James Joule (1818–1889) in England, Hermann von Helmholtz (1821–1894) in Germany, and L. A. Colding (1815–1888) in Denmark.*

It was Joule who showed by experiment that, when a given quantity of mechanical energy is converted to heat, the same quantity of heat is always developed. Thus, the equivalence of heat and mechanical work as two forms of energy was definitely established.

Helmholtz first expressed clearly the idea that not only heat and mechanical energy but all forms of energy are equivalent, and that a given amount of one form cannot disappear without an equal amount appearing in some of the other forms.

### 22–2    Quantity of Heat and Specific Heat

The unit of heat $Q$ is defined quantitatively in terms of a specified change produced in a body during a specified process. Thus, if the temperature of one kilogram of water is raised from 14.5 to 15.5° C by heating, we say that one *kilocalorie* (kcal) of heat has been added to the system. The *calorie* ($= 10^{-3}$ kcal) is also used as a heat unit. (Incidentally, the "calorie" used to measure the energy content of foods is actually a kilocalorie.) In the engineering system the unit of heat is the *British thermal unit* (Btu), which is defined as the heat necessary to raise the temperature of one pound of water from 63 to 64° F.

The reference temperatures are stated because, near room temperature, there is a slight variation in the heat needed for a one-degree temperature rise with the temperature interval chosen. We will neglect this variation for most practical purposes. The heat units are related as follows:

$$1.000 \text{ kcal} = 1000 \text{ cal} = 3.968 \text{ Btu}$$

Substances differ from one another in the quantity of heat needed to produce a given rise of temperature in a given mass. The ratio of the heat $\Delta Q$ supplied to a body to its corresponding temperature rise $\Delta T$ is called the *heat capacity* $C$ of the body; that is,

$$C = \text{heat capacity} = \frac{\Delta Q}{\Delta T}.$$

The word "capacity" may be misleading because it suggests the essentially meaningless statement "the amount of heat a body can hold," whereas what is meant is simply the heat added per unit temperature rise.

---

* From the posthumous publication of *Reflections* (1872) of the French engineer Sadi Carnot (1796–1832), it is clear that he arrived at the conservation of energy principle before all the others. It will give the student some food for thought to realize that of the five men who were the first to understand the conservation of energy principle, all were young and all were professionally outside the field of physics at the time of their contributions. Mayer was a physician, age 28; Helmholtz, a physiologist, age 32; Colding, an engineer, age 27; Joule, an industrialist, age 25; and Carnot, an engineer, age 34. Rumford was an old man, age 45, by comparison.

The heat capacity per unit mass of a body, called *specific heat,* is characteristic of the material of which the body is composed:

$$c = \frac{\text{heat capacity}}{\text{mass}} = \frac{\Delta Q}{m \, \Delta T}. \tag{22-1}$$

We properly speak, on the one hand, of the heat capacity of a penny but, on the other, of the specific heat of copper.

Neither the heat capacity of a body nor the specific heat of a material is constant but depends on the location of the temperature interval. The previous equations give only average values for these quantities in the temperature range of $\Delta T$. The specific heat $c$ of a material *at any temperature* is defined by

$$c = \frac{dQ}{m \, dT}. \tag{22-2}$$

Hence, the heat that must be given to a body of mass $m$, whose material has a specific heat capacity $c$, to increase its temperature from $T_i$ to $T_f$, is

$$Q = m \int_{T_i}^{T_f} c \, dT \tag{22-3}$$

where $c$ is a function of the temperature. At ordinary temperatures and over ordinary temperature intervals, specific heats can be considered to be constants. Figure 22-1 shows the variation in the specific heat of water with temperature. Information of this sort is obtained by using an electrical heating coil to supply heat at a rate that can be accurately determined. We see from the graph that the specific heat of water varies less than 1% from its value of 1.000 cal/gm C° at 15° C.

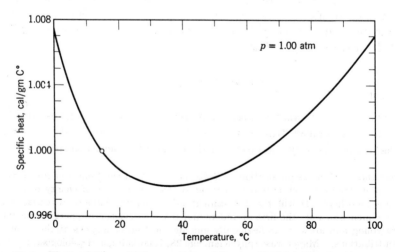

**Fig. 22-1**   The variation with temperature of the specific heat of water at a pressure of 1.00 atm. The circle, located at 15° C, suggests the definition of the calorie.

Equations 21–1 and 21–2 do not define specific heat uniquely. We must also specify the conditions under which the heat $\Delta Q$ is added to the specimen. We have implied that the condition is that the specimen remain at normal (constant) atmospheric pressure while we add the heat. This is a common condition, but there are many other possibilities, each leading, in general, to a different value for $c$. To obtain a unique value for $c$ we must specify the conditions, such as specific heat at constant pressure $c_p$, specific heat at constant volume $c_v$, etc.

Table 22–1 (second column) shows the specific heats at constant pressure of some solid elements; we will discuss the specific heats of gases later. The student should realize from the way the calorie and the Btu are defined that 1 cal/gm C° = 1 kcal/kg C° = 1 Btu/lb F°, exactly. Note that the specific heat of water, equal to 1.00 cal/gm C°, is large compared to that of most substances.

### Table 22–1

VALUES FOR $c_p$ FOR SOME SOLIDS
(At room temperature and for $p$ = 1.0 atm)

| Substance | Specific heat, cal/gm C° | Molecular weight gm/mole | Molar heat capacity cal/mole C° |
|---|---|---|---|
| Aluminum | 0.215 | 27.0 | 5.82 |
| Carbon | 0.121 | 12.0 | 1.46 |
| Copper | 0.0923 | 63.5 | 5.85 |
| Lead | 0.0305 | 207 | 6.32 |
| Silver | 0.0564 | 108 | 6.09 |
| Tungsten | 0.0321 | 184 | 5.92 |

▶ **Example 1.** A 75-gm block of copper, taken from a furnace, is dropped into a 300-gm glass beaker containing 200-gm of water. The temperature of the water rises from 12 to 27° C. What was the temperature of the furnace?

This is an example of two systems originally at different temperatures reaching thermal equilibrium after contact. No mechanical energy is involved, only heat exchange. Hence,

heat lost by copper = heat gained by (beaker + water),

$$m_C c_C (T_C - T_e) = (m_G c_G + m_W c_W)(T_e - T_W).$$

The subscript $C$ stands for copper, $G$ for glass, and $W$ for water. The initial copper temperature is $T_C$, the initial beaker water temperature is $T_W$, and $T_e$ is the final equilibrium temperature. Substituting the given values, with $c_C$ = 0.093 cal/gm C°, $c_G$ = 0.12, cal/gm C°, and $c_W$ = 1.0 cal/gm C°, we obtain

$$(75 \text{ gm})(0.093 \text{ cal/gm C°})(T_C - 27° \text{ C}) = [(300 \text{ gm})(0.12 \text{ cal/gm C°})$$
$$+ (200 \text{ gm})(1.0 \text{ cal/gm C°})](27° \text{ C} - 12° \text{ C})$$

or, solving for $T_C$,    $T_C = 530° \text{ C}$

What approximations, both experimental and theoretical, were used implicitly to arrive at this answer? ◀

## 22–3 Molar Heat Capacities of Solids

From the second column of Table 22–1 we conclude that the specific heats of solids vary widely from one material to another. However quite a different story emerges if we compare samples of materials that contain the same number of molecules rather than samples that have the same mass. We can do this by expressing specific heats (called when so expressed *molar heat capacities*) in cal/mole C° rather than in cal/gm C°.* In 1819 Dulong and Petit pointed out that the molar heat capacities of all substances, with few exceptions (see carbon in Table 22–1), have values close to 6 cal/mole C°. The molar heat capacity, listed in the fourth column of Table 22–1, is found by multiplying the specific heat (second column) by the molecular weight (third column). We see that the amount of heat required *per molecule* to raise the temperature of a solid by a given amount seems to be about the same for almost all materials. This is striking evidence for the molecular theory of matter.

Actually molar heat capacities vary with temperature, approaching zero as $T \rightarrow 0°$ K and approaching the Dulong-Petit value as $T \rightarrow \infty$. Since the number of molecules rather than the kind of molecule seems to be important in determining the heat required to increase the temperature of a body by a given amount, we are led to expect that the molar heat capacities of different substances will vary with temperature in much the same way. Figure 22–2 shows that, indeed, the molar heat capacities of various substances can be made to fall on the same curve by a simple, empirical adjustment in the temperature scale. The horizontal scale in Fig. 22–2 is the dimensionless ratio $T/T_D$, where $T$ is the Kelvin temperature and $T_D$ is a characteristic temperature, called the *Debye temperature*, that has a particular constant value for each material. For lead, $T_D$ has the empirical value of 88° K and for carbon, $T_D = 1860°$ K. From these data the student can show that a scale value of $T/T_D = 0.600$ corresponds to $T = 53°$ K for lead but to $T = 1120°$ K for carbon. Alternatively, room temperature ($\sim 300°$ K) corresponds to $T/T_D = 3.4$ for lead and to $T/T_D = 0.16$ for carbon. Thus we see from Fig. 22–2 that in the early days, when only room temperature specific heats were available, lead would conform to the Dulong and Petit rule but carbon would seem to be an exception.

The straight line *I* in Fig. 22–2 is the Dulong and Petit value of 1819; it agrees with experiment at high temperature but fails at low temperatures. It corresponds to the assumption that every atom in a solid vibrates independently like a classical oscillator. Curve II is due to Debye (1912). In the Debye theory, a characteristic temperature $T_D$, which is directly related to a vibrational frequency characteristic of the material, can be obtained independent of specific heat experi-

---

* A *mole* of any substance is that mass of the substance that contains a specified number of molecules, namely, $6.02252 \times 10^{23}$, called Avogadro's number. This number is the result of the defining relation that one mole of carbon (actually, of the isotope $C^{12}$) shall have a mass of 12 gm, exactly. The *molecular weight M* of a substance is a dimensionless quantity expressing the number of grams per mole of that substance. Thus the molecular weight of oxygen is 32.0 gm/mole. Although the mole is a unit of mass, we cannot translate it into, say, grams, until we know the chemical composition of the substance; for this reason we find it convenient to use a special symbol ($\mu$) for masses expressed in moles.

**Fig. 22–2** The molar heat capacities ($c_v$) showing a few selected points only. Line I represents the Dulong and Petit rule and curve II represents a theory due to Debye.

ments. One then uses quantum principles to analyze the coupled vibrations of the atoms in a solid and obtains a specific heat formula which, in terms of the dimensionless ratio $T/T_D$, is the same for all substances. The excellent agreement of this formula (curve II) with experiment is a triumph of quantum physics.*

The materials displayed in Fig. 22–2 are "normal" in that they do not melt, boil, change their crystal structure, etc., in the temperature range indicated. Specific heat measurements, which tell us how a solid absorbs energy as its temperature is raised, are a sensitive probe to detect such molecular, atomic, or electronic rearrangements. Figure 22–3, for example, shows the specific heat of tantalum near

**Fig. 22–3** The specific heat of tantalum near its superconducting transition temperature.

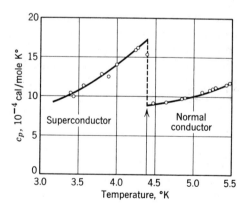

---

* The data reported in Fig. 22–2 are values of $c_v$ but those in Table 22–1 are $c_p$. The former is easier to calculate theoretically because the thermal expansion need not be taken into account, but (for solids) the latter is much easier to measure. The two are related by the simple thermodynamic formula

$$c_p = c_v + T\beta^2/\kappa\rho$$

in which $\beta$ is the thermal coefficient of volume expansion, $\kappa$ ($= -\Delta V/V\Delta p$) is the (isothermal) compressibility, and $\rho$ is the density. At room temperature the difference between $c_p$ and $c_v$ for typical solids is about 5%.

4.39° K. Below this transition temperature tantalum loses all its electric resistance—it becomes superconducting. Above this temperature it has the resistance expected of a normal metal.

## 22-4  Heat Conduction

The transfer of energy arising from the temperature difference between adjacent parts of a body is called *heat conduction*. Consider a slab of material of cross-sectional area $A$ and thickness $\Delta x$, whose faces are kept at different temperatures. We measure the heat $\Delta Q$ that flows perpendicular to the faces for a time $\Delta t$. Experiment shows that $\Delta Q$ is proportional to $\Delta t$ and to the cross-sectional area $A$ for a given temperature difference $\Delta T$, and that $\Delta Q$ is proportional to $\Delta T/\Delta x$ for a given $\Delta t$ and $A$, providing both $\Delta T$ and $\Delta x$ are small. That is,

$$\frac{\Delta Q}{\Delta t} \propto A \frac{\Delta T}{\Delta x} \quad \text{approximately.}$$

In the limit of a slab of infinitesimal thickness $dx$, across which there is a temperature difference $dT$, we obtain the fundamental law of heat conduction

$$\frac{dQ}{dt} = -kA \frac{dT}{dx}. \tag{22-4}$$

Here $dQ/dt$ is the time rate of heat transfer across the area $A$, $dT/dx$ is called the *temperature gradient*, and $k$ is a constant of proportionality called the *thermal conductivity*. We choose the direction of heat flow to be the direction in which $x$ increases; since heat flows in the direction of decreasing $T$, we introduce a minus sign in Eq. 22-4 (that is, we wish $dQ/dt$ to be positive when $dT/dx$ is negative).

A substance with a large thermal conductivity $k$ is a good heat conductor; one with a small thermal conductivity $k$ is a poor heat conductor, or a good thermal insulator. The value of $k$ depends on the temperature, increasing slightly with increasing temperature, but $k$ can be taken to be practically constant throughout a substance if the temperature difference between its parts is not too great. In Table 22-2 we list values of $k$ for various substances; we see that metals as a group are better heat conductors than nonmetals, and that gases are poor heat conductors.

Let us apply Eq. 22-4 to a rod of length $L$ and constant cross-sectional area $A$ in which a steady state has been reached (Fig. 22-4). In a steady state the temperature at each point is constant in time. Hence, $dQ/dt$ is the same at all cross-sections. (Why?) But $dQ/dt = -kA(dT/dx)$, so that, for a constant $k$ and $A$, the temperature gradient $dT/dx$ is the same at all cross-sections. Hence, $T$ decreases linearly along the rod so that

**Table 22–2**

THERMAL CONDUCTIVITIES, KCAL/SEC METER C°
(Gases at 0° C; others at about room temperature)

| Metals | | Hydrogen | $3.3 \times 10^{-5}$ |
|---|---|---|---|
| Aluminum | $4.9 \times 10^{-2}$ | Oxygen | $5.6 \times 10^{-6}$ |
| Brass | $2.6 \times 10^{-2}$ | Others | |
| Copper | $9.2 \times 10^{-2}$ | Asbestos | $2 \quad \times 10^{-5}$ |
| Lead | $8.3 \times 10^{-3}$ | Concrete | $2 \quad \times 10^{-4}$ |
| Silver | $9.9 \times 10^{-2}$ | Cork | $4 \quad \times 10^{-5}$ |
| Steel | $1.1 \times 10^{-2}$ | Glass | $2 \quad \times 10^{-4}$ |
| Gases | | Ice | $4 \quad \times 10^{-4}$ |
| Air | $5.7 \times 10^{-6}$ | Wood | $2 \quad \times 10^{-5}$ |

$-dT/dx = (T_2 - T_1)/L$. Therefore, the heat $\Delta Q$ transferred in time $\Delta t$ is

$$\frac{\Delta Q}{\Delta t} = kA \frac{T_2 - T_1}{L}. \qquad (22\text{–}5)$$

**Fig. 22–4** Conduction of heat through an insulated conducting bar.

The phenomenon of heat conduction also shows that the concepts of heat and temperature are distinctly different. Different rods, having the same temperature difference between their ends, may transfer entirely different quantities of heat in the same time.

▶ **Example 2.** Consider a compound slab, consisting of two materials having different thicknesses, $L_1$ and $L_2$, and different thermal conductivities, $k_1$ and $k_2$. If the temperatures of the outer surfaces are $T_2$ and $T_1$, find the rate of heat transfer through the compound slab (Fig. 22–5) in a steady state.

Let $T_x$ be the temperature at the interface between the two materials. Then

$$\frac{\Delta Q_2}{\Delta t} = \frac{k_2 A (T_2 - T_x)}{L_2}$$

and

$$\frac{\Delta Q_1}{\Delta t} = \frac{k_1 A (T_x - T_1)}{L_1}.$$

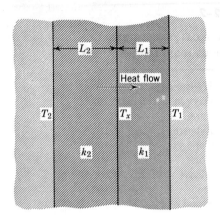

In a steady state $\Delta Q_1/\Delta t = \Delta Q_2/\Delta t$, so that

$$\frac{k_2 A (T_2 - T_x)}{L_2} = \frac{k_1 A (T_x - T_1)}{L_1}.$$

Let $\Delta Q/\Delta t$ be the rate of heat transfer (the same for all sections). Then, solving for $T_x$ and substituting into either of these equations, we obtain

$$\frac{\Delta Q}{\Delta t} = \frac{A (T_2 - T_1)}{(L_1/k_1) + (L_2/k_2)}.$$

The extension to any number of sections in series is obviously

**Fig. 22–5**  Example 2.  Conduction of heat through two layers of matter with different thermal conductivities.

$$\frac{\Delta Q}{\Delta t} = \frac{A (T_2 - T_1)}{\Sigma (L_i/k_i)}. \quad \blacktriangleleft$$

## 22–5  The Mechanical Equivalent of Heat

If heat is just another form of energy, any energy unit could be a heat unit. The calorie and Btu originated before it was generally accepted that heat is energy. It was Joule who first carefully measured the mechanical energy equivalent of heat energy, that is, the number of joules equivalent to 1 calorie, or the number of foot-pounds equivalent to 1 Btu.

The relative size of the "heat units" and the "mechanical units" can be found from experiments in which a measured quantity of mechanical energy is completely converted into a measured quantity of heat. Joule originally used an apparatus in which falling weights rotated a set of paddles in a water container (Fig. 22–6). The loss of mechanical energy was computed

**Fig. 22–6**  Joule's arrangement for measuring the mechanical equivalent of heat. The falling weights turn paddles which stir the water in the container, thus raising its temperature.

from a knowledge of the weights and the heights through which they fell and the gain in heat energy by determining the equivalent mass of water and its rise in temperature. Joule wanted to show that the same amount of heat energy would be obtained from a given expenditure of work regardless of the method used to produce the work. He produced heat by stirring mercury, by rubbing together iron rings in a mercury bath, by converting electrical energy into heat in a wire immersed in water, and in other ways. Always the constant of proportionality between heat produced and work performed agreed within his experimental error of 5%. Joule did not have at his disposal the accurately standardized thermometers of today, nor could he make such reliable corrections for heat losses from the system as are possible now. His pioneer experiments are noteworthy not only for the skill and ingenuity he showed but also for the influence they had in convincing scientists everywhere of the correctness of the concept that heat is a form of energy.

The accepted results* (see Appendix A for more precise values) are

$$1 \text{ kcal} = 1000 \text{ cal} = 4186 \text{ joules}$$
$$1 \text{ Btu} = 252.0 \text{ cal} = 777.9 \text{ ft lb};$$

that is, 4186 joules of mechanical energy, when converted to heat, will raise the temperature of 1 kg of water from 14.5 to 15.5° C.

In modern calorimetry heat is almost always measured in terms of the electrical energy transferred to a water bath by passing a current through a resistor that is immersed in the bath; it is rarely measured by observing the rise in temperature of a water bath. Thus the logical practical unit of heat is the joule (1 joule = 1 watt-sec) and this was indeed adopted as the accepted international unit for heat by the Ninth General Conference on Weights and Measures (1948). Indeed, in modern laboratory practice the calorie (or kilocalorie) is not much used or needed. It is, however, deeply embedded in the literature of science. To permit the continued use of this familiar unit—but to recognize the practical importance of the joule—a new kilocalorie, the *thermochemical kilocalorie*, is often defined:

$$1 \text{ kilocalorie (thermochemical)} = 4184.0 \text{ joules (exactly)}.$$

In ordinary laboratory practice this kilocalorie does not differ significantly from that defined earlier.

## 22–6  Heat and Work

We have seen that *heat is energy that flows from one body to another because of a temperature difference between them*. The idea that heat is something *in* a body, as the caloric theory assumed, contradicts many experimental facts. It is only as it flows, because of a temperature difference, that the energy

---

* Henry A. Rowland, in 1879, carried out a painstaking determination of the mechanical equivalent of heat which, to this day, remains a model of careful experimentation. His result differs from the accepted value today by only 1 part in 2000. Rowland graduated from Rensselaer Polytechnic Institute in 1870 and in 1876 became the first Professor of Physics at the then newly established Johns Hopkins University, where he conducted this experiment. See "The Education of an American Scientist, Henry A. Rowland" by Samuel Rezneck, *American Journal of Physics*, February 1960.

is called heat energy. If heat were a substance, or a definite kind of energy that kept its identity while contained in a system, it would not be possible to remove heat indefinitely from a system which does not change. Yet Rumford showed that this was possible. In fact, by continually performing mechanical work in Joule's apparatus, we can obtain an indefinite amount of heat out of the water, by connecting it to a cooler system, for example, without changing the condition of the water.

In the same way work is not something of which a system contains a definite amount. We can put an indefinite amount of work into a system without changing its condition, as Joule's apparatus again illustrates. Work, like heat, involves a transfer of energy. In mechanics, work is involved in energy transfers in which temperature played no role. If heat energy is transmitted by temperature differences, we can distinguish heat and work by defining *work as energy that is transmitted from one system to another in such a way that a difference of temperature is not directly involved.* This definition is consistent with our previous use of the term. That is, in the expression $dW = F\,dx$, the force $F$ can arise from electrical, magnetic, gravitational, and other sources. The term work includes all these energy transfer processes, but it specifically excludes energy transfer arising from temperature differences.

Consider another simple example, that of rubbing two surfaces together. There is no limit to the amount of heat that can be removed from this system or to the amount of work that can be put into it, so that there is no definite meaning to phrases such as "the heat in the system" or "the work in the system." The quantities $Q$ and $W$ are not characteristic of the (equilibrium) *state* of the system but rather of the *thermodynamic process* by which the system moves from one equilibrium state to another, by interacting with its environment. It is only during such a process that we can give meaning to heat and work; we can then identify $Q$ with the heat transferred to or from the system and $W$ with the work done on or by the system. The study of such processes and of the changes in energy involved in the performance of work and the flow of heat is the subject matter of *thermodynamics.*

In Fig. 22–7 we consider a general thermodynamic process. We must first state definitely what the system is and what the environment is. In the figure we draw a closed surface surrounding the system to define it. In (a) the system is in its *initial state*, in equilibrium with the environment external to it. In (b) the system interacts with its environment through some specific *thermodynamic process.* During this process, energy in the form of heat and/or work may go into or out of the system. Arrows representing the flow of $Q$ or $W$ must pierce the surface enclosing the system. In (c) the system has reached its *final state*, again in equilibrium with the environment external to it.

Figure 22–8 shows a falling weight which turns a generator, which in turn sends an electric current through a resistor immersed in a water container. Let us choose the system to be the generator and the attached electric circuit, the water, and its container. Then the environment is the weight and the earth, which pulls on the weight. The process consists of letting the weight fall a distance $h$ in the earth's gravitational field. During this process the environment (by means of the cord) does work $W$ on the system. There are no temperature differences between the system and its environment and hence $Q = 0$ for this process.

Our choice of a system in thermodynamic problems is arbitrary. Let us now choose the system to be only the water and its container in Fig. 22–8. The environment now is the generator and attached circuit as well as the weight and the earth. For this choice of system there now *is* a temperature difference between the environment (resistor) and the system (water), and heat $Q$ will flow into the system during the process. No forces act through the system boundary to product displacements, however, and hence $W = 0$ for this process. This example shows that we must first state definitely what the system is and what the environment is before we can decide whether the change in the state of the system is due to the flow of heat or to the performance of work or both. There will be a transfer of heat between system and environment only when a temperature difference exists across the system boundary; if no temperature difference exists, the energy transfer involves work.

Let us now compute $Q$ and $W$ for a specific thermodynamic process. Consider a gas in a cylindrical container with a movable piston. Let the gas be the system. Initially it is in equilibrium with the environment external to it (which is the heat reservoir and the piston, shown

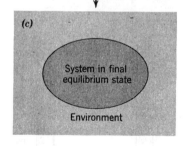

**Fig. 22–7** (a) A system in an initial state, in equilibrium with its surroundings. (b) A thermodynamic process during which the system may exchange heat $Q$ or work $W$ with its environment. (c) A final equilibrium state reached as the result of the process.

in Fig. 22–9) and has a pressure $p_i$ and a volume $V_i$. We can think of the containing walls as the system boundary. Heat can flow into the system or out of it through the bottom of the cylinder and work can be done on the system or by the system by compressing or expanding the gas, respectively,

**Fig. 22–8** Heat and work. A weight, in falling, does work on an electric generator which sends current through a resistor which heats the water in which it is immersed.

with the piston.   Consider a process whereby the system interacts with its environment and reaches a final equilibrium state characterized by a pressure $p_f$ and a volume $V_f$.

In Fig. 22–9 we show the gas expanding against the piston.   The work done by the gas in displacing the piston through an infinitesimal distance $s$ is

$$dW = \mathbf{F} \cdot d\mathbf{s} = pA \, ds = p \, dV$$

where $dV$ is the differential change in the volume of the gas.   In general, the pressure will not be constant during a displacement.   To obtain the total work $W$ done on the piston by the gas in a large displacement, we must know how $p$ varies with the displacement.   Then we compute the integral

$$W = \int dW = \int_{V_i}^{V_f} p \, dV$$

over the range in volume.   This integral can be evaluated graphically as the area under the curve in a $p$–$V$ diagram, as shown for a special case in Fig. 22–10.

There are many different ways in which the system can be taken from

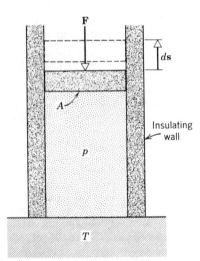

Heat reservoir of controllable temperature $T$

**Fig. 22–9**   Work is done by the gas at pressure $p$ as it expands against the piston.   Heat may enter or leave the system from the heat reservoir on which the cylinder rests.

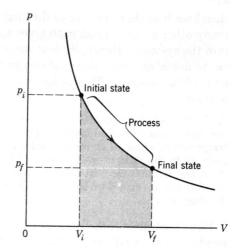

**Fig. 22–10** The work done by a gas is equal to the area under a $p$-$V$ curve.

the initial state $i$ to the final state $f$. For example (Fig. 22–11), the pressure may be kept constant from $i$ to $a$ and then the volume kept constant from $a$ to $f$. Then the work done by the expanding gas is equal to the area under the line $ia$. Another possibility is the path $ibf$, in which case the work done by the gas is the area under the line $bf$. The continuous curve from $i$ to $f$ is another possible path in which the work done by the gas is still different from the previous two paths. We can see, therefore, that *the work done by a system depends not only on the initial and final states but also on the intermediate states, that is, on the path of the process.*

A similar result follows if we compute the flow of heat during the process. State $i$ is characterized by a temperature $T_i$ and state $f$ by a temperature $T_f$. The heat flowing into the system, say, depends on how the system is heated. We can heat it at a constant pressure $p_i$, for example, until we reach the temperature $T_f$, and then change the pressure at constant temperature to the final value $p_f$. Or we can first lower the pressure to $p_f$ and

**Fig. 22–11** The work done by a system depends not only on the initial state ($i$) and the final state ($f$) but on the intermediate path as well.

then heat it at that pressure to the final temperature $T_f$.  Or we can follow many other paths.  Each path gives a different result for the heat flowing into the system.  Hence, *the heat lost or gained by a system depends not only on the initial and final states but also on the intermediate states, that is, on the path of the process.*  This is an experimental fact.  As J. C. Slater has written:

". . . It would be pleasant to be able to say, in a given state of the system, that the system has so and so much heat energy.  Starting from the absolute zero of temperature, where we could say that the heat energy was zero, we could heat the body up to the state we were interested in, find $\int dQ$ from absolute zero up to this state, and call that the heat energy.  But the stubborn fact remains that we would get different answers if we heated it up in different ways. . . . There is nothing to do about it."

Both heat and work "depend on the path" taken; neither one is independent of the path, and neither one can be conserved alone.

### 22–7   The First Law of Thermodynamics

We can now tie all these ideas together.  Let a system change from an initial equilibrium state $i$ to a final equilibrium state $f$ in a definite way, the heat absorbed by the system being $Q$ and the work done by the system being $W$.  Then we compute the $Q - W$.  Now we start over and change the system from the same state $i$ to the same state $f$, but this time in another way by a different path.  We do this over and over again, using different paths each time.  We find that in every case the quantity $Q - W$ *is the same.*  That is, although $Q$ and $W$ separately depend on the path taken, $Q - W$ does not depend at all on how we took the system from state $i$ to state $f$ but only on the initial and final (equilibrium) states.

The student will recall from mechanics that when an object is moved from an initial point $i$ to a final point $f$ in a gravitational field in the absence of friction, the work done depends only on the positions of the two points and not at all on the path through which the body is moved.  From this we concluded that there is a function of the space coordinates of the body whose final value minus is initial value equals the work done in displacing the body.  We called it the potential energy function.  Now in thermodynamics we find that when a system has its state changed from state $i$ to state $f$, the quantity $Q - W$ depends only on the initial and final coordinates and not at all on the path taken between these end points.  We conclude that there is a function of the thermodynamic coordinates whose final value minus its initial value equals the change $Q - W$ in the process. We call this function the *internal energy function.*

Now $Q$ is the energy added to the system by the transfer of heat and $W$ is the energy given up by the system in performing work, so that $Q - W$ represents, by definition, *the internal energy change of the system.*  Let us represent the internal energy function by the letter $U$.  Then the internal energy of the system in state $f$, $U_f$, minus the internal energy of the system in state $i$, $U_i$, is simply *the change in internal energy of the system,* and this quantity *has a definite value independent of how the system went from state i to state f.* We have

$$U_f - U_i = \Delta U = Q - W. \tag{22–6}$$

Just as for potential energy, so for internal energy too it is the change that matters. If some arbitrary value is chosen for the internal energy in some standard reference state, its value in any other state can be given a definite value. Equation 22–6 is known as the *first law of thermodynamics.* In applying Eq. 22–6 we must remember that $Q$ is considered positive when heat enters the system and $W$ is positive when work is done by the system.

If our system undergoes only an infinitesimal change in state, only an infinitesimal amount of heat $dQ$ is absorbed and only an infinitesimal amount of work $dW$ is done, so that the internal energy change $dU$ is also infinitesimal. In such a case, the first law is written in *differential\* form as*

$$dU = dQ - dW. \tag{22–7}$$

We may express the first law in words by saying: *Every thermodynamic system in an equilibrium state possesses a state variable called the internal energy U whose change dU in a differential process is given by Eq. 22–7.* Recall that the essential content of the zeroth law of thermodynamics (p. 526) is, speaking loosely: *there exists a useful thermodynamic quantity called "temperature."* The essential content of the first law is: *there exists a useful thermodynamic quantity called "internal energy";* the law also provides, in Eq. 22–6, a recipe for measuring changes in internal energy quantitatively.

The first law of thermodynamics is thought to apply to every process in nature that proceeds between equilibrium states. Note that the *process* may or may not involve equilibrium states. We may apply the first law to the explosion of a firecracker in an insulated steel drum, for example. Because of its generality, the information that the first law gives is far from complete, although exact and correct. There are some very general questions which it cannot answer. For example, although it tells us that energy is conserved in every process, it does not tell us whether any particular process can actually occur. An entirely different generalization, called the second law of thermodynamics, gives us this information, and much of the subject matter of thermodynamics depends on this second law (Chapter 25).

## 22–8    Some Applications of the First Law of Thermodynamics

We have seen that when a gas expands the work it does on its environment is

$$W = \int p \, dV,$$

---

\* $W$ and $Q$ are not actual functions of the state of a system, that is, they do not depend on the values of the system's coordinates. Hence, $dW$ and $dQ$ are not exact differentials as the term is used in mathematics. All they mean here is a very small quantity. More advanced books write them as đ$Q$ and đ$W$ to indicate their inexact nature. However, $dU$ *is* an exact differential, for $U$ is an exact function of the system's coordinates.

Frictionless and airtight contact

Sand

W

Steam

Liquid water

Q

**Fig. 22–12**   Water boiling at constant pressure (isobarically). The pressure is kept constant by the weight of the sand and the piston.

where $p$ is the pressure exerted on or by the gas and $dV$ is the differential change in volume of the gas.   Consider a special case in which the pressure remains constant while the volume changes by a finite amount, say from $V_i$ to $V_f$.   Then

$$W = \int_{V_i}^{V_f} p \, dV = p \int_{V_i}^{V_f} dV = p(V_f - V_i) \qquad \text{(constant pressure)}.$$

A process taking place at constant pressure is called an *isobaric* process. For example, water is heated in the boiler of a steam engine up to its boiling point and is vaporized to steam; then the steam is superheated, all processes proceeding at a constant pressure.

In Fig. 22–12 we show an isobaric process.   The system is $H_2O$ in a cylindrical container.   A frictionless airtight piston is loaded with sand to produce the desired pressure on the $H_2O$ and to maintain it automatically.   Heat can be transferred from the environment to the system by a Bunsen burner.   If the process continues long enough, the water boils and some is converted to steam; we assume that this occurs.   The system may expand, very slowly (quasi-statically) but the pressure it exerts on the piston is automatically always the same, for this pressure must be equal to the constant pressure which the piston exerts on the system.   If we wedged the piston so that it could not move, or if we added or took away some sand during the heating process, the process would not be isobaric.

Let us consider the boiling process. We know that substances will change their phase from liquid to vapor at a definite combination of values of pressure and temperature. Water will vaporize at 100° C and atmospheric pressure, for example. For a system to undergo a change of phase heat must be added to it, or taken from it, quite apart from the heat necessary to bring its temperature to the required value. Consider the change of phase of a mass $m$ of liquid to a vapor occurring at constant temperature and pressure. Let $V_l$ be the volume of liquid and $V_v$ the volume of vapor. The work done by this substance in expanding from $V_l$ to $V_v$ at constant pressure is

$$W = p(V_v - V_l).$$

Let $L$ represent the heat of vaporization, that is, the heat needed per unit mass to change a substance from liquid to vapor at constant temperature and pressure. Then the heat absorbed by the mass $m$ during the change of state is

$$Q = mL.$$

From the first law of thermodynamics, we have

$$\Delta U = Q - W$$

so that

$$\Delta U = mL - p(V_v - V_l)$$

for this process.

▶ **Example 3.** At atmospheric pressure 1.00 gm of water, having a volume of 1.00 cm³, becomes 1671 cm³ of steam when boiled. The heat of vaporization of water is 539 cal/gm at 1 atm. Hence, if $m = 1.00$ gm,

$$Q = mL = 539 \text{ cal.}$$

This quantity, which respresents heat *added* to the system from the environment, is positive.

$$W = p(V_v - V_l) = (1.013 \times 10^5 \text{ nt/meter}^2)[(1671 - 1) \times 10^{-6} \text{ meter}^3]$$

$$= 169.5 \text{ joules.}$$

This quantity, which represents work done *by* the system on the environment, is positive.

Since 1 cal equals 4.186 joules, $W = 41$ cal. Then,

$$\Delta U = U_v - U_l = mL - p(V_v - V_l) = (539 - 41) \text{ cal}$$

$$= 498 \text{ cal.}$$

This quantity is positive; the internal energy of the system *increases* during this process. Hence, of the 539 cal needed to boil 1 gm of water (at 100° C and 1 atm), 41 cal go into external work of expansion and 498 cal go into internal energy added to the system. This energy represents the internal work done in overcoming the strong attraction of $H_2O$ molecules for one another in the liquid state.

How would you expect the 80 cal that are needed to melt 1 gm of ice to water (at 0° C and 1 atm) to be shared by the external work and the internal energy? ◀

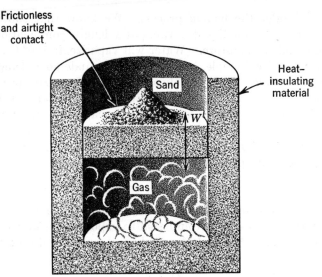

Frictionless
and airtight
contact

Sand

Heat-
insulating
material

$W$

Gas

**Fig. 22–13** In an adiabatic process there is no flow of heat to or from the system. Here the walls are insulated and, as sand is removed or added, the volume of the gas changes adiabatically.

A process that takes place in such a way that no heat flows into or out of the system is called an *adiabatic process*. Experimentally such processes are achieved either by sealing the system off from its surroundings with heat insulating material or by performing the process quickly. Because the flow of heat is somewhat slow, any process can be made practically adiabatic if it is performed quickly enough.

For an adiabatic process $Q$ equals zero, so that from the first law we obtain

$$\Delta U = U_f - U_i = -W.$$

Hence, the internal energy of a system increases exactly by the amount of work done *on* the system in an adiabatic process. If work is done *by* the system in an adiabatic process, the internal energy of the system decreases by exactly the amount of external work it performs. An increase of internal energy usually raises the system's temperature and conversely, a decrease of internal energy usually lowers the system's temperature. A gas that expands adiabatically does external work and its internal energy decreases; such a process is used to attain low temperatures. The increase of temperature during an adiabatic compression of air is well known from the heating of a bicycle pump.

In Fig. 22–13 we show a simple adiabatic process. The system is a gas inside a cylinder made of heat-insulating material. Heat cannot enter the system from its environment or leave the system to the environment.

Again we have a pile of sand on a frictionless airtight piston. The only interaction permitted between system and environment is through the performance of work. Such a process can occur when sand is added or removed from the piston, so that the gas can be compressed or can expand against the piston.

Among the many engineering examples of adiabatic processes are the expansion of steam in the cylinder of a steam engine, the expansion of hot gases in an internal combustion engine, and the compression of air in a Diesel engine or in an air compressor. These processes all take place rapidly enough so that only a very small amount of heat can enter or leave the system through its walls during that short time. The compressions and rarefactions in a sound wave are so rapid that the behavior of the transmitting gas is adiabatic (Example 6, Chapter 23).

The most important reason for studying adiabatic processes, however, is that ideal engines use processes that are exactly adiabatic. These ideal engines determine the theoretical limits to the operation and capabilities of real engines. We shall look further into this in Chapter 25.

A process of much theoretical interest is that of *free expansion*. This is an adiabatic process in which no work is performed on or by the system. Something like this can be achieved by connecting one vessel which contains a gas to another evacuated vessel with a stopcock connection, the whole system being enclosed with thermal insulation (Fig. 22–14). If the stopcock is suddenly opened, the gas rushes into the vacuum and expands freely. Because of the heat insulation this process is adiabatic, and because the walls of the vessels are rigid no external work is done on the system. Hence, in the first law we have $Q = 0$ and $W = 0$, so that $U_i = U_f$ for this process. The initial and final internal energies are equal in free expansion.

A free expansion differs from the other examples that we have given in that there is no way to carry it out very slowly (quasi-statically). After

Initial equilibrium state        Final equilibrium state

**Fig. 22–14** Free expansion. There is no change of internal energy $U$ since there is no flow of heat $Q$ and no external work $W$ is done.

we open the stopcock we have no further control over the process. At intermediate states the pressure, volume and temperature do not have unique values characteristic of the system as a whole, that is, the system passes through non-equilibrium states so that we cannot plot the course of the process by a curve on a $p\text{-}V$ diagram. We can plot the initial and final states as points on such plots because they are well-defined, equilibrium states. The free expansion is a good example of an irreversible process; see Section 25–2.

## QUESTIONS

**1.** Give examples to distinguish clearly between temperature and heat.

**2.** (a) Show how heat conduction and calorimetry could be explained by the caloric theory. (b) List some heat phenomena that cannot be explained by the caloric theory.

**3.** Can heat be considered a form of stored (or potential) energy? Would such an interpretation contradict the concept of heat as energy in process of transfer because of a temperature difference?

**4.** Apply Eq. 22–1 to boiling water.

**5.** Can heat be added to a substance without causing the temperature of the substance to rise? If so, does this contradict the concept of heat as energy in process of transfer because of a temperature difference?

**6.** Explain the fact that the presence of a large body of water nearby, such as a sea or ocean, tends to moderate the temperature extremes of the climate on adjacent land.

**7.** Theory shows that the coefficient of linear expansion $\alpha$ (see Sec. 21–8) is proportional to the heat capacity $C_v$. Show that this is to be expected. (Hint: heat capacity measures the rate of change of the vibrational energy with temperature.)

**8.** Give an example of a process in which no heat is transferred to or from the system but the temperature of the system changes.

**9.** Both heat conduction and wave propagation involve the transfer of energy. Is there any difference in principle between these two phenomena?

**10.** When a hot body warms a cool one are their temperature changes equal in magnitude? Give examples. Can one then say that temperature passes from one to the other?

**11.** What connection is there between an object's feeling hot or cold and its heat capacity? Between this and its thermal conductivity?

**12.** A block of wood and a block of metal are at the *same* temperature. When the blocks feel cold the metal feels colder than the wood; when the blocks feel hot the metal feels hotter than the wood. Explain. At what temperature will the blocks feel equally cold or hot?

**13.** On a winter day the temperature of the inside surface of a wall is much lower than room temperature and that of the outside surface is much higher than the outdoor temperature. Explain.

**14.** What requirements for thermal conductivity, specific heat capacity, and coefficient of expansion would you want a material to be used as a cooking utensil to satisfy?

**15.** In what way is steady-state heat flow analogous to the flow of an incompressible fluid?

**16.** Is the mechanical equivalent of heat, $J$, a physical quantity or merely a conversion factor for converting energy from heat units to mechanical units and vice versa?

**17.** Is the temperature of an isolated system (no interaction with the environment) conserved?

**18.** Can one distinguish between whether the internal energy of a body was acquired by heat transfer or acquired by performance of work?

**19.** If the pressure and volume of a system are given is the temperature always uniquely determined? (Hint: See Fig. 21–7).

**20.** Does a gas do any work when it expands adiabatically? If so, what is the source of the energy needed to do this work?

**21.** A gas is kept at a constant temperature as it expands. It does external work. Does the internal energy of the gas change during this process? If not, what is the source of the energy needed to do the work?

**22.** A quantity of gas occupies an initial volume $V_0$ at a pressure $p_0$ and a temperature $T_0$. It expands to a volume $V$ (a) at constant temperature and (b) at constant pressure. In which case does the gas do more work?

**23.** Discuss the process of the freezing of water from the point of view of the first law of thermodynamics. Remember that ice occupies a greater volume than an equal mass of water.

**24.** A thermos bottle contains coffee. The thermos bottle is vigorously shaken. Consider the coffee as the system. (*a*) Does its temperature rise? (*b*) Has heat been added to it? (*c*) Has work been done on it? (*d*) Has its internal energy changed?

## PROBLEMS

**1.** In a Joule experiment, a mass of 6.00 kg falls through a height of 50.0 meters and rotates a paddle wheel which stirs 0.600 kg of water. The water is initially at 15° C. By how much does its temperature rise?

**2.** Compute the possible increase in temperature for water going over Niagara Falls, 162 ft high. What factors would tend to prevent this possible rise?

**3.** An energetic athlete dissipates all the energy in a diet of 4000 kcal per day. If he were to release this heat at a steady rate, how would his heat output compare with the energy output of a 100-watt bulb?

**4.** A block of ice at 0° C whose mass is initially 50.0 kg slides along a horizontal surface, starting at a speed of 5.38 meters/sec and finally coming to rest after traveling 28.3 meters. Compute the mass of ice melted as a result of the friction between the block and the surface. List any assumptions you need to make in getting your answer.

**5.** Calculate the specific heat of a metal from the following data. A container made of the metal weighs 8.0 lb and contains in addition 30 lb of water. A 4.0-lb piece of the metal initially at a temperature of 350° F is dropped into the water. The water and container initially have a temperature of 60° F and the final temperature of the entire system is 65° F.

**6.** A thermometer of mass 0.055 kg and of specific heat 0.20 kcal/kgC° reads 15.0° C. It is then inserted into 0.300 kg of water and it comes to the same final temperature of the water. If the thermometer reads 44.4° C and is accurate, what was the temperature of the water before insertion of the thermometer, neglecting other heat losses?

**7.** Count Rumford weighed a metal object at low temperature and then at high temperature to see whether its "caloric content" increased. He concluded that (for gold) the "caloric" did not weigh more than $10^{-6}$ the weight of the sample. (*a*) Should the mass of a sample increase when heated, according to modern theories? (*b*) If so, by what order of magnitude? (c) Was Rumford safe in rejecting the caloric theory on this basis, in retrospect?

**8.** Take the average specific heat of copper to be 0.090 cal/gmC° in the temperature range 0 to 1000° C. If 1.00 kg of copper is heated from 0 to 1000° C, by how much does its mass increase?

**9.** A "flow calorimeter" is used to measure the specific heat of a liquid. Heat is added at a known rate to a stream of the liquid as it passes through the calorimeter at a known rate. Then a measurement of the resulting temperature difference between the inflow and the outflow points of the liquid stream enables us to compute the specific heat of the liquid.

A liquid of density 0.85 gm/cm³ flows through a calorimeter at the rate of 8.0 cm³/sec. Heat is added by means of a 250-watt electric heating coil, and a temperature difference of 15 C° is established in steady-state conditions between the inflow and outflow points. Find the specific heat of the liquid.

**10.** By means of a heating coil energy is transferred at a *constant* rate to a substance in a *thermally insulated* container. The temperature of the substance is measured as a function of the time. Show how we can deduce the way in which the heat capacity of the body depends on the temperature from this information.

**11.** Suppose the specific heat of a substance is found to vary with temperature in a parabolic fashion, that is

$$c = A + BT^2,$$

where $A$ and $B$ are constants and $T$ is Celsius temperature. Compare the *mean* specific heat of the substance in a temperature range $T = 0$ to $T = T$ to the specific heat at the midpoint $T/2$.

**12.** The specific heat of silver, measured at atmospheric pressure, is found to vary with temperature between 50 and 100° K by the empirical equation

$$c_p = 0.076T - 0.00026T^2 - 0.15,$$

where $c_p$ is in cal/mole K° and $T$ is the Kelvin temperature. Calculate the quantity of heat required to raise 216 gm of silver from 50 to 100° K.

**13.** Power is supplied at the rate of 0.40 hp for 2.0 min in drilling a hole in a 1.0-lb brass block. (a) How much heat is generated? (b) What is the rise in temperature of the brass if 75% of the heat generated warms the brass? (c) What happens to the other 25%?

**14.** A 2.0-gm lead bullet moving at a speed of 200 meters/sec becomes embedded in a 2.0-kg wooden block of a ballistic pendulum. Calculate the rise in temperature of the bullet, assuming that all the heat generated raises the bullet's temperature.

**15.** Consider the rod shown in Fig. 22–4. Suppose $L = 25$ cm, $A = 1.0$ cm², and the material is copper. If $T_2 = 125°$ C, $T_1 = 0°$ C, and a steady state is reached, find (a) the temperature gradient, (b) the rate of heat transfer, and (c) the temperature at a point in the rod 10 cm from the high-temperature end.

**16.** Show that in a compound slab the temperature gradient in each portion is inversely proportional to the thermal conductivity.

**17.** Assume that the thermal conductivity of copper is twice that of aluminum and four times that of brass. Three metal rods, made of copper, aluminum, and brass, respectively, are each 6.0 in. long and 1.0 in. in diameter. These rods are placed end-to-end, with the aluminum between the other two. The free ends of the copper and brass rods are maintained at 100 and 0° C, respectively. Find the equilibrium temperatures of the copper-aluminum junction and the aluminum-brass junction.

**18.** Assuming $k$ is constant, show that the radial rate of flow of heat in a substance between two concentric spheres is given by

$$\frac{dQ}{dt} = \frac{(T_1 - T_2)4\pi k r_1 r_2}{r_2 - r_1}$$

where the inner sphere has a radius $r_1$ and temperature $T_1$, and the outer sphere has a radius $r_2$ and temperature $T_2$.

**19.** Heat generated by radioactivity within the earth is conducted outward through the oceans. For purposes of approximate calculation, assume the average temperature gradient within the solid earth beneath the ocean to be 0.07 C°/meter and the average thermal conductivity to be $2 \times 10^{-4}$ kcal/meter sec C°, and determine the rate of heat transfer per square meter. Assume that this is approximately the rate for the entire surface of the earth, and determine how much heat is thereby transferred through the earth's surface each day.

**20.** Assuming $k$ is constant, show that the radial rate of flow of heat in a substance between two coaxial cylinders is given by

$$\frac{dQ}{dt} = \frac{(T_1 - T_2)2\pi L k}{\ln(r_2/r_1)}$$

where the inner cylinder has a radius $r_1$ and temperature $T_1$, and the outer cylinder has a radius $r_2$ and temperature $T_2$, each cylinder having a length $L$.

**21.** A long tungsten heater wire is rated at 3.0 kw/meter and is $5.0 \times 10^{-4}$ meter in diameter. It is embedded along the axis of a ceramic cylinder of diameter 0.12 meter. When operating at the rated power, the wire is at 1500° C; the outside of the cylinder is at 20° C. Find the thermal conductivity of the ceramic; use the result given in Problem 20.

**22.** Determine the value of $J$, the mechanical equivalent of heat, from the following data: 2000 cal of heat are supplied to a system; the system does 3350 joules of external work during that time; the increase in internal energy during the process is 5030 joules.

**23.** When a system is taken from state $i$ to state $f$ along the path $iaf$, it is found that $Q = 50$ cal and $W = 20$ cal. Along the path $ibf$, $Q = 36$ cal (Fig. 22–15). (a) What

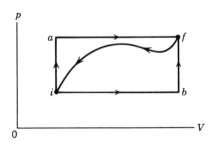

**Fig. 22–15**

is $W$ along the path $ibf$? (b) If $W = -13$ cal for the curved return path $fi$, what is $Q$ for this path? (c) Take $U_i = 10$ cal. What is $U_f$? (d) If $U_b = 22$ cal, what is $Q$ for the process $ib$? For the process $bf$?

**24.** A thermodynamic system is taken from an initial state $A$ to another $B$ and back again to $A$, via state $C$, as shown by the path $A$-$B$-$C$-$A$ in the $p$-$V$ diagram of Fig. 22–16a. (a) Complete the table in Fig. 22–16b by filling in appropriate $+$ or $-$ indi-

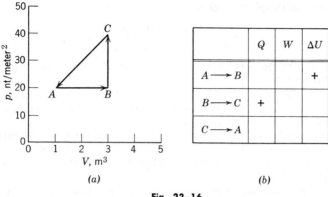

(a)                                   (b)

**Fig. 22–16**

cations for the signs of the thermodynamic quantities associated with each process.   (b)
Calculate the numerical value of the work done by the system for the complete cycle
A-B-C-A.

**25.** Figure 22–17a shows a cylinder containing gas and closed by a movable piston.
The cylinder is submerged in an ice-water mixture.   The piston is *quickly* pushed down
from position (1) to position (2).   The piston is held at position (2) until the gas is again
at 0° C and then is *slowly* raised back to position (1).   Figure 22–17b is a p-V diagram
for the process.   If 100 gm of ice are melted during the cycle, how much work has been
done *on* the gas?

(a)                                   (b)

**Fig. 22–17**

**26.** An iron ball is dropped onto a concrete floor from a height of 10 meters.   On the
first rebound it rises to a height of 0.50 meter.   Assume that all the macroscopic
mechanical energy lost in the collision with the floor goes into the ball.   The specific
heat of iron is 0.12 cal/gm C°.   During the collision (a) has heat been added to the ball?
(b) Has work been done on it?   (c) Has its internal energy changed?   If so, by how
much?   (d) How much has the temperature of the ball risen after the first collision?

# Kinetic Theory of Gases—I

## CHAPTER 23

### 23-1  Introduction

Thermodynamics deals only with macroscopic variables, such as pressure, temperature, and volume. Its basic laws, expressed in terms of such quantities, say nothing at all about the fact that matter is made up of atoms. Statistical mechanics, however, which deals with the same areas of science that thermodynamics does, presupposes the existence of atoms. Its basic laws are the laws of mechanics, which are applied to the atoms that make up the system.

No existing electronic computer could solve the problem of applying the laws of mechanics individually to every atom in a gas, say. If there were one, the results of such calculations would be too voluminous to be useful. Fortunately, the detailed life histories of individual atoms in a gas are not important if we want to calculate only the macroscopic behavior of the gas. We apply the laws of mechanics statistically, then, and we find that we are able to express all the thermodynamic variables as certain averages of atomic properties. For example, the pressure exerted by a gas on the wall of the containing vessel is the average rate per unit area at which the atoms of the gas transfer momentum to the wall as they collide with it. The number of atoms in a macroscopic system is usually so large that such averages are very sharply defined quantities indeed.

We can apply the laws of mechanics statistically to assemblies of atoms at two different levels. At the level called kinetic theory we proceed in a rather physical way, using relatively simple mathematical averaging techniques. In this chapter we will use these methods to enlarge our understanding of pressure, temperature, specific heat, and internal energy at the atomic level. Kinetic theory was developed by Robert Boyle (1627–1691), Daniel Bernoulli (1700–1782), James Joule (1818–1889), A. Kronig (1822–1879), Rudolph Clausius (1822–1888), and Clerk Maxwell (1831–1879), among others.* In this book we apply the kinetic theory to gases only, because the interactions between atoms in gases are much weaker than in liquids and solids; this greatly simplifies the mathematical difficulties.

At another level, we can apply the laws of mechanics statistically using techniques that are more formal and abstract than those of kinetic theory. This approach, developed by J. Willard Gibbs (1839–1903) and by Ludwig Boltzmann (1844–1906) among others, is called *statistical mechanics*, a term that includes kinetic theory as a sub-branch. Using these methods one can derive the laws of thermodynamics, thus establishing that science as a branch of mechanics. The fullest flowering of statistical mechanics (*quantum statistics*) involves the statistical application of the laws of quantum mechanics—rather than those of classical mechanics—to many-atom systems.†

## 23–2   Ideal Gas—A Macroscopic Description

Let a mass $\mathfrak{M}$ of a gas be confined in a container of volume $V$. The density $\rho$ of the gas is $\mathfrak{M}/V$ and it is clear that we can reduce $\rho$ either by removing some gas from the container (reducing $\mathfrak{M}$) or by putting the gas in a larger container (increasing $V$). We find from experiment that, at low enough densities, all gases, no matter what their chemical composition, tend to show a certain simple relationship among the thermodynamic variables $p$, $V$, and $T$. This suggests the concept of an *ideal gas*, one that would have the same simple behavior under all conditions. In this section we give a macroscopic or thermodynamic definition of an ideal gas. In Section 23–3 we will define an ideal gas microscopically, from the standpoint of kinetic theory, and we will see what we can learn by comparing these two approaches.

Given a mass $\mathfrak{M}$ of any gas in a state of thermal equilibrium we can measure its pressure $p$, its temperature $T$, and its volume $V$. For low enough values of the density experiment shows that (1) for a given mass of gas held at a constant temperature, the pressure is inversely proportional to the volume (Boyle's law), and (2) for a given mass of gas held at a constant pressure, the volume is directly proportional to the temperature (law of Charles and Gay-Lussac). We can summarize these two experimental results by the relation

$$\frac{pV}{T} = \text{a constant} \quad \text{(for a fixed mass of gas).} \quad (23\text{--}1)$$

---

* See "John James Waterston and the Kinetic Theory of Gases," by S. G. Brush, in *American Scientist*, June 1961, for an interesting aspect of the history of kinetic theory.

† See *Thermal Physics* by Philip M. Morse, W. A. Benjamin, Inc., New York, 1962, for a fuller treatment of thermodynamics, kinetic theory, and (particularly) statistical mechanics proper, than we can give here.

The volume occupied by a gas (real or ideal) at a given pressure and temperature is proportional to its mass. Thus the constant in Eq. 23–1 must also be proportional to the mass of the gas. In Section 22–2 (see Fig. 22–2) we saw the great simplification that occurs in studies of the specific heats of solids if we compare samples of solids that contain the same number of molecules rather than samples that have the same mass in grams. We did this by using the mole as our mass unit. Let us also do that here.

We therefore write the constant in Eq. 23–1 as $\mu R$, where $\mu$ is the mass of the gas in moles and $R$ is a constant that must be determined for each gas by experiment. Our expectation that simplicity will emerge if we compare gases on a molar basis is justified because experiment shows that, at low enough densities, $R$ has *the same value for all gases*, namely

$$R = 8.314 \text{ joule/mole K}° = 1.986 \text{ cal/mole K}°.$$

$R$ is called the *universal gas constant*. We then write Eq. 23–1 as

$$pV = \mu R T \qquad (23–2)$$

and we define an ideal gas as one that obeys this relation *under all conditions*. There is no such thing as a truly ideal gas, but it remains a useful and simple concept connected with reality by the fact that all real gases approach the ideal gas abstraction in their behavior if the density is low enough. Equation 23–2 is called the *equation of state* of an ideal gas.

If we could fill the bulb of an (ideal) constant-volume gas thermometer with an ideal gas, we see from Eq. 23–2 that we could define temperature in terms of its pressure readings, that is,

$$T = 273.16° \text{ K } \frac{p}{p_{tr}} \quad \text{(ideal gas)}.$$

Here $p_{tr}$ is the gas pressure at the triple point, at which the temperature $T_{tr}$ is 273.16° K by definition. In practice we must fill our thermometer with a real gas and measure the temperature by extrapolating to zero density using Eq. 21–4,

$$T = 273.16° \text{ K } \lim_{p_{tr}\to 0} \frac{p}{p_{tr}} \quad \text{(real gas)}.$$

▶ **Example 1.** A cylinder contains oxygen at a temperature of 20° C and a pressure of 15 atm in a volume of 100 liters. A piston is lowered into the cylinder decreasing the volume occupied by the gas to 80 liters and raising the temperature to 25° C. Assuming oxygen to behave like an ideal gas under these conditions, what then is the gas pressure?

From Eq. 23–1, since the mass of gas remains unchanged, we may write

$$\frac{p_i V_i}{T_i} = \frac{p_f V_f}{T_f}.$$

Our initial conditions are

$$p_i = 15 \text{ atm}, \qquad T_i = 293° \text{ K}, \qquad V_i = 100 \text{ liters}.$$

Our final conditions are

$$p_f = ?, \qquad T_f = 298° \text{ K}, \qquad V_f = 80 \text{ liters}.$$

Hence,

$$p_f = \left(\frac{T_f}{V_f}\right)\left(\frac{p_i V_i}{T_i}\right) = \left(\frac{298° \text{ K}}{80 \text{ liters}}\right)\left(\frac{15 \text{ atm} \times 100 \text{ liters}}{293° \text{ K}}\right) = 19 \text{ atm}.$$

▶ **Example 2.** Calculate the work per mole done by an ideal gas which expands isothermally, that is, at constant temperature, from an initial volume $V_i$ to a final volume $V_f$.

The work done may be represented as

$$W = \int_{V_i}^{V_f} p \, dV.$$

From the ideal gas law we have

$$p = \frac{\mu R T}{V},$$

so that $W/\mu$, the work per mole, is

$$\frac{W}{\mu} = \int_{V_i}^{V_f} \frac{RT}{V} \, dV.$$

The temperature is constant so that

$$\frac{W}{\mu} = RT \int_{V_i}^{V_f} \frac{dV}{V} = RT \ln \frac{V_f}{V_i}$$

is the work per mole done by an ideal gas in an isothermal expansion at temperature $T$ from an initial volume $V_i$ to a final volume $V_f$.

$pV = \mu RT$
$T = $ constant

Isothermal process

**Fig. 23–1** Example 2. The shaded area represents the work done by $\mu$ moles of gas in expanding from $V_i$ to $V_f$ with the temperature held constant.

Notice that when the gas expands, so that $V_f > V_i$, the work done by the gas is positive; when the gas is compressed, so that $V_f < V_i$, the work done by the gas is negative. This is consistent with the sign convention adopted for $W$ in the first law of thermodynamics. The work done is shown as the shaded area in Fig. 23–1. The solid line is an isotherm, that is, a curve giving the relation of $p$ to $V$ at a constant temperature.

In practice, how can we keep an expanding or contracting gas at constant temperature? ◀

## 23–3 An Ideal Gas—Microscopic Definition

From the microscopic point of view we define an ideal gas by making the following assumptions; it will then be our task to apply the laws of classical mechanics statistically to the gas atoms and to show that our microscopic definition is consistent with the macroscopic definition of the preceding section:

1. *A gas consists of particles called molecules.* Depending on the gas, each molecule will consist of one atom or a group of atoms. If the gas is an element or a compound and is in a stable state, we consider all its molecules to be identical.

2. *The molecules are in random motion and obey Newton's laws of motion.* The molecules move in all directions and with various speeds. In computing the properties of the motion, we assume that Newtonian mechanics works at the microscopic level. As for all our assumptions, this one will stand or fall depending on whether or not the experimental facts it predicts are correct.

3. *The total number of molecules is large.* The direction and speed of motion of any one molecule may change abruptly on collision with the wall or another molecule. Any particular molecule will follow a zigzag path because of these collisions. However, because there are so many molecules we assume that the resulting large number of collisions maintains the over-all distribution of molecular velocities and the randomness of the motion.

4. *The volume of the molecules is a negligibly small fraction of the volume occupied by the gas.* Even though there are many molecules, they are extremely small. We know that the volume occupied by a gas can be changed through a large range of values with little difficulty, and that when a gas condenses the volume occupied by the liquid may be thousands of times smaller than that of the gas. Hence, our assumption is plausible. Later we shall investigate the actual size of molecules and see whether we need to modify this assumption.

5. *No appreciable forces act on the molecules except during a collision.* To the extent that this is true a molecule moves with uniform velocity between collisions. Because we have assumed the molecules to be so small, the average distance between molecules is large compared to the size of a molecule. Hence, we assume that the range of molecular forces is comparable to the molecular size.

6. *Collisions are elastic and are of negligible duration.* Collisions between molecules and with the walls of the container conserve momentum and (we assume) kinetic energy. Because the collision time is negligible compared to the time spent by a molecule between collisions, the kinetic energy which is converted to potential energy during the collision is available again as kinetic energy after such a brief time that we can ignore this exchange entirely.

### 23–4   Kinetic Calculation of the Pressure

Let us now calculate the pressure of an ideal gas from kinetic theory. To simplify matters, we consider a gas in a cubical vessel whose walls are perfectly elastic. Let each edge be of length $l$. Call the faces normal to the $x$-axis (Fig. 23–2) $A_1$ and $A_2$, each of area $l^2$. Consider a molecule which has a velocity $\mathbf{v}$. We can resolve $\mathbf{v}$ into components $v_x$, $v_y$, and $v_z$ in the directions of the edges. If this particle collides with $A_1$, it will

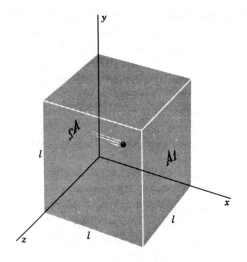

**Fig. 23–2** A cubical box of side $l$, containing an ideal gas. A molecule is shown moving toward $A_1$.

rebound with its $x$-component of velocity reversed.   There will be no effect on $v_y$ or $v_z$, so that the change $\Delta p$ in the particle's momentum will be

$$\Delta p = p_f - p_i = -mv_x - (mv_x) = -2mv_x,$$

normal to $A_1$.   Hence, the momentum imparted to $A_1$ will be $2mv_x$, since the total momentum is conserved.

Suppose that this particle reaches $A_2$ without striking any other particle on the way.   The time required to cross the cube will be $l/v_x$.   At $A_2$ it will again have its $x$-component of velocity reversed and will return to $A_1$.   Assuming no collisions in between, the round trip will take a time $2l/v_x$.   Hence, the number of collisions per unit time this particle makes with $A_1$ is $v_x/2l$, so that the rate at which it transfers momentum to $A_1$ is

$$2mv_x \frac{v_x}{2l} = \frac{mv_x^2}{l}.$$

To obtain the total force on $A_1$, that is, the rate at which momentum is imparted to $A_1$ by all the gas molecules, we must sum up $mv_x^2/l$ for all the particles.   Then, to find the pressure, we divide this force by the area of $A_1$, namely $l^2$.

If $m$ is the mass of each molecule, we have

$$p = \frac{m}{l^3} (v_{x1}^2 + v_{x2}^2 + \cdot\,\cdot\,\cdot),$$

where $v_{x1}$ is the $x$-component of the velocity of particle 1, $v_{x2}$ is that of particle 2, etc.   If $N$ is the total number of particles in the container and $n$ is the number per unit volume, then $N/l^3 = n$ or $l^3 = N/n$.   Hence,

$$p = mn \left( \frac{v_{x1}^2 + v_{x2}^2 + \cdot\,\cdot\,\cdot}{N} \right).$$

But $mn$ is simply the mass per unit volume, that is, the density $\rho$. The quantity $(v_{x1}^2 + v_{x2}^2 + \cdots)/N$ is the average value of $v_x^2$ for all the particles in the container. Let us call this $\overline{v_x^2}$. Then

$$p = \rho \overline{v_x^2}.$$

For any particle $v^2 = v_x^2 + v_y^2 + v_z^2$. Because we have many particles and because they are moving entirely at random, the average values of $v_x^2$, $v_y^2$, and $v_z^2$ are equal and the value of each is exactly one-third the average value of $v^2$. There is no preference among the molecules for motion along any one of the three axes. Hence, $\overline{v_x^2} = \frac{1}{3}\overline{v^2}$, so that

$$p = \rho \overline{v_x^2} = \frac{1}{3}\rho \overline{v^2}. \tag{23-3}$$

Although we derived this result by neglecting collisions between particles, the result is true even when we consider collisions. Because of the exchange of velocities in an elastic collision between identical particles, there will always be some one molecule that will collide with $A_2$ with momentum $mv_x$ corresponding to the one that left $A_1$ with this same momentum. Also, the time spent during collisions is negligible compared to the time spent between collisions. Hence, our neglect of collisions is merely a convenient device for calculation. Likewise, we could have chosen a container of any shape—the cube merely simplifies the calculation. Although we have calculated the pressure exerted only on the side $A_1$, it follows from Pascal's law that the pressure is the same on all sides and everywhere in the interior.*

The square root of $\overline{v^2}$ is called the *root-mean-square* speed of the molecules and is a kind of average molecular speed.† Using Eq. 23-3, we can calculate this root-mean-square speed from measured values of the pressure and density of the gas. Thus,

$$v_{\text{rms}} = \sqrt{\overline{v^2}} = \sqrt{\frac{3p}{\rho}}. \tag{23-4}$$

In Eq. 23-3 we relate a macroscopic quantity (the pressure $p$) to an average value of a microscopic quantity (that is, to $\overline{v^2}$ or $v_{\text{rms}}^2$. However, averages can be taken over short times or over long times, over small regions of space or large regions of space. The average computed in a small region for a short time might depend on the time or region chosen, so that the values obtained in this way may fluctuate. This could happen in a gas of very low density, for example. We can ignore fluctuations, however, when the number of particles in the system is large enough.

---

* We neglect the weight of the gas, a negligible effect unless the gas is of very large extent, as in the atmosphere. (See Section 17-3 and Problem 42.)

† We will consider this further in Section 24-2 in which we discuss the molecular distribution of speeds.

▶ **Example 3.** Calculate the root-mean-square speed of hydrogen molecules at 0.00° C and 1.00-atm pressure, assuming hydrogen to be an ideal gas. Under these conditions hydrogen has a density $\rho$ of $8.99 \times 10^{-2}$ kg/meter³. Then, since $p = 1.00$ atm $= 1.01 \times 10^5$ nt/meter²,

$$v_{rms} = \sqrt{\frac{3p}{\rho}} = 1840 \text{ meters/sec.}$$

This is of the order of a mile per second, or 3600 miles/hr.    ◀

Table 23-1 gives the results of similar calculations for some gases at 0° C.

### Table 23-1

| Gas | $v_{rms}$ (at 0° C), meters/sec | Molecular weight,* gm/mole | Translational kinetic energy per mole (at 0° C), $\frac{1}{2}Mv_{rms}^2$ joules/mole |
|---|---|---|---|
| $O_2$ | 461 | 32 | 3400 |
| $N_2$ | 493 | 28 | 3390 |
| Air | 485 | 28.8 | 3280 |
| CO | 493 | 28 | 3390 |
| $H_2$ | 1838 | 2.02 | 3370 |
| He | 1311 | 4.0 | 3430 |
| $CO_2$ | 393 | 44 | 3400 |
| $H_2O$ | 615 | 18 | 3400 |
| Ne | 584 | 20.1 | 3420 |

* The molecular weight and the mole are defined on page 550. We will discuss the last column in this table in the next section.

These molecular speeds are of the same order as the speed of sound at the same temperature. For example, in air at 0° C, $v_{rms} = 485$ meters/sec and the speed of sound is 331 meters/sec; in hydrogen $v_{rms} = 1838$ meters/sec and sound travels at 1286 meters/sec; in oxygen $v_{rms} = 461$ meters/sec and sound travels at 317 meters/sec. These results are to be expected in terms of our model of a gas; see Prob. 34. We visualize the propagation of sound waves as a directional motion of the molecules as a whole superimposed on their random motion. Hence, the energy of the sound wave is carried as kinetic energy from one molecule to the next one with which it collides. The molecules themselves, in spite of their high speeds, do not move very far during a period of the sound vibration; they are confined to a rather small space by the effects of a large number of collisions.*

---

* This explains why there is a time lag between opening an ammonia bottle at one end of the room and smelling it at the other end. Although molecular speeds are high, the large number of collisions restrains the advance of the ammonia molecules. They diffuse through the air at a speed that is rather small compared to molecular speeds.

However, the energy of the sound wave *is* communicated from one molecule to the next with that high speed, even though we do not expect the speed of sound to be *exactly* equal to $v_{\mathrm{rms}}$, a point that we will clarify in Example 6.

▶ **Example 4.** Assume that the speed of sound in a gas is the same as the root-mean-square speed of the molecules, and show how the speed of sound for an ideal gas depends on the temperature.

The density of a gas is

$$\rho = \frac{\mathfrak{M}}{V} = \frac{\mu M}{V}$$

in which $\mathfrak{M}$ is the mass of the gas, $M$ is the molecular weight (grams/mole), and $\mu$ is the mass in moles. Combining this with the ideal gas law

$$pV = \mu RT$$

yields

$$\frac{p}{\rho} = \frac{RT}{M}.$$

We obtain from Eq. 23-4

$$v_{\mathrm{rms}} = \sqrt{\frac{3p}{\rho}} = \sqrt{\frac{3RT}{M}},$$

so that the speed of sound $v_1$ at a temperature $T_1$ is related to the speed of sound $v_2$ in the same gas at a temperature $T_2$ by

$$\frac{v_1}{v_2} = \sqrt{\frac{T_1}{T_2}}.$$

For example, if the speed of sound at 273° K is 332 meters/sec in air, its speed in air at 300° K will be

$$\sqrt{\tfrac{300}{273}} \times 332 \text{ meters/sec} = 348 \text{ meters/sec}.$$

Would our result change if the speed of sound were proportional to, rather than equal to, the root-mean-square speed of the molecules of a gas?    ◀

## 23-5    Kinetic Interpretation of Temperature

If we multiply each side of Eq. 23-3 by the volume $V$, we obtain

$$pV = \tfrac{1}{3}\rho V \overline{v^2},$$

where $\rho V$ is simply the total mass $\mathfrak{M}$ of gas, $\rho$ being the density. We can also write the mass of gas as $\mu M$, in which $\mu$ is the mass in moles and $M$ is the molecular weight. Making this substitution yields

$$pV = \tfrac{1}{3}\mu M \overline{v^2}.$$

The quantity $\frac{1}{3}\mu M\overline{v^2}$ is two-thirds the total kinetic energy of translation of the molecules, that is, $\frac{2}{3}(\frac{1}{2}\mu M\overline{v^2})$*. We can then write

$$pV = \frac{2}{3}(\frac{1}{2}\mu M\overline{v^2}).$$

The equation of state of an ideal gas is

$$pV = \mu RT.$$

Combining these two expressions, we obtain

$$\frac{1}{2}M\overline{v^2} = \frac{3}{2}RT. \tag{23-5}$$

That is, *the total translational kinetic energy per mole of the molecules of an ideal gas is proportional to the temperature.* We may say that this result, Eq. 23–5, is necessary to fit the kinetic theory to the equation of state of an ideal gas, or we may consider Eq. 23–5 as a definition of gas temperature on a kinetic theory or microscopic basis. In either case, we gain some insight into the meaning of temperature for gases.

The temperature of a gas is related to the total translational kinetic energy measured with respect to the center of mass of the gas. The kinetic energy associated with the motion of the center of mass of the gas has no bearing on the gas temperature. In Section 23–3 we assumed random motion as part of our statistical definition of an ideal gas and in Section 23–4 we calculated $\overline{v^2}$ on this basis. For a random distribution of molecular velocities with direction the center of mass would be at rest, so that we must use a reference frame in which the center of mass of the gas is at rest. For all other frames the molecules will each have velocities greater by **u** (the velocity of the center of mass in that frame) than in the center of mass frame; hence, the motions will no longer be random and we will obtain different values for $\overline{v^2}$. The temperature of a gas in a container does not increase when we put the container on a moving train!

Let us now divide each side of Eq. 23–5 by Avogadro's number, $N_0$, which (see page 550, footnote) is the number of molecules per mole of a gas. Thus $M/N_0$ ($= m$) is the mass of a single molecule and we have

$$\frac{1}{2}(M/N_0)\overline{v^2} = \frac{1}{2}m\overline{v^2} = \frac{3}{2}(R/N_0)T.$$

Now $\frac{1}{2}m\overline{v^2}$ is the average translational kinetic energy per molecule. The ratio $R/N_0$—which we call $k$, the *Boltzmann constant*—plays the role of the gas constant per molecule. We have

$$\frac{1}{2}m\overline{v^2} = \frac{3}{2}kT \tag{23-6}$$

---

* If $N$ is the total number of molecules and $m$ is the mass of each molecule, then

$$\frac{1}{2}mv_1^2 + \frac{1}{2}mv_2^2 + \cdots = \frac{1}{2}mN\left[\frac{v_1^2 + v_2^2 + \cdots}{N}\right] = \frac{1}{2}mN\overline{v^2} \text{ in which } mN \ (= \mu M)$$

is the total mass of the gas.

in which*

$$k = \frac{R}{N_0} = \frac{8.317 \text{ joules/mole } K^\circ}{6.023 \times 10^{23} \text{ molecules/mole}}$$

$$= 1.380 \times 10^{-23} \text{ joule/molecule } K^\circ.$$

We shall return to Boltzmann's constant in Chapter 24.

In the last column of Table 23-1 we list calculated values of $\frac{1}{2}Mv_{\text{rms}}^2$. As Eq. 23-5 predicts, this quantity (the translational kinetic energy per mole) has (closely) the same value for all gases at the same temperatures, 0° C in this case. From Eq. 23-6 we conclude that at the same temperature $T$ the ratio of the root-mean-square speeds of molecules of two different gases is equal to the square root of the inverse ratio of their masses. That is, from

$$T = \frac{2}{3k} \frac{\overline{m_1 v_1^2}}{2} = \frac{2}{3k} \frac{\overline{m_2 v_2^2}}{2}$$

we obtain

$$\sqrt{\frac{\overline{v_1^2}}{\overline{v_2^2}}} = \frac{v_{1\text{rms}}}{v_{2\text{rms}}} = \sqrt{\frac{m_2}{m_1}}. \tag{23-7}$$

We can apply Eq. 23-7 to the diffusion of two different gases in a container with porous walls placed in an evacuated space. The lighter gas, whose molecules move more rapidly on the average, will escape faster than the heavier one. The ratio of the numbers of molecules of the two gases which find their way through the porous walls for a short time interval is equal to the square root of the inverse ratio of their masses, $\sqrt{m_2/m_1}$. This diffusion process is one method of separating (fissionable) $U^{235}$ (0.7 % abundance) from a normal sample of uranium containing mostly (non-fissionable) $U^{238}$ (99.3 % abundance). To quote from the Smyth report,†

As long ago as 1896 Lord Rayleigh showed that a mixture of gases of different atomic weight could be partly separated by allowing some of it to diffuse through a porous barrier into an evacuated space. Because of their higher average speed the molecules of the light gas diffuse through the barrier faster so that the gas which has passed through the barrier (i.e., the "diffusate") is enriched in the lighter constituent and the residual gas which has not passed through the barrier is impoverished in the lighter constituent. The gas most highly enriched in the lighter constituent is the so-called "instantaneous diffusate"; it is the part that diffuses before the impoverishment of the residue has become appreciable. . . . On the assumption that the diffusion rates are inversely proportional to the square roots of the molecular weights‡ the separation factor for the instantaneous diffusate, called the "ideal

---

* See footnote, p. 550.

† *A General Account of the Development of Methods of Using Atomic Energy for Military Purposes* . . . , H. D. Smyth, U. S. Government Printing Office, 1945.

‡ Note that the ratio $m_2/m_1$ of the masses of the two molecules of different gases is the same as the ratio $M_2/M_1$ of their molecular weights, because the molecular weights refer to the same number of molecules. Compare Eq. 23-7.

separation factor" $\alpha$, is given by

$$\alpha = \sqrt{M_2/M_1},$$

where $M_1$ is the molecular weight of the lighter gas and $M_2$ that of the heavier. Applying this formula to the case of uranium will illustrate the magnitude of the separation problem. Since uranium itself is not a gas, some gaseous compound of uranium must be used. The only one obviously suitable is uranium hexafluoride, $UF_6$. . . . Since fluorine has only one isotope, the two important uranium hexafluorides are $U^{235}F_6$ and $U^{238}F_6$; their molecular weights are 349 [gm/mole] and 352 [gm/mole]. Thus if a small fraction of a quantity of uranium hexafluoride is allowed to diffuse through a porous barrier, the diffusate will be enriched in $U^{235}F_6$ by a factor

$$\alpha = \sqrt{\tfrac{352}{349}} = 1.0043 \ldots$$

To separate the uranium isotopes, many successive diffusion stages (i.e., a cascade) must be used. . . . Studies by Cohen and others show that the best flow arrangement for the sucessive stages is that in which half the gas pumped into each stage diffused through the barrier, the other (impoverished) half being returned to the feed of the next lower stage. . . . If one desires to produce 99 per cent pure $U^{235}F_6$, and if one uses a cascade in which each stage has a reasonable overall enrichment factor, then it turns out that roughly 4000 stages are required. . . . Most of the material that eventually emerges from the cascade has been recycled many times. Calculation shows that for an actual uranium-separation plant it may be necessary to force through the barriers of the first stage 100,000 times the volume of gas that comes out the top of the cascade (i.e., as desired product $U^{235}F_6$).

## 23–6 Intermolecular Forces

Forces between molecules are of electromagnetic origin. All molecules contain electric charges in motion. These molecules are electrically neutral in the sense that the negative charge of the electrons is equal and opposite to the charge of the nuclei. This does not mean, however, that molecules do not interact electrically. For example, when two molecules approach each other, the charges on each are disturbed and depart slightly from their usual positions in such a way that the average distance between opposite charges in the two molecules is a little smaller than that between like charges. Hence, an attractive intermolecular force results. This internal rearrangement takes place only when molecules are fairly close together, so that these forces act only over short distances; they are short-range forces. If the molecules come very close together, so that their outer charges begin to overlap, the intermolecular force becomes repulsive. The molecules repel each other because there is no way for a molecule to rearrange itself internally to prevent repulsion of the adjacent external electrons. It is this repulsion on contact that accounts for the billiard-ball character of molecular collisions in gases. If it were not for this repulsion, molecules would move right through each other instead of rebounding on collision.

Let us assume that molecules are approximately spherically symmetrical. Then we can describe intermolecular forces graphically by plotting the mutual potential energy of two molecules, $U$, as a function of distance $r$ between their centers. The force $F$ acting on each molecule is related to the potential energy $U$ by $F = -dU/dr$. In Fig. 23–3a we plot a typical $U(r)$. Here we can imagine one molecule to be fixed at $O$. Then the other molecule will be repelled from $O$ when the slope of $U$ is negative and will be attracted to $O$ when the slope is positive. At $r_0$ no force acts between the molecules; the slope is zero there. In Fig. 23–3b we plot the mutual force $F(r)$ corresponding to this potential energy function. The line $E$ in Fig. 23–3a represents the total mechanical energy of the colliding molecules. The intersection of $U(r)$ with this line is a "turning point" of the motion

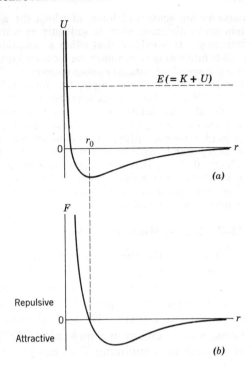

**Fig. 23–3** (*a*) The mutual potential energy of two molecules versus their separation. *E* shows their total mechanical energy ( = *K* + *U*). (*b*) The mutual force, $-dU/dr$, corresponding to this potential energy. *U* is a minimum at $r_0$, at which separation *F* = 0.

(see Section 8–5). The separation of the centers of two molecules at the turning point is the distance of closest approach. The separation distance at which the mutual potential energy is zero may be taken as the approximate distance of closest approach in a collision and hence as the diameter of the molecule. For simple molecules the diameter is about $2.5 \times 10^{-10}$ meter. The forces between molecules practically cease at about $10^{-9}$ meter or 4 diameters apart, so that molecular forces are very short-range ones. The distance $r_0$ at which the potential is a minimum (the equilibrium point) is about $3.5 \times 10^{-10}$ meter for simple molecules. Of course, different molecules have different sizes and internal arrangement of charges so that intermolecular forces vary from one molecule to another. However, they always show the qualitative behavior indicated in the figures.*

In the solid state molecules vibrate about the equilibrium position $r_0$, their total energy *E* being negative, that is, lying below the horizontal axis in Fig. 23–3*a*. The molecules do not have enough energy to escape from the potential valley (that is, from the attractive binding force). The centers of vibration *O* are more or less fixed in a solid. In a liquid the molecules have greater vibrational energy about centers which are free to move but which remain about the same distance from one another. These molecules have their greatest kinetic energy in the gaseous state. In a gas the average distance between the molecules is considerably greater than the effective range of intermolecular forces, and the molecules move in straight lines between collisions. Clerk Maxwell discusses the relation between the kinetic theory model of a gas and the intermolecular forces as follows: "Instead of saying that the particles are hard, spherical, and elastic, we may if we please say that the

---

* See "The Force between Molecules," by B. V. Derjaguin, *Scientific American*, July 1960, for a discussion of the measurement of molecular attractions between macroscopic bodies.

particles are centers of force, of which the action is insensible except at a certain small distance, when it suddenly appears as a repulsive force of very great intensity. It is evident that either assumption will lead to the same results."

It is interesting to compare the measured intermolecular forces with the gravitational force of attraction between molecules. If we choose a separation distance of $4 \times 10^{-10}$ meter, for example, the force between two helium atoms is about $6 \times 10^{-13}$ nt. The gravitational force at that separation is about $7 \times 10^{-42}$ nt, smaller than the intermolecular force by a factor of $10^{29}$! This is a typical result and shows that gravitational forces are negligible in comparison with intermolecular forces. Although the intermolecular forces appear to be small by ordinary standards, we must remember that the mass of a molecule is so small (about $10^{-26}$ kg) that these forces can impart instantaneous accelerations of the order of $10^{15}$ meters/sec$^2$ ($10^{14}g$). These accelerations may last for only a very short time, of course, because one molecule can very quickly move out of the range of influence of the other.

### 23–7   Specific Heats of an Ideal Gas

We picture the molecules in an ideal gas as hard elastic spheres; that is, we assume that there are no forces between the molecules except during collisions and that the molecules are not deformed by collisions. If this is so there is no internal potential energy and the internal energy of an ideal gas is entirely kinetic. We have already found that the average translational kinetic energy per molecule is $\frac{3}{2}kT$, so that the internal energy $U$ of an ideal gas containing $N$ molecules is*

$$U = \tfrac{3}{2}NkT = \tfrac{3}{2}\mu RT. \tag{23–8}$$

This prediction of kinetic theory says that *the internal energy of an ideal gas is proportional to the Kelvin temperature and depends only on the temperature*, being independent of pressure and volume. With this result we can now obtain information about the specific heats of an ideal gas.

The specific heat of a substance is the heat required per unit mass per unit temperature change. A convenient unit of mass is the mole. The corresponding specific heat is called the molar heat capacity and is represented by $C$. Only two varieties of molar heat capacity are important for gases, namely, that at constant volume, $C_v$, and that at constant pressure, $C_p$.

Let us confine a certain number of moles of an ideal gas in a piston-cylinder arrangement as in Fig. 23–4a. The cylinder rests on a heat reservoir whose temperature can be raised or lowered at will, so that we may add heat to the system or remove it, as we wish. The gas has a pressure $p$ such that its upward force on the (frictionless) piston just balances the weight of the piston and its sand load. The state of the system is represented by point $a$ in the $p$-$V$ diagram of Fig. 23–4d; this diagram shows two isothermal lines, all points on one corresponding to a

---

* We will see in Section 23–8 that this result applies only to monatomic gases, for which rotational and vibrational energies are not possible. Only in this case can we equate $U$ to the *translational* kinetic energy.

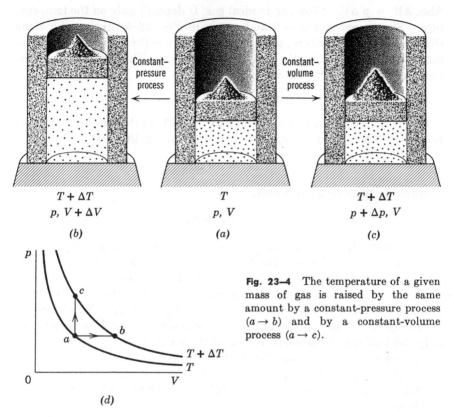

$T + \Delta T$
$p, V + \Delta V$

$(b)$

$T$
$p, V$

$(a)$

$T + \Delta T$
$p + \Delta p, V$

$(c)$

**Fig. 23–4** The temperature of a given mass of gas is raised by the same amount by a constant-pressure process $(a \to b)$ and by a constant-volume process $(a \to c)$.

$(d)$

temperature $T$ and all points on the other to a (higher) temperature $T + \Delta T$.

Now let us raise the temperature of the system by $\Delta T$, by slowly increasing the reservoir temperature. As we do this let us add sand to the piston so that the volume $V$ does not change. This *constant-volume process* carries the system from the initial state of Fig. 23–4a to the final state of Fig. 23–4c. Equivalently, it goes from point $a$ to point $c$ in Fig. 23–4d. Let us apply the first law of thermodynamics

$$\Delta Q = \Delta U + \Delta W$$

to this process. By definition of $C_v$ we have $\Delta Q = \mu C_v \Delta T$. Also, $\Delta W \ (= p \, \Delta V) = 0$ because $\Delta V = 0$. Thus

$$\Delta U = \mu C_v \Delta T. \qquad (23\text{–}9)$$

Let us restore the system to its original state and again raise its temperature by $\Delta T$, this time leaving the sand load undisturbed so that the pressure $p$ does not change. This *constant-pressure process* carries the system from the initial state of Fig. 23–4a to the final state of Fig. 23–4b. Equivalently, it goes from point $a$ to point $b$ in Fig. 23–4d. Let us apply the first law to *this* process. By definition of $C_p$ we have $\Delta Q = \mu C_p \Delta T$.

Also, $\Delta W = p \, \Delta V$. Now for an ideal gas, $U$ depends only on the temperature. Since processes $a \to b$ and $a \to c$ in Fig. 23–4 involve the same change $\Delta T$ in temperature, they must also involve the same change $\Delta U$ in internal energy, namely, that given by Eq. 23–9. Thus for the constant-pressure process the first law yields

$$\mu C_p \, \Delta T = \mu C_v \, \Delta T + p \, \Delta V.$$

Let us apply the equation of state $pV = \mu RT$ to the constant-pressure process $a \to b$. For $p$ constant we have, by taking differences,

$$p \, \Delta V = \mu R \, \Delta T.$$

Combining these equations yields

$$C_p - C_v = R. \tag{23–10}$$

This shows that the molar heat capacity of an ideal gas at constant pressure is always larger than that at constant volume by an amount equal to the universal gas constant $R$ ($= 8.31$ joules/mole $K°$ or $1.99$ cal/ mole $K°$). Although Eq. 23–10 is exact only for an ideal gas, it is nearly true for real gases at moderate pressure (see Table 23–2). Notice that in obtaining this result we did not use the specific relation $U = \frac{3}{2}\mu RT$, but only the fact that $U$ depends on temperature alone.

If we can compute $C_v$, then Eq. 23–10 will give us $C_p$ and vice versa. We *can* obtain $C_v$ by combining Eq. 23–9 with the kinetic theory result for the internal energy of an ideal gas, $U = \frac{3}{2}\mu RT$ (Eq. 23–8). Thus, in the limit of differential changes,

$$C_v = \frac{dU}{\mu \, dT} = \frac{d}{\mu \, dT} [\tfrac{3}{2}\mu RT] = \tfrac{3}{2}R. \tag{23–11}$$

This result (about 3 cal/mole $K°$) turns out to be rather good for monatomic gases. However, it is in serious disagreement with values obtained for diatomic and polyatomic gases (see Table 23–2). This suggests that Eq. 23–8 is not generally correct. Since that relation followed directly from the kinetic theory model, we conclude that we must change the model if kinetic theory is to survive as a useful approximation to the behavior of real gases.

▶ **Example 5.** Show that for an ideal gas undergoing an adiabatic process $pV^\gamma = $ a constant, where $\gamma = C_p/C_v$.

Let us apply the first law of thermodynamics

$$\Delta Q = \Delta U + \Delta W.$$

For an adiabatic process $\Delta Q = 0$. For $\Delta W$ we put $p \, \Delta V$. Since the gas is assumed to be ideal, $U$ depends only on temperature and, from Eq. 23–9, $\Delta U = \mu C_v \, \Delta T$. With these substitutions we have

$$0 = \mu C_v \, \Delta T + p \, \Delta V$$

or

$$\Delta T = -\frac{p\,\Delta V}{\mu C_v}.$$

For an ideal gas $pV = \mu RT$, so that, if $p$, $V$, and $T$ are allowed to take on small variations,

$$p\,\Delta V + V\,\Delta p = \mu R\,\Delta T$$

or

$$\Delta T = \frac{p\,\Delta V + V\,\Delta p}{\mu R}.$$

Equating these two expressions and using Eq. 23–10 ($C_p - C_v = R$), we obtain, after some rearrangement,

$$p\,\Delta VC_p + V\,\Delta pC_v = 0$$

Dividing by $pVC_v$ and recalling that, by definition, $C_p/C_v = \gamma$, we get

$$\frac{\Delta p}{p} + \gamma\frac{\Delta V}{V} = 0.$$

In the limiting case of differential changes this reduces to

$$\frac{dp}{p} + \gamma\frac{dV}{V} = 0,$$

which (assuming $\gamma$ to be constant) we can integrate as

$$\ln p + \gamma \ln V = \text{a constant}$$

or

$$pV^\gamma = \text{a constant.} \tag{23–12}$$

The value of the constant is proportional to the quantity of gas. In Fig. 23–5 we compare the isothermal and adiabatic behaviors of an ideal gas.

▶ **Example 6.** The compressions and rarefactions in a sound wave are practically adiabatic at audio frequencies. Show that in such a case the speed of sound in an ideal gas is given by

$$v = \sqrt{\frac{\gamma p}{\rho}}.$$

In Chapter 20 we showed the speed of sound to be $v = \sqrt{B/\rho}$, where $\rho$ is the gas density and $B$ is the bulk modulus of the gas, $B = -V(\Delta p/\Delta V)$. However, $B$ will depend on the conditions that prevail as the pressure is changed. If the pressure change is carried out slowly enough so that we can assume the temperature to remain constant we have, in the limit of differential changes,

$$B_{\text{isothermal}} = -V\left(\frac{dp}{dv}\right)_{\text{isothermal}} \tag{23–13}$$

In an isothermal process for an ideal gas we have

$$pV = \text{a constant}$$

**Fig. 23–5**   $T_1$, $T_2$, and $T_3$ show how the pressure of one mole of an ideal gas changes as its volume is changed, the temperature being held constant (isothermal process). $A_1$, $A_2$, and $A_3$ show how the pressure of an ideal gas changes as its volume is changed, no heat being allowed to flow to or from the gas (adiabatic process). An adiabatic *increase* in volume (for example going from $a$ to $b$ along $A_3$) is always accompanied by a *decrease* in temperature, since at $a$, $T = 400°$ K, whereas at $b$, $T = 300°$ K.

or, by differentiation with respect to $V$,

$$p + V\left(\frac{dp}{dV}\right)_{\text{isothermal}} = 0.$$

Combined with Eq. 23–13 this yields

$$B_{\text{isothermal}} = p.$$

In a sound wave, however, the variations are so rapid that the conditions are not isothermal but closely adiabatic. The appropriate bulk modulus is then

$$B_{\text{adiabatic}} = -V\left(\frac{dp}{dV}\right)_{\text{adiabatic}} \qquad (23\text{–}14)$$

In an adiabatic process for an ideal gas we have

$$pV^\gamma = \text{a constant}$$

or, by differentiating with respect to $V$,

$$p\gamma V^{\gamma-1} + V^\gamma \left(\frac{dp}{dV}\right)_{\text{adiabatic}} = 0.$$

This, combined with Eq. 23-14, yields

and, for the speed of sound,

$$B_{\text{adiabatic}} = \gamma p$$

$$v = \sqrt{\frac{B}{\rho}} = \sqrt{\frac{\gamma p}{\rho}}. \qquad (23\text{-}15)$$

Newton, in 1710, derived a formula for the speed of sound in which he assumed isothermal rather than adiabatic conditions. He obtained $v = \sqrt{p/\rho}$ rather than the (correct) value of $\sqrt{\gamma p/\rho}$. The error was pointed out by Laplace in 1816. We must remember that, at that date, the concept of energy was not yet understood and the science of thermodynamics did not exist. Does this result modify the result obtained in Example 4? Can you now explain why the speed of sound in a gas is not the same as the root-mean-square speed of the gas molecules? ◀

## 23-8   Equipartition of Energy

A modification of the kinetic theory model designed to explain the specific heats of gases was first suggested by Clausius in 1857. Recall that in our model we assumed a molecule to behave like a hard elastic sphere and we treated its kinetic energy as purely translational. The specific heat prediction was satisfactory for monatomic molecules. Further, because of the success of this simple model in other respects in predicting the correct behavior of gases of all kinds over wide temperature ranges, we feel confident that it is the average kinetic energy of translation which determines what we measure as the temperature of a gas.

However, in the case of specific heats we are concerned with all possible ways of absorbing energy and we must ask whether or not a molecule can store energy internally, that is, in a form other than kinetic energy of translation. This would certainly be so if we pictured a molecule, not as a rigid particle, but as an object with internal structure. For then a molecule could rotate and vibrate as well as move with translational motion. In collisions, the rotational and vibrational modes of motion could be excited, and this would contribute to the internal energy of the gas. Here then is a model which enables us to modify the kinetic theory formula for the internal energy of a gas.

Let us now find the total energy of a system containing a large number of such molecules, where each molecule is thought of as an object having internal structure. The energy will consist of kinetic energy of translation, with terms like $\frac{1}{2}mv_x^2$; of kinetic energy of rotation, with terms like $\frac{1}{2}I\omega_x^2$; of kinetic energy of vibration of the atoms in a molecule, with terms like $\frac{1}{2}\mu v^2$ (where $\mu$ is the reduced mass), and of potential energy of vibration of the atoms in a molecule, with terms like $\frac{1}{2}kx^2$. Although other kinds of energy contributions exist, such as magnetic, for gases we can describe the total energy quite accurately by terms such as these. Although these terms have different origins, they all have the same mathematical form, namely, a positive constant times the square of a quantity which can take on negative or positive values. We can show from statistical mechanics that *when the number of particles is large and Newtonian mechanics holds, all these terms have the same average value, and this average value depends only on the temperature.* In other words, the available energy depends only on the temperature and distributes itself in equal shares to each of the independent ways in which the molecules can absorb energy. This theorem, stated here without proof, is called the *equipartition of energy* and was deduced by Clerk Maxwell. Each such independent mode of energy absorption is called a *degree of freedom.*

From Eq. 23–8 we know that the kinetic energy of translation per mole of gaseous molecules is $\frac{3}{2}RT$. The kinetic energy of translation per mole is the sum of three terms, however, namely $\frac{1}{2}M\overline{v_x}^2$, $\frac{1}{2}M\overline{v_y}^2$, and $\frac{1}{2}M\overline{v_z}^2$. The theorem of equipartition requires that each such term contribute the same amount to the total energy per mole, or $\frac{1}{2}RT$ per degree of freedom.

For *monatomic gases* the molecules have only translational motion (no internal structure in kinetic theory), so that $U = \frac{3}{2}\mu RT$. It follows from Eq. 23–11 that $C_v = \frac{3}{2}R \cong 3$ cal/mole K°. Then from Eq. 23–10, $C_p = \frac{5}{2}R$, and the ratio of specific heat is

$$\gamma = \frac{C_p}{C_v} = \frac{5}{3} = 1.67.$$

For a *diatomic gas* we can think of each molecule as having a dumbbell shape (two spheres joined by a rigid rod). Such a molecule can rotate about any one of three mutually perpendicular axes. However, the rotational inertia about an axis along the rigid rod should be negligible compared to that about axes perpendicular to the rod, so that the rotational energy should consist of only two terms,* such as $\frac{1}{2}I\omega_y^2$ and $\frac{1}{2}I\omega_z^2$. Each rotational degree of freedom is required by equipartition to contribute the same energy as each translational degree, so that for a diatomic gas having both rotational and translational motion,

$$U = 3\mu(\tfrac{1}{2}T) + 2\mu(\tfrac{1}{2}RT) = \tfrac{5}{2}\mu RT,$$

or
$$C_v = \frac{dU}{\mu \, dt} = \tfrac{5}{2}R \cong 5 \text{ cal/mole K°}$$

---

* We have already ruled out the possibility that a monatomic molecule could rotate. Actually it could spin about any one of three mutually perpendicular axes if it had any extent, such as a finite sphere. Implicitly, therefore, we have adopted a point mass as our model of the atom. Hence, in a diatomic molecule we are rid of one rotational degree of freedom, for point masses joined by a rigid line have no motion about an axis along that line.

and $$C_p = C_v + R = \tfrac{7}{2}R,$$

or $$\gamma = \frac{C_p}{C_v} = \frac{7}{5} = 1.40.$$

For *polyatomic gases*, each molecule contains three or more spheres (atoms) joined together by rods in our model, so that the molecule is capable of rotating energetically about each of three mutually perpendicular axes. Hence, for a polyatomic gas having both rotational and translational motion,

$$U = 3\mu(\tfrac{1}{2}RT) + 3\mu(\tfrac{1}{2}RT) = 3\mu RT,$$

or $$C_v = \frac{dU}{\mu\, dT} = 3R = 6 \text{ cal/mole K}^\circ,$$

and $$C_p = 4R,$$

or $$\gamma = \frac{C_p}{C_v} = 1.33.$$

Let us now turn to experiment to test these ideas. In Table 23–2 we list the experimentally determined molar heat capacities for common gases at 20° C and 1.0 atm. Notice that for monatomic and diatomic gases the values of $C_v$, $C_p$, and $\gamma$ are close to the ideal gas predictions. In some diatomic gases, like chlorine, and in most polyatomic gases the specific heats are larger than the predicted values. Even $\gamma$ shows no simple regularity for polyatomic gases. This suggests that our model is not yet close enough to reality.

We have not yet considered energy contributions from the vibrations of the atoms in diatomic and polyatomic molecules. That is, we can

### Table 23–2

| Type of Gas | Gas | $C_p$, cal/mole K° | $C_v$, cal/mole K° | $C_p - C_v$ | $\gamma = C_p/C_v$ |
|---|---|---|---|---|---|
| Monatomic | He | 4.97 | 2.98 | 1.99 | 1.67 |
|  | A | 4.97 | 2.98 | 1.99 | 1.67 |
| Diatomic | $H_2$ | 6.87 | 4.88 | 1.99 | 1.41 |
|  | $O_2$ | 7.03 | 5.03 | 2.00 | 1.40 |
|  | $N_2$ | 6.95 | 4.96 | 1.99 | 1.40 |
|  | $Cl_2$ | 8.29 | 6.15 | 2.14 | 1.35 |
| Polyatomic | $CO_2$ | 8.83 | 6.80 | 2.03 | 1.30 |
|  | $SO_2$ | 9.65 | 7.50 | 2.15 | 1.29 |
|  | $C_2H_6$ | 12.35 | 10.30 | 2.05 | 1.20 |
|  | $NH_3$ | 8.80 | 6.65 | 2.15 | 1.31 |

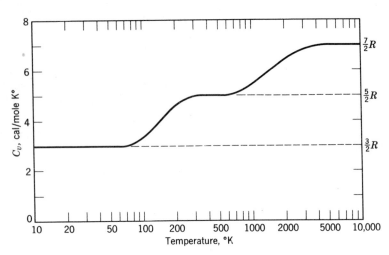

**Fig. 23–6**   Variation of the molar heat $C_v$ of hydrogen with temperature.   Note that $T$ is drawn on a logarithmic scale.

modify the dumbbell model and join the spheres instead by springs.   This new model will greatly improve our results in some cases.   However, instead of having a theoretical model for all gases, we now require an empirical model which differs from gas to gas.   We can obtain a reasonably good picture of molecular behavior this way and the empirical model is therefore useful; however it ceases to be fundamental.

To see this more clearly, let us consider Fig. 23–6, which shows the variation of the molar heat capacity of hydrogen with temperature.   The value of 5 cal/mole K°, which is predicted for diatomic molecules by our model, is characteristic of hydrogen only in the temperature range from about 250 to 750° K.   Above 750° K, $C_v$ increases steadily to 7 cal/mole K° and below 250° K, $C_v$ decreases steadily to 3 cal/mole K°.   Other gases show similar variations of molar heat with temperature.

Here is a possible explanation.   At low temperatures apparently (see Example 7) the hydrogen molecule has translational energy only and, for some reason, cannot rotate.   As the temperature rises rotation becomes possible so that at "ordinary" temperatures a hydrogen molecule acts like our dumbbell model.   At high temperatures the collisions between molecules cause the atoms in the molecule to vibrate and the molecule ceases to behave as a rigid body.   Different gases, because of their different molecular structure, may show these effects at different temperatures.   Thus a chlorine molecule appears to vibrate at room temperature.

Although this description is essentially correct, and we have obtained much insight into the behavior of molecules, this behavior contradicts classical kinetic theory.   For kinetic theory is based on Newtonian mechanics applied to a large collection of particles, and the equipartition of energy is a necessary consequence of this classical statistical mechanics.

But *if equipartition of energy holds, then, no matter what happens to the total internal energy as the temperature changes, each part of the energy—* translational, rotational, and vibrational—*must share equally in the change.* There is no classical mechanism for changing one mode of mechanical energy at a time in such a system. Kinetic theory requires that the specific heats of gases be independent of the temperature.

Hence, we have come to the limit of validity of classical mechanics when we try to explain the structure of the atom (or molecule). Just as New-tonian principles break down at very high speeds (near the speed of light), so here in the region of very small dimensions they also break down. Relativity theory modifies Newtonian ideas to account for the behavior of physical systems in the region of high speeds. It is quantum physics that modifies Newtonian ideas to account for the behavior of physical systems in the region of small dimensions. Both relativity theory and quantum mechanics are generalizations of classical theory in the sense that they give the (correct) Newtonian results in the regions in which Newtonian physics has accurately described experimental observations. In the following two chapters we shall confine our attention to the very fruitful application of thermodynamics and the kinetic theory to "classical" systems.

▶ **Example 7.** According to quantum theory the internal energy of an atom (or molecule) is "quantized"; that is, the atom cannot have any of a continuous set of internal energies but *only certain discrete ones.* After being raised from its lowest energy state to some higher one the atom can give up this energy by emitting radiation whose energy equals the difference in energy between the upper and lower internal energy states of the atom.

When two atoms collide, some of their translational kinetic energy may be converted into internal energy of one or both of the atoms. In such a case the collision is inelastic, for translational kinetic energy is not conserved. In a gas, the average translational kinetic energy of an atom is $\frac{3}{2}kT$. When the temperature is raised to a value where $\frac{3}{2}kT$ is about equal to some allowed internal excitation energy of the atom, then an appreciable number of the atoms can absorb enough energy through inelastic collisions to be raised to this higher internal energy state. We can detect this because, after an interval, radiation corresponding to the absorbed energy will be emitted.

(*a*) Compute the average translational kinetic energy per molecule in a gas at room temperature.

We have, for $T = 300°$ K,

$$\tfrac{3}{2}kT = \tfrac{3}{2}(1.38 \times 10^{-23} \text{ joule/molecule } °K)(300° \text{ K})$$

$$= 6.21 \times 10^{-21} \text{ joule/molecule}$$

$$= 3.88 \times 10^{-2} \text{ ev/molecule}$$

This is about $\frac{1}{25}$ ev per molecule. Some molecules will have larger energies and some smaller energies than this average value.

(*b*) The first allowed (internal) excited state of a hydrogen atom is 10.2 ev above its lowest (ground) state. What temperature is needed to excite a "large" number of hydrogen atoms to emit radiation of this energy?

We require
$$\tfrac{3}{2}kT = 10.2 \text{ ev}$$
and we have from above
$$\tfrac{3}{2}k(300° \text{ K}) = \tfrac{1}{25} \text{ ev}$$
Hence
$$T = 300° \text{ K} \times 10.2/(\tfrac{1}{25}) \simeq 7.5 \times 10^{4°} \text{ K}.$$

Actually, because many molecules have energies much greater than the average value, appreciable excitation may occur at somewhat lower temperatures.

We can now appreciate why the kinetic theory assumption, that molecules can be regarded as having no internal structure and collide elastically with one another, holds true at ordinary temperatures. Only at temperatures high enough to give the molecules an average translational kinetic energy comparable to the energy difference between the lowest and the first allowed excited state of the molecule will the internal structure of the molecule change and the collisions become inelastic. Indeed, in retrospect one may say that early evidence that the internal energy of an atom is quantized existed in experiments with gas collisions and that the seeds of quantum theory lay in the kinetic theory of gases.*          ◀

## QUESTIONS

**1.** In discussing the fact that it is impossible to apply the laws of mechanics individually to atoms in a macroscopic system, Mayer and Mayer state: "The very complexity of the problem [that is, the fact that the number of atoms is large] is the secret of its solution." Discuss this sentence.

**2.** In kinetic theory we assume that there are a large number of molecules in a gas. Real gases behave like an ideal gas at low densities. Are these statements contradictory? If not, what conclusion can you draw from them?

**3.** We have assumed that the walls of the container are elastic for molecular collisions. Actually, the walls may be inelastic. In practice this makes no difference as long as the walls are at the same temperature as the gas. Explain.

**4.** In large-scale inelastic collisions mechanical energy is lost through internal friction resulting in a rise in temperature owing to increased internal molecular agitation. Is there a loss of mechanical energy to heat in an inelastic collision between molecules?

**5.** What justification is there in neglecting the change in gravitational potential energy of molecules in a gas?

**6.** We have assumed that the force exerted by molecules on the wall of a container is steady in time. How is this justified?

**7.** The average velocity of the molecules in a gas must be zero if the gas as a whole and the container are not in translational motion. Explain how it can be that the average *speed* is not zero.

**8.** By considering quantities which must be conserved in an elastic collision, show that in general molecules of a gas cannot have the same speeds after a collision as they had before. Is it possible, then, for a gas to consist of molecules which all have the same speed?

**9.** Justify the fact that the pressure of a gas depends on the *square* of the speed of its particles by explaining the dependence of pressure on the collision frequency and the momentum transfer of the particles.

---

*See "On Teaching Quantum Phenomena," by Sir N. F. Mott in *Contemporary Physics*, August 1964.

10. The gas kinetic temperature in the upper atmosphere (see Eq. 23–5) is of the order of 1000° K. It is quite cold up there. Explain this paradox.

11. Why must the time allowed for diffusion separation be relatively short?

12. Suppose we want to obtain $U^{238}$ instead of $U^{235}$ as the end product of a diffusion process. Would we use the same process? If not, explain how the separation process would have to be modified.

13. Can you describe a centrifugal device for gaseous separation? Is a centrifuge better than a diffusion chamber for separation of gases?

14. Would you expect real molecules to be spherically symmetrical? If not, how would the potential energy function of Fig. 23–3 change?

15. Explain how we might keep a gas at a constant temperature during a thermodynamic process.

16. Explain why the temperature of a gas drops in an adiabatic expansion.

17. If hot air rises, why is it cooler at the top of a mountain than near sea level?

18. A sealed rubber balloon contains a very light gas. The balloon is released and it rises high into the atmosphere. Describe and explain the thermal and mechanical behavior of the balloon.

19. Explain why the specific heat at constant pressure is greater than the specific heat at constant volume.

20. It is more common to excite radiation from gaseous atoms by use of electrical discharge than by thermal methods. Why?

## PROBLEMS

1. At 0° C and 1.000-atm pressure the densities of air, oxygen, and nitrogen are, respectively, 1.293 kg/meter$^3$, 1.429 kg/meter$^3$, and 1.251 kg/meter$^3$. Calculate the percentage of nitrogen in the air from these data, assuming only these two gases to be present.

2. Suppose that, as happened historically, we are given Boyle's law

$$pV = \text{a constant} \quad (\text{constant } T)$$

and Charles' law

$$V/T = \text{a constant} \quad (\text{constant } p)$$

separately. Show how these two laws may be combined to yield

$$pV/T = \text{a constant}.$$

3. An air bubble of 20-cm$^3$ volume is at the bottom of a lake 40 meters deep where the temperature is 4° C. The bubble rises to the surface which is at a temperature of 20° C. Take the temperature to be the same as that of the surrounding water and find its volume just before it reaches the surface.

4. One mole of an ideal gas undergoes an isothermal expansion. Find the heat flow into the gas in terms of the initial and final volumes and the temperature.

5. Calculate the work done in compressing 1.00 mole of oxygen from a volume of 22.4 liters at 0° C and 1.00-atm pressure to 16.8 liters at the same temperature.

6. Oxygen gas having a volume of 1.0 liter at 40° C and a pressure of 76 cm-Hg expands until its volume is 1.5 liters and its pressure is 80 cm-Hg. Find the mass in moles of oxygen in the system and its final temperature.

7. An automobile tire has a volume of 1000 in.$^3$ and contains air at a gauge pressure of 24 lb/in.$^2$ when the temperature is 0° C. What is the gauge pressure of the air in the tires when its temperature rises to 27° C and its volume increases to 1020 in.$^3$?

**8.** A mercury-filled manometer with two unequal arms is sealed off with the same pressure $p_0$ in the two arms as in Fig. 23–7.   The cross-sectional area of the manometer arms is 1.0 cm$^2$.   With the temperature constant, an additional 10 cm$^3$ of mercury is admitted through the stopcock at the bottom; the level on the left increases 6.0 cm and that on the right increases 4.0 cm.   Find the pressure $p_0$.

50 cm

$p_0$

30 cm

Stopcock

**Fig. 23–7**

**9.** A thin tube, sealed at both ends, is 1.0 meter long.   It lies horizontally, the middle 10 cm containing mercury and the two equal ends containing air at standard atmospheric pressure.   If the tube is now turned to a vertical position, by what amount will the mercury be displaced?

**10.** The mass of the H$_2$ molecule is $3.32 \times 10^{-24}$ gm.   If $10^{23}$ hydrogen molecules per second strike 2.0 cm$^2$ of wall at an angle of 45° with the normal when moving with a speed of $10^5$ cm/sec, what pressure do they exert on the wall?

**11.** (a) Determine the average value of the kinetic energy of the molecules of an ideal gas at 0.0° C and at 100° C.   (b) What is the kinetic energy per mole of an ideal gas at these temperatures?

**12.** (a) Compute the root-mean-square speed of an argon atom at room temperature (20° C).   (b) At what temperature will the root-mean-square speed be half that value?  Twice that value?

**13.** (a) Compute the temperature at which the root-mean-square speed is equal to the speed of escape from the surface of the earth for hydrogen.   For oxygen.   (b) Do the same for the moon, assuming gravity on its surface to be 0.164$g$.   (c) The temperature high in the earth's upper atmosphere is about 1000° K.   Would you expect to find much hydrogen there?   Much oxygen?

**14.** At what temperature is the average translational kinetic energy of a molecule equal to the kinetic energy of an electron accelerated from rest through a potential difference of one volt (that is, an energy of 1.0 ev)?

**15.** Show how to find the root-mean-square speeds of helium and argon molecules at 40° C from that of oxygen molecules (460 meters/sec at 0.00° C).   The molecular weight of oxygen is 32 gm/mole, of argon 40, of helium 4.

**16.** Compute the number of molecules in a gas contained in a volume of 1.00 cm$^3$ at a pressure of $1.00 \times 10^{-3}$ atm and a temperature of 200° K.

**17.** If the water molecules in 1.0 gm of water were distributed uniformly over the surface of the earth, how many such molecules would there be in 1.0 cm$^2$ of the earth's surface?

**18.** Oxygen gas at 273° K and 1.00-atm pressure is confined to a cubical container 10 cm on a side.   (a) How long does it take a typical molecule to cross the container?

(b) Compare the change in gravitational potential energy of an oxygen molecule falling the height of the box with its mean kinetic energy.

**19.** (a) Consider an ideal gas at 273° K and 1.0-atm pressure. Imagine that the molecules are for the most part evenly spaced at the centers of identical cubes. Using Avogadro's number and taking the diameter of a molecule to be $3.0 \times 10^{-8}$ cm, find the length of an edge of such a cube and compare this length to the diameter of a molecule. (b) Now consider a mole of water having a volume of 18 cm³. Again imagine the molecules to be evenly spaced at the centers of identical cubes. Find the length of an edge of such a cube and compare this length to the diameter of a molecule.

**20.** At 300° K and 100 atm the density of a gas is $8.0 \times 10^{-2}$ gm/cm³. (a) Find $v_{\mathrm{rms}}$ for the gas molecules. (b) Find the molecular weight of the gas and identify it.

**21.** *Avogadro's law* states that under the same condition of temperature and pressure equal volumes of gas contain equal numbers of molecules. Derive this law from kinetic theory using Eq. 23-3 and the equipartition of energy assumption.

**22.** *Dalton's law* states that when mixtures of gases having no chemical interaction are present together in a vessel, the pressure exerted by each constituent at a given temperature is the same as it would exert if it alone filled the whole vessel, and that the total pressure is equal to the sum of the partial pressures of each gas. Derive this law from kinetic theory, using Eq. 23-3.

**23.** Plot and interpret physically (a) the variation of gas density with temperature for an isobaric (constant-pressure) process and (b) the variation of gas density with pressure for an isothermal process.

**24.** Consider a given mass of an ideal gas. Compare curves representing constant-pressure, constant-volume, and isothermal processes on (a) a $p$-$V$ diagram, (b) a $p$-$T$ diagram and (c) a $V$-$T$ diagram. (d) How do these curves depend on the mass of gas chosen?

**25.** The mass of a gas molecule can be computed from the specific heat at constant volume. Take $C_v = 0.75$ kcal/kg K° for argon and calculate (a) the mass of an argon atom and (b) the atomic weight of argon.

**26.** Take the mass of a helium atom to be $6.66 \times 10^{-27}$ kg. Compute the specific heat at constant volume for helium gas.

**27.** Calculate the mechanical equivalent of heat from the value of $R$ and the values of $C_v$ and $\gamma$ for oxygen from Table 23-2.

**28.** The following data are the result of accurate experimental measurements: 1.000 mole of a gas occupies a volume of $2.541 \times 10^{-2}$ meter³ at a pressure of $9.480 \times 10^4$ nt/meter² when its temperature is 290.0° K. The same mass of gas requires 125.0 cal to raise its temperature from 290.0 to 315.0° K while its volume is held constant. The ratio $(c_p/c_v)$ of its specific heats is 1.430. (a) Use these data to compute the mechanical equivalent of heat $J$. (b) Account for the fact that your value of $J$ differs from the accepted three-figure value—namely, 4.19 joules/cal.

**29.** One mole of oxygen is heated at a constant pressure starting at 0.00° C. How much heat energy must be added to the gas to double its volume?

**30.** Ten grams of oxygen are heated at constant atmospheric pressure from 27.0 to 127.0° C. How much heat is transferred to the oxygen? What fraction of the heat is used to raise the internal energy of the oxygen?

**31.** How would you explain the observed value of $C_v = 7.50$ cal/mole K° for gaseous $SO_2$ at 15.0° C and 1.00 atm?

**32.** Show that the speed of sound in a gas is independent of the pressure and density.

**33.** Show that the speed of sound in air increases about 2.0 ft/sec for each Celsius degree rise in temperature.

**34.** The speed of sound in different gases at the same temperature depends on the molecular weight of the gas. Show that $v_1/v_2 = \sqrt{M_2/M_1}$ (constant $T$) where $v_1$

is the speed of sound in the gas of molecular weight $M_1$ and $v_2$ is the speed of sound in the gas of molecular weight $M_2$.

**35.** Air at $0.00°$ C and $1.00$-atm pressure has a density of $1.291 \times 10^{-3}$ gm/cm³ and the speed of sound in air is 332 meters/sec at that temperature. Compute the ratio of specific heats of air.

**36.** (a) A monatomic ideal gas initially at $17°$ C is suddenly compressed to one-tenth its original volume. What is its temperature after compression? (b) Make the same calculation for a diatomic gas.

**37.** The atomic weight of iodine is 127. A standing wave in a tube filled with iodine gas at $400°$ K has nodes that are 6.77 cm apart when the frequency is 1000 vib/sec. Is iodine gas monatomic or diatomic?

**38.** A reversible heat engine carries 1.00 mole of an ideal monatomic gas around the cycle shown in Fig. 23–8. Process 1–2 takes place at constant volume, process 2–3 is adiabatic, and process 3–1 takes place at a constant pressure. (a) Compute the approximate numerical values for the heat $\Delta Q$, the change in internal energy $\Delta U$, and the work done $\Delta W$, for each of the three processes and for the cycle as a whole. (b) If the initial pressure at point 1 is 1.00 atm, find the pressure and the volume at points 2 and 3.

**Fig. 23–8**

**39.** A mass of gas occupies a volume of 4.0 liters at a pressure of 1.0 atm and a temperature of $300°$ K. It is compressed adiabatically to a volume of 1.0 liter. Determine (a) the final pressure and (b) the final temperature, assuming it to be an ideal gas for which $\gamma = 1.5$.

**40.** An ideal gas expands adiabatically from an initial temperature $T_1$ to a final temperature $T_2$. Prove that the work done by the gas is $C_v(T_1 - T_2)$.

**41.** (a) A liter of gas with $\gamma = 1.3$ is at $273°$ K and 1.0-atm pressure. It is suddenly compressed to half its original volume. Find its final pressure and temperature. (b) The gas is now cooled back to $0°$ C at constant pressure. What is its final volume?

**42.** (a) Show that the variation in pressure in the earth's atmosphere, assumed to be isothermal, is given by $p = p_0 e^{-Mgy/RT}$ where $M$ is the molecular weight of the gas. (See Example 1, Chapter 17.) (b) Show also that $n = n_0 e^{-Mgy/RT}$ where $n$ is the number of molecules per unit volume.

**43.** A hydrogen atom, in its lowest (ground) state and moving with 13-ev kinetic energy, collides head-on with another hydrogen atom which is *at rest* in its ground state. (a) Use the conservation laws of energy and momentum to show that this collision must be elastic. The first allowed excited state is about 10.2 ev above the ground state. (b) Show that the minimum initial kinetic energy that the incident atom needs to raise one of the atoms to the first excited state is *twice* the energy difference between ground state and first excited state.

# Kinetic Theory of Gases—II

## CHAPTER 24

### 24–1  Mean Free Path

Between successive collisions a molecule in a gas moves with constant speed along a straight line. The average distance between such successive collisions is called the *mean free path* (Fig. 24–1). If molecules were points, they would not collide at all and the mean free path would be infinite. Molecules, however, are not points and hence collisions occur. If they were so numerous that they completely filled the space available to them, leaving no room for translational motion, the mean free path would be zero. Thus the mean free path is related to the size of the molecules and to their number per unit volume.

Consider the molecules of a gas to be spheres of diameter $d$. The cross section for a collision is then $\pi d^2$. That is, a collision will take place when the centers of two molecules approach within a distance $d$ of one another. An equivalent description of collisions

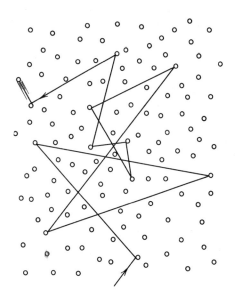

**Fig. 24–1**  A molecule traveling through a gas, colliding with other molecules in its path. Of course, all the other molecules are moving in a similar fashion.

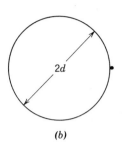

Fig. 24–2 (a) If a collision occurs when two molecules come within a distance $d$ of each other, the process can be treated equivalently (b) by thinking of one molecule as having an effective diameter $2d$ and the other as being a point mass.

(a)                    (b)

made by any one molecule is to regard that molecule as having a diameter $2d$ and all other molecules as point particles (see Fig. 24–2).

Imagine a typical molecule of equivalent diameter $2d$ moving with speed $v$ through a gas of equivalent point particles and let us assume, for the time being, that the molecule and the point particles exert no forces on each other. In time $t$ our molecule will sweep out a cylinder of cross-sectional area $\pi d^2$ and length $vt$. If $n$ is the number of molecules per unit volume the cylinder will contain $(\pi d^2 vt)\, n$ particles (see Fig. 24–3). Since our molecule and the point particles *do* exert forces on each other, this will be the number of collisions experienced by the molecule in time $t$. The cylinder of Fig. 24–3 will, in fact, be a broken one, changing direction with every collision.

The mean free path $\bar{l}$ is the average distance between successive collisions. Hence, $\bar{l}$ is the total distance $vt$ covered in time $t$ divided by the number of collisions that take place in this time, or

$$\bar{l} = \frac{vt}{\pi\, d^2 n v t} = \frac{1}{\pi n d^2}.$$

This equation is based on the picture of a molecule hitting stationary targets. Actually the molecule hits moving targets. The collision frequency is increased as a result (see below) and the mean free path is reduced to

$$\bar{l} = \frac{1}{\pi \sqrt{2}\, n d^2}. \qquad (24\text{--}1)$$

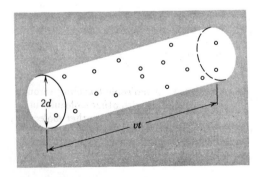

Fig. 24–3 A molecule of equivalent diameter $2d$ traveling with speed $v$ sweeps out a cylinder of base $\pi d^2$ and length $vt$ in a time $t$. It suffers a collision with every other molecule whose center lies within this cylinder.

When the target molecules are moving, the two $v$'s in the first equation above are not the same. The one in the numerator $(= \bar{v})$ is the mean molecular speed measured with respect to the container. The one in the denominator $(= \bar{v}_{rel})$ is the mean *relative* speed with respect to other molecules; it is this relative speed that determines the collision rate.

We can see qualitatively that $\bar{v}_{rel} > \bar{v}$. Thus two molecules of speed $v$ moving toward each other have a relative speed of $2v$ $(> v)$; two molecules with speed $v$ moving at right angles on a collision course have a relative speed of $\sqrt{2}\,v$ (also $> v$); two molecules moving with speed $v$ in the same direction have a relative speed of zero $(< v)$. Thus molecules arriving from *all of the forward hemisphere* and *part of the backward hemisphere* have $\bar{v}_{rel} > \bar{v}$. The molecules arriving from the rest of the backward hemisphere have $\bar{v}_{rel} < \bar{v}$ but, since their numbers are smaller, they do not determine the nature of the average over both hemispheres, which yields $\bar{v}_{rel} > \bar{v}$. A quantitative calculation, taking into account the actual speed distribution of the molecules, gives $\bar{v}_{rel} = \sqrt{2}\,\bar{v}$.

▶ **Example 1.** Let us calculate the magnitude of the mean free path and the collision frequency for air molecules at 0° C and 1-atm pressure.

We take $2 \times 10^{-8}$ cm as an effective molecular diameter $d$. For the conditions stated, the average speed of air molecules is about $1 \times 10^5$ cm/sec and there are about $3 \times 10^{19}$ molecules/cm³. The mean free path is then

$$\bar{l} = \frac{1}{\pi \sqrt{2}\,nd^2} = \frac{1}{\pi \sqrt{2}\,(3 \times 10^{19}/\text{cm}^3)(2 \times 10^{-8}\text{ cm})^2}$$

$$= 2 \times 10^{-5}\text{ cm}.$$

This is about a thousand molecular diameters.

The corresponding collision frequency is

$$\frac{v}{\bar{l}} = (1 \times 10^5\text{ cm/sec})/(2 \times 10^{-5}\text{ cm})$$

$$= 5 \times 10^9/\text{sec}.$$

Thus, on the average, *each molecule* makes five billion collisions per second!   ◀

In the earth's atmosphere the mean free path of air molecules at sea level (760 mm-Hg) is about $10^{-5}$ cm. At 100 km above the earth $(10^{-3}$ mm-Hg) the mean free path is 1 meter. At 300 km $(10^{-6}$ mm-Hg) it is 10 km or 6 miles, and yet there are about $10^8$ molecules/cm³ in this region. This emphasizes that molecules are indeed small. At great enough heights the mean free path concept fails because the upward-directed molecules follow ballistic paths and may escape from the atmosphere.

In the laboratory the mean free path concept is useful in situations such as that of Example 1. In even modest laboratory vacuums, however, it loses some of its meaning because nearly all the collisions are with the wall of the containing vessel rather than with other molecules. Consider a box 10 cm on edge containing air at $10^{-6}$ mm-Hg pressure. The mean free path (see above) is 6 miles, so that collisions between molecules are rare indeed. And yet this box contains about $10^{12}$ molecules!

Even in a finite "box," however, there are some conditions in which particles can travel great distances without striking the walls. In a typical proton synchrotron, used to accelerate protons to the billion-electron-volt range of energies, the protons are constrained by a magnetic field to move in a circular path and may travel *several hundred thousand miles* during the acceleration process. Mean free path considerations are important if the accelerating protons are to have essentially no collisions with residual air molecules. In this case the effective cross section of the proton is so much smaller than that of the air molecules that if we have a vacuum of about $10^{-6}$ mm-Hg, there is essentially no beam loss by proton scattering from gas molecules inside the vacuum chamber.

### 24–2  Distribution of Molecular Speeds

In Chapter 23 we discussed the root-mean-square speed of the molecules of a gas. However, the speeds of individual molecules vary over a wide range of magnitude; there is a characteristic distribution of molecular speeds for a given gas which depends, as we will see below, on the temperature. If all the molecules of a gas had the same speed $v$, this situation would not persist for very long because the molecular speeds would be changed by collisions. However, we do not expect many molecules to have speeds $\ll v_{rms}$ (that is, near zero) or $\gg v_{rms}$ because such extreme speeds would require an unlikely sequence of preferential collisions.

Clerk Maxwell first solved the problem of the most probable distribution of speeds in a large number of molecules of a gas. His molecular speed distribution law, for a sample of gas containing $N$ molecules, is*

$$N(v) = 4\pi N(m/2\pi kT)^{3/2}v^2 e^{-mv^2/2kt}. \qquad (24\text{--}2)$$

In this equation $N(v)\,dv$ is the number of molecules in the gas sample having speeds between $v$ and $v + dv$. $T$ is the absolute temperature, $k$ is Boltzmann's constant, and $m$ is the mass of a molecule. Note that for a given gas the speed distribution depends only on the temperature. We find $N$, the total number of molecules in the sample, by adding up (that is, by integrating) the number present in each differential speed interval from zero to infinity, or

$$N = \int_0^\infty N(v)\,dv. \qquad (24\text{--}3)$$

The unit of $N(v)$ is, say, molecules/(cm/sec). In Fig. 24–4 we plot the Maxwell distribution of speeds for molecules of oxygen at two different temperatures. The number of molecules having a speed between $v_1$ and $v_2$ equals the area under the curve between the vertical lines at $v_1$ and $v_2$. As Eq. 24–3 shows, the area under the speed distribution curve, which is the integral in that equation, is equal to the total number of molecules in the sample. At any temperature the number of

---

* A derivation of Eq. 24–2 appears in Supplementary Topic IV.

**Fig. 24–4**    The Maxwellian distribution of speeds of $10^6$ oxygen molecules at two different temperatures. The number of molecules within a certain range of speeds (say, 300 to 600 meters/sec) is the area under this section of the curve. The complete area under either curve is the total number of molecules (equals $10^6$); this area must be the same for each temperature if, as in this case, the curves refer to a given number of molecules.

molecules in a given speed interval* $\Delta v$ increases as the speed increases up to a maximum (the most probable speed $v_p$) and then decreases asymptotically toward zero. The distribution curve is not symmetrical about the most probable speed because the lowest speed must be zero, whereas there is no classical limit to the upper speed a molecule can attain. In this case the *average speed* $\bar{v}$ is somewhat larger than the most probable value. The root-mean-square value, $v_{rms}$, being the square root of the sum of the *squares* of the speeds, is still larger.

As the temperature increases, the root-mean-square speed $v_{rms}$ (and $\bar{v}$ and $v_p$ as well) increases, in accord with our microscopic interpretation of temperature. The range of typical speeds is now greater, so that the distribution broadens. Since the area under the distribution curve (which

---

* We cannot simply plot the "number of particles having speed $v$" against $v$, because there are a finite number of particles and an infinite number of possible speeds. Hence, the probability that a particle has a precisely stated speed, such as 279.343267 · · · meters/sec, is exactly zero. However, we can divide the range of speeds into intervals and the probability that a particle has a speed somewhere in a given interval (such as 279 meters/sec to 280 meters/sec) has a definite nonzero value.

is the total number of molecules in the sample) remains the same, the distribution must also flatten as the temperature rises. Hence the number of molecules which have speeds greater than some given speed increases as the temperature increases (see Fig. 24–4). This explains many phenomena, such as the increase in the rates of chemical reactions with rising temperature.

The distribution of speeds of molecules in a liquid also resembles the curves of Fig. 24–4. This explains why some molecules in a liquid (the fast ones) can escape through the surface (evaporate) at temperatures well below the normal boiling point. Only these molecules can overcome the attraction of the molecules in the surface and escape by evaporation. The average kinetic energy of the remaining molecules drops correspondingly, leaving the liquid at a lower temperature. This explains why evaporation is a cooling process.

From Eq. 24–2 we see that the distribution of molecular speeds depends on the mass of the molecule as well as on the temperature. The smaller the mass, the larger the proportion of high-speed molecules at any given temperature. Hence hydrogen is more likely to escape from the atmosphere at high altitudes than oxygen or nitrogen. The moon may have a tenuous atmosphere. For the molecules in this atmosphere not to have a great probability of escaping from the weak gravitational pull of the moon, even at the low temperatures there, we would expect them to be molecules or atoms of the heavier elements. Evidence points to the heavy inert gases, such as krypton and xenon, which were produced largely by radioactive decay early in the moon's history. The atmospheric pressure on the moon is believed to be about $10^{-13}$ of the earth's atmospheric pressure.

▶ **Example 2.** The speeds of ten particles in meters/sec are 0, 1.0, 2.0, 3.0, 3.0, 3.0, 4.0, 4.0, 5.0, and 6.0. Find (a) the average speed, (b) the root-mean-square speed, and (c) the most probable speed of these particles.

(a) The average speed is

$$\bar{v} = \frac{0 + 1.0 + 2.0 + 3.0 + 3.0 + 3.0 + 4.0 + 4.0 + 5.0 + 6.0}{10} = 3.1 \text{ meters/sec.}$$

(b) The mean-square speed is

$$\bar{v^2} = \frac{\begin{array}{c} 0 + (1.0)^2 + (2.0)^2 + (3.0)^2 + (3.0)^2 \\ + (3.0)^2 + (4.0)^2 + (4.0)^2 + (5.0)^2 + (6.0)^2 \end{array}}{10}$$

$$= 12.5 \text{ meters}^2/\text{sec}^2$$

and the root-mean-square speed is

$$v_{\text{rms}} = \sqrt{12.5 \text{ meters}^2/\text{sec}^2} = 3.5 \text{ meters/sec.}$$

(c) Of the ten particles three have speeds of 3.0 meters/sec, two have speeds of 4.0 meters/sec, and the other five each have a different speed. Hence, the most probable speed of a particle $v_p$ is

$$v_p = 3.0 \text{ meters/sec.}$$

**Example 3.**   Use Eq. 24–2 to determine the average speed $\bar{v}$, the root-mean-square speed $v_{\mathrm{rms}}$, and the most probable speed $v_p$ of the molecules in a gas in terms of the gas parameters.

The quantity $N(v) \, dv$ is the number of particles in the sample having a speed between $v$ and $v + dv$, $N(v)$ being given by Eq. 24–2.   We find the average speed $\bar{v}$ in the usual way: we multiply the number of particles in each speed interval by a speed $v$ characteristic of that interval; we sum these products over all speed intervals and we divide by the total number of particles.   Replacing the summation by an integration, we obtain

$$\bar{v} = \frac{\int_0^\infty N(v) v \, dv}{N}$$

Substituting Eq. 24–2 for $N(v)$ and integrating* we obtain

$$\bar{v} = \sqrt{\frac{8}{\pi} \frac{kT}{m}} = 1.59 \sqrt{\frac{kT}{m}} \quad \text{(average speed)}.$$

The mean-square speed is given by

$$\overline{v^2} = \frac{\int_0^\infty N(v) v^2 \, dv}{N}$$

which yields

$$v_{\mathrm{rms}} = \sqrt{\overline{v^2}} = \sqrt{\frac{3kT}{m}} = 1.73 \sqrt{\frac{kT}{m}} \quad \text{(root-mean-square speed)}.$$

The most probable speed $v_p$ is the speed at which $N(v)$ has its maximum value. It is given by requiring that

$$\frac{dN(v)}{dv} = 0.$$

By substituting Eq. 24–2 for $N(v)$ we obtain, as the student should show,

$$\bar{v}_p = \sqrt{\frac{2kT}{m}} = 1.41 \sqrt{\frac{kT}{m}} \quad \text{(most probable speed)}.$$

In Fig. 24–4 we show $v_p$, $\bar{v}$, and $v_{\mathrm{rms}}$ at 0° C for a molecular speed distribution in oxygen.   ◄

### 24–3   Experimental Confirmation of the Maxwellian Distribution

Maxwell derived his distribution law for molecular speeds (Eq. 24–2) in 1859. At that early date it was not possible to check this law by direct measurement and, indeed, it was not until 1920 that Stern made the first serious attempt to do so. Techniques improved rapidly in the hands of various workers but it was not until 1955 that a high-precision experimental verification of the law (for gas molecules) was provided, by Miller and Kusch.

Their apparatus is shown in Fig. 24–5.   The walls of oven $O$ were heated, in one

---

* Let $\lambda = m/2kT$.   From tables of integrals,

$$\int_0^\infty v^2 e^{-\lambda v^2} \, dv = \frac{1}{4} \sqrt{\frac{\pi}{\lambda^3}}; \quad \int_0^\infty v^3 e^{-\lambda v^2} \, dv = \frac{1}{2\lambda^2}; \quad \int_0^\infty v^4 e^{-\lambda v^2} \, dv = \frac{3}{8} \sqrt{\frac{\pi}{\lambda^5}}.$$

set of experiments, to a uniform temperature of 870 ± 4° K, some thallium having been placed in the oven.  At this temperature thallium vapor, at a pressure of $3.2 \times 10^{-3}$ mm-Hg, fills the oven.  Some molecules of thallium vapor escape from slit $S$ into the highly evacuated space outside the oven, falling on the rotating cylinder $R$.  This cylinder, of length $l$, has a number of helical grooves cut into it, only one of them being shown in Fig. 24–5.  For a given angular speed $\omega$ of the cylinder, only molecules of a sharply defined speed $v$ can pass along the grooves without striking the walls.  The speed $v$ can be found from:

$$\text{time of travel along the groove} = \frac{l}{v} = \frac{\phi}{\omega},$$

or $$v = l\omega/\phi \qquad (24\text{–}4)$$

in which $\phi$ (see Fig. 24–5) is the angular displacement between the entrance and the exit of a helical groove.  Thus the rotating cylinder is a *velocity selector*, the speed selected being proportional to the (controllable) angular speed $\omega$, as Eq. 24–4 shows.  One observes the beam intensity recorded by detector $D$ as a function of the selected speed $v$.  Figure 24–6 shows the remarkable agreement between theory (the solid line) and experiment (the triangles and circles) for thallium vapor.

The distribution of speeds in the *beam* (as distinguished from the distribution of speeds in the *oven*) is not proportional to $v^2 e^{-mv^2/2kt}$, as in Eq. 24–2, but to $v^3 e^{-mv^2/2kT}$.  Consider a group of molecules in the oven whose speeds lie within a certain small range $v_1$ to $v_1 + \Delta v$, where $v_1$ is less than the most probable speed $v_p$.  We can always find another equal speed interval $\Delta v$, extending from $v_2$ to $v_2 + \Delta v$, where $v_2$, which will be greater than $v_p$, is chosen so that the two speed intervals contain the same number of molecules. However, more molecules in the latter interval than in the former will escape from slit $S$ to form the beam, because molecules in the latter interval "bombard" the slit with a greater frequency, by precisely the factor $v_2/v_1$. Thus, other things being equal, fast molecules are favored in escaping from the oven, just in proportion to their speeds, and the molecules in the beam have a "$v^3$" rather than a "$v^2$" distribution. This effect is allowed for in computing the theoretical curve of Fig. 24–6.

Rainwater and Havens (1946) also provided a convincing experimental check of the Maxwell speed distribution law by using a "gas" of neutrons. The neutrons were produced (as fast neutrons) in continuous series of short bursts in a cyclotron and allowed to fall on a block of paraffin. By repeated collisions with the nuclei of the block, the neutrons rapidly slowed down and came into thermal equilibrium with the block, behaving like a "neutron gas" in a container. The container, however, is a leaky one because neutrons diffuse out through the walls of the block and move across the laboratory. It is possible, by electronic means, to measure the time between the production of the neutrons in the cyclotron and their arrival at a distant detector after escaping from the paraffin block. Thus one can measure the speed distribution in a collimated beam of escaping neutrons and can compare it to the prediction of Maxwell; the agreement of theory and experiment is excellent.

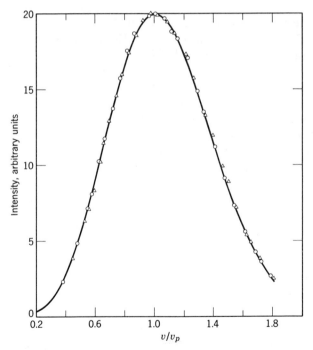

**Fig. 24–6**   The solid line shows Maxwell's molecular speed distribution. The circles (○) are experimental points for thallium atoms emerging from an oven at 870° K; the triangles (△) correspond to 944° K. The horizontal scale is a plot of $v/v_p$ where $v_p$ is the most probable speed. When speeds are plotted in this way the distributions for different temperatures should fall on the same curve. At 870° K, $v_p = 376$ meters/sec and at 944° K, it is 395 meters/sec. From Miller and Kusch, *Physical Review*, 99, 1314 (1955).

Although the Maxwell speed distribution for gases agrees remarkably well with observations under ordinary conditions, it fails at high densities, where the basic assumptions of the classical kinetic theory fail. In these regions we must use speed distributions founded on the principles of quantum physics, the Fermi-Dirac and the Bose-Einstein distributions. These quantum distributions agree closely with the Maxwell distribution in the classical region (low density) and agree with experiment where the classical distribution fails. Hence there are limits to the applicability of the Maxwell distribution, as in fact there are to any theory.

### 24–4 Brownian Motion

The prominence given to atomic and molecular theory during the last quarter of the nineteenth century was deplored by many able scientists. In spite of the many quantitative agreements between kinetic theory and the behavior of gases, no proof of the separate existence of atoms and molecules had been obtained, nor had any observation been made that could really demonstrate the continuous motions of the molecules. Ernst Mach (1838–1916) saw no point to "thinking of the world as a mosaic, since we cannot examine its individual pieces of stone." It had been established rather early in the development of kinetic theory that an atom should be about $10^{-7}$ cm or $10^{-8}$ cm in diameter. No one actually expected to see an atom or detect the effect of a single atom.

The leader of the opposition to the atomic theory was Wilhelm Ostwald. He was a champion of the principle of the conservation of energy and regarded energy as the ultimate reality. Ostwald argued that with a thermodynamical treatment of a process we know all that is essential about the process and that further mechanical assumptions about the mechanism of the reactions are unproved hypotheses. He abandoned the atomic and molecular theories and fought to free science "from hypothetical conception which lead to no immediate experimentally verifiable conclusions." Other prominent physicists were reluctant to admit the atom as an established scientific fact.

Ludwig Boltzmann felt compelled to protest this attitude in an article in 1897, stressing the indispensability of atomism in natural science. The progress of science is often guided by the analogies of nature's processes which occur in the minds of investigators. Kinetic theory was such a mechanical analogy. As with most analogies it suggests experiments to test the validity of our mental pictures and leads to further investigations and clearer knowledge.

As is always true in such controversies in science, the decision rests with experiment. The earliest and most direct experimental evidence for the reality of atoms was the proof of the atomic kinetic theory provided by the quantitative studies of Brownian motion. These observations convinced both Mach and Ostwald of the validity of the kinetic theory and the atomic description of matter on which it rests. The atomic theory gained unquestioned acceptance in later years when a wide variety of experiments all led to the same values of the fundamental atomic constants.

Brownian motion is named after the English botanist Robert Brown who discovered in 1827 that pollen suspended in water shows a continuous random motion when viewed under a microscope. At first these motions were considered a form of life, but it was soon found that small inorganic particles behave similarly. There was no quantitative explanation of this phenomenon until the development of kinetic theory. Then, in 1905, Albert Einstein developed a theory of Brownian motion.* In his *Autobiographical Notes*, Einstein writes, "My major aim in this was to find facts which would guarantee as much as possible the existence of atoms of definite size. In the midst of this I discovered that, according to atomistic theory, there would have to be a movement of suspended microscopic particles open to observation, without knowing that observations concerning the Brownian motion were already long familiar."

The basic assumption made by Einstein was that particles suspended in a liquid or a gas share in the thermal motions of the medium and that on the average the translational kinetic energy of each particle is $\frac{3}{2} kT$, in accordance with the principle of equipartition of energy. In this view the Brownian motions result from impacts by molecules of the fluid, and the suspended particles acquire the same mean kinetic energy as the molecules of the fluid.

The suspended particles are extremely large compared to the molecules of the fluid and are being continually bombarded on all sides by them. If the particles are sufficiently large and the number of molecules is sufficiently great, equal numbers of molecules strike the particles on all sides at each instant. For smaller particles and fewer molecules the number of molecules striking various sides of the particle at any instant, being merely a matter of chance, may not be equal; that is, fluctuations occur. Hence the particle at each instant suffers an unbalanced force causing it to move this way or that. The particles therefore act just like very large molecules in the fluid, and their motions should be qualitatively the same as the motions of the fluid molecules. If Avogadro's number were infinite there would be no statistical unbalance (fluctuations) and no Brownian motion. If Avogadro's number were very small, the Brownian motion would be very large. Hence we should be able to deduce the value of Avogadro's number from observations of the Brownian motion. Deeply ingrained in this picture is the idea of molecular motion and the smallness of molecules. The Brownian motion therefore offers a striking experimental test of the kinetic theory hypotheses.

The suspended particles are under the influence of gravity and would settle to the bottom of the fluid were it not for the molecular bombardment opposing this tendency. Since the suspended particles behave like gas molecules we are not surprised to learn that, as for molecules in the atmosphere, their density drops off exponentially with respect to height in the

---

* Einstein's theory appeared as an article in the same issue of the *Annalen der Physik* which contained his famous paper on the theory of relativity and also his paper on the theory of the photoelectric effect. It was for his work on the photoelectric effect that he won the Nobel prize in 1921.

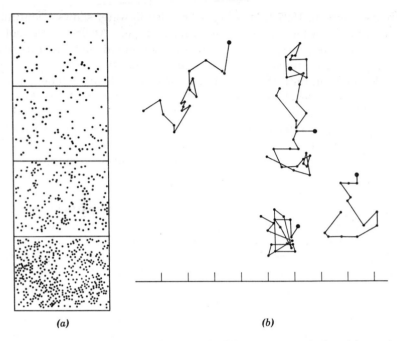

*(a)*                                        *(b)*

**Fig. 24–7**   (*a*) A gum resin suspension contained in a glass vessel viewed in a micro-scope by Perrin in 1909.   At first the distribution of particles was uniform, but in time they settled to the distribution shown.   The particles have a diameter of $0.6 \times 10^{-3}$ cm and the horizontal lines are $10 \times 10^{-3}$ cm apart.   (*b*) Sketch by V. Henri in 1908 from his cinematographic study of Brownian movement.   Henri used a microscope with a motion-picture camera which ran 20 frames/sec, each exposure being $\frac{1}{320}$ sec.   The zigzag lines show the position of five rubber particles as recorded by successive frames. The lines do not represent the actual paths of the particles for between exposures the particles may have traveled a similar erratic path.   The scale at the bottom is divided into microns ($10^{-4}$ cm).

fluid; they from a "miniature atmosphere"; see Example 1, Chapter 17; Problem 42, Chapter 23; and Problem 15, this chapter.   Jean Perrin, a French physical chemist, confirmed this prediction in 1908 by determining the numbers of small particles of gum resin suspended at different heights in a liquid drop (Fig. 24–7, left).   From his data he deduced a value of Avogadro's number $N_0 = 6 \times 10^{23}$ particles/mole.   Perrin also made measurements of the displacements of Brownian particles during many equal time intervals and found that they have the statistical distribution required by kinetic theory and the root-mean-square displacement pre-dicted by Einstein (Fig. 24–7, right).

Among the many subsequent experiments was that of Kappler, in 1931, who observed the Brownian motion of a rather gross object, a small mirror (area 0.7 mm²), mounted on a fine torsion fiber with light reflected from the mirror to a moving photographic film.   The mirror is mounted in a chamber with gas at low pressure ($10^{-2}$ mm-Hg); the record on the moving film yields the function $\theta(t)$

(angular displacement as a function of time). This shows clearly the rotational Brownian motion of the mirror which consists of a series of angular displacements produced by unbalanced impacts from the molecules. As the gas pressure is lowered, there is a gradual decrease in the motion. From the photographic record we can find the angular displacement $\theta$ and the angular velocity $\omega$. The equipartition of energy principle requires that

$$\tfrac{1}{2}I\overline{\omega^2} = \tfrac{1}{2}\kappa\overline{\theta^2} = \tfrac{1}{2}kT,$$

for $\tfrac{1}{2}I\overline{\omega^2}$ is the average rotational kinetic energy of the system and $\tfrac{1}{2}\kappa\overline{\theta^2}$ is the average potential energy of the system. Here $I$ is the rotational inertia of the system and $\kappa$ the torsion constant of the fiber. From his observations Kappler could calculate Boltzmann's constant $k$ and from the relation $N_0 = R/k$ he could obtain Avogadro's number. His values were $k = 1.36 \times 10^{-23}$ joule/molecule K° $\pm 3\%$ (the accepted value today of $1.380 \times 10^{-23}$ joule/molecule K° being within the limits of error) and $N_0 = 6.1 \times 10^{23}$ particles/mole.

## 24–5   The van der Waals Equation of State

In the preceding chapter we discussed the behavior of an ideal gas. On the macroscopic scale its fundamental relationship is the equation of state

$$pV = \mu RT.$$

From this equation and the principles of thermodynamics we can show that the internal energy $U$ of a gas depends only on the temperature. Real gases obey these relations fairly well at low densities, but their behavior may become markedly different as the density increases. We cannot neglect these deviations from ideal behavior in accurate scientific work. For example, to establish the Kelvin thermodynamic scale in the laboratory we must know how to make the necessary corrections to the scale of a constant-volume gas thermometer. We must therefore know the behavior of real gases rather accurately. Even more important, perhaps, is the fact that the behavior of real gases gives us information on the nature of intermolecular forces and the structure of molecules.

Kinetic theory provides the microscopic description of the behavior of an ideal gas. We have already suggested how the assumptions of kinetic theory could become invalid if applied to a real gas. Under some conditions we may not be justified in neglecting the facts that the molecules occupy a fraction of the volume available to the gas and that the range of molecular forces is greater than the size of the molecule. At high densities we cannot ignore these effects.

J. D. van der Waals (1837–1923) deduced a modified equation of state which takes these factors into account in a simple way. Let us imagine the molecules to be hard spheres of diameter $d$. The diameter of such a sphere would correspond to the distance between the centers of molecules at which strong collision forces come into play. During its motion the center of a molecule cannot approach within a distance $d/2$ from a wall or a distance $d$ from the center of another molecule. Hence the actual volume available to a molecule is smaller than the volume of the containing vessel. Just how much smaller depends on how many molecules there are. Let us represent the volume per mole, $V/\mu$, by $v$. Then the "free volume" per mole would be less than this by the "covolume" $b$. Hence we modify the equation of state from the ideal relation $pv = RT$ to

$$p(v - b) = RT$$

to allow for this. Because of the reduced volume, the number of impacts on the wall increases, thereby increasing the pressure; this relationship was first derived by Clausius.

We can also allow for the effect of attractive forces between molecules in a simple way. Imagine a plane passed through a gas and consider, at any instant, the intermolecular forces which act across it. Each molecule on the left, say, will attract and be attracted by some small number $n$ of those on the right. Now compare this situation with another similar in every way except that the number of molecules per unit volume is doubled. Here any particular molecule on the left will interact on the average with $2n$ of those on the right, for the range of the molecular force is the same, and twice as many molecules now fall into this range. Since there also are twice as many molecules on the left as before which attract in this way, it is clear that the number of attractive pairs across the plane has increased fourfold. Therefore, the effect of these forces varies as the *square* of the number of particles per unit volume or inversely as the square of the volume per mole, that is, as $(1/v)^2$. Because of these intermolecular force bonds, the gas should, for a given external pressure, occupy a volume less than the volume it would occupy as an ideal gas, in which there are no such attractive forces. Or, equivalently, the gas acts as though it is subject to a pressure in excess of the externally applied pressure. This excess pressure is proportional to $(1/v)^2$, or equal to $a/v^2$ where $a$ is a constant. Hence, we obtain the *van der Waals equation of state* of a gas,

$$\left(p + \frac{a}{v^2}\right)(v - b) = RT. \tag{24-5}$$

The values of $a$ and $b$ are to be found from experiment, and in this respect the equation is empirical. We must realize that these corrections to the ideal gas equation of state are of the simplest kind, and that failure of the van der Waals equation in any particular case is evidence that our assumptions are oversimplified for that case. No one simple formula is known which applies to all gases under all conditions.

We have seen that real gases do not follow the ideal gas law exactly. Our discussion suggests also that for real gases the internal energy $U$ depends on the volume as well as on the temperature. For if there are (long range) attractive forces between molecules, the potential energy increases as the average distance between molecules increases. Hence, we would expect the internal energy of most real gases to increase slightly with the volume at ordinary temperatures, and this is found to be the case. Of course, collisions can be regarded as arising from repulsive forces. If the molecules move rapidly so as to make many collisions, the potential energy

**Fig. 24–8** (a) Isotherms for an ideal gas. (b) Isotherms for a van der Waals gas. We have assumed $a = 3.59$ li$^2$atm/mole$^2$ and $b = 0.0427$ li/mole in Eq. 24.4. These values give the best fit of this equation to $p$-$V$-$T$ data for the real gas $CO_2$. $T_{cr}(= 304°$ K) is the critical temperature.

of the (short range) repulsive forces may be more important than that of the attractive forces and the internal energy could decrease as the volume increases. This is true for hydrogen and helium at ordinary temperatures. In either case, however, the internal energy $U$ is not a function of temperature alone but depends also on the volume. The dependence of the internal energy of a gas on the volume can be deduced readily from the observed results of the free expansion experiment, discussed in Chapter 22.

▶ **Example 4.** On a pressure-volume diagram compare the behavior of an ideal gas at constant temperature to that of a van der Waals gas.

In Fig. 24–8a we draw the isotherms (curves of constant $T$) according to the law $pv = RT$. Figure 24–8b shows the isotherms according to the law

$$(p + a/v^2)(v - b) = RT.$$

The ideal gas isotherms are each one branch of a rectangular hyperbola, $pv =$ constant. For the van der Waals gas the pressure varies with volume as

$$p = \frac{RT}{(v - b)} - \frac{a}{v^2}. \tag{24–6}$$

As the volume per mole $v$ decreases from large values, the pressure rises, but the $a/v^2$ term, which diminishes the pressure, climbs rapidly so that for sufficiently low $T$ the pressure passes through a maximum at $A$. As $v$ is further decreased, the $RT/(v - b)$ term climbs more rapidly so that the pressure goes through a minimum at $B$ and then rises rapidly without bound as $v$ tends to the value $b$. At neighboring higher temperatures, the maxima and minima are less pronounced and are closer to the inflection point that lies between them. At the so-called critical temperature $(T = T_{cr})$, they coincide in a horizontal inflection point called the critical point. For temperatures sufficiently higher than the critical temperature $T_{cr}$ the van der Waals isotherms have no inflection point and approach the rectangular-hyperbola behavior of the ideal-gas isotherms. For carbon dioxide the critical temperature is 304° K and the pressure at the critical point is 72.9 atm.

We can obtain the pressure $p_{cr}$, the molar volume $v_{cr}$, and the temperature $T_{cr}$ of the critical point quite generally from the conditions that the tangent to the isotherm is horizontal, $dp/dv = 0$ when $T$ = constant, and that the point is an inflection point, $d^2p/dv^2 = 0$ when $T$ = constant. We obtain

$$\frac{dp}{dv} = -\frac{RT}{(v-b)^2} + \frac{2a}{v^3} = 0 \quad (T = \text{constant})$$

and

$$\frac{d^2p}{dv^2} = \frac{2RT}{(v-b)^3} - \frac{6a}{v^4} = 0 \quad (T = \text{constant.})$$

This gives us

$$v_{cr} = 3b$$

and

$$T_{cr} = \frac{8a}{27bR}$$

Putting these in Eq. 24–6, we obtain

$$p_{cr} = \frac{a}{27b^2}.$$

The isotherms suggest the actual experimental behavior of liquids and gases. The maxima and minima of the isotherms below the critical temperature are not usually observed experimentally. At some point $x$ the gas begins to condense. As the volume is decreased, the pressure remains constant (dotted line) until at $y$ all the gas has been transformed into liquid. Beyond $y$, as we decrease the volume, we are compressing a liquid, with the consequent sharp rise in pressure needed to make even small volume changes. Actually the portions $xA$ and $By$ of the isotherms can be obtained experimentally by using very pure gases and liquids. We call these supersaturated vapors and supercooled liquids, and they are in metastable states. The portion $AB$ cannot be reproduced experimentally and is unstable.

The constants $a$ and $b$ in van der Waals equation can be calculated from the experimental values of the critical quantities. The term $a/v^2$ is called an *internal pressure*. Some values for air are of interest. For air at 0° C and external pressure $p$ of 1.00 atm, the internal pressure is 0.0028 atm; at 0°C and external pressure $p$ of 100 atm, the internal pressure is 26 atm. For air at $-75°$ C the corresponding values of the internal pressure are 0.0056 atm and 84.5 atm. When a gas expands under pressure and does work against outside compressing forces, it must also do work against these internal forces. For air at $-75°$ C and 100 atm, the work done against internal forces is nearly as great as that done against external forces. There is an important distinction between internal and external work, however. In the case of external work, energy is transferred from the body to an outside body; in the case of internal work, there is merely a transfer from one kind of energy to another within the body, as from potential to kinetic. The constant $b$ varies from gas to gas, but is usually of the order of 30 cm$^3$/mole. Hence the covolume is about 0.15% of the free volume available to a gas at standard conditions.

Although the van der Waals formula is a good qualitative guide, the quantitative experimental data cannot be matched everywhere with constant values for $a$ and $b$. The reason is that the model on which the formula is based is still an oversimplification. Instead of assuming that the molecules always have a well-defined diameter, for example, we must use the actual intermolecular force (Fig. 23–3). In this way a more accurate correction to the ideal gas law can be made. Van der Waals knew this would be necessary for accurate quantitative work.

## QUESTIONS

**1.** Consider the case in which the mean free path is greater than the longest straight line in a vessel. Is this a perfect vacuum for a molecule in this vessel?

**2.** Give a qualitative explanation of the connection between the mean free path of ammonia molecules in air and the time it takes to smell the ammonia when a bottle is opened across the room.

**3.** The two opposite walls of a container of gas are kept at different temperatures. Describe the mechanism of heat conduction through the gas.

**4.** A gas can transmit only those sound waves whose wavelength is long compared with the mean free path. Can you explain this? Where might this limitation arise?

**5.** If molecules are not spherical, what meaning can we give to $d$ in Eq. 24–1 for the mean free path? In which gases would the molecules act the most nearly as rigid spheres?

**6.** Suppose we dispense with the hypothesis of elastic collisions in kinetic theory and consider the molecules as centers of force acting at a distance. Does the concept of mean free path have any meaning under these circumstances?

**7.** Since the actual force between molecules depends on the distance between them, forces can cause deflections even when molecules are far from "contact" with one another. Furthermore, the deflection caused should depend on how long a time these forces act and hence on the relative speed of the molecules. (a) Would you then expect the measured mean free path to depend on temperature, even though the density remains constant? (b) If so, would you expect $l$ to increase or decrease with temperature? (c) How does this dependence enter into Eq. 24–1?

**8.** Justify qualitatively the statement that, in a mixture of molecules of different kinds in complete equilibrium, each kind of molecule has the same Maxwellian distribution in speed that it would have if the other kinds were not present.

**9.** The Maxwellian distribution of speeds among molecules in a gas is shown in Fig. 24–4. How would you expect the Maxwellian distribution of *velocities* to look? What would the average velocity be?

**10.** The fraction of molecules within a given range $\Delta v$ of the root-mean-square speed decreases as the temperature of a gas rises. Explain why.

**11.** (a) Do half the molecules in a gas in thermal equilibrium have speeds greater than $v_p$? Than $\bar{v}$? Than $v_{rms}$?

(b) Which speed, $v_p$, $\bar{v}$, or $v_{rms}$, corresponds to a molecule having average kinetic energy?

**12.** The slit system in Fig. 24–5 selects only those molecules moving in the $+x$-direction. Does this destroy the validity of the experiment as a measure of the distribution of speeds of molecules moving in all directions?

**13.** Why did Rainwater and Havens, in their investigation of the speed distribution of neutrons (page 607), select paraffin as a material to bring fast neutrons rather quickly into thermal equilibrium?

**14.** List examples of the Brownian motion in physical phenomena.

**15.** We have defined $n$ to be the number of molecules per unit volume in a gas. If we define $n$ for a very small volume in a gas, say one equal to ten times the volume of an atom, then $n$ fluctuates with time through the range of values zero to some maximum value. How then can we justify a statement that $n$ has a definite value at every point in the gas?

**16.** Show that as the volume per mole of a gas increases, the van der Waals equation tends to the equation of state of an ideal gas.

**17.** The covolume $b$ in van der Waals equation is often taken to be four times the actual volume of the gas molecules themselves. What factors would have to be taken into account to obtain such a result?

**18.** Keeping in mind that internal energy of a body consists of kinetic energy and potential energy of its particles how would you distinguish between the internal energy of a body and its temperature?

## PROBLEMS

**1.** The mean free path of nitrogen molecules at $0°$ C and 1 atm is $0.80 \times 10^{-5}$ cm. At this temperature and pressure there are $2.7 \times 10^{19}$ molecules/cm$^3$. What is the molecular diameter?

**2.** The best vacuum attained so far in the laboratory is $10^{-10}$ mm-Hg. How many molecules of gas remain per cubic centimeter at $20°$ C in this "vacuum"?

**3.** In the cosmotron at the Brookhaven National Laboratory the protons travel around a circular path of diameter 75 ft in a chamber of $10^{-6}$ mm-Hg pressure.
(a) Estimate the number of gas molecules per cubic centimeter at this pressure.
(b) What is the mean free path of the gas molecules under these conditions if the molecular diameter is $2.0 \times 10^{-8}$ cm?

**4.** At what frequency would the wavelength of sound be of the order of the mean free path in oxygen at 1-atm pressure and $0°$ C? Take the diameter of the oxygen molecule to be $3.00 \times 10^{-8}$ cm.

**5.** For a gas in which all molecules travel with the same speed $v$, show that $\bar{v}_{rel} = \frac{4}{3}v$ rather than $\sqrt{2}\,\bar{v}$ (which is the result obtained when we consider the actual distribution of molecular speeds). See p. 601.

**6.** At 2500 km above the earth's surface the density is about one molecule/cm$^3$. What is the mean free path and what is its significance under these conditions?

**7.** The mean free path of a molecule is $\bar{l}$. Prove that the probability that a molecule will go at least a distance $x$ before having its next collision is $e^{-x/\bar{l}}$.

**8.** The mean free path $\bar{l}$ of the molecules of a gas may be determined from measurements (e.g., from measurement of the viscosity of the gas). At $20°$ C and 75 cm-Hg pressure such measurements yield values of $\bar{l}_A$ (argon) $= 9.9 \times 10^{-6}$ cm and $\bar{l}_{N_2}$ (nitrogen) $= 27.5 \times 10^{-6}$ cm. (a) Find the ratio of the effective cross-section diameters of argon and nitrogen. (b) What would the value be of the mean free path of argon at $20°$ C and 15 cm-Hg? (c) What would the value be of the mean free path of argon at $-40°$ C and 75 cm-Hg?

**9.** A molecule of hydrogen (diameter $10^{-8}$ cm) escapes from a furnace ($T = 4000°$ K) with the root-mean-square speed into a chamber containing atoms of cold argon (diameter $3 \times 10^{-8}$ cm) at a density of $4 \times 10^{19}$ atoms/cm$^3$. (a) What is the speed of the hydrogen molecule? (b) On a collision between the molecule and an argon atom, what is the closest distance between their centers, considering each as spherical? (c) What is the initial number of collisions per unit time experienced by the hydrogen molecule?

10. You are given the following group of particles ($N_i$ represents the number of particles which have a speed $v_i$).

| $N_i$ | $v_i$(cm/sec) |
| --- | --- |
| 2 | 1.00 |
| 4 | 2.00 |
| 6 | 3.00 |
| 8 | 4.00 |
| 2 | 5.00 |

(a) Compute the average speed $\bar{v}$. (b) Compute the root-mean-square speed $v_{\text{rms}}$ (c) Among the five speeds shown, which is the most probable speed $v_p$ for the entire group?

11. Consider the distribution of speeds shown in Fig. 24–9. (a) List $v_{\text{rms}}$, $\bar{v}$, and $v_p$ in the order of increasing speed. (b) How does this compare with the Maxwellian distribution?

**Fig. 24–9**

12. In the apparatus of Miller and Kusch (Fig. 24–5) the length $l$ of the rotating cylinder is 20.4 cm and the angle $\phi$ is $(2\pi/74.7)$ radians. What rotational speed corresponds to a selected speed $v$ of 200 meters/sec?

13. Calculate the root-mean-square speed of smoke particles of mass $5.0 \times 10^{-14}$ gm in air at 0° C and 1-atm pressure.

14. Particles of mass $6.2 \times 10^{-14}$ gm are suspended in a liquid at 27° C and are observed to have a root-mean-square speed of 1.4 cm/sec. Calculate Avogadro's number from the equipartition theorem and these data.

15. Colloidal particles in solution are buoyed up by the liquid in which they are suspended. Let $\rho'$ be the density of liquid and $\rho$ the density of the particles. If $V$ is the volume of a particle, show that the number of particles per unit volume in the liquid varies with height as

$$n = n_0 \exp\left[ -\frac{N_0}{RT} V(\rho - \rho')gh \right].$$

This equation was tested by Perrin in his Brownian motion studies.

16. The average speed of hydrogen molecules at 0° C is 1694 meters/sec. Compute the average speed of colloidal particles of "molecular weight" $3.2 \times 10^6$ gm/mole.

17. Calculate the work done per mole in an isothermal expansion of a van der Waals gas from volume $V_i$ to $V_f$.

**18.** The constant $a$ in van der Waals equation is 0.37 nt-m$^4$/mole$^2$ for $CO_2$ and 0.025 nt-m$^4$/mole$^2$ for hydrogen. Compute the internal pressures for these gases and the ratio of the internal to the external pressure for values of $v/v_0$ (where $v_0 = 22.4$ liters/mole) of 1, 0.01, and 0.001.

**19.** (a) The constant $b$ in van der Waals equation is 43 cm$^3$/mole for $CO_2$. Using the value for $a$ in the previous problem, compute the pressure at 0° C for a specific volume of 0.55 liter/mole, assuming van der Waals equation to be strictly true. (b) What is the pressure under these same conditions, assuming $CO_2$ behaves as an ideal gas?

**20.** Van der Waals' $b$ for oxygen is 32 cm$^3$/mole. Assume $b$ is four times the actual volume of a mole of "billiard-ball" $O_2$ molecules and compute the diameter of an $O_2$ molecule.

**21.** The constants $a$ and $b$ in the van der Waals equation are different for different substances. Show, however, that if we take $v_{cr}$, $p_{cr}$, and $T_{cr}$ as the units of specific volume, pressure, and temperature, the van der Waals equation becomes identical for all substances.

# Entropy and the Second Law of Thermodynamics

## CHAPTER 25

### 25–1 Introduction

The first law of thermodynamics states that energy is conserved. However, we can think of many thermodynamic processes which conserve energy but which actually never occur. For example, when a hot body and a cold body are put into contact, it simply does not happen that the hot body gets hotter and the cold body colder. Or again, a pond does not suddenly freeze on a hot summer day by giving up heat to its environment. *And yet neither of these processes violates the first law of thermodynamics.* Similarly, the first law does not restrict our ability to convert work into heat or heat into work, except that energy must be conserved in the process. And yet in practice, although we can convert a given quantity of work completely into heat, we have never been able to find a scheme that converts a given amount of heat completely into work. The second law of thermodynamics deals with this question of whether processes, assumed to be consistent with the first law, do or do not occur in nature. Although the ideas contained in the second law may seem subtle or abstract, in application they prove to be extremely practical.

### 25–2 Reversible and Irreversible Processes

Consider a typical system in thermodynamic equilibrium, say a mass $\mathfrak{M}$ of a (real) gas confined in a cylinder-piston arrangement of volume $V$, the gas having a pressure $p$ and a temperature $T$. In an equilibrium state these thermodynamic variables remain constant with time. Suppose that the cylinder, whose walls are an (ideal) heat insulator but whose base is an (ideal) heat conductor is placed on a large heat reservoir maintained at this same temperature $T$, as in Fig. 22–9. Now let us change the system to another equilibrium state in which the temperature $T$ is the same but the volume $V$ is reduced by one-half. Of the many ways in which we could do this we discuss two extreme cases.

I. We depress the piston very rapidly; we then wait for equilibrium with the reservoir to be re-established. During this process the gas is turbulent and its pressure and temperature are not well defined; we cannot plot the process as a continuous line on a $p$-$V$ diagram because we would not know what value of pressure (or temperature) to associate with a given volume. The system passes from one equilibrium state $i$ to another $f$ through a series of nonequilibrium states (Fig. 25-1$a$).

II. We depress the piston (assumed to be frictionless) exceedingly slowly—perhaps by adding sand to the top of the piston—so that the pressure, volume, and temperature of the gas are, at all times, well-defined quantities. We first drop a few grains of sand on the piston. This will reduce the volume of the system a little and the temperature will tend to rise; the system will depart from equilibrium, but only slightly. A small amount of heat will be transferred to the reservoir and in a short time the system will reach a new equilibrium state, its temperature again being that of the reservoir. Then we drop a few more grains of sand on the piston, reducing the volume further. Again we wait for a new equilibrium state to be established, and so forth. By many repetitions of this procedure we finally reduce the volume by one-half. During this entire process the system is never in a state differing much from an equilibrium state. If we imagine carrying out this procedure with still smaller successive increases in pressure, the intermediate states will depart from equilibrium even less. By indefinitely increasing the number of changes and corre-

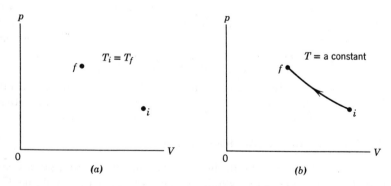

**Fig. 25–1**  We cause a real gas to go from an initial equilibrium state $i$ described by $p_i$, $V_i$, $T_i$ to a final equilibrium state $f$ described by $p_f$, $V_f$ ($= \frac{1}{2}V_i$), and $T_f$ ($= T_i$). We carry out the process ($a$) irreversibly, and ($b$) reversibly.

spondingly decreasing the size of each change, we arrive at an ideal process in which the system passes through a continuous succession of equilibrium states, which we can plot as a continuous line on a $p$-$V$ diagram (Fig. 25–1$b$). During this process a certain amount of heat $Q$ is transferred from the system to the reservoir.

Processes of type I are called *irreversible* and those of type II are called *reversible*. *A reversible process is one that, by a differential change in the environment, can be made to retrace its path.* Thus as we cause the piston to move slowly downward, in II, the external pressure on the piston exceeds the pressure exerted on it by the gas by only a differential amount $dp$. If at any instant we reduce the external pressure ever so slightly (by removing a few sand grains), so that it is *less than* the internal gas pressure by $dp$, the gas will expand instead of contracting and the system will retrace the equilibrium states through which it has just passed.* In practice all processes are irreversible, but we can approach reversibility arbitrarily closely by making appropriate experimental refinements. The strictly reversible process is a simple and useful abstraction that bears a similar relation to real processes that the ideal gas abstraction does to real gases.

The process described in II is not only reversible but *isothermal*, because we have assumed that the temperature of the gas differs at all times by only a differential amount $dT$ from the (constant) temperature of the reservoir on which the cylinder rests.

We could also reduce the volume *adiabatically* by removing the cylinder from the heat reservoir and putting it on a nonconducting stand. In an adiabatic process no heat is allowed to enter or to leave the system. An adiabatic process can be either reversible or irreversible—the definition does not exclude either. In a reversible adiabatic process we move the piston exceedingly slowly—perhaps using the sand-loading technique; in an irreversible adiabatic process we shove the piston down quickly.

The temperature of the gas will rise during an adiabatic compression because, from the first law, with $Q = 0$, the work $W$ done in pushing down the piston must appear as an increase $\Delta U$ in the internal energy of the system. $W$ will have different values for different rates of pushing down the piston, being given by $\int p \, dV$—that is, by the area under a curve on a $p$-$V$ diagram—only for reversible processes (for which $p$ has a well-defined value). Thus $\Delta U$ and the corresponding temperature change $\Delta T$ will not be the same for reversible and irreversible adiabatic processes.

---

* Not all processes carried out very slowly are reversible. For example, if the piston in our example exerted a frictional force against the cylinder walls, it would not reverse its motion if we made only a differential change $dp$ in the external pressure. We would have to make a change $\Delta p$ that might be an appreciable fraction of $p$. Thus our criterion for reversibility, which involves a response of the system to a *differential* change in the environment, is not met. The word *quasi-static* is used to describe processes that are carried out slowly enough so that the system passes through a continuous sequence of equilibrium states; a quasi-static process may or may not be reversible. See "Thermodynamics of an Irreversible Quasi-Static Process," by John S. Thomsen, *American Journal of Physics*, **28**, 119, 1960.

## 25–3 The Carnot Cycle

Suppose that we have a system (a real gas, say) in an equilibrium state in a cylinder-piston arrangement. By using our ability to make changes in the environment of the system we can carry out, at our pleasure, a wide variety of processes. We can let the gas expand or we can compress it; we can add or subtract energy in the form of heat; we can do these things and others irreversibly or reversibly. We can also choose to carry out a sequence of processes such that the system returns to its original equilibrium state; we call this a *cycle*. If the processes involved are all reversible, we call it a *reversible cycle*.

Figure 25–2 shows a reversible cycle on a $p$-$V$ diagram. Along the curve $abc$ we allow the system to expand, and the area under this curve represents the work done by the system during the expansion. Along the curve $cda$, which returns the system to its original state, we compress the system, and the area under this curve represents the work we must do on the system during the compression. Hence, the net work done by the system is represented by the area enclosed by the curve and is positive. If we decided to traverse the cycle in the opposite sense, that is, expanding along $adc$ and compressing along $cba$, the net work done by the system would be the negative of that of the previous case.

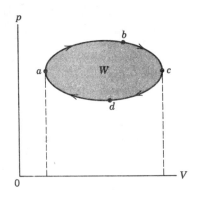

**Fig. 25–2** A $p$-$V$ diagram of a gas undergoing a reversible cycle. The shaded area $W$ represents the net work done by the gas in the cycle.

An important reversible cycle is the *Carnot cycle*, introduced by Sadi Carnot in 1824. We shall see later that this cycle will determine the limit of our ability to convert heat into work. The system consists of a "working substance," such as a gas, and the cycle is made up of two isothermal and two adiabatic reversible processes. The working substance, which we can think of as an ideal gas for concreteness, is contained in a cylinder with a heat-conducting base and nonconducting walls and piston. We also provide, as part of the environment, a heat reservoir in the form of a body of large heat capacity at a temperature $T_1$, another reservoir of large heat capacity at a temperature $T_2$, and two nonconducting stands. We carry out the Carnot cycle in four steps, as shown in Fig. 25–3. The cycle is shown on the $p$-$V$ diagram of Fig. 25–4.

*Step 1.* The gas is in an initial equilibrium state represented by $p_1$, $V_1$, $T_1$ ($a$, Fig. 25–4). We put the cylinder on the heat reservoir at tempera-

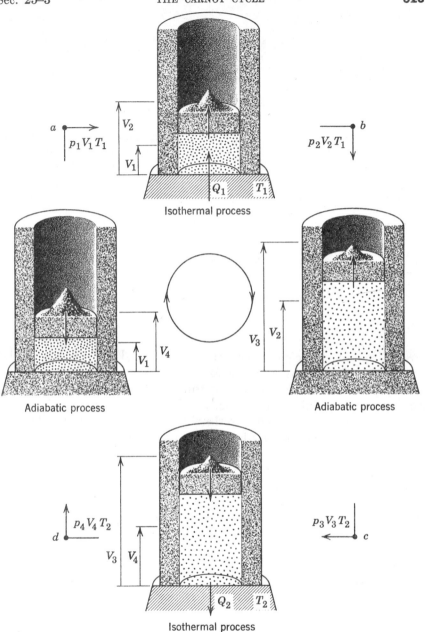

**Fig. 25–3** A Carnot cycle. The points $a$, $b$, $c$ and $d$ correspond to the points so labelled in Fig. 25.4. The cylinder-piston arrangements show intermediate steps in the processes that connect adjacent points. The arrows on the pistons suggest expansions (caused by removing sand) and compressions (caused by adding sand).

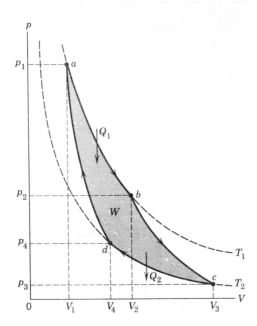

**Fig. 25–4**  The Carnot cycle illustrated in the previous figure, plotted on a $p$-$V$ diagram for an ideal gas.

ture $T_1$, and allow the gas to expand slowly to $p_2$, $V_2$, $T_1$ ($b$, Fig. 25–4). During the process heat energy $Q_1$ is absorbed by the gas by conduction through the base.  The expansion is isothermal at $T_1$ and the gas does work in raising the piston and its load.

*Step 2.*  We put the cylinder on the nonconducting stand and allow the gas to expand slowly to $p_3$, $V_3$, $T_2$ ($c$, Fig. 25–4).  The expansion is adiabatic because no heat can enter or leave the system.  The gas does work in raising the piston and its temperature falls to $T_2$.

*Step 3.*  We put the cylinder on the (colder) heat reservoir $T_2$ and compress the gas slowly to $p_4$, $V_4$, $T_2$ ($d$, Fig. 25–4).  During the process heat energy $Q_2$ is transferred from the gas to the reservoir by conduction through the base.  The compression is isothermal at $T_2$ and work is done *on* the gas by the piston and its load.

*Step 4.*  We put the cylinder on a nonconducting stand and compress the gas slowly to the initial condition $p_1$, $V_1$, $T_1$.  The compression is adiabatic because no heat can enter or leave the system.  Work is done on the gas and its temperature rises to $T_1$.

The net work $W$ done by the system during the cycle is represented by the area enclosed by path $abcd$ of Fig. 25–4.  The net amount of heat energy received by the system in the cycle is $Q_1 - Q_2$, where $Q_1$ is the heat absorbed in Step 1 and $Q_2$ is that given up in Step 3.  The initial and final states are the same so that there is no net change in the internal energy $U$ of the system.  Hence, from the first law of thermodynamics,

$$W = Q_1 - Q_2 \tag{25-1}$$

for the cycle, in which $Q_1$ and $Q_2$ are taken as positive quantities. The result of the cycle is that heat has been converted into work by the system. Any required amount of work can be obtained by simply repeating the cycle. Hence, the system acts like a *heat engine*.

We have used an ideal gas as an example of a working substance. The working substance can be anything at all, although the $p$-$V$ diagrams for other substances would be different. Common heat engines use steam or a mixture of fuel and air, or fuel and oxygen as their working substance. Heat may be obtained from the combustion of a fuel such as gasoline or coal, or from the annihilation of mass in nuclear fission processes in nuclear reactors. Heat may be discharged at the exhaust or to a condenser. Although real heat engines do not operate on a reversible cycle, the Carnot cycle, which is reversible, gives useful information about the behavior of any heat engine.

The efficiency $e$ of a heat engine is the ratio of the net work done by the engine during one cycle to the heat taken in from the high temperature source in one cycle.* Hence,

$$e = \frac{W}{Q_1} = \frac{Q_1 - Q_2}{Q_1} = 1 - \frac{Q_2}{Q_1}. \qquad (25\text{–}2)$$

Equation 25–2 shows that the efficiency of a heat engine is less than one (100%) so long as the heat $Q_2$ delivered to the exhaust is not zero. Experience shows that every heat engine rejects some heat during the exhaust stroke. This represents the heat absorbed by the engine that is not converted to work in the process.

We may choose to carry out the Carnot cycle by starting at any point, such as $a$ in Fig. 25–4, and traversing each process in a direction opposite to that of the arrowheads in that figure. Then an amount of heat $Q_2$ is *removed* from the lower temperature reservoir at $T_2$, and an amount of heat $Q_1$ is *delivered* to the higher temperature reservoir at $T_1$; work must be done *on* the system by an outside agency. In this reversed cycle work must be done *on* the system which extracts heat from the lower temperature reservoir. Any amount of heat can be removed from this reservoir by simply repeating the reverse cycle. Hence, the system acts like a *refrigerator*, transferring heat from a body at a lower temperature (the freezing compartment) to one at a higher temperature (the room) by means of work supplied to it (the electric power input).

▶ **Example 1.** Show that the efficiency of a Carnot engine using an ideal gas as the working substance is $e = (T_1 - T_2)/T_1$.

Along the isothermal path $ab$, the temperature, and hence the internal energy of an ideal gas, remains constant. From the first law, the heat $Q_1$ absorbed by the gas in its expansion must be equal to the work $W_1$ done in this expansion. From

---

* The definition reflects the economic importance of engines. Work $W$ is the desirable output; the heat $Q_1$, is the input that must be paid for in the form, say, of a fuel bill. An efficient engine has a large ratio of $W$ to $Q_1$.

Example 2, Chapter 23, we have,

$$Q_1 = W_1 = \mu R T_1 \ln (V_2/V_1).$$

Likewise, in the isothermal compression along the path $cd$, we have

$$Q_2 = W_2 = \mu R T_2 \ln (V_3/V_4).$$

On dividing the first equation by the second, we obtain

$$\frac{Q_1}{Q_2} = \frac{T_1 \ln (V_2/V_1)}{T_2 \ln (V_3/V_4)}.$$

From the equation describing an isothermal process for an ideal gas we obtain for the paths $ab$ and $cd$

$$p_1 V_1 = p_2 V_2,$$

$$p_3 V_3 = p_4 V_4.$$

From the equation describing an adiabatic process for an ideal gas we have for paths $bc$ and $da$

$$p_2 V_2{}^\gamma = p_3 V_3{}^\gamma,$$

$$p_4 V_4{}^\gamma = p_1 V_1{}^\gamma.$$

Multiplying these four equations together and canceling the factor $p_1 p_2 p_3 p_4$ appearing on both sides, we obtain

$$V_1 V_2{}^\gamma V_3 V_4{}^\gamma = V_2 V_3{}^\gamma V_4 V_1{}^\gamma,$$

from which    $$(V_2 V_4)^{\gamma-1} = (V_3 V_1)^{\gamma-1}$$

and    $$V_2/V_1 = V_3/V_4.$$

Using this result in our expression for $Q_1/Q_2$, we see that

$$Q_1/Q_2 = T_1/T_2, \tag{25-3}$$

so that

$$e = 1 - Q_2/Q_1 = 1 - T_2/T_1$$

or    $$e = \frac{Q_1 - Q_2}{Q_1} = \frac{T_1 - T_2}{T_1}.$$

The temperatures $T_1$ and $T_2$ are those measured on the ideal gas scale described in Chapter 21.    ◀

### 25–4  The Second Law of Thermodynamics

The first heat engines constructed were very inefficient devices. Only a small fraction of the heat absorbed at the high-temperature source could be converted to useful work. Even as engineering design improved, a sizable fraction of the absorbed heat was still discharged at the lower-temperature exhaust of the engine, remaining unconverted to mechanical energy. It remained a hope to devise an engine that could take heat from an abundant reservoir, like the ocean, and convert it completely into useful work. Then it would not be necessary to provide a source of heat at a higher temperature than the outside environment by burning fuels (Fig.

Actual heat engine                    "Perfect" heat engine

**Fig. 25–5**   In an actual heat engine, some of the heat $Q_1$ taken in by the engine is converted into work $W$, but the rest is rejected as heat $Q_2$. In a "perfect" heat engine all the heat input would be converted into work output.

25–5).   Likewise, we might hope to be able to devise a refrigerator that simply transfers heat from a cold body to a hot body, without requiring the expense of outside work (Fig. 25–6). *Neither of these hopeful ambitions violates the first law of thermodynamics.* The heat engine would simply convert heat energy completely into mechanical energy, the total energy being

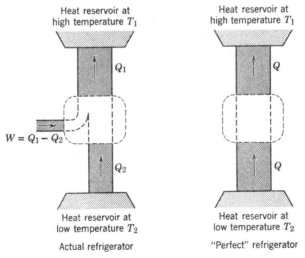

Actual refrigerator                   "Perfect" refrigerator

**Fig. 25–6**   In an actual refrigerator, work $W$ is needed to transfer heat from a low-temperature to a high-temperature reservoir. In a "perfect" refrigerator, heat would flow from the low-temperature to the high-temperature reservoir without any work being done on the engine.

conserved in the process. In the refrigerator, the heat energy would simply be transferred from cold body to hot body without any loss of energy in the process. Nevertheless *neither of these ambitions has ever been achieved*, and there is reason to believe they never will be.

The *second law of thermodynamics*, which is a generalization of experience, is an assertion that such devices do not exist. There have been many statements of the second law, each emphasizing another facet of the law, but all can be shown to be equivalent to one another. Clausius stated it as follows: *It is impossible for any cyclical machine to produce no other effect than to convey heat continuously from one body to another at a higher temperature*. This statement rules out our ambitious refrigerator, for it implies that to convey heat continuously from a cold to a hot object it is necessary to supply work by an outside agent. We know from experience that when two bodies are in contact, heat energy flows from the hot body to the cold body. The second law rules out the possibility of heat energy flowing from cold to hot body in such a case and so determines the direction of transfer of heat. The direction can be reversed only by an expenditure of work.

Kelvin (with Planck) stated the second law in words equivalent to these: *A transformation whose only final result is to transform into work heat extracted from a source which is at the same temperature throughout is impossible.*\* This statement rules out our ambitious heat engine, for it implies that we cannot produce mechanical work by extracting heat from a single reservoir without returning any heat to a reservoir at a lower temperature.

To show that the two statements are equivalent we need to show that, if either statement is false, the other statement must be false also. Suppose Clausius' statement were false so that we could have a refrigerator operating without needing a work input. We could use an ordinary engine to remove heat from a hot body, to do work and to return part of the heat to a cold body. But by connecting our "perfect" refrigerator into the system, this heat would be returned to the hot body without expenditure of work and would become available again for use by the heat engine. Hence, the combination of an ordinary engine and the "perfect" refrigerator would constitute a heat engine which violates the Kelvin-Planck statement. Or we can reverse the argument. If the Kelvin-Planck statement were incorrect, we could have a heat engine which simply takes heat from a source and converts it completely into work. By connecting this "perfect" heat engine to an ordinary refrigerator, we could extract heat from the hot body, convert it completely to work, use this work to run the

---

\* This statement needs to be supplemented if we extend thermodynamics to the region of negative Kelvin temperatures. All other formulations of the second law, and indeed, all other laws of thermodynamics apply to negative temperatures without revision. See an article, "Thermodynamics and Statistical Mechanics at Negative Absolute Temperatures," by N. F. Ramsey, in *Temperature, Its Measurement and Control in Science and Industry*, Vol. 3, Part 1, Reinhold Publishing Co., New York, 1962.

ordinary refrigerator, extract heat from the cold body, and deliver it plus the work converted to heat by the refrigerator to the hot body. The net result is a transfer of heat from cold to hot body without expenditure of work and this violates Clausius' statement.

The second law tells us that many processes are irreversible. For example, Clausius' statement specifically rules out a simple reversal of the process of heat transfer from hot body to cold body. Not only will some processes not run backward by themselves, but no combination of processes can undo the effect of an irreversible process without causing another corresponding change elsewhere. In later sections we shall develop these ideas more fully and formulate the second law quantitatively.

### 25–5  The Efficiency of Engines

Carnot first wrote scientifically on the theory of heat engines. In 1824 he published *Reflections on the Motive Power of Heat.* By then the steam engine was commonly used in industry. Carnot wrote:

> In spite of labor of all sorts expended on the steam engine, and in spite of the perfection to which it has been brought, its theory is very little advanced. . . .
> The production of motion in the steam engine is always accompanied by a circumstance which we should particularly notice. This circumstance is the passage of caloric from one body where the temperature is more or less elevated to another where it is lower. . . .
> The motive power of heat is independent of the agents employed to develop it; its quantity is determined solely by the temperature of the bodies between which, in the final result, the transfer of the caloric occurs.

Hence, Carnot directed attention to the facts that the difference in temperature was the real source of "motive power," that the transfer of heat played a significant role, and that the choice of working substance was of no theoretical importance.

Carnot's achievement was remarkable when we recall that the mechanical equivalence of heat and the conservation of energy principle were not known in 1824. In his later papers, published posthumously in 1872, it became clear that Carnot had foreseen the principle of the conservation of energy and had made an accurate determination of the mechanical equivalent of heat. He had planned a program of research which included all the important developments in the field made by other investigators during the following several decades. However, he died during a cholera epidemic in 1832 at the age of 36, leaving it to others to extend his work. It was William Thomson (later Lord Kelvin) who modified Carnot's reasoning to bring it into accord with the mechanical theory of heat, and who, together with Clausius, successfully developed the science of thermodynamics.

Carnot developed the concept of a reversible engine and the reversible cycle named after him. He stated a theorem of great practical importance: *The efficiency of all reversible engines operating between the same two temperatures is the same, and no irreversible engine working between the same two tem-*

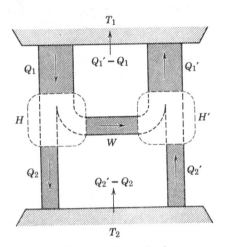

$T_1$

$Q_1$

$Q_1' - Q_1$

$Q_1'$

$H$

$H'$

$W$

$Q_2$

$Q_2' - Q_2$

$Q_2'$

$T_2$

**Fig. 25–7**   Proof of Carnot's theorem.

peratures can have a greater efficiency than this. Clausius and Kelvin showed that this theorem was a necessary consequence of the second law of thermodynamics. Notice that nothing is said about the working substance, so that the efficiency of a reversible engine is independent of the working substance and depends only on the temperatures. Furthermore, a reversible engine operates at the maximum efficiency possible for any engine working between the same two temperature limits. The proof of this theorem follows.

Let us call the two reversible engines $H$ and $H'$. They operate between the temperatures $T_1$ and $T_2$ where $T_1 > T_2$. They may differ, say, in their working substance or in their initial pressures and lengths of stroke. We choose $H$ to run forward and $H'$ to run backward (as a refrigerator). The forward-running engine $H$ takes in heat energy $Q_1$ at $T_1$ and gives out heat energy $Q_2$ at $T_2$. The backward-running engine (refrigerator) $H'$ takes in heat $Q_2'$ at $T_2$ and gives out heat $Q_1'$ at $T_1$. We now connect the engines mechanically and adjust the stroke lengths so that the work done per cycle by $H$ is just sufficient to operate $H'$ (Fig. 25–7). Suppose the efficiency $e$ of $H$ were greater than the efficiency $e'$ of $H'$. Then

$$e > e', \quad \text{(assumption)}$$

or

$$\frac{Q_1 - Q_2}{Q_1} > \frac{Q_1' - Q_2'}{Q_1'}$$

Since the work per cycle done by one engine equals the work per cycle done on the other engine,

$$W = W',$$

or

$$Q_1 - Q_2 = Q_1' - Q_2'.$$

Comparing these relations, we see that (since $Q_1 - Q_2 > 0$)

$$\frac{1}{Q_1} > \frac{1}{Q_1'}$$

or

$$Q_1 < Q_1'.$$

Hence (from the work equality),

$$Q_2 < Q_2'.$$

Thus, the hot source gains heat $Q_1' - Q_1$ (positive) and the cool source loses heat $Q_2' - Q_2$ (positive). But no work is done in the process by the combined system $H + H'$ so that we have transferred heat from a body at one temperature to a body at a higher temperature without performing work—in direct contradiction to Clausius' statement of the second law. Hence, we conclude that $e$ cannot be greater than $e'$.  Likewise, by reversing the engines we can use the same reasoning to prove that $e'$ cannot be greater than $e$.  Hence,

$$e = e',$$

proving the first part of Carnot's theorem.

Now suppose that $H$ is an *irreversible* engine.  Then by the exact same procedure we can prove that $e_{ir}$ cannot be greater than $e'$.  But $H$ cannot be reversed, so we cannot prove that $e'$ cannot be greater than $e_{ir}$.  Therefore, $e_{ir}$ is either equal to or less than $e'$.  Since $e' = e = e_{reversible}$, we have

$$e_{irreversible} \leqq e_{reversible},$$

thus proving the second part of Carnot's theorem.

▶ **Example 2.**  A steam engine takes steam from the boiler at 200° C (225 lb/in.² pressure) and exhausts directly into the air (14 lb/in.² pressure) at 100° C. What is its maximum possible efficiency?

Using the result of Example 1 (which applies to this case by virtue of Carnot's theorem, which we have just proved) we have

$$e = \frac{T_1 - T_2}{T_1} = \frac{473° \text{ K} - 373° \text{ K}}{473° \text{ K}} \times 100\% = 21.1\%.$$

Actual efficiencies of about 15% are usually realized.  Energy is lost by friction, turbulence, and heat conduction.  Lower exhaust temperatures on more complicated steam engines may raise the maximum possible efficiency to 35% and the actual efficiency to 20%.  The efficiency of an ordinary automobile engine is about 22% and that of a large Diesel oil engine about 40%.    ◀

## 25–6  The Thermodynamic Temperature Scale

The efficiency of a reversible engine is independent of the working substance and depends only on the two temperatures between which the engine works.  Since $e = 1 - Q_2/Q_1$, then $Q_2/Q_1$ can depend only on the temperatures.  This led Kelvin to suggest a new scale of temperature.  If we let $\theta_1$ and $\theta_2$ represent these two temperatures, his defining equation is

$$\theta_1/\theta_2 = Q_1/Q_2.$$

That is, two temperatures on this scale are to each other as the heats absorbed and rejected, respectively, by a Carnot engine operating between these temperatures. Such a temperature scale is called the *thermodynamic* (or *Kelvin*) *temperature scale*.

To complete the definition of the thermodynamic scale, we assign the arbitrary value of 273.16° to the temperature of the triple point of water.  Hence, $\theta_{tr} = 273.16°$ K.  Then for a Carnot engine operating between reservoirs at the temperatures $\theta$ and $\theta_{tr}$ we have

$$\frac{\theta}{\theta_{tr}} = \frac{Q}{Q_{tr}}$$

or
$$\theta = 273.16° \text{ K} \frac{Q}{Q_{tr}} \qquad (25\text{-}4)$$

If we compare this with the corresponding equation for the ideal gas temperature $T$, namely

$$T = 273.16° \text{ K} \lim_{p_{tr} \to 0} \frac{p}{p_{tr}} \qquad (25\text{-}5)$$

we see that on the thermodynamic scale $Q$ plays the role of a thermometric property. However, $Q$ does not depend on the characteristics of any substance because a Carnot engine is independent of the nature of the working substance. Therefore, we obtain a scale of temperature which is free of the objection we can raise to the ideal gas scale of Chapter 21, and in fact we arrive at a fundamental definition of temperature.

The definition of thermodynamic temperature enables us to rewrite the equation for the efficiency of a reversible engine as

$$e = \frac{Q_1 - Q_2}{Q_1} = \frac{\theta_1 - \theta_2}{\theta_1}. \tag{25-6}$$

But we have shown (Example 1) that the efficiency of a Carnot engine using an ideal gas as working substance is

$$e = \frac{Q_1 - Q_2}{Q_1} = \frac{T_1 - T_2}{T_1} \tag{25-7}$$

where $T$ is the temperature given by the constant-volume thermometer containing the ideal gas. Hence, $Q_1/Q_2 = T_1/T_2$ and $Q_1/Q_2 = \theta_1/\theta_2$. Since $\theta_{tr} = T_{tr} = 273.16°$ and $\theta/\theta_{tr} = T/T_{tr}$, it follows that $\theta = T$. Hence, *if an ideal gas were available for use in a constant-volume thermometer, the thermometer would yield the thermodynamic* (or *Kelvin*) *temperature*. We have seen that, although an ideal gas is not available, measurements made using the limiting process of Eq. 25–5 with real gases correspond to ideal gas behavior. We shall treat the ideal gas scale and the thermodynamic scale as identical and we shall use the designation °K interchangeably for each, as in fact we have already done.

In practice, we cannot have a gas below 1° K. One of the methods used in measuring temperature below 1° K employs the thermodynamic scale directly. The ratio of two thermodynamic temperatures is the ratio of two heats transferred during two isothermal processes bounded by the same two adiabatics (Fig. 25–8). The location of the adiabatic boundaries (on the $p$-$V$ diagram) can be found experimentally, and the heats transferred during two nearly reversible isothermal processes can be measured with great precision.

From the equations

$$T = 273.16° \text{ K} \frac{Q}{Q_{tr}} \quad \text{or} \quad \frac{T}{T_{tr}} = \frac{Q}{Q_{tr}}$$

it is clear that the heat $Q$ transferred in an isothermal process between two given adiabatics decreases as the temperature $T$ decreases. Conversely, the smaller $Q$ is the lower the corresponding temperature $T$ is. Now the smallest possible value of $Q$ is zero and the corresponding $T$ is absolute zero. That is, *if a system undergoes a reversible isothermal process with no transfer of heat, the temperature at which this process takes place is the absolute zero*. Hence, at absolute zero, an isothermal and an adiabatic process are identical (Fig. 25–8).

This definition of absolute zero applies to all substances and is independent of the properties of any one of them. Notice that no reference is made to molecules or molecular energy and that we have obtained a purely macroscopic definition of absolute zero.

The efficiency of a Carnot engine is

$$e = 1 - \frac{T_2}{T_1};$$

which is the maximum possible efficiency any engine can have operating between temperatures $T_1$ and $T_2$. To obtain 100% efficiency, $T_2$ must be zero. Only when the low-temperature reservoir is at absolute zero will all the heat absorbed at the high-temperature reservoir be converted to work.

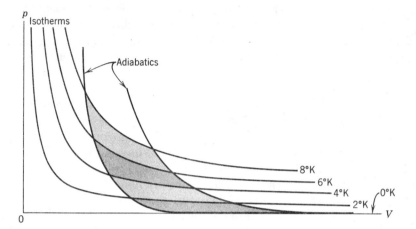

**Fig. 25-8** A series of Carnot cycles tending toward absolute-zero temperature, as used in establishing the thermodynamic scale of temperature. The difference in slope between isothermals and adiabatics has here been exaggerated for clarity.

The fundamental feature of all cooling processes is that the lower the temperature, the more difficult it is to go still lower. This experience has led to the formulation of the *third law of thermodynamics*, which can be stated in one form as follows: *It is impossible by any procedure, no matter how idealized, to reduce any system to the absolute zero of temperature in a finite number of operations.* Hence, because we cannot obtain a reservoir at absolute zero, a heat engine with 100% efficiency is a practical impossibility.

## 25-7   Entropy—Reversible Processes

The zeroth law of thermodynamics is related to the concept of *temperature T* and the first law is related to the concept of *internal energy U*. In this and the following sections we show that the second law of thermodynamics is related to a thermodynamic variable called *entropy, S,* and that we can express the second law quantitatively in terms of this variable. We start by considering a Carnot cycle. For such a cycle we have seen (Eq. 25-3) that

$$\frac{Q_1}{T_1} = \frac{Q_2}{T_2},$$

in which the $Q$'s were taken as positive quantities, that is, we dealt with the magnitudes, or absolute values, only of the $Q$'s. If we now interpret them again as algebraic quantities, $Q$ being positive when heat enters the system and negative when heat leaves the system, we can write this relation as

$$\frac{Q_1}{T_1} + \frac{Q_2}{T_2} = 0.$$

This equation states that the sum of the algebraic quantities $Q/T$ is zero for a Carnot cycle.

As a next step, we assert that *any* reversible cycle is equivalent, to as close an approximation as we wish, to an assembly of Carnot cycles. Figure 25–9a shows an arbitrary reversible cycle superimposed on a family of isotherms. We can approximate the actual cycle by connecting the isotherms by suitably chosen adiabatic lines (Fig. 25–9b), thus forming an assembly of Carnot cycles. The student should convince himself that traversing the individual Carnot cycles in Fig. 25–9b is exactly equivalent, in terms of heat transferred and work done, to traversing the jagged sequence of isotherms and adiabatic lines that approximates the actual cycle. This is so because adjacent Carnot cycles have a common isotherm and the two traversals, in opposite directions, cancel each other in the region of overlap as far as heat transfer and work done are concerned. By making the temperature interval between the isotherms in Fig. 25–9b small enough we can approximate the actual cycle as closely as we wish by an alternating sequence of isotherms and adiabatic lines.

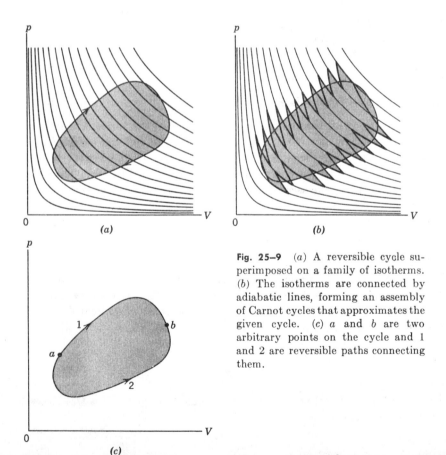

**Fig. 25–9**  (a) A reversible cycle superimposed on a family of isotherms. (b) The isotherms are connected by adiabatic lines, forming an assembly of Carnot cycles that approximates the given cycle. (c) a and b are two arbitrary points on the cycle and 1 and 2 are reversible paths connecting them.

We can write, then, for the isothermal-adiabatic sequence of lines in Fig. 25–9b,

$$\sum \frac{Q}{T} = 0,$$

or, in the limit of infinitesimal temperature differences between the isotherms of Fig. 25–9b,

$$\oint \frac{dQ}{T} = 0, \tag{25–8}$$

in which $\oint$ indicates that the integral is evaluated for a complete traversal of the cycle, starting (and ending) at any arbitrary point of the cycle.

If the integral of a quantity around any closed path is zero, that quantity is called a state variable, that is, it has a value that is characteristic only of the state of the system, regardless of how that state was arrived at. We call the variable in this case the *entropy S* and we have, from Eq. 25–8,

$$dS = \frac{dQ}{T} \quad \text{and} \quad \oint dS = 0. \tag{25–9}$$

Common units for entropy are joules/K° or cal/K°.

Gravitational potential energy $U_g$, internal energy $U$, pressure $p$, and temperature $T$ are other state variables and equations of the form $\oint dX = 0$ hold for each of them, where for $X$ we substitute the appropriate symbol. Heat $Q$ and work $W$ are *not* state variables and we know that, in general, $\oint dQ \neq 0$ and $\oint dW \neq 0$, as the student can easily show for the special case of a Carnot cycle.

The property of a state variable expressed by $\oint dX = 0$ can also be expressed by saying that $\int dX$ between any two equilibrium states has the same value for all (reversible) paths connecting those states. Let us prove this for the state variable called entropy. We can write Eq. 25–9 (see Fig. 25–9c) as

$$_1\int_a^b dS + {}_2\int_b^a dS = 0 \tag{25–10}$$

where $a$ and $b$ are arbitrary points and 1 and 2 describe the paths connecting these points. Since the cycle is reversible, we can write Eq. 25–10 as

$$_1\int_a^b dS - {}_2\int_a^b dS = 0$$

or

$$_1\int_a^b dS = {}_2\int_a^b dS \tag{25–11}$$

In Eq. 25–11 we have simply decided to traverse path 2 in the opposite direction, that is, from $a$ to $b$ rather than from $b$ to $a$. We do this by changing the order of the limits in the second integral of Eq. 25–10, which requires that we also change the sign of the integral, thus yielding Eq. 25–11. This latter equation tells us that the quantity $\int_a^b dS$ between any two equilibrium states of the system, such as $a$ and $b$, is independent of the path connecting those states, for 1 and 2 are quite arbitrary paths. The student will recall our almost identical discussion in Section 8–2, where we introduced the concept of a conservative force.

The change in entropy between $a$ and $b$ in Fig. 25–9c is, then

$$S_b - S_a = \int_a^b dS = \int_a^b \frac{dQ}{T} \quad \text{(reversible process)}, \quad (25\text{–}12)$$

where the integral is evaluated over *any reversible path* connecting these two states.

### 25–8    Entropy—Irreversible Processes

In Section 25–7 we spoke only of reversible processes. However, entropy, like all state variables, depends only on the state of the system and we must be able to calculate the change in entropy for irreversible processes, provided only that they begin and end in equilibrium states. Let us consider two examples.

1. *Free Expansion.* As in Section 22–7 (see Fig. 22–14) let a gas double its volume by expanding into an evacuated enclosure. Since no work is done against the vacuum, $W = 0$ and, since the gas is enclosed by non-conducting walls, $Q = 0$. From the first law, then $\Delta U = 0$ or

$$U_i = U_f \qquad (25\text{–}13)$$

where $i$ and $f$ refer to the initial and final (equilibrium) states. If the gas is an ideal gas, then $U$ depends on temperature alone and not on the pressure or the volume so that Eq. 25–13 implies $T_i = T_f$.

The free expansion is certainly irreversible because we lose control of the environment once we turn the stopcock in Fig. 22–14. There is, however, an entropy difference $S_f - S_i$ between the initial and final equilibrium states, but we cannot calculate it from Eq. 25–12 because that relation applies only to reversible paths; if we tried to use that equation we would have the immediate difficulty that $Q = 0$ for the free expansion and—further—we would not know how to assign meaningful values of $T$ to the intermediate, nonequilibrium states.

How, then, do we calculate $S_f - S_i$ for a free expansion? We do so by finding a *reversible* path (*any* reversible path) that connects the states $i$ and $f$ and we calculate the entropy change for that path. In the free expansion a convenient reversible path (assuming an ideal gas) is an isothermal expansion from $V_i$ to $V_f$ ($= 2V_i$). This corresponds to the isothermal expansion carried out between the points $a$ and $b$ of the Carnot cycle of Fig. 25–4. It represents quite a different set of operations from the free expansion and has in common with it *only* the fact that it connects the same set of equilibrium states, $i$ and $f$. From Eq. 25–12 and Example 1 we have

$$S_f - S_i = \int_i^f \frac{dQ}{T} = \mu R \ln (V_f/V_i)$$

$$= \mu R \ln 2.$$

This is positive so that the entropy of the system *increases* in this irreversible, adiabatic process.

2. *Heat Conduction.* For another example consider two bodies that are similar in every respect except that one is at a temperature $T_1$ and the other at temperature $T_2$, where $T_1 > T_2$. If we put both objects in contact inside a box with nonconducting walls, they will eventually reach a common temperature $T_m$, approximately half-way between $T_1$ and $T_2$. Like the free expansion, the process is irreversible because we lose control of the environment once we put the two bodies in the box. Like the free expansion this process is also (irreversibly) adiabatic because no heat enters or leaves the system during the process.

To calculate the entropy change for the system during this process we must again find a *reversible* process connecting the same initial and final states and calculate the system entropy change by applying Eq. 25–12 to that process. We can do so if we imagine that we have at our disposal a heat reservoir of large heat capacity whose temperature $T$ is at our control, by turning a knob, say. We first adjust the reservoir temperature to $T_1$ and put the first (hotter) object in contact with the reservoir. We then *slowly* (reversibly) lower the reservoir temperature from $T_1$ to $T_m$, extracting heat from the hot body as we do so. The hot body *loses* entropy in this process, the amount being approximately

$$\Delta S_1 = - \frac{Q}{T_{1,m}}$$

where $T_{1,m}$ is the average of $T_1$ and $T_m$ and $Q$ is the heat extracted.

We then adjust our reservoir temperature to $T_2$ and place it in contact with the second (cooler) object. We then *slowly* (reversibly) raise the reservoir temperature from $T_2$ to $T_m$, adding heat to the cool body as we do so. The cool body *gains* entropy in this process, the amount being approximately

$$\Delta S_2 = + \frac{Q}{T_{2,m}},$$

where $T_{2,m}$ is the average of $T_2$ and $T_m$ and $Q$ is the heat added.

The two bodies are now at the same temperature $T_m$ and the system, which consists of these two bodies, is now in its final equilibrium state. The change in entropy for the complete system is

$$S_f - S_i = \Delta S_1 + \Delta S_2$$

$$= - \frac{Q}{T_{1,m}} + \frac{Q}{T_{2,m}}.$$

Since $T_{1,m} > T_{2,m}$ we have $S_f > S_i$. Again, as for the free expansion, the entropy of the system has *increased* in this irreversible, adiabatic process.

In each of these examples we must distinguish carefully between the actual (irreversible) process (free expansion or heat conduction) and the reversible process that we introduce just so that we can calculate the entropy change in the actual process. We can choose *any* reversible process, as long as it connects the same initial and final state as the actual process; all such reversible processes will yield the same entropy change because this depends only on the initial and final states and not on the process connecting them—be it reversible or irreversible.

### 25–9   Entropy and the Second Law

We are now ready to formulate the second law of thermodynamics in terms of entropy. Since this law is a generalization from experience we cannot *prove* it but can only write it down and show that our statement is in agreement with experiment and is equivalent to other formulations of the second law that we have given earlier. In this spirit we assert that the second law is: *A natural process that starts in one equilibrium state and ends in another will go in the direction that causes the entropy of the system plus environment to increase.*

Following our pattern for the zeroth law and the first law of thermodynamics (see page 561) the essence of the second law, speaking loosely, is: *There exists a useful thermodynamic variable called entrophy.* The second law also tells us how to use this variable to predict whether a particular process will occur in nature.

The two experiments of Section 25–8 (free expansion and heat conduction) are consistent with the second law. The entropy of the system *increased* in each of these irreversible processes. Note that the entropy of the environment in these two cases remains unchanged because, both being carried out in adiabatic enclosures, there was no interchange of heat with the environment. Thus, as required by our statement of the second law, the entropy of the system plus environment increased for each of these (natural) processes.

In the form that we have written it the second law applies only to irreversible processes because only such processes have a "natural direction." Indeed (see Section 25–1) the understanding of the natural directions of such processes is the main concern of the second law. Reversible processes can go equally well in either direction, however, and *for reversible processes the entropy of the system plus environment remains unchanged.* This is so because if heat $dQ$ is transferred from the environment to the system the entropy of the environment *decreases* by $dQ/T$ while that of the system *increases* by $dQ/T$, the net change for the system plus environment being zero. The fact that the process is reversible means that the environment and the system can differ in temperature by only a differential amount $dT$ when the heat transfer takes place; this is in sharp contrast to our (irreversible) heat conduction problem of the previous section, in which the temperature difference of the two bodies placed in contact was large.

Another class of processes of particular interest are adiabatic processes (reversible or irreversible); they involve no transfer of heat with the environment so that the only entropy change possible is that of the system. From our statement of the second law and from our remarks about reversible processes in the paragraph above, we conclude that

$$S_f = S_i \qquad \text{(reversible adiabatic process)}$$

and

$$S_f > S_i \qquad \text{(irreversible adiabatic process)},$$

where $S_f$ and $S_i$ are the final and initial entropies of the system.

Our statement of the second law is consistent with the Clausius statement (page 628) which declares that there is no such thing as a "perfect" refrigerator (see Fig. 25-6). If there were, the entropy of the lower temperature reservoir would *decrease* by $Q/T_2$; that of the upper temperature reservoir would *increase* by $Q/T_1$; that of the system would remain unchanged because the system traverses a cycle, returning to its starting point. Thus the net change in the entropy of the system plus environment is a *decrease*, because $T_2 < T_1$. This violates the statement of the second law that we have just given and, if we wish to retain the statement, we must conclude (with Clausius) that there is no such thing as a "perfect" refrigerator.

Our statement of the second law is also consistent with the Kelvin-Planck statement (page 628) which declares that there is no such thing as a "perfect" heat engine (see Fig. 25-5). If there were, the entropy of the reservoir at temperature $T$ would *decrease* by $Q/T$; that of the system would remain unchanged because the system traverses a cycle, returning to its starting point. Thus the net change of entropy of the system plus environment is a *decrease*. This violates the statement of the second law that we have just given and, if we wish to retain the statement, we must conclude (with Kelvin) that there is no such thing as a "perfect" heat engine.

▶ **Example 3.** Compute the entropy change of a system consisting of 1.00 kg of ice at 0° C which melts (reversibly) to water at that same temperature. The latent heat of melting is 79.6 cal/gm.

The requirement that we melt the ice *reversibly* means that we must put it in contact with a heat reservoir whose temperature exceeds 0° C by only a differential amount; if we lower the reservoir temperature until it is a differential amount below 0° C, the melted ice will begin to freeze. Since the process is reversible, we can use Eq. 25-12 to compute the entropy change of the system. The temperature remains constant at 273° K. Therefore,

$$S_{\text{water}} - S_{\text{ice}} = \int_0^Q \frac{dQ}{T} = \frac{1}{T} \int_0^Q dQ = \frac{Q}{T}.$$

But

$$Q = 10^3 \text{ gm} \times 79.6 \text{ cal/gm} = 7.96 \times 10^4 \text{ cal}$$

or

$$S_{\text{water}} - S_{\text{ice}} = \frac{7.96 \times 10^4}{273} \text{ cal/°K} = 292 \text{ cal/K°}$$

$$= 1220 \text{ joules/K°}.$$

In this example of reversible melting the entropy change of the *system plus environment* is zero, as it must be for all reversible processes. The entropy change calculated above is the increase in entropy of the *system;* there is an exactly equal decrease in entropy of the environment ($-1220$ joules/K°) associated with the heat that leaves the reservoir (environment), at 273° K, to melt the ice.

In practice, melting is likely to be irreversible, as when we put an ice cube in a glass of water at room temperature. This process has only one natural direction—the ice will melt. The entropy of the system plus environment will *increase* in this process as required by the second law. The (irreversible) heat conduction example of the previous section should make this understandable.

▶ **Example 4.** Calculate the entropy change that an ideal gas undergoes in a reversible isothermal expansion from a volume $V_i$ to a volume $V_f$.

From the first law

$$dU = dQ - p\, dV.$$

But $dU = 0$, since $U$ depends only on temperature for an ideal gas and the temperature is constant. Hence,

$$dQ = p\, dV$$

and

$$dS = \frac{dQ}{T} = \frac{p\, dV}{T}.$$

But

$$pV = \mu RT,$$

so that

$$dS = \mu R \frac{dV}{V}$$

and

$$S_f - S_i = \int_{V_i}^{V_f} \mu R \frac{dV}{V} = \mu R \ln \frac{V_f}{V_i}. \tag{25-14}$$

Since $V_f > V_i$, $S_f > S_i$ and the *entropy of the gas increases.*

In order to carry out this process we must have a reservoir at temperature $T$ which is in contact with the system and supplies the heat to the gas. Hence, the *entropy of the reservoir decreases* by $\int dQ/T[= \mu R \ln (V_f/V_i)]$, so that in this process the entropy of system plus environment does not change. As in the previous example, this is characteristic of a reversible process.    ◀

## 25–10  Entropy and Disorder

Freeman Dyson, in an article* "What Is Heat?" writes:
"Heat is disordered energy. So with two words the nature of heat is explained. . . . Energy can exist without disorder. For example, a flying rifle bullet or an atom of $U^{235}$ carries ordered energy. The motion of the bullet is the kind we call kinetic. When the bullet hits a steel plate and is stopped, the energy of its motion is transferred to random motions of the atoms in the bullet and the plate. This disordered energy makes itself felt in the form of heat. . . . The energy dwelling in the uranium atom is the kind we call potential; it consists of the electric forces which tend to push the constituent protons apart. When the atom fissions, the energy of motion of the flying fragments is converted by collisions into random motions of the electrons and other atoms nearby in the surrounding matter—that is to say, into heat. This conversion of potential energy into heat is the working principle of nuclear reactors.

---

* *Scientific American*, September 1954.

These two examples illustrate the general principle that energy becomes heat as soon as it is disordered. It is conversely true that disorder can exist without energy, and that disorder becomes heat as soon as it is energized. The atoms of $U^{235}$ and $U^{238}$ in a piece of ordinary uranium are mixed in a random way, but this disorder carries no energy. . . .

In order to go further it is necessary to talk quantitatively. We must measure heat precisely in terms of numbers. . . . First it is clear that to specify heat we must use at least two numbers: one to measure the quantity of energy, the other to measure the quantity of disorder. The quantity of energy is measured in terms of a practical unit called the calorie. . . . The quantity of disorder is measured in terms of the mathematical concept called entropy. . . ."

If there is a connection between disorder and entropy then disorder, like entropy, must increase in natural processes. We will try to show that this is true by showing that in the examples of Section 25-8, the free expansion and heat conduction, the disorder of the system plus environment does in fact increase. We will use reasonable qualitative concepts of disorder first and will define disorder more rigorously afterwards.

1. *Free Expansion.* In a free expansion (Section 22-7) the gas molecules confined to one-half of a box are permitted to fill the entire box. By any reasonable definition of the word disorder the system has become more disordered, in the same sense that disorder increases if the litter on one vacant lot is spread over two lots. More precisely, the disorder has increased because we have lost some of our ability to classify molecules. The statement: "The molecules are in the box" is weaker from this point of view than the statement: "The molecules are in the left half of the box;" see below.

2. *Heat Conduction.* In this example two bodies of different temperatures $T_1$ and $T_2$ come to a uniform intermediate temperature $T$ when they are placed in contact. Here again the system has become more disordered in this natural process because we have lost some of our ability to classify molecules. The statement: "All molecules in the system correspond, by way of Eq. 23-6, to temperature $T$" is weaker from this point of view than the statement: "All molecules in body $A$ correspond to temperature $T_1$ and all molecules in body $B$ correspond to temperature $T_2$."

These two examples and the two given by Dyson at the beginning of this section (the bullet striking a steel plate and the fissioning uranium nucleus in a nuclear reactor) convince us that *there is a tendency for natural processes to proceed toward a state of greater disorder.*

In statistical mechanics we give a precise meaning to disorder and we express its connection with entropy by the relation

$$S = k \ln w. \qquad (25\text{-}15)$$

Here, $k$ is Boltzmann's constant, $S$ is the entropy of the system, and $w$, which we may call the *disorder parameter*, is the probability that the system will exist in the state it is in relative to all the possible states it could be in. This equation connects a thermodynamic or macroscopic quantity, the entropy, with a statistical or microscopic quantity, the probability.

Let us illustrate by computing the change in entropy of an ideal gas in an isothermal expansion. Here the number of molecules and the temperature do not change, but the volume does. The probability that a given molecule may be found in a region having a volume $V$ is proportional to $V$; that is, the greater $V$ is, the greater the chance of finding it in $V$. Hence, the probability of finding a *single* molecule in $V$ is

$$w_1 = cV$$

where $c$ is a constant. The probability of finding $N$ molecules simultaneously in the volume $V$ is the $N$-fold product of $w_1$. That is, the probability of a state consisting of $N$ molecules in a volume $V$ is

$$w = w_1^N = (cV)^N. \tag{25-16}$$

For example, if the probability of finding a single molecule in $V$ is $\frac{1}{2}$ (that is, there is a 50% chance of its being in $V$ and a 50% chance of its being outside $V$), the probability of finding two molecules in $V$ is $\frac{1}{4}$. There are four equally probable states here (both in; both out; one in, the other out; one out, the other in), and only one of them is a state with both molecules in $V$.

If we now combine Eq. 25–15 and Eq. 25–16 we obtain

$$S = kN \,(\ln c + \ln V).$$

Hence, the difference in entropy between a state of volume $V_f$ and a state of volume $V_i$ (temperature and number of molecules remaining constant) is

$$S_f - S_i = kN \,(\ln c + \ln V_f) - kN \,(\ln c + \ln V_i)$$

$$= kN \ln \frac{V_f}{V_i} = \frac{RN}{N_0} \ln \frac{V_f}{V_i} = \mu R \ln \frac{V_f}{V_i}$$

in exact agreement with the strictly thermodynamic result of Eq. 25–14.

It is on the basis of Eq. 25–16 that we stated above that disorder increases during a free expansion; that equation yields $(cV)^N$ for the disorder parameter before expansion and $(c2V)^N$ for that parameter when the volume is doubled by the expansion.

The statistical definition of entropy, Eq. 25–15, connects the thermodynamic and the statistical mechanical pictures and enables us to put the second law of thermodynamics on a statistical basis. The direction in which natural processes take place (toward higher entropy) is determined by the laws of probability (toward a more probable state). The equilibrium state is the state of maximum entropy thermodynamically and the most probable state statistically. We have seen, however, that fluctuations may occur about an equilibrium distribution (for example, the Brownian motion). From this point of view, then, it is not absolutely certain that the entropy increases in every spontaneous process. The entropy may sometimes decrease. If we waited long enough, even the most improbable states might occur: the water in a pond suddenly freezing on a hot summer day or a local vacuum occurring suddenly in a room. Although such occurrences are possible, the probability of their happening, when computed, turns out to be incredibly small. Hence, the second law of thermodynamics shows us the most probable course of events, not the only possible ones. But its area of application is so broad and the chance of nature's contradicting it so small that it occupies the distinction of being one of the most useful and general laws in all sciences.

## QUESTIONS

**1.** What requirements should a system meet in order to be in thermodynamic equilibrium?

**2.** In the irreversible process of Fig. 25–1a can we calculate the work done in terms of an area on a $p$-$V$ diagram? Is any work done?

**3.** Can a given amount of mechanical energy be converted completely into heat energy? If so, give an example.

**4.** Can you suggest a reversible process whereby heat can be added to a system? Would adding heat by means of a Bunsen burner be a reversible process?

**5.** Give some examples of irreversible processes in nature.

**6.** Give a qualitative explanation of how frictional forces between moving surfaces produce heat energy. Does the reverse process (heat energy producing relative motion of these surfaces) occur? Can you give a plausible explanation?

**7.** A block returns to its initial position after dissipating mechanical energy to heat through friction. Is this process reversible thermodynamically?

**8.** To carry out a Carnot cycle we need not start at point $a$ in Fig. 25–4, but may equally well start at points $b$, $c$, or $d$, or indeed any intermediate point. Explain.

**9.** If a Carnot engine is independent of the working substance, then perhaps real engines should be similarly independent, to a certain extent. Why then, for real engines, are we so concerned to find suitable fuels such as coal, gasoline, or fissionable material? Why not use stones as a fuel?

**10.** Couldn't we just as well define the efficiency of an engine as $e = W/Q_2$ rather than as $e = W/Q_1$? Why don't we?

**11.** What factors reduce the efficiency of a heat engine from its ideal value?

**12.** In order to increase the efficiency of a Carnot engine most effectively, would you increase $T_1$, keeping $T_2$ constant, or would you decrease $T_2$, keeping $T_1$ constant?

**13.** Can a kitchen be cooled by leaving the door of an electric refrigerator open? Explain.

**14.** Is there a change in entropy in purely mechanical motions?

**15.** Two samples of a gas initially at the same temperature and pressure are compressed from a volume $V$ to a volume $(V/2)$, one isothermally, the other adiabatically. In which sample is the final pressure greater? Does the entropy of the gas change in either process?

**16.** Suppose we had chosen to represent the state of a system by its entropy and its absolute temperature rather than by its pressure and volume. What would a Carnot cycle look like on a $T$-$S$ diagram?

**17.** Consider a box containing a very small number of molecules, say five. It must sometimes happen by chance that all of these molecules find themselves in the left half of the box, the right half being completely empty. This is just the reverse of a free expansion, a process that we have declared to be *irreversible*. What is your explanation?

**18.** Show that the total entropy increases when work is converted into heat by friction between sliding surfaces. Describe the increase in disorder.

**19.** Comment on the statement "A heat engine converts disordered mechanical motion into organized mechanical motion."

**20.** When we put cards together in a deck or put bricks together to build a house, for example, we increase the order in the physical world. Does this violate the second law of thermodynamics? Explain.

**21.** A rubber band feels warmer than its surroundings immediately after it is quickly stretched; it becomes noticeably cooler when it is allowed to contract rapidly; and a rubber band supporting a load contracts on being heated. Explain these observations using the fact that the molecules of rubber consist of intertwined and cross-linked long chains of atoms in roughly random orientation.

**22.** Explain the statement "Cosmic rays continually *decrease the entropy of the earth* on which they fall." Does this contradict the second law of thermodynamics?

**23.** Discuss the following comment of Panofsky and Phillips: "From the standpoint of formal physics there is only one concept which is asymmetric in the time, namely entropy. But this makes it reasonable to assume that the second law of thermodynamics can be used to ascertain the sense of time independently in any frame of reference; that is, we shall take the positive direction of time to be that of statistically increasing disorder, or increasing entropy . . .''

## PROBLEMS

**1.** An ideal gas heat engine operates in a Carnot cycle between 227 and 127° C. It absorbs $6.0 \times 10^4$ cal at the higher temperature. How much work per cycle is this engine capable of performing?

**2.** (a) A Carnot engine operates between a hot reservoir at 320° K and a cold reservoir at 260° K. If it absorbs 500 joules of heat at the hot reservoir, how much work does it deliver? (b) If the same engine, working in reverse, functions as a refrigerator between the same two reservoirs, how much work must be supplied to remove 1000 joules of heat from the cold reservoir?

**3.** In a two-stage heat engine a quantity of heat $Q_1$ is absorbed at a temperature $T_1$, work $W_1$ is done, and a quantity of heat $Q_2$ is expelled at a lower temperature $T_2$ by the first stage. The second stage absorbs the heat expelled by the first, does work $W_2$, and expels a quantity of heat $Q_3$ at a lower temperature $T_3$. Prove that the efficiency of the combination engine is $(T_1 - T_3)/T_1$.

**4.** A combination mercury-steam turbine takes saturated mercury vapor from a boiler at 876° F and exhausts it to heat a steam boiler at 460° F. The steam turbine receives steam at this temperature and exhausts it to a condenser at 100° F. What is the maximum efficiency of the combination?

**5.** Using the equation of state of an ideal gas and the equation describing an adiabatic process for an ideal gas, show that the slope, $dp/dV$, on a $p$-$V$ diagram of an adiabatic can be written as $-\gamma p/V$ and of an isothermal can be written as $-p/V$. From these results prove that adiabatics are steeper curves than isothermals.

**6.** (a) Plot an exact Carnot cycle on a $p$-$V$ diagram for 1 mole of an ideal gas. Let point $a$ correspond to $p = 1.0$ atm, $T = 300°$ K, and let $b$ correspond to $p = 0.5$ atm, $T = 300°$ K; take the low temperature reservoir to be at 100° K. Let $\gamma = 1.5$. (b) Compute graphically the work done in this cycle.

**7.** In a Carnot cycle, the isothermal expansion of the gas takes place at 400° K and the isothermal compression at 300° K. During the expansion 500 cal of heat energy are transferred to the gas. Determine (a) the work performed by the gas during the isothermal expansion, (b) the heat rejected from the gas during the isothermal compression, (c) the work done on the gas during the isothermal compression.

**8.** (a) If the Carnot cycle is run backward, we have an ideal refrigerator. A quantity of heat $Q_2$ is taken in at the lower temperature $T_2$ and a quantity of heat $Q_1$ is given out at the higher temperature $T_1$. The difference is the work $W$ that must be supplied to run the refrigerator. Show that

$$W = Q_2 \frac{T_1 - T_2}{T_2}.$$

(b) The *coefficient of performance* $K$ of a refrigerator is defined as the ratio of the heat extracted from the c_ld source to the work needed to run the cycle. Show that ideally

$$K = \frac{T_2}{T_1 - T_2}.$$

In actual refrigerators $K$ has a value of 5 or 6.

**9.** In a mechanical refrigerator the low-temperature coils are at a temperature of $-13°$ C, and the compressed gas in the condenser has a temperature of 27° C. What is the theoretical coefficient of performance?

**10.** How much work must be done to transfer 1.0 joule of heat from a reservoir at 7° C to one at 27° C by means of a refrigerator using a Carnot cycle? From one at −73° C to one at 27° C? From one at −173° C to one at 27° C? From one at −223° C to one at 27° C?

**11.** The motor in a refrigerator has a power output of 200 watts. If the freezing compartment is at 270° K and the outside air is at 300° K, assuming ideal efficiency, what is the maximum amount of heat that can be extracted from the freezing compartment in 10 min?

**12.** How is the efficiency of a reversible heat engine related to the coefficient of performance of the reversible refrigerator obtained by running the engine backward?

**13.** In a heat pump, heat $Q_2$ is extracted from the outside atmosphere at $T_2$ and a larger quantity of heat $Q_1$ is delivered to the inside of the house at $T_1$, with the performance of work $W$. (a) Draw a schematic diagram of a heat pump. (b) How does it differ in principle from a refrigerator? In practical use? (c) How are $Q_1$, $Q_2$, and $W$ related to one another? (d) Can a heat pump be reversed for use in summer? Explain. (e) What advantages does such a pump have over other heating devices?

**14.** In a heat pump, heat from the outdoors at −5° C is transferred to a room at 17° C, energy being supplied by an electric motor. How many joules of heat will be delivered to the room for each joule of electric energy consumed, ideally?

**15.** Suppose that we were to take as our measure of temperature $−1/T$ rather than $T$. The unit of this new measure might be the Nivlek (Kelvin spelled backwards) degree (°N). Write a sequence of temperatures in °N extending from positive to negative values of $T$. (See footnote, page 532.)

**16.** (a) Show that when a substance of mass $m$ having a constant specific heat $c$ is heated from $T_1$ to $T_2$ the entropy change is

$$S_2 - S_1 = mc \ln \frac{T_2}{T_1}.$$

(b) Does the entropy of the substance decrease on cooling? If so, does the total entropy decrease in such a process? Explain.

**17.** In a specific heat experiment 100 gm of lead ($c_p = 0.0345$ cal/gmC°) at 100° C is mixed with 200 gm of water at 20° C. Find the difference in entropy of the system at the end from its value before mixing.

**18.** Four moles of an ideal gas are caused to expand from a volume $V_1$ to a volume $V_2(= 2V_1)$. (a) If the expansion is isothermal at the temperature $T = 400°$ K, deduce an expression for the work done by the expanding gas. (b) For the isothermal expansion just described, deduce an expression for the change in entropy, if any. (c) If the expansion were reversibly adiabatic instead of isothermal, would the change in entropy be positive, negative, or zero?

**19.** Heat can be removed from water at 0° C and atmospheric pressure without causing the water to freeze, if done with little disturbance of the water. Suppose the water is cooled to −5.0° C before ice begins to form. What is the change in entropy per unit mass occurring during the sudden freezing that then takes place?

**20.** An 8.00-gm ice cube at −10.0° C is dropped into a thermos flask containing 100 cm³ of water at 20.0° C. What is the change in entropy of the system when a final equilibrium state is reached?

**21.** A brass rod is in contact thermally with a heat reservoir at 127° C at one end and a heat reservoir at 27° C at the other end. Compute the total change in the entropy arising from the process of conduction of 1200 cal of heat through the rod. Does the entropy of the rod change in the process?

**22.** A mole of a monatomic ideal gas is taken from an initial state of pressure $p$ and volume $V$ to a final state of pressure $2p$ and volume $2V$ by two different processes.

(I) It expands isothermally until its volume is doubled, and then its pressure is increased at constant volume to the final state.    (II) It is compressed isothermally until its pressure is doubled, and then its volume is increased at constant pressure to the final state.

Show the path of each process on a $p$-$V$ diagram.    For each process calculate in terms of $p$ and $V$, or of $T$, (a) the heat absorbed by the gas in each part of the process; (b) the work done on the gas in each part of the process; (c) the change in internal energy of the gas $U_f - U_i$; (d) the change in entropy of the gas $S_f - S_i$.

**23.** One mole of hydrogen gas and 1.0 mole of nitrogen gas are in adjacent containers at the same pressure $p$ and temperature $T$.    The pressure and temperature are such that both gases behave virtually ideally.    (a) If the rms speed of the $H_2$ molecules is 1850 meters/sec at temperature $T$, what will the rms speed be of the $N_2$ molecules? (b) For which gas will a larger percentage or fraction of the molecules have speeds within $\pm 50$ meters/sec of the rms speed?    (c) If the containers are connected so that the $H_2$ and $N_2$ mix, will the change in entropy be positive, negative, or zero?

**24.** (a) A body of finite mass is originally at temperature $T_2$, higher than that of a heat reservoir at a temperature $T_1$.    An engine operates in infinitesimal cycles between the body and the reservoir until it lowers the temperature of the body from $T_2$ to $T_1$. Prove that the maximum work obtainable from the engine is $W_{max} = Q - T_1(S_2 - S_1)$, where $S_1 - S_2$ is the entropy change in the body and $Q$ is the heat extracted from the body by the engine.    (b) A body of finite mass is originally at temperature $T_1$, the same as that of a heat reservoir.    A refrigerator operates in infinitesimal cycles between the body and reservoir until it lowers the temperature of the body from $T_1$ to $T_0$.    Prove that the minimum amount of work which must be supplied to the refrigerator is $W_{min} = T_1(S_1 - S_0) - Q$, where $S_0 - S_1$ is the entropy change in the body and $Q$ is the heat extracted from the body by the refrigerator.

**25.** In general, the probability $w_{12}$ of a complex event, which consists of two unrelated simple events, is equal to the product of their respective probabilities $w_1$, $w_2$.    The entropy $S_{12}$ of a complex system which consists of two simple systems is just the sum of their respective entropies, $S_1$, $S_2$.    Show that Eq. 25-15, which relates probability and entropy, is consistent with the additive property of entropy and the multiplicative property of probability for a complex system.

# Physics   PART II

# Charge and Matter

## CHAPTER 26

## 26–1   Electromagnetism—A Preview

The science of electricity has its roots in the observation, known to Thales of Miletus in 600 B.C., that a rubbed piece of amber will attract bits of straw. The study of magnetism goes back to the observation that naturally occurring "stones" (that is, magnetite) will attract iron. These two sciences developed quite separately until 1820, when Hans Christian Oersted (1777–1851) observed a connection between them, namely, that an *electric* current in a wire can affect a *magnetic* compass needle (Section 33–1).

The new science of electromagnetism was developed further by many workers, of whom one of the most important was Michael Faraday (1791–1867). It fell to James Clerk Maxwell (1831–1879) to put the laws of electromagnetism in the form in which we know them today. These laws, often called *Maxwell's equations*, are displayed in Table 38–3, which the student may want to examine at this time. These laws play the same role in electromagnetism that Newton's laws of motion and of gravitation do in mechanics.

Although Maxwell's synthesis of electromagnetism rests heavily on the work of his predecessors, his own contribution is central and vital. Maxwell deduced that light is electromagnetic in nature and that its speed can be found by making purely electric and magnetic measurements. Thus the science of optics was intimately connected with those of electricity and of magnetism. The scope of Maxwell's equations is remarkable, including as it does the fundamental principles of all large-scale electromagnetic and optical devices such as motors, cyclotrons, electronic computers, radio, television, microwave radar, microscopes, and telescopes.

The development of classical electromagnetism did not end with Maxwell. The English physicist Oliver Heaviside (1850–1925) and especially the Dutch physicist H. A. Lorentz (1853–1928) contributed substantially to the clarification of Maxwell's theory. Heinrich Hertz (1857–1894) * took a great step forward when, more than twenty years after Maxwell set up his theory, he produced in the laboratory electromagnetic "Maxwellian waves" of a kind that we would now call short radio waves. It remained for Marconi and others to exploit this practical application of the electromagnetic waves of Maxwell and Hertz.

Present interest in electromagnetism takes two forms. At the level of engineering applications Maxwell's equations are used constantly and universally in the solution of a wide variety of practical problems. At the level of the foundations of the theory there is a continuing effort to extend its scope in such a way that electromagnetism is revealed as a special case of a more general theory. Such a theory would also include (say) the theories of gravitation and of quantum physics. This grand synthesis has not yet been achieved.

### 26–2  Electric Charge

The rest of this chapter deals with electric charge and its relationship to matter. We can show that there are *two kinds* of charge by rubbing a glass rod with silk and hanging it from a long silk thread as in Fig. 26–1. If a second glass rod is rubbed with silk and held near the rubbed end of the first rod, the rods will repel each other. On the other hand, a hard-rubber rod rubbed with fur will *attract* the glass rod. Two hard-rubber rods rubbed with fur will repel each other. We explain these facts by saying that rubbing a rod gives it an *electric charge* and that the charges on the two rods exert forces on each other. Clearly the charges on the glass and on the hard rubber must be different in nature.

Benjamin Franklin (1706–1790), who, among his other achievements, was the first American physicist, named the kind of electricity that appears on the glass *positive* and the kind that appears on the hard rubber *negative;* these names have remained to this day. We can sum up these experiments by saying that *like charges repel and unlike charges attract.*

Electric effects are not limited to glass rubbed with silk or to hard rubber rubbed with fur. Any substance rubbed with any other under suitable conditions will become charged to some extent; by comparing the unknown charge with a charged glass rod or a charged hard-rubber rod, it can be labeled as either positive or negative.

The modern view of bulk matter is that, in its normal or neutral state, it contains equal amounts of positive and negative electricity. If two bodies like glass and silk are rubbed together, a small amount of charge is transferred from one to the other, upsetting the electric neutrality of each. In this case the glass would become positive, the silk negative.

---

* "Heinrich Hertz," by P. and E. Morrison, *Scientific American,* December 1957.

**Fig. 26–1**   Two positively charged
glass rods repel each other.

## 26–3   Conductors and Insulators

A metal rod held in the hand and rubbed with fur will not seem to develop
a charge.  It is possible to charge such a rod, however, if it is furnished with
a glass or hard-rubber handle and if the metal is not touched with the hands
while rubbing it.  The explanation is that metals, the human body, and the
earth are *conductors* of electricity and that glass, hard rubber, plastics, etc.,
are *insulators* (also called *dielectrics*).

In conductors electric charges are free to move through the material,
whereas in insulators they are not.  Although there are no perfect insulators,
the insulating ability of fused quartz is about $10^{25}$ times as great as that of
copper, so that for many practical purposes some materials behave as if they
were perfect insulators.

In metals a fairly subtle experiment called the *Hall effect* (see Section 33–5)
shows that only negative charge is free to move.  Positive charge is as im-
mobile as it is in glass or in any other dielectric.  The actual charge carriers in
metals are the *free electrons*.  When isolated atoms are combined to form a
metallic solid, the outer electrons of the atom do not remain attached to
individual atoms but become free to move throughout the volume of the
solid.  For some conductors, such as electrolytes, both positive and negative
charges can move.

A class of materials called *semiconductors* is intermediate between conductors and insulators in its ability to conduct electricity. Among the elements, silicon and germanium are well-known examples. In semiconductors the electrical conductivity can often be greatly increased by adding very small amounts of other elements; traces of arsenic or boron are often added to silicon for this purpose. Semiconductors have many practical applications, among which is their use in the construction of transistors. The mode of action of semiconductors cannot be described adequately without some understanding of the basic principles of quantum physics.

## 26–4 Coulomb's Law

Charles Augustin de Coulomb (1736–1806) in 1785 first measured electrical attractions and repulsions quantitatively and deduced the law that governs them. His apparatus, shown in Fig. 26–2, resembles the hanging rod of Fig. 26–1, except that the charges in Fig. 26–2 are confined to small spheres *a* and *b*.

If *a* and *b* are charged, the electric force on *a* will tend to twist the suspension fiber. Coulomb canceled out this twisting effect by turning the suspension head through the angle $\theta$ needed to keep the two charges at the particular distance apart in which he was interested. The angle $\theta$ is then a relative measure of the electric force acting on charge *a*. The device of Fig. 26–2 is called a *torsion balance;* a similar arrangement was used later by Cavendish to measure gravitational attractions (Section 16–3).

Coulomb's first experimental results can be represented by

$$F \propto \frac{1}{r^2}.$$

$F$ is the magnitude of the force that acts on each of the two charges *a* and *b*; *r* is their distance apart. These forces, as Newton's third law requires, act along the line joining the charges but point in opposite directions. Note that the magnitude of the force on each charge is the same, even though the charges may be different.

Coulomb also studied how the electrical force varied with the relative size of the charges on the spheres of his torsion balance. For example, if we touch a charged conducting sphere to an exactly similar but uncharged conducting sphere, the original charge must divide equally between the spheres. By such techniques Coulomb extended the inverse square relationship to

$$F \propto \frac{q_1 q_2}{r^2}, \tag{26–1}$$

where $q_1$ and $q_2$ are relative measures of the charges on spheres *a* and *b*. Equation 26–1, which is called *Coulomb's law*, holds only for charged objects whose sizes are much smaller than the distance between them. We often say that it holds only for *point charges*.

Coulomb's law resembles the inverse square law of gravitation which was already more than 100 years old at the time of Coulomb's experiments; *q* plays the role of *m* in that law. In gravity, however, the forces are always

**Fig. 26–2** Coulomb's torsion balance from his 1785 memoir to the French Academy of Sciences.

attractive; this corresponds to the fact that there are two kinds of electricity but (apparently) only one kind of mass.

Our belief in Coulomb's law does not rest quantitatively on Coulomb's experiments. Torsion balance measurements are difficult to make to an accuracy of better than a few per cent. Such measurements could not, for example, convince us that the exponent in Eq. 26–1 is exactly 2 and not, say, 2.01. In Section 28–5 we show that Coulomb's law can also be deduced from an indirect experiment which shows that the exponent in Eq. 26–1 lies between the limits of approximately 2.000000002 and 1.999999998. Small wonder that we usually assume the exponent to be exactly 2.

Although we have established the physical concept of electric charge, we have not yet defined a unit in which it may be measured. It is possible to do so operationally by putting equal charges $q$ on the spheres of a torsion balance and by measuring the magnitude $F$ of the force that acts on each when the charges are a measured distance $r$ apart. One could then define $q$ to have a unit value if a unit force acts on each charge when the charges are separated by a unit distance and one can give a name to the unit of charge so defined.*

For practical reasons having to do with the accuracy of measurements, the unit of charge in the mks system is not defined using a torsion balance but is derived from the unit of electric current. If the ends of a long wire are connected to the terminals of a battery, it is common knowledge that an *electric current* $i$ is set up in the wire. We visualize this current as a flow of charge. The mks unit of current is the *ampere* (abbr. *amp*). In Section 34–4 we describe the operational procedures in terms of which the ampere is defined.

The mks unit of charge is the *coulomb* (abbr. *coul*). *A coulomb is defined as the amount of charge that flows through a given cross section of a wire in 1 second if there is a steady current of 1 ampere in the wire.* In symbols

$$q = it, \qquad (26\text{–}2)$$

where $q$ is in coulombs if $i$ is in amperes and $t$ is in seconds. Thus, if a wire is connected to an insulated metal sphere, a charge of $10^{-6}$ coul can be put on the sphere if a current of 1.0 amp exists in the wire for $10^{-6}$ sec.

▶ **Example 1.** A copper penny has a mass of 3.1 gm. Being electrically neutral, it contains equal amounts of positive and negative electricity. What is the magnitude $q$ of these charges? A copper atom has a positive nuclear charge of $4.6 \times 10^{-18}$ coul and a negative electronic charge of equal magnitude.

The number $N$ of copper atoms in a penny is found from the ratio

$$\frac{N}{N_0} = \frac{m}{M},$$

where $N_0$ is Avogadro's number, $m$ the mass of the coin, and $M$ the atomic weight of copper. This yields, solving for $N$,

$$N = \frac{(6.0 \times 10^{23} \text{ atoms/mole})(3.1 \text{ gm})}{64 \text{ gm/mole}} = 2.9 \times 10^{22} \text{ atoms}.$$

The charge $q$ is

$$q = (4.6 \times 10^{-18} \text{ coul/atom})(2.9 \times 10^{22} \text{ atoms}) = 1.3 \times 10^5 \text{ coul}.$$

In a 100-watt, 110-volt light bulb the current is 0.91 amp. The student should verify that it would take 40 hr for a charge of this amount to pass through this bulb. ◀

---

* This scheme is the basis for the definition of the unit of charge called the *statcoulomb*. However, in this book we do not use this unit or the systems of units of which it is a part; see Appendix L, however.

Equation 26-1 can be written as an equality by inserting a constant of proportionality. Instead of writing this simply as, say, $k$, it is usually written in a more complex way as $1/4\pi\epsilon_0$ or

$$F = \frac{1}{4\pi\epsilon_0} \frac{q_1 q_2}{r^2}. \qquad (26\text{-}3)$$

Certain equations that are derived from Eq. 26-3, but are used more often than it is, will be simpler in form if we do this.

In the mks system we can measure $q_1$, $q_2$, $r$, and $F$ in Eq. 26-3 in ways that do not depend on Coulomb's law. Numbers with units can be assigned to them. There is no choice about the so-called *permittivity constant* $\epsilon_0$; it must have that value which makes the right-hand side of Eq. 26-3 equal to the left-hand side. This (measured) value turns out to be *

$$\epsilon_0 = 8.85418 \times 10^{-12} \text{ coul}^2/\text{nt-m}^2.$$

In this book the value $8.9 \times 10^{-12}$ coul$^2$/nt-m$^2$ will be accurate enough for all problems. For direct application of Coulomb's law or in any problem in which the quantity $1/4\pi\epsilon_0$ occurs we may use, with sufficient accuracy for this book,

$$1/4\pi\epsilon_0 = 9.0 \times 10^9 \text{ nt-m}^2/\text{coul}^2.$$

▶ **Example 2.** Let the total positive and the total negative charges in a copper penny be separated to a distance such that their force of attraction is 1.0 lb ($= 4.5$ nt). How far apart must they be?

We have (Eq. 26-3)

$$F = \frac{1}{4\pi\epsilon_0} \frac{q_1 q_2}{r^2}.$$

Putting $q_1 q_2 = q^2$ (see Example 1) and solving for $r$ yields

$$r = q \sqrt{\frac{1/4\pi\epsilon_0}{F}} = 1.3 \times 10^5 \text{ coul} \sqrt{\frac{9.0 \times 10^9 \text{ nt-m}^2/\text{coul}^2}{4.5 \text{ nt}}}$$

$$= 5.8 \times 10^9 \text{ meters} = 3.6 \times 10^6 \text{ miles.}$$

This suggests that it is not possible to upset the electrical neutrality of gross objects by any very large amount. What would be the force between the two charges if they were placed 1.0 meter apart? ◀

If more than two charges are present, Eq. 26-3 holds for every pair of charges. Let the charges be $q_1$, $q_2$, and $q_3$, etc.; we calculate the force exerted on any one (say $q_1$) by all the others from the vector equation

$$\mathbf{F}_1 = \mathbf{F}_{12} + \mathbf{F}_{13} + \mathbf{F}_{14} + \cdots, \qquad (26\text{-}4)$$

where $\mathbf{F}_{12}$, for example, is the force exerted on $q_1$ by $q_2$.

---

* For practical reasons this value is not actually measured by direct application of Eq. 26-3 but in an equivalent although more circuitous way that is described in Section 30-2.

▶ **Example 3.** Figure 26–3 shows three charges $q_1$, $q_2$, and $q_3$. What force acts on $q_1$? Assume that $q_1 = -1.0 \times 10^{-6}$ coul, $q_2 = +3.0 \times 10^{-6}$ coul, $q_3 = -2.0 \times 10^{-6}$ coul, $r_{12} = 15$ cm, $r_{13} = 10$ cm, and $\theta = 30°$.

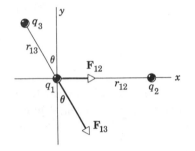

**Fig. 263** Example 3. Showing the forces exerted on $q_1$ by $q_2$ and $q_3$.

From Eq. 26–3, ignoring the signs of the charges, since we are interested only in the magnitudes of the forces,

$$F_{12} = \frac{1}{4\pi\epsilon_0} \frac{q_1 q_2}{r_{12}^2}$$

$$= \frac{(9.0 \times 10^9 \text{ nt-m}^2/\text{coul}^2)(1.0 \times 10^{-6} \text{ coul})(3.0 \times 10^{-6} \text{ coul})}{(1.5 \times 10^{-1} \text{ meter})^2}$$

$$= 1.2 \text{ nt}$$

and
$$F_{13} = \frac{(9.0 \times 10^9 \text{ nt-m}^2/\text{coul}^2)(1.0 \times 10^{-6} \text{ coul})(2.0 \times 10^{-6} \text{ coul})}{(1.0 \times 10^{-1} \text{ meter})^2}$$

$$= 1.8 \text{ nt.}$$

The directions of $\mathbf{F}_{12}$ and $\mathbf{F}_{13}$ are as shown in the figure.

The components of the resultant force $\mathbf{F}_1$ acting on $q_1$ (see Eq. 26–4) are

$$F_{1x} = F_{12x} + F_{13x} = F_{12} + F_{13} \sin \theta$$

$$= 1.2 \text{ nt} + (1.8 \text{ nt})(\sin 30°) = 2.1 \text{ nt}$$

and
$$F_{1y} = F_{12y} + F_{13y} = 0 - F_{13} \cos \theta$$

$$= -(1.8 \text{ nt})(\cos 30°) = -1.6 \text{ nt.}$$

The student should find the magnitude of $\mathbf{F}_1$ and the angle it makes with the $x$-axis.

◀

### 26–5 Charge Is Quantized

In Franklin's day electric charge was thought of as a continuous fluid, an idea that was useful for many purposes. The atomic theory of matter, however, has shown that fluids themselves, such as water and air, are not continuous but are made up of atoms. Experiment shows that the "electric fluid" is not continuous either but that it is made up of integral multiples of a certain minimum electric charge. This fundamental charge, to which we give the symbol $e$, has the magnitude $1.60210 \times 10^{-19}$ coul. Any physically existing charge $q$, no matter what its origin, can be written as $ne$ where $n$ is a positive or a negative integer.

When a physical property such as charge exists in discrete "packets" rather than in continuous amounts, the property is said to be *quantized*. Quantization is basic to modern physics. The existence of atoms and of particles like the electron and the proton indicates that *mass* is quantized also. Later the student will learn that several other properties prove to be quantized when suitably examined on the atomic scale; among them are energy and angular momentum.

The *quantum of charge e* is so small that the "graininess" of electricity does not show up in large-scale experiments, just as we do not realize that the air we breathe is made up of atoms. In an ordinary 110-volt, 100-watt light bulb, for example, $6 \times 10^{18}$ elementary charges enter and leave the filament every second.

There exists today no theory that predicts the quantization of charge (or the quantization of mass, that is, the existence of fundamental particles such as protons, electrons, pions, etc.). Even assuming quantization, the classical theory of electromagnetism and Newtonian mechanics are incomplete in that they do not correctly describe the behavior of charge and matter on the atomic scale. The classical theory of electromagnetism, for example, describes correctly what happens when a bar magnet is thrust through a closed copper loop; it fails, however, if we wish to explain the magnetism of the bar in terms of the atoms that make it up. The more detailed theories of quantum physics are needed for this and similar problems.

### 26–6  Charge and Matter

Matter as we ordinarily experience it can be regarded as composed of three kinds of elementary particles, the proton, the neutron, and the electron. Table 26–1 shows their masses and charges. Note that the masses of the neutron and the proton are approximately equal but that the electron is lighter by a factor of about 1840.

Atoms are made up of a dense, positively charged *nucleus*, surrounded by a

### Table 26–1

PROPERTIES OF THE PROTON, THE NEUTRON, AND THE ELECTRON

| Particle | Symbol | Charge | Mass |
|----------|--------|--------|------|
| Proton | $p$ | $+e$ | $1.67252 \times 10^{-27}$ kg |
| Neutron | $n$ | $0$ | $1.67482 \times 10^{-27}$ kg |
| Electron | $e^-$ | $-e$ | $9.1091 \ \times 10^{-31}$ kg |

**Fig. 26–4** An atom, suggesting the electron cloud and, above, an enlarged view of the nucleus.

cloud of electrons; see Fig. 26–4. The nucleus varies in radius from about $1 \times 10^{-15}$ meter for hydrogen to about $7 \times 10^{-15}$ meter for the heaviest atoms. The outer diameter of the electron cloud, that is, the diameter of the the atom, lies in the range $1$–$3 \times 10^{-10}$ meter, about $10^5$ times larger than the nuclear diameter.

▶ **Example 4.** The distance $r$ between the electron and the proton in the hydrogen atom is about $5.3 \times 10^{-11}$ meter. What are the magnitudes of (a) the electrical force and (b) the gravitational force between these two particles?

From Coulomb's law,

$$F_e = \frac{1}{4\pi\epsilon_0} \frac{q_1 q_2}{r^2}$$

$$= \frac{(9.0 \times 10^9 \text{ nt-m}^2/\text{coul}^2)(1.6 \times 10^{-19} \text{ coul})^2}{(5.3 \times 10^{-11} \text{ meter})^2}$$

$$= 8.1 \times 10^{-8} \text{ nt.}$$

The gravitational force is given by Eq. 16–1, or

$$F_g = G \frac{m_1 m_2}{r^2}$$

$$= \frac{(6.7 \times 10^{-11} \text{ nt-m}^2/\text{kg}^2)(9.1 \times 10^{-31} \text{ kg})(1.7 \times 10^{-27} \text{ kg})}{(5.3 \times 10^{-11} \text{ meter})^2}$$

$$= 3.7 \times 10^{-47} \text{ nt.}$$

Thus the electrical force is about $10^{39}$ times stronger than the gravitational force. ◀

The significance of Coulomb's law goes far beyond the description of the forces acting between charged balls or rods. This law, when incorporated into the structure of quantum physics, correctly describes (a) the electric forces that bind the electrons of an atom to its nucleus, (b) the forces that bind atoms together to form molecules, and (c) the forces that bind atoms or molecules together to form solids or liquids. Thus most of the forces of our daily experience that are not gravitational in nature are electrical. A force transmitted by a steel cable is basically an electrical force because, if we pass an imaginary plane through the cable at right angles to it, it is only the attractive electrical interatomic forces acting between atoms on opposite sides of the plane that keep the cable from parting. We ourselves are an assembly of nuclei and electrons bound together in a stable configuration by Coulomb forces.

In the atomic *nucleus* we encounter a new force which is neither gravitational nor electrical in nature. This strong attractive force, which binds together the protons and neutrons that make up the nucleus, is called simply *the nuclear force*. If this force were not present, the nucleus would fly apart at once because of the strong Coulomb repulsion force that acts between its protons. The nature of the nuclear force is only partially understood today and forms the central problem of present-day researches in nuclear physics.

▶ **Example 5.** What repulsive Coulomb force exists between two protons in a nucleus of iron? Assume a separation of $4.0 \times 10^{-15}$ meter.

From Coulomb's law,

$$F = \frac{1}{4\pi\epsilon_0} \frac{q_1 q_2}{r^2}$$

$$= \frac{(9.0 \times 10^9 \text{ nt-m}^2/\text{coul}^2)(1.6 \times 10^{-19} \text{ coul})^2}{(4.0 \times 10^{-15} \text{ meter})^2}$$

$$= 14 \text{ nt.}$$

This enormous repulsive force must be more than compensated for by the strong attractive nuclear forces. This example, combined with Example 4, shows that nuclear binding forces are much stronger than atomic binding forces. Atomic binding forces are, in turn, much stronger than gravitational forces for the same particles separated by the same distance.  ◀

The repulsive Coulomb forces acting between the protons in a nucleus make the nucleus less stable than it otherwise would be. The spontaneous emission of alpha particles from heavy nuclei and the phenomenon of nuclear fission are evidences of this instability.

The fact that heavy nuclei contain significantly more neutrons than protons is still another effect of the Coulomb forces. Consider Fig. 26–5 in which a particular atomic species is represented by a circle, the coordinates being $Z$, the number of protons in the nucleus (that is, the *atomic number*), and $N$, the number of neutrons in the nucleus (that is, the *neutron number*). Stable nuclei are represented by filled circles and radio-active nuclei, that is, nuclei that disintegrate spontaneously, emitting electrons or $\alpha$-particles, by open circles. Note that all elements (iron, for example, for which $Z = 26$; see arrow) exist in a number of different forms, called *isotopes*.

Figure 26–5 shows that light nuclei, for which the Coulomb forces are relatively unimportant,* lie on or close to the line labeled "$N = Z$" and thus have about equal numbers of neutrons and protons. The heavier nuclei have a pronounced neutron excess, $U^{238}$ having 92 protons and $238 - 92$ or 146 neutrons.† In the absence of Coulomb forces we would assume, extending the $N = Z$ rule, that the most stable nucleus with 238 particles would have 119 protons and 119 neutrons. However, such a nucleus, if assembled, would fly apart at once because of Coulomb repulsion. Relative stability is found only if 27 of the protons are replaced by neutrons, thus diluting the total Coulomb repulsion. Even in $U^{238}$ Coulomb repulsion is still very important because (a) this nucleus is radioactive and emits $\alpha$-particles, and (b) it may break up into two large fragments (*fission*) if it absorbs a neutron; both processes result in separation of the nuclear charge and are Coulomb repulsion effects. Figure 26–5 shows that *all* nuclei with $Z > 83$ are unstable.

We have pointed out that matter, as we ordinarily experience it, is made up of electrons, neutrons, and protons. Nature exhibits much more variety than this, however. No fewer than 28 distinct elementary particles are now known, most of them having been discovered since 1940, either in the penetrating cosmic rays that come to us from beyond our atmosphere or in the reaction products of giant cyclotron-like devices.

Appendix E, which lists some properties of these particles, shows that, like the more familiar particles of Table 26–1, their charges are quantized, the quantum of charge again being $e$. An understanding of the nature of these particles and of their relationships to each other is perhaps the most significant research goal of modern physics.

---

* Coulomb forces are important in relation to the strong nuclear attractive forces only for large nuclei, because Coulomb repulsion occurs between *every pair* of protons in the nucleus but the attractive nuclear force does not. In $U^{238}$, for example, every proton exerts a force of repulsion on each of the other 91 protons. However, each proton (and neutron) exerts a nuclear attraction on only a small number of other neutrons and protons that happen to be near it. As we proceed to larger nuclei, the amount of energy associated with the repulsive Coulomb forces increases much faster than that associated with the attractive nuclear forces.

† The superscript in this notation is the *mass number A* ($= N + Z$). This is the total number of particles in the nucleus.

**Fig. 26-5** The filled circles represent stable nuclei, the open ones radioactive nuclei. This figure does not show the more recently discovered radioactive nuclei, which appear throughout the chart, extending up to $Z = 103$.

## 26–7 Charge Is Conserved

When a glass rod is rubbed with silk, a positive charge appears on the rod. Measurement shows that a negative charge of equal magnitude appears on the silk. This suggests that rubbing does not create charge but merely transfers it from one object to another, disturbing slightly the electrical neutrality of each. This hypothesis of the *conservation of charge* has stood up under close experimental scrutiny both for large-scale events and at the atomic and nuclear level; no exceptions have ever been found.

An interesting example of charge conservation comes about when an electron (charge $= -e$) and a positron (charge $= +e$) are brought close to each other. The two particles may simply disappear, converting all their rest mass into energy according to the well-known $E = mc^2$ relationship; this *annihilation* process was described in Section 8–9. The energy appears in the form of two oppositely directed *gamma rays*, which are similar in character to X-rays. The net charge is zero both before and after the event so that charge is conserved. Rest mass is *not* conserved, being turned completely into energy.

Another example of charge conservation is found in radioactive decay, of which the following process is typical:

$$U^{238} \to Th^{234} + He^4. \tag{26-5}$$

The radioactive "parent" nucleus, $U^{238}$, contains 92 protons (that is, its atomic number $Z = 92$). It disintegrates spontaneously by emitting an $\alpha$-particle (He$^4$; $Z = 2$) transmuting itself into the nucleus Th$^{234}$, with $Z = 90$. Thus the amount of charge present before disintegration $(+92e)$ is the same as that present after the disintegration.

A final example of charge conservation is found in nuclear reactions, of which the bombardment of Ca$^{44}$ with cyclotron-accelerated protons is typical. In a particular collision a neutron may emerge from the nucleus, leaving Sc$^{44}$ as a "residual" nucleus:

$$Ca^{44} + p \to Sc^{44} + n.$$

The sum of the atomic numbers before the reaction $(20 + 1)$ is exactly equal to the sum of the atomic numbers after the reaction $(21 + 0)$. Again charge is conserved.

## QUESTIONS

1. You are given two metal spheres mounted on portable insulating supports. Find a way to give them equal and opposite charges. You may use a glass rod rubbed with silk but may not touch it to the spheres. Do the spheres have to be of equal size for your method to work?

2. A charged rod attracts bits of dry cork dust which, after touching the rod, often jump violently away from it. Explain.

3. If a charged glass rod is held near one end of an insulated uncharged metal rod as in Fig. 26–6, electrons are drawn to one end, as shown. Why does the flow of electrons cease? There is an almost inexhaustible supply of them in the metal rod.

4. In Fig. 26–6 does any net electrical force act on the metal rod? Explain.

5. An insulated rod is said to carry an electric charge. How could you verify this and determine the sign of the charge?

6. Why do electrostatic experiments not work well on humid days?

7. A person standing on an insulated stool touches a charged, insulated conductor. Is the conductor discharged completely?

8. (a) A positively charged glass rod attracts a suspended object. Can we conclude that the object is negatively charged? (b) A positively charged glass rod *repels* a suspended object. Can we conclude that the object is *positively* charged?

**Fig. 26–6**

9. Is the Coulomb force that one charge exerts on another changed if other charges are brought nearby?

10. The quantum of charge is $1.60 \times 10^{-19}$ coul. Is there a corresponding single quantum of mass?

11. Verify the fact that the decay schemes for the elementary particles in Appendix E are consistent with charge conservation.

12. What does it mean to say that a physical quantity is (a) quantized or (b) conserved? Give some examples.

13. A nucleus $U^{238}$ splits into two identical parts. Are the nuclei so produced likely to be stable or radioactive?

## PROBLEMS

1. Protons in the cosmic rays strike the earth's upper atmosphere at a rate, averaged over the earth's surface, of 0.15 protons/cm²-sec. What total current does the earth receive from beyond its atmosphere in the form of incident cosmic ray protons? The earth's radius is $6.4 \times 10^{6}$ meters.

2. A point charge of $+3.0 \times 10^{-6}$ coul is 12 cm distant from a second point charge of $-1.5 \times 10^{-6}$ coul. Calculate the magnitude and direction of the force on each charge.

3. Two similar balls of mass $m$ are hung from silk threads of length $l$ and carry similar charges $q$ as in Fig. 26–7. Assume that $\theta$ is so small that $\tan \theta$ can be replaced by its approximate equal, $\sin \theta$. To this approximation show that

$$ x = \left( \frac{q^2 l}{2 \pi \epsilon_0 m g} \right)^{\frac{1}{3}} $$

where $x$ is the separation between the balls. If $l = 120$ cm, $m = 10$ gm, and $x = 5.0$ cm, what is $q$?

4. Assume that each ball in Problem 3 is losing charge at the rate of $1.0 \times 10^{-9}$ coul/sec. At what instantaneous relative speed ($= dx/dt$) do the balls approach each other initially?

5. Three small balls, each of mass 10 gm, are suspended separately from a common point by silk threads, each 1.0 meter

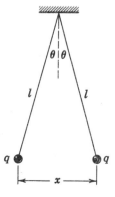

**Fig. 26–7**

long. The balls are identically charged and hang at the corners of an equilateral triangle 0.1 meter long on a side. What is the charge on each ball?

6. In Fig. 26–8 what is the resultant force on the charge in the lower left corner of the square? Assume that $q = 1.0 \times 10^{-7}$ coul and $a = 5.0$ cm.

**Fig. 26–8**

7. A charge $Q$ is placed at each of two opposite corners of a square. A charge $q$ is placed at each of the other two corners. (a) If the resultant electrical force on $Q$ is zero, how are $Q$ and $q$ related? (b) Could $q$ be chosen to make the resultant force on *every* charge zero?

8. How far apart must two protons be if the electrical repulsive force acting on either one is equal to its weight?

9. (a) What equal positive charges would have to be placed on the earth and on the moon to neutralize their gravitational attraction? (b) Do you need to know the lunar distance to solve this problem? (c) How many pounds of hydrogen would be needed to provide the positive charge calculated in a?

10. A certain charge $Q$ is to be divided into two parts, $q$ and $Q - q$. What is the relationship of $Q$ to $q$ if the two parts, placed a given distance apart, are to have a maximum Coulomb repulsion?

11. Each of two small spheres is charged positively, the combined charge being $5.0 \times 10^{-5}$ coul. If each sphere is repelled from the other by a force of 1.0 newton when the spheres are 2.0 meters apart, how is the total charge distributed between the spheres?

12. Two equal positive point charges are separated by a distance $2a$. A point test charge is located in a plane which is normal to the line joining these charges and midway between them. (a) Calculate the radius $r$ of the circle of symmetry in this plane for which the force on the test charge has a maximum value. (b) What is the direction of this force, assuming a positive test charge.

13. A cube of edge $a$ carries a point charge $q$ at each corner. (a) Show that the magnitude of the resultant force on any one of the charges is

$$F = \frac{0.261q^2}{\epsilon_0 a^2}.$$

(b) What is the direction of $\mathbf{F}$ relative to the cube edges?

14. Estimate roughly the number of coulombs of positive charge in a glass of water.

15. (a) How many electrons would have to be removed from a penny to leave it with a charge of $+10^{-7}$ coul? (b) What fraction of the electrons in the penny does this correspond to?

16. The radius of a copper nucleus is about $1.9 \times 10^{-13}$ cm. Calculate the density of the material that makes up the nucleus. Does your answer seem reasonable? (The atomic weight of copper is 64 gm/mole; ignore the mass of the electrons in comparison to that of the nucleus.)

17. In the radioactive decay of $U^{238}$ (see Eq. 26–5) the center of the emerging $\alpha$-particle is, at a certain instant, $9 \times 10^{-15}$ meter from the center of the residual nucleus $Th^{234}$. At this instant (a) what is the force on the $\alpha$-particle and (b) what is its acceleration?

# The Electric Field

## 27-1 The Electric Field

With every point in space near the earth we can associate a *gravitational field strength* vector $\mathbf{g}$ (see Eq. 16–12). This is the gravitational acceleration that a test body, placed at that point and released, would experience. If $m$ is the mass of the body and $\mathbf{F}$ the gravitational force acting on it, $\mathbf{g}$ is given by

$$\mathbf{g} = \mathbf{F}/m. \tag{27-1}$$

This is an example of a *vector field*. For points near the surface of the earth the field is often taken as *uniform*; that is, $\mathbf{g}$ is the same for all points.

The flow of water in a river provides another example of a vector field, called a *flow field* (see Section 18–7). Every point in the water has associated with it a vector quantity, the velocity $\mathbf{v}$ with which the water flows past the point. If $\mathbf{g}$ and $\mathbf{v}$ do not change with time, the corresponding fields are described as *stationary*. In the case of the river note that even though the water is moving the vector $\mathbf{v}$ at any point does not change with time for steady-flow conditions.

The space surrounding a charged rod is affected by the presence of the rod, and we speak of an *electric field* in this space. In the same way we speak of a *magnetic field* in the space around a bar magnet. In the classical theory of electromagnetism the electric and magnetic fields are central concepts.

Before Faraday's time, the force acting between charged particles was thought of as a direct and instantaneous interaction between the two particles. This *action-at-a-distance* view was also held for magnetic and for gravitational forces. Today we prefer to think in terms of electric fields as follows:

1. Charge $q_1$ in Fig. 27–1 sets up an electric field in the space around itself. This field is suggested by the shading in the figure; later we shall show how to represent electric fields more concretely.

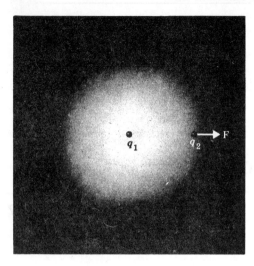

**Fig. 27–1**   Charge $q_1$ sets up a field that exerts a force **F** on charge $q_2$.

2. The field acts on charge $q_2$; this shows up in the force **F** that $q_2$ experiences.

The field plays an intermediary role in the forces between charges. There are two separate problems: (*a*) calculating the fields that are set up by given distributions of charge and (*b*) calculating the forces that given fields will exert on charges placed in them. We think in terms of

$$\text{charge} \rightleftharpoons \text{field}$$

and not, as in the action-at-a-distance point of view, in terms of

$$\text{charge} \rightleftharpoons \text{charge}.$$

In Fig. 27–1 we can also imagine that $q_2$ sets up a field and that this field acts on $q_1$, producing a force $-\mathbf{F}$ on it. The situation is completely symmetrical, each charge being immersed in a field associated with the other charge.

If the only problem in electromagnetism was that of the forces between stationary charges, the field and the action-at-a-distance points of view would be perfectly equivalent. Suppose, however, that $q_1$ in Fig. 27–1 suddenly accelerates to the right. How quickly does the charge $q_2$ learn that $q_1$ has moved and that the force which it ($q_2$) experiences must increase? Electromagnetic theory predicts that $q_2$ learns about $q_1$'s motion by a *field disturbance* that emanates from $q_1$, traveling with the speed of light. The action-at-a-distance point of view requires that information about $q_1$'s acceleration be communicated *instantaneously* to $q_2$; this is not in accord with experiment. Accelerating electrons in the antenna of a radio transmitter influence electrons in a distant receiving antenna only after a time $l/c$ where $l$ is the separation of the antennas and $c$ is the speed of light.

## 27-2   The Electric Field Strength E

To define the electric field operationally, we place a small test body carrying a test charge $q_0$ (assumed positive for convenience) at the point in space that is to be examined, and we measure the electrical force **F** (if any) that acts on this body. The *electric field strength* **E** at the point is defined as *

$$E = F/q_0. \qquad (27\text{-}2)$$

Here **E** is a vector because **F** is one, $q_0$ being a scalar. The direction of **E** is the direction of **F**, that is, it is the direction in which a resting positive charge placed at the point would tend to move.

The definition of gravitational field strength **g** is much like that of electric field strength, except that the mass of the test body rather than its charge is the property of interest. Although the units of **g** are usually written as meters/sec$^2$, they could also be written as nt/kg (Eq. 27-1); those for **E** are nt/coul (Eq. 27-2). Thus both **g** and **E** are expressed as a force divided by a property (mass or charge) of the test body.

▶ **Example 1.** What is the magnitude of the electric field strength **E** such that an electron, placed in the field, would experience an electrical force equal to its weight? From Eq. 27-2, replacing $q_0$ by $e$ and $F$ by $mg$, where $m$ is the electron mass, we have

$$E = \frac{F}{q_0} = \frac{mg}{e}$$

$$= \frac{(9.1 \times 10^{-31} \text{ kg})(9.8 \text{ meters/sec}^2)}{1.6 \times 10^{-19} \text{ coul}}$$

$$= 5.6 \times 10^{-11} \text{ nt/coul}.$$

This is a very weak electric field. Which way will **E** have to point if the electric force is to cancel the gravitational force? ◀

In applying Eq. 27-2 we must use a test charge as small as possible. A large test charge might disturb the primary charges that are responsible for the field, thus changing the very quantity that we are trying to measure. Equation 27-2 should, strictly, be replaced by

$$E = \lim_{q_0 \to 0} \frac{F}{q_0}. \qquad (27\text{-}3)$$

This equation instructs us to use a smaller and smaller test charge $q_0$, evaluating the ratio $F/q_0$ at every step. The electric field **E** is then the limit of this ratio as the size of the test charge approaches zero.

## 27-3   Lines of Force

The concept of the electric field as a vector was not appreciated by Michael Faraday, who always thought in terms of *lines of force*. The lines of force still form a convenient way of visualizing electric-field patterns. We shall use them for this purpose but we shall not employ them quantitatively.

---

* This definition of **E**, though conceptually sound and quite appropriate to our present purpose, is rarely carried out in practice because of experimental difficulties. **E** is normally found by calculation from more readily measurable quantities such as the electric potential; see Section 29-7.

The relationship between the (imaginary) lines of force and the electric field strength vector is this:

1. The tangent to a line of force at any point gives the *direction* of **E** at that point.

2. The lines of force are drawn so that the number of lines per unit cross-sectional area is proportional to the *magnitude* of **E**. Where the lines are close together $E$ is large and where they are far apart $E$ is small.

It is not obvious that it is possible to draw a continuous set of lines to meet these requirements. Indeed, it turns out that if Coulomb's law were not true it would *not* be possible to do so; see Problem 4.

Figure 27–2 shows the lines of force for a uniform sheet of positive charge. We assume that the sheet is infinitely large, which, for a sheet of finite dimensions, is equivalent to considering only those points whose distance from the sheet is small compared to the distance to the nearest edge of the sheet. A positive test charge, released in front of such a sheet, would move away from the sheet along a perpendicular line. Thus the electric field strength vector at any point near the sheet must be at right angles to the sheet. The lines of force are uniformly spaced, which means that **E** has the same magnitude for all points near the sheet.

Figure 27–3 shows the lines of force for a negatively charged sphere. From symmetry, the lines must lie along radii. They point inward because a free positive charge would be accelerated in this direction. The electric field $E$ is not constant but decreases with increasing distance from the charge. This is evident in the lines of force, which are farther apart at greater distances. From symmetry, $E$ is the same for all points that lie a given distance from the center of the charge.

▶ **Example 2.** In Fig. 27–3 how does $E$ vary with the distance $r$ from the center of the charged sphere?

Suppose that $N$ lines originate on the sphere. Draw an imaginary concentric sphere of radius $r$; the number of lines per unit cross-sectional area at every point on the sphere is $N/4\pi r^2$. Since $E$ is proportional to this, we can write that

$$E \propto 1/r^2.$$

We derive an exact relationship in Section 27–4. How should $E$ vary with distance from an infinitely long uniform cylinder of charge?　◀

**Fig. 27–2** Lines of force for a section of an infinitely large sheet of positive charge.

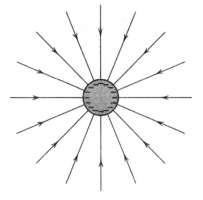

**Fig. 27–3**  Lines of force for a negatively charged sphere.

Figures 27–4 and 27–5 show the lines of force for two equal like charges and for two equal unlike charges, respectively.  Michael Faraday, as we have said, used lines of force a great deal in his thinking.  They were more real for him than they are for most scientists and engineers today.  It is possible

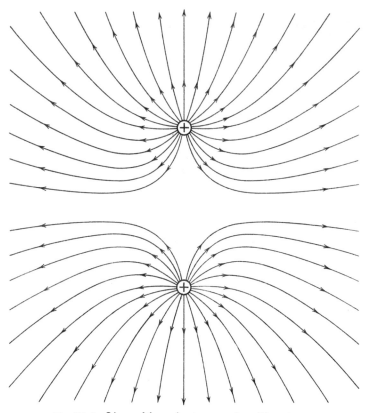

**Fig. 27–4**  Lines of force for two equal positive charges.

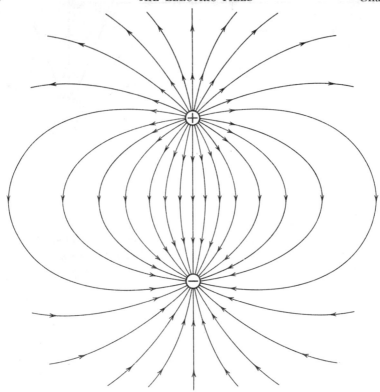

**Fig. 27-5**  Lines of force for equal but opposite charges.

to sympathize with Faraday's point of view. Can we not almost "see" the charges being pushed apart in Fig. 27-4 and pulled together in Fig. 27-5 by the lines of force? The student should compare Fig. 27-5 with Fig. 18-15, which represents a flow field. Figure 27-6 shows a representation of lines of force around charged conductors, using grass seeds suspended in an insulating liquid.

Lines of force give a vivid picture of the way **E** varies through a given region of space. However, the equations of electromagnetism (see Table 38-3) are written in terms of the electric field strength **E** and other field vectors and not in terms of the lines of force. The electric field **E** varies in a perfectly continuous way as any path in the field is traversed; see Fig. 27-7a. This kind of physical continuity, however, is different from the continuity of the lines of force, which has no real physical meaning. To illustrate this point we assert that the lines of force need not be continuous but can be drawn as in Fig. 27-7b. This figure agrees with the two properties of lines of force laid down at the beginning of this section. This point of view has been especially emphasized by Joseph Slepian.*

---

\* See *American Journal of Physics,* **19,** 87 (1951).

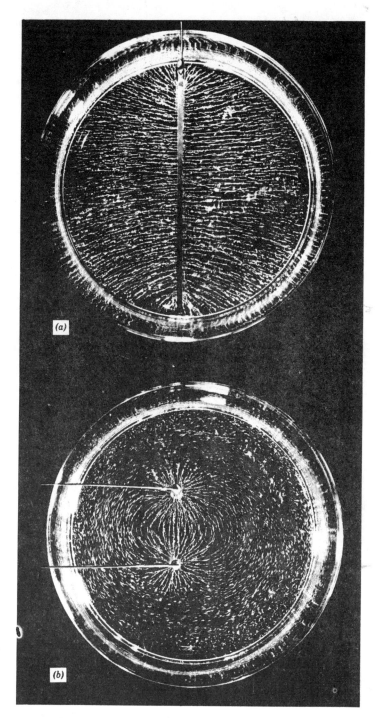

**Fig. 27–6** Photographs of the patterns of electric lines of force around (a) a charged plate (compare Fig. 27–2), and (b) two rods with equal and opposite charges (compare Fig. 27–5). The patterns were made by suspending grass seed in an insulating liquid. (Courtesy Educational Services Incorporated, Watertown, Mass.)

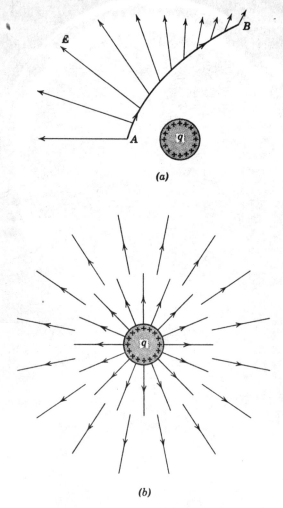

**Fig. 27-7** (a) **E** varies continuously as we move along any path $AB$ in the field set up by $q$. (b) Lines of force need not be continuous.

## 27-4 Calculation of E

Let a test charge $q_0$ be placed a distance $r$ from a point charge $q$. The magnitude of the force acting on $q_0$ is given by Coulomb's law, or

$$F = \frac{1}{4\pi\epsilon_0}\frac{qq_0}{r^2}.$$

The electric field strength at the site of the test charge is given by Eq. 27-2, or

$$E = \frac{F}{q_0} =: \frac{1}{4\pi\epsilon_0}\frac{q}{r^2}. \tag{27-4}$$

The direction of **E** is on a radial line from $q$, pointing outward if $q$ is positive and inward if $q$ is negative.

To find **E** for a group of point charges: ($a$) Calculate $E_n$ due to each charge at the given point *as if it were the only charge present.* ($b$) Add these separately calculated fields vectorially to find the resultant field **E** at the point. In equation form,

$$\mathbf{E} = \mathbf{E_1} + \mathbf{E_2} + \mathbf{E_3} + \cdots = \Sigma \mathbf{E}_n \qquad n = 1, 2, 3, \ldots. \qquad (27\text{-}5)$$

The sum is a vector sum, taken over all the charges.

If the charge distribution is a continuous one, the field it sets up at any point $P$ can be computed by dividing the charge into infinitesimal elements $dq$. The field $d\mathbf{E}$ due to each element at the point in question is then calculated, treating the elements as point charges. The magnitude of $d\mathbf{E}$ (see Eq. 27–4) is given by

$$dE = \frac{1}{4\pi\epsilon_0}\frac{dq}{r^2}, \qquad (27\text{-}6)$$

where $r$ is the distance from the charge element $dq$ to the point $P$. The resultant field at $P$ is then found by adding (that is, integrating) the field contributions due to all the charge elements, or,

$$\mathbf{E} = \int d\mathbf{E}. \qquad (27\text{-}7)$$

The integration, like the sum in Eq. 27–5, is a vector operation; in Example 5 we will see how such an integral is handled in a simple case.

▶ **Example 3.** *An electric dipole.* Figure 27–8 shows a positive and a negative charge of equal magnitude $q$ placed a distance $2a$ apart, a configuration called an elec-

**Fig. 27–8**   Example 3.

tric dipole. The pattern of lines of force is that of Fig. 27–5, which also shows an electric dipole. What is the field **E** due to these charges at point $P$, a distance $r$ along the perpendicular bisector of the line joining the charges? Assume $r \gg a$.

Equation 27–5 gives the vector equation

$$\mathbf{E} = \mathbf{E_1} + \mathbf{E_2},$$

where, from Eq. 27–4,*

$$E_1 = E_2 = \frac{1}{4\pi\epsilon_0}\frac{q}{a^2 + r^2}.$$

---

* Note that the $r$'s in Eq. 27–4 and in this equation have different meanings.

The vector sum of $E_1$ and $E_2$ points vertically downward and has the magnitude

$$E = 2E_1 \cos \theta.$$

From the figure we see that

$$\cos \theta = \frac{a}{\sqrt{a^2 + r^2}}.$$

Substituting the expressions for $E_1$ and for $\cos \theta$ into that for $E$ yields

$$E = \frac{2}{4\pi\epsilon_0} \frac{q}{(a^2 + r^2)} \frac{a}{\sqrt{a^2 + r^2}} = \frac{1}{4\pi\epsilon_0} \frac{2aq}{(a^2 + r^2)^{3/2}}.$$

If $r \gg a$, we can neglect $a$ in the denominator; this equation then reduces to

$$E \cong \frac{1}{4\pi\epsilon_0} \frac{(2a)(q)}{r^3}. \qquad (27\text{–}8a)$$

The essential properties of the charge distribution in Fig. 27–8, the magnitude of the charge $q$ and the separation $2a$ between the charges, enter Eq. 27–8a only as a product. This means that, if we measure $E$ at various distances from the electric dipole (assuming $r \gg a$), we can never deduce $q$ and $2a$ separately but only the product $2aq$; if $q$ were doubled and $a$ simultaneously cut in half, the electric field *at large distances from the dipole* would not change.

The product $2aq$ is called the *electric dipole moment p.* Thus we can rewrite this equation for $E$, *for distant points along the perpendicular bisector,* as

$$E = \frac{1}{4\pi\epsilon_0} \frac{p}{r^3}. \qquad (27\text{–}8b)$$

The result for distant points *along the dipole axis* (see Problem 10) and the general result for any distant point (see Problem 23) also contain the quantities $2a$ and $q$ only as the product $2aq \,(= p)$. The variation of $E$ with $r$ in the general result for distant points is also as $1/r^3$, as in Eq. 27–8b.

The dipole of Fig. 27–8 is two equal and opposite charges placed close to each other so that their separate fields at distant points almost, but not quite, cancel. On this point of view it is easy to understand that $E(r)$ for a dipole varies as $1/r^3$ (Eq. 27–8b), whereas for a point charge $E(r)$ drops off more slowly, namely as $1/r^2$ (Eq. 27–4).

**Example 4.** Figure 27–9 shows a charge $q_1 \,(= +1.0 \times 10^{-6}$ coul) 10 cm from a charge $q_2 \,(= +2.0 \times 10^{-6}$ coul). At what point on the line joining the two charges is the electric field strength zero?

**Fig. 27–9** Example 4.

The point must lie between the charges because only here do the forces exerted by $q_1$ and $q_2$ on a test charge oppose each other. If $E_1$ is the electric field strength due to $q_1$ and $E_2$ that due to $q_2$, we must have

$$E_1 = E_2$$

or (see Eq. 27–4)

$$\frac{1}{4\pi\epsilon_0} \frac{q_1}{x^2} = \frac{1}{4\pi\epsilon_0} \frac{q_2}{(l - x)^2}.$$

where $x$ is the distance from $q_1$ and $l$ equals 10 cm. Solving for $x$ yields

$$x = \frac{l}{1 + \sqrt{q_2/q_1}} = \frac{10 \text{ cm}}{1 + \sqrt{2}} = 4.1 \text{ cm}.$$

The student should supply the missing steps. On what basis was the second root of the resulting quadratic equation discarded?

**Example 5.** Figure 27–10 shows a ring of charge $q$ and of radius $a$. Calculate **E** for points on the axis of the ring a distance $x$ from its center.

Consider a differential element of the ring of length $ds$, located at the top of the ring in Fig. 27–10. It contains an element of charge given by

$$dq = q \frac{ds}{2\pi a}$$

where $2\pi a$ is the circumference of the ring. This element sets up a differential electric field $d\mathbf{E}$ at point $P$.

The resultant field **E** at $P$ is found by integrating the effects of all the elements that make up the ring. From symmetry this resultant field must lie along the ring axis. Thus only the component of $d\mathbf{E}$ parallel to this axis contributes to the final result. The component perpendicular to the axis is canceled out by an equal but opposite component established by the charge element on the opposite side of the ring.

Thus the general vector integral (Eq. 27–7)

$$\mathbf{E} = \int d\mathbf{E}$$

becomes a scalar integral $\qquad E = \int dE \cos \theta.$

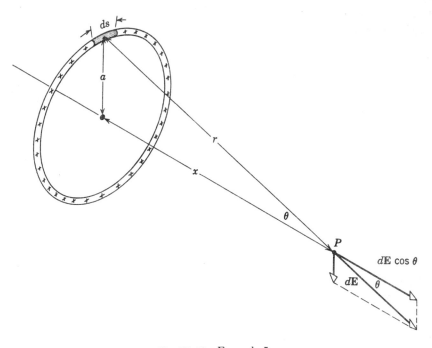

**Fig. 27–10**   Example 5

The quantity $dE$ follows from Eq. 27–6, or

$$dE = \frac{1}{4\pi\epsilon_0} \frac{dq}{r^2} = \frac{1}{4\pi\epsilon_0} \left(\frac{q\,ds}{2\pi a}\right) \frac{1}{a^2 + x^2}.$$

From Fig. 27–10 we have $\qquad \cos\theta = \dfrac{x}{\sqrt{a^2 + x^2}}.$

Noting that, for a given point $P$, $x$ has the same value for all charge elements and is not a variable, we obtain

$$E = \int dE \cos\theta = \int \frac{1}{4\pi\epsilon_0} \frac{q\,ds}{(2\pi a)(a^2 + x^2)} \frac{x}{\sqrt{a^2 + x^2}}$$

$$= \frac{1}{4\pi\epsilon_0} \frac{qx}{(2\pi a)(a^2 + x^2)^{3/2}} \int ds.$$

The integral is simply the circumference of the ring $(= 2\pi a)$, so that

$$E = \frac{1}{4\pi\epsilon_0} \frac{qx}{(a^2 + x^2)^{3/2}}.$$

Does this expression for $E$ reduce to an expected result for $x = 0$? For $x \gg a$ we can neglect $a$ in the denominator of this equation, yielding

$$E \cong \frac{1}{4\pi\epsilon_0} \frac{q}{x^2}.$$

This is an expected result (compare Eq. 27–4) because at great enough distances the ring behaves like a point charge $q$.

**Example 6.** *Line of charge.* Figure 27–11 shows a section of an infinite line of charge whose linear charge density (that is, the charge per unit length, measured

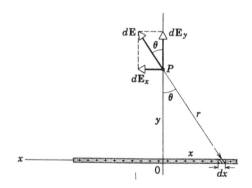

**Fig. 27–11** Example 6. A section of an infinite line of charge.

in coul/meter) has the constant value $\lambda$. Calculate the field $\mathbf{E}$ a distance $y$ from the line.

The magnitude of the field contribution $dE$ due to charge element $dq$ $(= \lambda\,dx)$ is given, using Eq. 27–6, by

$$dE = \frac{1}{4\pi\epsilon_0} \frac{dq}{r^2} = \frac{1}{4\pi\epsilon_0} \frac{\lambda\,dx}{y^2 + x^2}.$$

The vector $d\mathbf{E}$, as Fig. 27–11 shows, has the components

$$dE_x = -dE \sin \theta \quad \text{and} \quad dE_y = dE \cos \theta.$$

The minus sign in front of $dE_x$ indicates that $d\mathbf{E}_x$ points in the negative $x$ direction. The $x$ and $y$ components of the resultant vector $\mathbf{E}$ at point $P$ are given by

$$E_x = \int dE_x = -\int_{x=-\infty}^{x=+\infty} \sin \theta \, dE \quad \text{and} \quad E_y = \int dE_y = \int_{x=-\infty}^{x=+\infty} \cos \theta \, dE.$$

$E_x$ must be zero because every charge element on the right has a corresponding element on the left such that their field contributions in the $x$ direction cancel. Thus $\mathbf{E}$ points entirely in the $y$ direction. Because the contributions to $E_y$ from the right- and left-hand halves of the rod are equal, we can write

$$E = E_y = 2 \int_{x=0}^{x=+\infty} \cos \theta \, dE.$$

Note that we have changed the lower limit of integration and have introduced a factor of two.

Substituting the expression for $dE$ into this equation gives

$$E = \frac{\lambda}{2\pi\epsilon_0} \int_{x=0}^{x=\infty} \cos \theta \, \frac{dx}{y^2 + x^2}.$$

From Fig. 27–11 we see that the quantities $\theta$ and $x$ are not independent. We must eliminate one of them, say $x$. The relation between $x$ and $\theta$ is (see figure)

$$x = y \tan \theta.$$

Differentiating, we obtain $\qquad dx = y \sec^2 \theta \, d\theta.$

Substituting these two expressions leads finally to

$$E = \frac{\lambda}{2\pi\epsilon_0 y} \int_{\theta=0}^{\theta=\pi/2} \cos \theta \, d\theta.$$

The student should check this step carefully, noting that the limits must now be on $\theta$ and not on $x$. For example as $x \to +\infty$, $\theta \to \pi/2$, as Fig. 27–11 shows. This equation integrates readily to

$$E = \frac{\lambda}{2\pi\epsilon_0 y} \left. \sin \theta \right|_0^{\pi/2} = \frac{\lambda}{2\pi\epsilon_0 y}.$$

The student may wonder about the usefulness of solving a problem involving an infinite rod of charge when any actual rod must have a finite length (see Problem 15). However, for points close enough to finite rods and not near their ends, the equation that we have just derived yields results that are so close to the correct values that the difference can be ignored in many practical situations. It is usually unnecessary to solve exactly every geometry encountered in practical problems. Indeed, if idealizations or approximations are not made, the vast majority of significant problems of all kinds in physics and engineering cannot be solved at all. ◀

## 27–5   A Point Charge in an Electric Field

An electric field will exert a force on a charged particle given by (Eq. 27–2)

$$\mathbf{F} = \mathbf{E}q.$$

This force will produce an acceleration

$$\mathbf{a} = \mathbf{F}/m,$$

where $m$ is the mass of the particle. We will consider two examples of the acceleration of a charged particle in a uniform electric field. Such a field can be produced by connecting the terminals of a battery to two parallel metal plates which are otherwise insulated from each other. If the spacing between the plates is small compared with the dimensions of the plates, the field between them will be fairly uniform except near the edges. Note that in calculating the motion of a particle in a field set up by external charges the field due to the particle itself (that is, its *self-field*) is ignored. For example, the earth's gravitational field can have no effect on the earth itself but only on a second object, say a stone, placed in that field.

▶ **Example 7.**   A particle of mass $m$ and charge $q$ is placed at rest in a u..iform electric field (Fig. 27–12) and released. Describe its motion.

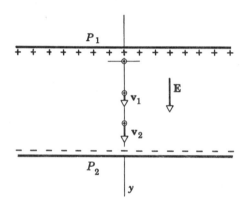

**Fig. 27–12**   A charge is released from rest in a uniform electric field set up between two oppositely charged metal plates $P_1$ and $P_2$.

The motion resembles that of a body falling in the earth's gravitational field. The (constant) acceleration is given by

$$a = \frac{F}{m} = \frac{qE}{m}.$$

The equations for uniformly accelerated motion (Table 3–1) then apply. With $v_0 = 0$, they are

$$v = at = \frac{qEt}{m},$$

$$y = \tfrac{1}{2}at^2 = \frac{qEt^2}{2m},$$

and

$$v^2 = 2ay = \frac{2qEy}{m}.$$

The kinetic energy attained after moving a distance $y$ is found from

$$K = \tfrac{1}{2}mv^2 = \tfrac{1}{2}m\left(\frac{2qEy}{m}\right) = qEy.$$

This result also follows directly from the work-energy theorem because a constant force $qE$ acts over a distance $y$.

**Example 8.** *Deflecting an electron beam.* Figure 27-13 shows an electron of mass $m$ and charge $e$ projected with speed $v_0$ at right angles to a uniform field **E**. Describe its motion.

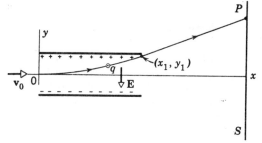

**Fig. 27-13**    Example 8. An electron is projected into a uniform electric field.

The motion is like that of a projectile fired horizontally in the earth's gravitational field. The considerations of Section 4-3 apply, the horizontal $(x)$ and vertical $(y)$ motions being given by

$$x = v_0 t$$

and

$$y = \tfrac{1}{2}at^2 = \frac{eE}{2m}\,t^2.$$

Eliminating $t$ yields

$$y = \frac{eE}{2mv_0^2}\,x^2 \tag{27-9}$$

for the equation of the trajectory.

When the electron emerges from the plates in Fig. 27-13, it travels (neglecting gravity) in a straight line tangent to the parabola at the exit point. We can let it fall on a fluorescent screen $S$ placed some distance beyond the plates. Together with other electrons following the same path, it will then make itself visible as a small luminous spot; this is the principle of the electrostatic *cathode-ray oscilloscope.*

**Example 9.** The electric field between the plates of a cathode-ray oscilloscope is $1.2 \times 10^4$ nt/coul. What deflection will an electron experience if it enters at right angles to the field with a kinetic energy of 2000 ev ($= 3.2 \times 10^{-16}$ joule), a typical value? The deflecting assembly is 1.5 cm long.

Recalling that $K_0 = \tfrac{1}{2}mv_0^2$, we can rewrite Eq. 27-9 as

$$y = \frac{eEx^2}{4K_0}.$$

If $x_1$ is the horizontal position of the far edge of the plate, $y_1$ will be the corresponding deflection (see Fig. 27-13), or

$$y_1 = \frac{eEx_1^2}{4K_0}$$

$$= \frac{(1.6 \times 10^{-19}\ \text{coul})(1.2 \times 10^4\ \text{nt/coul})(1.5 \times 10^{-2}\ \text{meter})^2}{(4)(3.2 \times 10^{-16}\ \text{joule})}$$

$$= 3.4 \times 10^{-4}\ \text{meter} = 0.34\ \text{mm}.$$

The deflection measured, not at the deflecting plates but at the fluorescent screen, is much larger.

**Example 10.** A positive point test charge $q_0$ is placed halfway between two equal positive charges $q$. What force acts on it at or near this point $P$?

From symmetry the force *at* the point is zero so that the particle is in equilibrium; the nature of the equilibrium remains to be found. Figure 27–14 (compare Fig. 27–4)

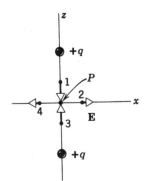

**Fig. 27–14** Example 10. The electric field at four points near a point $P$ which is centered between two equal positive charges.

shows the E vectors for four points near $P$. If the test charge is moved along the $z$ axis, a *restoring* force is brought into play; however, the equilibrium is unstable for motion in the $x$-$y$ plane. Thus we have the three-dimensional equivalent of *saddle point equilibrium;* see Fig. 14–8. What is the nature of the equilibrium for a negative test charge? ◀

## 27–6  A Dipole in an Electric Field

An electric dipole moment can be regarded as a vector **p** whose magnitude $p$, for a dipole like that described in Example 3, is the product $2aq$ of the magnitude of either charge $q$ and the distance $2a$ between the charges. The direction of **p** for such a dipole is from the negative to the positive charge. The vector nature of the electric dipole moment permits us to cast many expressions involving electric dipoles into concise form, as we shall see.

Figure 27–15a shows an electric dipole formed by placing two charges $+q$ and $-q$ a fixed distance $2a$ apart. The arrangement is placed in a uniform *external* electric field **E**, its dipole moment **p** making an angle $\theta$ with this field. Two equal and opposite forces **F** and $-$**F** act as shown, where

$$F = qE.$$

The net force is clearly zero, but there is a net torque about an axis through $O$ (see Eq. 12–2) given by

$$\tau = 2F(a \sin \theta) = 2aF \sin \theta.$$

Combining these two equations and recalling that $p = (2a)(q)$, we obtain

$$\tau = 2aqE \sin \theta = pE \sin \theta. \qquad (27\text{–}10)$$

Thus an electric dipole placed in an external electric field **E** experiences a torque tending to align it with the field. Equation 27–10 can be written in vector form as

$$\boldsymbol{\tau} = \mathbf{p} \times \mathbf{E}, \qquad (27\text{–}11)$$

the appropriate vectors being shown in Fig. 27–15b.

**Fig. 27–15**  (a) An electric dipole in a uniform external field.  (b) An oblique view, illustrating $\tau = \mathbf{p} \times \mathbf{E}$.

(a)

(b)

Work (positive or negative) must be done by an external agent to change the orientation of an electric dipole in an external field. This work is stored as potential energy $U$ in the system consisting of the dipole and the arrangement used to set up the external field. If $\theta$ in Fig. 27–15a has the initial value $\theta_0$, the work required to turn the dipole axis to an angle $\theta$ is given (see Table 12–2) from

$$W = \int dW = \int_{\theta_0}^{\theta} \tau \, d\theta = U,$$

where $\tau$ is the torque exerted by the agent that does the work. Combining this equation with Eq. 27–10 yields

$$U = \int_{\theta_0}^{\theta} pE \sin \theta \, d\theta = pE \int_{\theta_0}^{\theta} \sin \theta \, d\theta$$

$$= pE \left| - \cos \theta \right|_{\theta_0}^{\theta}$$

Since we are interested only in *changes* in potential energy, we choose the reference orientation $\theta_0$ to have any convenient value, in this case 90°. This gives

$$U = -pE \cos \theta \qquad (27\text{–}12)$$

or, in vector form,

$$U = -\mathbf{p} \cdot \mathbf{E}. \qquad (27\text{–}13)$$

▶ **Example 11.**   An electric dipole consists of two opposite charges of magnitude $q = 1.0 \times 10^{-6}$ coul separated by $d = 2.0$ cm. The dipole is placed in an external field of $1.0 \times 10^5$ nt/coul.

(a) What maximum torque does the field exert on the dipole? The maximum torque is found by putting $\theta = 90°$ in Eq. 27–10 or

$$\tau = pE \sin \theta = qdE \sin \theta$$

$$= (1.0 \times 10^{-6} \text{ coul})(0.020 \text{ meter})(1.0 \times 10^5 \text{ nt/coul})(\sin 90°)$$

$$= 2.0 \times 10^{-3} \text{ nt-m.}$$

(b) How much work must an external agent do to turn the dipole end for end, starting from a position of alignment ($\theta = 0$)? The work is the difference in potential energy $U$ between the positions $\theta = 180°$ and $\theta = 0$. From Eq. 27–12,

$$W = U_{180°} - U_{0°} = (-pE \cos 180°) - (-pE \cos 0)$$

$$= 2pE = 2qdE$$

$$= (2)(1.0 \times 10^{-6} \text{ coul})(0.020 \text{ meter})(1.0 \times 10^5 \text{ nt/coul})$$

$$= 4.0 \times 10^{-3} \text{ joule.} \qquad ◀$$

## QUESTIONS

1. Name as many scalar fields and vector fields as you can.

2. (a) In the gravitational attraction between the earth and a stone, can we say that the earth lies in the gravitational field of the stone? (b) How is the gravitational field due to the stone related to that due to the earth?

3. A positively charged ball hangs from a long silk thread. We wish to measure $\mathbf{E}$ at a point in the same horizontal plane as that of the hanging charge. To do so, we put a positive test charge $q_0$ at the point and measure $\mathbf{F}/q_0$. Will $F/q_0$ be less than, equal to, or greater than $E$ at the point in question?

4. Taking into account the quantization of electric charge (the single electron providing the basic charge unit), how can we justify the procedure suggested by Eq. 27–3?

5. In Fig. 27–5 the force on the lower charge points up and is finite. The crowding of the lines of force, however, suggests that $E$ is infinitely great at the site of this (point) charge. A charge immersed in an infinitely great field should have an infinitely great force acting on it. What is the solution to this dilemma?

6. Electric lines of force never cross. Why?

7. In Fig. 27–4 why do the lines of force around the edge of the figure appear, when extended backwards, to radiate uniformly from the center of the figure?

8. Figure 27–2 shows that $\mathbf{E}$ has the same value for all points in front of an infinite uniformly charged sheet. Is this reasonable? One might think that the field should be stronger near the sheet because the charges are so much closer.

9. Two point charges of unknown magnitude and sign are a distance $d$ apart. The electric field strength is zero at one point between them, on the line joining them. What can you conclude about the charges?

10. Compare the way $E$ varies with $r$ for (a) a point charge (Eq. 27–4), (b) a dipole (Eq. 27–8a), and (c) a quadrupole (Problem 18).

11. If a point charge $q$ of mass $m$ is released from rest in a nonuniform field, will it follow a line of force?

12. An electric dipole is placed in a *nonuniform* electric field. Is there a net force on it?

13. An electric dipole is placed at rest in a uniform external electric field, as in Fig. 27–15a, and released. Discuss its motion.

14. An electric dipole has its dipole moment **p** aligned with a uniform external electric field **E**. (a) Is the equilibrium stable or unstable?   (b) Discuss the nature of the equilibrium if **p** and **E** point in opposite directions.

## PROBLEMS

1. Sketch qualitatively the lines of force associated with a thin, circular, uniformly charged disk of radius $R$. (Hint: Consider as limiting cases points very close to the surface and points very far from it.) Show the lines only in a plane containing the axis of the disk.

2. (a) Sketch qualitatively the lines of force associated with three equal positive point charges placed at the corners of an equilateral triangle. Use symmetry arguments and limiting cases (see hint in Problem 1). Show the lines in the plane of the triangle only. (b) Discuss the nature of the equilibrium of a test charge placed at the center of the triangle.

3. In Fig. 27-4 consider any two lines of force leaving the upper charge. If the angle between their tangents for points near the charge is $\theta$, it becomes $\theta/2$ at great distances. Verify this statement and explain it. (Hint: Consider how the lines must behave both close to either charge and far from the charges.)

4. Assume that the exponent in Coulomb's law is not "two" but $n$. Show that for $n \neq 2$ it is impossible to construct lines that will have the properties listed for lines of force in Section 27-3. For simplicity, treat an isolated point charge.

5. What is the magnitude of a point charge chosen so that the electric field 50 cm away has the magnitude 2.0 nt/coul?

6. Two equal and opposite charges of magnitude $2.0 \times 10^{-7}$ coul are 15 cm apart. (a) What are the magnitude and direction of **E** at a point midway between the charges? (b) What force (magnitude and direction) would act on an electron placed there?

7. Two point charges are a distance $d$ apart (Fig. 27-16). Plot $E(x)$, assuming $x = 0$ at the left-hand charge. Consider both positive and negative values of $x$. Plot $E$ as positive if **E** points to the right and negative if **E** points to the left. Assume $q_1 = +1.0 \times 10^{-6}$ coul, $q_2 = +3.0 \times 10^{-6}$ coul, and $d = 10$ cm.

Fig. 27-16

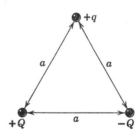

Fig. 27-17

8. Three charges are arranged in an equilateral triangle as in Fig. 27-17. What is the direction of the force on $+q$?

9. Two point charges of magnitude $+2.0 \times 10^{-7}$ coul and $+8.5 \times 10^{-8}$ coul are 12 cm apart. (a) What electric field does each produce at the site of the other? (b) What force acts on each?

10. *Axial field due to an electric dipole.* In Fig. 27-8, consider a point a distance $r$ from the center of the dipole *along its axis*. (a) Show that, at large values of $r$, the electric field is

$$E = \frac{1}{2\pi\epsilon_0}\frac{p}{r^3},$$

which is twice the value given for the conditions of Example 3. (b) What is the direction of **E**?

11. In Fig. 27–8 assume that both charges are positive. (a) Show that $E$ at point $P$ in that figure, assuming $r \gg a$, is given by

$$E = \frac{1}{4\pi\epsilon_0} \frac{2q}{r^2}.$$

(b) What is the direction of **E**? (c) Is it reasonable that $E$ should vary as $r^{-2}$ here and as $r^{-3}$ for the dipole of Fig. 27–8?

12. (a) In Fig. 27–18 locate the point (or points) at which the electric field strength is zero. (b) Sketch qualitatively the lines of force. Take $a = 50$ cm.

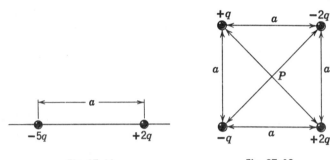

Fig. 27–18                     Fig. 27–19

13. What is **E** in magnitude and direction at the center of the square of Fig. 27–19? Assume that $q = 1.0 \times 10^{-8}$ coul and $a = 5.0$ cm.

14. Two point charges of unknown magnitude and sign are placed a distance $d$ apart. (a) If it is possible to have **E** = 0 at any point *not* between the charges but on the line joining them, what are the necessary conditions and where is the point located? (b) Is it possible, for any arrangement of two point charges, to find *two* points (neither at infinity) at which **E** = 0; if so, under what conditions?

15. A thin nonconducting rod of finite length $l$ carries a total charge $q$, spread uniformly along it. Show that $E$ at point $P$ on the perpendicular bisector in Fig. 27–20 is given by

$$E = \frac{q}{2\pi\epsilon_0 y} \frac{1}{\sqrt{l^2 + 4y^2}}.$$

Show that as $l \to \infty$ this result approaches that of Example 6.

Fig. 27–20

16. A thin nonconducting rod is bent to form the arc of a circle of radius $a$ and subtends an angle $\theta_0$ at the center of the circle. A total charge $q$ is spread uniformly along its length. Find the electric field strength at the center of the circle in terms of $a$, $q$, and $\theta_0$.

17. A nonconducting hemispherical cup of inner radius $a$ has a total charge $q$ spread uniformly over its inner surface. Find the electric field at the center of curvature.

18. *Electric quadrupole.* Figure 27–21 shows a typical electric quadrupole. It consists of two dipoles whose effects at external points do not quite cancel. Show that the value of $E$ on the axis of the quadrupole for points distant $r$ from its center (assume $r \gg a$) is given by

$$E = \frac{3Q}{4\pi\epsilon_0 r^4}$$

where $Q$ ( $= 2qa^2$) is called the *quadrupole moment* of the charge distribution.

**Fig. 27–21**

19. An electron is constrained to move along the axis of the ring of charge in Example 5. Show that the electron can perform oscillations whose frequency is given by

$$\omega = \sqrt{\frac{eq}{4\pi\epsilon_0 ma^3}}.$$

This formula holds only for small oscillations, that is, for $x \ll a$ in Fig. 27–10. (Hint: Show that the motion is simple harmonic and use Eq. 15–11.)

20. For the ring of charge in Example 5, show that the maximum value of $E$ occurs at $x = a/\sqrt{2}$.

21. Consider the ring of charge of Example 5. Suppose that the charge $q$ is not distributed uniformly over the ring but that charge $q_1$ is distributed uniformly over half the circumference and charge $q_2$ is distributed uniformly over the other half. Let $q_1 + q_2 = q$. (a) Find the *component* of the electric field at any point on the axis directed *along* the axis and compare with the uniform case of Example 5. (b) Find the *component* of the electric field at any point on the axis *perpendicular* to the axis and compare with the uniform case of Example 5.

22. A thin circular disk of radius $a$ is charged uniformly so as to have a charge per unit area of $\sigma$. Find the electric field on the axis of the disk at a distance $r$ from the disk.

23. *Field due to an electric dipole.* Show that the components of **E** due to a dipole are given, at distant points, by

$$E_x = \frac{1}{4\pi\epsilon_0} \frac{3pxy}{(x^2 + y^2)^{5/2}}$$

$$E_y = \frac{1}{4\pi\epsilon_0} \frac{p(2y^2 - x^2)}{(x^2 + y^2)^{5/2}},$$

where $x$ and $y$ are coordinates of a point in Fig. 27–22. Show that this general result includes the special results of Eq. 27–8$b$ and of Problem 10.

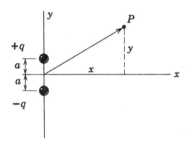

**Fig. 27–22**

24. What is the magnitude and direction of an electric field that will balance the weight of (a) an electron and (b) an alpha particle?

25. A particle having a charge of $-2.0 \times 10^{-9}$ coul is acted on by a downward electric force of $3.0 \times 10^{-6}$ newton in a uniform electric field. (a) What is the strength of the electric field? (b) What is the magnitude and direction of the *electric* force exerted on a proton placed in this field? (c) What is the *gravitational* force on the proton? (d) What is the ratio of the electric to the gravitational forces in this case?

26. (a) What is the acceleration of an electron in a uniform electric field of $10^6$ nt/coul? (b) How long would it take for the electron, starting from rest, to attain one-tenth the speed of light? (c) What considerations limit the applicability of Newtonian mechanics to such problems?

27. An electron moving with a speed of $5.0 \times 10^8$ cm/sec is shot parallel to an electric field of strength $1.0 \times 10^3$ nt/coul arranged so as to retard its motion. (a) How far will the electron travel in the field before coming (momentarily) to rest, and (b) how much time will elapse? (c) If the electric field ends abruptly after 0.8 cm, what fraction of its initial energy will the electron lose in traversing it?

28. An electron is projected as in Fig. 27–23 at a speed of $6.0 \times 10^6$ meters/sec and at an angle $\theta$ of 45°; $E = 2.0 \times 10^3$ nt/coul (directed upward), $d = 2.0$ cm, and $l = 10.0$ cm (a) Will the electron strike either of the plates? (b) If it strikes a plate, where does it do so?

29. *Dipole in a nonuniform field.* Derive an expression for $dE/dz$ at a point midway between two equal positive charges, where $z$ is the distance from one of the charges, measured along the line joining them. Would there be a force on a small dipole placed at this point, its axis being aligned with the $z$ axis? Recall that $E = 0$ at this point.

**Fig. 27–23**

**30.** *Oil drop experiment.* R. A. Millikan set up an apparatus (Fig. 27–24) in which a tiny, charged oil drop, placed in an electric field **E**, could be "balanced" by adjusting $E$ until the electric force on the drop was equal and opposite to its weight. If the radius of the drop is $1.64 \times 10^{-4}$ cm and $E$ at balance is $1.92 \times 10^5$ nt/coul, (a) what charge is on the drop? (b) Why did Millikan not try to balance electrons in his apparatus instead of oil drops? The density of the oil is 0.851 gm/cm³. (Millikan first measured the electronic charge in this way. He measured the drop radius by observing the limiting speed that the drops attained when they fell in air with the electric field turned off. He charged the oil drops by irradiating them with bursts of X-rays.)

**Fig. 27–24** Millikan's oil drop apparatus. Charged oil drops from atomizer $A$ fall through the hole in plate $B$.

31. In a particular early run (1911), Millikan observed that the following measured charges, among others, appeared at different times on a single drop:

| | | |
|---|---|---|
| $6.563 \times 10^{-19}$ coul | $13.13 \times 10^{-19}$ coul | $19.71 \times 10^{-19}$ coul |
| $8.204 \times 10^{-19}$ coul | $16.48 \times 10^{-19}$ coul | $22.89 \times 10^{-19}$ coul |
| $11.50 \ \times 10^{-19}$ coul | $18.08 \times 10^{-19}$ coul | $26.13 \times 10^{-19}$ coul |

What value for the elementary charge $e$ can be deduced from these data?

32. An electric field **E** with an average magnitude of about 150 nt/coul points upward in the earth's atmosphere. We wish to "float" a sulfur sphere weighing 1.0 lb in this field by charging it. (a) What charge (sign and magnitude) must be used? (b) Why is the experiment not practical? Give a qualitative reason supported by a very rough numerical calculation to prove your point.

# Gauss's Law

## CHAPTER 28

## 28–1  Flux of the Electric Field

*Flux* (symbol $\Phi$) is a property of any vector field; it refers to a hypothetical surface in the field, which may be closed or open.  For a *flow field* the flux ($\Phi_v$) is measured by the number of streamlines that cut through such a surface.  For an *electric field* the flux ($\Phi_E$) is measured by the number of lines of force that cut through such a surface.

For closed surfaces we shall see that $\Phi_E$ is positive if the lines of force point outward everywhere and negative if they point inward.  Figure 28–1 shows two equal and opposite charges and their lines of force.  Curves $S_1, S_2, S_3$, and $S_4$ are the intersections with the plane of the figure of four hypothetical closed surfaces.  From the statement just given, $\Phi_E$ is positive for surface $S_1$ and negative for $S_2$.  The flux of the electric field is important because Gauss's law, one of the four basic equations of electromagnetism (see Table 38–3), is expressed in terms of it.  Although the concept of flux may seem a little abstract at first, the student will soon see its value in solving problems.

To define $\Phi_E$ precisely, consider Fig. 28–2, which shows an arbitrary closed surface immersed in an electric field.  Let the surface be divided into elementary squares $\Delta S$, each of which is small enough so that it may be considered to be plane.  Such an element of area can be represented as a vector $\Delta \mathbf{S}$, whose magnitude is the area $\Delta S$; the direction of $\Delta \mathbf{S}$ is taken as the *outward-drawn normal* to the surface.

At every square in Fig. 28–2 we can also construct an electric field vector $\mathbf{E}$.  Since the squares have been taken to be arbitrarily small, $\mathbf{E}$ may be taken as constant for all points in a given square.

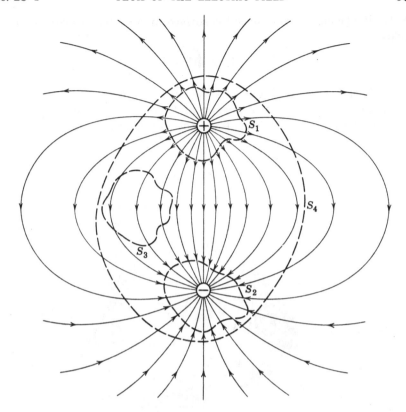

**Fig. 28–1**   Two equal and opposite charges.   The dashed lines represent hypothetical closed surfaces.

The vectors **E** and Δ**S** that characterize each square make an angle $\theta$ with each other.   Figure 28–2b shows an enlarged view of the three squares on the surface of Fig. 28–2a marked $x$, $y$, and $z$.   Note that at $x$, $\theta > 90°$; at $y$, $\theta = 90°$; and at $z$, $\theta < 90°$.

A semiquantitative definition of flux is

$$\Phi_E \cong \Sigma \mathbf{E} \cdot \Delta \mathbf{S}, \qquad (28\text{–}1)$$

which instructs us to add up the scalar quantity **E**·Δ**S** for all elements of area into which the surface has been divided.   For points such as $x$ in Fig. 28–2 the contribution to the flux is negative; at $y$ it is zero and at $z$ it is positive. Thus if **E** is everywhere outward, $\theta < 90°$, **E**·Δ**S** will be positive, and $\Phi_E$ for the entire surface will be positive; see Fig. 28–1, surface $S_1$.   If **E** is everywhere inward, $\theta > 90°$, **E**·Δ**S** will be negative, and $\Phi_E$ for the surface will be negative; see Fig. 28–1, surface $S_2$.   From Eq. 28–1 we see that the appropriate mks unit for $\Phi_E$ is the newton-meter$^2$/coul.

The exact definition of electric flux is found in the differential limit of Eq.

**28-1.** Replacing the sum over the surface by an integral over the surface yields

$$\Phi_E = \oint \mathbf{E} \cdot d\mathbf{S}. \tag{28-2}$$

This *surface integral* indicates that the surface in question is to be divided into infinitesimal elements of area $d\mathbf{S}$ and that the scalar quantity $\mathbf{E} \cdot d\mathbf{S}$ is to be evaluated for each element and the sum taken for the entire surface.

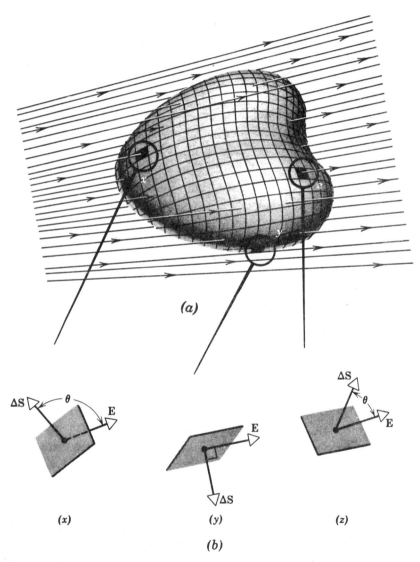

(a)

(x)　　　　　(y)　　　　　(z)

(b)

**Fig. 28-2** (a) A hypothetical surface immersed in an electric field. (b) Three elements of area on this surface, shown enlarged.

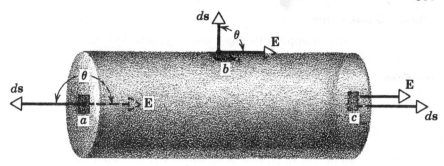

**Fig. 28–3**   Example 1.   A cylindrical surface immersed in a uniform field **E** parallel to its axis.

The circle on the integral sign indicates that the surface of integration is a closed surface.*

▶ **Example 1.** Figure 28–3 shows a hypothetical cylinder of radius $R$ immersed in a uniform electric field **E**, the cylinder axis being parallel to the field. What is $\Phi_E$ for this closed surface?

The flux $\Phi_E$ can be written as the sum of three terms, an integral over $(a)$ the left cylinder cap, $(b)$ the cylindrical surface, and $(c)$ the right cap. Thus

$$\Phi_E = \oint \mathbf{E} \cdot d\mathbf{S}$$

$$= \int_{(a)} \mathbf{E} \cdot d\mathbf{S} + \int_{(b)} \mathbf{E} \cdot d\mathbf{S} + \int_{(c)} \mathbf{E} \cdot d\mathbf{S}.$$

For the left cap, the angle $\theta$ for all points is 180°, **E** has a constant value, and the vectors $d\mathbf{S}$ are all parallel. Thus

$$\int_{(a)} \mathbf{E} \cdot d\mathbf{S} = \int E \cos 180° \, dS$$

$$= -E \int dS = -ES,$$

where $S \, (= \pi R^2)$ is the cap area. Similarly, for the right cap,

$$\int_{(c)} \mathbf{E} \cdot d\mathbf{S} = +ES,$$

the angle $\theta$ for all points being zero here. Finally, for the cylinder wall,

$$\int_{(b)} \mathbf{E} \cdot d\mathbf{S} = 0,$$

because $\theta = 90°$, hence $\mathbf{E} \cdot d\mathbf{S} = 0$ for all points on the cylindrical surface. Thus

$$\Phi_E = -ES + 0 + ES = 0. \qquad \blacktriangleleft$$

---

* Similarly, a circle on a *line* integral sign indicates a closed *path*. It will be clear from the context and from the differential element ($d\mathbf{S}$ in this case) whether we are dealing with a surface integral or a line integral.

## 28-2   Gauss's Law

Gauss's law, which applies to any closed hypothetical surface (called a *Gaussian surface*), gives a connection between $\Phi_E$ for the surface and the net charge $q$ enclosed by the surface.   It is

$$\epsilon_0 \Phi_E = q \qquad (28\text{-}3)$$

or, using Eq. 28-2,        $\epsilon_0 \oint \mathbf{E} \cdot d\mathbf{S} = q.$        (28-4)

The fact that $\Phi_E$ proves to be zero in Example 1 is predicted by Gauss's law because no charge is enclosed by the Gaussian surface in Fig. 28-3 ($q = 0$).

Note that $q$ in Eq. 28-3 (or in Eq. 28-4) is the *net* charge, taking its algebraic sign into account.   If a surface encloses equal and opposite charges, the flux $\Phi_E$ is zero.   Charge outside the surface makes no contribution to the value of $q$, nor does the exact location of the inside charges affect this value.

Gauss's law can be used to evaluate $\mathbf{E}$ if the charge distribution is so symmetric that by proper choice of a Gaussian surface we can easily evaluate the integral in Eq. 28-4.   Conversely, if $\mathbf{E}$ is known for all points on a given closed surface, Gauss's law can be used to compute the charge inside.   If $\mathbf{E}$ has an outward component for every point on a closed surface, $\Phi_E$, as Eq. 28-2 shows, will be positive and, from Eq. 28-4, there must be a net positive charge within the surface (see Fig. 28-1, surface $S_1$).   If $\mathbf{E}$ has an inward component for every point on a closed surface, there must be a net negative charge within the surface (see Fig. 28-1, surface $S_2$).   Surface $S_3$ in Fig. 28-1 encloses no charge, so that Gauss's law predicts that $\Phi_E = 0$.   This is consistent with the fact that lines of $\mathbf{E}$ pass directly through surface $S_3$, the contribution to the integral on one side canceling that on the other.   What would be the value of $\Phi_E$ for surface $S_4$ in Fig. 28-1, which encloses both charges?

## 28-3   Gauss's Law and Coulomb's Law

Coulomb's law can be deduced from Gauss's law and symmetry considerations.   To do so, let us apply Gauss's law to an isolated point charge $q$ as in Fig. 28-4.   Although Gauss's law holds for any surface whatever, information can most readily be extracted for a spherical surface of radius $r$ centered

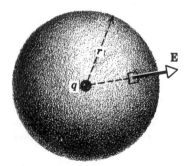

**Fig. 28-4**   A spherical Gaussian surface of radius $r$ surrounding a point charge $q$.

on the charge.  The advantage of this surface is that, from symmetry, $\mathbf{E}$ must be normal to it and must have the same (as yet unknown) magnitude for all points on the surface.

In Fig. 28–4 both $\mathbf{E}$ and $d\mathbf{S}$ at any point on the Gaussian surface are directed radially outward.  The angle between them is zero and the quantity $\mathbf{E} \cdot d\mathbf{S}$ becomes simply $E\, dS$.  Gauss's law (Eq. 28–4) thus reduces to

$$\epsilon_0 \oint \mathbf{E} \cdot d\mathbf{S} = \epsilon_0 \oint E\, dS = q.$$

Because $E$ is constant for all points on the sphere, it can be factored from inside the integral sign, leaving

$$\epsilon_0 E \oint dS = q,$$

where the integral is simply the area of the sphere.*  This equation gives

$$\epsilon_0 E (4\pi r^2) = q$$

or
$$E = \frac{1}{4\pi\epsilon_0} \frac{q}{r^2}. \tag{28–5}$$

Equation 28–5 gives the magnitude of the electric field strength $\mathbf{E}$ at any point a distance $r$ from an isolated point charge $q$.  The direction of $\mathbf{E}$ is already known from symmetry.

Let us put a second point charge $q_0$ at the point at which $\mathbf{E}$ is calculated.  The magnitude of the force that acts on it (see Eq. 27–2) is

$$F = Eq_0.$$

Combining with Eq. 28–5 gives

$$F = \frac{1}{4\pi\epsilon_0} \frac{qq_0}{r^2},$$

which is precisely Coulomb's law.  Thus we have deduced Coulomb's law from Gauss's law and considerations of symmetry.

Gauss's law is one of the fundamental equations of electromagnetic theory and is displayed in Table 38–3 as one of Maxwell's equations.  Coulomb's law is not listed in that table because, as we have just proved, it can be deduced from Gauss's law and from simple assumptions about the symmetry of $\mathbf{E}$ due to a point charge.

It is interesting to note that writing the proportionality constant in Coulomb's law as $1/4\pi\epsilon_0$ (see Eq. 26–3) permits a particularly simple form for Gauss's law (Eq. 28–3).  If we had written the Coulomb law constant simply as $k$, Gauss's law would have to be written as $(1/4\pi k)\Phi_E = q$.  We prefer to leave the factor $4\pi$ in Coulomb's law so that it will not appear in Gauss's law or in other much used relations that will be derived later.

---

* The usefulness of Gauss's law depends on our ability to find a surface over which, from symmetry, both $E$ and $\theta$ (see Fig. 28–2) have constant values.  Then $E \cos \theta$ can be factored out of the integral and $E$ can be found simply, as in this example.

### 28–4   An Insulated Conductor

Gauss's law can be used to make an important prediction, namely: *An excess charge, placed on an insulated conductor, resides entirely on its outer surface.* This hypothesis was shown to be true by experiment (see Section 28–5) before either Gauss's law or Coulomb's law were advanced. Indeed, the experimental proof of the hypothesis is the experimental foundation upon which both laws rest: We have already pointed out that Coulomb's torsion balance experiments, although direct and convincing, are not capable of great accuracy. In showing that the italicized hypothesis is predicted by Gauss's law, we are simply reversing the historical situation.

Figure 28–5 is a cross section of an insulated conductor of arbitrary shape carrying an excess charge $q$. The dashed lines show a Gaussian surface that lies a small distance below the actual surface of the conductor. Although the Gaussian surface can be as close to the actual surface as we wish, it is important to keep in mind that the Gaussian surface is *inside* the conductor.

When an excess charge is placed at random on an insulated conductor, it will set up electric fields inside the conductor. These fields act on the charge carriers of the conductor and cause them to move, that is, they set up internal currents. These currents redistribute the excess charge in such a way that the internal electric fields are automatically reduced in magnitude. Eventually the electric fields inside the conductor become zero everywhere, the currents automatically stop, and electrostatic conditions prevail. This redistribution of charge normally takes place in a time that is negligible for most purposes. What can be said about the distribution of the excess charge when such electrostatic conditions have been achieved?

If, at electrostatic equilibrium, E is zero everywhere inside the conductor, it must be zero for every point on the Gaussian surface. This means that the flux $\Phi_E$ for this surface must be zero. Gauss's law then predicts (see Eq. 28–3) that there must be no net charge inside the Gaussian surface. If the excess charge $q$ is not *inside* this surface, it can only be *outside* it, that is, *it must be on the actual surface of the conductor.*

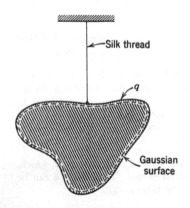

**Fig. 28–5**   An insulated conductor.

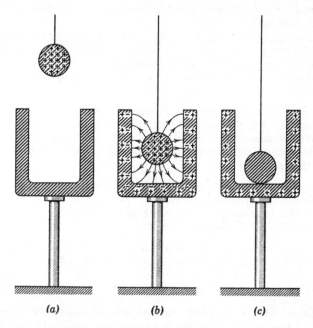

*(a)*          *(b)*          *(c)*

**Fig. 28–6**   The *entire* charge on the ball is transferred to the *outside* of the can.   This statement and the discussion of the first paragraph of Section 28–5 are strictly correct only if the can is provided with a conducting lid which can be closed after the ball is inserted.

## 28–5   Experimental Proof of Gauss's and Coulomb's Laws

Let us turn to the experiments that prove that the hypothesis of Section 28–4. is true.   For a simple test, charge a metal ball and lower it with a silk thread deep into a metal can as in Fig. 28–6.   Touch the ball to the inside of the can; when the ball is removed from the can, all its charge will have vanished.   When the metal ball touches the can, the ball and can together form an "insulated conductor" to which the hypothesis of Section 28–4 applies.   That the charge moves entirely to the outside surface of the can can be shown by touching a small insulated metal object to the can; only on the *outside* of the can will it be possible to pick up a charge.

Benjamin Franklin seems to have been the first to notice that there can be no charge inside an insulated metal can.   In 1755 he wrote to a friend:

> I electrified a silver pint cann, on an electric stand, and then lowered into it a cork-ball, of about an inch diameter, hanging by a silk string, till the cork touched the bottom of the cann.   The cork was not attracted to the inside of the cann as it would have been to the outside, and though it touched the bottom, yet when drawn out, it was not found to be electrified by that touch, as it would have been by touching the outside.   The fact is singular.   You require the reason; I do not know it. . . .

About ten years later Franklin recommended this "singular fact" to the attention of his friend Joseph Priestley (1733–1804).   In 1767 (about twenty years before Coulomb's experiments) Priestley checked Franklin's observation and, with remarkable insight, realized that the inverse square law of force followed from it.   Thus the indirect approach is not only more accurate than the direct approach of Section 26–4 but was carried out earlier.

Priestley, reasoning by analogy with gravitation, said that the fact that no electric force acted on Franklin's cork ball when it was surrounded by a deep metal can is similar to the fact (see Section 16–6) that no gravitational force acts on a mass inside a spherical shell of matter; if gravitation obeys an inverse square law, perhaps the electrical force does also. In Priestley's words:

> May we not infer from this [that is, Franklin's experiment] that the attraction of electricity is subject to the same laws with that of gravitation and is therefore according to the squares of the distances; since it is easily demonstrated that were the earth in the form of a shell, a body in the inside of it would not be attracted to one side more than another?

Michael Faraday also carried out experiments designed to show that excess charge resides on the outside surface of a conductor. In particular, he built a large metal-covered box which he mounted on insulating supports and charged with a powerful electrostatic generator. In Faraday's words:

> I went into the cube and lived in it, and using lighted candles, electrometers, and all other tests of electrical states, I could not find the least influence upon them . . . though all the time the outside of the cube was very powerfully charged, and large sparks and brushes were darting off from every part of its outer surface.

Henry Cavendish (1731–1810) carried out an improved version of the experiment of Fig. 28–6. With the instruments available to him, Cavendish proved experimentally that the exponent in the force law lay, with high probability, between 2.02 and 1.98. Cavendish, however, did not publish his results so that almost nobody knew about them at the time. Maxwell repeated Cavendish's experiment with more accuracy and set these limits as 2.00005 and 1.99995. In 1936 Plimpton and Lawton repeated the experiment again; they set the probability limits as 2.000000002 and 1.999999998.

Figure 28–7 is an idealized sketch of the apparatus of Plimpton and Lawton. It consists in principle of two concentric metal shells, $A$ and $B$, the former being 5 ft in diameter. The inner shell contains a sensitive electrometer $E$ connected so that it will indicate whether any charge moves between shells $A$ and $B$.

By throwing switch $S$ to the left, a substantial charge can be placed on the sphere assembly. If any of this charge moves to shell $B$, it will have to pass through the electrometer and will cause a deflection, which can be observed optically using telescope $T$, mirror $M$, and windows $W$.

However, when the switch $S$ is thrown alternately from left to right, thus connecting the shell assembly either to the battery or to the ground, no effect is observed on the galvanometer. This is the strongest experimental evidence to date that the hypothesis of Section 28–4 is correct. Knowing the sensitivity of their electrometer, Plimpton and Lawton calculated that the exponent in Coulomb's law lies, with high probability, between the limits already stated.

**Fig. 28–7**   The apparatus of Plimpton and Lawton.

## 28–6   Gauss's Law—Some Applications

Gauss's law can be used to calculate **E** if the symmetry of the charge distribution is high.   One example of this, the calculation of **E** for a point charge, has already been discussed (Eq. 28–5).   Here we present other examples.

▶ **Example 2.**   *Spherically symmetric charge distribution.*   Figure 28–8 shows a spherical distribution of charge of radius $R$.   The *charge density* $\rho$ (that is, the charge per unit volume, measured in coul/meter$^3$) at any point depends only on the distance of the point from the center and not on the direction, a condition called *spherical symmetry*.   Find an expression for $E$ for points ($a$) outside and ($b$) inside the charge distribution.   Note that the object in Fig. 28–8 cannot be a conductor or, as we have seen, the excess charge will reside on its surface.

Applying Gauss's law to a spherical Gaussian surface of radius $r$ in Fig. 28–8$a$ (see Section 28–3) leads exactly to Eq. 28–5, or

$$E = \frac{1}{4\pi\epsilon_0} \frac{q}{r^2}, \tag{28–5}$$

where $q$ is the total charge.   Thus for points outside a spherically symmetric dis-

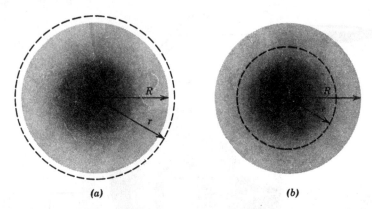

(a)                                        (b)

**Fig. 28-8**   Example 2.  A spherically symmetric charge distribution, showing two Gauss-ian surfaces.  The density of charge, as the shading suggests, varies with distance from the center but not with direction.

tribution of charge, the electric field has the value that it would have if the charge were concentrated at its center.  This reminds us that a sphere of mass $m$ behaves gravitationally, for outside points, as if the mass were concentrated at its center.  At the root of this similarity lies the fact that both Coulomb's law and the law of gravita-tion are inverse square laws.  The gravitational case was proved in detail in Section 16–6; the proof using Gauss's law in the electrostatic case is certainly much simpler.

Figure 28–8$b$ shows a spherical Gaussian surface of radius $r$ drawn *inside* the charge distribution.  Gauss's law (Eq. 28–4) gives

$$\epsilon_0 \oint \mathbf{E} \cdot d\mathbf{S} = \epsilon_0 E(4\pi r^2) = q'$$

or

$$E = \frac{1}{4\pi\epsilon_0} \frac{q'}{r^2},$$

in which $q'$ is that part of $q$ contained within the sphere of radius $r$.  The part of $q$ that lies outside this sphere makes no contribution to $\mathbf{E}$ at radius $r$.  This corresponds, in the gravitational case (Section 16–6), to the fact that a spherical shell of matter exerts no gravitational force on a body inside it.

An interesting special case of a spherically symmetric charge distribution is a uni-form sphere of charge.  For such a sphere, which would be suggested by uniform shading in Fig. 28–8, the charge density $\rho$ would have a constant value for all points within a sphere of radius $R$ and would be zero for all points outside this sphere.  For points inside such a uniform sphere of charge we can put

$$q' = q \frac{\frac{4}{3}\pi r^3}{\frac{4}{3}\pi R^3}$$

or

$$q' = q \left(\frac{r}{R}\right)^3$$

where $\frac{4}{3}\pi R^3$ is the volume of the spherical charge distribution.  The expression for $E$ then becomes

$$E = \frac{1}{4\pi\epsilon_0} \frac{qr}{R^3}. \tag{28–6}$$

This equation becomes zero, as it should, for $r = 0$. Note that Eqs. 28–5 and 28–6 give the same result, as they must, for points on the surface of the charge distribution (that is, if $r = R$). Note that Eq. 28–6 does not apply to the charge distribution of Fig. 28–8b because the charge density, suggested by the shading, is *not* constant in that case.

**Example 3.** *The Thomson atom model.* At one time the positive charge in the atom was thought to be distributed uniformly throughout a sphere with a radius of about $1.0 \times 10^{-10}$ meter, that is, throughout the entire atom. Calculate the electric field strength at the surface of a gold atom ($Z = 79$) on this (erroneous) assumption. Neglect the effect of the electrons.

The positive charge of the atom is $Ze$ or $(79)(1.6 \times 10^{-19}$ coul). Equation 28–5 yields, for $E$ at the surface,

$$E = \frac{1}{4\pi\epsilon_0} \frac{q}{r^2}$$

$$= \frac{(9.0 \times 10^9 \text{ nt-m}^2/\text{coul}^2)(79)(1.6 \times 10^{-19} \text{ coul})}{(1.0 \times 10^{-10} \text{ meter})^2}$$

$$= 1.1 \times 10^{13} \text{ nt/coul.}$$

Figure 28–9 is a plot of $E$ as a function of distance from the center of the atom, using Eqs. 28–5 and 28–6. We see that $E$ has its maximum value on the surface and decreases linearly to zero at the center (see Eq. 28–6). Outside the sphere $E$ decreases as the inverse square of the distance (see Eq. 28–5).

**Example 4.** *The Rutherford, or nuclear, atom.* We shall see in Section 28–7 that the positive charge of the atom is *not* spread uniformly throughout the atom (see Example 3) but is concentrated in a small region (the *nucleus*) at the center of the atom. For gold the radius of the nucleus is about $6.9 \times 10^{-15}$ meter. What is the electric field strength at the nuclear surface? Again neglect effects associated with the atomic electrons.

The problem is the same as that of Example 3, except that the radius is much smaller. This will make the electric field strength at the surface larger, in proportion to the ratio of the squares of the radii. Thus

$$E = (1.1 \times 10^{13} \text{ nt/coul}) \frac{(1.0 \times 10^{-10} \text{ meter})^2}{(6.9 \times 10^{-15} \text{ meter})^2}$$

$$= 2.3 \times 10^{21} \text{ nt/coul.}$$

This is an enormous electric field, much stronger than could be produced and maintained in the laboratory. It is about $10^8$ times as large as the field calculated in Example 3.

**Fig. 28–9** Example 3. The electric field due to the positive charge in a gold atom, according to the (erroneous) Thomson model.

**Fig. 28–10** Example 5. An infinite rod of charge, showing a cylindrical Gaussian surface.

**Example 5.** *Line of charge.* Figure 28–10 shows a section of an infinite rod of charge, the *linear charge density* λ (that is, the charge per unit length, measured in coul/meter) being constant for all points on the line. Find an expression for $E$ at a distance $r$ from the line.

From symmetry, **E** due to a uniform linear charge can only be radially directed. As a Gaussian surface we choose a circular cylinder of radius $r$ and length $h$, closed at each end by plane caps normal to the axis. $E$ is constant over the cylindrical surface and the flux of **E** through this surface is $E(2\pi rh)$ where $2\pi rh$ is the area of the surface. There is no flux through the circular caps because **E** here lies in the surface at every point.

The charge enclosed by the Gaussian surface of Fig. 28–10 is $\lambda h$. Gauss's law (Eq. 28–4),

$$\epsilon_0 \oint \mathbf{E} \cdot d\mathbf{S} = q,$$

then becomes

$$\epsilon_0 E(2\pi rh) = \lambda h,$$

whence

$$E = \frac{\lambda}{2\pi \epsilon_0 r}. \qquad (28\text{–}7)$$

The direction of **E** is radially outward for a line of positive charge.

Note how much simpler the solution using Gauss's law is than that using integration methods, as in Example 6, Chapter 27. Note too that the solution using Gauss's law is possible only if we choose our Gaussian surface to take full advantage of the radial symmetry of the electric field set up by a long line of charge. We are free to choose any surface, such as a cube or a sphere, for a Gaussian surface. Even though Gauss's law holds for all such surfaces, they are not all useful for the problem at hand; only the cylindrical surface of Fig. 28–10 is appropriate in this case.

Gauss's law has the property that it provides a useful technique for calculation only in problems that have a certain degree of symmetry, but in these problems the solutions are strikingly simple.

**Example 6.** *A sheet of charge.* Figure 28–11 shows a portion of a thin, *nonconducting*, infinite sheet of charge, the *surface charge density* σ (that is, the charge per unit area, measured in coul/meter²) being constant. What is **E** at a distance $r$ in front of the plane?

A convenient Gaussian surface is a "pill box" of cross-sectional area $A$ and height $2r$, arranged to pierce the plane as shown. From symmetry, **E** points at right angles

**Fig. 28–11**   Example 6.   An infinite sheet of charge pierced by a cylindrical Gaussian surface.   The cross section of the cylinder need not be circular, as shown, but can have an arbitrary shape.

to the end caps and away from the plane.   Since **E** does not pierce the cylindrical surface, there is no contribution to the flux from this source.   Thus Gauss's law,

$$\epsilon_0 \oint \mathbf{E} \cdot d\mathbf{S} = q$$

becomes                                 $\epsilon_0 (EA + EA) = \sigma A$

where $\sigma A$ is the enclosed charge.   This gives

$$E = \frac{\sigma}{2\epsilon_0}.$$     (28–8)

Note that $E$ is the same for all points on each side of the plane; compare Fig. 27–2. Although an infinite sheet of charge cannot exist physically, this derivation is still useful in that Eq. 28–8 yields substantially correct results for real (not infinite) charge sheets if we consider only points not near the edges whose distance from the sheet is small compared to the dimensions of the sheet.

**Example 7.**   *A charged conductor.*   Figure 28–12 shows a *conductor* carrying on its surface a charge whose surface charge density at any point is $\sigma$; in general $\sigma$ will vary from point to point.   What is **E** for points a short distance above the surface?

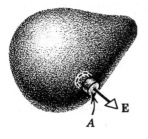

**Fig. 28–12**   Example 7.   A charged insulated conductor, showing a Gaussian surface.   The cross section of the surface need not be circular, as shown, but can have an arbitrary shape.

The direction of **E** *for points close to the surface* is at right angles to the surface, pointing away from the surface if the charge is positive. If **E** were *not* normal to the surface, it would have a component lying in the surface. Such a component would act on the charge carriers in the conductor and set up surface currents. Since there are no such currents under the assumed electrostatic conditions, **E** must be normal to the surface.

The magnitude of **E** can be found from Gauss's law using a small flat "pill box" of cross section $A$ as a Gaussian surface. Since **E** equals zero everywhere inside the conductor (see Section 28–4), the only contribution to $\Phi_E$ is through the plane cap of area $A$ that lies outside the conductor. Gauss's law

$$\epsilon_0 \oint \mathbf{E} \cdot d\mathbf{S} = q$$

becomes                                $\epsilon_0(EA) = \sigma A$

where $\sigma A$ is the net charge within the Gaussian surface. This yields

$$E = \frac{\sigma}{\epsilon_0}. \tag{28-9}$$

Comparison with Eq. 28–8 shows that the electric field is *twice as great* near a conductor carrying a charge whose surface charge density is $\sigma$ as that near a nonconducting sheet with the same surface charge density. The student should compare the Gaussian surfaces in Figs. 28–11 and 28–12 carefully. In Fig. 28–11 lines of force leave the surface through *each* end cap, an electric field existing on *both* sides of the sheet. In Fig. 28–12 the lines of force leave only through the *outside* end cap, the inner end cap being inside the conductor where no electric field exists. If we assume the same surface charge density and cross-sectional area $A$ for the two Gaussian surfaces, the enclosed charge $(= \sigma A)$ will be the same. Since, from Gauss's law, the flux $\Phi_E$ must then be the same in each case, it follows that $E\,(= \Phi_E/A)$ must be twice as large in Fig. 28–12 as in Fig. 28–11. It is helpful to note that in Fig. 28–11 half the flux emerges from one side of the surface and half from the other, whereas in Fig. 28–12 all the flux emerges from the outside surface.                ◀

### 28-7   The Nuclear Model of the Atom

Ernest Rutherford (1871–1937) was first led, in 1911, to assume that the atomic nucleus existed when he tried to interpret some experiments carried out at the University of Manchester by his collaborators H. Geiger and E. Marsden.* The results of Examples 3 and 4 played an important part in Rutherford's analysis of these experiments.

These workers, at Rutherford's suggestion, allowed a beam of $\alpha$-particles † to strike and be deflected by a thin film of a heavy element such as gold. They counted the number of particles deflected through various angles $\phi$. Figure 28–13 shows the experimental setup schematically. Figure 28–14 shows the paths taken by typical $\alpha$-particles as they scatter from a gold atom; the angles $\phi$ through which the $\alpha$-particles are deflected range from 0 to 180° as the character of the collision varies from "grazing" to "head-on."

---

* See "The Birth of the Nuclear Atom," E. N. da C. Andrade, *Scientific American*, November 1956. See also Example 5, Chapter 10.

† $\alpha$-Particles are helium nuclei that are emitted spontaneously by some radioactive materials such as radium. They move with speeds of the order of one-thirtieth that of light when so emitted.

**Fig. 28–13**   Experimental arrangement for studying the scattering of α-particles. Particles from radioactive source $S$ are allowed to fall on a thin metal "target" $T$; α-particles scattered by the target through an (adjustable) angle $\phi$ are counted by detector $D$.

The electrons in the gold atom, being so light, have almost no effect on the motion of an oncoming α-particle; the electrons are themselves strongly deflected, just as a swarm of insects would be by a stone hurled through them. Any deflection of the α-particle must be caused by the repulsive action of the positive charge of the gold atom, which is known to possess most of the mass of the atom.

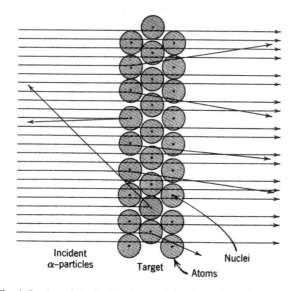

Incident α-particles    Target    Nuclei    Atoms

**Fig. 28–14**   The deflection of the incident α-particles depends on the nature of the nuclear collision. (From Andrade, *Scientific American*, November 1956.)

At the time of these experiments most physicists believed in the so-called "plum pudding" model of the atom that had been suggested by J. J. Thomson (1856–1940). In this view (see Example 3) the positive charge of the atom was thought to be spread out through the whole atom, that is, through a spherical volume of radius about $10^{-10}$ meter. The electrons were thought to vibrate about fixed centers inside this sphere.

Rutherford showed that this model of the atom was not consistent with the $\alpha$-scattering experiments and proposed instead the nuclear model of the atom that we now accept. Here the positive charge is confined to a very much smaller sphere whose radius is about $10^{-14}$ meter (the *nucleus*). The electrons move around this nucleus and occupy a roughly spherical volume of radius about $10^{-10}$ meter. This brilliant deduction by Rutherford laid the foundation for modern atomic and nuclear physics.

The feature of the $\alpha$-scattering experiments that attracted Rutherford's attention at once was that a few $\alpha$-particles are deflected through very large angles, up to 180°. To scientists accustomed to thinking in terms of the "plum pudding" model, this was a very surprising result. In Rutherford's words: "It was quite the most incredible event that ever happened to me in my life. It was almost as incredible as if you had fired a 15-inch shell at a piece of tissue paper and it came back and hit you."

The $\alpha$-particle must pass through a region in which the electric field strength is very high indeed in order to be deflected so strongly.* Example 3 shows that, in Thomson's model, the maximum electric field strength is $1.1 \times 10^{13}$ nt/coul. Compare this with the value calculated in Example 4 for a point on the surface of a gold nucleus ($2.3 \times 10^{21}$ nt/coul). Thus the deflecting force acting on an $\alpha$-particle can be up to $10^8$ times as great if the positive charge of the atom is compressed into a small enough region (the nucleus) at the center of the atoms. Rutherford made his hypothesis about the existence of nuclei only after a much more detailed mathematical analysis than that given here.

### QUESTIONS

1. A point charge is placed at the center of a spherical Gaussian surface. Is $\Phi_E$ changed (a) if the surface is replaced by a cube of the same volume, (b) if the sphere is replaced by a cube of one-tenth the volume, (c) if the charge is moved off-center in the original sphere, still remaining inside, (d) if the charge is moved just outside the original sphere, (e) if a second charge is placed near, and outside, the original sphere, and (f) if a second charge is placed inside the Gaussian surface?

2. By analogy with $\Phi_E$, how would you define the flux $\Phi_g$ of a gravitational field? What is the flux of the earth's gravitational field through the boundaries of a room, assumed to contain no matter?

3. In Gauss's law,

$$\epsilon_0 \oint \mathbf{E} \cdot d\mathbf{S} = q,$$

is $\mathbf{E}$ the electric field intensity attributable to the charge $q$?

---

* The chance that a big deflection can result from the combined effects of many small deflections can be shown to be very small.

4. Show that Eq. 18–3 illustrates what might be called *Gauss's law for incompressible fluids*, or

$$\Phi_v = \oint \mathbf{v} \cdot d\mathbf{S} = 0.$$

5. A surface encloses an electric dipole. What can you say about $\Phi_E$ for this surface?

6. Suppose that a Gaussian surface encloses no net charge. Does Gauss's law require that **E** equal zero for all points on the surface? Is the converse of this statement true, that is, if **E** equals zero everywhere on the surface, does Gauss's law require that there be no net charge inside?

7. Would Gauss's law hold if the exponent in Coulomb's law were not exactly two?

8. Does Gauss's law, as applied in Section 28–4, require that all the conduction electrons in an insulated conductor reside on the surface?

9. In Section 28–4 we assumed that **E** equals zero everywhere inside a conductor. However, there are certainly very large electric fields inside the conductor, at points close to the electrons or to the nuclei. Does this invalidate the proof of Section 28–4?

10. It is sometimes said that excess charge resides entirely on the outer surface of a conductor because like charges repel and try to get as far away as possible from one another. Comment on this plausibility argument.

11. Is Gauss's law useful in calculating the field due to three equal charges located at the corners of an equilateral triangle? Explain.

12. The use of line, surface, and volume densities of charge to calculate the charge contained in an element of a charged object implies a continuous distribution of charge, whereas, in fact, charge on the microscopic scale is discontinuous. How, then, is this procedure justified?

13. Is **E** necessarily zero inside a charged rubber balloon if the balloon is (*a*) spherical or (*b*) sausage-shaped? For each shape assume the charge to be distributed uniformly over the surface.

14. A spherical rubber balloon carries a charge that is uniformly distributed over its surface. How does $E$ vary for points (*a*) inside the balloon, (*b*) at the surface of the balloon, and (*c*) outside the balloon, as the balloon is blown up?

15. As you penetrate a uniform sphere of charge, $E$ should decrease because less charge lies inside a sphere drawn through the observation point. On the other hand, $E$ should increase because you are closer to the center of this charge. Which effect predominates and why?

16. Given a spherically symmetric charge distribution (not of uniform density of charge), is $E$ necessarily a maximum at the surface? Comment on various possibilities.

17. An atom is normally *electrically neutral*. Why then should an $\alpha$-particle be deflected by the atom under any circumstances?

18. If an $\alpha$-particle, fired at a gold nucleus, is deflected through 135°, can you conclude (*a*) that any force has acted on the $\alpha$-particle or (*b*) that any net work has been done on it?

## PROBLEMS

1. Calculate $\Phi_E$ through a hemisphere of radius $R$. The field of **E** is uniform and is parallel to the axis of the hemisphere.

2. In Example 1 compute $\Phi_E$ for the cylinder if it is turned so that its axis is perpendicular to the electric field. Do not use Gauss's law.

3. A plane surface of area $A$ is inclined so that its normal makes an angle $\theta$ with a uniform field of **E**. Calculate $\Phi_E$ for this surface.

4. A point charge of $1.0 \times 10^{-6}$ coul is at the center of a cubical Gaussian surface 0.50 meter on edge. What is $\Phi_E$ for the surface?

5. Charge on an originally uncharged insulated conductor is separated by holding a positively charged rod nearby, as in Fig. 28-15. What can you learn from Gauss's law about the flux for the five Gaussian surfaces shown? The induced negative charge on the conductor is equal to the positive charge on the rod.

6. "Gauss's law for gravitation" is

$$\frac{1}{4\pi G}\Phi_g = \frac{1}{4\pi G}\oint \mathbf{g}\cdot d\mathbf{S} = m,$$

where $m$ is the enclosed mass and $G$ is the universal gravitation constant (Section 16-3). Derive Newton's law of gravitation from this.

**Fig. 28-15**

7. Figure 28-16 shows a point charge of $1.0 \times 10^{-7}$ coul at the center of a spherical cavity of radius 3.0 cm in a piece of metal. Use Gauss's law to find the electric field at point $a$, halfway from the center to the surface, and at point $b$.

8. An uncharged spherical thin metallic shell has a point charge $q$ at its center. Give expressions for the electric field (a) inside the shell, and (b) outside the shell, using Gauss's law. (c) Has the shell any effect on the field due to $q$? (d) Has the presence of $q$ any effect on the shell? (e) If a second point charge is held outside the shell, does this outside charge experience a force? (f) Does the inside charge experience a force? (g) Is there a contradiction with Newton's third law here?

9. Two large nonconducting sheets of positive charge face each other as in Fig. 28-17. What is $\mathbf{E}$ at points (a) to the left of the sheets, (b) between them, and (c) to the right of the sheets? Assume the same surface charge density $\sigma$ for each sheet. Consider only points not near the edges whose distance from the sheets is small compared to the dimensions of the sheet. (Hint: $\mathbf{E}$ at any point is the vector sum of the separate electric field strengths set up by each sheet.)

**Fig. 28-16**

**Fig. 28-17**

**Fig. 28-18**

10. Two large metal plates face each other as in Fig. 28–18 and carry charges with surface charge density $+\sigma$ and $-\sigma$, respectively, on their inner surfaces. What is **E** at points (a) to the left of the sheets, (b) between them, and (c) to the right of the sheets. Consider only points not near the edges whose distance from the sheets is small compared to the dimensions of the sheet.

11. Two large metal plates of area 1.0 meter² face each other. They are 5.0 cm apart and carry equal and opposite charges on their inner surfaces. If $E$ between the plates is 55 nt/coul, what is the charge on the plates? Neglect edge effects. See Problem 10.

12. A thin-walled metal sphere has a radius of 25 cm and carries a charge of $2.0 \times 10^{-7}$ coul. Find $E$ for a point (a) inside the sphere, (b) just outside the sphere, and (c) 3.0 meters from the center of the sphere.

13. A 100-ev electron is fired directly toward a large metal plate that has a surface charge density of $-2.0 \times 10^{-6}$ coul/meter². From what distance must the electron be fired if it is to just fail to strike the plate?

14. Charge is distributed uniformly throughout an infinitely long cylinder of radius $R$. Show that $E$ at a distance $r$ from the cylinder axis ($r < R$) is given by

$$ E = \frac{\rho r}{2\epsilon_0} $$

where $\rho$ is the density of charge (coul/meter³). What result do you expect for $r > R$?

15. Figure 28–19 shows a spherical nonconducting shell of charge of uniform density $\rho$ (coul/meter³). Plot $E$ for distances $r$ from the center of the shell ranging from zero to 30 cm. Assume that $\rho = 1.0 \times 10^{-6}$ coul/meter³, $a = 10$ cm, and $b = 20$ cm.

16. Figure 28–20 shows a section through a long, thin-walled metal tube of radius $R$, carrying a charge per unit length $\lambda$ on its surface. Derive expressions for $E$ for various distances $r$ from the tube axis, considering both $r > R$ and $r < R$. Plot your re-

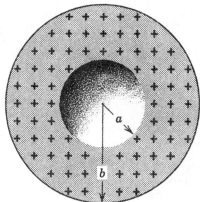

**Fig. 28–19**

sults for the range $r = 0$ to $r = 5$ cm, assuming that $\lambda = 2.0 \times 10^{-8}$ coul/meter and $R = 3.0$ cm.

17. Figure 28–21 shows a section through two long concentric cylinders of radii $a$ and $b$. The cylinders carry equal and opposite charges per unit length $\lambda$. Using Gauss's law,

**Fig. 28–20**

**Fig. 28–21**

prove (a) that $E = 0$ for $r > b$ and for $r < a$ and (b) that between the cylinders $E$ is given by

$$E = \frac{1}{2\pi\epsilon_0} \frac{\lambda}{r}.$$

18. In Problem 17 an electron revolves in a circular path of radius $r$, between and concentric with the cylinders. What must be its kinetic energy $K$? Assume $a = 2.0$ cm, $b = 3.0$ cm, and $\lambda = 3.0 \times 10^{-8}$ coul/meter.

19. A long conducting cylinder carrying a total charge $+q$ is surrounded by a conducting cylindrical shell of total charge $-2q$, as shown in cross section in Fig. 28–22. Use Gauss's

**Fig. 28–22**

law to find (a) the electric field strength at points outside the conducting shell, (b) the distribution of the charge on the conducting shell, and (c) the electric field strength in the region between the cylinders. List the assumptions made in arriving at your answers.

20. A thin metallic spherical shell of radius $a$ carries a charge $q_a$. Concentric with it is another thin metallic spherical shell of radius $b$ ($b > a$) carrying a charge $q_b$. Use Gauss's law to find the electric field strength at radial points $r$ where (a) $r < a$; (b) $a < r < b$; (c) $r > b$. (d) Discuss the criterion one would use to determine how the charges are distributed on the inner and outer surfaces of each shell.

21. A small sphere whose mass $m$ is $1.0 \times 10^{-3}$ gm carries a charge $q$ of $2.0 \times 10^{-8}$ coul. It hangs from a silk thread which makes an angle of $30°$ with a large, charged conducting sheet as in Fig. 28–23. Calculate the surface charge density $\sigma$ for the sheet.

**Fig. 28–23**

22. Equation 28–9 ($E = \sigma/\epsilon_0$) gives the electric field at points near a charged conducting surface. Show that this equation leads to a familiar result when applied to a conducting sphere of radius $r$, carrying a charge $q$.

23. An $\alpha$-particle, approaching the surface of a nucleus of gold, is a distance equal to one nuclear radius ($6.9 \times 10^{-15}$ meter) away from that surface. What are the forces on the $\alpha$-particle and its acceleration at that point? The mass of the $\alpha$-particle, which may be treated here as a point, is $6.7 \times 10^{-27}$ kg.

24. A gold foil used in a Rutherford scattering experiment is $3 \times 10^{-5}$ cm thick. (a) What fraction of its surface area is "blocked out" by gold nuclei, assuming a nuclear radius of $6.9 \times 10^{-15}$ meter? Assume that no nucleus is screened by any other. (b) What fraction of the volume of the foil is occupied by the nuclei? (c) What fills all the rest of the space in the foil?

25. The electric field components in Fig. 28–24 are $E_x = bx^{\frac{1}{2}}$, $E_y = E_z = 0$, in which $b = 800$ nt/coul-m$^{\frac{1}{2}}$. Calculate (a) the flux $\Phi_E$ through the cube and (b) the charge within the cube. Assume that $a = 10$ cm.

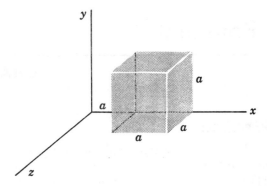

**Fig. 28–24**

# Electric Potential

## CHAPTER 29

## 29–1 Electric Potential

The electric field around a charged rod can be described not only by a (vector) electric field strength $\mathbf{E}$ but also by a scalar quantity, the *electric potential V*. These quantities are intimately related, and often it is only a matter of convenience which is used in a given problem.

To find the *electric potential difference* between two points $A$ and $B$ in an electric field, we move a test charge $q_0$ from $A$ to $B$, always keeping it in equilibrium, and we measure the work $W_{AB}$ that must be done by the agent moving the charge. The electric potential difference * is defined from

$$V_B - V_A = \frac{W_{AB}}{q_0}. \qquad (29\text{--}1)$$

The work $W_{AB}$ may be (a) positive, (b) negative, or (c) zero. In these cases the electric potential at $B$ will be (a) higher, (b) lower, or (c) the same as the electric potential at $A$.

The mks unit of potential difference that follows from Eq. 29–1 is the joule/coul. This combination occurs so often that a special unit, the *volt*, is used to represent it; that is,

$$1 \text{ volt} = 1 \text{ joule/coul.}$$

---

\* This definition of potential difference, though conceptually sound and suitable for our present purpose, is rarely carried out in practice because of technical difficulties. Equivalent and more technically feasible methods are usually adopted.

Usually point $A$ is chosen to be at a large (strictly an infinite) distance from all charges, and the electric potential $V_A$ at this infinite distance is arbitrarily taken as zero.   This allows us to define the *electric potential at a point.*   Putting $V_A = 0$ in Eq. 29–1 and dropping the subscripts leads to

$$V = \frac{W}{q_0},\qquad(29\text{--}2)$$

where $W$ is the work that an external agent must do to move the test charge $q_0$ from infinity to the point in question.   The student should keep in mind that *potential differences* are of fundamental concern and that Eq. 29–2 depends on the arbitrary assignment of the value zero to the potential $V_A$ at the reference position (infinity); this reference potential could equally well have been chosen as any other value, say $-100$ volts.   Similarly any other agreed-upon point could be chosen as a reference position.   In many circuit problems the *earth* is taken as a reference of potential and assigned the value zero.

Bearing in mind the assumptions made about the reference position, we see from Eq. 29–2 that $V$ near an isolated positive charge is positive because positive work must be done by an outside agent to push a (positive) test charge in from infinity.   Similarly, the potential near an isolated negative charge is negative because an outside agent must exert a restraining force on (that is, must do negative work on) a (positive) test charge as it comes in from infinity.   Electric potential as defined in Eq. 29–2 is a scalar because $W$ and $q_0$ in that equation are scalars.

Both $W_{AB}$ and $V_B - V_A$ in Eq. 29–1 are independent of the path followed in moving the test charge from point $A$ to point $B$.   If this were not so, point $B$ would not have a unique electric potential (with respect to point $A$ as a defined reference position) and the concept of potential would have limited usefulness.

We can easily prove that potential differences are path-independent for the special case shown in Fig. 29–1.   This figure illustrates the case in which the two points $A$ and $B$ are in a field set up by a spherical charge $q$; the two points are further chosen, for simplicity, to lie along a radial line.   Although our

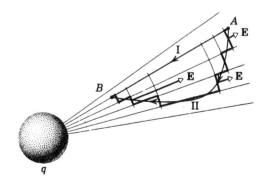

**Fig. 29–1**   A test charge $q_0$ is moved from $A$ to $B$ in the field of charge $q$ along either of two paths. The open arrows show **E** at three points on path II.

path-independence proof applies only to this special case, it illustrates the general principles involved.

Point $A$ in Fig. 29–1 may be taken as a defined reference point, and we imagine a positive test charge $q_0$ moved by an external agent from $A$ to $B$. We consider two paths, path I being a radial line between $A$ and $B$ and path II being a completely arbitrary path between these two points. The open arrows on path II show the electric force per unit charge that would act at various points on a test charge $q_0$.

Path II may be approximated by a broken path made up of alternating elements of arc and of radius. Since these elements can be arbitrarily small, the broken path can be made arbitrarily close to the actual path. On path II the external agent does work *only along the radial segments* because along the arcs the force **F** and the displacement $d\mathbf{l}$ are at right angles, $\mathbf{F} \cdot d\mathbf{l}$ being zero in such cases. The sum of the work done on the radial segments that make up path II is the same as the work done on path I because each path has the same array of radial segments. Since path II is arbitrary, we have proved that the work done is the same for *all* paths connecting $A$ and $B$. Although this proof holds only for the special case of Fig. 29–1, the potential difference is path-independent for *any* two points in *any* electrostatic field. We discussed path independence in Section 8–2 for the general class of *conservative forces;* electrostatic forces, like gravitational forces, are conservative.

The locus of points, all of which have the same electric potential, is called an *equipotential surface.* A family of equipotential surfaces, each surface corresponding to a different value of the potential, can be used to give a general description of the electric field in a certain region of space. We have seen earlier (Section 27–3) that electric lines of force can also be used for this purpose; in later sections (see, for example, Fig. 29–15) we explore the intimate connection between these two ways of describing the electric field.

No work is required to move a test charge between any two points on an equipotential surface. This follows from Eq. 29–1,

$$V_B - V_A = \frac{W_{AB}}{q_0},$$

because $W_{AB}$ must be zero if $V_A = V_B$. This is true, because of the path independence of potential difference, even if the path connecting $A$ and $B$ does not lie entirely in the equipotential surface.

Figure 29–2 shows an arbitrary family of equipotential surfaces. The work to move a charge along paths I and II is zero because all these paths begin and end on the same equipotential surface. The work to move a charge along paths I′ and II′ is not zero but is the same for each path because the initial and the final potentials are identical; paths I′ and II′ connect the same pair of equipotential surfaces.

From symmetry, the equipotential surfaces for a spherical charge are a family of concentric spheres. For a uniform field they are a family of planes at right angles to the field. In all cases (including these two examples) the equipotential surfaces are at right angles to the lines of force and thus to **E**

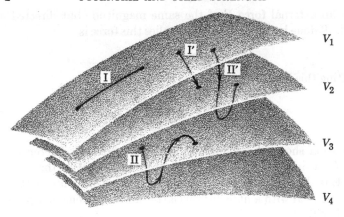

$V_1$

$V_2$

$V_3$

$V_4$

**Fig. 29–2**  Portions of four equipotential surfaces. The heavy lines show four paths along which a test charge is moved.

(see Fig. 29–15). If **E** were *not* at right angles to the equipotential surface, it would have a component lying in that surface. Then work would have to be done in moving a test charge about on the surface. Work cannot be done if the surface is an equipotential, so **E** must be at right angles to the surface.

There is a strong analogy between electrostatic forces and gravitational forces, based on the fact that their fundamental laws are inverse square laws (see Eqs. 26–3 and 16–1):

$$F_E = \frac{1}{4\pi\epsilon_0} \frac{q_1 q_2}{r^2} \quad \text{and} \quad F_g = G \frac{m_1 m_2}{r^2}.$$

Thus we can define the *gravitational potential* $V_g$ (compare Eq. 29–2) from

$$V_g = \frac{W}{m},$$

where $W$ is the work required to move a test body of mass $m$ from infinity to the point in question. Gravitational equipotential surfaces can also be constructed; they prove to be everywhere at right angles to the gravitational field strength vector **g**. For a uniform gravitational field, such as that near the surface of the earth, these surfaces are horizontal planes. This correlates with the facts that (*a*) no net work is required to move a stone of mass $m$ between two points with the same elevation and (*b*) the same net work is required to move a stone along any path starting on a given horizontal surface and ending on another.

### 29–2  Potential and Field Strength

Let $A$ and $B$ in Fig. 29–3 be two points in a uniform electric field **E**, set up by an arrangement of charges not shown, and let $A$ be a distance $d$ in the field direction from $B$. Assume that a positive test charge $q_0$ is moved, by an external agent and without acceleration, from $A$ to $B$ along the straight line connecting them.

The *electric* force on the charge is $q_0$**E** and points down. To move the charge in the way we have described we must counteract this force by applying an external force $\mathbf{F}$ of the same magnitude but directed upward. The work $W$ done by the agent that supplies this force is

$$W_{AB} = Fd = q_0 Ed. \tag{29-3}$$

Substituting this into Eq. 29-1 yields

$$V_B - V_A = \frac{W_{AB}}{q_0} = Ed. \tag{29-4}$$

This equation shows the connection between potential difference and field strength for a simple special case. Note from this equation that another mks unit for $\mathbf{E}$ is the volt/meter. The student may wish to prove that a volt/meter is identical with a nt/coul; this latter unit is the one first presented for $\mathbf{E}$ in Section 27-2.

In Fig. 29-3 $B$ has a higher potential than $A$. This is reasonable because an external agent would have to do positive work to push a positive test charge from $A$ to $B$. Figure 29-3 could be used as it stands to illustrate the act of lifting a stone from $A$ to $B$ in the uniform gravitational field near the earth's surface.

What is the connection between $V$ and $\mathbf{E}$ in the more general case in which the field is *not* uniform and in which the test body is moved along a path that is *not* straight, as in Fig. 29-4? The electric field exerts a force $q_0\mathbf{E}$ on the test charge, as shown. To keep the test charge from accelerating, an external agent must apply a force $\mathbf{F}$ chosen to be exactly equal to $-q_0\mathbf{E}$ for all positions of the test body.

If the external agent causes the test body to move through a displacement $d\mathbf{l}$ along the path from $A$ to $B$, the element of work done by the external agent

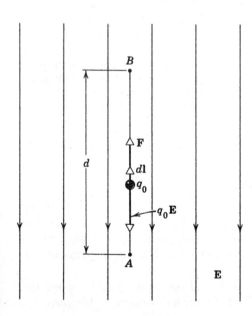

**Fig. 29-3**   A test charge $q_0$ is moved from $A$ to $B$ in a uniform electric field $\mathbf{E}$ by an external agent that exerts a force $\mathbf{F}$ on it.

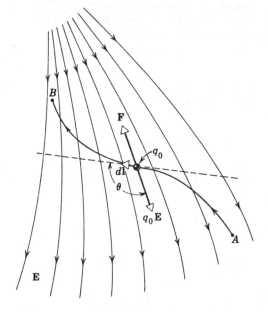

**Fig. 29-4** A test charge $q_0$ is moved from $A$ to $B$ in a nonuniform electric field by an external agent that exerts a force **F** on it.

is **F**·$d\mathbf{l}$. To find the total work $W_{AB}$ done by the external agent in moving the test charge from $A$ to $B$, we add up (that is, integrate) the work contributions for all the infinitesimal segments into which the path is divided. This leads to

$$W_{AB} = \int_A^B \mathbf{F} \cdot d\mathbf{l} = -q_0 \int_A^B \mathbf{E} \cdot d\mathbf{l}.$$

Such an integral is called a *line integral*. Note that we have substituted $-q_0\mathbf{E}$ for its equal, **F**.

Substituting this expression for $W_{AB}$ into Eq. 29–1 leads to

$$V_B - V_A = \frac{W_{AB}}{q_0} = -\int_A^B \mathbf{E} \cdot d\mathbf{l}. \tag{29-5}$$

If point $A$ is taken to be infinitely distant and the potential $V_A$ at infinity is taken to be zero, this equation gives the potential $V$ at point $B$, or, dropping the subscript $B$,

$$V = -\int_\infty^B \mathbf{E} \cdot d\mathbf{l}. \tag{29-6}$$

These two equations allow us to calculate the potential difference between any two points (or the potential at any point) if **E** is known at various points in the field.

▶ **Example 1.** In Fig. 29–3 calculate $V_B - V_A$ using Eq. 29–5. Compare the result with that obtained by direct analysis of this special case (Eq. 29–4).

In moving the test charge the element of path $d\mathbf{l}$ always points in the direction of motion; this is upward in Fig. 29–3. The electric field $\mathbf{E}$ in this figure points down so that the angle $\theta$ between $\mathbf{E}$ and $d\mathbf{l}$ is 180°.

Equation 29–5 then becomes

$$V_B - V_A = -\int_A^B \mathbf{E} \cdot d\mathbf{l} = -\int_A^B E \cos 180° \, dl = \int_A^B E \, dl.$$

$E$ is the constant for all parts of the path in this problem and can thus be taken outside the integral sign, giving

$$V_B - V_A = E \int_A^B dl = Ed,$$

which agrees with Eq. 29–4, as it must.

**Example 2.**   In Fig. 29–5 let a test charge $q_0$ be moved without acceleration from $A$ to $B$ over the path shown. Compute the potential difference between $A$ and $B$.

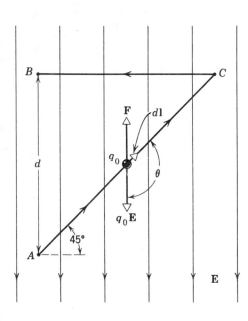

**Fig. 29–5** Example 2. A test charge $q_0$ is moved along path $ACB$ in a uniform electric field by an external agent.

For the path $AC$ we have $\theta = 135°$ and, from Eq. 29–5,

$$V_C - V_A = -\int_A^C \mathbf{E} \cdot d\mathbf{l} = -\int_A^C E \cos 135° \, dl = \frac{E}{\sqrt{2}} \int_A^C dl.$$

The integral is the length of the line $AC$ which is $\sqrt{2}d$. Thus

$$V_C - V_A = \frac{E}{\sqrt{2}} (\sqrt{2}d) = Ed.$$

Points $B$ and $C$ have the same potential because no work is done in moving a charge between them, $\mathbf{E}$ and $d\mathbf{l}$ being at right angles for all points on the line $CB$. In other words, $B$ and $C$ lie on the same equipotential surface at right angles to the lines of force. Thus

$$V_B - V_A = V_C - V_A = Ed.$$

This is the same value derived for a direct path connecting $A$ and $B$, a result to be expected because the potential difference between two points is path independent.  ◀

### 29-3  Potential Due to a Point Charge

Figure 29-6 shows two points $A$ and $B$ near an isolated point charge $q$. For simplicity we assume that $A$, $B$, and $q$ lie on a straight line. Let us compute the potential difference between points $A$ and $B$, assuming that a test charge $q_0$ is moved without acceleration along a radial line from $A$ to $B$.

In Fig. 29-6 **E** points to the right and $d\mathbf{l}$, which is always in the direction of motion, points to the left. Therefore, in Eq. 29-5,

$$\mathbf{E} \cdot d\mathbf{l} = E \cos 180° \, dl = -E \, dl.$$

However, as we move a distance $dl$ to the left, we are moving in the direction of decreasing $r$ because $r$ is measured from $q$ as an origin. Thus

$$dl = -dr.$$

Combining yields        $$\mathbf{E} \cdot d\mathbf{l} = E \, dr.$$

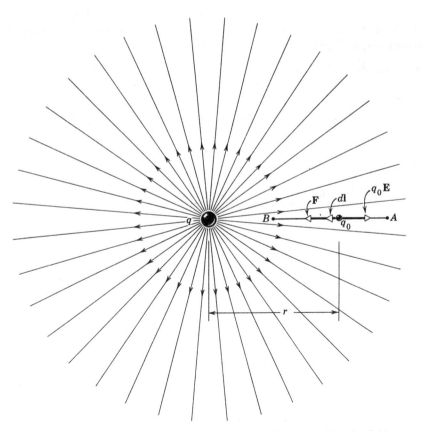

**Fig. 29-6**  A test charge $q_0$ is moved by an external agent from $A$ to $B$ in the field set up by a point charge $q$.

Substituting this into Eq. 29–5 gives

$$V_B - V_A = -\int_A^B \mathbf{E} \cdot d\mathbf{l} = -\int_{r_A}^{r_B} E \, dr.$$

Combining with Eq. 27–4,

$$E = \frac{1}{4\pi\epsilon_0} \frac{q}{r^2}$$

leads to $\quad V_B - V_A = -\frac{q}{4\pi\epsilon_0} \int_{r_A}^{r_B} \frac{dr}{r^2} = \frac{q}{4\pi\epsilon_0}\left(\frac{1}{r_B} - \frac{1}{r_A}\right).$   (29–7)

Choosing reference position $A$ to be at infinity (that is, letting $r_A \to \infty$), choosing $V_A = 0$ at this position, and dropping the subscript $B$ leads to

$$V = \frac{1}{4\pi\epsilon_0} \frac{q}{r}.$$   (29–8)

This equation shows clearly that equipotential surfaces for an isolated point charge are spheres concentric with the point charge (see Fig. 29-15$i$). A study of the derivation will show that this relation also holds for points external to spherically symmetric charge distributions.

▶ **Example 3.**   What must the magnitude of an isolated positive point charge be for the electric potential at 10 cm from the charge to be $+100$ volts?
Solving Eq. 29–8 for $q$ yields

$$q = V4\pi\epsilon_0 r = (100 \text{ volts})(4\pi)(8.9 \times 10^{-12} \text{ coul}^2/\text{nt-m}^2)(0.10 \text{ meter})$$

$$= 1.1 \times 10^{-9} \text{ coul.}$$

This charge is comparable to charges that can be produced by friction.

**Example 4.**   What is the electric potential at the surface of a gold nucleus?   The radius is $6.6 \times 10^{-15}$ meter and the atomic number $Z = 79$.
The nucleus, assumed spherically symmetrical, behaves electrically for external points as if it were a point charge.   Thus we can use Eq. 29–8, or, recalling that the proton charge is $1.6 \times 10^{-19}$ coul,

$$V = \frac{1}{4\pi\epsilon_0} \frac{q}{r} = \frac{(9.0 \times 10^9 \text{ nt-m}^2/\text{coul}^2)(79)(1.6 \times 10^{-19} \text{ coul})}{6.6 \times 10^{-15} \text{ meter}}$$

$$= 1.7 \times 10^7 \text{ volts.}$$   ◀

## 29–4   A Group of Point Charges

The potential at any point due to a group of point charges is found by (a) calculating the potential $V_n$ due to each charge, as if the other charges were not present, and (b) adding the quantities so obtained, or (see Eq. 29–8)

$$V = \sum_n V_n = \frac{1}{4\pi\epsilon_0} \sum_n \frac{q_n}{r_n},$$   (29–9)

where $q_n$ is the value of the $n$th charge and $r_n$ is the distance of this charge from the point in question. The sum used to calculate $V$ is an *algebraic sum* and not a vector sum like the one used to calculate $\mathbf{E}$ for a group of point charges (see Eq. 27–5). Herein lies an important computational advantage of potential over electric field strength.

If the charge distribution is continuous, rather than being a collection of points, the sum in Eq. 29–9 must be replaced by an integral, or

$$V = \int dV = \frac{1}{4\pi\epsilon_0} \int \frac{dq}{r}, \tag{29-10}$$

where $dq$ is a differential element of the charge distribution, $r$ is its distance from the point at which $V$ is to be calculated, and $dV$ is the potential it establishes at that point.

▶ **Example 5.** What is the potential at the center of the square of Fig. 29–7? Assume that $q_1 = +1.0 \times 10^{-8}$ coul, $q_2 = -2.0 \times 10^{-8}$ coul, $q_3 = +3.0 \times 10^{-8}$ coul, $q_4 = +2.0 \times 10^{-8}$ coul, and $a = 1.0$ meter.

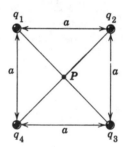

**Fig. 29–7**  Example 5

The distance $r$ of each charge from $P$ is $a/\sqrt{2}$ or 0.71 meter. From Eq. 29–9

$$V = \sum_n V_n = \frac{1}{4\pi\epsilon_0} \frac{q_1 + q_2 + q_3 + q_4}{r}$$

$$= \frac{(9.0 \times 10^9 \text{ nt-m}^2/\text{coul}^2)(1.0 - 2.0 + 3.0 + 2.0) \times 10^{-8} \text{ coul}}{0.71 \text{ meter}}$$

$$= 500 \text{ volts.}$$

Is the potential constant within the square? Does any point inside have a negative potential? Can you sketch roughly the intersection of the plane of Fig. 29–7 with the equipotential surface corresponding to zero volts?

**Example 6.** *A charged disk.* Find the electric potential for points on the axis of a uniformly charged circular disk whose surface charge density is $\sigma$ (see Fig. 29–8).

Consider a charge element $dq$ consisting of a flat circular strip of radius $y$ and width $dy$. We have

$$dq = \sigma(2\pi y)(dy),$$

where $(2\pi y)(dy)$ is the area of the strip. All parts of this charge element are the same distance $r'$ $(= \sqrt{y^2 + r^2})$ from axial point $P$ so that their contribution $dV$ to the

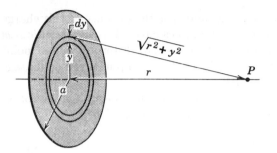

**Fig. 29-8** Example 6. A point $P$ on the axis of a uniformly charged circular disk of radius $a$.

electric potential at $P$ is given by Eq. 29–8, or

$$dV = \frac{1}{4\pi\epsilon_0}\frac{dq}{r'} = \frac{1}{4\pi\epsilon_0}\frac{\sigma 2\pi y\,dy}{\sqrt{y^2 + r^2}}.$$

The potential $V$ is found by integrating over all the strips into which the disk can be divided (Eq. 29–10) or

$$V = \int dV = \frac{\sigma}{2\epsilon_0}\int_0^a (y^2 + r^2)^{-\frac{1}{2}}y\,dy$$

$$= \frac{\sigma}{2\epsilon_0}(\sqrt{a^2 + r^2} - r).$$

This general result is valid for all values of $r$. In the special case of $r \gg a$ the quantity $\sqrt{a^2 + r^2}$ can be approximated as

$$\sqrt{a^2 + r^2} = r\left(1 + \frac{a^2}{r^2}\right)^{\frac{1}{2}} = r\left(1 + \frac{1}{2}\frac{a^2}{r^2} + \cdots\right) \cong r + \frac{a^2}{2r},$$

in which the quantity in parentheses in the second member of this equation has been expanded by the binomial theorem (see Appendix $I$). This equation means that $V$ becomes

$$V \cong \frac{\sigma}{2\epsilon_0}\left(r + \frac{a^2}{2r} - r\right) = \frac{\sigma\pi a^2}{4\pi\epsilon_0 r} = \frac{1}{4\pi\epsilon_0}\frac{q}{r},$$

where $q$ ($= \sigma\pi a^2$) is the total charge on the disk. This limiting result is expected because the disk behaves like a point charge for $r \gg a$. ◄

## 29–5 Potential Due to a Dipole

Two equal charges, $q$, of opposite sign, separated by a distance $2a$, constitute an electric dipole; see Example 3, Chapter 27. The electric dipole moment $\mathbf{p}$ has the magnitude $2aq$ and points from the negative charge to the positive charge. Here we derive an expression for the electric potential $V$ at any point of space due to a dipole, provided only that the point is not too close to the dipole.

A point $P$ is specified by giving the quantities $r$ and $\theta$ in Fig. 29–9. From symmetry, it is clear that the potential will not change as point $P$ rotates about the $z$ axis, $r$ and $\theta$ being fixed. Thus we need only find $V(r,\theta)$ for any plane containing this axis; the plane of Fig. 29–9 is such a plane. Applying

Eq. 29–9 gives

$$V = \sum_n V_n = V_1 + V_2 = \frac{1}{4\pi\epsilon_0}\left(\frac{q}{r_1} - \frac{q}{r_2}\right) = \frac{q}{4\pi\epsilon_0}\frac{r_2 - r_1}{r_1 r_2},$$

which is an exact relationship.

We now limit consideration to points such that $r \gg 2a$. These approximate relations then follow from Fig. 29–9:

$$r_2 - r_1 \cong 2a \cos \theta \quad \text{and} \quad r_1 r_2 \cong r^2,$$

and the potential reduces to

$$V = \frac{q}{4\pi\epsilon_0}\frac{2a \cos \theta}{r^2} = \frac{1}{4\pi\epsilon_0}\frac{p \cos \theta}{r^2}, \qquad (29\text{--}11)$$

in which $p \ (= 2aq)$ is the dipole moment. Note that $V$ vanishes everywhere in the equatorial plane ($\theta = 90°$). This reflects the fact that it takes no work to bring a test charge in from infinity along the perpendicular bisector of the dipole. For a given radius, $V$ has its greatest positive value for $\theta = 0$ and its greatest negative value for $\theta = 180°$. Note that the potential does not depend separately on $q$ and $2a$ but only on their product $p$.

It is convenient to call *any* assembly of charges, for which $V$ at distant points is given by Eq. 29–11, an *electric dipole*. Two point charges separated by a small distance behave this way, as we have just proved. However, other charge configurations also obey Eq. 29–11. Suppose that by measurement at points outside an imaginary box (Fig. 29–10) we find a pattern of lines of force that can be described quantitatively by Eq. 29–11. We then declare that the object inside the box is an *electric dipole*, that its axis is the line $zz'$, and that its dipole moment **p** points vertically upward.

Many molecules have electric dipole moments. That for $H_2O$ in its vapor state is $6.1 \times 10^{-30}$ coul-m. Figure 29–11 is a representation of this molecule, showing the three nuclei and the surrounding electron cloud. The dipole moment **p** is represented

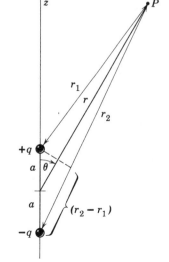

**Fig. 29–9**   A point $P$ in the field of an electric dipole.

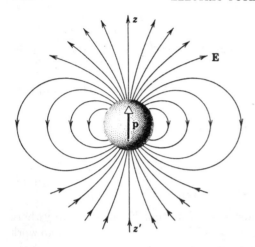

**Fig. 29–10** If an object inside the spherical box sets up the electric field shown (described quantitatively by Eq. 29–11), it is an electric dipole.

by the arrow on the axis of symmetry of the molecule. In this molecule the effective center of positive charge does not coincide with the effective center of negative charge. It is precisely because of this separation that the dipole moment exists.

Atoms, and many molecules, do *not* have permanent dipole moments. However, dipole moments may be induced by placing any atom or molecule in an external electric field. The action of the field (Fig. 29–12) is to separate the centers of positive and of negative charge. We say that the atom becomes *polarized* and acquires an *induced electric dipole moment*. Induced dipole moments disappear when the electric field is removed.

Electric dipoles are important in situations other than atomic and molecular ones. Radio and radar antennas are often in the form of a metal wire or rod in which electrons surge back and forth periodically. At a certain time one end of the wire or rod will be negative and the other end positive. Half a cycle later the polarity of the ends is exactly reversed. This is an *oscillating* electric dipole. It is so named because its dipole moment changes in a periodic way with time.

**Fig. 29–11** A schematic representation of a water molecule, showing the three nuclei, the electron cloud, and the orientation of the dipole moment.

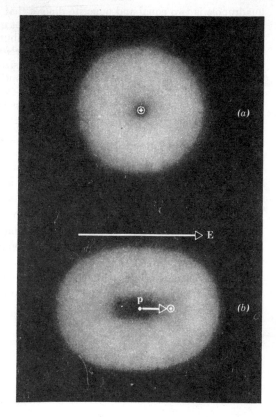

**Fig. 29-12** (*a*) An atom, showing the nucleus and the electron cloud. The center of negative charge coincides with the center of positive charge, that is, with the nucleus. (*b*) If an external field **E** is applied, the electron cloud is distorted so that the center of negative charge, marked by the dot, and the center of positive charge no longer coincide. An electric dipole appears.

▶ **Example 7.** *An electric quadrupole.* An electric quadrupole, of which Fig. 27–21 is an example, consists of two electric dipoles so arranged that they almost, but not quite, cancel each other in their electric effects at distant points.* Calculate $V(r)$ for points on the axis of this quadrupole.

Applying Eq. 29–9 to Fig. 27–21 yields

$$V = \sum_n V_n = \frac{1}{4\pi\epsilon_0}\left(\frac{q}{r-a} - \frac{2q}{r} + \frac{q}{r+a}\right)$$

$$= \frac{q}{4\pi\epsilon_0}\frac{2a^2}{(r-a)(r)(r+a)}.$$

Assuming that $r \gg a$ allows us to put $a = 0$ in the sum and difference terms in the denominator, yielding

$$V = \frac{1}{4\pi\epsilon_0}\frac{Q}{r^3},$$

where $Q$ ($= 2qa^2$) is the *electric quadrupole moment* of the charge assembly of Fig. 27–21. Note that $V$ varies (*a*) as $1/r$ for a point charge (see Eq. 29–8), (*b*) as $1/r^2$ for a dipole (see Eq. 29–11), and (*c*) as $1/r^3$ for a quadrupole.

Note too that (*a*) a dipole is two equal and opposite charges that do not coincide in space so that their electric effects at distant points do not quite cancel, and (*b*) a

---

* See Problem 18, Chapter 27.

quadrupole is two equal and opposite dipoles that do not coincide in space so that their electric effects at distant points again do not quite cancel. This pattern can be extended to define higher orders of charge distribution such as *octupoles*.

The potential at points at distances from an *arbitrary* charge distribution (continuous or discrete) that are large compared with the size of the distribution can always be written as the sum of separate potential distributions due to (*a*) a single charge—sometimes, in this context, called a *monopole*—(*b*) a dipole, (*c*) a quadrupole, etc. This process is called an *expansion in multipoles* and is a very useful technique in problem solving. ◄

### 29–6    Electric Potential Energy *

If we raise a stone from the earth's surface, the work that we do against the earth's gravitational attraction is stored as *potential energy* in the system earth + stone. If we release the stone, the stored potential energy changes steadily into kinetic energy as the stone drops. After the stone comes to rest on the earth, this kinetic energy, equal in magnitude just before the time of contact to the originally stored potential energy, is transformed into heat energy in the system earth + stone.

A similar situation exists in electrostatics. Consider two charges $q_1$ and $q_2$ a distance $r$ apart, as in Fig. 29–13. If we increase the separation between

Fig. 29–13

them, an external agent must do work that will be positive if the charges are opposite in sign and negative otherwise. The energy represented by this work can be thought of as stored in the system $q_1 + q_2$ as *electric potential energy*. This energy, like all varieties of potential energy, can be transformed into other forms. If $q_1$ and $q_2$, for example, are charges of opposite sign and we release them, they will accelerate toward each other, transforming the stored potential energy into kinetic energy of the accelerating masses. The analogy to the earth + stone system is exact, save for the fact that electric forces may be either attractive or repulsive whereas gravitational forces are always attractive.

We define the electric potential energy of a system of point charges as the work required to assemble this system of charges by bringing them in from an infinite distance. We assume that the charges are all at rest when they are infinitely separated, that is, they have no initial kinetic energy.

In Fig. 29–13 let us imagine $q_2$ removed to infinity and at rest. The

---

* In mechanics the concept of *potential energy* (of compressed springs, falling masses, etc.) is more commonly used than the concept of *potential*. In electrostatics the reverse is true, electric potential being perhaps a more common concept than electric potential energy. In what follows the student must be careful not to confuse these quite different quantities, potential and potential energy.

*electric potential* at the original site of $q_2$, caused by $q_1$, is given by Eq. 29–8, or

$$V = \frac{1}{4\pi\epsilon_0} \frac{q_1}{r}.$$

If $q_2$ is moved in from infinity to the original distance $r$, the work required is, from the definition of electric potential, that is, from Eq. 29–2,

$$W = V q_2. \tag{29–12}$$

Combining these two equations and recalling that this work $W$ is precisely the *electric potential energy* $U$ of the system $q_1 + q_2$ yields

$$U (= W) = \frac{1}{4\pi\epsilon_0} \frac{q_1 q_2}{r_{12}}. \tag{29–13}$$

The subscript of $r$ emphasizes that the distance involved is that between the point charges $q_1$ and $q_2$.

For systems containing more than two charges the procedure is to compute the potential energy for every pair of charges separately and to add the results algebraically. This procedure rests on a physical picture in which (*a*) charge $q_1$ is brought into position, (*b*) $q_2$ is brought from infinity to its position near $q_1$, (*c*) $q_3$ is brought from infinity to its position near $q_1$ and $q_2$, etc.

The potential energy of continuous charge distributions (an ellipsoid of charge, for example) can be found by dividing the distribution into infinitesimal elements $dq$, treating each such element as a point charge, and using the procedures of the preceding paragraph, with the summation process replaced by an integration. We have not considered such problems in this text.

▶ **Example 8.** Two protons in a nucleus of $U^{238}$ are $6.0 \times 10^{-15}$ meter apart. What is their mutual electric potential energy?
From Eq. 29–13

$$U = \frac{1}{4\pi\epsilon_0} \frac{q_1 q_2}{r} = \frac{(9.0 \times 10^9 \text{ nt-m}^2/\text{coul}^2)(1.6 \times 10^{-19} \text{ coul})^2}{6.0 \times 10^{-15} \text{ meter}}$$

$$= 3.8 \times 10^{-14} \text{ joule} = 2.4 \times 10^5 \text{ ev}.$$

**Example 9.** Three charges are arranged as in Fig. 29–14. What is their mutual potential energy? Assume that $q = 1.0 \times 10^{-7}$ coul and $a = 10$ cm.

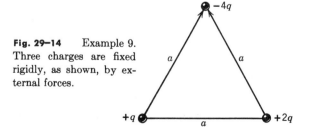

**Fig. 29–14**     Example 9. Three charges are fixed rigidly, as shown, by external forces.

The total energy of the configuration is the sum of the energies of each pair of particles. From Eq. 29–13,

$$U = U_{12} + U_{13} + U_{23}$$

$$= \frac{1}{4\pi\epsilon_0} \left[ \frac{(+q)(-4q)}{a} + \frac{(+q)(+2q)}{a} + \frac{(-4q)(+2q)}{a} \right]$$

$$= -\frac{10}{4\pi\epsilon_0} \frac{q^2}{a}$$

$$= -\frac{(9.0 + 10^9 \text{ nt-m}^2/\text{coul}^2)(10)(1.0 \times 10^{-7} \text{ coul})^2}{0.10 \text{ meter}} = -9.0 \times 10^{-3} \text{ joule.}$$

The fact that the total energy is negative means that negative work would have to be done to assemble this structure, starting with the three charges separated and at rest at infinity. Expressed otherwise, $9.0 \times 10^{-3}$ joule of work must be done to dismantle this structure, removing the charges to an infinite separation from one another.

When, as is common practice, infinity is taken as the zero of electric potential, a positive potential energy (as in Example 8) corresponds to repulsive electric forces and a negative potential energy (as in this example) to attractive electric forces. If the protons in Example 8 were not held in place by attractive (nonelectrical) nuclear forces, they would move away from each other. If the three particles in this example were released from their fixed positions, in which they are held by external forces, they would move toward each other.     ◄

### 29–7  Calculation of E from V

We have stated that $V$ and $E$ are equivalent descriptions and have determined (Eq. 29–6) how to calculate $V$ from $E$. Let us now consider how to calculate $E$ if $V$ is known throughout a certain region.

This problem has already been solved graphically. If $E$ is known at every point in space, the lines of force can be drawn; then a family of equipotentials can be sketched in by drawing surfaces at right angles. These equipotentials describe the behavior of $V$. Conversely, if $V$ is given as a function of position, a set of equipotential surfaces can be drawn. The lines of force can then be found by drawing lines at right angles, thus describing the behavior of $E$. It is the mathematical equivalent of this second graphical process that we seek here. Figure 29–15 shows some examples of lines of force and of the corresponding equipotential surfaces.

Figure 29–16 shows the intersection with the plane of the figure of a family of equipotential surfaces. The figure shows that $E$ at a typical point $P$ is at right angles to the equipotential surface through $P$, as it must be.

Let us move a test charge $q_0$ from $P$ along the path marked $\Delta l$ to the equipotential surface marked $V + \Delta V$. The work that must be done by the agent exerting the force $F$ (see Eq. 29–1) is $q_0\Delta V$.

From another point of view we can calculate the work from *

$$\Delta W = F \cdot \Delta l,$$

---

* We assume that the equipotentials are so close together that $F$ is constant for all parts of the path $\Delta l$. In the limit of a differential path ($dl$) there will be no difficulty.

where **F** is the force that must be exerted on the charge to overcome exactly the electrical force $q_0\mathbf{E}$. Since **F** and $q_0\mathbf{E}$ have opposite signs and are equal in magnitude,

$$\Delta W = -q_0\mathbf{E}\cdot\Delta\mathbf{l} = -q_0E\cos(\pi - \theta)\,\Delta l = q_0E\cos\theta\,\Delta l.$$

These two expressions for the work must be equal, which gives

$$q_0\,\Delta V = q_0E\cos\theta\,\Delta l$$

or
$$E\cos\theta = \frac{\Delta V}{\Delta l}. \tag{29–14}$$

Now $E\cos\theta$ is the component of **E** in the direction $-\mathbf{l}$ in Fig. 29–16; the quantity $-E\cos\theta$, which we call $E_l$, would then be the component of **E** in the $+\mathbf{l}$ direction. In the differential limit Eq. 29–14 can then be written as

$$E_l = -\frac{dV}{dl}. \tag{29–15}$$

In words, this equation says: If we travel through an electric field along a straight line and measure $V$ as we go, the rate of change of $V$ with distance that we observe, when changed in sign, is the component of **E** in that direction. The minus sign implies that **E** points in the direction of decreasing $V$, as in Fig. 29–16. It is particularly clear from Eq. 29–15 that appropriate units for **E** are the volts/meter.

There will be one direction **l** for which the quantity $dV/dl$ is a maximum. From Eq. 29–15, $E_l$ will also be a maximum for this direction and will in fact be $E$ itself. Thus

$$E = -\left(\frac{dV}{dl}\right)_{\text{max}} \tag{29–16}$$

The maximum value of $dV/dl$ at a given point is called the *potential gradient* at that point. The direction **l** for which $dV/dl$ has its maximum value is always at right angles to the equipotential surface, corresponding to $\theta = 0$ in Fig. 29–16.

If we take the direction **l** to be, in turn, the directions of the $x$, $y$, and $z$ axes, we can find the three components of **E** at any point, from Eq. 29–15.

$$E_x = -\frac{\partial V}{\partial x}; \qquad E_y = -\frac{\partial V}{\partial y}; \qquad E_z = -\frac{\partial V}{\partial z}. \tag{29–17}$$

Thus if $V$ is known for all points of space, that is, if the function $V(x, y, z)$ is known, the components of **E**, and thus **E** itself, can be found by taking derivatives.*

---

\* The symbol $\partial V/\partial x$ is a *partial derivative*. It implies that in taking this derivative of the function $V(x, y, z)$ the quantity $x$ is to be viewed as a variable and $y$ and $z$ are to be regarded as constants. Similar considerations hold for $\partial V/\partial y$ and $\partial V/\partial z$.

*(a)*

*(b)*

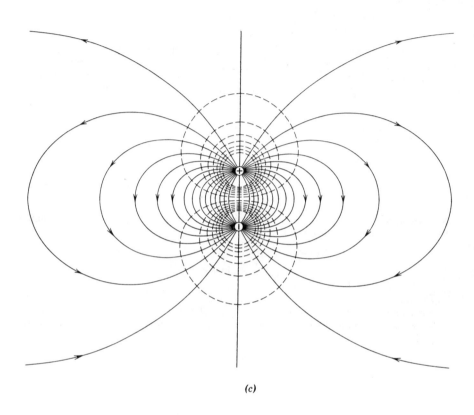

(c)

**Fig. 29-15**   Equipotential surfaces (dashed lines) and lines of force (solid lines) for ($a$) a point charge, ($b$) a uniform electric field, and ($c$) an electric dipole.   In all figures there is a constant difference of potential $\Delta V$ between adjacent equipotential surfaces.   Thus from Eq. 29-14, written for the case of $\theta = 180°$ as $\Delta l = -\Delta V/E$, the surfaces will be relatively close together where $E$ is relatively large and relatively far apart where $E$ is small.   Similarly (see Section 27-3) the lines of force are relatively close together where $E$ is large and far apart where $E$ is small.   See discussion and figures of Section 18-7 for other examples.

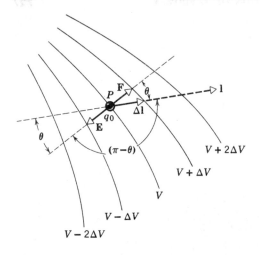

**Fig. 29–16** A test charge $q_0$ is moved from one equipotential surface to another along an arbitrarily selected direction marked 1.

▶ **Example 10.** Calculate $E(r)$ for a point charge $q$, using Eq. 29–16 and assuming that $V(r)$ is given as (see Eq. 29–8)

$$V = \frac{1}{4\pi\epsilon_0}\frac{q}{r}.$$

From symmetry, **E** must be directed radially outward for a (positive) point charge. Consider a point $P$ in the field a distance $r$ from the charge. It is clear that $dV/dl$ at $P$ has its greatest value if the direction $l$ is identified with that of $r$. Thus, from Eq. 29–16,

$$E = -\frac{dV}{dr} = -\frac{d}{dr}\left(\frac{1}{4\pi\epsilon_0}\frac{q}{r}\right)$$

$$= -\frac{q}{4\pi\epsilon_0}\frac{d}{dr}\left(\frac{1}{r}\right) = \frac{1}{4\pi\epsilon_0}\frac{q}{r^2}.$$

This result agrees exactly with Eq. 27–4, as it must.

**Example 11.** **E** *for a dipole.* Figure 29–17 shows a (distant) point $P$ in the field of a dipole located at the origin of an $xy$-axis system. $V$ is given by Eq. 29–11, or

$$V = \frac{1}{4\pi\epsilon_0}\frac{p\cos\theta}{r^2}.$$

Calculate **E** as a function of position.

From symmetry, **E**, for points in the plane of Fig. 29–17, lies in this plane. Thus it can be expressed in terms of its components $E_x$ and $E_y$. Let us first express the potential function in rectangular coordinates rather than polar coordinates, making use of

$$r = (x^2 + y^2)^{1/2} \quad \text{and} \quad \cos\theta = \frac{y}{(x^2 + y^2)^{1/2}}.$$

The result is

$$V = \frac{p}{4\pi\epsilon_0}\frac{y}{(x^2 + y^2)^{3/2}}.$$

We find $E_y$ from Eq. 29–17, recalling that $x$ is to be treated as a constant in this calculation:

$$E_y = -\frac{\partial V}{\partial y} = -\frac{p}{4\pi\epsilon_0}\frac{(x^2+y^2)^{3/2} - y\frac{3}{2}(x^2+y^2)^{1/2}(2y)}{(x^2+y^2)^3}$$

$$= -\frac{p}{4\pi\epsilon_0}\frac{x^2-2y^2}{(x^2+y^2)^{5/2}}.$$

Note that putting $x = 0$ describes points along the dipole axis (that is, the $y$ axis), and the expression for $E_y$ reduces to

$$E_y = \frac{2p}{4\pi\epsilon_0}\frac{1}{y^3}.$$

This result agrees exactly with that found in Chapter 27 (see Problem 10), for, from symmetry, $E_x$ equals zero on the dipole axis.

Putting $y = 0$ in the expression for $E_y$ describes points in the median plane of the dipole and yields

$$E_y = -\frac{p}{4\pi\epsilon_0}\frac{1}{x^3},$$

which agrees exactly with the result found in Chapter 27 (see Example 3), for, again from symmetry, $E_x$ equals zero in the median plane. The minus sign in this equation indicates that **E** points in the negative $y$ direction (see Fig. 29–10).

The component $E_x$ is also found from Eq. 29–17, recalling that $y$ is to be taken as a constant during this calculation:

$$E_x = -\frac{\partial V}{\partial x} = -\frac{py}{4\pi\epsilon_0}(-\tfrac{3}{2})(x^2+y^2)^{-5/2}(2x)$$

$$= \frac{3p}{4\pi\epsilon_0}\frac{xy}{(x^2+y^2)^{5/2}}.$$

As expected, $E_x$ vanishes both on the dipole axis ($x = 0$) and in the median plane ($y = 0$); see Fig. 29–10. ◀

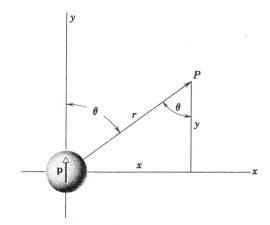

**Fig. 29–17** Showing a point $P$ in the field of an electric dipole **p**.

## 29-8    An Insulated Conductor

We proved in Section 28–4, using Gauss's law, that after a steady state is reached an excess charge $q$ placed on an insulated conductor will move to its outer surface. We now assert that this charge $q$ will distribute itself on this surface so that all points of the conductor, including *those on the surface and those inside*, have the same potential.

Consider any two points $A$ and $B$ in or on the conductor. If they were not at the same potential, the charge carriers in the conductor near the point of lower potential would tend to move toward the point of higher potential. We have assumed, however, that a steady-state situation, in which such currents do not exist, has been reached; thus all points, both on the surface and inside

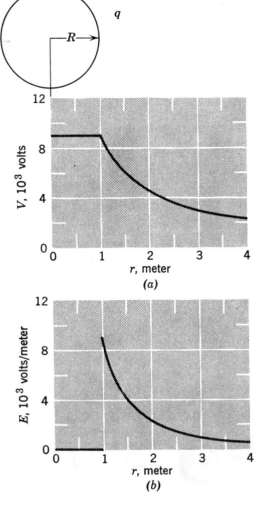

**Fig. 29–18** (a) The potential and (b) the electric field strength, for points near a conducting spherical shell of 1.0 meter radius carrying a charge of $+1.0 \times 10^{-6}$ coul.

it, must have the same potential.  Since the surface of the conductor is an equipotential surface, **E** for points on the surface must be at right angles to the surface.

We saw in Section 28–4 that a charge placed on an insulated conductor will spread over the surface until **E** equals zero for all points inside.  We now have an alternative way of saying the same thing; the charge will move until all points of the conductor (surface points and interior points) are brought to the same potential, for if $V$ is constant in the conductor then **E** is zero everywhere in the conductor ($E_l = -dV/dl$).

Figure 29–18$a$ is a plot of potential against radial distance for an isolated spherical conducting shell of 1.0-meter radius carrying a positive charge of $1.0 \times 10^{-6}$ coul.  For points outside the shell $V(r)$ can be calculated from Eq. 29–8 because the charge $q$ behaves, for such points, as if it were concentrated at the center of the sphere.  Equation 29–8 is correct right up to the surface of the shell.  Now let us push the test charge through the surface, assuming that there is a small hole, and into the interior.  No extra work is needed because no electrical forces act on the test charge once it is inside the shell.  Thus the potential everywhere inside is the same as that on the surface, as Fig. 29–18$a$ shows.

Figure 29–18$b$ shows the electric field strength for this same sphere.  Note that $E$ equals zero inside.  The lower of these curves can be derived from the upper by differentiation with respect to $r$, using Eq. 29–16; the upper can be derived from the lower by integration with respect to $r$, using Eq. 29–6.

Figure 29–18 holds without change if the conductor is a solid sphere rather than a spherical shell as we have assumed.  It is constructive to compare Fig. 29–18$b$ (conducting shell or sphere) with Fig. 28–9, which holds for a *nonconducting* sphere.  The student should try to understand the difference between these two figures, bearing in mind that in the first the charge lies on the surface whereas in the second it was assumed to have been spread uniformly throughout the volume of the sphere.

Finally we note that, as a general rule, the charge density tends to be high on isolated conducting surfaces whose radii of curvature are small, and conversely.  For example, the charge density tends to be relatively high on sharp points and relatively low on plane regions on a conducting surface.  The electric field strength $E$ at points immediately above a charged surface is proportional to the charge density $\sigma$ so that $E$ may also reach very high values near sharp points.  Glow discharges from sharp points during thunderstorms are a familiar example.  The lightning rod acts in this way to neutralize charged clouds and thus prevent lightning strokes.

We can examine the qualitative relationship between $\sigma$ and the curvature of the surface in a particular case by considering two spheres of different radii connected by a very long fine wire; see Fig. 29–19.  Suppose that this entire assembly is raised

**Fig. 29–19** Two spheres connected by a long fine wire.

to some arbitrary potential $V$. The (equal) potentials of the two spheres are, from Eq. 29–8,*

$$V = \frac{1}{4\pi\epsilon_0}\frac{q_1}{R_1} = \frac{1}{4\pi\epsilon_0}\frac{q_2}{R_2},$$

which yields

$$\frac{q_1}{q_2} = \frac{R_1}{R_2}, \tag{29–18}$$

where $q_1$ is the charge on the sphere of radius $R_1$ and $q_2$ is the charge on the sphere of radius $R_2$.

The *surface charge densities* for each sphere are given by

$$\sigma_1 = \frac{q_1}{4\pi R_1{}^2} \quad \text{and} \quad \sigma_2 = \frac{q_2}{4\pi R_2{}^2}.$$

Dividing gives

$$\frac{\sigma_1}{\sigma_2} = \frac{q_1}{q_2}\frac{R_2{}^2}{R_1{}^2}.$$

Combining with Eq. 29–18 yields

$$\frac{\sigma_1}{\sigma_2} = \frac{R_2}{R_1},$$

which is consistent with our qualitative statement above. Note that the larger sphere has the larger total charge but the smaller charge density.

The fact that $\sigma$, and thus **E**, can become very large near sharp points is important in the design of high-voltage equipment. *Corona discharge* can result from such points if the conducting object is raised to high potential and surrounded by air. Normally air is thought of as a nonconductor. However, it contains a small number of ions produced, for example, by the cosmic rays. A positively charged conductor will attract negative ions from the surrounding air and thus will slowly neutralize itself.

---

* Equation 29–8 holds only for an *isolated* point charge or spherically symmetric charge distribution. The spheres must be assumed to be so far apart that the charge on either one has a negligible effect on the distribution of charge on the other.

If the charged conductor has sharp points, the value of **E** in the air near the points can be very high. If the value is high enough, the ions, as they are drawn toward the conductor, will receive such large accelerations that, by collision with air molecules, they will produce vast additional numbers of ions. The air is thus made much more conducting, and the discharge of the conductor by this corona discharge may be very rapid indeed. The air surrounding sharp conducting points may even glow visibly because of light emitted from the air molecules during these collisions.

### 29–9  The Electrostatic Generator

The electrostatic generator was conceived by Lord Kelvin in 1890 and put into useful practice in essentially its modern form by R. J. Van de Graaff in 1931. It is a device for producing electric potential differences of the order of several millions of volts. Its chief application in physics is the use of this potential difference to accelerate charged particles to high energies. Beams of energetic particles made in this way can be used in many different "atom-smashing" experiments. The technique is to let a charged particle "fall" through a potential difference $V$, gaining kinetic energy as it does so.

Let a particle of (positive) charge $q$ move in a vacuum under the influence of an electric field from one position $A$ to another position $B$ whose electric potential is lower by $V$. The electric potential energy of the system is reduced by $qV$ because this is the work that an external agent would have to do to restore the system to its original condition. This decrease in potential energy appears as kinetic energy of the particle, or

$$K = qV. \tag{29–19}$$

$K$ is in joules if $q$ is in coulombs and $V$ in volts. If the particle is an electron or a proton, $q$ will be the quantum of charge $e$.

If we adopt the quantum of charge $e$ as a unit in place of the coulomb, we arrive at another unit for energy, the *electron volt*, which is used extensively in atomic and nuclear physics. By substituting into Eq. 29–19,

$$1 \text{ electron volt} = (1 \text{ quantum of charge})(1 \text{ volt})$$

$$= (1.60 \times 10^{-19} \text{ coul})(1.00 \text{ volt})$$

$$= 1.60 \times 10^{-19} \text{ joule}.$$

The electron volt can be used interchangeably with any other energy unit. Thus a 10-gm object moving at 1000 cm/sec can be said to have a kinetic energy of $3.1 \times 10^{18}$ ev. Most physicists would prefer to express this result as 0.50 joule, the electron volt being inconveniently small. In atomic and nuclear problems, however, the electron volt (ev) and its multiples the Mev ($= 10^6$ ev), the Bev ($= 10^9$ ev) and the Gev ($= 10^{12}$ ev) are the usual units of choice.

▶ **Example 12.** *The electrostatic generator.* Figure 29–20, which illustrates the basic operating principle of the electrostatic generator, shows a small sphere of radius $r$ placed inside a large spherical shell of radius $R$. The two spheres carry charges $q$ and $Q$, respectively. Calculate their potential difference.

The potential of the large sphere is caused in part by its own charge and in part because it lies in the field set up by the charge $q$ on the small sphere. From Eq. 29–8,

$$V_R = \frac{1}{4\pi\epsilon_0}\left(\frac{Q}{R} + \frac{q}{R}\right).$$

The potential of the small sphere is caused in part by its own charge and in part because it is inside the large sphere; see Fig. 29–18a. From Eq. 29–8,

$$V_r = \frac{1}{4\pi\epsilon_0}\left(\frac{q}{r} + \frac{Q}{R}\right).$$

The potential difference is

$$V_r - V_R = \frac{q}{4\pi\epsilon_0}\left(\frac{1}{r} - \frac{1}{R}\right).$$

Thus, assuming $q$ is positive, the inner sphere will always be higher in potential than the outer sphere. If the spheres are connected by a fine wire, the charge $q$ will flow *entirely* to the outer sphere, regardless of the charge $Q$ that may already be present.

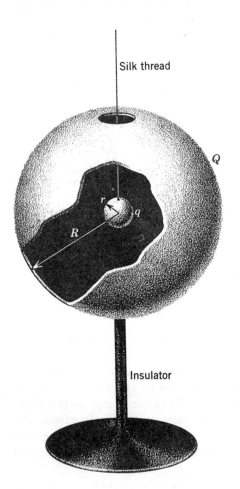

Silk thread

**Fig. 29–20** Example 12. A small charged sphere of radius $r$ is suspended inside a charged spherical shell whose outer surface has radius $R$.

Insulator

Removable tank cover

Electronic circuits

Built-in 2 kw power supply

Charge collector

Equipotential planes

Insulating column 18′ long

Windows

2–50 hp 1,800 rpm motors

Belt tension adjustment

Lead shielding

Dry ice trap

Pumping system

Equipotential shield, 68″ I.D.

High voltage terminal, 38″ diam

Positive ion source

400 lb/in.$^2$ steel pressure tank

Field control rods

Insulating belt

Positive ion accelerating tube

Manhole

Movable platform

Main valve

Flexible coupling

Analyzing magnet

Beam axis

Adjustable magnet base

0   2   4   6   8
Feet

**Fig. 29–21**   An electrostatic generator at MIT capable of producing 9-Mev protons. The proton beam is accelerated vertically downward, being deflected into a horizontal plane by the analyzing magnet shown at the bottom. (Courtesy of J. G. Trump.)

From another point of view, we note that since the spheres when electrically connected form a single conductor at electrostatic equilibrium there can be only a single potential. This means that $V_r - V_R = 0$, which can occur only if $q = 0$.

In actual electrostatic generators charge is carried into the shell on rapidly moving belts made of insulating material. Charge is "sprayed" onto the belts outside the shell by corona discharge from a series of sharp metallic points connected to a source of moderately high potential difference. Charge is removed from the belts inside the shell by a similar series of points connected to the shell. Electrostatic generators can be built commercially to accelerate protons to energies up to 10 Mev, using a single acceleration. Figure 29–21 shows a schematic diagram of an electrostatic generator at MIT that can produce 9–Mev protons.

Generators can be built in which the accelerated particles are subject to successive accelerations. An electrostatic generator at the University of Pittsburgh subjects particles to three successive accelerations.

## QUESTIONS

1. Are we free to call the potential of the earth $+100$ volts instead of zero? What effect would such an assumption have on measured values of (a) potentials and (b) potential differences?

2. What would happen to a person on an insulated stand if his potential was increased by 10,000 volts?

3. Do electrons tend to go to regions of high potential or of low potential?

4. Suppose that the earth has a net charge that is *not* zero. Is it still possible to adopt the earth as a standard reference point of potential and to assign the potential $V = 0$ to it?

5. Does the potential of a positively charged insulated conductor have to be positive? Give an example to prove your point.

6. Can two different equipotential surfaces intersect?

7. If E equals zero at a given point, must $V$ equal zero for that point? Give some examples to prove your answer.

8. If you know E at a given point, can you calculate $V$ at that point? If not, what further information do you need?

9. If $V$ equals a constant throughout a given region of space, what can you say about E in that region?

10. In Section 16–6 we saw that the gravitational field strength is zero inside a spherical shell of matter. The electrical field strength is zero not only inside an isolated charged spherical conductor but inside an isolated conductor of *any* shape. Is the gravitational field strength inside, say, a cubical shell of matter zero? If not, in what respect is the analogy not complete?

11. How can you insure that the electric potential in a given region of space will have a constant value?

12. An isolated conducting spherical shell carries a negative charge. What will happen if a positively charged metal object is placed in contact with the shell interior? Assume that the positive charge is (a) less than, (b) equal to, and (c) greater than the negative charge in magnitude.

13. An uncharged metal sphere suspended by a silk thread is placed in a uniform external electric field E. What is the magnitude of the electric field for points inside the sphere? Is your answer changed if the sphere carries a charge?

14. A charge is placed on an insulated conductor in the form of a perfect cube. What will be the relative charge density at various points on the cube (surfaces, edges, corners); what will happen to the charge if the cube is in air?

## PROBLEMS

1. An infinite charged sheet has a surface charge density $\sigma$ of $1.0 \times 10^{-7}$ coul/meter$^2$. How far apart are the equipotential surfaces whose potentials differ by 5.0 volts?

2. A charge $q$ is distributed uniformly throughout a nonconducting spherical volume of radius $R$. (a) Show that the potential a distance $a$ from the center, where $a < R$, is given by

$$V = \frac{q(3R^2 - a^2)}{8\pi\epsilon_0 R^3}.$$

(b) Is it reasonable that, according to this expression, $V$ is not zero at the center of the sphere?

3. A charge of $10^{-8}$ coul can be produced by simple rubbing. To what potential would such a charge raise an insulated conducting sphere of 10-cm radius?

4. Consider a point charge with $q = 1.5 \times 10^{-8}$ coul. (a) What is the radius of an equipotential surface having a potential of 30 volts? (b) Are surfaces whose potentials differ by a constant amount (say 1.0 volt) evenly spaced in radius?

5. In Fig. 29–22, locate the points (a) where $V = 0$ and (b) where $\mathbf{E} = 0$. Consider only points on the axis and choose $d = 1.0$ meter.

**Fig. 29–22**

6. In Fig. 29–22 (see Problem 5) sketch qualitatively (a) the lines of force and (b) the intersections of the equipotential surfaces with the plane of the figure. (Hint: Consider the behavior close to each point charge and at considerable distances from the pair of charges.)

7. In Fig. 29–23 derive an expression for $V_A - V_B$. Does your result reduce to the expected answer when $d = 0$? When $q = 0$?

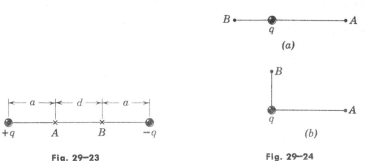

**Fig. 29–23**                **Fig. 29–24**

8. A point charge has $q = +1.0 \times 10^{-6}$ coul. Consider point $A$ which is 2.0 meters distant and point $B$ which is 1.0 meter distant in a direction diametrically opposite, as in Fig. 29–24a. (a) What is the potential difference $V_A - V_B$? (b) Repeat if points $A$ and $B$ are located as in Fig. 29–24b.

9. Calculate the dipole moment of a water molecule under the assumption that all ten electrons in the molecule circulate symmetrically about the oxygen atom, that the OH distance is $0.96 \times 10^{-8}$ cm, and that the angle between the two OH bonds is 104°. Compare with the value quoted on p. 719; see Fig. 29–11.

10. For the charge configuration of Fig. 29–25, show that $V(r)$ for points on the vertical axis, assuming $r \gg a$, is given by

$$V = \frac{1}{4\pi\epsilon_0}\left(\frac{q}{r} + \frac{2qa}{r^2}\right).$$

Is this an expected result? (Hint: The charge configuration can be viewed as the sum of an isolated charge and a dipole.)

**Fig. 29–25**

11. In a typical lightning flash the potential difference between discharge points is about $10^9$ volts and the quantity of charge transferred is about 30 coul. How much ice would it melt at $0\,°C$ if all the energy released could be used for this purpose?

12. Calculate (a) the electric potential established by the nucleus of a hydrogen atom at the mean distance of the circulating electron ($r = 5.3 \times 10^{-11}$ meter), (b) the electric potential energy of the atom when the electron is at this radius, and (c) the kinetic energy of the electron, assuming it to be moving in a circular orbit of this radius centered on the nucleus. (d) How much energy is required to ionize the hydrogen atom? Express all energies in electron volts.

13. What is the electric potential energy of the charge configuration of Fig. 29–7? Use the numerical values of Example 5.

14. (a) A spherical drop of water carrying a charge of $3 \times 10^{-6}$ coul has a potential of 500 volts at its surface. What is the radius of the drop? (b) If two such drops, of the same charge and radius, combine to form a single spherical drop, what is the potential at the surface of the new drop so formed?

15. If the earth had a net charge equivalent to 1 electron/meter$^2$ of surface area, (a) what would the earth's potential be? (b) What would the electric field due to the earth be just outside its surface?

16. Figure 29–26 shows an idealized representation of a $U^{238}$ nucleus ($Z = 92$) on the verge of fission. Calculate (a) the repulsive force acting on each fragment and (b) the mutual electric potential energy of the two fragments. Assume that the fragments are

**Fig. 29–26**

equal in size and charge, spherical, and just touching. The radius of the initially spherical $U^{238}$ nucleus is $8.0 \times 10^{-15}$ meter. Assume that the material out of which nuclei are made has a constant density.

17. In the Millikan oil drop experiment (see Fig. 27–24) an electric field of $1.92 \times 10^5$ nt/coul is maintained at balance across two plates separated by 1.50 cm. Find the potential difference between the plates.

18. (a) Show that the electric potential at a point on the axis of a ring of charge of radius $a$, computed directly from Eq. 29–10, is given by

$$V = \frac{1}{4\pi\epsilon_0} \frac{q}{\sqrt{x^2 + a^2}}.$$

(b) From this result derive an expression for $E$ at axial points; compare with the direct calculation of $E$ in Example 5, Chapter 27.

19. In Example 6 the potential at an axial point for a charged disk was shown to be

$$V = \frac{\sigma}{2\epsilon_0} \left( \sqrt{a^2 + r^2} - r \right).$$

From this result show that $E$ for axial points is given by

$$E = \frac{\sigma}{2\epsilon_0} \left( 1 - \frac{r}{\sqrt{a^2 + r^2}} \right).$$

Does this expression for $E$ reduce to an expected result for (a) $r \gg a$ and (b) for $r = 0$?

20. (a) Starting from Eq. 29–11, find the magnitude $E_r$ of the radial component of the electric field due to a dipole. (b) For what values of $\theta$ is $E_r$ zero?

21. Can a conducting sphere 10 cm in radius hold a charge of $4 \times 10^{-6}$ coul in air without breakdown? The dielectric strength (minimum field required to produce breakdown) of air at 1 atm is $3 \times 10^6$ volts/meter.

22. A Geiger counter has a metal cylinder 2.0 cm in diameter along whose axis is stretched a wire 0.005 in. in diameter. If 850 volts are applied between them, what is the electric field strength at the surface of (a) the wire and (b) the cylinder?

23. Two metal spheres are 3.0 cm in radius and carry charges of $+1.0 \times 10^{-8}$ coul and $-3.0 \times 10^{-8}$ coul, respectively, assumed to be uniformly distributed. If their centers are 2.0 meters apart, calculate (a) the potential of the point halfway between their centers and (b) the potential of each sphere.

24. In Fig. 29–19 let $R_1 = 1.0$ cm and $R_2 = 2.0$ cm. Before the spheres are connected by the fine wire, a charge of $2.0 \times 10^{-7}$ coul is placed on the smaller sphere, the larger sphere being uncharged. Calculate (a) the charge, (b) the charge density, and (c) the potential for each sphere after they are connected.

25. The metal object in Fig. 29–27 is a figure of revolution about the horizontal axis. If it is charged negatively, sketch roughly a few equipotentials and lines of force. Use physical reasoning rather than mathematical analysis.

Axis

**Fig. 29–27**

26. Devise an arrangement of three point charges, separated by finite distances, that has zero electric potential energy.

27. Derive an expression for the work required to put the four charges together as indicated in Fig. 29–28.

**Fig. 29–28**

28. A gold nucleus contains a positive charge equal to that of 79 protons. An $\alpha$-particle ($Z = 2$) has a kinetic energy $K$ at points far from this charge and is traveling directly toward the charge. The particle just touches the surface of the charge (assumed spherical) and is reversed in direction. Calculate $K$, assuming a nuclear radius of $5.0 \times 10^{-15}$ meter. The actual $\alpha$-particle energy used in the experiments of Rutherford and his collaborators was 5.0 Mev. What do you conclude?

29. What is the potential gradient, in volts/meter, at a distance of $10^{-12}$ meter from the center of the gold nucleus? What is the gradient at the nuclear surface?

30. For the spheres of Fig. 29–19, what is the ratio of electric field strengths at the surface?

31. (a) Through what potential difference must an electron fall, according to Newtonian mechanics, to acquire a speed $v$ equal to the speed $c$ of light? (b) Newtonian mechanics fails as $v \rightarrow c$. Therefore, using the correct relativistic expression for the kinetic energy

$$K = mc^2 \left[ \frac{1}{\sqrt{1 - (v/c)^2}} - 1 \right]$$

in place of the Newtonian expression $K = \frac{1}{2}mv^2$, determine the actual electron speed acquired in falling through the potential difference computed in (a). Express this speed as an appropriate fraction of the speed of light.

32. Two insulated concentric conducting spheres of radii $R_1$ and $R_2$ carry charges $q_1$ and $q_2$, respectively. Derive expressions for $E(r)$ and $V(r)$, where $r$ is the distance from the center of the spheres. Plot $E(r)$ and $V(r)$ from $r = 0$ to $r = 4.0$ meters for $R_1 = 0.50$ meter, $R_2 = 1.0$ meter, $q_1 = +2.0 \times 10^{-6}$ coul, and $q_2 = +1.0 \times 10^{-6}$ coul. Compare with Fig. 29–18.

33. Let the potential difference between the shell of an electrostatic generator and the point at which charges are sprayed onto the moving belt be $3.0 \times 10^6$ volts. If the belt transfers charge to the shell at the rate of $3.0 \times 10^{-3}$ coul/sec, what power must be provided to drive the belt, considering only electrical forces?

34. (a) How much charge is required to raise an isolated metallic sphere of 1.0-meter radius to a potential of $1.0 \times 10^6$ volts? Repeat for a sphere of 1.0-cm radius. (b) Why use a large sphere in an electrostatic generator since the same potential can be achieved for a smaller charge with a small sphere?

35. An alpha particle is accelerated through a potential difference of one million volts in an electrostatic generator. (a) What kinetic energy does it acquire? (b) What kinetic energy would a proton acquire under these same circumstances? (c) Which particle would acquire the greater speed, starting from rest?

# Capacitors and Dielectrics

## CHAPTER 30

### 30-1 Capacitance

In Section 29-3 we showed that the potential of a charged conducting sphere, assumed to be completely isolated with no other bodies (conducting or nonconducting) nearby, is given by

$$V_+' = \frac{1}{4\pi\epsilon_0}\frac{q}{R},\qquad(30\text{-}1)$$

in which $q$ is the charge on the sphere and $R$ is the sphere radius. The subscript on $V$ indicates that we assume the charge to be positive. We represent this potential in Fig. 30-1 by the line marked $V_+'$. The line marked $V_\infty$ in that figure represents the potential of an infinitely distant reference position; it has been assigned the value zero, following the usual convention.

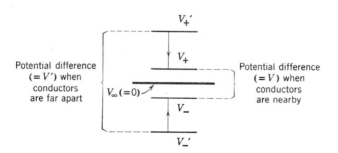

**Fig. 30-1** The potential difference between two conductors that carry constant, equal, and opposite charges is reduced as the conductors are brought closer together.

**741**

Let us now imagine a second sphere of radius $R$, carrying a negative charge $-q$ and located a large distance ($\gg R$) from the first sphere so that each may still be considered to be electrically isolated. The potential of the second sphere is given by

$$V_-' = -\frac{1}{4\pi\epsilon_0}\frac{q}{R}, \tag{30-2}$$

and this quantity also is represented in Fig. 30–1.

The potential difference $V'$ between the two spheres is

$$V' = V_+' - V_-' = \frac{1}{4\pi\epsilon_0}\frac{2q}{R}.$$

This shows that $V'$, the potential difference, and $q$, the magnitude of the charge on either sphere, are proportional to each other. We may rewrite the equation as

$$q = (2\pi\epsilon_0 R)V' = C'V', \tag{30-3}$$

in which the proportionality constant in parentheses is called the *capacitance* of the two spheres and assigned the symbol $C'$.

Let us move the two spheres close together. The presence of each will now spoil the spherical symmetry of the lines of force emanating from the other. Lines from a given sphere, which, for large sphere separations, radiated uniformly in all directions to infinity, now terminate, in part, on the other sphere. Under these conditions Eqs. 30–1 and 30–2 no longer apply, since they were derived (see Section 29–3) on the assumption that spherical symmetry existed, permitting the useful application of Gauss's law.

A positive charge brought near to an isolated object serves to raise the potential of that object and a negative charge serves to lower it, as the student can see by considering the work required to move a positive test charge from infinity to points near such charges. Thus the potential of the positively charged sphere will be lowered by the presence nearby of the negatively charged sphere, from $V_+'$ to some lower value $V_+$. Similarly the potential of the negative sphere will be raised from $V_-'$ to a higher value $V_-$. These new potentials are shown in Fig. 30–1, the potential changes for each sphere being suggested by the vertical arrows.

From Fig. 30–1, although the *charges* on the spheres have not changed, it is clear that the *potential difference* between the spheres has been considerably reduced. Put another way, the *capacitance* of the system of two spheres (see Eq. 30–3), defined from

$$C = \frac{q}{V}, \tag{30-4}$$

has been made considerably larger than its initial value $C'$ by bringing the spheres closer together.

It is also possible to use Eq. 30–4 to define the capacitance of a single isolated conductor such as a sphere. In such cases one may imagine that the second "plate," carrying an equal and opposite charge, is a conducting sphere of very large—essentially infinite—radius centered about the conductor. The potential of this infinitely distant sphere, according to the usual convention for potential measurements, is zero. The capacitance of an isolated sphere of radius $R$ is given from Eqs. 30–4 and 30–1 as

$$C = \frac{q}{V} = 4\pi\epsilon_0 R.$$

The mks unit of capacitance that follows from Eq. 30–4 is the coul/volt. A special unit, the *farad*, is used to represent it. It is named in honor of Michael Faraday who, among other contributions, developed the concept of capacitance. Thus

$$1 \text{ farad} = 1 \text{ coul/volt.}$$

The submultiples of the farad, the *microfarad* (1 $\mu$f $= 10^{-6}$ farad) and the *micromicrofarad* (1 $\mu\mu$f $= 10^{-12}$ farad), are more convenient units in practice.

An analogy can be made between a capacitor carrying a charge $q$ and a rigid container of volume $\mathcal{V}$ containing $\mu$ moles of an ideal gas.

The gas pressure $p$ is directly proportional to $\mu$ for a fixed temperature, according to the ideal gas law (Eq. 23–2)

$$\mu = \left(\frac{\mathcal{V}}{RT}\right) p.$$

For the capacitor (Eq. 30–4)

$$q = (C)V.$$

Comparison shows that the capacitance $C$ of the capacitor, assuming a fixed temperature, is analogous to the volume $\mathcal{V}$ of the container.

Note that any amount of charge can be put on the capacitor, and any mass of gas can be put in the container, up to certain limits. These correspond to electrical breakdown ("arcing over") for the capacitor and to rupture of the walls for the container.

Figure 30–2 shows a more general case of two nearby conductors, which are now permitted to be of any shape, carrying equal and opposite charges. Such an arrangement is called a *capacitor*, the conductors being called *plates*. The equal and opposite charges might be established by connecting the plates momentarily to opposite poles of a battery. The capacitance $C$ of any capacitor is defined from Eq. 30–4 in which we remind the student that $V$ is the *potential difference between the plates* and $q$ is the magnitude of the *charge on either plate; q* must not be taken as the net charge of the capacitor, which is zero. The capacitance of a capacitor depends on the geometry of each plate, their spatial relationship to each other, and the medium in which the plates are immersed. For the present, we take this medium to be a vacuum.

Capacitors are very useful devices, of great interest to physicists and engineers. For example:

1. In this book we stress the importance of *fields* to the understanding of natural phenomena. A capacitor can be used to establish desired electric field configurations for various purposes. In Section 27–5 we described the deflection of an electron beam in a uniform field set up by a capacitor, al-

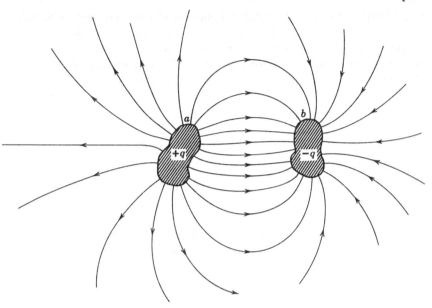

**Fig. 30–2**   Two insulated conductors carrying equal and opposite charges form a capacitor.

though we did not use this term in that section.   In later sections we discuss the behavior of dielectric materials when placed in an electric field (provided conveniently by a capacitor) and we shall see how the laws of electromagnetism can be generalized to take the presence of dielectric bodies more readily into account.

2. A second important concept stressed in this book is *energy*.  By analyzing a charged capacitor we show that electric energy may be considered to be stored in the electric field between the plates and indeed in any electric field, however generated.   Because capacitors can confine strong electric fields to small volumes, they can serve as useful devices for storing energy.  In many electron synchrotrons, which are cyclotron-like devices for accelerating electrons, energy accumulated and stored in a large bank of capacitors over a relatively long period of time is made available intermittently to accelerate the electrons by discharging the capacitor in a much shorter time.  Many researches and devices in plasma physics also make use of bursts of energy stored in this way.

3. The electronic age could not exist without capacitors.  They are used, in conjunction with other devices, to reduce voltage fluctuations in electronic power supplies, to transmit pulsed signals, to generate or detect electromagnetic oscillations at radio frequencies, and to provide time delays.   In most of these applications the potential difference between the plates will not be constant, as we assume in this chapter, but will vary with time, often in a sinusoidal or a pulsed fashion.   In later chapters we consider some aspects of the capacitor used as a circuit element.

### 30–2    Calculating Capacitance

Figure 30–3 shows a *parallel-plate* capacitor formed of two parallel conducting plates of area $A$ separated by a distance $d$. If we connect each plate to the terminal of a battery, a charge $+q$ will appear on one plate and a charge $-q$ on the other. If $d$ is small compared with the plate dimensions, the electric field strength $\mathbf{E}$ between the plates will be uniform, which means that the lines of force will be parallel and evenly spaced. The laws of electromagnetism (see Problem 20, Chapter 35) require that there be some "fringing" of the lines at the edges of the plates, but for small enough $d$ it can be neglected for our present purpose.

We can calculate the capacitance of this device using Gauss's law. Figure 30–3 shows (dashed lines) a Gaussian surface of height $h$ closed by plane caps of area $A$ that are the shape and size of the capacitor plates. The flux of $\mathbf{E}$ is zero for the part of the Gaussian surface that lies inside the top capacitor plate because the electric field inside a conductor carrying a static charge is zero. The flux of $\mathbf{E}$ through the wall of the Gaussian surface is zero because, to the extent that the fringing of the lines of force can be neglected, $\mathbf{E}$ lies in the wall.

This leaves only the face of the Gaussian surface that lies between the plates. Here $\mathbf{E}$ is constant and the flux $\Phi_E$ is simply $EA$. Gauss's law gives

$$\epsilon_0 \Phi_E = \epsilon_0 E A = q. \tag{30–5}$$

The work required to carry a test charge $q_0$ from one plate to the other can be expressed either as $q_0 V$ (see Eq. 29–1) or as the product of a force $q_0 E$ times a distance $d$ or $q_0 E d$. These expressions must be equal, or

$$V = Ed. \tag{30–6}$$

More formally, Eq. 30–6 is a special case of the general relation (Eq. 29–5; see also Example 1, Chapter 29)

$$V = -\int \mathbf{E} \cdot d\mathbf{l},$$

where $V$ is the difference in potential between the plates. The integral may

**Fig. 30–3**    A parallel-plate capacitor with plates of area $A$. The dashed line represents a Gaussian surface whose height is $h$ and whose top and bottom caps are the same shape and size as the capacitor plates.

be taken over any path that starts on one plate and ends on the other because each plate is an equipotential surface and the electrostatic force is path independent. Although the simplest path between the plates is a perpendicular straight line, Eq. 30–6 follows no matter what path of integration we choose.

If we substitute Eqs. 30–5 and 30–6 into the relation $C = q/V$, we obtain

$$C = \frac{q}{V} = \frac{\epsilon_0 E A}{Ed} = \frac{\epsilon_0 A}{d}. \tag{30–7}$$

Equation 30–7 holds only for capacitors of the parallel-plate type; different formulas hold for capacitors of different geometry.

In Section 26–4 we stated that $\epsilon_0$, which we first met in connection with Coulomb's law, was not measured in terms of that law because of experimental difficulties. Equation 30–7 suggests that $\epsilon_0$ might be measured by building a capacitor of accurately known plate area and plate spacing and determining its capacitance experimentally by measuring $q$ and $V$ in the relation $C = q/V$. Thus Eq. 30–7 can be solved for $\epsilon_0$ and a numerical value found in terms of the measured quantities $A$, $d$, and $C$; $\epsilon_0$ has been measured accurately in this way.

▶ **Example 1.** The parallel plates of an air-filled capacitor are everywhere 1.0 mm apart. What must the plate area be if the capacitance is to be 1.0 farad?

From Eq. 30–7

$$A = \frac{dC}{\epsilon_0} = \frac{(1.0 \times 10^{-3} \text{ meter})(1.0 \text{ farad})}{8.9 \times 10^{-12} \text{ coul}^2/\text{nt-m}^2} = 1.1 \times 10^8 \text{ meter}^2.$$

This is the area of a square sheet more than 6 miles on edge; the farad is indeed a large unit.

**Example 2.** *A cylindrical capacitor.* A cylindrical capacitor consists of two coaxial cylinders (Fig. 30–4) of radius $a$ and $b$ and length $l$. What is the capacitance of this device? Assume that the capacitor is very long (that is, that $l \gg b$) so that fringing of the lines of force at the ends can be ignored for the purpose of calculating the capacitance.

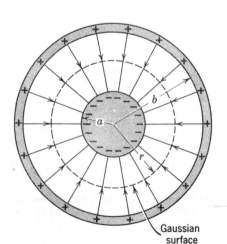

**Fig. 30–4** Example 2. A cross section of a cylindrical capacitor. The dashed circle is a cross section of a cylindrical Gaussian surface of radius $r$ and length $l$.

Gaussian
surface

As a Gaussian surface construct a coaxial cylinder of radius $r$ and length $l$, closed by plane caps. Gauss's law

$$\epsilon_0 \oint \mathbf{E} \cdot d\mathbf{S} = q$$

gives          $\epsilon_0 E(2\pi r)(l) = q,$

the flux being entirely through the cylindrical surface and not through the end caps. Solving for $E$ yields

$$E = \frac{q}{2\pi \epsilon_0 r l}.$$

The potential difference between the plates is given by Eq. 29–5 [note that $\mathbf{E}$ and $d\mathbf{l}$ ($= d\mathbf{r}$) point in opposite directions] or

$$V = -\int_a^b \mathbf{E} \cdot d\mathbf{l} = \int_a^b E \, dr = \int_a^b \frac{q}{2\pi \epsilon_0 l} \frac{dr}{r} = \frac{q}{2\pi \epsilon_0 l} \ln \frac{b}{a}.$$

Finally, the capacitance is given by

$$C = \frac{q}{V} = \frac{2\pi \epsilon_0 l}{\ln (b/a)}.$$

Like the relation for the parallel-plate capacitor (Eq. 30–7), this relation also depends only on geometrical factors.

**Example 3.** *Capacitors in parallel.* Figure 30–5 shows three capacitors connected in parallel. What single capacitance $C$ is equivalent to this combination? "Equivalent" means that if the parallel combination and the single capacitance were each in a box with wires $a$ and $b$ connected to terminals, it would not be possible to distinguish the two by electrical measurements external to the box.

**Fig. 30–5** Example 3. Three capacitors in parallel.

The potential difference across each capacitor in Fig. 30–5 will be the same. This follows because all of the upper plates are connected together and to terminal $a$, whereas all of the lower plates are connected together and to terminal $b$. Applying the relation $q = CV$ to each capacitor yields

$$q_1 = C_1 V; \qquad q_2 = C_2 V; \qquad \text{and} \qquad q_3 = C_3 V.$$

The total charge $q$ on the combination is

$$q = q_1 + q_2 + q_3$$
$$= (C_1 + C_2 + C_3)V.$$

The equivalent capacitance $C$ is

$$C = \frac{q}{V} = C_1 + C_2 + C_3.$$

This result can easily be extended to any number of parallel-connected capacitors.

**Example 4.** *Capacitors in series.* Figure 30–6 shows three capacitors connected in series. What single capacitance $C$ is "equivalent" (see Example 3) to this combination?

For capacitors connected as shown, the magnitude $q$ of the charge on each plate must be the same. This is true because the net charge on the part of the circuit enclosed by the dashed line in Fig. 30–6 must be zero; that is, the charge present on these plates initially is zero and connecting a battery between $a$ and $b$ will only produce a charge separation, the *net* charge on these plates still being zero. Assuming that neither $C_1$ nor $C_2$ "sparks over," there is no way for charge to enter or leave the region enclosed by the dashed line.

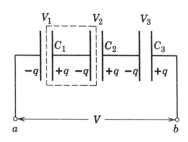

**Fig. 30–6**  Example 4.  Three capacitors in series.

Applying the relation $q = CV$ to each capacitor yields

$$V_1 = q/C_1; \qquad V_2 = q/C_2; \qquad \text{and} \qquad V_3 = q/C_3.$$

The potential difference for the series combination is

$$V = V_1 + V_2 + V_3$$

$$= q \left( \frac{1}{C_1} + \frac{1}{C_2} + \frac{1}{C_3} \right).$$

The equivalent capacitance

$$C = \frac{q}{V} = \frac{1}{\dfrac{1}{C_1} + \dfrac{1}{C_2} + \dfrac{1}{C_3}},$$

or

$$\frac{1}{C} = \frac{1}{C_1} + \frac{1}{C_2} + \frac{1}{C_3}.$$

The equivalent series capacitance is always less than the smallest capacitance in the chain.  ◀

## 30–3  Parallel-Plate Capacitor with Dielectric

Equation 30–7 holds only for a parallel-plate capacitor with its plates in a vacuum. Michael Faraday, in 1837, first investigated the effect of filling the space between the plates with a dielectric, say mica or oil. In Faraday's words:

> The question may be stated thus: suppose $A$ an electrified plate of metal suspended in air, and $B$ and $C$ two exactly similar plates, placed parallel to and on each side of $A$ at equal distances and insulated; $A$ will then induce equally toward $B$ and $C$ [that is, equal charges will appear on these plates]. If in this position of the plates some other dielectric than air, as shell-lac, be introduced between $A$ and

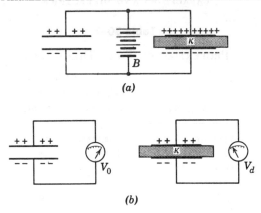

(a)

(b)

**Fig. 30-7**    (a) Battery $B$ supplies the same potential difference to each capacitor; the one on the right has the higher charge.    (b) Both capacitors carry the same charge; the one on the right has the lower potential difference, as indicated by the meter readings.

$C$, will the induction between them remain the same?    Will the relation of $C$ and $B$ to $A$ be unaltered, notwithstanding the difference of the dielectrics interposed between them?

Faraday answered this question by constructing two identical capacitors, in one of which he placed a dielectric, the other containing air at normal pressure.    When both capacitors were charged to the *same potential difference*, Faraday found by experiment that *the charge on the one containing the dielectric was greater than that on the other;* see Fig. 30-7a.

Faraday measured the relative charges on the plates of the two capacitors by touching a metal ball (fitted with an insulating handle) to the plates, thus sampling the charge quantitatively.    He then put this ball in a Coulomb torsion balance and measured the force of Coulomb repulsion on a second (standard) charged ball mounted on the balance arm.

Since $q$ is larger, for the same $V$, if a dielectric is present, it follows from the relation $C = q/V$ that *the capacitance of a capacitor increases if a dielectric is placed between the plates.*    The ratio of the capacitance with the dielectric * to that without is called the *dielectric constant* $\kappa$ of the material; see Table 30-1.

Instead of maintaining the two capacitors at the same potential difference, we can place the *same charge* on them, as in Fig. 30-7b.    Experiment then shows that the potential difference $V_d$ between the plates of the right-hand capacitor is smaller than that for the left-hand capacitor by the factor $1/\kappa$, or

$$V_d = V_0/\kappa.$$

We are led once again to conclude, from the relation $C = q/V$, that the effect of the dielectric is to increase the capacitance by a factor $\kappa$.

---

* Assumed to fill completely the space between the plates.

**Table 30–1**

PROPERTIES OF SOME DIELECTRICS

| Material | Dielectric Constant | Dielectric Strength * (kv/mm) |
|---|---|---|
| Vacuum | 1.00000 | ∞ |
| Air | 1.00054 | 0.8 |
| Water | 78 | — |
| Paper | 3.5 | 14 |
| Ruby mica | 5.4 | 160 |
| Amber | 2.7 | 90 |
| Porcelain | 6.5 | 4 |
| Fused quartz | 3.8 | 8 |
| Pyrex glass | 4.5 | 13 |
| Bakelite | 4.8 | 12 |
| Polyethylene | 2.3 | 50 |
| Polystyrene | 2.6 | 25 |
| Teflon | 2.1 | 60 |
| Neoprene | 6.9 | 12 |
| Pyranol oil | 4.5 | 12 |
| Titanium dioxide | 100 | 6 |

* This is the maximum potential gradient that may exist in the dielectric without the occurrence of electrical breakdown. Dielectrics are often placed between conducting plates to permit a higher potential difference to be applied between them than would be possible with air as the dielectric.

For a parallel-plate capacitor we can write, as an experimental result,

$$C = \frac{\kappa \epsilon_0 A}{d}. \tag{30–8}$$

Equation 30–7 is a special case of this relation found by putting $\kappa = 1$, corresponding to a vacuum between the plates. Experiment shows that the capacitance of *all* types of capacitor is increased by the factor $\kappa$ if the space between the plates is filled with a dielectric. Thus the capacitance of any capacitor can be written as

$$C = \kappa \epsilon_0 L,$$

where $L$ depends on the geometry and has the dimensions of a length. For a parallel-plate capacitor (see Eq. 30–7) $L$ is $A/d$; for a cylindrical capacitor (see Example 2) it is $2\pi l/\ln (b/a)$.

### 30–4   Dielectrics—An Atomic View

We now seek to understand, in atomic terms, what happens when a dielectric is placed in an electric field. There are two possibilities. The molecules of some dielectrics, like water, have permanent electric dipole moments.

In such materials (called *polar*) the electric dipole moments **p** tend to align themselves with an external electric field, as in Fig. 30–8; see also Section 27–6. Because the molecules are in constant thermal agitation, the degree of alignment will not be complete but will increase as the applied electric field is increased or as the temperature is decreased.

Whether or not the molecules have permanent electric dipole moments, they acquire them by *induction* when placed in an electric field. In Section 29–5 we saw that the external electric field tends to separate the negative and the positive charge in the atom or molecule. This *induced electric dipole moment* is present only when the electric field is present. It is proportional to the electric field (for normal field strengths) and is created already lined up with the electric field as Fig. 29–12 suggests.

Let us use a parallel-plate capacitor, carrying a fixed charge $q$ and not connected to a battery (see Fig. 30–7b), to provide a uniform external electric field $E_0$ into which we place a dielectric slab. The over-all effect of alignment and induction is to separate the center of positive charge of the entire slab slightly from the center of negative charge. The slab, as a whole, although remaining electrically neutral, becomes *polarized*, as Fig. 30–9b suggests. The net effect is a pile-up of positive charge on the right face of the slab and of negative charge on the left face; within the slab no excess charge appears in any given volume element. Since the slab as a whole remains neutral, the positive *induced surface charge* must be equal in magnitude to the negative induced surface charge. Note that in this process electrons in the dielectric

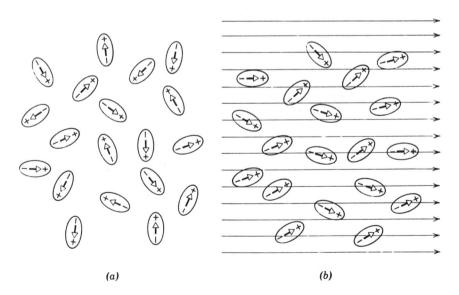

*(a)*                                        *(b)*

**Fig. 30-8**   (*a*) Molecules with a permanent electric dipole moment, showing their random orientation in the absence of an external electric field. (*b*) An electric field is applied, producing partial alignment of the dipoles. Thermal agitation prevents complete alignment.

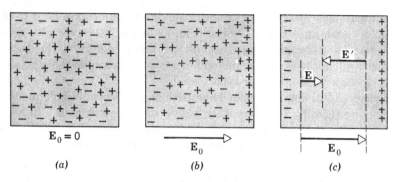

$E_0 = 0$

(a)

$E_0$

(b)

$E_0$

(c)

**Fig. 30–9**   (a) A dielectric slab, showing the random distribution of plus and minus charges. (b) An external field $E_0$, established by putting the slab between the plates of a parallel-plate capacitor (not shown), separates the center of plus charge in the slab slightly from the center of minus charge, resulting in the appearance of surface charges. No *net* charge exists in any volume element located in the *interior* of the slab. (c) The surface charges set up a field $E'$ which opposes the external field $E_0$ associated with the charges on the capacitor plates. The resultant field $E$ $(= E_0 + E')$ in the dielectric is thus less than $E_0$.

are displaced from their equilibrium positions by distances that are considerably less than an atomic diameter. There is no transfer of charge over macroscopic distances such as occurs when a current is set up in a conductor.

Figure 30–9c shows that the induced surface charges will always appear in such a way that the electric field set up *by them* ($E'$) opposes the external electric field $E_0$. The *resultant* field in the dielectric $E$ is the vector sum of $E_0$ and $E'$. It points in the same direction as $E_0$ but is smaller. *If a dielectric is placed in an electric field, induced surface charges appear which tend to weaken the original field within the dielectric.*

This weakening of the electric field reveals itself in Fig. 30–7b as a reduction in potential difference between the plates of a charged isolated capacitor when a dielectric, is introduced between the plates. The relation $V = Ed$ for a parallel-plate capacitor (see Eq. 30–6) holds whether or not dielectric is present and shows that the reduction in $V$ described in Fig. 30–7b is directly connected to the reduction in $E$ described in Fig. 30–9. More specifically, if a dielectric slab is introduced into a charged parallel-plate capacitor, then

$$\frac{E_0}{E} = \frac{V_0}{V_d} = \kappa \tag{30–9}$$

where the symbols on the left refer to Fig. 30–9 and the symbols $V_0$ and $V_d$ refer to Fig. 30–7b.*

Induced surface charge is the explanation of the most elementary fact of static electricity, namely, that a charged rod will attract uncharged bits of

---

* Equation 30–9 does not hold if the battery remains connected while the dielectric slab is introduced. In this case $V$ (hence $E$) could not change. Instead, the charge $q$ on the capacitor plates would increase by a factor $\kappa$, as Fig. 30–7a suggests.

**Fig. 30–10**  A charged rod attracts an uncharged piece of paper because unbalanced forces act on the induced surface charges.

paper, etc.  Figure 30–10 shows a bit of paper in the field of a charged rod. Surface charges appear on the paper as shown.  The negatively charged end of the paper will be pulled toward the rod and the positively charged end will be repelled.  These two forces do not have the same magnitude because the negative end, being closer to the rod, is in a stronger field and experiences a stronger force.  The net effect is an attraction.  A dielectric body in a *uniform* electric field will not experience a net force.

### 30–5  Dielectrics and Gauss's Law

So far our use of Gauss's law has been confined to situations in which no dielectric was present.  Now let us apply this law to a parallel-plate capacitor filled with a dielectric of dielectric constant $\kappa$.

Figure 30–11 shows the capacitor both with and without the dielectric.  It is assumed that the charge $q$ on the plates is the same in each case.  Gaussian surfaces have been drawn after the fashion of Fig. 30–3.

**Fig. 30–11**  A parallel-plate capacitor (a) without and (b) with a dielectric.  The charge $q$ on the plates is assumed to be the same in each case.

If no dielectric is present (Fig. 30–11a), Gauss's law (see Eq. 30–5) gives

$$\epsilon_0 \oint \mathbf{E} \cdot d\mathbf{S} = \epsilon_0 E_0 A = q$$

or
$$E_0 = \frac{q}{\epsilon_0 A}. \tag{30–10}$$

If the dielectric is present (Fig. 30–11b), Gauss's law gives

$$\epsilon_0 \oint \mathbf{E} \cdot d\mathbf{S} = \epsilon_0 E A = q - q'$$

or
$$E = \frac{q}{\epsilon_0 A} - \frac{q'}{\epsilon_0 A}, \tag{30–11}$$

in which $-q'$, the *induced surface charge*, must be distinguished from $q$, the so-called *free charge* on the plates. These two charges, both of which lie within the Gaussian surface, are opposite in sign; $q - q'$ is the *net* charge within the Gaussian surface.

Equation 30–9 shows that in Fig. 30–11

$$E = \frac{E_0}{\kappa}.$$

Combining this with Eq. 39–10, we have

$$E = \frac{E_0}{\kappa} = \frac{q}{\kappa \epsilon_0 A}. \tag{30–12}$$

Inserting this in Eq. 30–11 yields

$$\frac{q}{\kappa \epsilon_0 A} = \frac{q}{\epsilon_0 A} - \frac{q'}{\epsilon_0 A} \tag{30–13a}$$

or
$$q' = q\left(1 - \frac{1}{\kappa}\right). \tag{30–13b}$$

This shows correctly that the induced surface charge $q'$ is always less in magnitude than the free charge $q$ and is equal to zero if no dielectric is present, that is, if $\kappa = 1$.

Now we write Gauss's law for the case of Fig. 30–11b in the form

$$\epsilon_0 \oint \mathbf{E} \cdot d\mathbf{S} = q - q', \tag{30–14}$$

$q - q'$ again being the net charge within the Gaussian surface. Substituting from Eq. 30–13b for $q'$ leads, after some rearrangement, to

$$\epsilon_0 \oint \kappa \mathbf{E} \cdot d\mathbf{S} = q. \tag{30–15}$$

This important relation, although derived for a parallel-plate capacitor, is true generally and is the form in which Gauss's law is usually written when dielectrics are present. Note the following:

1. The flux integral now contains a factor $\kappa$.
2. The charge $q$ contained within the Gaussian surface is taken to be the *free charge only*. Induced surface charge is deliberately ignored on the right side of this equation, having been taken into account by the introduction of $\kappa$ on the left side. Equations 30–14 and 30–15 are completely equivalent formulations.

▶ **Example 5.** Figure 30–12 shows a dielectric slab of thickness $b$ and dielectric constant $\kappa$ placed between the plates of a parallel-plate capacitor of plate area $A$ and separation $d$. A potential difference $V_0$ is applied with no dielectric present. The battery is then disconnected and the dielectric slab inserted. Assume that $A = 100$ cm², $d = 1.0$ cm, $b = 0.50$ cm, $\kappa = 7.0$, and $V_0 = 100$ volts and (*a*) calculate the capacitance $C_0$ before the slab is inserted.

**Fig. 30–12**   Example 5. A parallel-plate capacitor containing a dielectric slab.

From Eq. 30–7, $C_0$ is found:

$$C_0 = \frac{\epsilon_0 A}{d} = \frac{(8.9 \times 10^{-12} \text{ coul}^2/\text{nt-m}^2)(10^{-2} \text{ meter}^2)}{10^{-2} \text{ meter}} = 8.9 \ \mu\mu\text{f}.$$

(*b*) Calculate the free charge $q$.
From Eq. 30–4,

$$q = C_0 V_0 = (8.9 \times 10^{-12} \text{ farad})(100 \text{ volts}) = 8.9 \times 10^{-10} \text{ coul}.$$

Because of the technique used to charge the capacitor, the free charge remains unchanged as the slab is introduced. If the charging battery had *not* been disconnected, this would not be the case.

(*c*) Calculate the electric field strength in the gap.
Applying Gauss's law in the form given in Eq. 30–15 to the Gaussian surface of Fig. 30–12 (upper plate) yields

$$\epsilon_0 \oint \kappa \mathbf{E} \cdot d\mathbf{S} = \epsilon_0 E_0 A = q,$$

or   $$E_0 = \frac{q}{\epsilon_0 A} = \frac{8.9 \times 10^{-10} \text{ coul}}{(8.9 \times 10^{-12} \text{ coul}^2/\text{nt-m}^2)(10^{-2} \text{ meter}^2)} = 1.0 \times 10^4 \text{ volts/meter}.$$

Note that we put $\kappa = 1$ here because the surface over which we evaluate flux integral does not pass through any dielectric. Note too that $E_0$ remains unchanged when the slab is introduced; this derivation takes no specific account of the presence of the dielectric.

(d) Calculate the electric field strength in the dielectric. Applying Eq. 30–15 to the Gaussian surface of Fig. 30–12 (lower plate) yields

$$\epsilon_0 \oint \kappa \mathbf{E} \cdot d\mathbf{S} = \epsilon_0 \kappa E A = q.$$

Note that $\kappa$ appears here because the surface cuts through the dielectric and that only the free charge $q$ appears on the right. Thus we have

$$E = \frac{q}{\kappa \epsilon_0 A} = \frac{E_0}{\kappa} = \frac{1.0 \times 10^4 \text{ volts/meter}}{7.0} = 0.14 \times 10^4 \text{ volts/meter}.$$

(e) Calculate the potential difference between the plates. Applying Eq. 29–5 to a straight perpendicular path from the lower plate (L) to the upper one (U) yields

$$V = -\int_L^U \mathbf{E} \cdot d\mathbf{l} = -\int_L^U E \cos 180° \, dl = \int_L^U E \, dl = E_0(d - b) + Eb.$$

Numerically

$$V = (1.0 \times 10^4 \text{ volts/meter})(5 \times 10^{-3} \text{ meter})$$

$$+ (0.14 \times 10^4 \text{ volts/meter})(5 \times 10^{-3} \text{ meter}) = 57 \text{ volts}.$$

This contrasts with the original applied potential difference of 100 volts; compare Fig. 30–7b.

(f) Calculate the capacitance with the slab in place. From Eq. 30–4,

$$C = \frac{q}{V} = \frac{8.9 \times 10^{-10} \text{ coul}}{57 \text{ volts}} = 16 \, \mu\mu\text{f}.$$

When the dielectric slab is introduced, the potential difference drops from 100 to 57 volts and the capacitance rises from 8.9 to 16 $\mu\mu$f, a factor of 1.8. If the dielectric slab had filled the capacitor, the capacitance would have risen by a factor of $\kappa$ ( = 7.0) to 62 $\mu\mu$f. ◀

### 30–6 Three Electric Vectors

For all situations that we encounter in this book our discussion of the behavior of dielectrics in an electric field is adequate. However, the problems that we treat are simple ones, such as that of a rectangular slab placed at right angles to a uniform external electric field. For more difficult problems, such as that of finding $\mathbf{E}$ at the center of a dielectric ellipsoid placed in a (possibly nonuniform) external electric field, it greatly simplifies the labor and leads to deeper insight if we introduce a new formalism. We do so largely so that students who take a second course in electromagnetism will have some familiarity with the concepts.

Let us rewrite Eq. 30–13a, which applies to a parallel-plate capacitor containing a dielectric, as

$$\frac{q}{A} = \epsilon_0 \left( \frac{q}{\kappa \epsilon_0 A} \right) + \frac{q'}{A}. \qquad (30\text{–}16)$$

The quantity in parentheses (see Eq. 30–12) is simply the electric field strength $E$ in the dielectric. The last term in Eq. 30–16 is the *induced surface charge per unit area*. We call it the *electric polarization P*, or

$$P = \frac{q'}{A}. \qquad (30\text{–}17)$$

**Fig. 30–13**  (a) Showing **D**, $\epsilon_0\mathbf{E}$, and **P** in the dielectric (*upper right*) and in the gap (*upper left*) for a parallel-plate capacitor.  (b) Showing samples of the lines associated with **D** (free charge), $\epsilon_0\mathbf{E}$ (all charges), and **P** (polarization charge).

The name is suitable because the induced surface charge $q'$ appears when the dielectric is polarized.

The electric polarization $P$ can be defined in an equivalent way by multiplying the numerator and denominator in Eq. 30–17 by $d$, the thickness of the dielectric slab in Fig. 30–11,

$$P = \frac{q'd}{Ad}. \tag{30–18}$$

The numerator is the product $q'd$ of the magnitude of the (equal and opposite) polarization charges by their separation. It is thus the induced electric dipole moment of the dielectric slab. Since the denominator $Ad$ is the volume of the slab, we see that the electric polarization can also be defined as the induced electric dipole moment per unit volume in the dielectric. This definition suggests that since the electric dipole moment is a vector the electric polarization is also a vector, its magnitude being $P$. The direction of **P** is from the negative induced charge to the positive induced charge, as for any dipole. In Fig. 30–13, which shows a capacitor with a dielectric slab filling half the space between the plates, **P** points down.

We can now rewrite Eq. 30–16 as

$$\frac{q}{A} = \epsilon_0 E + P. \tag{30–19}$$

The quantity on the right occurs so often in electrostatic problems that we give it the special name *electric displacement D*, or

$$D = \epsilon_0 E + P \qquad (30\text{-}20a)$$

in which

$$D = \frac{q}{A}. \qquad (30\text{-}20b)$$

The name has historical significance only.

Since **E** and **P** are vectors, **D** must also be one, so that in the more general case we have

$$\mathbf{D} = \epsilon_0\mathbf{E} + \mathbf{P}. \qquad (30\text{-}21)$$

In Fig. 30–13 all three vectors point down and each has a constant magnitude for every point in the dielectric (and also at every point in the air gap) so that the vector nature of Eq. 30–21 is not very important in this case. In more complicated problems, however, **E**, **P**, and **D** may vary in magnitude and direction from point to point.

From their definitions we see the following:

1. **D** (see Eq. 30–20b) is connected with the *free charge* only. We can represent the vector field of **D** by *lines of D*, just as we represent the field of **E** by lines of force. Figure 30–13b shows that the lines of **D** begin and end on the free charges.

2. **P** (see Eq. 30–17) is connected with the *polarization charge* only. It is also possible to represent this vector field by lines. Figure 30–13b shows that the lines of **P** begin and end on the polarization charges.

3. **E** is connected with all charges that are actually present, whether free or polarization. The lines of **E** reflect the presence of both kinds of charge, as Fig. 30–13b shows. Note (Eqs. 30–17 and 30–20b) that the units for **P** and **D** (coul/meter²) differ from those of **E** (nt/coul).

The electric field vector **E**, which is what determines the force that acts on a suitably placed test charge, remains of fundamental interest. **D** and **P** are auxiliary vectors useful as aids in the solution of problems more complex than that of Fig. 30–13.

The vectors **D** and **P** can both be expressed in terms of **E** alone. A convenient starting point is the identity

$$\frac{q}{A} = \kappa\epsilon_0 \left(\frac{q}{\kappa\epsilon_0 A}\right).$$

Comparison with Eqs. 30–12 and 30–20b shows that this, extended to vector form, can be written as

$$\mathbf{D} = \kappa\epsilon_0\mathbf{E}. \qquad (30\text{-}22)$$

We can also write the polarization (see Eqs. 30–17 and 30–13b) as

$$P = \frac{q'}{A} = \frac{q}{A}\left(1 - \frac{1}{\kappa}\right).$$

Since $q/A = D$, we can rewrite this, using Eq. 30–22 and casting the result into vector form, as

$$\mathbf{P} = \epsilon_0(\kappa - 1)\mathbf{E}. \qquad (30\text{-}23)$$

This shows clearly that in a vacuum ($\kappa = 1$) the polarization vector **P** is zero.*

---

* Certain waxes, when polarized in their molten state, retain a permanent polarization after solidifying, even though the external polarizing field is removed. *Electrets*, manufactured in this way, are the electrostatic analog of permanent magnets in that they possess a gross permanent electric dipole moment. Materials from which electrets can be constructed are called *ferroelectric*. Electrets do not obey Eq. 30–23 because they have a nonvanishing value of **P** even though **E** = 0.

Equations 30–22 and 30–23 show that for isotropic materials, to which a single dielectric constant $\kappa$ can be assigned, $\mathbf{D}$ and $\mathbf{P}$ both point in the direction of $\mathbf{E}$ at any given point.

The definition of $\mathbf{D}$ given by Eq. 30–22 allows us to write Eq. 30–15, that is, Gauss's law in the presence of a dielectric, simply as

$$\oint \mathbf{D} \cdot d\mathbf{S} = q, \qquad (30\text{–}24)$$

where, as before, $q$ represents the free charge only, the induced surface charges being excluded.

▶ **Example 6.** In Figure 30–13, using data from Example 5, calculate $E$, $D$, and $P$: (a) in the dielectric and (b) in the air gap.

(a) The electric field in the dielectric is calculated in Example 5 to be $1.43 \times 10^3$ volts/meter. From Eq. 30–22,

$$D = \kappa\epsilon_0 E$$

$$= (7.0)(8.9 \times 10^{-12} \text{ coul}^2/\text{nt-m}^2)(1.43 \times 10^3 \text{ volts/meter})$$

$$= 8.9 \times 10^{-8} \text{ coul/meter}^2$$

and, from Eq. 30–23,

$$P = \epsilon_0(\kappa - 1)E$$

$$= (8.9 \times 10^{-12} \text{ coul}^2/\text{nt-m}^2)(7.0 - 1)(1.43 \times 10^3 \text{ volts/meter})$$

$$= 7.5 \times 10^{-8} \text{ coul/meter}^2.$$

(b) The electric field $E_0$ in the air gap is calculated in Example 5 to be $1.00 \times 10^4$ volts/meter. From Eq. 30–22,

$$D_0 = \kappa\epsilon_0 E_0$$

$$= (1)(8.9 \times 10^{-12} \text{ coul}^2/\text{nt-m}^2)(1.00 \times 10^4 \text{ volts/meter})$$

$$= 8.9 \times 10^{-8} \text{ coul/meter}^2$$

and, from Eq. 30–23, recalling that $\kappa = 1$ in the air gap,

$$P_0 = \epsilon_0(\kappa - 1)E_0 = 0.$$

Note that $\mathbf{P}$ vanishes outside the dielectric, $\mathbf{D}$ has the same value in the dielectric and in the gap, and $\mathbf{E}$ has different values in the dielectric and in the gap. The student should verify that Eq. 30–21 ($\mathbf{D} = \epsilon_0\mathbf{E} + \mathbf{P}$) is correct both in the gap and in the dielectric.

It can be shown from Maxwell's equations that no matter how complex the problem the component of $\mathbf{D}$ *normal* to the surface of the dielectric has the same value on each side of the surface. In this problem $\mathbf{D}$ itself is normal to the surface, there being no component but the normal one. It can also be shown that the component of $\mathbf{E}$ *tangential* to the dielectric surface has the same value on each side of the surface. This *boundary condition*, like the one for $\mathbf{D}$, is trivial in this problem, both tangential components being zero. In more complex problems these boundary conditions on $\mathbf{D}$ and $\mathbf{E}$ are very important. Table 30–2 summarizes the properties of the electric vectors $\mathbf{E}$, $\mathbf{D}$, and $\mathbf{P}$.          ◀

**Table 30–2**

THREE ELECTRIC VECTORS

| Name | Symbol | Associated with | Boundary Condition |
|---|---|---|---|
| Electric field strength | E | All charges | Tangential component continuous |
| Electric displacement | D | Free charges only | Normal component continuous |
| Polarization (electric dipole moment per unit volume) | P | Polarization charges only | Vanishes in a vacuum |

| | | |
|---|---|---|
| Defining equation for **E** | $\mathbf{F} = q\mathbf{E}$ | Eq. 27–2 |
| General relation among the three vectors | $\mathbf{D} = \epsilon_0 \mathbf{E} + \mathbf{P}$ | Eq. 30–21 |
| Gauss's law when dielectric media are present | $\oint \mathbf{D} \cdot d\mathbf{S} = q$ <br> ($q$ = free charge only) | Eq. 30–24 |
| Empirical relations for certain dielectric materials * | $\mathbf{D} = \kappa \epsilon_0 \mathbf{E}$ <br> $\mathbf{P} = (\kappa - 1)\epsilon_0 \mathbf{E}$ | Eq. 30–22 <br> Eq. 30–23 |

\* Generally true, with $\kappa$ independent of **E**, except for certain materials called *ferroelectrics*; see footnote on page 758.

## 30–7   Energy Storage in an Electric Field

In Section 29–6 we saw that all charge configurations have a certain *electric potential energy* $U$, equal to the work $W$ (which may be positive or negative) that must be done to assemble them from their individual components, originally assumed to be infinitely far apart and at rest. This potential energy reminds us of the potential energy stored in a compressed spring or the gravitational potential energy stored in, say, the earth-moon system.

For a simple example, work must be done to separate two equal and opposite charges. This energy is stored in the system and can be recovered if the charges are allowed to come together again. Similarly, a charged capacitor has stored in it an electrical potential energy $U$ equal to the work $W$ required to charge it. This energy can be recovered if the capacitor is allowed to discharge. We can visualize the work of charging by imagining that an external agent pulls electrons from the positive plate and pushes them onto the negative plate, thus bringing about the charge separation; normally the work of charging is done by a battery, at the expense of its store of chemical energy.

Suppose that at a time $t$ a charge $q'(t)$ has been transferred from one plate to the other. The potential difference $V(t)$ between the plates at that moment will be $q'(t)/C$. If an extra increment of charge $dq'$ is transferred, the small amount of additional work needed will be

$$dW = V \, dq = \left(\frac{q'}{C}\right) dq'.$$

If this process is continued until a total charge $q$ has been transferred, the total work will be found from

$$W = \int dW = \int_0^q \frac{q'}{C} \, dq' = \frac{1}{2} \frac{q^2}{C}. \tag{30-25}$$

From the relation $q = CV$ we can also write this as

$$W \, (= U) = \tfrac{1}{2}CV^2. \tag{30-26}$$

It is reasonable to suppose that the energy stored in a capacitor resides in the electric field. As $q$ or $V$ in Eqs. 30-25 and 30-26 increase, for example, so does the electric field $E$; when $q$ and $V$ are zero, so is $E$.

In a parallel-plate capacitor, neglecting fringing, the electric field has the same value for all points between the plates. Thus the *energy density u*, which is the stored energy per unit volume, should also be uniform; $u$ (see Eq. 30-26) is given by

$$u = \frac{U}{Ad} = \frac{\tfrac{1}{2}CV^2}{Ad},$$

where $Ad$ is the volume between the plates. Substituting the relation $C = \kappa\epsilon_0 A/d$ (Eq. 30-8) leads to

$$u = \frac{\kappa\epsilon_0}{2}\left(\frac{V}{d}\right)^2.$$

However, $V/d$ is the electric field strength $E$, so that

$$u = \tfrac{1}{2}\kappa\epsilon_0 E^2. \tag{30-27}$$

Although this equation was derived for the special case of a parallel-plate capacitor, it is true in general. *If an electric field **E** exists at any point in space, we can think of that point as the site of stored energy in amount, per unit volume, of $\tfrac{1}{2}\kappa\epsilon_0 E^2$.*

▶ **Example 7.** A capacitor $C_1$ is charged to a potential difference $V_0$. This charging battery is then removed and the capacitor is connected as in Fig. 30–14 to an uncharged capacitor $C_2$.

(a) What is the final potential difference $V$ across the combination?

**Fig. 30–14** Example 7. $C_1$ is charged and then connected to $C_2$ by closing switch $S$.

The original charge $q_0$ is now shared by the two capacitors. Thus

$$q_0 = q_1 + q_2.$$

Applying the relation $q = CV$ to each of these terms yields

$$C_1 V_0 = C_1 V + C_2 V$$

or

$$V = V_0 \frac{C_1}{C_1 + C_2}.$$

This suggests a way to measure an unknown capacitance ($C_2$, say) in terms of a known one.

(b) What is the stored energy before and after the switch in Fig. 30–14 is thrown?
The initial stored energy is

$$U_0 = \tfrac{1}{2} C_1 V_0{}^2.$$

The final stored energy is

$$U = \tfrac{1}{2} C_1 V^2 + \tfrac{1}{2} C_2 V^2 = \tfrac{1}{2}(C_1 + C_2)\left(\frac{V_0 C_1}{C_1 + C_2}\right)^2 = \left(\frac{C_1}{C_1 + C_2}\right) U_0.$$

Thus $U$ is less than $U_0$! The "missing" energy appears as heat in the connecting wires as the charges move through them.

**Example 8.** A parallel-plate capacitor has plates with area $A$ and separation $d$. A battery charges the plates to a potential difference $V_0$. The battery is then disconnected, and a dielectric slab of thickness $d$ is introduced. Calculate the stored energy both before and after the slab is introduced and account for any difference.
The energy $U_0$ before introducing the slab is

$$U_0 = \tfrac{1}{2} C_0 V_0{}^2.$$

After the slab is in place, we have

$$C = \kappa C_0 \quad \text{and} \quad V = V_0/\kappa$$

and thus

$$U = \tfrac{1}{2} C V^2 = \tfrac{1}{2}\kappa C_0 \left(\frac{V_0}{\kappa}\right)^2 = \frac{1}{\kappa} U_0.$$

The energy after the slab is introduced is *less* by a factor $1/\kappa$. The "missing" energy would be apparent to the person who inserted the slab. He would feel a "tug" on the slab and would have to restrain it if he wished to insert the slab without acceleration. This means that he would have to do negative work on it, or, alternatively, that the condenser + slab system would do positive work on him. This positive work is

$$W = U_0 - U = \tfrac{1}{2} C_0 V_0{}^2 \left(1 - \frac{1}{\kappa}\right).$$

Figure 30–15 shows how the forces that do this work arise, in terms of attraction between the free charge on the plates and the induced surface charges that appear on the slab when it is introduced between the plates.

**Fig. 30–15**   When we introduce a dielectric slab into a charged capacitor, as shown, forces arise which tend to pull the slab into the capacitor.

**Example 9.**   A conducting sphere of radius $R$, in a vacuum, carries a charge $q$. (a) Compute the total electrostatic energy stored in the surrounding space. At any radius $r$ from the center of the sphere (assuming $r > R$) $E$ is given by

$$E = \frac{1}{4\pi\epsilon_0} \frac{q}{r^2}.$$

The energy density at any radius $r$ is found from Eq. 30–27, assuming $\kappa = 1$, or

$$u = \tfrac{1}{2}\epsilon_0 E^2 = \frac{q^2}{32\pi^2\epsilon_0 r^4}.$$

The energy $dU$ that lies in a spherical shell between the radii $r$ and $r + dr$ is

$$dU = (4\pi r^2)(dr)u = \frac{q^2}{8\pi\epsilon_0} \frac{dr}{r^2},$$

where $(4\pi r^2)(dr)$ is the volume of the spherical shell.  The total energy $U$ is found by integration, or

$$U = \int dU = \frac{q^2}{8\pi\epsilon_0} \int_R^\infty \frac{dr}{r^2} = \frac{q^2}{8\pi\epsilon_0 R}.$$

Note that this relation follows at once from Eq. 30–25 ($U = q^2/2C$), where $C$ (see p. 651) is the capacitance ($= 4\pi\epsilon_0 R$) of an isolated sphere of radius $R$.

(b) What is the radius $R_0$ of a spherical surface such that half the stored energy lies within it?

In the equation just given we put

$$\tfrac{1}{2}U = \frac{q^2}{8\pi\epsilon_0} \int_R^{R_0} \frac{dr}{r^2}$$

or

$$\frac{q^2}{16\pi\epsilon_0 R} = \frac{q^2}{8\pi\epsilon_0}\left(\frac{1}{R} - \frac{1}{R_0}\right),$$

which yields, after some rearrangement,

$$R_0 = 2R.$$

## QUESTIONS

1. A capacitor is connected across a battery. (a) Why does each plate receive a charge of exactly the same magnitude? (b) Is this true even if the plates are of different sizes?

2. Can there be a potential difference between two adjacent conductors that carry the same positive charge?

Foil

**Fig. 30-16**

3. The relation $\sigma \propto 1/R$ suggests that the charge placed on an isolated conductor concentrates on points and avoids flat surfaces, where $R = \infty$. How do we reconcile this with Fig. 30-3 in which the charge is definitely on the flat surface of either plate?

4. A sheet of aluminum foil of negligible thickness is placed between the plates of a capacitor as in Fig. 30-16. What effect has it on the capacitance if (a) the foil is electrically insulated and (b) the foil is connected to the upper plate.

5. Discuss similarities and differences when (a) a dielectric slab and (b) a conducting slab are inserted between the plates of a parallel-plate capacitor. Assume the slab thicknesses to be one-half the plate separation.

6. An oil-filled parallel-plate capacitor has been designed to have a capacitance $C$ and to operate safely at or below a certain maximum potential difference $V_m$ without arcing over. However, the designer did not do a good job and the capacitor occasionally arcs over. What can be done to redesign the capacitor, keeping $C$ and $V_m$ unchanged and using the same dielectric?

7. Would you expect the dielectric constant, for substances containing permanent molecular electric dipoles, to vary with temperature?

8. What is your estimate of the amount by which the center of positive charge and the center of negative charge are displaced in a situation like that of Fig. 30-9b? An intuitive guess is all that is called for.

9. For a given potential difference does a capacitor store more or less charge with a dielectric than it does without a dielectric (vacuum)? Explain in terms of the microscopic picture of the situation.

10. An isolated conducting sphere is given a positive charge. Does its mass increase, decrease, or remain the same?

11. A dielectric slab is inserted in one end of a charged parallel-plate capacitor (the plates being horizontal and the charging battery having been disconnected) and then released. Describe what happens. Neglect friction.

12. A capacitor is charged by using a battery, which is then disconnected. A dielectric slab is then slipped between the plates. Describe qualitatively what happens to the charge, the capacitance, the potential difference, the electric field strength, and the stored energy.

13. While a capacitor remains connected to a battery, a dielectric slab is slipped between the plates. Describe qualitatively what happens to the charge, the capacitance, the potential difference, the electric field strength, and the stored energy. Is work required to insert the slab?

**Fig. 30-17**

14. Two identical capacitors are connected as shown in Fig. 30-17. A dielectric slab is slipped between the plates of one capacitor, the battery remaining connected. Describe qualitatively what happens to the charge, the capacitance, the potential difference, the electric field strength, and the stored energy for each capacitor.

15. Show that the dielectric constant of a conductor can be taken to be infinitely great.

## PROBLEMS

1. A potential difference of 300 volts is applied to a 2.0-$\mu$f capacitor and an 8.0-$\mu$f capacitor connected in series. (a) What are the charge and the potential difference for each capacitor? (b) The charged capacitors are reconnected with their positive plates together and their negative plates together, no external voltage being applied. What are the charge and the potential difference for each? (c) The charged capacitors in (a) are reconnected with plates of *opposite* sign together. What are the charge and the potential difference for each?

2. Calculate the capacitance of the earth, viewed as a spherical conductor of radius 6400 km.

3. A 100-$\mu\mu$f capacitor is charged to a potential difference of 50 volts, the charging battery then being disconnected. The capacitor is then connected, as in Fig. 30-14, to a second capacitor. If the measured potential difference drops to 35 volts, what is the capacitance of this second capacitor?

4. If we solve Eq. 30-7 for $\epsilon_0$, we see that its mks units are farads/meter. Show that these units are equivalent to those obtained earlier for $\epsilon_0$, namely coul$^2$/nt-m$^2$.

5. Figure 30-18 shows two capacitors in series, the rigid center section of length $b$ being movable vertically. Show that the equivalent capacitance of the series combination is independent of the position of the center section and is given by

$$C = \frac{\epsilon_0 A}{a - b}.$$

**Fig. 30-18**                              **Fig. 30-19**

6. In Fig. 30-19 a variable air capacitor of the type used in tuning radios is shown. Alternate plates are connected together, one group being fixed in position, the other group being capable of rotation. Consider a pile of $n$ plates of alternate polarity, each having an area $A$ and separated from adjacent plates by a distance $d$. Show that this capacitor has a maximum capacitance of

$$C = \frac{(n - 1)\epsilon_0 A}{d}.$$

7. A spherical capacitor consists of two concentric spherical shells of radii $a$ and $b$, with $b > a$. Show that its capacitance is

$$C = 4\pi\epsilon_0 \frac{ab}{b - a}.$$

8. A capacitor has square plates, each of side $a$, making an angle of $\theta$ with each other as shown in Fig. 30-20. Show that for small $\theta$ the capacitance is given by

$$C = \frac{\epsilon_0 a^2}{d}\left(1 - \frac{a\theta}{2d}\right)$$

(Hint: The capacitor may be divided into differential strips which are effectively in parallel.)

**Fig. 30–20**

9. Suppose that the two spherical shells of a spherical capacitor have their radii approximately equal. Under these conditions the device approximates a parallel plate capacitor with $b - a = d$. Show that the formula in Problem 7 does indeed reduce to Eq. 30–7 in this case.

10. A parallel-plate capacitor has circular plates of 8.0-cm radius and 1.0-mm separation. What charge will appear on the plates if a potential difference of 100 volts is applied?

11. In Fig. 30–21 find the equivalent capacitance of the combination. Assume that $C_1 = 10 \ \mu f$, $C_2 = 5 \ \mu f$, $C_3 = 4 \ \mu f$, and $V = 100$ volts.

12. In Fig. 30–21 suppose that capacitor $C_3$ breaks down electrically, becoming equivalent to a conducting path. What *changes* in (a) the charge and (b) the potential difference occur for capacitor $C_1$?

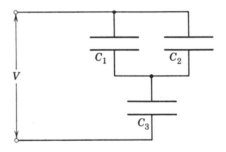

**Fig. 30–21**

13. Find the effective capacitance between points $x$ and $y$ in Fig. 30–22. Assume that $C_2 = 10 \ \mu f$ and that the other capacitors are all 4.0 $\mu f$. (Hint: Apply a potential difference $V$ between $x$ and $y$ and write down all the relationships that involve the charges and potential differences for the separate capacitors.)

**Fig. 30–22**

14. If you have available several 2.0-$\mu$f capacitors, each capable of withstanding 200 volts without breakdown, how would you assemble a combination having an equivalent capacitance of (a) 0.40 $\mu$f or of (b) 1.2 $\mu$f, each capable of withstanding 1000 volts?

15. In Fig. 30–23 find the equivalent capacitance of the combination. Assume that $C_1 = 10$ $\mu$f, $C_2 = 5$ $\mu$f, $C_3 = 4$ $\mu$f, and $V = 100$ volts.

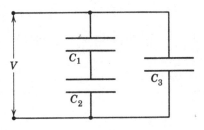

**Fig. 30–23**

16. In Fig. 30–24 the battery $B$ supplies 12 volts. (a) Find the charge on each capacitor when switch $S_1$ is closed and (b) when switch $S_2$ is also closed. Take $C_1 = 1$ $\mu$f, $C_2 = 2$ $\mu$f, $C_3 = 3$ $\mu$f, and $C_4 = 4$ $\mu$f.

**Fig. 30–24**

17. A parallel-plate capacitor is filled with two dielectrics as in Fig. 30–25. Show that the capacitance is given by

$$C = \frac{\epsilon_0 A}{d} \left( \frac{\kappa_1 + \kappa_2}{2} \right).$$

Check this formula for all the limiting cases that you can think of. (Hint: Can you justify regarding this arrangement as two capacitors in parallel?)

**Fig. 30–25**          **Fig. 30–26**

18. A parallel-plate capacitor is filled with two dielectrics as in Fig. 30–26. Show that the capacitance is given by

$$C = \frac{2\epsilon_0 A}{d} \left( \frac{\kappa_1 \kappa_2}{\kappa_1 + \kappa_2} \right).$$

Check this formula for all the limiting cases that you can think of. (Hint: Can you justify regarding this arrangement as two capacitors in series?)

19. A dielectric slab of thickness $b$ is inserted between the plates of a parallel-plate capacitor of plate separation $d$. Show that the capacitance is given by

$$ C = \frac{\kappa \epsilon_0 A}{\kappa d - b(\kappa - 1)}. $$

(Hint: Derive the formula following the pattern of Example 5.) Does this formula predict the correct numerical result of Example 5? Does the formula seem reasonable for the special cases of $b = 0$, $\kappa = 1$, and $b = d$?

20. A slab of copper of thickness $b$ is thrust into a parallel-plate capacitor as shown in Fig. 30–27; it is exactly halfway between the plates. What is the capacitance before and after the slab is introduced?

**Fig. 30–27**

21. For making a capacitor you have available two plates of copper, a sheet of mica (thickness = 0.10 mm, $\kappa = 6$), a sheet of glass (thickness = 2.0 mm, $\kappa = 7$), and a slab of paraffin (thickness = 1.0 cm, $\kappa = 2$). To obtain the largest capacitance, which sheet (or sheets) should you place between the copper plates?

22. In Example 5, suppose that the 100-volt battery remains connected during the time that the dielectric slab is being introduced. Calculate (a) the charge on the capacitor plates, (b) the electric field in the gap, (c) the electric field in the slab, and (d) the capacitance. For all of these quantities give the numerical values before and after the slab is introduced. Contrast your results with those of Example 5 by constructing a tabular listing.

23. A parallel-plate capacitor has a capacitance of 100 $\mu\mu$f, a plate area of 100 cm², and a mica dielectric. At 50 volts potential difference, calculate (a) $E$ in the mica, (b) the free charge on the plates, and (c) the induced surface charge.

24. Two parallel plates of area 100 cm² are each given equal but opposite charges of $8.9 \times 10^{-7}$ coul. Within the dielectric material filling the space between the plates the electric field strength is $1.4 \times 10^6$ volts/meter. ·(a) Find the dielectric constant of the material. (b) Determine the magnitude of the charge induced on each dielectric surface.

25. Hard rubber has a dielectric constant of 2.8 and a dielectric strength of $18 \times 10^6$ volts/meter. If it is used as the dielectric material in a parallel-plate capacitor, what minimum area may the plates of the capacitor have in order that the capacitance be $7.0 \times 10^{-2}$ $\mu$f and that the capacitor be able to withstand a potential difference of 4000 volts?

26. A cylindrical capacitor has radii $a$ and $b$ as in Fig. 30–4. Show that half the stored electric potential energy lies within a cylinder whose radius is

$$ r = \sqrt{ab}. $$

27. An isolated metal sphere whose diameter is 10 cm has a potential of 8000 volts. What is the energy density at the surface of the sphere?

28. A parallel-plate capacitor has plates of area $A$ and separation $d$ and is charged to a potential difference $V$. The charging battery is then disconnected and the plates are pulled

apart until their separation is $2d$. Derive expressions in terms of $A$, $d$, and $V$ for ($a$) the new potential difference, ($b$) the initial and the final stored energy, and ($c$) the work required to separate the plates.

29. Show that the plates of a parallel-plate capacitor attract each other with a force given by

$$F = \frac{q^2}{2\epsilon_0 A}.$$

Prove this by calculating the work necessary to increase the plate separation from $x$ to $x + dx$.

30. In the capacitor of Example 5 the dielectric slab fills half the space between the plates. ($a$) What per cent of the energy is stored in the air gaps? ($b$) What per cent is stored in the slab?

31. A parallel-plate air capacitor has a capacitance of 100 $\mu\mu$f. ($a$) What is the stored energy if the applied potential difference is 50 volts? ($b$) Can you calculate the energy density for points between the plates?

32. For the capacitors of Problem 1, compute the energy stored for the three different connections of parts ($a$), ($b$), and ($c$). Compare your answers and explain any differences.

33. A charge $q$ is placed on the surface of an originally uncharged soap bubble of radius $R_0$. Because of the mutual repulsion of the charged surface, the radius is increased to a somewhat larger value $R$. Show that

$$q = [\tfrac{3}{3}\tfrac{2}{3}\pi^2\epsilon_0 pR_0R(R^2 + R_0R + R_0^2)]^{\frac{1}{2}}$$

in which $p$ is the pressure of the atmosphere. Find $q$ for $p = 1.00$ atm, $R_0 = 2.00$ cm, and $R = 2.10$ cm. (Hint: The work done by the bubble in pushing back the atmosphere must equal the decrease in the stored electric field energy that accompanies the expansion, from the conservation of energy principle.)

34. Two capacitors (2.0 $\mu$f and 4.0 $\mu$f) are connected in parallel across a 300-volt potential difference. Calculate the total stored energy in the system.

35. A parallel-connected bank of 2000 5.0-$\mu$f capacitors is used to store electric energy. What does it cost to charge this bank to 50,000 volts, assuming a rate of 2¢/kw-hr?

36. In Fig. 30–21 find ($a$) the charge, ($b$) the potential difference, and ($c$) the stored energy for each capacitor. Assume the numerical values of Problem 11.

37. In Fig. 30–23 find ($a$) the charge, ($b$) the potential difference, and ($c$) the stored energy for each capacitor. Assume the numerical values of Problem 15.

# Current and Resistance

## CHAPTER 31

### 31–1 Current and Current Density

The free electrons in an isolated metallic conductor, such as a length of copper wire, are in random motion like the molecules of a gas confined to a container. They have no net directed motion along the wire. If a hypothetical plane is passed through the wire, the rate at which electrons pass through it from right to left is the same as the rate at which they pass through from left to right; the *net* rate is zero.

If the ends of the wire are connected to a battery, an electric field will be set up at every point within the wire. If the potential difference maintained by the battery is 10 volts and if the wire (assumed uniform) is 5 meters long, the strength of this field at every point will be 2 volts/meter. This field **E** will act on the electrons and will give them a resultant motion in the direction of $-\mathbf{E}$. We say that an *electric current* $i$ is established; if a net charge $q$ passes through any cross section of the conductor in time $t$ the current, assumed constant, is

$$i = q/t. \tag{31-1}$$

The appropriate mks units are amperes for $i$, coulombs for $q$, and seconds for $t$. The student will recall (Section 26–4) that Eq. 31–1 is the defining equation for the coulomb and that we have not yet given an operational definition of the ampere; we do so in Section 34–4.

If the rate of flow of charge with time is not constant, the current varies with time and is given by the differential limit of Eq. 31–1, or

$$i = dq/dt. \tag{31-2}$$

In the rest of this chapter we consider only constant currents.

The current $i$ is the same for all cross sections of a conductor, even though the cross-sectional area may be different at different points. In the same way the rate at which water (assumed incompressible) flows past any cross section of a pipe is the same even if the cross section varies. The water flows faster where the pipe is smaller and slower where it is larger, so that the volume rate, measured perhaps in gal/min, remains unchanged. This constancy of the electric current follows because charge must be conserved; it does not pile up steadily or drain away steadily from any point in the conductor under the assumed steady-state conditions. In the language of Section 18-3 there are no "sources" or "sinks" of charge.

The existence of an electric field inside a conductor does not contradict Section 28-4, in which we asserted that E equals zero inside a conductor. In that section, which dealt with a state in which all net motion of charge had stopped (*electrostatics*), we assumed that the conductor was insulated and that no potential difference was deliberately maintained between any two points on it, as by a battery. In this chapter, which deals with charges in motion, we relax this restriction.

The electric field that acts on the electrons in a conductor does not produce a *net* acceleration because the electrons keep colliding with the atoms (strictly, ions) that make up the conductor. This array of ions, coupled together by strong spring-like forces of electric origin, is called the *lattice* (see Fig. 21-5). The over-all effect of these collisions is to transfer kinetic energy from the accelerating electrons into vibrational energy of the lattice. The electrons acquire a constant average *drift speed* $v_d$ in the direction $-\mathbf{E}$. The analogy is to a marble rolling down a long flight of stairs and not to a marble falling freely from the same height. In the first case the acceleration caused by the (gravitational) field is effectively canceled by the decelerating effects of collisions with the stair treads so that, under proper conditions, the marble rolls down the stairs with zero average acceleration, that is, at constant average speed.

Although in metals the charge carriers are electrons, in electrolytes or in gaseous conductors they may also be positive or negative ions or both. A convention for labeling the directions of currents is needed because charges of opposite sign move in opposite directions in a given field. A positive charge moving in one direction is equivalent in nearly all external effects to a negative charge moving in the opposite direction. Hence, for simplicity and algebraic consistency, *we assume that all charge carriers are positive and we draw the current arrows in the direction that such charges would move.* If the charge carriers are negative, they simply move opposite to the direction of the current arrow (see Fig. 31-1). When we encounter a case (as in the *Hall effect;* see Section 33-5) in which the sign of the charge carriers makes a difference in the external effects, we will disregard the convention and take the actual situation into account.

Current $i$ is a characteristic of a particular conductor. It is a macroscopic quantity, like the mass of an object, the volume of an object, or the length of a rod. A related microscopic quantity is the current density $\mathbf{j}$. It is a

**Fig. 31-1**    Electrons drift in a direction opposite to the electric field in a conductor.

vector and is characteristic of a point inside a conductor rather than of the conductor as a whole. If the current is distributed uniformly across a conductor of cross-sectional area $A$, the magnitude of the current density for all points on that cross section is

$$j = i/A. \qquad (31\text{--}3)$$

The vector $\mathbf{j}$ at any point is oriented in the direction that a positive charge carrier would move at that point. An electron at that point would move in the direction $-\mathbf{j}$.

The general relationship between $\mathbf{j}$ and $i$ is that, for a particular surface in a conductor, $i$ is the flux of the vector $\mathbf{j}$ over that surface, or

$$i = \int \mathbf{j} \cdot d\mathbf{S}, \qquad (31\text{--}4)$$

where $d\mathbf{S}$ is an element of surface area and the integral is taken over the surface in question. Equation 31–3 (written as $i = jA$) is a special case of this relationship in which the surface of integration is a cross section of the conductor and in which $\mathbf{j}$ is constant over this surface and at right angles to it. However, Eq. 31–4 may be applied to any surface through which we wish to know the current. Equation 31–4 shows clearly that $i$ is a scalar because the integrand $\mathbf{j} \cdot d\mathbf{S}$ is a scalar.

The arrow often associated with the current in a wire does not indicate that current is a vector but merely shows the *sense* of charge flow. Positive charge carriers either move in a certain direction along the wire or in the opposite direction, these two possibilities being represented by $+$ or $-$ in algebraic equations. Note that (a) the current in a wire remains unchanged if the wire is bent, tied into a knot, or otherwise distorted, and (b) the arrows representing the sense of currents do not in any way obey the laws of vector addition.

The drift speed $v_d$ of charge carriers in a conductor can be computed from the current density $j$. Figure 31–1 shows the conduction electrons in a wire moving to the right at an assumed constant drift speed $v_d$. The number of conduction electrons in the wire is $nAl$ where $n$ is the number of conduction electrons per unit volume and $Al$ is the volume of the wire. A charge of magnitude

$$q = (nAl)e$$

passes out of the wire, through its right end, in a time $t$ given by

$$t = \frac{l}{v_d}.$$

The current $i$ is given by

$$i = \frac{q}{t} = \frac{nAle}{l/v_d} = nAev_d.$$

Solving for $v_d$ and recalling that $j = i/A$ (Eq. 31-3) yields

$$v_d = \frac{i}{nAe} = \frac{j}{ne}. \tag{31-5}$$

▶ **Example 1.** An aluminum wire whose diameter is 0.10 in. is welded end to end to a copper wire with a diameter of 0.064 in. The composite wire carries a steady current of 10 amp. What is the current density in each wire?

The current is distributed uniformly over the cross section of each conductor, except near the junction, which means that the current density may be taken as constant for all points within each wire. The cross-sectional area of the aluminum wire is 0.0079 in.$^2$ Thus, from Eq. 31-3,

$$j_{Al} = \frac{i}{A} = \frac{10 \text{ amp}}{0.0079 \text{ in.}^2} = 1300 \text{ amp/in.}^2$$

The cross-sectional area of the copper wire is 0.0032 in.$^2$ Thus

$$j_{Cu} = \frac{i}{A} = \frac{10 \text{ amp}}{0.0032 \text{ in.}^2} = 3100 \text{ amp/in.}^2$$

The fact that the wires are of different materials does not enter into consideration here.

**Example 2.** What is $v_d$ for the copper wire in Example 1?

We can write the current density for the copper wire as 480 amp/cm$^2$. To compute $n$ we start from the fact that there is one free electron per atom in copper. The number of atoms per unit volume is $dN_0/M$ where $d$ is the density, $N_0$ is Avogadro's number, and $M$ is the atomic weight. The number of free electrons per unit volume is then

$$n = \frac{dN_0}{M} = \frac{(9.0 \text{ gm/cm}^3)(6.0 \times 10^{23} \text{ atoms/mole})(1 \text{ electron/atom})}{64 \text{ gm/mole}}$$

$$= 8.4 \times 10^{22} \text{ electrons/cm}^3.$$

Finally, $v_d$ is, from Eq. 31-5,

$$v_d = \frac{j}{ne} = \frac{480 \text{ amp/cm}^2}{(8.4 \times 10^{22} \text{ electrons/cm}^3)(1.6 \times 10^{-19} \text{ coul/electron})}$$

$$= 3.6 \times 10^{-2} \text{ cm/sec.}$$

It takes 28 sec for the electrons in this wire to drift 1.0 cm. Would you have guessed that $v_d$ was so low? The drift speed of electrons must not be confused with the speed at which changes in the electric field configuration travel along wires, a speed which approaches that of light. When pressure is applied to one end of a long water-filled tube, a *pressure wave* travels rapidly along the tube. The speed at which *water* moves through the tube is much lower, however.    ◀

## 31–2  Resistance, Resistivity, and Conductivity

If the same potential difference is applied between the ends of a rod of copper and of a rod of wood, very different currents result. The characteristic of the conductor that enters here is its *resistance*. We define the resistance of a conductor (often called a *resistor;* symbol -WW-) between two points by applying a potential difference $V$ between those points, measuring the current $i$, and dividing:

$$R = V/i. \tag{31–6}$$

If $V$ is in volts and $i$ in amperes, the resistance $R$ will be in *ohms*.

The flow of charge through a conductor is often compared with the flow of water through a pipe, which occurs because there is a difference in pressure between the ends of the pipe, established perhaps by a pump. This pressure difference can be compared with the potential difference established between the ends of a resistor by a battery. The flow of water ($ft^3$/sec, say) is compared with the current (coul/sec or amp). The rate of flow of water for a given pressure difference is determined by the nature of the pipe. Is it long or short? Is it narrow or wide? Is it empty or filled, perhaps with gravel? These characteristics of the pipe are analogous to the resistance of a conductor.

Primary standards of resistance, kept at the National Bureau of Standards, are spools of wire whose resistances have been accurately measured. Because resistance varies with temperature, these standards, when used, are placed in an oil bath at a controlled temperature. They are made of a special alloy, called *manganin*, for which the change of resistance with temperature is very small. They are carefully annealed to eliminate strains, which also affect the resistance. These primary standard resistors are used chiefly to calibrate secondary standards for other laboratories.

Operationally, the primary resistance standards are not measured by using Eq. 31–6 but are measured in an indirect way which involves magnetic fields. Equation 31–6 is, in fact, used to measure $V$, by setting up an accurately known current $i$ (using a *current balance;* see Section 34–4) in an accurately known resistance $R$. This operational procedure for potential difference is the one normally used in place of the conceptual definition introduced in Section 29–1, in which one measures the work per unit charge required to move a test charge between two points.

Related to resistance is the *resistivity* $\rho$, which is a characteristic of a material rather than of a particular specimen of a material; it is defined, for isotropic materials,* from

$$\rho = \frac{E}{j}. \tag{31–7}$$

The resistivity of copper is $1.7 \times 10^{-8}$ ohm-m; that of fused quartz is about $10^{16}$ ohm-m. Few physical properties are measurable over such a range of values; Table 31–1 lists some values for common metals.

---

* These are materials whose properties (electrical in this case) do not vary with direction in the material.

**Table 31–1**

PROPERTIES OF METALS AS CONDUCTORS

|  | Resistivity (at 20°C), ohm-m | Temperature Coefficient of Resistivity,* $\alpha$, per C° | Density, gm/cm³ | Melting Point, °C |
|---|---|---|---|---|
| Aluminum | $2.8 \times 10^{-8}$ | $3.9 \times 10^{-3}$ | 2.7 | 659 |
| Copper | $1.7 \times 10^{-8}$ | $3.9 \times 10^{-3}$ | 8.9 | 1080 |
| Carbon (amorphous) | $3.5 \times 10^{-5}$ | $-5 \times 10^{-4}$ | 1.9 | 3500 |
| Iron | $1.0 \times 10^{-7}$ | $5.0 \times 10^{-3}$ | 7.8 | 1530 |
| Manganin | $4.4 \times 10^{-7}$ | $1 \times 10^{-5}$ | 8.4 | 910 |
| Nickel | $7.8 \times 10^{-8}$ | $6 \times 10^{-3}$ | 8.9 | 1450 |
| Silver | $1.6 \times 10^{-8}$ | $3.8 \times 10^{-3}$ | 10.5 | 960 |
| Steel | $1.8 \times 10^{-7}$ | $3 \times 10^{-3}$ | 7.7 | 1510 |
| Wolfram (tungsten) | $5.6 \times 10^{-8}$ | $4.5 \times 10^{-3}$ | 19 | 3400 |

* This quantity, defined from

$$\alpha = \frac{1}{\rho}\frac{d\rho}{dT}. \tag{31-8}$$

is the fractional change in resistivity $(d\rho/\rho)$ per unit change in temperature. It varies with temperature, the values here referring to 20°C. For copper ($\alpha = 3.9 \times 10^{-3}/\text{C}°$) the resistivity increases by 0.39 per cent for a temperature increase of 1 C° near 20°C. Note that $\alpha$ for carbon is negative, which means that the resistivity *decreases* with increasing temperature.

Consider a cylindrical conductor, of cross-sectional area $A$ and length $l$, carrying a steady current $i$. Let us apply a potential difference $V$ between its ends. If the cylinder cross sections at each end are equipotential surfaces, the electric field strength and the current density will be constant for all points in the cylinder and will have the values

$$E = \frac{V}{l} \quad \text{and} \quad j = \frac{i}{A}.$$

The resistivity $\rho$ may then be written as

$$\rho = \frac{E}{j} = \frac{V/l}{i/A}.$$

But $V/i$ is the resistance $R$ which leads to

$$R = \rho\frac{l}{A}. \tag{31-9}$$

$V$, $i$, and $R$ are *macroscopic* quantities, applying to a particular body or extended region. The corresponding *microscopic* quantities are $\mathbf{E}$, $\mathbf{j}$, and $\rho$; they have values at every point in a body. The macroscopic quantities are related to each other by Eq. 31-6 ($V = iR$) and the microscopic quantities by Eq. 31-7, which can be written in vector form as $\mathbf{E} = \mathbf{j}\rho$.

The macroscopic quantities can be found by integrating over the microscopic quantities, using relations already given, namely

$$i = \int \mathbf{j} \cdot d\mathbf{S} \qquad (31\text{-}4)$$

and
$$V_{ab} = -\int_a^b \mathbf{E} \cdot d\mathbf{l}. \qquad (29\text{-}5)$$

The integral in Eq. 31-4 is a surface integral, carried out over any cross section of the conductor. The integral in Eq. 29-5 is a line integral carried out along an arbitrary line drawn along the conductor, connecting any two equipotential surfaces, identified by $a$ and $b$. For a long wire connected to a battery equipotential surface $a$ might be chosen as a cross section of the wire near the positive battery terminal and $b$ might be a cross section near the negative terminal.

The resistance of a conductor between $a$ and $b$ can be expressed in microscopic terms by dividing the two equations, or

$$R = \frac{V_{ab}}{i} = \frac{-\int_a^b \mathbf{E} \cdot d\mathbf{l}}{\int \mathbf{j} \cdot d\mathbf{S}}.$$

If the conductor is a long cylinder of cross section $A$ and length $l$ and if points $a$ and $b$ are its ends, the foregoing equation for $R$ (see Eq. 31-7) reduces to

$$R = \frac{El}{jA} = \rho\,\frac{l}{A},$$

which is Eq. 31-9.

The macroscopic quantities $V$, $i$, and $R$ are of primary interest when we are making electrical measurements on real conducting objects. They are the quantities that one reads on meters. The microscopic quantities $\mathbf{E}$, $\mathbf{j}$, and $\rho$ are of primary importance when we are concerned with the fundamental behavior of matter (rather than of specimens of matter), as we usually are in the research area of *solid state physics*. Thus Section 31-4 deals appropriately with an atomic view of the *resistivity* of a metal and not of the *resistance* of a metallic specimen. The microscopic quantities are also important when we are interested in the interior behavior of irregularly shaped conducting objects.

▶ **Example 3.** A rectangular carbon block has dimensions 1.0 cm × 1.0 cm × 50 cm. (a) What is the resistance measured between the two square ends? (b) Between two opposing rectangular faces? The resistivity of carbon at 20°C is 3.5 × 10$^{-5}$ ohm-m.

(a) The area of a square end is 1.0 cm$^2$ or 1.0 × 10$^{-4}$ meter$^2$. Equation 31-9 gives for the resistance between the square ends:

$$R = \rho\,\frac{l}{A} = \frac{(3.5 \times 10^{-5}\text{ ohm-m})(0.50\text{ meter})}{1.0 \times 10^{-4}\text{ meter}^2} = 0.18\text{ ohm}.$$

(b) For the resistance between opposing rectangular faces (area = 5.0 × 10$^{-3}$ meter$^2$), we have

$$R = \rho\,\frac{l}{A} = \frac{(3.5 \times 10^{-5}\text{ ohm-m})(10^{-2}\text{ meter})}{5.0 \times 10^{-3}\text{ meter}^2} = 7.0 \times 10^{-5}\text{ ohm}.$$

Thus a given conductor can have a number of resistances, depending on how the potential difference is applied to it. The ratio of resistances for these two cases is 2600. We assume in each that the potential difference is applied to the block in such a way that the surfaces between which the resistance is desired are equipotential. Otherwise Eq. 31-9 would not be valid.    ◀

Figure 31-2 shows (solid curve) how the resistivity of copper varies with temperature. Sometimes, for practical use, such data are expressed in equation form. If we are interested in only a limited range of temperatures extending, say, from 0 to 500°C, we can fit a straight line to the curve of Fig. 31-2, making it pass through two arbitrarily selected points; see the dashed line. We choose the point labeled $T_0$, $\rho_0$ in the figure as a reference point, $T_0$ being 0°C in this case and $\rho_0$ being $1.56 \times 10^{-8}$ ohm-m. The resistivity $\rho$ at any temperature $T$ can be found from the empirical equation of the dashed straight line in Fig. 31-2, which is

$$\rho = \rho_0[1 + \bar{\alpha}(T - T_0)]. \tag{31-10}$$

This relation shows correctly that $\rho \to \rho_0$ as $T \to T_0$. If we solve Eq. 31-10 for $\bar{\alpha}$, we obtain

$$\bar{\alpha} = \frac{1}{\rho_0} \frac{\rho - \rho_0}{T - T_0}.$$

Comparison with Eq. 31-8 shows that $\bar{\alpha}$ is a *mean temperature coefficient of resistivity* for a selected pair of temperatures rather than the temperature coefficient of resistivity at a particular temperature, which is the definition of $\alpha$. For most practical purposes Eq. 31-10 gives results that are within the acceptable range of accuracy.

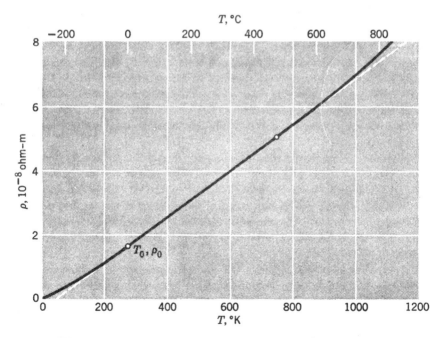

**Fig. 31-2**  The resistivity of copper as a function of temperature. The dashed line is an approximation chosen to fit the curve at the two circled points. The point marked $T_0$, $\rho_0$ is chosen as a reference point.

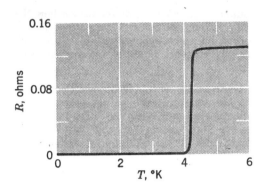

**Fig. 31-3** The resistance of mercury disappears below about 4°K.

The curve of Fig. 31-2 does not go to zero at the absolute zero of temperature, even though it appears to do so, the residual resistivity at this temperature being $0.02 \times 10^{-8}$ ohm-m. For many substances the resistance *does* become zero at some low temperature. Figure 31-3 shows the resistance of a specimen of mercury for temperatures below 6°K. In the space of about 0.05 K° the resistance drops abruptly to an immeasurably low value. This phenomenon, called *superconductivity,*[*] was discovered by Kamerlingh Onnes in the Netherlands in 1911. The resistance of materials in the superconducting state seems to be truly zero; currents, once established in closed superconducting circuits, persist for weeks without diminution, even though there is no battery in the circuit. If the temperature is raised slightly above the superconducting point, such currents drop rapidly to zero.

### 31-3   Ohm's Law

Let us apply a variable potential difference $V$ between the ends of a 100-foot coil of #18 copper wire. For each applied potential difference, let us measure the current $i$ and plot it against $V$ as in Fig. 31-4. The straight line that results means that *the resistance of this conductor is the same no matter what applied voltage is used to measure it.* This important result, which holds for metallic conductors, is known as *Ohm's law.* We assume that the temperature of the conductor is essentially constant throughout the measurements.

Many conductors do not obey Ohm's law. Figure 31-5, for example, shows a $V$–$i$ plot for a type 2A3 vacuum tube. The plot is not straight and the resistance depends on the voltage used to measure it. Also, the current for this device is almost vanishingly small if the polarity of the applied potential difference is reversed. For metallic conductors the current reverses direction when the potential difference is reversed, but its magnitude does not change.

Figure 31-6 shows a typical $V$–$i$ plot for another nonohmic device, a *thermistor.* This is a semiconductor (see p. 650) with a large and negative temperature coefficient of resistivity $\alpha$ (see Table 31-1) that varies greatly with temperature. We note that two different currents through the thermistor can correspond to the same potential difference between its ends.

---

[*] See "Superconductivity" by B. T. Matthias, *Scientific American*, p. 92, November 1957.

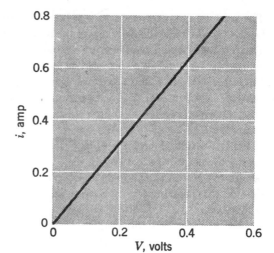

**Fig. 31–4**  The current in a particular copper conductor as a function of potential difference. This conductor obeys Ohm's law.

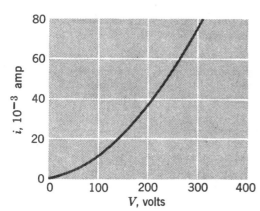

**Fig. 31–5**  The current in a type 2A3 vacuum tube as a function of potential difference. This conductor does not obey Ohm's law.

**Fig. 31–6**  A plot of current as a function of potential difference in a Western Electric 1–B thermistor. The curve shows how the voltage across the thermistor varies as the current through it is increased. The shape of the curve can be accounted for in terms of the large negative temperature coefficient of resistivity of the material of which the device is made.

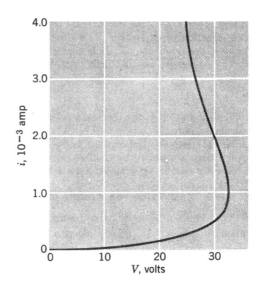

Thermistors are often used to measure the rate of energy flow in microwave beams by allowing the microwave beam to fall on the thermistor and heat it. The relatively small temperature rise so produced results in a relatively large change in resistance, which serves as a measure of the microwave power. Modern electronics, and therefore much of the character of our present technological civilization, depends in a fundamental way on the fact that many conductors, such as vacuum tubes, crystal rectifiers, thermistors, and transistors, do *not* obey Ohm's law.

We stress that the relationship $V = iR$ is *not* a statement of Ohm's law. A conductor obeys this law only if its $V - i$ curve is linear, that is, if $R$ is independent of $V$ and $i$. The relationship $R = V/i$ remains as the general definition of the resistance of a conductor whether or not the conductor obeys Ohm's law.

The microscopic equivalent of the relationship $V = iR$ is Eq. 31–7, or **E** = **j**$\rho$. A conducting *material* is said to obey Ohm's law if a plot of $E$ versus $j$ is linear, that is, if the resistivity $\rho$ is independent of $E$ and $j$. Ohm's law is a specific property of certain materials and is not a general law of electromagnetism, for example, like Gauss's law.

A close analogy exists between the flow of charge because of a potential difference and the flow of heat because of a temperature difference. Consider a thin electrically conducting slab of thickness $\Delta x$ and area $A$. Let a potential difference $\Delta V$ be maintained between opposing faces. The current $i$ is given by Eqs. 31–6 ($i = V/R$) and 31–9 ($R = \rho l/A$), or

$$i = \frac{\Delta V}{R} = \frac{\Delta V A}{\rho \Delta x}.$$

In the limiting case of a slab of thickness $dx$ this becomes

$$i = \frac{1}{\rho} A \frac{dV}{dx}$$

or
$$\frac{dq}{dt} = -\sigma A \frac{dV}{dx}, \qquad (31\text{–}11)$$

where $\sigma \; (= 1/\rho)$ is the *conductivity* of the material. Since positive charge flows in the direction of decreasing $V$, we introduce a minus sign into Eq. 31–11, that is, $dq/dt$ is positive when $dV/dx$ is negative.

The analogous heat flow equation (see Section 22–4) is

$$\frac{dQ}{dt} = -kA \frac{dT}{dx}, \qquad (31\text{–}12)$$

which shows that $k$, the thermal conductivity, corresponds to $\sigma$ and $dT/dx$, the temperature gradient, corresponds to $dV/dx$, the potential gradient. There is more than a formal mathematical analogy between Eqs. 31–11 and 31–12. Both heat energy and charge are carried by the free electrons in a metal; empirically, a good electrical conductor (silver, say) is also a good heat conductor and conversely.

### 31–4 Resistivity—an Atomic View

One can understand why metals obey Ohm's law on the basis of simple classical ideas. If these ideas are modified when necessary by the requirements of quantum physics, it is possible to go further and to calculate theoretical values of the resistivity $\rho$ for various metals. These calculations are not simple, but when they have been carried out the agreement with the experimental value of $\rho$ has usually been good.

In a metal the valence electrons are not attached to individual atoms but are free to move about within the lattice and are called *conduction electrons*. In copper there is one such electron per atom, the other 28 remaining bound to the copper nuclei to form ionic cores.

The speed distribution of conduction electrons can be described correctly only in terms of quantum physics. For our purposes, however, it suffices to consider only a suitably defined average speed $\bar{v}$; for copper $\bar{v} = 1.6 \times 10^8$ cm/sec. In the absence of an electron field, the directions in which the electrons move are completely random, like those of the molecules of a gas confined to a container.

The electrons collide constantly with the ionic cores of the conductor, that is, they interact with the lattice, often suffering sudden changes in speed and direction. These collisions remind us of the collisions of gas molecules confined to a container. As in the case of molecular collisions, we can describe electron-lattice collisions by a *mean free path* $\lambda$, where $\lambda$ is the average distance that an electron travels between collisions.*

In an ideal metallic crystal at 0°K electron-lattice collisions would not occur, according to the predictions of quantum physics, that is, $\lambda \to \infty$ as $T \to 0°K$ for ideal crystals. Collisions take place in actual crystals because (a) the ionic cores at any temperature $T$ are vibrating about their equilibrium positions in a random way, (b) impurities, that is, foreign atoms, may be present, and (c) the crystal may contain lattice imperfections, such as rows of missing atoms and displaced atoms. On this view it is not surprising that the resistivity of a metal can be increased by (a) raising its temperature, (b) adding small amounts of impurities, and (c) straining it severely, as by drawing it through a die, to increase the number of lattice imperfections.

When an electric field is applied to a metal, the electrons modify their random motion in such a way that they drift slowly, in the opposite direction to that of the field, with an average drift speed $v_d$. This drift speed is much less than the effective average speed $\bar{v}$ mentioned above (see Example 2). Figure 31-7 suggests the relationship between these two speeds. The solid lines suggest a possible random path followed by an electron in the absence of an applied field; the electron proceeds from $x$ to $y$, making six collisions on the way. The dashed curves show how this same event *might* have occurred if an electric field $E$ had been applied. Note that the electron drifts steadily to the right, ending at $y'$ rather than at $y$. In preparing Fig. 31-7, it has been assumed that the drift speed $v_d$ is $0.02\bar{v}$; actually, it is more like $10^{-10}\bar{v}$, so that the "drift" exhibited in the figure is greatly exaggerated.

The drift speed $v_d$ can be calculated in terms of the applied electric field $E$ and of $\bar{v}$ and $\lambda$. When a field is applied to an electron in the metal it will experience a force $eE$ which will impart to it an acceleration $a$ given by Newton's second law,

$$a = \frac{eE}{m}.$$

---

* It can be shown that collisions between electrons occur only rarely and have little effect on the resistivity.

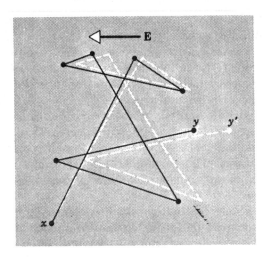

**Fig. 31-7**   The solid lines show an electron moving from $x$ to $y$, making six collisions. The dashed curves show what the electron path *might* have been in the presence of an electric field **E**. Note the steady drift in the direction of $-$**E**.

Consider an electron that has just collided with an ion core.   The collision, in general, will momentarily destroy the tendency to drift and the electron will have a truly random direction after the collision.   At its next collision the electron's velocity will have changed, on the average, by $a(l/\bar{v})$ where $l/\bar{v}$ is the mean time between collisions.   We call this the drift speed $v_d$, or

$$v_d = a\left(\frac{\lambda}{\bar{v}}\right) = \frac{eE\lambda}{m\bar{v}}. \qquad (31\text{--}13)$$

The electron's motion through the conductor is analogous to the constant rate of fall of a stone in water.   The gravitational force $F_g$ on the stone is opposed by a viscous resisting force that is proportional to the velocity, or

$$F_g = mg = bv,$$

where $b$ is a viscous coefficient (see Section 15–8).   Thus the constant terminal speed of the stone is

$$v = \left(\frac{1}{b}\right)F_g.$$

We can rewrite Eq. 31–13 as

$$v_d = \left(\frac{\lambda}{m\bar{v}}\right)F_E,$$

where $F_E$ ($= eE$) is the electrical force.   Comparison of these equations shows that the equivalent "viscous coefficient" for the motion of an electron in a particular conductor is $\lambda/2m\bar{v}$.   If $\lambda$ is short, the conductor exhibits a greater "viscous effect" on the electron motion, and the drift speed $v_d$ is proportionally lower.

We may express $v_d$ in terms of the current density (Eq. 31–5) and combine with Eq. 31–13 to obtain

$$v_d = \frac{j}{ne} = \frac{eE\lambda}{m\bar{v}}.$$

Combining this with Eq. 31–7 ($\rho = E/j$) leads finally to

$$\rho = \frac{m\bar{v}}{ne^2\lambda}. \tag{31-14}$$

Equation 31–14 can be taken as a statement that metals obey Ohm's law *if* we can show that $\bar{v}$ and $\lambda$ do not depend on the applied electric field $E$. In this case $\rho$ will not depend on $E$, which (see Section 31–3) is the criterion that a material obey Ohm's law. The quantities $\bar{v}$ and $\lambda$ depend on the speed distribution of the conduction electrons. We have seen that this distribution is affected only slightly by the application of even a relatively large electric field, since $\bar{v}$ is of the order of $10^8$ cm/sec and $v_d$ (see Example 1) only of the order of $10^{-2}$ cm/sec, a ratio of $10^{10}$. We may be sure that whatever the values of $\bar{v}$ and $\lambda$ are (for copper at 20°C, say) in the absence of a field they remain essentially unchanged when the field is applied. Thus the right side of Eq. 31–14 is independent of $E$ and the material obeys Ohm's law. The numerical calculation of $\rho$ from Eq. 31–14 is hampered by the difficulty of calculating $\lambda$, although the calculation has been carried out in a number of cases.

▶ **Example 4.** What are (a) the mean time $\tau$ between collisions and (b) the mean free path for free electrons in copper?

(a) From Eq. 31–14 (see also Example 2), we have

$$\tau = \frac{\lambda}{\bar{v}} = \frac{m}{ne^2\rho} = \frac{(9.1 \times 10^{-31}\,\text{kg})}{(8.4 \times 10^{28}/\text{meter}^3)(1.6 \times 10^{-19}\,\text{coul})^2(1.7 \times 10^{-8}\,\text{ohm-m})}$$

$$= 2.5 \times 10^{-14}\,\text{sec}.$$

(b) The mean free path is

$$\lambda = \tau\bar{v} = (2.5 \times 10^{-14}\,\text{sec})(1.6 \times 10^8\,\text{cm/sec}) = 4.0 \times 10^{-6}\,\text{cm}.$$

This is about 200 ionic diameters.    ◀

### 31–5  Energy Transfers in an Electric Circuit

Figure 31–8 shows a circuit consisting of a battery $B$ connected to a "black box." A steady current $i$ exists in the connecting wires and a steady potential difference $V_{ab}$ exists between the terminals $a$ and $b$. The box might contain a resistor, a motor, or a storage battery, among other things.

**Fig. 31–8**  A battery $B$ sets up a current in a circuit containing a "black box."

Terminal $a$, connected to the positive battery terminal, is at a higher potential than terminal $b$. If a charge $dq$ moves through the box from $a$ to $b$, this charge will decrease its electric potential energy by $dq\ V_{ab}$ (see Section 29–6). The conservation-of-energy principle tells us that this energy is transferred in the box from electric potential energy to some other form. What that other form will be depends on what is in the box. In a time $dt$ the energy $dU$ transferred inside the box is then

$$dU = dq\ V_{ab} = i\ dt\ V_{ab}.$$

We find the *rate* of energy transfer $P$ by dividing by the time, or

$$P = \frac{dU}{dt} = iV_{ab}. \qquad (31\text{--}15)$$

If the device in the box is a motor, the energy appears largely as mechanical work done by the motor; if the device is a storage battery that is being charged, the energy appears largely as stored chemical energy in this second battery.

If the device is a resistor, we assert that the energy appears as heat in the resistor. To see this, consider a stone of mass $m$ that falls through a height $h$. It decreases its gravitational potential energy by $mgh$. If the stone falls in a vacuum or—for practical purposes—in air, this energy is transformed into kinetic energy of the stone. If the stone falls in water, however, its speed eventually becomes constant, which means that the kinetic energy no longer increases. The potential energy that is steadily being made available as the stone falls then appears as thermal energy in the stone and the surrounding water. It is the viscous, friction-like drag of the water on the surface of the stone that stops the stone from accelerating, and it is at this surface that thermal energy appears.

The course of the electrons through the resistor is much like that of the stone through water. The electrons travel with a constant drift speed $v_d$ and thus do not gain kinetic energy. The electric potential energy that they lose is transferred to the resistor as heat. On a microscopic scale this can be understood in that collisions between the electrons and the lattice (see Fig. 21–5) increase the amplitude of the thermal vibrations of the lattice; on a macroscopic scale this corresponds to a temperature increase. This effect, which is thermodynamically irreversible, is called *Joule heating*.

For a resistor we can combine Eqs. 31–15 and 31–6 ($R = V/i$) and obtain either

$$P = i^2 R \qquad (31\text{--}16)$$

or

$$P = \frac{V^2}{R}. \qquad (31\text{--}17)$$

Note that Eq. 31–15 applies to electrical energy transfer of *all* kinds; Eqs. 31–16 and 31–17 apply only to the transfer of electrical energy to heat energy in a resistor. Equations 31–16 and 31–17 are known as *Joule's law*. This law is a particular way of writing the conservation-of-energy principle for the special case in which electrical energy is transferred into heat energy.

The unit of power that follows from Eq. 31–15 is the volt-amp. It can be written as

$$1 \text{ volt-amp} = 1 \text{ volt-amp} \left( \frac{1 \text{ joule}}{1 \text{ volt} \times 1 \text{ coul}} \right) \left( \frac{1 \text{ coul}}{1 \text{ amp} \times 1 \text{ sec}} \right)$$

$$= 1 \text{ joule/sec.}$$

The first conversion factor in parenthesis comes from the definition of the volt (Eq. 29–1); the second comes from the definition of the coulomb. The joule/sec is such a common unit that it is given a special name of its own, the *watt;* see Section 7–7. Power is not an exclusively electrical concept, of course, and we can express in watts the power ($= \mathbf{F} \cdot \mathbf{v}$) expended by an agent that exerts a force $\mathbf{F}$ while it moves with a velocity $\mathbf{v}$.

▶ **Example 5.** You are given a 20-ft length of heating wire made of the special alloy Nichrome; it has a resistance of 24 ohms. Can you obtain more heat by winding one coil or by cutting the wire in two and winding two separate coils? In each case the coils are to be connected individually across a 110-volt line.

The power $P$ for the single coil is given by Eq. 31–17:

$$P = \frac{V^2}{R} = \frac{(110 \text{ volts})^2}{24 \text{ ohms}} = 500 \text{ watts.}$$

The power for a coil of half the length is given by

$$P' = \frac{(110 \text{ volts})^2}{12 \text{ ohms}} = 1000 \text{ watts.}$$

There are two "half-coils," so that the total power obtained by cutting the wire in half is 2000 watts, or four times that for the single coil. This would seem to suggest that we could buy a 500-watt heating coil, cut it in half, and rewind it to obtain 2000 watts. Why is this not a practical idea?    ◀

## QUESTIONS

1. Name other physical quantities that, like current, are scalars having a sense represented by an arrow in a diagram.

2. What conclusions can you draw by applying Eq. 31–4 to a closed surface through which a number of wires pass in random directions, carrying steady currents of different sizes?

3. A potential difference $V$ is applied to a circular cylinder of carbon by clamping it between circular copper electrodes, as in Fig. 31–9. Discuss the difficulty of calculating the resistance of the carbon cylinder, using the relation $R = \rho L/A$.

Copper

Carbon

Copper

**Fig. 31–9**

4. How would you measure the resistance of a pretzel-shaped conductor? Give specific details to clarify the concept.

5. Discuss the difficulties of testing whether the filament of a light bulb obeys Ohm's law.

6. Does the relation $V = iR$ apply to nonohmic resistors?

7. The temperature coefficient of resistance of a thermistor is negative and varies greatly with temperature. Account qualitatively for the shape of the curve of $i$ versus $V$ for the thermistor of Fig. 31–6.

8. A potential difference $V$ is applied to a copper wire of diameter $d$ and length $l$. What is the effect on the electron drift speed of (a) doubling $V$, (b) doubling $l$, and (c) doubling $d$?

9. If the drift speeds of the electrons in a conductor under ordinary circumstances are so slow (see Example 2), why do the lights in a room turn on so quickly after the switch is closed?

10. Can you think of a way to measure the drift speed for electrons by timing their travel along a conductor?

11. Why are the dashed white lines in Fig. 31–7 curved slightly?

12. A current $i$ enters the top of a copper sphere of radius $R$ and leaves at a diametrically opposite point. Are all parts of the sphere equally effective in dissipating Joule heat?

13. What special characteristics must (a) heating wire and (b) fuse wire have?

14. Equation 31–16 ($P = i^2R$) seems to suggest that the rate of Joule heating in a resistor is reduced if the resistance is made less; Eq. 31–17 ($P = V^2/R$) seems to suggest just the opposite. How do you reconcile this apparent paradox?

15. Is the filament resistance lower or higher in a 500-watt light bulb than in a 100-watt bulb? Both bulbs are designed to operate on 110 volts.

16. Five wires of the same length and diameter are connected in turn between two points maintained at constant potential difference. Will heat be developed at the fastest rate in the wire of ($a$) the smallest or ($b$) the largest resistance?

## PROBLEMS

1. A current of 5 amp exists in a 10-ohm resistance for 4 min. ($a$) How many coulombs and ($b$) how many electrons pass through any cross section of the resistor in this time?

2. A current is established in a gas discharge tube when a sufficiently high potential difference is applied across the two electrodes in the tube. The gas ionizes; electrons move toward the positive terminal and positive ions toward the negative terminal. What are the magnitude and sense of the current in a hydrogen discharge tube in which $3.1 \times 10^{18}$ electrons and $1.1 \times 10^{18}$ protons move past a cross-sectional area of the tube each second?

3. A copper wire and an iron wire of the same length have the same potential difference applied to them. ($a$) What must be the ratio of their radii if the current is to be the same? ($b$) Can the current density be made the same by suitable choices of the radii?

4. A current $i$ enters one corner of a square sheet of copper and leaves at the opposite corner. Sketch arrows for various points within the square to represent the relative values of $j$. Intuitive guesses rather than detailed mathematical analysis are called for.

5. The belt of an electrostatic generator is 50 cm wide and travels at 30 meters/sec. The belt carries charge into the sphere at a rate corresponding to $10^{-4}$ amp. Compute the surface charge density on the belt.

6. A square aluminum rod is 1.0 meter long and 5.0 mm on edge. ($a$) What is the resistance between its ends? ($b$) What must be the diameter of a circular 1.0-meter copper rod if its resistance is to be the same?

7. A wire with a resistance of 6.0 ohms is drawn out so that its new length is three times its original length. Find the resistance of the longer wire, assuming that the resistivity and density of the material are not changed during the drawing process.

8. A copper wire and an iron wire of equal length $l$ and diameter $d$ are joined and a potential difference $V$ is applied between the ends of the composite wire. Calculate ($a$) the electric field strength in each wire, ($b$) the current density in each wire, and ($c$) the potential difference across each wire. Assume that $l = 10$ meters, $d = 2.0$ mm, and $V = 100$ volts.

9. A rod of a certain metal is 1.00 meter long and 0.550 cm in diameter. The resistance between its ends (at 20°C) is $2.87 \times 10^{-3}$ ohm. A round disk is formed of this same material, 2.00 cm in diameter and 1.00 mm thick. ($a$) What is the resistance between the opposing round faces? ($b$) What is the material?

10. Steel trolley-car rail has a cross-sectional area of 7.1 in.$^2$ What is the resistance of 10 miles of single track? The resistivity of the steel is $6.0 \times 10^{-7}$ ohm-m.

11. ($a$) At what temperature would the resistance of a copper conductor be double its resistance at 0°C? ($b$) Does this same temperature hold for all copper conductors, regardless of shape or size?

12. It is desired to make a long cylindrical conductor whose temperature coefficient of resistivity at 20°C will be close to zero. ($a$) If such a conductor is made by assembling alternate disks of iron and carbon, what is the ratio of the thickness of a carbon disk to that of an iron disk? Assume that the temperature remains essentially the same in each disk. ($b$) What is the ratio of the rate of Joule heating in a carbon disk to that in an iron disk?

13. When a metal rod is heated, not only its resistance but also its length and its cross-sectional area change. The relation $R = \rho l/A$ suggests that all three factors should be taken into account in measuring $\rho$ at various temperatures. If the temperature changes by 1.0 C°, what per cent changes in $R$, $l$, and $A$ occur for a copper conductor. What conclusion do you draw? The coefficient of linear expansion is $1.7 \times 10^{-5}/\mathrm{C}°$.

14. The copper windings of a motor have a resistance of 50 ohms at 20°C, when the motor is idle. After running for several hours the resistance rises to 58 ohms: What is the temperature of the windings?

15. (a) Using data from Fig. 31–5, plot the resistance of the vacuum tube as a function of applied potential difference. (b) Repeat for the thermistor of Fig. 31–6.

16. A small but measurable current of $10^{-10}$ amp exists in a copper wire whose diameter is 0.10 in. Calculate the electron drift speed.

17. Heat is developed in a resistor at a rate of 100 watts when the current is 3.0 amp. What is the resistance in ohms?

18. A potential difference of 1.0 volt is applied to a 100-ft length of #18 copper wire (diameter = 0.040 in.). Calculate (a) the current, (b) the current density, (c) the electric field strength, and (d) the rate of Joule heating.

19. The National Board of Fire Underwriters has fixed safe current-carrying capacities for various sizes and types of wire. For #10 rubber-coated copper wire (wire diameter = 0.10 in.) the maximum safe current is 25 amp. At this current, find (a) the current density, (b) the electric field strength, (c) the potential difference for 1000 ft of wire, and (d) the rate of Joule heating for 1000 ft of wire.

20. A 500-watt immersion heater is placed in a pot containing 2.0 liters of water at 20°C. (a) How long will it take to bring the water to boiling temperature, assuming that 80% of the available energy is absorbed by the water? (b) How much longer will it take to boil half the water away?

21. A nichrome heater dissipates 500 watts when the applied potential difference is 110 volts and the wire temperature is 800°C. How much power would it dissipate if the wire temperature were held to 200°C by immersion in a bath of cooling oil? The applied potential difference remains the same; $\bar{a}$ for nichrome is about $4 \times 10^{-4}/\mathrm{C}°$.

22. A beam of 16-Mev deuterons from a cyclotron falls on a copper block. The beam is equivalent to a current of $15 \times 10^{-6}$ amp. (a) At what rate do deuterons strike the block? (b) At what rate is heat produced in the block?

23. A "500-watt" heating unit is designed to operate from a 115-volt line. (a) By what percentage will its heat output drop if the line voltage drops to 110 volts? Assume no change in resistance. (b) Taking the variation of resistance with temperature into account, would the actual heat output drop be larger or smaller than that calculated in (a)?

24. Show that $p$, the power per unit volume transformed into Joule heat in a resistor, can be written as

$$p = j^2\rho \qquad \text{or} \qquad p = E^2/\rho.$$

# Electromotive Force
# and Circuits

CHAPTER 32

## 32–1  Electromotive Force

There exist in nature certain devices such as batteries and electric generators which are able to maintain a potential difference between two points to which they are attached.  Such devices are called seats of *electromotive force* (abbr. emf).  In this chapter we do not discuss their internal construction or detailed mode of action but confine ourselves to describing their gross electrical characteristics and to exploring their usefulness in electric circuits.

Figure 32–1a shows a seat of emf $B$, represented by a battery, connected to a resistor $R$.  The seat of emf maintains its upper terminal positive and its lower terminal negative, as shown by the $+$ and $-$ signs.  In the circuit external to $B$ positive charge carriers would be driven in the direction shown by the arrows marked $i$.  In other words, a clockwise current would be set up.

An emf is represented by an arrow which is placed next to the seat and points in the direction in which the seat, acting alone, would cause a positive charge carrier to move in the external circuit.  A small circle is drawn on the tail of an emf arrow so that it will not be confused with a current arrow.

A seat of emf must be able to do work on charge carriers that enter it.  In the circuit of Fig. 32–1a, for example, the seat acts to move positive charges from a point of low potential (the negative terminal) through the seat to a point of high potential (the positive terminal).  This reminds us of a pump, which can cause water to move from a place of low gravitational potential to a place of high potential.

In Fig. 32–1a a charge $dq$ passes through *any* cross section of the circuit in time $dt$.  In particular, this charge enters the seat of emf $\mathcal{E}$ at its low-potential

789

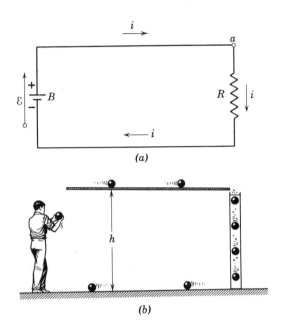

**Fig. 32–1** (a) A simple electric circuit and (b) its gravitational analog.

end and leaves at its high-potential end. The seat must do an amount of work $dW$ on the (positive) charge carriers to force them to go to the point of higher potential. The emf $\mathcal{E}$ of the seat is defined from

$$\mathcal{E} = dW/dq. \tag{32–1}$$

The unit of emf is the joule/coul (see Eq. 29–1) which is the *volt*. We might be inclined to say that a battery has an emf of 1 volt if it maintains a difference of potential of 1 volt between its terminals. This is true only under certain conditions, which we describe in Section 32–4.

If a seat of emf does work on a charge carrier, energy must be transferred within the seat. In a battery, for example, chemical energy is transferred into electrical energy. Thus we can describe a seat of emf as a device in which chemical, mechanical, or some other form of energy is changed (reversibly) into electrical energy. The chemical energy provided by the battery in Fig. 32–1a is stored in the electric and the magnetic * fields that surround the circuit. This stored energy does not increase because it is being drained away, by transfer to Joule heat in the resistor, at the same rate at which it is supplied. The electric and magnetic fields play an intermediary role in the energy transfer process, acting as a storage reservoir.

Figure 32–1b shows a gravitational analog of Fig. 32–1a. In the top figure the seat of emf $B$ does work on the charge carriers. This energy, stored temporarily as electromagnetic field energy, appears eventually as Joule heat in resistor $R$. In the lower figure the man, in lifting the bowling balls from

---

* A current in a wire is surrounded by a magnetic field, and this field, like the electric field, can also be viewed as a site of stored energy (see Section 36–4).

**Fig. 32–2**  Two batteries, a resistor, and a motor, connected in a single-loop circuit. It is given that $\mathcal{E}_B > \mathcal{E}_A$.

the floor to the shelf, does work on them. This energy is stored temporarily as gravitational field energy. The balls roll slowly and uniformly along the shelf, dropping from the right end into a cylinder full of viscous oil. They sink to the bottom at constant speed, are removed by a trapdoor mechanism not shown, and roll back along the floor to the left. The energy put into the system by the man appears eventually as heat in the viscous fluid. The energy supplied by the man comes from his own internal (chemical) energy. The circulation of charges in Fig. 32–1a will stop eventually if battery $B$ is not charged; the circulation of bowling balls in Fig. 32–1b will stop eventually if the man does not replenish his store of internal energy by eating.

Figure 32–2 shows a circuit containing two (ideal) batteries, $A$ and $B$, a resistor $R$, and an (ideal) electric motor employed in lifting a weight. The batteries are connected so that they tend to send charges around the circuit in opposite directions; the actual direction of the current is determined by $B$, which supplies the larger potential difference. The energy transfers in this circuit are

The chemical energy in $B$ is being steadily depleted, the energy appearing in the three forms shown on the right. Battery $A$ is being "charged" while battery $B$ is being discharged. Again, the electric and magnetic fields that surround the circuit act as an intermediary.

It is part of the definition of an emf that the energy transfer process be *reversible*, at least in principle. The student will recall that a reversible process is one that passes through equilibrium states; its course can be reversed by making an infinitesimal change in the environment of the system; see Section 25–2. A battery, for example, can either be on charge or discharge; a generator can be driven mechanically, producing electric energy, or it can be operated backward as a motor. The (reversible) energy transfers here are

$$\text{electrical} \rightleftarrows \text{chemical}$$

and
$$\text{electrical} \rightleftarrows \text{mechanical.}$$

Joule heating is an electric energy transfer that is *not* reversible. We can easily heat a conductor by supplying electric energy to it, but it is not possible to set up a current in a closed copper loop by heating the loop uniformly. Because of this lack of reversibility, we do not associate an emf with Joule heating.

### 32–2  Calculating the Current

In a time $dt$ an amount of energy given by $i^2R \, dt$ will appear in the resistor of Fig. 32–1a as Joule heat. During this same time a charge $dq$ ($= i \, dt$) will have moved through the seat of emf, and the seat will have done work on this charge (see Eq. 32–1) given by

$$dW = \mathcal{E}dq = \mathcal{E}i \, dt.$$

From the conservation of energy principle, the work done by the seat must equal the Joule heat, or

$$\mathcal{E}i \, dt = i^2R \, dt.$$

Solving for $i$, we obtain

$$i = \mathcal{E}/R. \tag{32–2}$$

We can also derive Eq. 32–2 by considering that if electric potential is to have any meaning a given point can have only one value of potential at any given time. If we start at any point in the circuit of Fig. 32–1a and, in imagination, go around the circuit in either direction, adding up algebraically the changes in potential that we encounter, we must arrive at the same potential when we return to our starting point. In other words, *the algebraic sum of the changes in potential encountered in a complete traversal of the circuit must be zero.*

In Fig. 32–1a let us start at point $a$, whose potential is $V_a$,* and traverse the circuit clockwise. In going through the resistor, there is a change in potential of $-iR$. The minus sign shows that the top of the resistor is higher

---

* The actual value of $V_a$ depends on assumptions made in the definition of potential (as described in Section 29–1). The numerical value of $V_a$ is not important because, as in most electric circuit situations, we are concerned here with *differences* of potential. Point $a$ in Fig. 32–1a (or any other single point in that figure) could be connected to ground (symbol $\rightleftharpoons$) and assigned the potential $V_a = 0$, following a common practice.

in potential than the bottom, which must be true, because positive charge carriers move of their own accord from high to low potential. As we traverse the battery from bottom to top, there is an *increase* of potential $+\mathcal{E}$ because the battery does (positive) work on the charge carriers, that is, it moves them from a point of low potential to one of high potential. Adding the algebraic sum of the changes in potential to the initial potential $V_a$ must yield the identical value $V_a$, or

$$V_a - iR + \mathcal{E} = V_a.$$

We write this as

$$-iR + \mathcal{E} = 0,$$

which is independent of the value of $V_a$ and which asserts explicitly that the algebraic sum of the potential changes for a complete circuit traversal is zero. This relation leads directly to Eq. 32–2.

These two ways to find the current in single-loop circuits, based on the conservation of energy and on the concept of potential, are completely equivalent because potential differences are defined in terms of work and energy (Section 29–1). The statement that the sum of the changes in potential encountered in making a complete loop is zero is called *Kirchhoff's second rule;* for brevity we call it the *loop theorem.* It must always be borne in mind that this theorem is simply a particular way of stating the law of conservation of energy for electric circuits.

To prepare for the study of more complex circuits, let us examine the rules for finding potential differences; these rules follow from the previous discussion. They are not meant to be memorized but rather to be so thoroughly understood that it becomes trivial to re-derive them on each application.

1. If a resistor is traversed in the direction of the current, the change in potential is $-iR$; in the opposite direction it is $+iR$.

2. If a seat of emf is traversed in the direction of the emf, the change in potential is $+\mathcal{E}$; in the opposite direction it is $-\mathcal{E}$.

### 32–3    Other Single-Loop Circuits

Figure 32–3a shows a circuit which emphasizes that all seats of emf have an intrinsic internal resistance $r$. This resistance cannot be removed—although we would usually like to do so—because it is an inherent part of the device. The figure shows the internal resistance $r$ and the emf separately, although, actually, they occupy the same region of space.

If we apply the loop theorem, starting at $b$ and going around clockwise, we obtain

$$V_b + \mathcal{E} - ir - iR = V_b$$

or

$$+\mathcal{E} - ir - iR = 0.$$

The student should compare these equations with Fig. 32–2b, which shows the changes in potential graphically. In writing these equations, note that we traversed $r$ and $R$ in the direction of the current and $\mathcal{E}$ in the direction of the

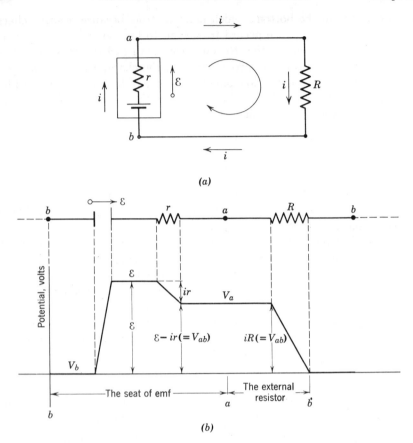

(a)

(b)

**Fig. 32-3** A single-loop circuit. The rectangular block is a seat of emf with internal resistance $r$. (b) The same circuit is drawn for convenience as a straight line. Directly below are shown the changes in potential that one encounters in traversing the circuit clockwise from point $b$.

emf. The same equation follows if we start at any other point in the circuit or if we traverse the circuit in a counterclockwise direction. Solving for $i$ gives

$$i = \frac{\mathcal{E}}{R + r}. \tag{32-3}$$

▶ **Example 1.** *Resistors in series.* Resistors in series are connected so that there is only one conducting path through them, as in Fig. 32-4. What is the equivalent resistance $R$ of this series combination? The equivalent resistance is the single resistance $R$ which, substituted for the series combination between the terminals $ab$, will leave the current $i$ unchanged.

Applying the loop theorem (going clockwise from $a$) yields

$$-iR_1 - iR_2 - iR_3 + \mathcal{E} = 0$$

or

$$i = \frac{\mathcal{E}}{R_1 + R_2 + R_3}.$$

**Fig. 32–4**   Example 1.   Three resistors are connected in series between terminals $a$ and $b$.

For the equivalent resistance $R$

$$i = \frac{\mathcal{E}}{R}$$

or $$R = R_1 + R_2 + R_3. \tag{32-4}$$

The extension to more than three resistors is clear.   ◄

### 32–4   Potential Differences

We often want to compute the potential difference between two points in a circuit.   In Fig. 32–3a for example, what is the relationship between the potential difference $V_{ab} (= V_a - V_b)$ between points $b$ and $a$ and the fixed circuit parameters $\mathcal{E}$, $r$, and $R$?   To find this relationship, let us start from point $b$ and traverse the circuit to point $a$, passing through resistor $R$ against the current.   If $V_b$ and $V_a$ are the potentials at $b$ and $a$, respectively, we have

$$V_b + iR = V_a$$

because we experience an increase in potential in traversing a resistor against the current arrow.   We rewrite this relation as

$$V_{ab} = V_a - V_b = +iR,$$

which tells us that $V_{ab}$, the potential difference between points $a$ and $b$, has the magnitude $iR$ and that point $a$ is more positive than point $b$.   Combining this last equation with Eq. 32–3 yields

$$V_{ab} = \mathcal{E}\,\frac{R}{R + r}. \tag{32-5}$$

To sum up: To find the potential difference between any two points in a circuit start at one point and traverse the circuit to the other, following any path, and add up algebraically the potential changes encountered.   This algebraic sum will be the potential difference.   This procedure is similar to that for finding the current in a closed loop, except that here the potential differences are added up over part of a loop and not over the whole loop.

The potential difference between any two points can have only one value; thus we must obtain the same answer for all paths that connect these points.

If we consider two points on the side of a hill, the measured difference in gravitational potential (that is, in altitude) between them is the same no matter what path is followed in going from one to the other.   In Fig. 32–3a let us calculate $V_{ab}$, using a path passing through the seat of emf.   We have

$$V_b + \mathcal{E} - ir = V_a$$

or (see also **Fig. 32–3b**)

$$V_{ab} = V_a - V_b = +\mathcal{E} - ir.$$

Again, combining with Eq. 32–3 leads to Eq. 32–5.

The terminal potential difference of the battery $V_{ab}$, as Eq. 32–5 shows, is less than $\mathcal{E}$ unless the battery has no internal resistance ($r = 0$) or if it is on open circuit ($R = \infty$); then $V_{ab}$ is equal to $\mathcal{E}$.   Thus the emf of a device is equal to its terminal potential difference *when on open circuit*.

▶ **Example 2.**   In Fig. 32–5a let $\mathcal{E}_1$ and $\mathcal{E}_2$ be 2.0 volts and 4.0 volts, respectively; let the resistances $r_1$, $r_2$, and $R$ be 1.0 ohm, 2.0 ohms, and 5.0 ohms, respectively. What is the current?

(a)

(b)

**Fig. 32–5**   (a) A single-loop circuit.   (b) The same circuit is shown schematically as a straight line, the potential differences encountered in traversing the circuit clockwise from point a being displayed directly below.   In the lower figure the potential of point a was assumed to be zero for convenience.

Emfs $\mathcal{E}_1$ and $\mathcal{E}_2$ oppose each other, but because $\mathcal{E}_2$ is larger it controls the direction of the current. Thus $i$ will be counterclockwise. The loop theorem, going clockwise from $a$, yields

$$-\mathcal{E}_2 + ir_2 + iR + ir_1 + \mathcal{E}_1 = 0.$$

The student should check that the same result is obtained by going around counterclockwise. He should also compare this equation carefully with Fig. 32–5b, which shows the potential changes graphically.

Solving for $i$ yields

$$i = \frac{\mathcal{E}_2 - \mathcal{E}_1}{R + r_1 + r_2} = \frac{4.0 \text{ volts} - 2.0 \text{ volts}}{5.0 \text{ ohms} + 1.0 \text{ ohm} + 2.0 \text{ ohms}}$$

$$= 0.25 \text{ amp.}$$

It is not necessary to know in advance what the actual direction of the current is. To show this, let us assume that the current in Fig. 32–5a is clockwise, an assumption that we know is incorrect. The loop theorem then yields (going clockwise from $a$)

$$-\mathcal{E}_2 - ir_2 - iR - ir_1 + \mathcal{E}_1 = 0$$

or

$$i = \frac{\mathcal{E}_1 - \mathcal{E}_2}{R + r_1 + r_2}.$$

Substituting numerical values (see above) yields $-0.25$ amp for the current. The minus sign tells us that the current is in the opposite direction from the one we have assumed.

In more complex circuit problems involving many loops and branches it is often impossible to know in advance the correct directions for the currents in all parts of the circuit. We can assume directions for the currents at random. Those currents for which positive numerical values are obtained will have the correct directions; those for which negative values are obtained will be exactly opposite to the assumed directions. In all cases the numerical values will be correct.

**Example 3.** What is the potential difference (a) between points $b$ and $a$ in Fig. 32–5a? (b) Between points $a$ and $c$?

(a) For points $a$ and $b$ we start at $b$ and traverse the circuit to $a$, obtaining

$$V_{ab} (= V_a - V_b) = -ir_2 + \mathcal{E}_2 = -(0.25 \text{ amp})(2.0 \text{ ohms}) + 4.0 \text{ volts}$$

$$= +3.5 \text{ volts.}$$

Thus $a$ is more positive than $b$ and the potential difference (3.5 volts) is *less than* the emf (4.0 volts); see Fig. 32–5b.

(b) For points $c$ and $a$, we start at $c$ and traverse the circuit to $a$, obtaining

$$V_{ac} (= V_a - V_c) = +\mathcal{E}_1 + ir_1 = +2.0 \text{ volts} + (0.25 \text{ amp})(1.0 \text{ ohm})$$

$$= +2.25 \text{ volts.}$$

This tells us that $a$ is at a higher potential than $c$. The terminal potential difference of $\mathcal{E}_1$ (2.25 volts) is *larger than* the emf (2.0 volts); see Fig. 32–5b. Charge is being forced through $\mathcal{E}_1$ in a direction opposite to the one in which it would send charge if it were acting by itself; if $\mathcal{E}_1$ is a storage battery, it is being charged at the expense of $\mathcal{E}_2$.

Let us test the first result by proceeding from $b$ to $a$ along a different path, namely, through $R$, $r_1$, and $\mathcal{E}_1$. We have

$$V_{ab} = iR + ir_1 + \mathcal{E}_1 = (0.25 \text{ amp})(5.0 \text{ ohms})$$

$$+ (0.25 \text{ amp})(1.0 \text{ ohm}) + 2.0 \text{ volts} = +3.5 \text{ volts,}$$

which is the same as the earlier result. ◀

### 32–5 Multiloop Circuits

Figure 32–6 shows a circuit containing two loops. For simplicity, we have neglected the internal resistances of the batteries. There are two *junctions*, $b$ and $d$, and three *branches* connecting these junctions. The branches are the left branch *bad*, the right branch *bcd*, and the central branch *bd*. If the emfs and the resistances are given, what are the currents in the various branches?

We label the currents in the branches as $i_1$, $i_2$, and $i_3$, as shown. Current $i_1$ has the same value for any cross section of the left branch from $b$ to $d$. Similarly, $i_2$ has the same value everywhere in the right branch and $i_3$ in the central branch. The directions of the currents have been chosen arbitrarily. The careful reader will note that $i_3$ must point in a direction opposite to the one we have shown. We have deliberately drawn it in wrong to show how the formal mathematical procedures will always indicate this to us.

The three currents $i_1$, $i_2$, and $i_3$ carry charge either toward junction $d$ or away from it. Charge does not accumulate at junction $d$, nor does it drain away from this junction because the circuit is in a steady-state condition. Thus charge must be removed from the junction by the currents at the same rate that it is brought into it. If we arbitrarily call a current approaching the junction positive and the one leaving the junction negative, then

$$i_1 + i_3 - i_2 = 0.$$

This equation suggests a general principle for the solution of multiloop circuits: *At any junction the algebraic sum of the currents must be zero.* This *junction theorem* is also known as *Kirchhoff's first rule.* Note that it is simply a statement of the conservation of charge. Thus our basic tools for solving circuits are (a) the conservation of energy (see p. 793) and (b) the conservation of charge.

For the circuit of Fig. 32–6, the junction theorem yields only one relationship among the three unknowns. Applying the theorem at junction $b$ leads to exactly the same equation, as the student should verify. To solve for the three unknowns, we need two more independent equations; they can be found from the loop theorem.

In single-loop circuits there is only one conducting loop around which to apply the loop theorem, and the current is the same in all parts of this loop.

**Fig. 32–6**   A multiloop circuit.

In multiloop circuits there is more than one loop, and the current in general will not be the same in all parts of any given loop.

If we traverse the left loop of Fig. 32–6 in a counterclockwise direction, the loop theorem gives

$$\mathcal{E}_1 - i_1R_1 + i_3R_3 = 0. \qquad (32–6)$$

The right loop gives

$$-i_3R_3 - i_2R_2 - \mathcal{E}_2 = 0. \qquad (32–7)$$

These two equations, together with the relation derived earlier with the junction theorem, are the three simultaneous equations needed to solve for the unknowns $i_1$, $i_2$, and $i_3$. Doing so yields

$$i_1 = \frac{\mathcal{E}_1(R_2 + R_3) - \mathcal{E}_2R_3}{R_1R_2 + R_2R_3 + R_1R_3}, \qquad (32–8a)$$

$$i_2 = \frac{\mathcal{E}_1R_3 - \mathcal{E}_2(R_1 + R_3)}{R_1R_2 + R_2R_3 + R_1R_3}, \qquad (32–8b)$$

and
$$i_3 = \frac{-\mathcal{E}_1R_2 - \mathcal{E}_2R_1}{R_1R_2 + R_2R_3 + R_1R_3}. \qquad (32–8c)$$

The student should supply the missing steps. Equation 32–8c shows that no matter what numerical values are given to the emfs and to the resistances the current $i_3$ will always have a negative value. This means that it will always point up in Fig. 32–6 rather than down, as we deliberately assumed. The currents $i_1$ and $i_2$ may be in either direction, depending on the particular numerical values given.

The student should verify that Eqs. 32–8 reduce to sensible conclusions in special cases. For $R_3 = \infty$, for example, we find

$$i_1 = i_2 = \frac{\mathcal{E}_1 - \mathcal{E}_2}{R_1 + R_2} \quad \text{and} \quad i_3 = 0.$$

What do these equations reduce to for $R_2 = \infty$?

The loop theorem can be applied to a large loop consisting of the entire circuit *abcda* of Fig. 32–6. This fact might suggest that there are more equations than we need, for there are only three unknowns and we already have three equations written in terms of them. However, the loop theorem yields for this loop

$$-i_1R_1 - i_2R_2 - \mathcal{E}_2 + \mathcal{E}_1 = 0,$$

which is nothing more than the sum of Eqs. 32–6 and 32–7. Thus this large loop does not yield another *independent* equation. It will never be found in solving multiloop circuits that there are more independent equations than variables.

▶ **Example 4.** *Resistors in parallel.* Figure 32–7 shows three resistors connected across the same seat of emf. Resistances across which the identical potential difference is applied are said to be in parallel. What is the equivalent resistance $R$ of this parallel combination? The equivalent resistance is that single resistance which, substituted for the parallel combination between terminals $ab$, would leave the current $i$ unchanged.

**Fig. 32–7** Example 4. Three resistors are connected in parallel betweeen terminals $a$ and $b$.

The currents in the three branches are

$$i_1 = \frac{V}{R_1}, \quad i_2 = \frac{V}{R_2}, \quad \text{and} \quad i_3 = \frac{V}{R_3},$$

where $V$ is the potential difference that appears between points $a$ and $b$. The total current $i$ is found by applying the junction theorem to junction $a$, or

$$i = i_1 + i_2 + i_3 = V\left(\frac{1}{R_1} + \frac{1}{R_2} + \frac{1}{R_3}\right).$$

If the equivalent resistance is used instead of the parallel combination, we have

$$i = \frac{V}{R}.$$

Combining these two equations gives

$$\frac{1}{R} = \frac{1}{R_1} + \frac{1}{R_2} + \frac{1}{R_3}. \tag{32–9}$$

This formula can easily be extended to more than three resistances. Note that the equivalent resistance of a parallel combination is less than any of the resistances that make it up.     ◀

### 32–6  Measuring Currents and Potential Differences

A meter to measure currents is called an *ammeter* (or a *milliammeter* or *microammeter*, depending on the size of the current to be measured). To determine the current in a wire, it is necessary to break or cut the wire and to insert the ammeter, so that the current to be measured passes through the meter (see Fig. 32–8).*

It is essential that the resistance $R_A$ of the ammeter be *small* compared to other resistances in the circuit. Otherwise the act of inserting the meter will in itself change

---

* The meter must be connected so that the direction of current through it (assuming positive charge carriers) is *into* the meter terminal marked +. Otherwise the meter will deflect in a direction opposite to that intended.

**Fig. 32-8**  An ammeter $(A)$ is connected to read the current in a circuit, and a voltmeter $(V)$ is connected to read the potential difference across resistor $R_1$.

the current to be measured.  An ideal ammeter would have zero resistance.  In the circuit of Fig. 32-8 the required condition, assuming that the voltmeter is not connected, is

$$R_A \ll r + R_1 + R_2.$$

A meter to measure potential differences is called a *voltmeter* (or a *millivoltmeter* or *microvoltmeter*).  To find the potential difference between two points in a circuit, it is necessary to connect one of the voltmeter terminals to each of the circuit points, without breaking the circuit (see Fig. 32-8).*

It is essential that the resistance of the voltmeter $R_V$ be *large* compared to any circuit resistance across which the voltmeter is connected.  Otherwise the meter will itself constitute an important circuit element and will alter the circuit current and the potential difference to be measured.  An ideal voltmeter would have an infinite resistance.  In Fig. 32-8 the required condition is

$$R_V \gg R_1$$

In measuring potential difference in electronic circuits, where the effective circuit resistance may be of the order of $10^6$ ohms or higher, it becomes necessary to use a *vacuum-tube voltmeter*, which is an electron-tube device designed specifically to have an extremely high effective resistance between its input terminals.

### 32-7  The Potentiometer

Figure 32-9 shows the rudiments of a *potentiometer*, which is a device for measuring an unknown emf $\mathcal{E}_x$.  The currents and emfs are marked as shown.  Applying the loop theorem to loop $abcd$ yields

$$-\mathcal{E}_x - ir + (i_0 - i)R = 0,$$

where $i_0 - i$, by application of the junction theorem at $a$, is the current in resistor $R$.  Solving for $i$ yields

$$i = \frac{i_0 R - \mathcal{E}_x,}{R + r}$$

in which $R$ is a variable resistor.  This relation shows that if $R$ is adjusted to have the value $R_x$ where

$$i_0 R_x = \mathcal{E}_x, \qquad\qquad (32\text{-}10)$$

the current $i$ in the branch $abcd$ becomes zero.  To *balance* the potentiometer in this way, $R$ must be adjusted manually until the sensitive meter $G$ reads zero.

---

\* The voltmeter terminal marked + must be connected to the point of higher potential.  Otherwise the meter will deflect in a direction opposite to that intended.

Fig. 32-9   Elements of a potentiometer

The emf can be obtained from Eq. 32–10 if the current $i_0$ is known. However, it is standard practice to replace $\mathcal{E}_x$ by a known standard emf $\mathcal{E}_s$, and once again to adjust $R$ to the zero-current condition. This yields, assuming the current $i_0$ remains unchanged,

$$i_0 R_s = \mathcal{E}_s.$$

Combining the last two equations yields

$$\mathcal{E}_x = \mathcal{E}_s \frac{R_x}{R_s}, \tag{32–11}$$

which allows us to compare emfs with precision. Note that the internal resistance $r$ of the emf plays no role. In practice, potentiometers are conveniently packaged units, containing a *standard cell* which, after calibration at the National Bureau of Standards or elsewhere, serves as a convenient known standard seat of emf $\mathcal{E}_s$. Switching arrangements for replacing the unknown emf by the standard and arrangements for ascertaining that the current $i_0$ remains constant are also incorporated.

### 32–8   RC Circuits

The preceding sections dealt with circuits in which the circuit elements were resistors and in which the currents did not vary with time. Here we introduce the capacitor as a circuit element, which will lead us to the concept of time-varying currents. In Fig. 32–10 let switch $S$ be thrown to position $a$. What current is set up in the single-loop circuit so formed? Let us apply conservation of energy principles.

In time $dt$ a charge $dq$ $(= i\,dt)$ moves through any cross section of the circuit. The work done by the seat of emf $(= \mathcal{E}\,dq$; see Eq. 32–1) must equal the energy that appears as Joule heat in the resistor during time

Fig. 32-10   An RC circuit.

$dt$ ($= i^2R\,dt$) plus the increase in the amount of energy $U$ that is stored in the capacitor [$= dU = d(q^2/2C)$; see Eq. 30–25]. In equation form

$$\varepsilon\,dq = i^2R\,dt + d\left(\frac{q^2}{2C}\right)$$

or
$$\varepsilon\,dq = i^2R\,dt + \frac{q}{C}\,dq.$$

Dividing by $dt$ yields

$$\varepsilon\frac{dq}{dt} = i^2R + \frac{q}{C}\frac{dq}{dt}.$$

But $dq/dt$ is simply $i$, so that this equation becomes

$$\varepsilon = iR + \frac{q}{C}. \tag{32–12}$$

This equation also follows from the loop theorem, as it must, since the loop theorem was derived from the conservation of energy principle. Starting from point $x$ and traversing the circuit clockwise, we experience an increase in potential in going through the seat of emf and decreases in potential in traversing the resistor and the capacitor, or

$$\varepsilon - iR - \frac{q}{C} = 0,$$

which is identical with Eq. 32–12.

We cannot immediately solve Eq. 32–12 because it contains two variables, $q$ and $i$, which, however, are related by

$$i = \frac{dq}{dt}. \tag{32–13}$$

Substituting for $i$ into Eq. 32–12 gives

$$\varepsilon = R\frac{dq}{dt} + \frac{q}{C}. \tag{32–14}$$

Our task now is to find the function $q(t)$ that satisfies this *differential equation*. Although this particular equation is not difficult to solve, we choose to avoid mathematical complexity by simply presenting the solution, which is

$$q = C\varepsilon(1 - e^{-t/RC}). \tag{32–15}$$

We can easily test whether this function $q(t)$ is really a solution of Eq. 32–14 by substituting it into that equation and seeing whether an identity results. Differentiating Eq. 32–15 with respect to time yields

$$\frac{dq}{dt}(= i) = \frac{\varepsilon}{R}e^{-t/RC}. \tag{32–16}$$

Substituting $q$ (Eq. 32–15) and $dq/dt$ (Eq. 32–16) into Eq. 32–14 yields an identity, as the student should verify. Thus Eq. 32–15 is a solution of Eq. 32–14.

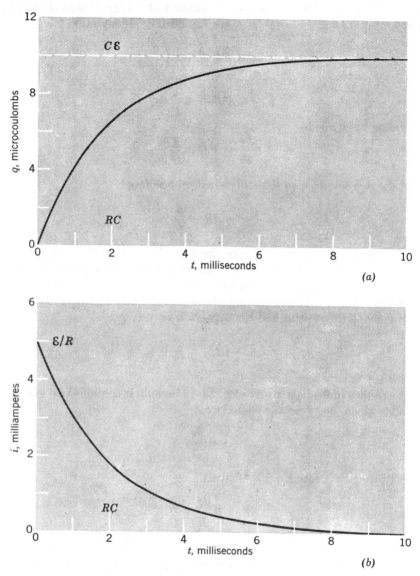

**Fig. 32–11** If, in Fig. 32–10, we assume that $R = 2000$ ohms, $C = 1.0$ $\mu$f, and $\varepsilon = 10$ volts, then (a) shows the variation of $q$ with $t$ during the charging process and (b) the variations of $i$ with $t$. The time constant is $RC = 2.0 \times 10^{-3}$ sec.

Figure 32–11 shows some plots of Eqs. 32–15 and 32–16 for a particular case. Study of these plots and of the corresponding equations shows that (a) at $t = 0$, $q = 0$ and $i = \varepsilon/R$, and (b) as $t \to \infty$, $q \to C\varepsilon$ and $i \to 0$: that is, the current is initially $\varepsilon/R$ and finally zero; the charge on the capacitor plates is initially zero and finally $C\varepsilon$.

The quantity $RC$ in Eqs. 32–15 and 32–16 has the dimensions of time (since the exponent must be dimensionless) and is called the *capacitative time constant* of the circuit. It is the time at which the charge on the capacitor has increased to within a factor of $(1 - e^{-1})$ ($= 63\%$) of its equilibrium value. To show this, we put $t = RC$ in Eq. 32–15 to obtain

$$q = C\mathcal{E}(1 - e^{-1}) = 0.63 C\mathcal{E}.$$

Since $C\mathcal{E}$ is the equilibrium charge on the capacitor, corresponding to $t \to \infty$, the foregoing statement follows.

▶ **Example 5.** After how many time constants will the energy stored in the capacitor in Fig. 32–10 reach one-half its equilibrium value?

The energy is given by Eq. 30–25, or

$$U = \frac{1}{2C}\, q^2,$$

the equilibrium energy $U_\infty$ being $(1/2C)(C\mathcal{E})^2$. From Eq. 32–15, we can write the energy as

$$U = \frac{1}{2C}(C\mathcal{E})^2(1 - e^{-t/RC})^2$$

or                    $$U = U_\infty(1 - e^{-t/RC})^2.$$

Putting $U = \tfrac{1}{2}U_\infty$ yields

$$\tfrac{1}{2} = (1 - e^{-t/RC})^2$$

and solving this relation for $t$ yields finally

$$t = 1.22\, RC = 1.22 \text{ time constants.} \qquad ◀$$

Figure 32–11 shows that if a resistance is included in the circuit the rate of increase of the charge of a capacitor toward its final equilibrium value is *delayed* in a way measured by the time constant $RC$. With no resistor present ($RC = 0$), the charge would rise immediately to its equilibrium value. Although we have shown that this time delay follows from an application of the loop theorem to $RC$ circuits, it is important that the student develop a physical understanding of the causes of the delay.

When switch $S$ in Fig. 32–10 is closed on $a$, the resistor experiences instantaneously an applied potential difference of $\mathcal{E}$, and an initial current of $\mathcal{E}/R$ is set up. Initially, the capacitor experiences no potential difference because its initial charge is zero, the potential difference always being given by $q/C$. The flow of charge through the resistor starts to charge the capacitor, which has several effects. First, the existence of a capacitor charge means that there must now be a potential difference ($= q/C$) across the capacitor; this, in turn, means that the potential difference across the resistor must decrease by this amount, since the sum of the two potential differences must always equal $\mathcal{E}$. This decrease in the potential difference across $R$ means that the charging current is reduced. Thus the charge of the capacitor builds up and the charging current decreases until the capacitor is fully charged. At this point the full emf $\mathcal{E}$ is applied to the capacitor, there being no potential drop ($i = 0$) across the resistor. This is precisely the reverse of the initial situation. The student should review the derivations of Eqs. 32–15 and 32–16 and should study Fig. 32–11 with the qualitative arguments of this paragraph in mind.

Assume now that the switch $S$ in Fig. 32–10 has been in position $a$ for a time $t$ such that $t \gg RC$. The capacitor is then fully charged for all practical purposes. The switch $S$ is then thrown to position $b$. How do the charge of the capacitor and the current vary with time?

With the switch $S$ closed on $b$, there is no emf in the circuit and Eq. 32–12 for the circuit, with $\mathcal{E} = 0$, becomes simply

$$iR + \frac{q}{C} = 0. \tag{32–17}$$

Putting $i = dq/dt$ allows us to write, as the differential equation of the circuit (compare Eq. 32–14),

$$R\frac{dq}{dt} + \frac{q}{C} = 0. \tag{32–18a}$$

The solution is

$$q = q_0 e^{-t/RC}, \tag{32–18b}$$

as the student may readily verify by substitution, $q_0$ being the initial charge on the capacitor. The capacitative time constant $RC$ appears in this expression for capacitor discharge as well as in that for the charging process (Eq. 32–15). We see that at a time such that $t = RC$ the capacitor charge is reduced to $q_0 e^{-1}$, which is 37% of the initial charge $q_0$.

The current during discharge follows from differentiating Eq. 32–18b, or

$$i = \frac{dq}{dt} = -\frac{q_0}{RC} e^{-t/RC}. \tag{32–19}$$

The negative sign shows that the current is in the direction opposite to that shown in Fig. 32–10. This is as it should be, since the capacitor is discharging rather than charging. Since $q_0 = C\mathcal{E}$, we can write Eq. 32–19 as

$$i = -\frac{\mathcal{E}}{R} e^{-t/RC},$$

in which $\mathcal{E}/R$ appears as the initial current, corresponding to $t = 0$. This is reasonable because the initial potential difference for the fully charged capacitor is $\mathcal{E}$.

The behavior of the $RC$ circuit of Fig. 32–10 during charge and discharge can be studied with a cathode-ray oscilloscope. This familiar laboratory device can display on its fluorescent screen plots of the variation of potential with time. Figure 32–12 shows the circuit of Fig. 32–10 with connections made to display (a) the potential difference $V_C$ across the capacitor and (b) the potential difference $V_R$ across the resistor as functions of time. $V_C$ and $V_R$ are given by

$$V_C = \left(\frac{1}{C}\right) q$$

and

$$V_R = (R)i,$$

the former being proportional to the charge and the latter to the current.

Figure 32–13 shows oscillograph plots of $V_C$ and $V_R$ that result when, in effect, switch $S$ in Fig. 32–10 is thrown regularly back and forth between positions $a$ and $b$, being left in each position for a time equal to several time constants. Intervals during which the charge is building up are labeled $ch$ and those during which it is decaying are labeled $dis$.

**Fig. 32–12** The circuit of Fig. 32–10 with connections made to display the potential variations across the resistor and the capacitor on a cathode ray oscilloscope.

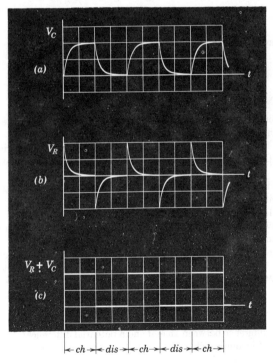

**Fig. 32–13** In Fig. 32–10 switch $S$ is thrown periodically, by electronic means, between positions $a$ and $b$. The variations with time of the potential differences across $(a)$ the capacitor, and $(b)$ the resistor are shown, as displayed on a cathode ray oscilloscope. $(c)$ The appearance of the screen when the oscilloscope is connected to display the sum of $V_R$ and $V_C$. (Courtesy E. K. Hege, Rensselaer Polytechnic Institute.)

The "charge" intervals in plot $a$ (see Eq. 32–15) are represented by

$$V = \left(\frac{1}{C}\right) q = \mathcal{E}(1 - e^{-t/RC})$$

and the "discharge" intervals (see Eq. 32–18$b$) by

$$V = \left(\frac{1}{C}\right) q = \mathcal{E}e^{-t/RC}.$$

Note that the current, as indicated by plot $b$, is in opposite directions during the charge and discharge intervals, in agreement with Eqs. 32–16 and 32–19.

In plot $c$ in Fig. 32–13 the oscillograph has been connected to show the algebraic sum of plots $a$ and $b$. According to the loop theorem this sum should equal $\mathcal{E}$ during the charge intervals and should be zero during the discharge intervals, when the battery is no longer in the circuit, that is,

$$V_R + V_C = \mathcal{E} \text{ during charge (see Eq. 32–12)}$$

$$V_R + V_C = 0 \text{ during discharge (see Eq. 32–17).}$$

Plot $c$ is in exact agreement with this expectation.

## QUESTIONS

1. Does the direction of the emf provided by a battery depend on the direction of current flow through the battery?

2. Figure 32–1$b$ shows a gravitational analog of a single-loop electric circuit. Is the source of "gravitational emf" in this figure reversible as far as energy exchanges are concerned?

3. Discuss in detail the statement that the energy method and the loop theorem method for solving circuits are perfectly equivalent.

4. It is possible to generate a 10,000-volt potential difference by rubbing a pocket comb with wool. Why is this large voltage not dangerous when the much lower voltage provided by an ordinary electric outlet is very dangerous?

5. Devise a method for measuring the emf and the internal resistance of a battery.

6. A 25-watt, 110-volt bulb glows at normal brightness when connected across a bank of batteries. A 500-watt, 110-volt bulb glows only dimly when connected across the same bank. Explain.

7. Under what circumstances can the terminal potential difference of a battery exceed its emf?

8. What is the difference between an emf and a potential difference?

9. In the flow of incompressible fluids, what are the analogies to ($a$) the loop theorem and ($b$) the junction theorem?

10. Compare and contrast the formulas for the effective values of ($a$) capacitors and ($b$) resistors, in series and in parallel.

11. Does the time required for the charge on a capacitor in an $RC$ circuit to build up to a given fraction of its equilibrium value depend on the value of the applied emf?

12. Devise a method whereby an $RC$ circuit can be used to measure very high resistances.

# PROBLEMS

1. A 5.0-amp current is set up in an external circuit by a 6.0-volt storage battery for 6.0 min. By how much is the chemical energy of the battery reduced?

2. The current in a simple series circuit is 5 amp. When an additional resistance of 2 ohms is inserted, the current drops to 4 amp. What was the resistance of the original circuit?

3. In Example 2 an ammeter whose resistance is 0.05 ohm is inserted in the circuit. What per cent change in the current results because of the presence of the meter?

4. In Fig. 32–3a put $\varepsilon$ = 2.0 volts and $r$ = 100 ohms. Plot (a) the current, and (b) the potential difference across $R$, as functions of $R$ over the range 0 to 500 ohms. Make both plots on the same graph. (c) Make a third plot by multiplying together, for each value of $R$, the two curves plotted. What is the physical significance of this plot?

5. (a) In the circuit of Fig. 32–3a show that the power delivered to $R$ as Joule heat is a maximum when $R$ is equal to the internal resistance $r$ of the battery. (b) Show that this maximum power is $P = \varepsilon^2/4r$.

6. Heat is to be generated in a 0.10-ohm resistor at the rate of 10 watts by connecting it to a battery whose emf is 1.5 volts. (a) What is the internal resistance of the battery? (b) What potential difference exists across the resistor?

7. (a) In Fig. 32–14 what value must $R$ have if the current in the circuit is to be 0.001 amp? Take $\varepsilon_1$ = 2.0 volts, $\varepsilon_2$ = 3.0 volts, and $r_1 = r_2 = 3.0$ ohms. (b) What is the rate of Joule heating in $R$?

8. A wire of resistance 5.0 ohms is connected to a battery whose emf $\varepsilon$ is 2.0 volts and whose internal resistance is 1.0 ohm. In 2.0 min (a) how much energy is transferred from chemical to electric form? (b) How much energy appears in the wire as Joule heat? (c) Account for the difference between (a) and (b).

**Fig. 32–14**

9. In Fig. 32–6 calculate the potential difference between points $c$ and $d$ by as many paths as possible. Assume that $\varepsilon_1$ = 4.0 volts, $\varepsilon_2$ = 1.0 volt, $R_1 = R_2 = 10$ ohms, and $R_3 = 5$ ohms.

10. In Fig. 32–5 calculate the potential difference between $a$ and $c$ by considering a path that contains $R$ and $\varepsilon_2$.

11. (a) In Fig. 32–15 what is the equivalent resistance of the network shown? (b) What are the currents in each resistor? Put $R_1$ = 100 ohms, $R_2 = R_3 = 50$ ohms, $R_4 = 75$ ohms, and $\varepsilon$ = 6.0 volts.

**Fig. 32–15**

**Fig. 32–16**

12. In Fig. 32–16 imagine an ammeter inserted in the branch containing $R_3$. (a) What will it read, assuming $\varepsilon$ = 5.0 volts, $R_1$ = 2.0 ohms, $R_2$ = 4.0 ohms, and $R_3$ = 6.0 ohms? (b) The ammeter and the source of emf are now physically interchanged. Show that the

ammeter reading remains unchanged. This reciprocity relationship holds for any circuit that contains only one source of emf.

13. Two batteries of emf $\mathcal{E}$ and internal resistance $r$ are connected in parallel across a resistor $R$ as in Fig. 32–20$b$. ($a$) For what value of $R$ is the power delivered to the resistor a maximum? ($b$) What is the maximum power?

14. By using only two resistance coils—singly, in series, or in parallel—a student is able to obtain resistances of 3, 4, 12, and 16 ohms. What are the separate resistances of the coils?

15. *The Wheatstone bridge.* In Fig. 32–17 $R_s$ is to be adjusted in value until points $a$ and $b$ are brought to exactly the same potential. (One tests for this condition by momentarily connecting a sensitive meter between $a$ and $b$; if these points are at the same potential, the meter will not deflect.) Show that when this adjustment is made the following relation holds:

$$R_x = R_s \frac{R_2}{R_1}.$$

Unknown resistors ($R_x$) can be measured in terms of standards ($R_s$) using this device, which is called a Wheatstone bridge.

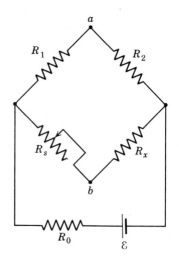

**Fig. 32–17**

16. If points $a$ and $b$ in Fig. 32–17 are connected by a wire of resistance $r$, show that the current in the wire is

$$i = \frac{\mathcal{E}(R_s - R_x)}{(R + 2r)(R_s + R_x) + 2R_s R_x},$$

where $\mathcal{E}$ is the emf of the battery. Assume that $R_1$ and $R_2$ are equal ($R_1 = R_2 = R$) and that $R_0$ equals zero. Is this formula consistent with the result of Problem 15?

17. Two resistors, $R_1$ and $R_2$, may be connected either in series or parallel across a (resistanceless) battery with emf $\mathcal{E}$. We desire the Joule heating for the parallel combination to be five times that for the series combination. If $R_1$ equals 100 ohms, what is $R_2$?

18. Four 100-watt heating coils are to be connected in all possible series-parallel combinations and plugged into a 100-volt line. What different rates of heat dissipation are possible?

19. What is the equivalent resistance between the terminal points $x$ and $y$ of the circuits shown in ($a$) Fig. 32–18$a$, ($b$) Fig. 32–18$b$, and ($c$) Fig. 32–18$c$? Assume that the resistance of each resistor is 10 ohms.

*(a)*            *(b)*            *(c)*

**Fig. 32-18**

20. In Fig. 32–19 find the current in each resistor and the potential difference between $a$ and $b$. Put $\mathcal{E}_1 = 6.0$ volts, $\mathcal{E}_2 = 5.0$ volts, $\mathcal{E}_3 = 4.0$ volts, $R_1 = 100$ ohms, and $R_2 = 50$ ohms.

**Fig. 32-19**            **Fig. 32-20**

21. You are given two batteries of emf $\mathcal{E}$ and internal resistance $r$. They may be connected either in series or in parallel and are used to establish a current in a resistor $R$, as in Fig. 32–20. Derive expressions for the current in $R$ for both methods of connection. Which connection yields the larger current if $(a)$ $R > r$ and if $(b)$ $R < r$?

22. $(a)$ In Fig. 32–21 what power appears as Joule heat in $R_1$? In $R_2$? In $R_3$? $(b)$ What power is supplied by $\mathcal{E}_1$? By $\mathcal{E}_2$? $(c)$ Discuss the energy balance in this circuit. Assume that $\mathcal{E}_1 = 3.0$ volts, $\mathcal{E}_2 = 1.0$ volt, $R_1 = 5.0$ ohms, $R_2 = 2.0$ ohms, and $R_3 = 4.0$ ohms.

**Fig. 32-21**

**23.** For manual control of the current in a circuit, a student uses a parallel combination of variable resistors of the sliding contact type, as in Fig. 32–22, with $R_1 = 20R_2$. (a) What procedure is used to adjust the current to the desired value? (b) Why is the parallel combination better than a single-variable resistor?

**Fig. 32-22**

**24.** *Resistance measurement.* A voltmeter (resistance $R_V$) and an ammeter (resistance $R_A$) are connected to measure a resistance $R$, as in Fig. 32–23a. The resistance is given by $R = V/i$, where $V$ is the voltmeter reading and $i$ is the current *in the resistor R*. Some of the current registered by the ammeter ($i'$) goes through the voltmeter so that the ratio of the meter readings ($= V/i'$) gives only an *apparent* resistance reading $R'$. Show that $R$ and $R'$ are related by

$$\frac{1}{R} = \frac{1}{R'} - \frac{1}{R_V}.$$

Note that if $R_V \gg R$, then $R \cong R'$.

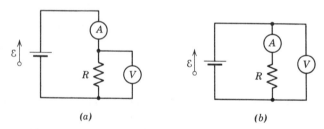

(a)                    (b)

**Fig. 32-23**

**25.** *Resistance measurement.* If meters are used to measure resistance, they may also be connected as they are in Fig. 32–23b. Again the ratio of the meter readings gives only an apparent resistance reading $R'$. Show that $R'$ is related to $R$ by

$$R = R' - R_A,$$

in which $R_A$ is the ammeter resistance. Note that if $R_A \ll R$, then $R \cong R'$.

**26.** In Fig. 32–8 assume that $\mathcal{E} = 5.0$ volts, $r = 2.0$ ohms, $R_1 = 5.0$ ohms, and $R_2 = 4.0$ ohms. If $R_A = 0.10$ ohm, what per cent error is made in reading the current? Assume that the voltmeter is not present.

**27.** In Fig. 32–8 assume that $\mathcal{E} = 5.0$ volts, $r = 20$ ohms, $R_1 = 50$ ohms, and $R_2 = 40$ ohms. If $R_v = 1000$ ohms, what per cent error is made in reading the potential differences across $R_1$? Ignore the presence of the ammeter.

28. (a) Find the three currents in Fig. 32–24. (b) Find $V_{ab}$. Assume that $R_1 = 1.0$ ohm, $R_2 = 2.0$ ohms, $\mathcal{E}_1 = 2.0$ volts, and $\mathcal{E}_2 = \mathcal{E}_3 = 4.0$ volts.

**Fig. 32–24**

29. How many time constants must elapse before a capacitor in an $RC$ circuit is charged to within 1.0 per cent of its equilibrium charge?

30. In the circuit of Fig. 32–25 let $i_1$, $i_2$, and $i_3$ be the currents through resistors $R_1$, $R_2$, and $R_3$, respectively, and let $V_1$, $V_2$, $V_3$, and $V_C$ be the corresponding potential differences across the resistors and across the capacitor $C$. (a) Plot qualitatively as a function of time after switch $S$ is closed the currents and voltages listed above. (b) After being closed for a large number of time constants, the switch $S$ is now opened. Plot qualitatively as a function of time after the switch is opened the currents and voltages listed above.

**Fig. 32–25**

31. Show that the units of $RC$ are indeed time units, that is, that 1 ohm $\times$ 1 farad $= 1$ sec.

32. Prove that when switch $S$ in Fig. 32–10 is thrown from $a$ to $b$ all the energy stored in the capacitor is transformed into Joule heat in the resistor. Assume that the capacitor is fully charged before the switch is thrown.

33. A $3.0 \times 10^6$-ohm resistor and a $1.0$-$\mu$f capacitor are connected in a single-loop circuit with a seat of emf with $\mathcal{E} = 4.0$ volts. At $1.0$ sec after the connection is made, what are the rates at which (a) the charge of the capacitor is increasing, (b) energy is being stored in the capacitor, (c) Joule heat is appearing in the resistor, and (d) energy is being delivered by the seat of emf?

# The Magnetic Field

## CHAPTER 33

### 33-1  The Magnetic Field

The science of magnetism grew from the observation that certain "stones" (magnetite) would attract bits of iron. The word *magnetism* comes from the district of Magnesia in Asia Minor, which is one of the places at which the stones were found. Figure 33–1 shows a modern permanent magnet, the lineal descendant of these natural magnets. Another "natural magnet" is the earth itself, whose orienting action on a magnetic compass needle has been known since ancient times.

In 1820 Oersted first discovered that a current in a wire can also produce magnetic effects, namely, that it can change the orientation of a compass needle. We pointed out in Section 26–1 how this important discovery linked the then separate sciences of magnetism and electricity. The magnetic ef-

**Fig. 33-1**  A permanent magnet. Lines of magnetic induction leave the north pole face, marked N, and enter the south pole face on the other side of the air gap.

**Fig. 33-2** A research-type electromagnet showing iron frame $F$, pole faces $P$, and coils $C$. The pole faces are 12 in. in diameter. (Courtesy Varian Associates.)

fect of a current in a wire can be intensified by forming the wire into a coil of many turns and by providing an iron core. Figure 33-2 shows how this is done in a large electromagnet of a type commonly used for research involving magnetism.

We define the space around a magnet or a current-carrying conductor as the site of a *magnetic field*, just as we defined the space near a charged rod as the site of an electric field. The basic magnetic field vector **B**, which we define in the following section, is called the *magnetic induction:* * it can be represented by *lines of induction*, just as the electric field was represented by lines of force. As for the electric field (see Section 27-3), the magnetic field vector is related to its lines of induction in this way:

1. The tangent to a line of induction at any point gives the *direction* of **B** at that point.

2. The lines of induction are drawn so that the number of lines per unit cross-sectional area is proportional to the *magnitude* of the magnetic field vector **B**. Where the lines are close together $B$ is large and where they are far apart $B$ is small.

As for the electric field, the field vector **B** is of fundamental importance, the lines of induction simply giving a graphic representation of the way **B** varies throughout a certain region of space.

The *flux* $\Phi_B$ for a magnetic field can be defined in exact analogy with the flux $\Phi_E$ for the electric field, namely

$$\Phi_B = \int \mathbf{B} \cdot d\mathbf{S}, \qquad (33\text{-}1)$$

in which the integral is taken over the surface (closed or open) for which $\Phi_B$ is defined.

---

* *Magnetic field strength* would be a more suitable name for **B**, but it has been usurped for historical reasons by another vector connected with the magnetic field (see Section 37-7).

## 33–2 The Definition of B

This chapter is not concerned with the *causes* of the magnetic field; we seek to determine (a) whether a magnetic field exists at a given point and (b) the action of this field on charges moving through it. As for the electric field, a particle of charge $q_0$ serves as a test body. We assume that there is no electric field present, which means that, neglecting gravity, no force will act on the test body if it is placed *at rest* at the point in question.

Let us fire a positive test charge with arbitrary velocity **v** through a point *P*. *If a sideways deflecting force* **F** *acts on it, we assert that a magnetic field is present at P* and we define the magnetic induction **B** of this field in terms of **F** and other measured quantities.

If we vary the direction of **v** through point *P*, keeping the magnitude of **v** unchanged, we find, in general, that although **F** will always remain at right angles to **v** its magnitude *F* will change. For a particular orientation of **v** (and also for the opposite orientation −**v**) the force **F** becomes zero. We define this direction as the direction of **B**, the specification of the sense of **B** (that is, the way it points along this line) being left to the more complete definition of **B** that we give below.

Having found the *direction* of **B**, we are now able to orient **v** so that the test charge moves at right angles to **B**. We will find that the force **F** is now a maximum, and we define the *magnitude* of **B** from the measured magnitude of this maximum force $F_\perp$, or

$$B = \frac{F_\perp}{q_0 v}. \tag{33–2}$$

Let us regard this definition of **B** (in which we have specified its magnitude and direction, but not its sense) as preliminary to the complete vector definition that we now give: *If a positive test charge $q_0$ is fired with velocity* **v** *through a point P and if a (sideways) force* **F** *acts on the moving charge, a magnetic induction* **B** *is present at point P, where* **B** *is the vector that satisfies the relation*

$$\mathbf{F} = q_0 \mathbf{v} \times \mathbf{B}, \tag{33–3a}$$

**v**, $q_0$, and **F** being measured quantities. The magnitude of the magnetic deflecting force **F**, according to the rules for vector products, is given by *

$$F = q_0 v B \sin\theta, \tag{33–3b}$$

in which $\theta$ is the angle between **v** and **B**.

Figure 33–3 shows the relations among the vectors. We see that **F**, being at right angles to the plane formed by **v** and **B**, will always be at right angles to **v** (and also to **B**) and thus will always be a sideways force. Equation 33–3a is consistent with the observed facts that (a) the magnetic force vanishes as $v \to 0$, (b) the magnetic force vanishes if **v** is either parallel or antiparallel to the direction of **B** (in these cases $\theta = 0$ or $180°$ and $\mathbf{v} \times \mathbf{B} = 0$), and (c) if **v** is at right angles to **B** ($\theta = 90°$), the deflecting force has its maximum value, given by Eq. 33–2, that is, $F_\perp = q_0 v B$.

---

* The student may wish to review Section 2–4, which deals with vector products.

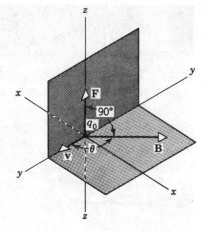

**Fig. 33-3** Illustrating $\mathbf{F} = q_0\mathbf{v} \times \mathbf{B}$   (Eq. 33-3a).

This definition of **B** is similar in spirit, although more complex, than the definition of the electric field strength **E**, which we can cast into this form: *If a positive test charge $q_0$ is placed at point P and if an (electric) force **F** acts on the stationary charge, an electric field **E** is present at P, where **E** is the vector satisfying the relation*

$$\mathbf{F} = q_0\mathbf{E},$$

$q_0$ and **F** being measured quantities. In defining **E**, the only characteristic direction to appear is that of the electric force $\mathbf{F}_E$ which acts on the positive test body; the direction of **E** is taken to be that of $\mathbf{F}_E$. In defining **B**, *two* characteristic directions appear, those of **v** and of the magnetic force $\mathbf{F}_B$; they prove always to be at right angles.

In Fig. 33-4 a positive and a negative electron are created at point $P$ in a bubble chamber. A magnetic field is perpendicular to the chamber, pointing out of the plane of the figure (symbol $\odot$).* The relation $\mathbf{F} = q_0\mathbf{v} \times \mathbf{B}$ (Eq. 33-3a) shows that the deflecting forces acting on the two particles are as indicated in the figure. These deflecting forces would make the tracks deflect as shown.

The unit of **B** that follows from Eq. 33-3 is the (nt/coul)/(meter/sec). This is given the special name weber/meter$^2$, or tesla. Recalling that a coul/sec is an ampere,

$$1 \text{ weber/meter}^2 = \frac{1 \text{ nt}}{\text{coul (meter/sec)}} = \frac{1 \text{ nt}}{\text{amp-m}}.$$

An earlier unit for **B**, still in common use, is the *gauss;* the relationship is

$$1 \text{ weber/meter}^2 = 10^4 \text{ gauss}.$$

The *weber* is used to measure $\Phi_B$, the flux of **B**; see Eq. 33-1.

The fact that the magnetic force is always at right angles to the direction of motion means that (for steady magnetic fields) the work done by this

---

* The symbol $\otimes$ indicates a vector into the page, the $\times$ being thought of as the tail of an arrow; the symbol $\odot$ indicates a vector out of the page, the dot being thought of as the tip of an arrow.

**Fig. 33–4** A *bubble chamber* is a device for rendering visible, by means of small bubbles, the tracks of charged particles that pass through the chamber. The figure is a photograph taken with such a chamber immersed in a field of magnetic induction $B$ and exposed to radiations from a large cyclotron-like accelerator. The curved $V$ at point $P$ is formed by a positive and a negative electron, which deflect in opposite directions in the magnetic field. The spirals $S$ are the tracks of three low-energy electrons. (Courtesy E. O. Lawrence Radiation Laboratory, University of California.)

force on the particle is zero. For an element of the path of the particle of length $dl$, this work $dW$ is $\mathbf{F}_B \cdot d\mathbf{l}$; $dW$ is zero because $\mathbf{F}_B$ and $d\mathbf{l}$ are always at right angles. Thus a static magnetic field cannot change the kinetic energy of a moving charge; it can only deflect it sideways.

If a charged particle moves through a region in which both an electric field and a magnetic field are present, the resultant force is found by combining Eqs. 27–2 and 33–3a, or

$$\mathbf{F} = q_0\mathbf{E} + q_0\mathbf{v} \times \mathbf{B}. \tag{33–4}$$

This is sometimes called the *Lorentz relation* in tribute to H. A. Lorentz who did so much to develop and clarify the concepts of the electric and magnetic fields.

▶ **Example 1.** A uniform field of magnetic induction **B** points horizontally from south to north; its magnitude is 1.5 webers/meter². If a 5.0-Mev proton moves vertically downward through this field, what force will act on it?

The kinetic energy of the proton is

$$K = (5.0 \times 10^6 \text{ ev})(1.6 \times 10^{-19} \text{ joule/ev}) = 8.0 \times 10^{-13} \text{ joule.}$$

Its speed can be found from the relation $K = \frac{1}{2}mv^2$, or

$$v = \sqrt{\frac{2K}{m}} = \sqrt{\frac{(2)(8.0 \times 10^{-13} \text{ joule})}{1.7 \times 10^{-27} \text{ kg}}} = 3.1 \times 10^7 \text{ meters/sec.}$$

Equation 33-3b gives

$$F = qvB \sin \theta = (1.6 \times 10^{-19} \text{ coul})(3.1 \times 10^7 \text{ meters/sec})(1.5 \text{ webers/meter}^2)(\sin 90°)$$

$$= 7.4 \times 10^{-12} \text{ nt.}$$

The student can show that this force is about $4 \times 10^{14}$ times greater than the weight of the proton.

The relation $\mathbf{F} = q\mathbf{v} \times \mathbf{B}$ shows that the *direction* of the deflecting force is to the east. If the particle had been negatively charged, the deflection would have been to the west. This is predicted automatically by Eq. 33-3a if we substitute $-e$ for $q_0$. ◀

## 33-3  Magnetic Force on a Current

A current is an assembly of moving charges. Because a magnetic field exerts a sideways force on a moving charge, we expect that it will also exert a sideways force on a wire carrying a current. Figure 33-5 shows a length $l$ of wire carrying a current $i$ and placed in a field of magnetic induction **B**. For simplicity we have oriented the wire so that the current density vector **j** is at right angles to **B**.

The current $i$ in a metal wire is carried by the free (or conduction) electrons, $n$ being the number of such electrons per unit volume of the wire. The magnitude of the average force on one such electron is given by Eq. 33-3b, or, since $\theta = 90°$,

$$F' = q_0 v B \sin \theta = e v_d B$$

where $v_d$ is the drift speed. From the relation $v_d = j/ne$ (Eq. 31-5),

$$F' = e\left(\frac{j}{ne}\right)B = \frac{jB}{n}.$$

**Fig. 33-5** A wire carrying a current $i$ is placed at right angles to a field of magnetic induction **B**.

The length $l$ of the wire contains $nAl$ free electrons, $Al$ being the volume of the section of wire of cross section $A$ that we are considering. The total force on the free electrons in the wire, and thus on the wire itself, is

$$F = (nAl)F' = nAl\frac{jB}{n}.$$

Since $jA$ is the current $i$ in the wire, we have

$$F = ilB. \tag{33-5}$$

The negative charges, which move to the right in the wire of Fig. 33-5, are equivalent to positive charges moving to the left, that is, in the direction of the current arrow. For such a positive charge the velocity $\mathbf{v}$ would point to the left and the force on the wire, given by Eq. 33-3$a$ ($\mathbf{F} = q_0\mathbf{v} \times \mathbf{B}$) points up, out of the page. This same conclusion follows if we consider the actual negative charge carriers for which $\mathbf{v}$ points to the right but $q_0$ has a negative sign. Thus by measuring the sideways magnetic force on a wire carrying a current and placed in a magnetic field we cannot tell whether the current carriers are negative charges moving in a given direction or positive charges moving in the opposite direction.

Equation 33-5 holds only if the wire is at right angles to $\mathbf{B}$. We can express the more general situation in vector form as

$$\mathbf{F} = i\mathbf{l} \times \mathbf{B}, \tag{33-6a}$$

where $\mathbf{l}$ is a (displacement) vector that points along the (straight) wire in the direction of the current. Equation 33-6$a$ is equivalent to the relation $\mathbf{F} = q_0\mathbf{v} \times \mathbf{B}$ (Eq. 33-3$a$); either can be taken as a defining equation for $\mathbf{B}$. The student should note that the vector $\mathbf{l}$ in Fig. 33-5 points to the left and that the magnetic force $\mathbf{F}$ ($= i\mathbf{l} \times \mathbf{B}$) points up, out of the page. This agrees with the conclusion obtained by analyzing the forces that act on the individual charge carriers.

If we consider a differential element of a conductor of length $d\mathbf{l}$, the force $d\mathbf{F}$ acting on it can be found, by analogy with Eq. 33-6$a$, from

$$d\mathbf{F} = i\,d\mathbf{l} \times \mathbf{B}. \tag{33-6b}$$

By integrating this formula in an appropriate way we can find the force $\mathbf{F}$ on a nonlinear conductor.

▶ **Example 2.** A wire bent as shown in Fig. 33-6 carries a current $i$ and is placed in a uniform field of magnetic induction $\mathbf{B}$ that emerges from the plane of the figure. Calculate the force acting on the wire. The magnetic field is represented by lines of induction, shown emerging from the page. The dots show that the sense of $\mathbf{B}$ is up, out of the page.

The force on each straight section, from Eq. 33-6$a$, has the magnitude

$$F_1 = F_3 = ilB$$

and points down as shown by the arrows in the figure.

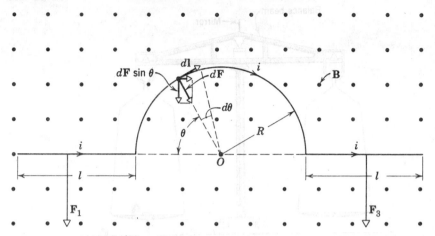

**Fig. 33–6**  Example 2.

A segment of wire of length $dl$ on the arc has a force $d\mathbf{F}$ on it whose magnitude is

$$dF = iB\,dl = iB(R\,d\theta)$$

and whose direction is radially toward $O$, the center of the arc. Only the downward component of this force is effective, the horizontal component being canceled by an oppositely directed component associated with the corresponding arc segment on the other side of $O$. Thus the total force on the semicircle of wire about $O$ points down and is

$$F_2 = \int_0^\pi dF \sin\theta = \int_0^\pi (iBR\,d\theta)\sin\theta = iBR\int_0^\pi \sin\theta\,d\theta = 2iBR.$$

The resultant force on the whole wire is

$$F = F_1 + F_2 + F_3 = 2ilB + 2iBR = 2iB(l + R).$$

Notice that this force is the same as that acting on a straight wire of length $2l + 2R$.
◀

Figure 33–7 shows the arrangement used by Thomas, Driscoll, and Hipple at the National Bureau of Standards to measure the magnetic induction provided by a laboratory magnet such as that of Fig. 33–2. The rectangle is a coil of nine turns whose width $a$ and length $b$ are about 10 cm and 70 cm, respectively. The lower end of the coil is placed in the field of magnetic induction $\mathbf{B}$ and the upper end is hung from the arm of a balance; $\mathbf{B}$ enters the plane of the figure at right angles.

An accurately known current $i$ of about 0.10 amp is set up in the coil in the direction shown, and weights are placed in the right-hand balance pan until the system is balanced. The magnetic force $\mathbf{F}$ ($= i\mathbf{l} \times \mathbf{B}$; see Eq. 33–6a) on the bottom leg of the coil points upward, as shown in the figure. Equation 33–5 also shows that the force *on each wire* at the bottom of the coil is $iaB$. Since there are nine wires, the total force on the bottom leg of the coil is $9iaB$. The forces on the vertical sides of the coil ($= i\mathbf{l} \times \mathbf{B}$) are sideways; because they are equal and opposite, they cancel and produce no effect.

After balancing the system, the experimenters reversed the direction of the current, which changed the sign of all the magnetic forces acting on the coil. In particular, $\mathbf{F}$ then pointed downward, which caused the rest point of the balance to move. A mass

**Fig. 33-7** Apparatus used to measure **B**. The zero point of the balance is observed by means of a light beam reflected from the mirror attached to the balance beam.

$m$ of about 8.78 gm had to be added to the left balance pan to restore the original rest point. The *change* in force when the current is reversed is $2F$, and this must equal the weight added to the left balance pan, or

$$mg = 2(9iaB) = 18iaB.$$

This gives

$$B = \frac{mg}{18ai} = \frac{(8.78 \times 10^{-3} \text{ kg})(9.80 \text{ meters/sec}^2)}{(18)(0.10 \text{ meter})(0.10 \text{ amp})} = 0.48 \text{ weber/meter}^2 = 4800 \text{ gauss.}$$

The Bureau of Standards' workers made this measurement with much more care than these approximate numbers suggest. In one series of measurements, for example, they found a magnetic induction of 4697.55 gauss.

### 33-4  Torque on a Current Loop

Figure 33-8 shows a rectangular loop of wire of length $a$ and width $b$ placed in a uniform field of induction **B**, with sides 1 and 3 always normal to the field direction. The normal $nn'$ to the plane of the loop makes an angle $\theta$ with the direction of **B**.

Assume the current to be as shown in the figure. Wires must be provided to lead the current into the loop and out of it. If these wires are twisted tightly together, there will be no net magnetic force on the twisted pair because the currents in the two wires are in opposite directions. Thus the lead wires may be ignored. Also, some way of supporting the loop must be provided. Let us imagine it to be suspended from a long string attached to the loop at its center of mass. In this way the loop will be free to turn, through a small angle at least, about any axis through the center of mass.

The net force on the loop is the resultant of the forces on the four sides of the loop. On side 2 the vector $\mathbf{l}$ points in the direction of the current and has the magnitude $b$. The angle between $\mathbf{l}$ and **B** for side 2 (see Fig. 33-8$b$) is

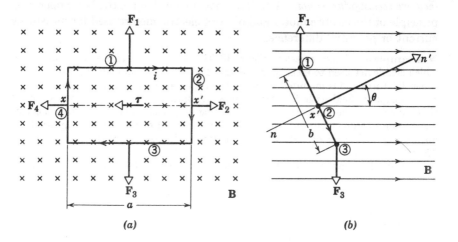

(a)    (b)

**Fig. 33-8**  A rectangular coil carrying a current $i$ is placed in a uniform external magnetic field.

$90° - \theta$. Thus the magnitude of the force on this side is

$$F_2 = ibB \sin (90° - \theta) = ibB \cos \theta.$$

From the relation $\mathbf{F} = i\mathbf{l} \times \mathbf{B}$ (Eq. 33–6a), we find the direction of $\mathbf{F}_2$ to be out of the plane of Fig. 33–8b. The student can show that the force $\mathbf{F}_4$ on side 4 has the same magnitude as $\mathbf{F}_2$ but points in the opposite direction. Thus $\mathbf{F}_2$ and $\mathbf{F}_4$, taken together, have no effect on the motion of the loop. The net force they provide is zero, and, since they have the same line of action, the net torque due to these forces is also zero.

The common magnitude of $\mathbf{F}_1$ and $\mathbf{F}_3$ is $iaB$. These forces, too, are oppositely directed so that they do not tend to move the coil bodily. As Fig. 33–8b shows, however, they do *not* have the same line of action if the coil is in the position shown; there is a net torque, which tends to rotate the coil clockwise about the line $xx'$. The coil can be supported on a rigid axis that lies along $xx'$, with no loss of its freedom of motion. This torque can be represented in Fig. 33–8b by a vector pointing into the figure at point $x'$ or in Fig. 33–8a by a vector pointing along the $xx'$ axis from right to left.

The magnitude of the torque $\tau'$ is found by calculating the torque caused by $\mathbf{F}_1$ about axis $xx'$ and doubling it, for $\mathbf{F}_3$ exerts the same torque about this axis that $\mathbf{F}_1$ does. Thus

$$\tau' = 2(iaB) \left(\frac{b}{2}\right) (\sin \theta) = iabB \sin \theta.$$

This torque acts on every turn of the coil. If there are $N$ turns, the torque on the entire coil is

$$\tau = N\tau' = NiabB \sin \theta = NiAB \sin \theta, \tag{33–7}$$

in which $A$, the area of the coil, is substituted for $ab$.

This equation can be shown to hold for *all plane loops of area $A$, whether they are rectangular or not*. A torque on a current loop is the basic operating principle of the electric motor and of most electric meters used for measuring current or potential difference.

▶ **Example 3.** *A galvanometer.* Figure 33–9 shows the rudiments of a galvanometer, which is a device used to measure currents. The coil is 2.0 cm high and 1.0 cm wide; it has 250 turns and is mounted so that it can rotate about a vertical axis in a uniform *radial* magnetic field with $B = 2000$ gauss. A spring $Sp$ provides a countertorque that cancels out the magnetic torque, resulting in a steady angular deflection $\phi$ corresponding to a given current $i$ in the coil. If a current of $1.0 \times 10^{-4}$ amp produces an angular deflection of 30°, what is the *torsional constant* $\kappa$ of the spring (see Eq. 15–21)?

Equating the magnetic torque to the torque caused by the spring (see Eq. 33–7) yields

$$\tau = NiAB \sin \theta = \kappa\phi$$

or

$$\kappa = \frac{NiAB \sin \theta}{\phi}$$

$$= \frac{(250)(1.0 \times 10^{-4}\ \text{amp})(2.0 \times 10^{-4}\ \text{meter}^2)(0.20\ \text{weber/meter}^2)(\sin 90°)}{30°}$$

$$= 3.3 \times 10^{-8}\ \text{nt-m/deg.}$$

Scale

Permanent
magnet

Coil

N          Sp          S
          Pivot

Soft-iron
core

Uniform radial
magnetic field

**Fig. 33-9** Example 3. The elements of a galvanometer, showing the coil, the helical spring $Sp$, and pointer $P$.

Note that the normal to the plane of the coil (that is, the pointer $P$) is always at right angles to the (radial) magnetic field so that $\theta = 90°$.  ◀

A current loop orienting itself in an external magnetic field reminds us of the action of a compass needle in such a field. One face of the loop behaves like the north pole of the needle; * the other face behaves like the south pole. Compass needles, bar magnets, and current loops can all be regarded as *magnetic dipoles*. We show this here for the current loop, reasoning entirely by analogy with *electric* dipoles.

A structure is called an electric dipole if (a) when placed in an *external* electric field it experiences a torque given by Eq. 27–11,

$$\tau = \mathbf{p} \times \mathbf{E}, \tag{33-8}$$

where $\mathbf{p}$ is the electric dipole moment, and (b) it sets up a field of its own at distant points, described qualitatively by the lines of force of Fig. 29–10 and quantitatively by Eq. 29–11. These two requirements are not independent; if one is fulfilled, the other follows automatically.

The magnitude of the torque described by Eq. 33–8 is

$$\tau = pE \sin \theta, \tag{33-9}$$

where $\theta$ is the angle between $\mathbf{p}$ and $\mathbf{E}$. Let us compare this with Eq. 33–7, the expression for the torque on a current loop:

$$\tau = (NiA)B \sin \theta. \tag{33-7}$$

---

* The north pole of a compass needle is the end that points toward the geographic north.

In each case the appropriate field ($E$ or $B$) appears, as does a term $\sin \theta$. Comparison suggests that $NiA$ in Eq. 33–7 can be taken as the *magnetic dipole moment* $\mu$, corresponding to $p$ in Eq. 33–9, or

$$\mu = NiA. \tag{33-10}$$

Equation 33–7 suggests that we write the torque on a current loop in vector form, in analogy with Eq. 33–8, or

$$\boldsymbol{\tau} = \boldsymbol{\mu} \times \mathbf{B}. \tag{33-11}$$

The magnetic dipole moment of the loop $\boldsymbol{\mu}$ must be taken to lie along the axis of the loop; its direction is given by the following rule: Let the fingers of the right hand curl around the loop in the direction of the current; the extended right thumb will then point in the direction of $\boldsymbol{\mu}$. The student should check carefully that, if $\boldsymbol{\mu}$ is defined by this rule and Eq. 33–10, Eq. 33–11 correctly describes in every detail the torque acting on a current loop in an external field (see Fig. 33–8).

Since a torque acts on a current loop, or other magnetic dipole, when it is placed in an external magnetic field, it follows that work (positive or negative) must be done by an external agent to change the orientation of such a dipole. Thus a magnetic dipole has *potential energy* associated with its orientation in an external magnetic field. This energy may be taken to be zero for any arbitrary position of the dipole. By analogy with the assumption made for electric dipoles in Section 27–6, we assume that the magnetic energy $U$ is zero when $\boldsymbol{\mu}$ and $\mathbf{B}$ are at right angles, that is, when $\theta = 90°$. This choice of a zero-energy configuration for $U$ is arbitrary because we are interested only in the *changes* in energy that occur when the dipole is rotated.

The magnetic potential energy in any position $\theta$ is defined as the work that an external agent must do to turn the dipole from its zero-energy position ($\theta = 90°$) to the given position $\theta$. Thus

$$U = \int_{90°}^{\theta} \tau \, d\theta = \int_{90°}^{\theta} NiAB \sin \theta \, d\theta = \mu B \int_{90°}^{\theta} \sin \theta \, d\theta = -\mu B \cos \theta,$$

in which Eq. 33–7 is used to substitute for $\tau$. In vector symbolism this relation can be written as

$$U = -\boldsymbol{\mu} \cdot \mathbf{B}, \tag{33-12}$$

which is in perfect correspondence with Eq. 27–13, the expression for the energy of an *electric* dipole in an external *electric* field,

$$U = -\mathbf{p} \cdot \mathbf{E}.$$

▶ **Example 4.** A circular coil of $N$ turns has an effective radius $a$ and carries a current $i$. How much work is required to turn it in an external magnetic field $\mathbf{B}$ from a position in which $\theta$ equals zero to one in which $\theta$ equals 180°? Assume that $N = 100$, $a = 5.0$ cm, $i = 0.10$ amp, and $B = 1.5$ webers/meter$^2$.

The work required is the difference in energy between the two positions, or, from Eq. 33–12,

$$W = U_{\theta = 180°} - U_{\theta = 0} = (-\mu B \cos 180°) - (-\mu B \cos 0) = 2\mu B.$$

But $\mu = NiA$, so that

$$W = 2NiAB = 2Ni(\pi a^2)B$$

$$= (2)(100)(0.10 \text{ amp})(\pi)(5 \times 10^{-2} \text{ meter})^2(1.5 \text{ webers/meter}^2) = 0.24 \text{ joule.} \quad \blacktriangleleft$$

### 33–5 The Hall Effect

In 1879 E. H. Hall devised an experiment that gives the sign of the charge carriers in a conductor; see p. 771. Figure 33–10 shows a flat strip of copper, carrying a current $i$ in the direction shown. As usual, the direction of the current arrow, labeled $i$, is the direction in which the charge carriers would move *if* they were positive. The current arrow can represent either positive charges moving down (as in Fig. 33–10a) or negative charges moving up (as in Fig. 33–10b). The Hall effect can be used to decide between these two possibilities.

A field of magnetic induction **B** is set up at right angles to the strip by placing the strip between the polefaces of an electromagnet. This field exerts a deflecting force **F** on the strip (given by $i\mathbf{l} \times \mathbf{B}$), which points to the right in the figure. Since the sideways force on the strip is due to the sideways forces on the charge carriers (given by $q\mathbf{v} \times \mathbf{B}$), it follows that these carriers, whether they are positive or negative, will tend to drift toward the right in Fig. 33–10 as they drift along the strip, producing a *transverse Hall potential difference* $V_{xy}$ between points such as $x$ and $y$. The sign of the charge carriers is determined by the sign of this Hall potential difference. If the carriers are positive, $y$ will be at a higher potential than $x$; if they are negative, $y$ will be at a lower potential than $x$. Experiment shows that in metals the charge carriers are negative.

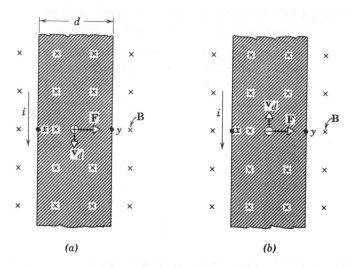

*(a)*                 *(b)*

**Fig. 33–10** A current $i$ is set up in a copper strip placed in a field of magnetic induction **B**, assuming (a) positive carriers and (b) negative carriers.

To analyze the Hall effect quantitatively, let us use the *free-electron* model of a metal, the same model used in Section 31-4 to explain resistivity. The charge carriers can be assumed to move along the conductor with a certain constant drift speed $v_d$. The magnetic deflecting force that causes the moving charge carriers to drift toward the right edge of the strip is given by $q\mathbf{v}_d \times \mathbf{B}$ (see Eq. 33-3a).

The charge carriers do not build up without limit on the right edge of the strip because the displacement of charge gives rise to a transverse *Hall electric field* $\mathbf{E}_H$, which acts, inside the conductor, to oppose the sideways drift of the carriers. This Hall electric field is another manifestation of the Hall potential difference and is related to it by

$$E_H = V_{xy}/d.$$

Eventually an equilibrium is reached in which the sideways magnetic deflecting force on the charge carriers is just canceled by the oppositely directed electric force $q\mathbf{E}_H$ caused by the Hall electric field, or

$$q\mathbf{E}_H + q\mathbf{v}_d \times \mathbf{B} = 0,$$

which can be written

$$\mathbf{E}_H = -\mathbf{v}_d \times \mathbf{B}. \qquad (33\text{-}13)$$

This equation shows explicitly that if $\mathbf{E}_H$ and $\mathbf{B}$ are measured $\mathbf{v}_d$ can be determined both in magnitude and direction; given the direction of $\mathbf{v}_d$, the sign of the charge carriers follows at once, as Fig. 33-10 shows.

The number of charge carriers per unit volume ($n$) can also be found from Hall effect measurements. If we write Eq. 33-13 in terms of magnitudes, for the case in which $v_d$ and $\mathbf{B}$ are at right angles, we obtain $E_H = v_d B$. Combining this with Eq. 31-5 ($v_d = j/ne$) leads to

$$E_H = \frac{j}{ne} B \qquad \text{or} \qquad n = \frac{jB}{eE_H}. \qquad (33\text{-}14)$$

The agreement between experiment and Eq. 33-14 is rather good for monovalent metals, as Table 33-1 shows.

### Table 33-1

NUMBER OF CONDUCTION ELECTRONS PER UNIT VOLUME

| Metal | Based on Hall Effect Data, $10^{22}/cm^3$ | Calculated, Assuming One Electron/Atom, $10^{22}/cm^3$ |
|---|---|---|
| Li | 3.7 | 4.8 |
| Na | 2.5 | 2.6 |
| K | 1.5 | 1.3 |
| Cs | 0.80 | 0.85 |
| Cu | 11 | 8.4 |
| Ag | 7.4 | 6.0 |
| Au | 8.7 | 5.9 |

For nonmonovalent metals, for iron and similar magnetic materials, and for so-called semiconductors such as germanium, the simple interpretation of the Hall effect in terms of the free-electron model is not valid. A theoretical interpretation of the

Hall effect based on modern quantum physics gives a reasonable agreement with experiment in all cases.

▶ **Example 5.**   A copper strip 2.0 cm wide and 1.0 mm thick is placed in a magnetic field with $B = 1.5$ webers/meter$^2$, as in Fig. 33–10. If a current of 200 amp is set up in the strip, what Hall potential difference appears across the strip?

From Eq. 33–14,

$$E_H = \frac{jB}{ne},$$

but

$$E_H = \frac{V_{xy}}{d} \quad \text{and} \quad j = \frac{i}{A} = \frac{i}{dh},$$

where $h$ is the thickness of the strip. Combining these equations gives

$$V_{xy} = \frac{iB}{neh} = \frac{(200 \text{ amp})(1.5 \text{ webers/meter}^2)}{(8.4 \times 10^{28}/\text{meter}^3)(1.6 \times 10^{-19} \text{ coul})(1.0 \times 10^{-3} \text{ meter})}$$

$$= 2.2 \times 10^{-5} \text{ volt} = 22\mu\text{v}.$$

These potential differences are not large. See p. 681 for the calculation of $n$.   ◀

### 33–6   Circulating Charges

Figure 33–11 shows a negatively charged particle introduced with velocity **v** into a uniform field of magnetic induction **B**. We assume that **v** is at right angles to **B** and thus lies entirely in the plane of the figure. The relation $\mathbf{F} = q\mathbf{v} \times \mathbf{B}$ (Eq. 33–3a) shows that the particle will experience a sideways deflecting force of magnitude $qvB$. This force will lie in the plane of the figure, which means that the particle cannot leave this plane.

This reminds us of a stone held by a rope and whirled in a horizontal circle on a smooth surface. Here, too, a force of constant magnitude, the tension in the rope, acts in a plane and at right angles to the velocity. The charged particle, like the stone, also moves with constant speed in a circular

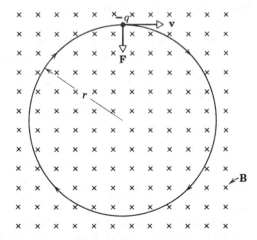

**Fig. 33–11**   A charge $-q$ circulates at right angles to a uniform magnetic field.

path. From Newton's second law we have

$$qvB = \frac{mv^2}{r} \quad \text{or} \quad r = \frac{mv}{qB}, \tag{33-15}$$

which gives the radius of the path. The three spirals in Fig. 33-4 show relatively low-energy electrons in a bubble chamber. The paths are not circles because the electrons lose energy by collisions in the chamber as they move. The angular velocity $\omega$ is given by $v/r$ or, from Eq. 33-15,

$$\omega = \frac{v}{r} = \frac{qB}{m}.$$

The frequency $\nu$ measured, say, in rev/sec, is given by

$$\nu = \frac{\omega}{2\pi} = \frac{qB}{2\pi m}. \tag{33-16}$$

Note that $\nu$ *does not depend on the speed of the particle.* Fast particles move in large circles (Eq. 33-15) and slow ones in small circles, but all require the same time $T$ (the *period*) to complete one revolution in the field.

The frequency $\nu$ is a characteristic frequency for the charged particle in the field and may be compared to the characteristic frequency of a swinging pendulum in the earth's gravitational field or to the characteristic frequency of an oscillating mass-spring system. It is sometimes called the *cyclotron frequency* of the particle in the field because particles circulate at this frequency in the cyclotron.

▶ **Example 6.** A 10-ev electron is circulating in a plane at right angles to a uniform field of magnetic induction of $1.0 \times 10^{-4}$ weber/meter$^2$ ($= 1.0$ gauss).
(a) What is its orbit radius?
The velocity of an electron whose kinetic energy is $K$ can be found from

$$v = \sqrt{\frac{2K}{m}}.$$

The student should verify that this yields $1.9 \times 10^6$ meters/sec for $v$. Then, from Eq. 33-15,

$$r = \frac{mv}{qB} = \frac{(9.1 \times 10^{-31} \text{ kg})(1.9 \times 10^6 \text{ meters/sec})}{(1.6 \times 10^{-19} \text{ coul})(1.0 \times 10^{-4} \text{ weber/meter}^2)} = 0.11 \text{ meter} = 11 \text{ cm}.$$

(b) What is the cyclotron frequency? From Eq. 33-16,

$$\nu = \frac{qB}{2\pi m} = \frac{(1.6 \times 10^{-19} \text{ coul})(1.0 \times 10^{-4} \text{ weber/meter}^2)}{(2\pi)(9.1 \times 10^{-31} \text{ kg})} = 2.8 \times 10^6 \text{ rev/sec}.$$

(c) What is the period of revolution $T$?

$$T = \frac{1}{\nu} = \frac{1}{2.8 \times 10^6 \text{ rev/sec}} = 3.6 \times 10^{-7} \text{ sec}.$$

Thus an electron requires 0.36 μsec to make 1 revolution in a 1.0-gauss field.
(d) What is the direction of circulation as viewed by an observer sighting along the field?
In Fig. 33-11 the magnetic force $q\mathbf{v} \times \mathbf{B}$ must point radially inward, since it provides the centripetal force. Since $\mathbf{B}$ points into the plane of the paper, $\mathbf{v}$ would have to

point to the left at the position shown in the figure if the charge $q$ were positive. However, the charge is an electron, with $q = -e$, which means that $\mathbf{v}$ must point to the right. Thus the charge circulates clockwise as viewed by an observer sighting in the direction of $\mathbf{B}$.                                                                                ◀

### 33-7  The Cyclotron

The cyclotron, first put into operation by Ernest Lawrence (1902–1958) in 1932, accelerates charged particles, such as protons or deuterons,* to high energies so that they can be used in atom-smashing experiments. Figure 33-12 shows the University of Pittsburgh cyclotron.

**Fig. 33-12**  The University of Pittsburgh cyclotron. Note vacuum chamber $V$, magnet frame $F$, magnetic pole faces $P$, magnet coils $C$, and the deuteron beam emerging into the air of the laboratory. The rule is 6 ft long. (Courtesy A. J. Allen.)

In an *ion source* at the center of the cyclotron molecules of deuterium are bombarded with electrons whose energy is high enough (say 100 ev) so that many positive ions are formed during the collisions. Many of these ions are free deuterons, which enter the cyclotron proper through a small hole in the wall of the ion source and are available to be accelerated.

---

* Deuterons are the nuclei of heavy hydrogen.

The cyclotron uses a modest potential difference for accelerating (say $10^5$ volts), but it requires the ion to pass through this potential difference a number of times. To reach 10 Mev with $10^5$ volts accelerating potential requires 100 passages. A magnetic field is used to bend the ions around so that they may pass again and again through the same accelerating potential.

Figure 33–13 is a top view of the part of the cyclotron that is inside the vacuum tank marked $V$ in Fig. 33–12. The two D-shaped objects, called *dees*, are made of copper sheet and form part of an electric oscillator which establishes an accelerating potential difference across the gap between the dees. The direction of this potential difference is made to change sign some millions of times per second.

The dees are immersed in a magnetic field ($B \cong 1.6$ webers/meter$^2$) whose direction is out of the plane of Fig. 33–13. The field is set up by a large electromagnet, marked $F$ in Fig. 33–12. Finally, the space in which the ions move is evacuated to a pressure of about $10^{-6}$ mm-Hg. If this were not done, the ions would continually collide with air molecules.

Suppose that a deuteron, emerging from the ion source, finds the dee that it is facing to be negative; it will accelerate toward this dee and will enter it. Once inside, it is screened from electrical forces by the metal walls of the dees. The magnetic field is not screened by the dees so that the ion bends in a circular path whose radius, which depends on the velocity, is given by Eq. 33–15, or

$$r = \frac{mv}{qB}.$$

After a time $t_0$ the ion emerges from the dee on the other side of the ion source. Let us assume that the accelerating potential has now changed sign. Thus the ion *again* faces a negative dee, is further accelerated, and again describes a semicircle, of somewhat larger radius (see Eq. 33–15), in the dee.

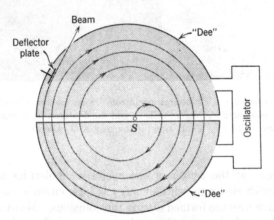

**Fig. 33-13**   The elements of a cyclotron showing the ion source $S$ and the dees. The deflector plate, held at a suitable negative potential, deflects the particles out of the dee system.

*The time of passage through this dee, however, is still $t_0$.* This follows because the period of revolution $T$ of an ion circulating in a magnetic field does not depend on the speed of the ion; see Eq. 33-16. This process goes on until the ion reaches the outer edge of one dee where it is pulled out of the system by a negatively charged deflector plate.

The key to the operation of the cyclotron is that the characteristic frequency $\nu$ at which the ion circulates in the field must be equal to the fixed frequency $\nu_0$ of the electric oscillator, or

$$\nu = \nu_0.$$

This *resonance condition* says that if the energy of the circulating ion is to increase energy must be fed to it at a frequency $\nu_0$ that is equal to the natural frequency $\nu$ at which the ion circulates in the field. In the same way we feed energy to a swing by pushing it at a frequency equal to the natural frequency of oscillation of the swing.

From Eq. 33-16 ($\nu = qB/2\pi m$), we can rewrite the resonance equation as

$$\frac{qB}{2\pi m} = \nu_0. \qquad (33\text{-}17)$$

Once we have selected an ion to be accelerated, $q/m$ is fixed; usually the oscillator is designed to work at a single frequency $\nu_0$. We then "tune" the cyclotron by varying $B$ until Eq. 33-17 is satisfied and an accelerated beam appears.

The *energy* of the particles produced in the cyclotron depends on the radius $R$ of the dees. From Eq. 33-15 ($r = mv/qB$), the velocity of a particle circulating at this radius is given by

$$v = \frac{qBR}{m}.$$

The kinetic energy is then

$$K = \tfrac{1}{2}mv^2 = \frac{q^2B^2R^2}{2m}. \qquad (33\text{-}18)$$

▶ **Example 7.** The University of Pittsburgh cyclotron has an oscillator frequency of $12 \times 10^6$ cycles/sec and a dee radius of 21 in. (*a*) What value of magnetic induction $B$ is needed to accelerate deuterons?

From Eq. 33-17, $\nu_0 = qB/2\pi m$, so that

$$B = \frac{2\pi\nu_0 m}{q} = \frac{(2\pi)(12 \times 10^6/\text{sec})(3.3 \times 10^{-27}\text{ kg})}{1.6 \times 10^{-19}\text{ coul}} = 1.6\text{ webers/meter}^2.$$

Note that the deuteron has the same charge as the proton but (very closely) twice the mass.

(*b*) What deuteron energy results?

From Eq. 33-18,

$$K = \frac{q^2B^2R^2}{2m} = \frac{(1.6 \times 10^{-19}\text{ coul})^2(1.6\text{ webers/meter}^2)^2(21 \times 0.0254\text{ meter})^2}{(2)(3.3 \times 10^{-27}\text{ kg})}$$

$$= (2.8 \times 10^{-12}\text{ joule})\left(\frac{1\text{ ev}}{1.6 \times 10^{-19}\text{ joule}}\right) = 17\text{ Mev.} \qquad ◀$$

The cyclotron fails to operate at high energies because one of its assumptions, that the frequency of rotation of an ion circulating in a magnetic field is independent of its

speed, is true only for speeds much less than that of light. As the particle speed
increases, we must use the *relativistic mass* $m$ in Eq. 33–16. The relativistic mass
increases with velocity (Eq. 8–20) so that at high enough speeds $v$ decreases with
velocity. Thus the ions get out of step with the electric oscillator, and eventually
the energy of the circulating ion stops increasing.

Another difficulty associated with the acceleration of particles to high energies is
that the size of the magnet that would be required to guide such particles in a circular
path is very large. For a 30-Bev proton, for example, in a field of 15,000 gauss the
radius of curvature is 65 meters. A magnet of the cyclotron type of this size (about
430 ft in diameter) would be prohibitively expensive. Incidentally, a 30-Bev proton
has a speed equal to 0.99998 that of light.

Both the relativistic and the economic limitations have been removed by techniques that can be understood in terms of Eq. 33–17 in which $m$ is now taken to be
the relativistic mass, given by Eq. 8–13, or

$$m = \frac{m_0}{\sqrt{1 - (v/c)^2}},$$

$v$ being the speed of the particle and $c$ being that of light.

As the particle speed increases, the relativistic mass $m$ also increases. To maintain
the equality in Eq. 33–17, and thus insure resonance, one may decrease the oscillator frequency $v_0$ as the particle (assumed to be a proton) accelerates in such a way
that the product $v_0 m$ remains constant. Accelerators that use this technique are
called *synchrocyclotrons*.

To remove the magnet cost limitation one can vary *both* $B$ and $v_0$ in a cyclic
fashion in such a way that not only is Eq. 33–17 satisfied at all times but the particle
orbit radius remains constant during the acceleration process. This permits the
use of an annular (or ring-shaped) magnet, rather than the conventional cyclotron
type, at great saving in cost. With the *two* variables $B$ and $v_0$ at our disposal, it is
possible to preserve *two* equalities during the acceleration process, one being Eq.
33–17 and the other being the relation

$$v = \omega_0 R_0 = (2\pi v_0) R_0$$

in which $R_0$ is the desired (fixed) orbit radius. Accelerators that use this technique are called *synchrotrons*. Table 33–2 shows some characteristics of the accel-

### Table 33–2

#### THE CERN PROTON SYNCHROTRON

| | |
|---|---|
| Orbit diameter | 560 ft |
| Vacuum chamber cross section | 5.5 in. × 2.7 in. |
| Maximum magnetic field | 1.4 webers/meter$^2$ |
| Frequency range per cycle | 7 mc/sec |
| Pulse rate | 20/min |
| Maximum proton energy | 28 Bev |
| Energy gain per cycle | 54 kev |
| Distance traveled by a proton | 5 × 10$^4$ miles |
| Protons per pulse | 10$^{11}$ |
| Cost | $28 × 10$^6$ |

erator built at Geneva, Switzerland, by the European Council for Nuclear Research (CERN), and embodying these principles.

## 33-8  Thomson's Experiment

In 1897 J. J. Thomson, working at the Cavendish Laboratory in Cambridge, measured the ratio of the charge $e$ of the electron to its mass $m$ by observing its deflection in combined electric and magnetic fields. The discovery of the electron is usually said to date from this historic experiment, although H. A. Lorentz and P. Zeeman (1865–1943), during the previous year, had measured this same quantity for electrons bound in atoms, using a method entirely different from Thomson's.

In Fig. 33-14, which is a modernized version of Thomson's apparatus, electrons are emitted from hot filament $F$ and accelerated by an applied potential difference $V$. They then enter a region in which they move at right angles to an electric field $\mathbf{E}$ and a field of magnetic induction $\mathbf{B}$; $\mathbf{E}$ and $\mathbf{B}$ are themselves at right angles to each other. The beam is made visible as a spot of light when it strikes fluorescent screen $S$. The entire region in which the electrons move is highly evacuated so that collisions with air molecules will not occur.

The resultant force on a charged particle moving through an electric and a magnetic field is given by Eq. 33-4, or

$$\mathbf{F} = q_0\mathbf{E} + q_0\mathbf{v} \times \mathbf{B}.$$

Study of Fig. 33-14 shows that the electric field deflects the particle upward and the magnetic field deflects it downward. If these deflecting forces are to

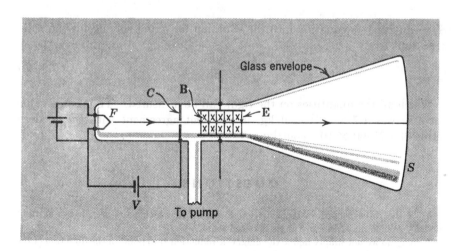

**Fig. 33-14**   Electrons from the heated filament $F$ are accelerated by a potential difference $V$ and pass through a hole in the screen $C$. After passing through a region in which perpendicular electric and magnetic fields are present, they strike the fluorescent screen $S$.

cancel (that is, if **F** = 0), this equation, for this problem, reduces to

$$eE = evB$$

or $$E = vB.$$ (33–19)

Thus for a given electron speed $v$ the condition for zero deflection can be satisfied by adjusting $E$ or $B$.

Thomson's procedure was (a) note the position of the undeflected beam spot, with **E** and **B** both equal to zero; (b) apply a fixed electric field **E**, measuring on the fluorescent screen the deflection so caused; and (c) apply a magnetic field and adjust its value until the beam deflection is restored to zero.

In Section 27–5 we saw that the deflection $y$ of an electron in a purely electric field (step b), measured at the far edge of the deflecting plates, is given by Eq. 27–9, or, with small changes in notation,

$$y = \frac{eEl^2}{2mv^2},$$

where $v$ is the electron speed and $l$ is the length of the deflecting plates; $y$ is not measurable directly, but it may be calculated from the measured displacement of the spot on the screen if the geometry of the apparatus is known. Thus $y$, $E$, and $l$ are known; the ratio $e/m$ and the velocity $v$ are unknown. We cannot calculate $e/m$ until we have found the velocity, which is the purpose of step $c$ above.

If (step $c$) the electric force is set equal and opposite to the magnetic force, the net force is zero and we can write (Eq. 33–19)

$$v = \frac{E}{B}.$$

Substituting this equation into the equation for $y$ and solving for the ratio $e/m$ leads to

$$\frac{e}{m} = \frac{2yE}{B^2l^2},$$ (33–20)

in which all the quantities on the right can be measured. Thomson's value for $e/m$ was $1.7 \times 10^{11}$ coul/kg, in excellent agreement with the modern value of $1.75890 \times 10^{11}$ coul/kg.

## QUESTIONS

1. Of the three vectors in the equation $\mathbf{F} = q\mathbf{v} \times \mathbf{B}$, which pairs are always at right angles? Which may have any angle between them?

2. Why do we not simply define the magnetic induction **B** to point in the direction of the magnetic force that acts on the moving charge?

3. Imagine that you are sitting in a room with your back to one wall and that an electron beam, traveling horizontally from the back wall toward the front wall, is deflected to your right. What is the direction of the field of magnetic induction that exists in the room?

4. If an electron is not deflected in passing through a certain region of space, can we be sure that there is no magnetic field in that region?

5. If a moving electron is deflected sideways in passing through a certain region of space, can we be sure that a magnetic field exists in that region?

6. A beam of protons is deflected sideways. Could this deflection be caused (a) by an electric field? (b) By a magnetic field? (c) If either could be responsible, how would you be able to tell which was present?

7. A conductor, even though it is carrying a current, has zero net charge. Why, then, does a magnetic field exert a force on it?

8. Equation 33–11 ($\tau = \mu \times B$) shows that there is no torque on a current loop in an external magnetic field if the angle between the axis of the loop and the field is (a) 0° or (b) 180°. Discuss the nature of the equilibrium (that is, is it stable, neutral, or unstable?) for these two positions.

9. In Example 4 we showed that the work required to turn a current loop end-for-end in an external magnetic field is $2\mu B$. Does this hold no matter what the original orientation of the loop was?

10. Imagine that the room in which you are seated is filled with a uniform magnetic field with B pointing vertically upward. A circular loop of wire has its plane horizontal. For what direction of current in the loop, as viewed from above, will the loop be in stable equilibrium with respect to forces and torques of magnetic origin?

11. A rectangular current loop is in an arbitrary orientation in an external magnetic field. Is any work required to rotate the loop about an axis perpendicular to its plane?

12. (a) In measuring Hall potential differences, why must we be careful that points $x$ and $y$ in Fig. 33–10 are exactly opposite to each other? (b) If one of the contacts is movable, what procedure might we follow in adjusting it to make sure that the two points are properly located?

13. A uniform magnetic field fills a certain cubical region of space. Can an electron be fired into this cube from the outside in such a way that it will travel in a closed circular path inside the cube?

14. Imagine the room in which you are seated to be filled with a uniform magnetic field with B pointing vertically downward. At the center of the room two electrons are suddenly projected horizontally with the same speed but in opposite directions. (a) Discuss their motions. (b) Discuss their motions if one particle is an electron and one a positron.

15. In Fig. 33–4, why are the low-energy electron tracks spirals? That is, why does the radius of curvature change in the constant magnetic field in which the chamber is immersed?

16. What are the primary functions of (a) the electric field and (b) the magnetic field in the cyclotron?

17. For Thomson's $e/m$ experiment to work properly (Section 33–8), is it essential that the electrons have a fairly constant speed?

# PROBLEMS

1. The electrons in the beam of a television tube have an energy of 12 kev. The tube is oriented so that the electrons move horizontally from south to north. The vertical component of the earth's magnetic field points down and has $B = 5.5 \times 10^{-5}$ weber/meter$^2$. (a) In what direction will the beam deflect? (b) What is the acceleration of a given electron? (c) How far will the beam deflect in moving 20 cm through the television tube?

2. In a nuclear experiment a 1.0-Mev proton moves in a uniform magnetic field in a circular path. What energy must (a) an alpha particle and (b) a deuteron have if they are to circulate in the same orbit?

3. A wire 1.0 meter long carries a current of 10 amp and makes an angle of 30° with a uniform magnetic field with $B = 1.5$ webers/meter$^2$. Calculate the magnitude and direction of the force on the wire.

4. A wire of 60 cm length and mass 10 gm is suspended by a pair of flexible leads in a magnetic field of induction 0.40 weber/meter². What are the magnitude and direction of the current required to remove the tension in the supporting leads? See Fig. 33–15.

**Fig. 33–15**

5. Express magnetic induction $B$ and magnetic flux $\Phi$ in terms of the fundamental dimensions $M$, $L$, $T$, and $Q$ (mass, length, time, and charge).

6. A metal wire of mass $m$ slides without friction on two rails spaced a distance $d$ apart, as in Fig. 33–16. The track lies in a verti-

**Fig. 33–16**

cal uniform field of magnetic induction **B**. A *constant current* $i$ flows from generator $G$ along one rail, across the wire, and back down the other rail. Find the velocity (speed and direction) of the wire as a function of time, assuming it to be at rest at $t = 0$.

7. A U-shaped wire of mass $m$ and length $l$ is immersed with its two ends in mercury (Fig. 33–17). The wire is in a homogeneous field of magnetic induction **B**. If a charge, that is, a current pulse $q = \int i \, dt$, is sent through the wire, the wire will jump up. Calculate, from the height $h$ that the wire reaches, the size of the charge or current pulse, assuming that the time of the current pulse is very small in comparison with the time of flight. Make use of the fact that impulse of force equals $\int F \, dt$, which equals $mv$. (Hint: Try to relate $\int i \, dt$ to $\int F \, dt$.) Evaluate $q$ for $B = 0.1$ weber/meter², $m = 10$ gm, $l = 20$ cm, and $h = 3$ meters.

**Fig. 33–17**

8. Figure 33-18 shows a wire ring of radius $a$ at right angles to the general direction of a radially symmetric diverging magnetic field. The magnetic induction at the ring is everywhere of the same magnitude $B$, and its direction at the ring is everywhere at an angle $\theta$ with a normal to the plane of the ring. The twisted lead wires have no effect on the problem. Find the magnitude and direction of the force the field exerts on the ring if the ring carries a current $i$ as shown in the figure.

**Fig. 33-18**

9. A copper rod weighing 0.30 lb rests on two rails 1.0 ft apart and carries a current of 50 amp from one rail to the other. The coefficient of starting friction is 0.60. What is the smallest magnetic field that would cause the bar to slide and what is its direction?

10. Figure 33-19 shows a wire of arbitrary shape carrying a current $i$ between points $a$ and $b$. The wire lies in a plane at right angles to a uniform field of magnetic induction **B**. Prove that the force on the wire is the same as that on a straight wire carrying a current $i$ directly from $a$ to $b$. (Hint: Replace the wire by a series of "steps" parallel and perpendicular to the straight line joining $a$ and $b$.)

**Fig. 33-19**

**Fig. 33-20**

11. Figure 33-20 shows a rectangular twenty-turn loop of wire, 10 cm by 5.0 cm. It carries a current of 0.10 amp and is hinged at one side. What torque (direction and magnitude) acts on the loop if it is mounted with its plane at an angle of 30° to the direction of a uniform field of magnetic induction 0.50 weber/meter²?

12. Prove that the relation $\tau = NAiB \sin \theta$ holds for closed loops of arbitrary shape. (Hint: Replace the loop of arbitrary shape by an assembly of adjacent long, thin—approximately rectangular—loops which are equivalent to it as far as the distribution of current is concerned.)

13. A length $L$ of wire carries a current $i$. Show that if the wire is formed into a circular coil the maximum torque in a given magnetic field is developed when the coil has *one* turn only and the maximum torque has the value

$$\tau = \frac{1}{4\pi} L^2 iB.$$

14. Figure 33–21 shows a wooden cylinder with a mass $m$ of 0.25 kg, a radius $R$, and a length $l$ of 0.1 meter with $N$ equal to ten turns of wire wrapped around it longitudinally, so that the plane of the wire loop contains the axis of the cylinder. What is the least current through the loop that will prevent the cylinder from rolling down an inclined plane whose surface is inclined at an angle $\theta$ to the horizontal, in the presence of a vertical field of magnetic induction 0.5 weber/meter$^2$, if the plane of the windings is parallel to the inclined plane?

**Fig. 33–21**                                    **Fig. 33–22**

15. A current $i$, indicated by the crosses in Fig. 33–22, is established in a strip of copper of height $h$ and width $w$. A uniform field of magnetic induction **B** is applied at right angles to the strip. (a) Calculate the drift speed $v_d$ for the electrons. (b) What are the magnitude and direction of the magnetic force **F** acting on the electrons? (c) What would the magnitude and direction of a homogeneous electric field **E** have to be in order to counterbalance the effect of the magnetic field? (d) What is the voltage $V$ necessary between two sides of the conductor in order to create this field **E**? Between which sides of the conductor would this voltage have to be applied? (e) If no electric field is applied *from the outside*, the electrons will be pushed somewhat to one side and therefore will give rise to a uniform electric field $\mathbf{E}_H$ across the conductor until the forces of this electrostatic field $\mathbf{E}_H$ balance the magnetic forces encountered in part (b). What will be the magnitude and direction of the field $\mathbf{E}_H$? Assume that $n$, the number of conduction electrons per unit volume, is $1.1 \times 10^{29}$/meter$^3$ and that $h = 0.02$ meter, $w = 0.1$ cm, $i = 50$ amp, and $B = 2$ webers/meter$^2$.

16. (a) Show that the ratio of the Hall electric field $E_H$ to the electric field $E$ responsible for the current is

$$\frac{E_H}{E} = \frac{B}{ne\rho}.$$

(b) What is the angle between $\mathbf{E}_H$ and $\mathbf{E}$? (c) Evaluate this ratio for the conditions of Example 5.

17. A proton, a deuteron, and an $\alpha$-particle, accelerated through the same potential difference, enter a region of uniform magnetic field, moving at right angles to **B**. (a) Compare their kinetic energies. (b) If the radius of the proton's circular path is 10 cm, what are the radii of the deuteron and the $\alpha$-particle paths?

18. A proton, a deuteron, and an $\alpha$-particle with the same kinetic energies enter a region of uniform magnetic field, moving at right angles to **B**. Compare the radii of their circular paths.

19. An $\alpha$-particle travels in a circular path of radius 0.45 meter in a magnetic field with $B = 1.2$ webers/meter$^2$. Calculate (a) its speed, (b) its period of revolution, (c) its kinetic energy, and (d) the potential difference through which it would have to be accelerated to achieve this energy.

20. An electron is accelerated through 15,000 volts and is then allowed to circulate at right angles to a uniform magnetic field with $B = 250$ gauss. What is its path radius?

21. Electrons are observed to be ejected in various directions with negligible speed from the negative plate of a parallel-plate capacitor when the plate is illuminated by light of a certain wavelength (photoelectric effect). The plates are separated by a distance $d$ and a potential difference $V$ is maintained between them. Show that none of these electrons will reach the positive plate if a magnetic field is applied at right angles to the electric field and the magnetic induction has a value

$$B > \left(\frac{2Vm}{ed^2}\right)^{\frac{1}{2}},$$

in which $m$ and $e$ are the electron mass and charge, respectively.

22. Show that the radius of curvature of a charged particle moving at right angles to a magnetic field is proportional to its momentum.

23. What is the smallest magnetic field (magnitude and direction) that can be set up at the equator to permit a proton of speed $1.0 \times 10^7$ meters/sec to circulate around the earth?

24. A deuteron in a large cyclotron is moving in a magnetic field with $B = 1.5$ webers/meter$^2$ and an orbit radius of 2.0 meters. Because of a grazing collision with a target, the deuteron breaks up, with a negligible loss of kinetic energy, into a proton and a neutron. Discuss the subsequent motions of each. Assume that the deuteron energy is shared equally by the proton and neutron at breakup.

25. A 2-kev positron is projected into a uniform field of induction **B** of 0.10 weber/meter$^2$ with its velocity vector making an angle of 89° with **B**. Convince yourself that the path will be a helix, its axis being the direction of **B**. Find the period, the pitch $p$, and the radius $r$ of the helix; see Fig. 33–23.

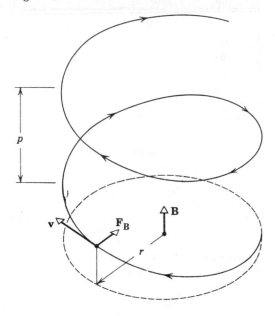

**Fig. 33–23**

26. (a) In a magnetic field with $B = 0.50$ weber/meter$^2$, for what path radius will an electron circulate at 0.1 the speed of light? (b) What will its kinetic energy be?

**27.** *Time-of-flight spectrometer.* S. A. Goudsmit has devised a method for measuring accurately the masses of heavy ions by timing their period of circulation in a known magnetic field. A singly charged ion of iodine makes 7 rev in a field of $4.5 \times 10^{-2}$ weber/meter$^2$ in about $1.29 \times 10^{-3}$ sec. What (approximately) is its mass in kilograms? Actually, the mass measurements are carried out to much greater accuracy than these approximate data suggest.

**28.** *Mass spectrometer.* Figure 33–24 shows an arrangement used by Dempster to measure the masses of ions. An ion of mass $M$ and charge $+q$ is produced essentially at rest in source $S$, a chamber in which a gas discharge is taking place. The ion is accelerated by potential difference $V$ and allowed to enter a field of magnetic induction **B**. In the field it moves in a semicircle, striking a photographic plate at distance $x$ from the entry slit and being recorded. Show that the mass $M$ is given by

$$M = \frac{B^2 q}{8V} x^2.$$

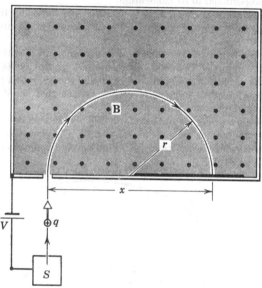

**Fig. 33–24**

**29.** *Zeeman effect.* In Bohr's theory of the hydrogen atom the electron can be thought of as moving in a circular orbit of radius $r$ about the proton. Suppose that such an atom is placed in a magnetic field, with the plane of the orbit at right angles to **B**. (*a*) If the electron is circulating clockwise, as viewed by an observer sighting along **B**, will the angular frequency increase or decrease? (*b*) What if the electron is circulating counterclockwise? Assume that the orbit radius does not change. [Hint: The centripetal force is now partially electric ($\mathbf{F}_E$) and partially magnetic ($\mathbf{F}_B$) in origin.]

**30.** In Problem 29 show that the change in frequency of rotation caused by the magnetic field is given approximately by

$$\Delta \nu = \pm \frac{Be}{4\pi m}.$$

Such frequency shifts were actually observed by Zeeman in 1896. (Hint: Calculate the frequency of rotation without the magnetic field and also with it. Subtract, bearing in mind that because the effect of the magnetic field is very small some—but not all—terms containing $B$ can be set equal to zero with little error.)

**31.** The University of Pittsburgh cyclotron is normally adjusted to accelerate deuterons. (a) What energy of protons could it produce, using the same oscillator frequency as that used for deuterons? (b) What magnetic induction would be required? (c) What energy of protons could be produced if the magnetic induction was left at the value used for deuterons? (d) What oscillator frequency would then be required? (e) Answer the same questions for α-particles.

**32.** Estimate the total path length traversed by a deuteron in the University of Pittsburgh cyclotron during the acceleration process. Assume an accelerating potential between the dees of 80,000 volts.

**33.** In a synchrocyclotron producing 400-Mev protons, what must the ratio be of the oscillator frequency at the beginning of an accelerating cycle to that at the end? Such a proton has a speed of 0.70c, where c is the speed of light.

**34.** A 10-kev electron moving horizontally enters a region of space in which there is a downward-directed electric field of magnitude 100 volts/cm. (a) What are the magnitude and direction of the (smallest) field of magnetic induction that will allow the electron to continue to move horizontally? Ignore gravitational forces, which are rather small. (b) Is it possible for a proton to pass through this combination of fields undeflected? If so, under what circumstances?

**35.** An electric field of 1500 volts/meter and a magnetic field of 0.40 weber/meter² act on a moving electron to produce no force. (a) Calculate the minimum electron speed v. (b) Draw the vectors **E**, **B**, and **v**.

# Ampère's Law

CHAPTER 34

### 34-1 Ampère's Law

One class of problems involving magnetic fields, dealt with in Chapter 33, concerns the forces exerted by a magnetic field on a moving charge or on a current-carrying conductor and the torque exerted on a magnetic dipole. A second class concerns the *production* of a magnetic field by a current-carrying conductor or by moving charges. This chapter deals with problems of this second class.

The discovery that currents produce magnetic effects was made by Oersted in 1820. Figure 34-1, which shows a wire surrounded by a number of small magnets, illustrates a modification of his experiment. If there is no current in the wire, all the magnets are aligned with the earth's magnetic field. When a strong current is present, the magnets point so as to suggest that the magnetic lines of induction form closed circles around the wire. This view is strengthened by the experiment of Fig. 34-2, which shows iron filings on a horizontal glass plate, through the center of which a current-carrying conductor passes.

Today we write the quantitative relationship between current $i$ and the magnetic field $\mathbf{B}$ as

$$\oint \mathbf{B} \cdot d\mathbf{l} = \mu_0 i, \tag{34-1}$$

which is known as *Ampère's law*. Ampère, being an advocate of the action-at-a-distance point of view, did not formulate his results in terms of fields; this was first done by Maxwell. Ampère's law, including an important ex-

**Fig. 34-1** An array of compass needles near a wire carrying a strong current. The black ends of the compass needles are their north poles. The dot shows the current emerging from the page. As usual, the direction of a current is taken as the direction of flow of positive charge.

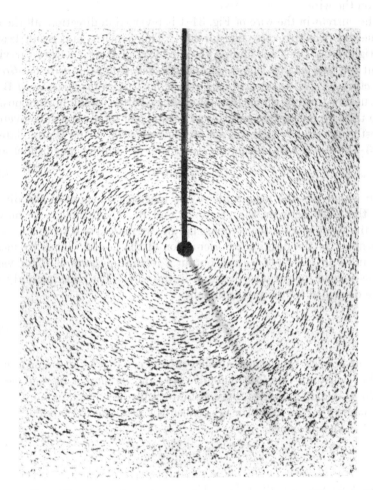

**Fig. 34-2** Iron filings around a wire carrying a strong current. (Courtesy Physical Science Study Committee.)

tension of it made later by Maxwell, is one of the basic equations of electromagnetism (see Table 38–3).

We can gain an appreciation of the way Ampère's law developed historically by considering a hypothetical experiment which has, in fact, much in common with experiments that were actually carried out. The experiment consists of measuring **B** at various distances $r$ from a long straight wire of circular cross section and carrying a current $i$. This can be done by making quantitative the qualitative observation of Fig. 34–1.

Let us put a small compass needle a distance $r$ from the wire. Such a needle, a small magnetic dipole, tends to line up with an external magnetic field, with its north pole pointing in the direction of **B**. Figure 34–1 makes it clear that **B** at the site of the dipole is tangent to a circle of radius $r$ centered on the wire.

If the current in the wire of Fig. 34–1 is reversed in direction, all the compass needles would reverse end-for-end. This experimental result leads to the "right-hand rule" for finding the direction of **B** near a wire carrying a current $i$: *Grasp the wire with the right hand, the thumb pointing in the direction of the current. The fingers will curl around the wire in the direction of* **B**.

Let us now turn the dipole through an angle $\theta$ from its equilibrium position. To do this, we must exert an external torque just large enough to overcome the restoring torque $\tau$ that will act on the dipole. $\tau$, $\theta$, and **B** are related by Eq. 33–11 ($\boldsymbol{\tau} = \boldsymbol{\mu} \times \mathbf{B}$), which can be written in terms of magnitudes as

$$\tau = \mu B \sin \theta \qquad (34–2)$$

and in which $\mu$ is the magnitude of the magnetic moment of the dipole, $\theta$ being the angle between the vectors $\boldsymbol{\mu}$ and **B**. Even though we may not know the value of $\mu$ for the compass needle, we may take it to be a constant, independent of the position or orientation of the needle. Thus by measuring $\tau$ and $\theta$ in Eq. 34–2 we can obtain a *relative* measure of $B$ for various distances $r$ and for various currents $i$ in the wire. The experimental results can be described by the proportionality

$$B \propto \frac{i}{r}. \qquad (34–3)$$

We can convert this proportionality into an equality by inserting a proportionality constant. As for Coulomb's law, and for similar reasons (see Section 26–4), we do not write this constant simply as $k$ but in a more complex form, namely $\mu_0/2\pi$, in which $\mu_0$ is called the *permeability constant.** Equation 34–3 then becomes

$$B = \frac{\mu_0 i}{2\pi r}, \qquad (34–4)$$

which we choose to write in the form

$$(B)(2\pi r) = \mu_0 i. \qquad (34–5)$$

---

* $\mu_0$ has no connection with the dipole moment $\mu$ that appears in Eq. 34–2.

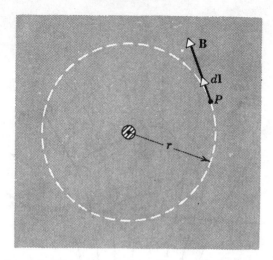

**Fig. 34–3**   A circular path of integration surrounding a wire.  The central dot suggests a current $i$ in the wire emerging from the page.  Note that the angle between **B** and $d\mathbf{l}$ is zero so that $\mathbf{B}\cdot d\mathbf{l} = B\,dl$.

The left side of Eq. 34–5 can easily be shown to be $\oint \mathbf{B}\cdot d\mathbf{l}$ for a path consisting of a circle of radius $r$ centered on the wire.  For all points on this circle **B** has the same (constant) magnitude $B$ and $d\mathbf{l}$, which is always tangent to the path of integration, points in the same direction as **B**, as Fig. 34–3 shows.  Thus

$$\oint \mathbf{B}\cdot d\mathbf{l} = \oint B\,dl = B\oint dl = (B)(2\pi r),$$

$\oint dl$ being simply the circumference of the circle.  *In this special case,* therefore, we can write the experimentally observed connection between the field and the current as

$$\oint \mathbf{B}\cdot d\mathbf{l} = \mu_0 i, \tag{34–1}$$

which is Ampère's law.  A host of other experiments suggests that Eq. 34–1 is true in general * for *any* magnetic field configuration, for *any* assembly of currents, and for *any* path of integration.

In applying Ampère's law in the general case, we construct a *closed linear path* in the magnetic field as shown in Fig. 34–4.  This path is divided into elements of length $d\mathbf{l}$, and for each element the quantity $\mathbf{B}\cdot d\mathbf{l}$ is evaluated.  Recall that $\mathbf{B}\cdot d\mathbf{l}$ has the magnitude $B\,dl\cos\theta$ and can be interpreted as the product of $dl$ and the component of **B** $(= B\cos\theta)$ parallel to $d\mathbf{l}$.  The inte-

---

* We must modify Eq. 34–1 if a time-varying electric field is present within the path of integration.   In this chapter we assume that if electric fields are present, they are constant in magnitude and direction.

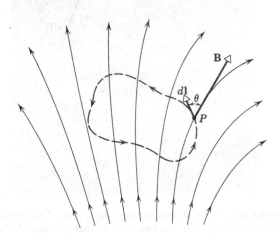

**Fig. 34-4**   A path of integration in a magnetic field.

gral is the sum of the quantities **b**·**u** ior all path elements in the complete loop.   The term $i$ on the right of Eq. 34–1 is the *net* current that passes through the area bounded by the closed path.

The permeability constant in Ampère's law has an assigned value of

$$\mu_0 = 4\pi \times 10^{-7} \text{ weber/amp-meter}$$

Both this and the permittivity constant ($\epsilon_0$) occur in electromagnetic formulas when the mks system of units is used.

The student may wonder why $\epsilon_0$ in Coulomb's law is a measured quantity, whereas $\mu_0$ in Ampère's law is an assigned quantity.   The answer is that the ampere, which is the mks unit for the current $i$ in Ampère's law, is defined by a laboratory technique (the *current balance*) that involves forces exerted by magnetic fields and in which this same constant $\mu_0$ appears.   In effect, as we show in detail in Section 34–4, the size of the current that we agree to define as one ampere is adjusted so that $\mu_0$ may have exactly the value assigned to it above.   In Coulomb's law, on the other hand, the quantities **F**, $q$, and $r$ are measured in ways in which the constant $\epsilon_0$ plays no role. This constant must then take on the particular value that makes the left side of Coulomb's law equal to the right side; no arbitrary assignment is possible.

### 34-2   B Near a Long Wire

We have seen that the lines of magnetic induction for a long straight wire carrying a current $i$ are concentric circles centered on the wire and that $B$ at a distance $r$ from the wire is given by Eq. 34–4:

$$B = \frac{\mu_0 i}{2\pi r}. \tag{34-4}$$

We may regard this as an experimental result consistent with, and readily derivable from, Ampère's law.

It is interesting to compare Eq. 34–4 with the expression for the electric field near a long line of charge, or

$$E = \frac{1}{2\pi\epsilon_0}\frac{\lambda}{r}. \tag{28–7}$$

In each case there are multiplying constants, namely $\mu_0/2\pi$ and $1/2\pi\epsilon_0$, and factors describing the device responsible for the field, namely $i$ and $\lambda$. Finally, each field varies as $1/r$.

Equation 28–7 may be derived from Gauss's law by relating the electric field at a Gaussian surface to the net charge within this surface. The (surface) integral in Gauss's law is evaluated for a closed cylindrical surface to which the lines of $E$ are everywhere perpendicular.

Equation 34–4 may be derived from Ampère's law by relating the magnetic field at a path of integration to the net current that pierces this path. The (line) integral in Ampère's law is evaluated for a closed circular path to which the lines of $B$ are everywhere tangent.

▶ **Example 1**   Derive an expression for $B$ at a distance $r$ from the center of a long cylindrical wire of radius $R$, where $r < R$. The wire carries a current $i_0$, distributed uniformly over the cross section of the wire.

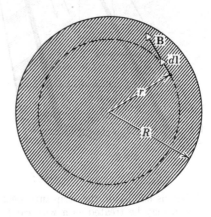

**Fig. 34–5**   Example 1. A circular path of integration inside a wire. A current $i_0$, distributed uniformly over the cross section of the wire, emerges from the page.

Figure 34–5 shows a circular path of integration inside the wire. Symmetry suggests that $B$ is tangent to the path as shown. Ampère's law,

$$\oint B \cdot dl = \mu_0 i,$$

gives

$$(B)(2\pi r) = \mu_0 i_0 \frac{\pi r^2}{\pi R^2},$$

since only the fraction of the current that passes through the path of integration is included in the factor $i$ on the right. Solving for $B$ and dropping the subscript on the current yields

$$B = \frac{\mu_0 i r}{2\pi R^2}.$$

At the surface of the wire ($r = R$) this equation reduces to the same expression as that found by putting $r = R$ in Eq. 34–4 ($B = \mu_0 i/2\pi R$).

**Example 2.** Figure 34–6 shows a flat strip of copper of width $a$ and negligible thickness carrying a current $i$. Find the magnetic field at a distance $R$ from the center of the strip, at right angles to the strip.

**Fig. 34–6** Example 2. A flat strip of width $a$ carries a current $i$.

Let us subdivide the strip into long infinitesimal filaments of width $dx$, each of which may be treated as a wire carrying a current $di$ given by $i(dx/a)$. The field contribution $dB$ at point $P$ in Fig. 34–6 is given, for the element shown, by the differential form of Eq. 34–4, or

$$dB = \frac{\mu_0}{2\pi} \frac{di}{r} = \frac{\mu_0}{2\pi} \frac{i(dx/a)}{R \sec \theta}.$$

Note that the vector $d\mathbf{B}$ is at right angles to the line marked $r$.

Only the horizontal component of $d\mathbf{B}$, namely $dB \cos \theta$, is effective, the vertical component being canceled by the contribution associated with a symmetrically located filament on the other side of the origin. Thus $B$ at point $P$ is given by the (scalar) integral

$$B = \int dB \cos \theta = \int \frac{\mu_0 i(dx/a)}{2\pi R \sec \theta} \cos \theta$$

$$= \frac{\mu_0 i}{2\pi a R} \int \frac{dx}{\sec^2 \theta}.$$

The variables $x$ and $\theta$ are not independent, being related by

$$x = R \tan \theta$$

or $$dx = R \sec^2 \theta \, d\theta.$$

Bearing in mind that the limits on $\theta$ are $\pm \tan^{-1}(a/2R)$ and eliminating $dx$ from this expression for $B$, we find

$$B = \frac{\mu_0 i}{2\pi a R} \int \frac{R \sec^2 \theta \, d\theta}{\sec^2 \theta}$$

$$= \frac{\mu_0 i}{2\pi a} \int_{-\tan^{-1}a/2R}^{+\tan^{-1}a/2R} d\theta = \frac{\mu_0 i}{\pi a} \tan^{-1} \frac{a}{2R}.$$

At points far from the strip, $a/2R$ is a small angle, for which $\tan^{-1} \alpha \cong \alpha$. Thus we have, as an approximate result,

$$B \cong \frac{\mu_0 i}{\pi a} \left( \frac{a}{2R} \right) = \frac{\mu_0}{2\pi} \frac{i}{R}.$$

This result is expected because at distant points the strip cannot be distinguished from a cylindrical wire (see Eq. 34–4).  ◄

### 34–3  Magnetic Lines of Induction

Figure 34–7 shows the lines of magnetic induction representing the field of $B$ near a long straight wire. Note the increase in the spacing of the lines with increasing distance from the wire. This represents the $1/r$ decrease in $B$ predicted by Eq. 34–4.

Figure 34–8 shows the resultant lines of magnetic induction associated with a current in a wire that is oriented at right angles to a uniform *external* field $B_e$. At any point the resultant magnetic induction $B$ will be the vector sum of $B_e$ and $B_i$, where $B_i$ is the magnetic induction set up by the current in the wire. The fields $B_e$ and $B_i$ tend to cancel above the wire and to reenforce each other below the wire. At point $P$ in Fig. 34–8 $B_e$ and $B_i$ cancel exactly. Very near the wire the field is represented by circular lines and is essentially $B_i$.

Michael Faraday, who originated the concept of lines of induction, endowed them with more reality than they are currently given. He imagined

**Fig. 34–7**  Lines of $B$ near a long cylindrical wire. A current $i$, suggested by the central dot, emerges from the page.

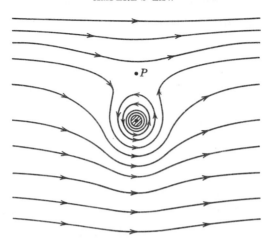

**Fig. 34–8** Lines of **B** near a long current-carrying wire immersed in a uniform external field $\mathbf{B}_e$ that points to the right. The current $i$ is emerging from the page.

that, like stretched rubber bands, they represent the site of mechanical forces. On this picture can we not visualize that the wire in Fig. 34–8 will be pushed up? Today we use lines of induction largely for purposes of visualization. For quantitative calculations we use the field vectors, describing the force on the wire in Fig. 34–8, for example, from the relation $\mathbf{F} = i\mathbf{l} \times \mathbf{B}$.

In applying this relation to Fig. 34–8, we recall that **B** is always the *external field* in which the wire is immersed; that is, it is $\mathbf{B}_e$ and thus points to the right. Since **l** points out of the page, the magnetic force on the wire ($= i\mathbf{l} \times \mathbf{B}_e$) does indeed point up. It is necessary to use only the external field in such calculations because the field set up by the current in the wire cannot exert a force on the wire, just as the gravitational field of the earth cannot exert a force on the earth itself but only on another body. In Fig. 34–7, for example, there is no magnetic force on the wire because no external magnetic field is present.

Faraday's idea of lines of induction was instrumental in overthrowing the older action-at-a-distance theory of magnetic (and electric) attraction. Like many new ideas, it was not immediately accepted. In 1851, for example, Faraday wrote:

> I cannot refrain from again expressing my conviction of the truthfulness of the representation, which the idea of lines of force affords in regard to magnetic action. All the points that are experimentally established in regard to that action—i.e., all that is not hypothetical—appear to be well and truly represented by it.

On the other hand, four years later another well-known British scientist, Sir George Airy, wrote:

> I declare that I can hardly imagine anyone who practically and numerically knows this agreement [with the action-at-a-distance theory] to hesitate an instant in the choice between this simple and precise action, on the one hand, and anything so vague as lines of force, on the other hand.

## 34-4  Two Parallel Conductors

Figure 34-9 shows two long parallel wires separated by a distance $d$ and carrying currents $i_a$ and $i_b$. It is an experimental fact, noted by Ampère only one week after word of Oersted's experiments reached Paris, that two such conductors attract each other.

Some of Ampère's colleagues thought that in view of Oersted's experiment this attraction between two conductors was an obvious result and did not need to be proved. They reasoned that if wire $a$ and wire $b$ each exert forces on a compass needle they should exert forces on each other. This conclusion is wrong. When he heard it, Arago, a contemporary of Ampère, drew two iron keys from his pocket and replied, "Each of these keys attracts a magnet. Do you believe that they therefore also attract each other?"

Wire $a$ in Fig. 34-9 will produce a field of induction $\mathbf{B}_a$ at all nearby points. The magnitude of $\mathbf{B}_a$, due to the current $i_a$, at the site of the second wire is, from Eq. 34-4,

$$B_a = \frac{\mu_0 i_a}{2\pi d}.$$

The right-hand rule shows that the direction of $\mathbf{B}_a$ at wire $b$ is down, as shown in the figure.

Wire $b$, which carries a current $i_b$, finds itself immersed in an *external* field of magnetic induction $\mathbf{B}_a$. A length $l$ of this wire will experience a sideways magnetic force ($= i\mathbf{l} \times \mathbf{B}$) whose magnitude is

$$F_b = i_b l B_a = \frac{\mu_0 l i_b i_a}{2\pi d}. \tag{34-6}$$

The vector rule of signs tells us that $\mathbf{F}_b$ lies in the plane of the wires and points to the left in Fig. 34-9.

We could have started with wire $b$, computed the field of induction which it produces at the site of wire $a$, and then computed the force on wire $a$. The

**Fig. 34-9**  Two parallel wires that carry parallel currents attract each other.

force on wire $a$ would, for parallel currents, point to the right. The forces that the two wires exert on each other are equal and opposite, as they must be according to Newton's law of action and reaction. For antiparallel currents the two wires repel each other.

This discussion reminds us of our discussion of the electric field between two point charges in Section 27–1. There we saw that the charges act on each other through the intermediary of the electric field. The conductors in Fig. 34–9 act on each other through the intermediary of the *magnetic* field. We think in terms of

$$\text{current} \rightleftharpoons \text{field}$$

and not, as in the action-at-a-distance point of view, in terms of

$$\text{current} \rightleftharpoons \text{current}.$$

The attraction between long parallel wires is used to define the ampere. Suppose that the wires are 1 meter apart ($d = 1.0$ meter) and that the two currents are equal ($i_a = i_b = i$). If this common current is adjusted until, by measurement, the force of attraction per unit length between the wires is $2 \times 10^{-7}$ nt/meter, the current is defined to be 1 *ampere*. From Eq. 34–6,

$$\frac{F}{l} = \frac{\mu_0 i^2}{2\pi d} = \frac{(4\pi \times 10^{-7} \text{ weber/amp-m})(1 \text{ amp})^2}{(2\pi)(1 \text{ meter})}$$

$$= 2 \times 10^{-7} \text{ nt/meter}$$

as expected.*

At the National Bureau of Standards primary measurements of current are made with a *current balance*. This consists of a carefully wound coil placed between two other coils, as in Fig. 34–10. The outer pair of coils is fastened to the table, and the inner one is hung from the arm of a balance. The coils are so connected that the current to be measured exists, as a common current, in all three of them.

The coils exert forces on one another—just as the parallel wires of Fig. 34–9 do—which can be measured by loading weights on the balance pan. The current is defined in terms of this measured force and the dimensions of the coils. The current balance is perfectly equivalent to the long parallel wires of Fig. 34–9 but is a much more practical arrangement. Current balance measurements are used primarily to standardize other, more convenient, secondary methods of measuring currents.

▶ **Example 3.** A long horizontal rigidly supported wire carries a current $i_a$ of 100 amp. Directly above it and parallel to it is a fine wire that carries a current $i_b$ of 20 amp and weighs 0.0050 lb/ft (= 0.073 nt/meter). How far above the lower wire should this second wire be strung if we hope to support it by magnetic repulsion?

To provide a repulsion, the two currents must point in opposite directions. For equilibrium, the magnetic force per unit length must equal the weight per unit length and must be oppositely directed.

---

* Note that $\mu_0$ appears in this relation used to define the ampere. As stated on page 848, $\mu_0$ is assigned the (arbitrary) value of $4\pi \times 10^{-7}$ weber/amp-m, and the size of the current that we define as 1 ampere is adjusted to give the required force of attraction per unit length.

**Fig. 34–10**   A current balance.

Solving Eq. 34–6 for $d$ yields

$$d = \frac{\mu_0 i_a i_b}{2\pi(F/l)} = \frac{(4\pi \times 10^{-7} \text{ weber/amp-m})(100 \text{ amp})(20 \text{ amp})}{(2\pi)(0.073 \text{ nt/meter})}$$

$$= 5.5 \times 10^{-3} \text{ meter} = 5.5 \text{ mm.}$$

We assume that the wire diameters are much smaller than their separation. This assumption is necessary because in deriving Eq. 34–6 we tacitly assumed that the magnetic induction produced by one wire is uniform for all points within the second wire.

Is the equilibrium of the suspended wire stable or unstable against vertical displacements? This can be tested by displacing the wire vertically and examining how the forces on the wire change.

Suppose that the fine wire is suspended *below* the rigidly supported wire. How may it be made to "float"? Is the equilibrium against vertical displacements stable or unstable?

**Example 4.** Two parallel wires a distance $d$ apart carry equal currents $i$ in opposite directions. Find the magnetic induction for points between the wires and at a distance $x$ from one wire.

Study of Fig. 34–11 shows that $\mathbf{B}_a$ due to the current $i_a$ and $\mathbf{B}_b$ due to the current $i_b$ point in the same direction at $P$. Each is given by Eq. 34–4 ($B = \mu_0 i/2\pi r$) so that

$$B = B_a + B_b = \frac{\mu_0 i}{2\pi}\left(\frac{1}{x} + \frac{1}{d - x}\right).$$

Fig. 34–11 Example 4.

This relationship does not hold for points inside the wires because Eq. 34–4 is not valid there. ◀

### 34–5  B for a Solenoid

A *solenoid* is a long wire wound in a close-packed helix and carrying a current $i$. We assume that the helix is very long compared with its diameter. What is the nature of the field of **B** that is set up?

For points close to a single turn of the solenoid, the observer is not aware that the wire is bent in an arc. The wire behaves magnetically almost like a long straight wire, and the lines of **B** due to this single turn are almost concentric circles.

The solenoid field is the vector sum of the fields set up by all the turns that make up the solenoid. Figure 34–12, which shows a "solenoid" with widely spaced turns, suggests that the fields tend to cancel between the wires. It suggests also that, at points inside the solenoid and reasonably far from the wires, **B** is parallel to the solenoid axis. In the limiting case of adjacent square tightly packed wires, the solenoid becomes essentially a cylindrical current sheet and the requirements of symmetry then make the statement just given necessarily true. We assume that it is true in what follows.

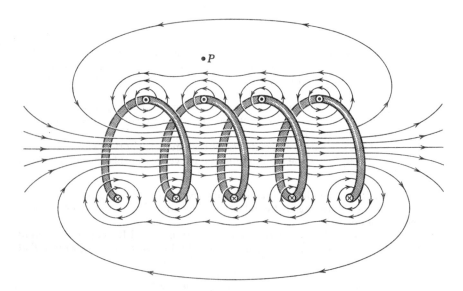

Fig. 34–12  A loosely wound solenoid.

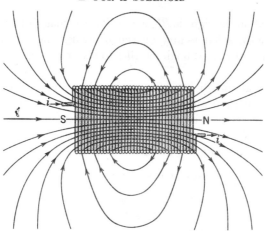

**Fig. 34–13** A solenoid of finite length. The right end, from which lines of **B** emerge, behaves like the north pole of a compass needle. The left end behaves like the south pole.

For points such as $P$ in Fig. 34–12 the field set up by the upper part of the solenoid turns (marked $\odot$) points to the left and tends to cancel the field set up by the lower part of the solenoid turns (marked $\otimes$), which points to the right. As the solenoid becomes more and more ideal, that is, as it approaches the configuration of an infinitely long cylindrical current sheet, the field of induction at outside points approaches zero. Taking the external field to be zero is not a bad assumption for a practical solenoid if its length is much greater than its diameter and if we consider only external points near the central region of the solenoid, that is, away from the ends. Figure 34–13 shows the lines of induction for a real solenoid, which is far from ideal in that the length is not much greater than the diameter. Even here the spacing of the lines of induction in the central plane shows that the external field is much weaker than the internal field.

Let us apply Ampère's law,

$$\oint \mathbf{B} \cdot d\mathbf{l} = \mu_0 i,$$

to the rectangular path $abcd$ in the ideal solenoid of Fig. 34–14. We write the integral $\oint \mathbf{B} \cdot d\mathbf{l}$ as the sum of four integrals, one for each path segment:

$$\oint \mathbf{B} \cdot d\mathbf{l} = \int_a^b \mathbf{B} \cdot d\mathbf{l} + \int_b^c \mathbf{B} \cdot d\mathbf{l} + \int_c^d \mathbf{B} \cdot d\mathbf{l} + \int_d^a \mathbf{B} \cdot d\mathbf{l}.$$

**Fig. 34–14** A section of an ideal solenoid, made of adjacent square turns, equivalent to an infinitely long cylindrical current sheet.

The first integral on the right is $Bh$, where $B$ is the magnitude of the magnetic induction inside the solenoid and $h$ is the arbitrary length of the path from $a$ to $b$. Note that path $ab$, though parallel to the solenoid axis, need not coincide with it.

The second and fourth integrals are zero because for every element of these paths $\mathbf{B}$ is at right angles to the path. This makes $\mathbf{B} \cdot d\mathbf{l}$ zero and thus the integrals are zero. The third integral, which includes the part of the rectangle that lies outside the solenoid, is zero because we have taken $\mathbf{B}$ as zero for all external points for an ideal solenoid.

Thus $\oint \mathbf{B} \cdot d\mathbf{l}$ for the entire rectangular path has the value $Bh$. The net current $i$ that passes through the area bounded by the path of integration is not the same as the current $i_0$ in the solenoid because the path of integration encloses more than one turn. Let $n$ be the *number of turns per unit length;* then

$$i = i_0(nh).$$

Ampère's law then becomes

$$Bh = \mu_0 i_0 nh$$

or $\qquad\qquad B = \mu_0 i_0 n. \qquad\qquad (34\text{-}7)$

Although Eq. 34-7 was derived for an infinitely long ideal solenoid, it holds quite well for actual solenoids for internal points near the center of the solenoid. It shows that $B$ does not depend on the diameter or the length of the solenoid and that $B$ is constant over the solenoid cross section. A solenoid is a practical way to set up a known uniform magnetic field for experimentation, just as a parallel-plate capacitor is a practical way to set up a known uniform electric field.

▶ **Example 5.** A solenoid is 1.0 meter long and 3.0 cm in mean diameter. It has five layers of windings of 850 turns each and carries a current of 5.0 amp.
(a) What is $B$ at its center? From Eq. 34-7,

$$B = \mu_0 i_0 n = (4\pi \times 10^{-7} \text{ weber/amp-m})(5.0 \text{ amp})(5 \times 850 \text{ turns/meter})$$

$$= 2.7 \times 10^{-2} \text{ weber/meter}^2.$$

We can use Eq. 34-7 even if the solenoid has more than one layer of windings because the diameter of the windings does not enter.
(b) What is the magnetic flux $\Phi_B$ for a cross section of the solenoid at its center? To the extent that $\mathbf{B}$ is constant, we can calculate the flux from

$$\Phi_B = \int \mathbf{B} \cdot d\mathbf{S} = BA,$$

where $A$ is the effective cross-sectional area. Let us assume that $A$ represents the area of a circular disk whose diameter is the mean diameter of the windings (3.0 cm). The effective area can then be shown to be $7.1 \times 10^{-4} \text{ meter}^2$, and

$$\Phi_B = BA = (2.7 \times 10^{-2} \text{ weber/meter}^2)(7.1 \times 10^{-4} \text{ meter}^2)$$

$$= 1.9 \times 10^{-5} \text{ weber}.$$

**Example 6.** *A toroid.* Figure 34–15 shows a toroid, which may be described as a solenoid of finite length bent into the shape of a doughnut. Calculate **B** at interior points.

**Fig. 34–15**　Example 6. A toroid.

From symmetry the lines of **B** form concentric circles inside the toroid, as shown in the figure. Let us apply Ampère's law to the circular path of integration of radius $r$:

$$\oint \mathbf{B} \cdot d\mathbf{l} = \mu_0 i$$

or

$$(B)(2\pi r) = \mu_0 i_0 N,$$

where $i_0$ is the current in the toroid windings and $N$ is the total number of turns. This gives

$$B = \frac{\mu_0}{2\pi} \frac{i_0 N}{r}.$$

In contrast to the solenoid, $B$ is not constant over the cross section of a toroid. Show from Ampère's law that $B$ equals zero for points outside an ideal toroid.　　◀

## 34–6　The Biot-Savart Law

Ampère's law can be used to calculate magnetic fields only if the symmetry of the current distribution is high enough to permit the easy evaluation of the line integral $\oint \mathbf{B} \cdot d\mathbf{l}$. This requirement limits the usefulness of the law in practical problems. The law does not fail; it simply becomes difficult to apply in a useful way.

Similarly, in electrostatics, Gauss's law can be used to calculate electric fields only if the symmetry of the charge distribution is high enough to permit the easy evaluation of the surface integral $\oint \mathbf{E} \cdot d\mathbf{S}$. We can, for example, use Gauss's law to find the electric field due to a long uniformly charged rod but we cannot apply it usefully to an electric dipole, for the symmetry is not high enough in this case.

To compute **E** at a given point for an *arbitrary* charge distribution, we divided the distribution into *charge elements dq* and (see Section 27–4) we used Coulomb's law to calculate the field contribution $d\mathbf{E}$ due to each ele-

**Fig. 34–16**   The current element $d$l establishes a magnetic field contribution $d$B at point $P$.

ment at the point in question. We found the field **E** at that point by adding, that is, by integrating, the field contributions $d$**E** for the entire distribution.

We now describe a similar procedure for computing **B** at any point due to an arbitrary current distribution. We divide the current distribution into *current elements* and, using the law of Biot and Savart (which we describe below), we calculate the field contribution $d$**B** due to each current element at the point in question. We find the field **B** at that point by integrating the field contributions for the entire distribution.

Figure 34–16 shows an arbitrary current distribution consisting of a current $i$ in a curved wire. The figure also shows a typical current element; it is a length $d$l of the conductor carrying a current $i$. Its direction is that of the tangent to the conductor (dashed line). A current element cannot exist as an isolated entity because a way must be provided to lead the current into the element at one end and out of it at the other. Nevertheless, we can think of an actual circuit as made up of a large number of current elements placed end to end.

Let $P$ be the point at which we want to know the magnetic induction $d$**B** associated with the current element. According to the Biot-Savart law, $d$**B** is given in magnitude by

$$dB = \frac{\mu_0 i}{4\pi} \frac{dl \sin\theta}{r^2},$$
(34–8)

where **r** is a displacement vector from the element to $P$ and $\theta$ is the angle between this vector and $d$l. The direction of $d$**B** is that of the vector $d$l ✕ **r**. In Fig. 34–16, for example, $d$**B** at point $P$ for the current element shown is directed into the page at right angles to the plane of the figure. Note that Eq. 34–8, being an inverse square law that describes the magnetic induction due to a current element, may be viewed as the magnetic equivalent of Coulomb's law, which is an inverse square law that describes the electric field due to a charge element.

The law of Biot and Savart may be written in vector form as

$$d\mathbf{B} = \frac{\mu_0 i}{4\pi} \frac{d\mathbf{l} \times \mathbf{r}}{r^3}.$$
(34–9)

This formulation reduces to that of Eq. 34–8 when expressed in terms of magnitudes; it also gives complete information about the direction of $d\mathbf{B}$, namely that it is the same as the direction of the vector $d\mathbf{l} \times \mathbf{r}$.

The resultant field at $P$ is found by integrating Eq. 34–9, or

$$\mathbf{B} = \int d\mathbf{B}, \tag{34–10}$$

where the integral is a vector integral.

▶ **Example 7.** *A long straight wire.* We illustrate the law of Biot and Savart by applying it to find $\mathbf{B}$ due to a current $i$ in a long straight wire. We discussed this problem at length in connection with Ampère's law in Section 34–1.

**Fig. 34–17**   Example 7.

Figure 34–17, a side view of the wire, shows a typical current element $dx$. The magnitude of the contribution $d\mathbf{B}$ of this element to the magnetic field at $P$ is found from Eq. 34–8, or

$$dB = \frac{\mu_0 i}{4\pi} \frac{dx \sin\theta}{r^2}.$$

The directions of the contributions $d\mathbf{B}$ at point $P$ for all elements are the same, namely, into the plane of the figure at right angles to the page. Thus the vector integral of Eq. 34–10 reduces to a scalar integral, or

$$B = \int dB = \frac{\mu_0 i}{4\pi} \int_{x=-\infty}^{x=+\infty} \frac{\sin\theta \, dx}{r^2}.$$

Now, $x$, $\theta$, and $r$ are not independent, being related (see Fig. 34–17) by

$$r = \sqrt{x^2 + R^2}$$

and

$$\sin\theta \, [= \sin(\pi - \theta)] = \frac{R}{\sqrt{x^2 + R^2}},$$

so that the expression for $B$ becomes

$$B = \frac{\mu_0 i}{4\pi} \int_{-\infty}^{+\infty} \frac{R \, dx}{(x^2 + R^2)^{\frac{3}{2}}}$$

$$= \frac{\mu_0 i}{4\pi R} \left. \frac{x}{(x^2 + R^2)^{\frac{1}{2}}} \right|_{x=-\infty}^{x=+\infty}$$

$$= \frac{\mu_0}{2\pi} \frac{i}{R}.$$

This is the result that we arrived at earlier for this problem (see Eq. 34–4). The law of Biot and Savart will always yield results that are consistent with Ampère's law and with experiment.

This problem reminds us of its electrostatic equivalent. We derived an expression for $E$ due to a long charged rod, using Gauss's law (Section 28–6); we also solved this problem by integration methods, using Coulomb's law (Section 27–4).

**Example 8.** *A circular current loop.* Figure 34–18 shows a circular loop of radius $R$ carrying a current $i$. Calculate $B$ for points on the axis.

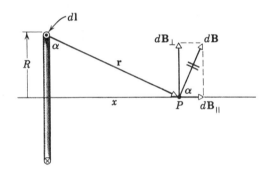

**Fig. 34–18**   Example 8.   A ring of radius $R$ carrying a current $i$.

The vector $dl$ for a current element at the top of the loop points perpendicularly out of the page. The angle $\theta$ between $dl$ and $r$ is 90°, and the plane formed by $dl$ and $r$ is normal to the page. The vector $dB$ for this element is at right angles to this plane and thus lies in the plane of the figure and at right angles to $r$, as the figure shows.

Let us resolve $dB$ into two components, one, $dB_\parallel$, along the axis of the loop and another, $dB_\perp$, at right angles to the axis. Only $dB_\parallel$ contributes to the total induction $B$ at point $P$. This follows because the components $dB_\parallel$ for all current elements lie on the axis and add directly; however, the components $dB_\perp$ point in different directions perpendicular to the axis, and their resultant for the complete loop is zero, from symmetry. Thus

$$B = \int dB_\parallel,$$

where the integral is a simple scalar integration over the current elements.

For the current element shown in Fig. 34–18 we have, from the Biot-Savart law (Eq. 34–8),

$$dB = \frac{\mu_0 i}{4\pi} \frac{dl \sin 90°}{r^2}.$$

We also have $$dB_{\parallel} = dB \cos \alpha.$$

Combining gives $$dB_{\parallel} = \frac{\mu_0 i \cos \alpha \, dl}{4\pi r^2}.$$

Figure 34–18 shows that $r$ and $\alpha$ are not independent of each other. Let us express each in terms of a new variable $x$, the distance from the center of the loop to the point $P$. The relationships are

$$r = \sqrt{R^2 + x^2}$$

and $$\cos \alpha = \frac{R}{r} = \frac{R}{\sqrt{R^2 + x^2}}.$$

Substituting these values into the expression for $dB_{\parallel}$ gives

$$dB_{\parallel} = \frac{\mu_0 i R}{4\pi (R^2 + x^2)^{3/2}} \, dl.$$

Note that $i$, $R$, and $x$ have the same values for all current elements. Integrating this equation, noting that $\int dl$ is simply the circumference of the loop ($= 2\pi R$), yields

$$B = \int dB_{\parallel} = \frac{\mu_0 i R}{4\pi (R^2 + x^2)^{3/2}} \int dl$$

$$= \frac{\mu_0 i R^2}{2(R^2 + x^2)^{3/2}}. \tag{34–11}$$

◀

If we put $x \gg R$ in Example 8 so that points close to the loop are not considered, Eq. 34–11 reduces to

$$B = \frac{\mu_0 i R^2}{2x^3}.$$

Recalling that $\pi R^2$ is the area $A$ of the loop and considering loops with $N$ turns, we can write this equation as

$$B = \frac{\mu_0}{2\pi} \frac{(NiA)}{x^3} = \frac{\mu_0}{2\pi} \frac{\mu}{x^3},$$

where $\mu$ is the *magnetic dipole moment* of the current loop. This reminds us of the result derived in Problem 10, Chapter 27 $[E = (1/2\pi\epsilon_0)(p/x^3)]$, which is the formula for the *electric* field strength on the axis of an *electric* dipole.

Thus we have shown in two ways that a current loop can be regarded as a magnetic dipole: It experiences a torque given by $\tau = \mu \times B$ when placed in an *external* magnetic field (Eq. 33–11); it generates its own magnetic field given, for points on the axis, by the equation just developed.

Table 34–1 is a summary of the properties of electric and magnetic dipoles.

**Table 34–1**

SOME DIPOLE EQUATIONS

| Property | Dipole Type | Equation |
|----------|-------------|----------|
| Torque in an external field | electric | $\tau = \mathbf{p} \times \mathbf{E}$ |
| | magnetic | $\tau = \boldsymbol{\mu} \times \mathbf{B}$ |
| Energy in an external field | electric | $U = -\mathbf{p} \cdot \mathbf{E}$ |
| | magnetic | $U = -\boldsymbol{\mu} \cdot \mathbf{B}$ |
| Field at distant points along axis | electric | $E = \dfrac{1}{2\pi\epsilon_0}\dfrac{p}{x^3}$ |
| | magnetic | $B = \dfrac{\mu_0}{2\pi}\dfrac{\mu}{x^3}$ |
| Field at distant points along perpendicular bisector | electric | $E = \dfrac{1}{4\pi\epsilon_0}\dfrac{p}{x^3}$ |
| | magnetic | $B = \dfrac{\mu_0}{4\pi}\dfrac{\mu}{x^3}$ |

▶ **Example 9.** In the Bohr model of the hydrogen atom the electron circulates around the nucleus in a path of radius $5.1 \times 10^{-11}$ meter at a frequency $\nu$ of $6.8 \times 10^{15}$ rev/sec. (a) What value of $B$ is set up at the center of the orbit?

The current is the rate at which charge passes any point on the orbit and is given by

$$i = e\nu = (1.6 \times 10^{-19} \text{ coul})(6.8 \times 10^{15}/\text{sec}) = 1.1 \times 10^{-3} \text{ amp.}$$

$B$ at the center of the orbit is given by Eq. 34–11 with $x = 0$, or

$$B = \frac{\mu_0 i R^2}{2(R^2 + x^2)^{3/2}} = \frac{\mu_0 i}{2R}$$

$$= \frac{(4\pi \times 10^{-7} \text{ weber/amp-m})(1.1 \times 10^{-3} \text{ amp})}{(2)(5.1 \times 10^{-11} \text{ meter})}$$

$$= 14 \text{ webers/meter}^2.$$

(b) What is the equivalent magnetic dipole moment? From Eq. 33–10,

$$\mu = NiA = (1)(1.1 \times 10^{-3} \text{ amp})(\pi)(5.1 \times 10^{-11} \text{ meter})^2$$

$$= 9.0 \times 10^{-24} \text{ amp-m}^2. \qquad ◀$$

# QUESTIONS

1. Can the path of integration around which we apply Ampère's law pass *through* a conductor?

2. Suppose we set up a path of integration around a cable that contains twelve wires with different currents (some in opposite directions) in each wire. How do we calculate $i$ in Ampère's law in such a case?

3. Apply Ampère's law qualitatively to the three paths shown in Fig. 34–19.

**Fig. 34–19**

4. Is **B** constant in magnitude for points that lie on a given line of induction?

5. Discuss and compare Gauss's law and Ampère's law.

6. A current is set up in a long copper pipe. Is there a magnetic field (a) inside and (b) outside the pipe?

7. Equation 34–4 ($B = \mu_0 i/2\pi r$) suggests that a strong magnetic field is set up at points near a long wire carrying a current. Since there is a current $i$ and a magnetic field **B**, why is there not a force on the wire in accord with the equation $\mathbf{F} = i\mathbf{l} \times \mathbf{B}$?

8. In electronics, wires that carry equal but opposite currents are often twisted together to reduce their magnetic effect at distant points. Why is this effective?

9. A beam of 20-Mev protons emerges from a cyclotron. Is a magnetic field associated with these particles?

10. Test the "floating" wire of Example 3 for equilibrium under *horizontal* displacements. Consider that the wire floats above the rigidly supported wire and also below it. Summarize the equilibrium situation for both wire positions and for both vertical and horizontal displacements.

11. Explain qualitatively the forces of interaction between parallel wires carrying parallel or antiparallel currents in terms of Faraday's lines of induction representation.

12. Comment on this statement: "The magnetic induction outside a long solenoid cannot be zero, if only for the reason that the helical nature of the windings produces a field for external points like that of a straight wire along the solenoid axis."

13. A current is sent through a vertical spring from whose lower end a weight is hanging; what will happen?

14. Does Eq. 34–7 ($B = \mu_0 i n$) hold for a solenoid of square cross section?

15. What is the direction of the magnetic fields at points $a$, $b$, and $c$ in Fig. 34–16 set up by the particular current element shown?

16. In a circular loop of wire carrying a current $i$, is **B** uniform for all points within the loop?

17. Discuss analogies and differences between Coulomb's law and the Biot-Savart law.

18. Equation 34–9 gives the law of Biot and Savart in vector form. Write its electrostatic equivalent [that is, Eq. 27–6, or $dE = dq/(4\pi\epsilon_0 r^2)$] in vector form.

19. How might you measure the magnetic dipole moment of a compass needle?

20. What is the basis for saying that a current loop is a magnetic dipole?

## PROBLEMS

1. A #10 bare copper wire (0.10 in. in diameter) can carry a current of 50 amp without overheating. For this current, what is $B$ at the surface of the wire?

2. A surveyor is using a compass 20 ft below a power line in which there is a steady current of 100 amp. Will this interfere seriously with the compass reading? The horizontal component of the earth's magnetic field at the site is 0.2 gauss.

3. A long straight wire carries a current of 50 amp. An electron, traveling at $10^7$ meters/sec, is 5.0 cm from the wire. What force acts on the electron if the electron velocity is directed (a) toward the wire, (b) parallel to the wire, and (c) at right angles to the directions defined by (a) and (b)?

4. A conductor consists of an infinite number of adjacent wires, each infinitely long and carrying a current $i$. Show that the lines of **B** will be as represented in Fig. 34–20 and that $B$ for all points in front of the infinite current sheet will be given by

$$B = \tfrac{1}{2}\mu_0 n i,$$

where $n$ is the number of conductors per unit length. Derive both by direct application of Ampère's law and by considering the problem as a limiting case of Example 2.

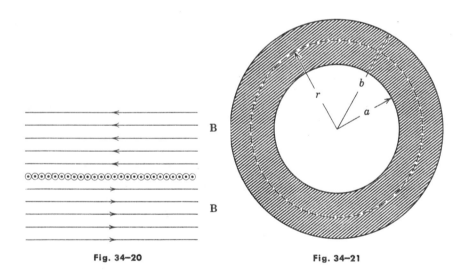

Fig. 34–20                    Fig. 34–21

5. Figure 34–21 shows a hollow cylindrical conductor of radii $a$ and $b$ which carries a current $i$ uniformly spread over its cross section. (a) Show that the magnetic field $B$ for points inside the body of the conductor (that is, $a < r < b$) is given by

$$B = \frac{\mu_0 i}{2\pi(b^2 - a^2)} \frac{r^2 - a^2}{r}.$$

Check this formula for the limiting case of $a = 0$. (b) Make a rough plot of the general behavior of $B(r)$ from $r = 0$ to $r \to \infty$.

6. A long coaxial cable consists of two concentric conductors with the dimensions shown in Fig. 34–22. There are equal and opposite currents $i$ in the conductors. (a) Find the magnetic induction $B$ at $r$ within the inner conductor ($r < a$). (b) Find $B$ between the two conductors ($a < r < b$). (c) Find $B$ within the outer conductor ($b < r < c$). (d) Find $B$ outside the cable ($r > c$).

Fig. 34–22                         Fig. 34–23

7. A long copper wire carries a current of 10 amp. Calculate the magnetic flux per meter of wire for a plane surface $S$ inside the wire, as in Fig. 34–23.

8. Two long, parallel #10 copper wires (diameter = 0.10 in.) carry currents of 10 amp in opposite directions. (a) If their centers are 2.0 cm apart, calculate the flux per meter that exists in the space between the axes of the wires. (b) What fraction of the flux in (a) lies inside the wires? (c) Repeat the calculation of (a) for parallel currents.

9. A long wire carrying a current of 100 amp is placed in a uniform external magnetic field of 50 gauss. The wire is at right angles to this external field. Locate the points at which the *resultant* magnetic field is zero.

10. Two long wires a distance $d$ apart carry equal antiparallel currents $i$, as in Fig. 34–24. Show that $B$ at point $P$, which is equidistant from the wires, is given by

$$B = \frac{2\mu_0 i d}{\pi(4R^2 + d^2)}.$$

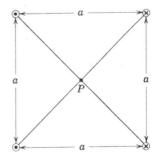

Fig. 34–24                         Fig. 34–25

11. Four long #10 copper wires are parallel to each other, their cross section forming a square 20 cm on edge. A 20-amp current is set up in each wire in the direction shown in Fig. 34–25. What are the magnitude and direction of **B** at the center of the square?

12. In Problem 11 what is the force per meter acting on the lower left wire, in magnitude and direction?

13. Figure 34–26 shows a long wire carrying a current of 30 amp. The rectangular loop carries a current of 20 amp. Calculate the resultant force acting on the loop. Assume that $a = 1.0$ cm, $b = 8.0$ cm, and $l = 30$ cm.

14. Derive the solenoid equation (Eq. 34–7) starting from the expression for the field on the axis of a circular loop (Example 8). (Hint: Subdivide the solenoid into a series of current loops of infinitesimal thickness and integrate.)

15. A square loop of wire of edge $a$ carries a current $i$. Show that the value of $B$ at the center is given by

$$B = \frac{2\sqrt{2}\,\mu_0 i}{\pi a}.$$

16. A square loop of wire of edge $a$ carries a current $i$. (a) Show that $B$ for a point on the axis of the loop and a distance $x$ from its center is given by

$$B = \frac{4\mu_0 i a^2}{\pi(4x^2 + a^2)(4x^2 + 2a^2)^{1/2}}.$$

(b) Does this reduce to the result of Problem 15 for $x = 0$? (c) Does the square loop behave like a dipole for points such that $x \gg a$? If so, what is its dipole moment?

17. A straight wire segment of length $l$ carries a current $i$. (a) Show that the field of induction $B$ to be associated with this segment, at a distance $R$ from the segment along a perpendicular bisector (see Fig. 34–27), is given in magnitude by

$$B = \frac{\mu_0 i}{2\pi R}\frac{l}{(l^2 + 4R^2)^{1/2}}.$$

(b) Does this expression reduce to an expected result as $l \rightarrow \infty$?

18. The wire shown in Fig. 34–28 carries a current $i$. What is the magnetic induction at the center $C$ of the semicircle arising from (a) each straight segment of length $l$, (b) the semicircular segment of radius $R$, and (c) the entire wire?

19. (a) A wire in the form of a regular polygon of $n$ sides is just enclosed by a circle of radius $a$. If the current in this

**Fig. 34–26**

**Fig. 34–27**

**Fig. 34–28**

wire is $i$, show that the magnetic induction at the center of the circle is given by

$$B = \frac{\mu_0 n i}{2\pi a}\tan(\pi/n).$$

(b) Show that as $n \rightarrow \infty$ this result approaches that of a circular loop.

20. (a) Show that $B$ at the center of a rectangle of length $l$ and width $d$, carrying a current $i$, is given by

$$B = \frac{2\mu_0 i}{\pi} \frac{(l^2 + d^2)^{1/2}}{ld}.$$

(b) What does $B$ reduce to for $l \gg d$? Is this a result that you expect?

21. *Helmholtz coils.* Two 300-turn coils are arranged a distance apart equal to their radius, as in Fig. 34–29. For $R = 5.0$ cm and $i = 50$ amp, plot $B$ as a function of distance $x$ along the common axis over the range $x = -5$ cm to $x = +5$ cm, taking $x = 0$ at point $P$. (Such coils provide an especially uniform field of $B$ near point $P$.)

22. In Problem 21 let the separation of the coils be a variable $z$. Show that if $z$ equals $R$, then not only the first derivative $(dB/dx)$ but also the second $(d^2B/dx^2)$ of $B$ is zero at point $P$. This accounts for the uniformity of $B$ near point $P$ for this particular coil separation.

**Fig. 34–29**

23. A long "hairpin" is formed by bending a piece of wire as shown in Fig. 34–19. If a 10-amp current is set up, what are the direction and magnitude of **B** at point $a$? At point $b$? Take $R = 0.50$ cm.

24. Calculate **B** at point $P$ in Fig. 34–30. Assume that $i = 10$ amp and $a = 8.0$ cm.

**Fig. 34–30**

25. A plastic disk of radius $R$ has a charge $q$ uniformly distributed over its surface. If the disk is rotated at an angular frequency $\omega$ about its axis, show that (a) the induction at the center of the disk is

$$B = \frac{\mu_0 \omega q}{2\pi R}$$

and (b) the magnetic dipole moment of the disk is

$$\mu = \frac{\omega q R^2}{4}.$$

(Hint: The rotating disk is equivalent to an array of current loops; see Example 8.)

26. You are given a length $l$ of wire in which a current $i$ may be established. The wire may be formed into a circle or a square. Which yields the larger value for $B$ at the central point? See Problem 15.

27. A circular copper loop of radius 10 cm carries a current of 15 amp. At its center is placed a second loop of radius 1.0 cm, having 50 turns and a current of 1.0 amp. (a) What magnetic induction **B** does the large loop set up at its center? (b) What torque acts on the small loop? Assume that the planes of the two loops are at right angles and that the induction **B** provided by the large loop is essentially uniform throughout the volume occupied by the small loop.

28. Show that it is impossible for a uniform magnetic field **B** to drop abruptly to zero as one moves at right angles to it, as suggested by the horizontal arrow in Fig. 34–31 (see point $a$). In actual magnets fringing of the lines of force always occurs, which means that **B** approaches zero in a continuous and gradual way. (Hint: Apply Ampère's law to the rectangular path shown by the dashed lines.)

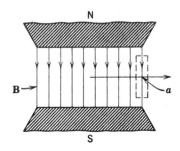

**Fig. 34–31**

# Faraday's Law

## CHAPTER 35

## 35-1 Faraday's Experiments

For some physical laws it is hard to find experiments that lead in a direct and convincing way to the formulation of the law. Gauss's law, for example, emerged only slowly as the common factor with whose aid all electrostatic experiments could be interpreted and correlated. In Chapter 28 we found it best to state Gauss's law first and then to show that the underlying experiments were consistent with it.

Faraday's *law of electromagnetic induction*, which is one of the basic equations of electromagnetism (see Table 38-3), is different in that there are a number of simple experiments from which the law can be—and was—deduced directly. Such experiments were carried out by Michael Faraday in England in 1831 and by Joseph Henry in the United States at about the same time.

Figure 35-1 shows the terminals of a coil connected to a galvanometer. Normally we would not expect this instrument to deflect because there seems to be no electromotive force in this circuit; but if we push a bar magnet toward the coil, with its north pole facing the coil, a remarkable thing happens. *While the magnet is moving*, the galvanometer deflects, showing that a current has been set up in the coil. If the magnet is held stationary with respect to the coil, the galvanometer does not deflect. If the magnet is moved away from the coil, the galvanometer again deflects, but in the opposite direction, which means that the current in the coil is in the opposite direction. If we use the south pole end of a magnet instead of the north pole end, the experiment works as described but the deflections are reversed. Further experimentation shows that *what matters is the relative motion of the*

**Fig. 35–1**  Galvanometer $G$ deflects while the magnet is moving with respect to the coil.

*magnet and the coil.*  It makes no difference whether the magnet is moved toward the coil or the coil toward the magnet.

The current that appears in this experiment is called an *induced current* and is said to be set up by an *induced electromotive force.*  Faraday was able to deduce from experiments like this the law that gives their magnitude and direction.  Such emfs are very important in practice.  The chances are good that the lights in the room in which you are reading this book are operated from an induced emf produced in a commercial electric generator.

In another experiment the apparatus of Fig. 35–2 is used.  The coils are placed close together but at rest with respect to each other.  When the switch $S$ is closed, thus setting up a steady current in the right-hand coil, the galvanometer deflects momentarily; when the switch is opened, thus interrupting this current, the galvanometer again deflects momentarily, but in the opposite direction.  No gross objects are moving in this experiment. In Faraday's words:

> When the contact was made, there was a sudden and very slight effect at the galvanometer, and there was also a similar slight effect when the contact with the battery was broken.  But whilst the voltaic current was continuing to pass through the one helix, no galvanometrical appearances nor any effect like induction upon the other helix could be perceived, although the active power of the battery was proved to be very great. . . .

Experiment shows that there will be an induced emf in the left coil of Fig. 35–2 whenever the current in the right coil is *changing.*  It is the *rate at which the current is changing* and *not the size of the current* that is significant.

**Fig. 35–2**  Galvanometer $G$ deflects momentarily when switch $S$ is closed or opened.

### 35-2 Faraday's Law of Induction

Faraday had the insight to perceive that the change in the flux $\Phi_B$ of magnetic induction for the left coil in the preceding experiments is the important common factor. This flux may be set up by a bar magnet or a current loop. Faraday's law of induction says that the induced emf $\mathcal{E}$ in a circuit is equal to the negative rate at which the flux through the circuit is changing. If the rate of change of flux is in webers/sec, the emf $\mathcal{E}$ will be in volts. In equation form

$$\mathcal{E} = -\frac{d\Phi_B}{dt}. \tag{35-1}$$

This equation is called *Faraday's law of induction*. The minus sign is an indication of the *direction* of the induced emf, a matter we discuss further in Section 35-3.

If Eq. 35-1 is applied to a coil of $N$ turns, an emf appears in every turn and these emfs are to be added. If the coil is so tightly wound that each turn can be said to occupy the same region of space, the flux through each turn will then be the same. The flux through each turn is also the same for (ideal) toroids and solenoids (see Section 34-5). The induced emf in all such devices is given by

$$\mathcal{E} = -N\frac{d\Phi_B}{dt} = -\frac{d(N\Phi_B)}{dt}, \tag{35-2}$$

where $N\Phi_B$ measures the so-called *flux linkages* in the device.

Figures 35-1 and 35-2 suggest that there are at least two ways in which we can make the flux through a circuit change and thus induce an emf in that circuit. The coil that is connected to the galvanometer cannot tell in which of these experiments it is participating; it is aware only that the flux passing through its cross-sectional area is changing. The flux through a circuit can also be changed by changing its shape, that is, by squeezing or stretching it.

▶ **Example 1.** A long solenoid has 200 turns/cm and carries a current of 1.5 amp; its diameter is 3.0 cm. At its center we place a 100-turn, close-packed coil of diameter 2.0 cm. This coil is arranged so that **B** at the center of the solenoid is parallel to its axis. The current in the solenoid is reduced to zero and then raised to 1.5 amp in the other direction at a steady rate over a period of 0.050 sec. What induced emf appears in the coil while the current is being changed?

The induction $B$ at the center of the solenoid is given by Eq. 34-7, or

$$B = \mu_0 n i = (4\pi \times 10^{-7} \text{ weber/amp-m})(200 \times 10^2 \text{ turns/meter})(1.5 \text{ amp})$$

$$= 3.8 \times 10^{-2} \text{ weber/meter}^2.$$

The area of the coil (not of the solenoid) is $3.1 \times 10^{-4}$ meter$^2$. The initial flux $\Phi_B$ through each turn of the coil is given by

$$\Phi_B = BA = (3.8 \times 10^{-2} \text{ weber/meter}^2)(3.1 \times 10^{-4} \text{ meter}^2) = 1.2 \times 10^{-5} \text{ weber}.$$

The flux goes from an initial value of $1.2 \times 10^{-5}$ weber to a final value of $-1.2 \times 10^{-5}$ weber. The *change* in flux $\Delta\Phi_B$ for each turn of the coil during the 0.050-sec period is thus twice the initial value. The induced emf is given by

$$\mathcal{E} = -\frac{N\Delta\Phi_B}{\Delta t} = -\frac{(100)(2 \times 1.2 \times 10^{-5} \text{ weber})}{0.050 \text{ sec}} = -4.8 \times 10^{-2} \text{ volt} = -48 \text{ mv.}$$

The minus sign deals with the *direction* of the emf, as we explain below.    ◄

### 35-3   Lenz's Law

So far we have not specified the directions of the induced emfs. Although these directions can be found from a formal analysis of Faraday's law, we prefer to find them from the conservation-of-energy principle which, in this context, takes the form of Lenz's law: *The induced current will appear in such a direction that it opposes the change that produced it.* * The minus sign in Faraday's law suggests this opposition. In mechanics the energy principle

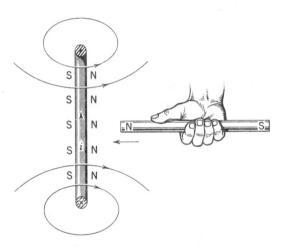

**Fig. 35-3**  If the magnet is moved toward the loop, the induced current points as shown, setting up a magnetic field that opposes the motion of the magnet.

often allows us to draw conclusions about mechanical systems without analyzing them in detail. We use the same approach here.

Lenz's law refers to induced *currents*, which means that it applies only to closed circuits. If the circuit is open, we can usually think in terms of what would happen if it were closed and in this way find the direction of the induced emf.

Consider the first of Faraday's experiments described in Section 35-1. Figure 35-3 shows the north pole of a magnet and a cross section of a nearby conducting loop. As we push the magnet toward the loop, an induced current is set up in the loop. What is its direction?

---

* Heinrich Friedrich Lenz (1804-1865) deduced this law in 1834. Faraday also discovered how to determine the directions of induced emfs, but he did not express his results as succinctly as Lenz.

A current loop sets up a magnetic field at distant points like that of a magnetic dipole, one face of the loop being a north pole, the opposite face being a south pole. The north pole, as for bar magnets, is that face *from* which the lines of **B** emerge. If, as Lenz's law predicts, the loop in Fig. 35–3 is to oppose the motion of the magnet toward it, the face of the loop toward the magnet must become a north pole. The two north poles—one of the current loop and one of the magnet—will repel each other. The right-hand rule shows that for the magnetic field set up by the loop to emerge from the right face of the loop the induced current must be as shown. The current will be counterclockwise as we sight along the magnet toward the loop.

When we push the magnet toward the loop (or the loop toward the magnet), an induced current appears. In terms of Lenz's law this pushing is the "change" that produces the induced current, and, according to this law, the induced current will oppose the "push." If we pull the magnet away from the coil, the induced current will oppose the "pull" by creating a *south* pole on the right-hand face of the loop of Fig. 35–3. To make the right-hand face a south pole, the current must be opposite to that shown in Fig. 35–3. Whether we pull or push the magnet, its motion will always be automatically opposed.

The agent that causes the magnet to move, either toward the coil or away from it, will always experience a resisting force and will thus be required to do work. From the conservation-of-energy principle this work done on the system must be exactly equal to the Joule heat produced in the coil, since these are the only two energy transfers that occur in the system. If we move the magnet more rapidly, we will have to do work at a faster rate and the rate of the Joule heating will increase correspondingly. If we cut the loop and then perform the experiment, there will be no induced current, no Joule heating, no force on the magnet, and no work required to move it. There will still be an emf in the loop, but, like a battery connected to an open circuit, it will not set up a current.

If the current in Fig. 35–3 were in the *opposite* direction to that shown, the face of the loop toward the magnet would be a south pole, which would pull the bar magnet toward the loop. We would only need to push the magnet slightly to start the process and then the action would be self-perpetuating. The magnet would accelerate toward the loop, increasing its kinetic energy all the time. At the same time Joule heat would appear in the loop at a rate that would increase with time. This would indeed be a something-for-nothing situation! Needless to say, it does not occur.

Let us apply Lenz's law to Fig. 35–3 in a different way. Figure 35–4 shows the lines of **B** for the bar magnet.* On this point of view the "change" is the increase in $\Phi_B$ through the loop caused by bringing the magnet nearer. The induced current opposes this change by setting up a field that tends to oppose the increase in flux caused by the moving magnet. Thus the field

---

* There are two fields of **B** in this problem—one connected with the current loop and one with the bar magnet. The student must always be certain which one is meant.

**Fig. 35–4** In moving the magnet toward the loop, we increase $\Phi_B$ through the loop.

due to the induced current must point from left to right through the plane of the coil, in agreement with our earlier conclusion.

It is not significant here that the induced field opposes the magnet *field* but rather that it opposes the *change*, which in this case is the *increase* in $\Phi_B$ through the loop. If we withdraw the magnet, we reduce $\Phi_B$ through the loop. The induced field will now oppose this decrease in $\Phi_B$ (that is, the change) by *re-enforcing* the magnet field. In each case the induced field opposes the change that gives rise to it.

### 35–4   Induction—A Quantitative Study

The example of Fig. 35–4, although easy to understand qualitatively, does not lend itself to quantitative calculations. Consider then Fig. 35–5, which shows a rectangular loop of wire of width $l$, one end of which is in a uniform field **B** pointing at right angles to the plane of the loop. This field of **B** may be produced in the gap of a large electromagnet like that of Fig. 33–2. The dashed lines show the assumed limits of the magnetic field. The experiment consists in pulling the loop to the right at a constant speed $v$.

**Fig. 35–5**  A rectangular loop is pulled out of a magnetic field with velocity $v$.

Note that the situation described by Fig. 35–5 does not differ in any essential particular from that of Fig. 35–4. In each case a conducting loop and a magnet are in relative motion; in each case the flux of the field of the magnet through the loop is being caused to change with time.

The flux $\Phi_B$ enclosed by the loop in Fig. 35–5 is

$$\Phi_B = Blx,$$

where $lx$ is the area of that part of the loop in which $B$ is not zero. The emf $\mathcal{E}$ is found from Faraday's law, or

$$\mathcal{E} = -\frac{d\Phi_B}{dt} = -\frac{d}{dt}(Blx) = -Bl\frac{dx}{dt} = Blv, \qquad (35\text{–}3)$$

where we have set $-dx/dt$ equal to the speed $v$ at which the loop is pulled out of the magnetic field. Note that the only dimension of the loop that enters into Eq. 35–3 is the length $l$ of the left end conductor. As we shall see later, the induced emf in Fig. 35–5 may be regarded as localized here. An induced emf such as this, produced by pulling a conductor through a magnetic field, is sometimes called a *motional emf*.

The emf $Blv$ sets up a current in the loop given by

$$i = \frac{\mathcal{E}}{R} = \frac{Blv}{R}, \qquad (35\text{–}4)$$

where $R$ is the loop resistance. From Lenz's law, this current (and thus $\mathcal{E}$) must be clockwise in Fig. 35–5; it opposes the "change" (the decrease in $\Phi_B$) by setting up a field that is parallel to the external field within the loop.

The current in the loop will cause forces $\mathbf{F}_1$, $\mathbf{F}_2$, and $\mathbf{F}_3$ to act on the three conductors, in accord with Eq. 33–6a, or

$$\mathbf{F} = i\mathbf{l} \times \mathbf{B}. \qquad (35\text{–}5)$$

Because $\mathbf{F}_2$ and $\mathbf{F}_3$ are equal and opposite, they cancel each other; $\mathbf{F}_1$, which is the force that opposes our effort to move the loop, is given in magnitude from Eqs. 35–5 and 35–4 as

$$F_1 = ilB \sin 90° = \frac{B^2l^2v}{R}.$$

The agent that pulls the loop must do work at the steady rate of

$$P = F_1v = \frac{B^2l^2v^2}{R}. \qquad (35\text{–}6)$$

From the principle of the conservation of energy, Joule heat must appear in the resistor at this same rate. We introduced the conservation-of-energy principle into our derivation when we wrote down the expression for the current (Eq. 35–4); the student will recall that the relation $i = \mathcal{E}/R$ for single-loop circuits is a direct consequence of this principle. Thus we should be able to write down the expression for the rate of Joule heating in the loop with the expectation that we will obtain a result identical with Eq. 35–6. Recalling Eq. 35–4, we put

$$P_J = i^2 R = \left(\frac{Blv}{R}\right)^2 R = \frac{B^2 l^2 v^2}{R},$$

which is indeed the expected result. This example provides a quantitative illustration of the conversion of mechanical energy (the work done by an external agent) into electrical energy (the induced emf) and finally into thermal energy (the Joule heating).

Figure 35–6 shows a side view of the coil in the field. In Fig. 35–6a the coil is stationary; in Fig. 35–6b we are moving it to the right; in Fig. 35–6c we are moving it to the left. The lines of induction in these figures represent the *resultant field* produced by the vector addition of the field $B_0$ due to the magnet and the field $B_i$ due to the induced current, if any, in the coil.

**Fig. 35–6**    Side view of a rectangular loop in a magnetic field showing the loop (a) at rest, (b) being pulled out, and (c) being pushed in.

These lines suggest convincingly that the agent moving the coil always experiences an opposing force.

▶ **Example 2.** Figure 35–7 shows a rectangular loop of resistance $R$, width $l$, and length $a$ being pulled at constant speed $v$ through a region of thickness $d$ in which a uniform field of induction **B** is set up by a magnet.

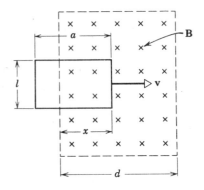

**Fig. 35–7** Example 2. A rectangular loop is caused to move with a velocity **v** through a magnetic field. The position of the loop is measured by $x$, the distance between the effective left edge of the field **B** and the right end of the loop.

(a) Plot the flux $\Phi_B$ through the loop as a function of the coil position $x$. Assume that $l = 4$ cm, $a = 10$ cm, $d = 15$ cm, $R = 16$ ohms, $B = 2.0$ webers/meter², and $v = 1.0$ meter/sec.

The flux $\Phi_B$ is zero when the loop is not in the field; it is $Bla$ when the loop is entirely in the field; it is $Blx$ when the loop is entering the field and $Bl[a - (x - d)]$ when the loop is leaving the field. These conclusions, which the student should verify, are shown graphically in Fig. 35–8a.

(b) Plot the induced emf $\mathcal{E}$.

The induced emf $\mathcal{E}$ is given by $\mathcal{E} = -d\Phi_B/dt$, which can be written as

$$\mathcal{E} = -\frac{d\Phi_B}{dt} = -\frac{d\Phi_B}{dx}\frac{dx}{dt} = -\frac{d\Phi_B}{dx}v,$$

where $d\Phi_B/dx$ is the slope of the curve of Fig. 35–8a. $\mathcal{E}(x)$ is plotted in Fig. 35–8b. Lenz's law, from the same type of reasoning as that used for Fig. 35–5, shows that when the coil is entering the field the emf $\mathcal{E}$ acts counterclockwise as seen from above. Note that there is no emf when the coil is entirely in the magnetic field because the flux $\Phi_B$ through the coil is not changing with time, as Fig. 35–8a shows.

(c) Plot the rate $P$ of Joule heating in the loop.

This is given by $P = \mathcal{E}^2/R$. It may be calculated by squaring the ordinate of the curve of Fig. 35–8b and dividing by $R$. The result is plotted in Fig. 35–8c.

If the fringing of the magnetic field, which cannot be avoided in practice (see Problem 34–28), is taken into account, the sharp bends and corners in Fig. 35–8 will be replaced by smooth curves. What changes would occur in the curves of Fig. 35–8 if the coil were open circuited?

**Example 3.** A copper rod of length $L$ rotates at angular frequency $\omega$ in a uniform field of magnetic induction **B** as shown in Fig. 35–9. Find the emf $\mathcal{E}$ developed between the two ends of the rod.

If a wire of length $dl$ is moved at velocity **v** at right angles to a field **B**, a motional emf $d\mathcal{E}$ will be developed (see Eq. 35–3) given by

$$d\mathcal{E} = Bv\,dl.$$

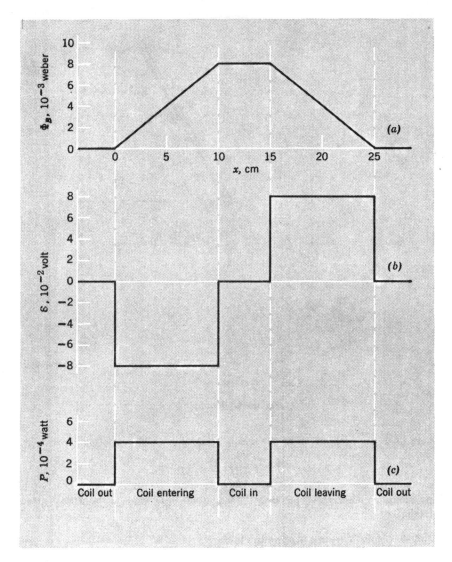

**Fig. 35–8**    Example 2.

The rod of Fig. 35–9 may be divided into elements of length $dl$, the linear speed $v$ of each element being $\omega l$. Each element is perpendicular to **B** and is also moving in a direction at right angles to **B** so that

$$\mathcal{E} = \int d\mathcal{E} = \int_0^L Bv \, dl = \int_0^L B(\omega l) \, dl = \tfrac{1}{2}B\omega L^2.$$

For a second approach, consider that at any instant the flux enclosed by the sector $aOb$ in Fig. 35–9 is given by

$$\Phi_B = BA = B(\tfrac{1}{2}L^2\theta),$$

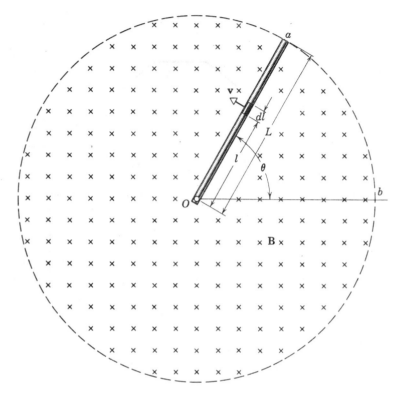

**Fig. 35–9**   Example 3.

where $\frac{1}{2}L^2\theta$ can be shown to be the area of the sector.  Differentiating gives

$$\frac{d\Phi_B}{dt} = \frac{1}{2}BL^2\frac{d\theta}{dt} = \frac{1}{2}B\omega L^2.$$

From Faraday's law, this is precisely the magnitude of $\mathcal{E}$, which agrees with the result just derived.                                                                    ◀

### 35–5  Time-Varying Magnetic Fields

So far we have considered emfs induced by the relative motion of magnets and coils.  In this section we assume that there is no physical motion of gross objects but that the magnetic field may vary with time.  If a conducting loop is placed in such a time-varying field, the flux through the loop will change and an induced emf will appear in the loop.  This emf will set the charge carriers in motion, that is, it will induce a current.

From a microscopic point of view we can say, equally well, that the changing flux of **B** sets up an induced electric field **E** at various points around the loop.  These induced electric fields are just as real as electric fields set up by static charges and will exert a force **F** on a test charge $q_0$ given by **F** = $q_0$**E**.  Thus we can restate Faraday's law of induction in a loose but informative way as: *A changing magnetic field produces an electric field.*

To fix these ideas, consider Fig. 35-10, which shows a uniform field of induction **B** at right angles to the plane of the page. We assume that **B** is increasing in magnitude at the same constant rate $dB/dt$ at every point. This could be done by causing the current in the windings of the electromagnet that establishes the field to increase with time in the proper way.

The circle of arbitrary radius $r$ shown in Fig. 35-10 encloses, at any instant, a flux $\Phi_B$. Because this flux is changing with time, an induced emf given by $\mathcal{E} = -d\Phi_B/dt$ will appear around the loop. The electric fields **E** induced at various points of the loop must, from symmetry, be tangent to the loop. Thus the electric lines of force that are set up by the changing magnetic field are in this case concentric circles.

If we consider a test charge $q_0$ moving around the circle of Fig. 35-10, the work $W$ done on it per revolution is, in terms of the definition of an emf, simply $\mathcal{E}q_0$. From another point of view, it is $(q_0E)(2\pi r)$, where $q_0E$ is the force that acts on the charge and $2\pi r$ is the distance over which the force acts. Setting the two expressions for $W$ equal and canceling $q_0$ yields

$$\mathcal{E} = E2\pi r. \tag{35-7}$$

In a more general case than that of Fig. 35-10 we must write

$$\mathcal{E} = \oint \mathbf{E}\cdot d\mathbf{l}. \tag{35-8}$$

If this integral is evaluated for the conditions of Fig. 35-10, we obtain Eq. 35-7 at once. If Eq. 35-8 is combined with Eq. 35-1 ($\mathcal{E} = -d\Phi_B/dt$), Faraday's law of induction can be written as

$$\oint \mathbf{E}\cdot d\mathbf{l} = -\frac{d\Phi_B}{dt}, \tag{35-9}$$

which is the form in which this law is expressed in Table 38-3.

**Fig. 35-10** The induced electric fields at four points produced by an increasing magnetic field. We assume that $B$ has symmetry about an axis perpendicular to the page through the center of the circle of radius $r$. This can be arranged by assuming that the magnetic induction decreases slightly along a radius starting from the center of the figure, the value of $B$ being constant for a particular value of $r$. (The magnetic field cannot end abruptly at radius $R$—unless a special arrangement of currents is provided—but must approach zero gradually. This "fringing" does not change any of the arguments of this section.

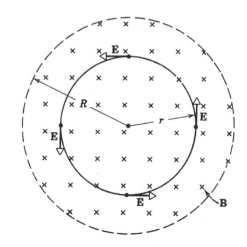

▶ **Example 4.** Let $B$ in Fig. 35–10 be increasing at the rate $dB/dt$. Let $R$ be the radius of the cylindrical region in which the magnetic field is assumed to exist. What is the magnitude of the electric field $E$ at any radius $r$? Assume that $dB/dt = 0.10$ weber/m²-sec and $R = 10$ cm.

(a) For $r < R$, the flux $\Phi_B$ through the loop is

$$\Phi_B = B(\pi r^2).$$

Substituting into Faraday's law (Eq. 35–9),

$$\oint \mathbf{E} \cdot d\mathbf{l} = -\frac{d\Phi_B}{dt}$$

yields

$$(E)(2\pi r) = -\frac{d\Phi_B}{dt} = -(\pi r^2)\frac{dB}{dt}.$$

Solving for $E$ yields

$$E = -\tfrac{1}{2}r\frac{dB}{dt}.$$

The minus sign is retained to suggest that the induced electric field $\mathbf{E}$ acts to *oppose* the change of the magnetic field. Note that $E(r)$ depends on $dB/dt$ and not on $B$. Substituting numerical values, assuming $r = 5$ cm, yields, for the magnitude of $E$,

$$E = \tfrac{1}{2}r\frac{dB}{dt} = (\tfrac{1}{2})(5 \times 10^{-2} \text{ meter})\left(\frac{0.10 \text{ weber}}{\text{m}^2\text{-sec}}\right) = 2.5 \times 10^{-3} \text{ volt/meter.}$$

(b) For $r > R$ the flux through the loop is

$$\Phi_B = \int \mathbf{B} \cdot d\mathbf{S} = B(\pi R^2).$$

This equation is true because $\mathbf{B} \cdot d\mathbf{S}$ is zero for those points of the loop that lie outside the effective boundary of the magnetic field.

From Faraday's law (Eq. 35–9),

$$(E)(2\pi r) = -\frac{d\Phi_B}{dt} = -(\pi R^2)\frac{dB}{dt}.$$

Solving for $E$ yields

$$E = -\frac{1}{2}\frac{R^2}{r}\frac{dB}{dt}.$$

These two expressions for $E(r)$ yield the same result, as they must, for $r = R$. Figure 35–11 is a plot of the magnitude of $E(r)$ for the numerical values given. ◀

**Fig. 35–11**   Example 4. If the fringing of the field in Fig. 35–10 were to be taken into account, the result would be a rounding of the sharp cusp at $r = R$ ( = 10 cm).

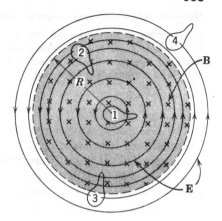

**Fig. 35–12** Showing the circular lines of E from an increasing magnetic field. The four loops are imaginary paths around which an emf can be calculated.

In applying Lenz's law to Fig. 35–10, imagine that a circular conducting loop is placed concentrically in the field. Since $\Phi_B$ through this loop is increasing, the induced current in the loop will tend to oppose this "change" by setting up a magnetic field of its own that points up within the loop. Thus the induced current $i$ must be counterclockwise, which means that the lines of the induced electric field E, which is responsible for the current, must also be counterclockwise. If the magnetic field in Fig. 35–10 were *decreasing* with time, the induced current and the lines of force of the induced electric field E would be clockwise, again opposing the *change* in $\Phi_B$.

Figure 35–12 shows four of many possible loops to which Faraday's law may be applied. For loops 1 and 2, the induced emf $\mathcal{E}$ is the same because these loops lie entirely within the changing magnetic field and thus have the

same value of $d\Phi_B/dt$. Note that even though the emf $\mathcal{E}$ ($= \oint \mathbf{E} \cdot d\mathbf{l}$) is the

same for these two loops, the distribution of electric fields E around the perimeter of each loop, as indicated by the electric lines of force, is different. For loop 3 the emf is less because $\Phi_B$ and $d\Phi_B/dt$ for this loop are less, and for loop 4 the induced emf is zero.

The induced electric fields that are set up by the induction process are not associated with charges but with a changing magnetic flux. Although both kinds of electric fields exert forces on charges, there is a difference between them. The simplest manifestation of this difference is that lines of E associated with a changing magnetic flux can form closed loops (see Fig. 35–12); lines of E associated with charges cannot but can always be drawn to start on a positive charge and end on a negative charge.

Equation 29–5, which defined the potential difference between two points $a$ and $b$, is

$$V_b - V_a = \frac{W_{ab}}{q_0} = -\int_a^b \mathbf{E} \cdot d\mathbf{l}.$$

We have insisted that if potential is to have any useful meaning this integral (and $W_{ab}$) must have the same value for every path connecting $a$ with $b$. This proved to be true for every case examined in earlier chapters.

An interesting special case comes up if $a$ and $b$ are the same point. The path connecting them is now a closed loop; $V_a$ must be identical with $V_b$ and this equation reduces to

$$\oint \mathbf{E} \cdot d\mathbf{l} = 0. \qquad (35\text{--}10)$$

However, when changing magnetic flux is present, $\oint \mathbf{E} \cdot d\mathbf{l}$ is precisely *not* zero but is, according to Faraday's law (see Eq. 35–9), $-d\Phi_B/dt$. Electric fields associated with stationary charges are *conservative*, but those associated with changing magnetic fields are *nonconservative;* see Section 8–2. Electric potential, which can be defined only for a conservative force, *has no meaning for electric fields produced by induction.*

### 35–6   The Betatron

The betatron is a device used to accelerate electrons to high speeds by allowing them to be acted upon by induced electric fields that are set up by a changing magnetic flux. It provides an excellent illustration of the "reality" of such induced fields. The energetic electrons can be used for fundamental research in physics or to produce penetrating X-rays which are useful in cancer therapy and in industry.

Figure 35–13 shows the 100-Mev betatron at the General Electric Company. At this energy the electron speed is $0.999986c$, where $c$ is the speed of light, so that relativistic mechanics must certainly be used in the analysis of its operation. Figure 35–14 shows a vertical cross section through the central part of the betatron to which the man in Fig. 35–13 is pointing.

The magnetic field in the betatron has several functions: ($a$) it guides the electrons in a circular path; ($b$) it accelerates the electrons in this path;

**Fig. 35–13**   A 100-Mev betatron. $M$ shows the magnet, $C$ the magnetizing coils, and $D$ the region in which the "doughnut" is located. (Courtesy General Electric Company.)

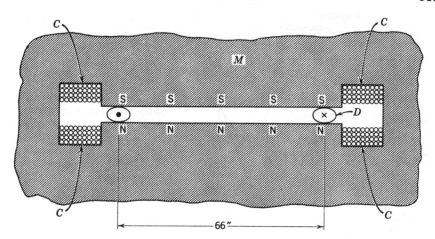

**Fig. 35–14**  Cross section of a betatron, showing magnet $M$, coils $C$, and "doughnut" $D$. Electrons emerge from the page at the left and enter it at the right.

(c) it keeps the radius of the orbit in which the electrons are moving a constant; (d) it introduces the electrons into the orbit initially and removes them from the orbit after they have reached full energy; and finally (e) it provides a restoring force that resists any tendency for the electrons to leave their orbit, either vertically or radially.  It is remarkable that it is possible to do all these things by proper shaping and control of the magnetic field.

The object marked $D$ in Fig. 35–14 is an evacuated glass "doughnut" inside which the electrons travel.  Their orbit is a circle at right angles to the plane of the figure.  The electrons emerge from the plane at the left ($\cdot$) and enter it at the right ($\times$).  In the General Electric machine the radius of the electron path is 33 in.  The coils $C$ and the 130-ton steel magnet shown in Fig. 35–13 provide the magnetic flux that passes through the plane of this orbit.

The current in coils $C$ is made to alter periodically, 60 times/sec, to produce a changing flux through the orbit, shown in Fig. 35–15.  Here $\Phi_B$ is taken as positive when **B** is pointing up, as in Fig. 35–14.  If the electrons are to circulate in the direction shown, they must do so during the positive half-cycle, marked $ac$ in Fig. 35–15.  The student should verify this (see Section 33–6).  The electrons are accelerated by electric fields set up by the changing flux.  The direction of these induced fields depends on the sign of $d\Phi_B/dt$ and must be chosen to accelerate, and not to decelerate, the electrons.  Thus only half the positive half-cycle in Fig. 35–15 can be used for acceleration; it will prove to be $ab$.

The average value of $d\Phi_B/dt$ during the quarter-cycle $ab$ is the slope of the dashed line, or

$$\frac{\overline{d\Phi_B}}{dt} = \frac{1.8 \text{ weber}}{4.2 \times 10^{-3} \text{ sec}} = 430 \text{ volts.}$$

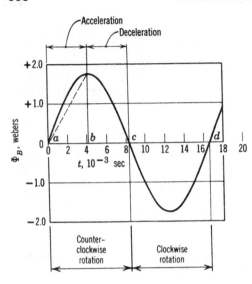

**Fig. 35–15** The flux through the orbit of a betatron, during one cycle. Rotation of the electrons in the desired direction (counterclockwise as viewed from above in Fig. 35–14) is possible only during half-cycle *ac*.

From Faraday's law (Eq. 35–1), this is also the emf in volts. The electron will thus increase its energy by 430 ev every time it makes a trip around the orbit in the changing flux. If the electron gains only 430 ev of energy per revolution, it must make about 230,000 rev to gain its full 100 Mev. For an orbit radius of 33 in., this corresponds to a length of path of some 750 miles.

The betatron provides a good example of the fact that electric potential has no meaning for electric fields produced by induction. If a potential exists, it must be true that, as Eq. 35–10 shows, $\oint \mathbf{E} \cdot d\mathbf{l} = 0$ for any closed path. In the betatron, however, this integral, evaluated around the orbit, is precisely *not* zero but is, in our example, 430 volts. It must not be thought, of course, that the betatron violates the conservation of energy principle. The gain in kinetic energy of the circulating electron (430 ev/rev) must be supplied by an identifiable energy source. It comes, in fact, from the generator that energizes the magnet coils, thus providing the changing magnetic field. The energy is transmitted to the electron through the intermediary of this changing field.

▶ **Example 5.** In the betatron of Fig. 35–13, which is the "accelerating" quarter-cycle?

Let us assume that it is *ab* in Fig. 35–15, during which $\Phi_B$ through the orbit is *increasing*. If a conducting loop were placed to coincide with the orbit, an induced current would appear in the loop to oppose the tendency of $\Phi_B$ to increase. This means that a magnetic field would be set up that would oppose the field of the large magnet. Thus E would point outward at the right side of "doughnut" *D* in Fig. 35–14 and inward on the left side. The force $(-e\mathbf{E})$ acting on the electron is in the opposite direction to E because of the negative charge of the electron. Thus the tangential force acting on the electron is in the same direction as that at which it circulates in its orbit; this means that the speed of the electron will increase, as desired. The student should go through this same analysis carefully, assuming (incorrectly, as it will turn out) that the accelerating half-cycle is *bc* in Fig. 35–15 rather than *ab*.

## 35-7   Induction and Relative Motion

Faraday's law, in the form $\mathcal{E} = -d\Phi_B/dt$, gives correctly the induced emf no matter whether the change in $\Phi_B$ is produced by moving a coil, moving a magnet, changing the strength of a magnetic field, changing the shape of a conducting loop, or in other ways.   However, observers who are in relative motion with respect to each other, even though they would all agree on the numerical value of the emf, would give different microscopic descriptions of the induction process.   In electromagnetic systems, as well as in mechanical systems, it is important that the state of motion of the observer with respect to his environment be made perfectly clear.

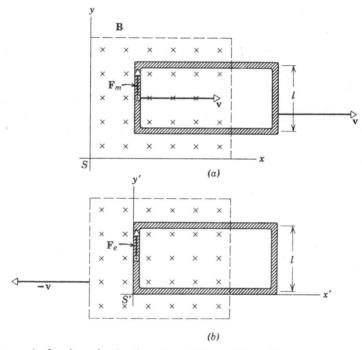

*(a)*

*(b)*

**Fig. 35-16**   A closed conducting loop in relative motion with respect to a magnetic field.   (*a*) An observer *S*, fixed with respect to the magnet that produces the field **B**, sees the loop moving to the right.   (*b*) An observer *S'*, fixed with respect to the loop, sees the magnet moving to the left.

Figure 35-16 shows a closed loop which is caused to move at velocity **v** with respect to a magnet that provides a uniform field **B** in the region shown.   We consider first an observer, identified as *S*, who is *at rest with respect to the magnet* used to establish the field **B**; see Fig. 35-16*a*.   The induced emf in this case is called a *motional emf* because the conducting loop is moving with respect to this observer.

Consider a positive charge carrier at the center of the left end of the conducting loop.   To observer *S*, this charge, constrained to move to the right along with the loop, is a charge $q$ moving, for an instant at least when the loop has just been set in motion, with a velocity $\mathbf{v}$ in the magnetic field $\mathbf{B}$ and as such it experiences a sideways magnetic deflecting force given by Eq. 33–3a ($\mathbf{F} = q\mathbf{v} \times \mathbf{B}$). This force causes the carriers to move upward along the conductor, so that they acquire a drift velocity $v_d$ also, as shown in Fig. 35–16a.

The resultant equilibrium speed of the carrier when the velocity $\mathbf{v}$ of the loop has become constant is now $\mathbf{V}$, which we find by adding $\mathbf{v}$ and $\mathbf{v}_d$ vectorially in Fig. 35–16a. The magnetic deflecting force $\mathbf{F}_m$ is, as always, at right angles to the resultant velocity $\mathbf{V}$ of the carrier and is given by

$$\mathbf{F}_m = q\mathbf{V} \times \mathbf{B} \tag{35–13}$$

Now $\mathbf{F}_m$ acting alone would tend to push the carriers through the left wall of the conductor. Because this does not happen the conductor wall must exert a normal force $\mathbf{N}$ on the carriers (see Fig. 35–16a) of magnitude such that $\mathbf{v}_d$ lies parallel to the axis of the wire; in other words, $\mathbf{N}$ exactly cancels the horizontal component $\mathbf{F}_m$, leaving only the component $\mathbf{F}_m \cos \theta$ that lies along the direction of the conductor. This component of force on the carrier is also cancelled out, this time by the average force $\overline{\mathbf{F}_i}$ associated with the internal collisions that the carrier experiences as it drifts with (constant) speed $v_d$ through the wire.

The kinetic energy of the charge carrier as it drifts through the wire remains constant. This is consistent with the fact that the resultant force acting on the charge carrier ($= \mathbf{F}_m + \overline{\mathbf{F}_i} + \mathbf{N}$) is zero. The work done by $\mathbf{F}_m$ is zero because magnetic forces, acting at right angles to the velocity of a moving charge, can do no work on that charge. Thus the (negative) work done on the carrier by the average internal collision force $\mathbf{F}_i$ must be exactly cancelled by the (positive) work done on the carrier by the force $\mathbf{N}$. In the last analysis $\mathbf{N}$ is exerted by the agent who pulls the loop through the magnetic field, and the mechanical energy expended by this agent appears as heat energy in the loop, as we have seen in Section 35–4.

Let us then calculate the work $dW$ done on the carrier in time $dt$ by the force $\mathbf{N}$; it is

$$dW = N(v\, dt) \tag{35–14}$$

in which $v\, dt$ is the distance that the loop (and the carrier) have moved to the right in Fig. 35–16a in time $dt$. We can write for $N$ (see Fig. 35–16a and Eq. 35–13).

$$N = \mathbf{F}_m \sin \theta = (qVB)(v_d/V) = qBv_d \tag{35–15}$$

Substituting Eq. 35–15 into Eq. 35–14 yields

$$dW = (qBv_d)(v\, dt)$$
$$= (qBv)(v_d\, dt) = qBv\, dl \tag{35–16}$$

in which $dl(= v_d\, dt)$ is the distance the carrier drifts along the conductor in time $dt$.

The work done on the carrier as it makes a complete circuit of the loop is found by integrating Eq. 35–16 around the loop and is

$$W = \oint dW = qBvl \tag{35–17}$$

This follows because work contributions for the top and the bottom of the loops are opposite in sign and cancel and no work is done in those portions of the loop that lie outside the magnetic field.

An agent that does work on charge carriers, thus establishing a current in a closed conducting loop, can be viewed as an emf. We can write, making use of Eq. 35–17,

$$\mathcal{E} = \frac{W}{q} = \frac{qBvl}{q} = Blv, \tag{35–18}$$

which is, of course, the same result that we derived from Faraday's law of induction; see Eq. 35–3. Thus a motional emf is intimately connected with the sideways deflection of a charged particle moving through a magnetic field.

We now consider how the situation of Fig. 35–16 would appear to an observer $S'$ who is *at rest with respect to the loop*. To this observer, the magnet is moving to the left in Fig. 35–16$b$ with velocity $-\mathbf{v}$, and the charge $q$ is at rest as far as its left-to-right motion is concerned. However $S'$, like $S$, observes that the charge drifts clockwise around the loop and he measures the same emf $\mathcal{E}$ that $S$ measures. $S'$ accounts for this, at the microscopic level, by postulating that an electric field $\mathbf{E}$ is induced in the loop by the action of the moving magnet. This induced field $\mathbf{E}$, which has the same origin as the induced fields that we discussed in Section 35–5, exerts a force on the charge carrier given by $q\mathbf{E}$.

The induced field $\mathbf{E}$, which exists in the end of the loop only, is associated with an emf $\mathcal{E}$ and generates a current in the closed loop. Note that, in any closed loop in which there is a current, an internal electric field must exist at every point at which charges are moving. These electric fields however are set up by the emf, as in the case of a closed loop connected to a battery, and are *not* induced by the motion of the magnet. It is only this induced field $\mathbf{E}$ that we associate with the emf, through the relation (Eq. 35–8)

$$\mathcal{E} = \mathbf{E} \cdot d\mathbf{l}$$

which reduced to

$$\mathcal{E} = El \tag{35–19}$$

in this case. This is so because no *induced* electric field appears in the upper and lower bars, because of the nature of their motions, and none appears in the part of the loop outside the magnetic field.

The emfs given by Eqs. 35–19 and 35–18 must be identical because the relative motion of the loop and the magnet is identical in the two cases shown in Fig. 35–16. Equating these relations yields

$$El = Blv,$$

or

$$E = vB. \tag{35–20a}$$

In Fig. 35–16$b$ the vector $\mathbf{E}$ points upward along the axis of the left end of the conducting loop because this is the direction in which positive charges are observed to drift. The directions of $\mathbf{v}$ and $\mathbf{B}$ are clearly shown in this figure. We see, then, that Eq. 35–20$a$ is consistent with the more general vector relation

$$\mathbf{E} = \mathbf{v} \times \mathbf{B}. \tag{35–20b}$$

We have not proved Eq. 35-20$b$ except for the special case of Fig. 35-16; nevertheless it proves to be true in general, that is, no matter what the angle between $\mathbf{v}$ and $\mathbf{B}$.

An experiment carried out in 1926 by the German physicist Wilhelm Wien (1864–1928) gives concrete support to our descriptions of the effect of the motion of an observer on the nature of the electric and magnetic fields that he observes. The radiations emitted from atoms vary slightly in wavelength if the atom is immersed in either a magnetic or an electric field. The atom can thus be used as a probe to examine the nature of such fields. Wien fired a beam of atoms with velocity $\mathbf{v}$ through a magnetic field $\mathbf{B}$. The radiations emitted were identical in the distribution of their wavelengths with those that would have been emitted by a *resting* atom immersed in (a) the magnetic field $\mathbf{B}$ *and* (b) an induced electric field $\mathbf{E}$ given by Eq. 35-20$b$.

We interpret Eq. 35-20$b$ in the following way: Observer $S$ fixed with respect to the magnet is aware only of a magnetic field. The force to him arises from the motion of the charges through $\mathbf{B}$. Observer $S'$ fixed on the charge carrier is aware of an electric field $\mathbf{E}$ also and attributes the force on the charge (at rest with respect to him initially) to the electric field. $S$ says the force is of purely magnetic origin and $S'$ says the force is of purely electric origin. From the point of view of $S$, the induced emf is given by $\oint (\mathbf{v} \times \mathbf{B}) \cdot d\mathbf{l}$. From the point of view of $S'$, the same induced emf is given by $\oint \mathbf{E} \cdot d\mathbf{l}$, where $\mathbf{E}$ is the induced) electric vector that he observes at points along the circuit.

For a third observer $S''$ who judges that both the magnet and the loop are moving, the force tending to move charges around the loop is neither purely electric nor purely magnetic, but a bit of each. In summary, in the equation

$$\mathbf{F}/q = \mathbf{E} + \mathbf{v} \times \mathbf{B},$$

different observers form different assessments of $\mathbf{E}$, $\mathbf{B}$, and $\mathbf{v}$ but, when these are combined, all observers form the same assessment of $\mathbf{F}/q$ and all obtain the same value for the induced emf in the loop (this depends only on the relative motion). That is, the total force is the same for all observers, but each observer forms a different estimate of the separate electric and magnetic forces contributing to the same total force.

▶ **Example 7.** In Fig. 35-16 assume that $B = 2.0$ webers/meter$^2$, $l = 10$ cm, and $v = 1.0$ meter/sec. Calculate (a) the induced electric field observed by $S'$, and (b) the emf induced in the loop.

(a) The electric field, which is apparent only to observer $S'$, is associated with the moving magnet and is given in magnitude (see Eq. 35-20a) by

$$\begin{aligned} E &= vB \\ &= (1.0 \text{ meter/sec})(2.0 \text{ webers/meter}^2) \\ &= 2.0 \text{ volt/meter.} \end{aligned}$$

(b) Observer $S$ would calculate the induced (motional) emf from

$$\begin{aligned} \mathcal{E} &= Blv \\ &= (2.0 \text{ webers/meters}^2)(1.0 \times 10^{-1} \text{ meter})(1.0 \text{ meter/sec}) \\ &= 0.20 \text{ volt.} \end{aligned}$$

Observer $S'$ would not regard the emf as motional and would use the relationship

$$\mathcal{E} = El$$

$$= (2.0 \text{ volt/meter})(1.0 \times 10^{-1} \text{ meter})$$

$$= 0.20 \text{ volt.}$$

As must be the case, both observers agree as to the numerical value of the emf. ◀

## QUESTIONS

1. The north pole of a magnet is moved away from a metallic ring, as in Fig. 35–17. In the part of the ring farthest from the reader, which way does the current point?

**Fig. 35–17**

2. *Eddy currents.* A sheet of copper is placed in a magnetic field as shown in Fig. 35–18. If we attempt to pull it out of the field or push it further in, an automatic resisting force appears. Explain its origin. (Hint: Currents, called eddy currents, are induced in the sheet in such a way as to oppose the motion.)

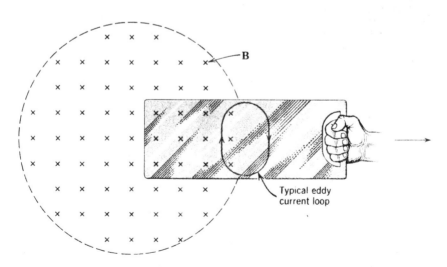

**Fig. 35–18**

**3.** *Electromagnetic shielding.* Consider a conducting sheet lying in a plane perpendicular to a magnetic field **B**, as shown in Fig. 35–19. (*a*) If **B** suddenly changes, the full *change* in **B** is not immediately detected in region *P*. Explain. (*b*) If the resistivity of the sheet is zero, the *change* is not ever detected at *P*. Explain. (*c*) If **B** changes periodically at high frequency and the conductor is made of a material of low resistivity, the region near *P* is almost completely shielded from the *changes* in flux. Explain. (*d*) Is such a conductor useful as a shield from *static* magnetic fields? Explain.

**Fig. 35–19**                                                **Fig. 35–20**

**4.** *Magnetic damping.* A strip of copper is mounted as a pendulum about *O* in Fig. 35–20. It is free to swing through a magnetic field normal to the page. If the strip has slots cut in it as shown, it can swing freely through the field. If a strip without slots is substituted, the vibratory motion is strongly damped. Explain. (Hint: Use Lenz's law; consider the paths that the charge carriers in the strip must follow if they are to oppose the motion.)

**5.** Two conducting loops face each other a distance *d* apart (Fig. 35–21). An observer sights along their common axis. If a clockwise current *i* is suddenly established in the larger loop, (*a*) what is the direction of the induced current in the smaller loop? (*b*) What is the direction of the force (if any) that acts on the smaller loop?

**Fig. 35–21**                                                **Fig. 35–22**

**6.** What is the direction, if any, of the conventional current through resistor *R* in Fig. 35–22 (*a*) immediately after switch *S* is closed, (*b*) some time after switch *S* was closed, and (*c*) immediately after switch *S* is opened. (*d*) When switch *S* is held closed, which end of the coil acts as a north pole?

7. A current-carrying solenoid is moved toward a conducting loop as in Fig. 35–23. What is the direction of circulation of current in the loop as we sight toward it as shown?

**Fig. 35–23**

8. If the resistance $R$ in the left-hand circuit of Fig. 35–24 is increased, what is the direction of the induced current in the right-hand circuit?

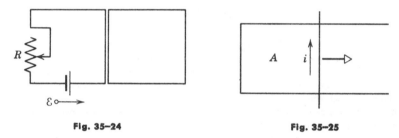

**Fig. 35–24**                    **Fig. 35–25**

9. In Fig. 35–25 the movable wire is moved to the right, causing an induced current as shown. What is the direction of **B** in region $A$?

10. A loop, shown in Fig. 35–26, is removed from the magnet by pulling it vertically upward. (a) What is the direction of the induced current? (b) Is a force required to remove the loop? (c) Does the total amount of Joule heat produced in removing the loop depend on the time taken to remove it?

**Fig. 35–26**

11. A magnet is dropped down a long vertical copper tube. Show that, even neglecting air resistance, the magnet will reach a constant terminal velocity.

12. A magnet is dropped from the ceiling along the axis of a copper loop lying flat on the floor. If the falling magnet is photographed with a time sequence camera, what differences, if any, will be noted if (a) the loop is at room temperature and (b) the loop is packed in dry ice?

13. A copper ring and a wooden ring of the same dimensions are placed so that there is the same changing magnetic flux through each. How do the induced electric fields in each ring compare?

14. In Fig. 35–12 how can the induced emfs around paths 1 and 2 be identical? The induced electric fields are much weaker near path 1 than near path 2, as the spacing of the lines of force shows. See also Fig. 35–11.

15. In a certain betatron the electrons rotate counterclockwise as seen from above. In what direction must the magnetic field point and how must it change with time while the electron is being accelerated?

16. Why can a betatron be used for acceleration only during one-quarter of a cycle?

17. To make the electrons in a betatron orbit spiral outward, would it be necessary to increase or to decrease the central flux? Assume that **B** at the orbit remains essentially unchanged.

18. A cyclotron is a so-called *resonance device*. Does a betatron depend on resonance?

## PROBLEMS

1. A hundred turns of insulated copper wire are wrapped around an iron cylinder of cross-sectional area 0.001 meter² and are connected to a resistor. The total resistance in the circuit is 10 ohms. If the longitudinal magnetic induction in the iron changes from 1 weber/meter² in one direction to 1 weber/meter² in the opposite direction, how much charge flows through the circuit?

2. In Fig. 35–27 a closed copper coil with 100 turns and a total resistance of 5.0 ohms is placed *outside* a solenoid like that of Example 1. If the current in the solenoid is changed as in that example, what current appears in the coil?

**Fig. 35–27**

3. A circular loop of wire 10 cm in diameter is placed with its normal making an angle of 30° with the direction of a uniform 5000-gauss magnetic field. The loop is "wobbled" so that its normal rotates about the field direction at the constant rate of 100 rev/min; the angle between the normal and the field direction ( = 30°) remains unchanged during this process. What emf appears in the loop?

4. A uniform field of induction **B** is normal to the plane of a circular ring 10-cm in diameter made of #10 copper wire (diameter = 0.10 in.). At what rate must B change with time if an induced current of 10 amp is to appear in the ring?

5. A uniform field of induction **B** is changing in magnitude at a constant rate $dB/dt$. You are given a mass $m$ of copper which is to be drawn into a wire of radius $r$ and formed into a circular loop of radius $R$. Show that the induced current in the loop does not depend

on the size of the wire or of the loop and, assuming **B** perpendicular to the loop, is given by

$$i = \frac{m}{4\pi\rho\delta} \frac{dB}{dt},$$

where $\rho$ is the resistivity and $\delta$ the density of copper.

6. You are given 50 cm of #18 copper wire (diameter = 0.040 in.). It is formed into a circular loop and placed at right angles to a uniform magnetic field that is increasing with time at the constant rate of 100 gauss/sec. At what rate is Joule heat generated in the loop?

7. A small bar magnet is pulled rapidly through a conducting loop, along its axis. Sketch qualitatively (a) the induced current and (b) the rate of Joule heating as a function of the position of the center of the magnet. Assume that the north pole of the magnet enters the loop first and that the magnet moves at constant speed. Plot the induced current as positive if it is clockwise as viewed along the path of the magnet.

8. *Alternating current generator.* A rectangular loop of $N$ turns and of length $a$ and width $b$ is rotated at a frequency $\nu$ in a uniform field of induction **B**, as in Fig. 35–28. (a) Show that an induced emf given by

$$\mathcal{E} = 2\pi\nu NbaB \sin 2\pi\nu t = \mathcal{E}_0 \sin 2\pi\nu t$$

appears in the loop. This is the principle of the commercial alternating-current generator. (b) Design a loop that will produce an emf with $\mathcal{E}_0$ = 150 volts when rotated at 60 rev/sec in a field of magnetic induction of 5000-gauss.

**Fig. 35–28**

9. A stiff wire bent into a semicircle of radius $R$ is rotated with a frequency $\nu$ in a uniform field of induction **B**, as shown in Fig. 35–29. What are the amplitude and frequency of the induced voltage and of the induced current when the internal resistance of the meter $M$ is $R_M$ and the remainder of the circuit has negligible resistance?

**Fig. 35–29**

10. A circular copper disk 10 cm in diameter rotates at 1800 rev/min about an axis through its center and at right angles to the disk. A uniform field of induction **B** of 10,000 gauss is perpendicular to the disk. What potential difference develops between the axis of the disk and its rim?

11. Figure 35–30 shows a copper rod moving with velocity **v** parallel to a long straight wire carrying a current $i$. Calculate the induced emf in the rod, assuming that $v = 5.0$ meters/sec, $i = 100$ amp, $a = 1.0$ cm, and $b = 20$ cm.

**Fig. 35–30**          **Fig. 35–31**

12. A metal wire of mass $m$ slides without friction on two rails spaced a distance $d$ apart, as in Fig. 35–31. The track lies in a vertical uniform field of induction **B**. (a) A *constant current $i$* flows from generator $G$ along one rail, across the wire, and back down the other rail. Find the velocity (speed and direction) of the wire as a function of time, assuming it to be at rest at $t = 0$. (b) The generator is replaced by a battery with *constant emf* $\varepsilon$. The velocity of the wire now approaches a constant final value. What is this terminal speed? (c) What is the current in part (b) when the terminal speed has been reached?

13. In Fig. 35–32 the magnetic flux through the loop perpendicular to the plane of the coil and directed into the paper is varying according to the relation

$$\Phi_B = 6t^2 + 7t + 1,$$

where $\Phi_B$ is in milliwebers (1 milliweber $= 10^{-3}$ weber) and $t$ is in seconds. (a) What is the magnitude of the emf induced in the loop when $t = 2$ sec? (b) What is the direction of the current through $R$?

**Fig. 35–32**          **Fig. 35–33**

14. In Fig. 35–33 a conducting rod $AB$ makes contact with the metal rails $AD$ and $BC$ which are 50 cm apart in a uniform magnetic field of induction 1.0 weber/meter$^2$ perpendicular to the plane of the paper as shown. The total resistance of the circuit $ABCD$ is 0.4 ohm (assumed constant). (a) What is the magnitude and direction of the emf induced in the rod when it is moved to the left with a velocity of 8 meters/sec? (b) What force is required to keep the rod in motion? (c) Compare the rate at which mechanical work is done by the force **F** with the rate of development of heat in the circuit.

15. A square wire of length $l$, mass $m$, and resistance $R$ slides without friction down parallel conducting rails of negligible resistance, as in Fig. 35–34. The rails are connected

to each other at the bottom by a resistanceless rail parallel to the wire, so that the wire and rails form a closed rectangular conducting loop. The plane of the rails makes an angle $\theta$ with the horizontal, and a uniform vertical field of magnetic induction **B** exists throughout the region. (*a*) Show that the wire acquires a steady-state velocity of magnitude

$$v = \frac{mgR \sin \theta}{B^2 l^2 \cos^2 \theta}.$$

(*b*) Prove that this result is consistent with the conservation-of-energy principle. (*c*) What change, if any, would there be if **B** were directed down instead of up?

**Fig. 35-34**                **Fig. 35-35**

16. Prove that if the flux of magnetic induction through the coil of $N$ turns of Fig. 35-35 changes in any way from $\Phi_1$ to $\Phi_2$, then the charge $q$ that flows through the circuit of total resistance $R$ is given by

$$q = \frac{N(\Phi_2 - \Phi_1)}{R}.$$

17. Figure 35-36 shows a uniform field of induction **B** confined to a cylindrical volume of radius $R$. **B** is decreasing in magnitude at a constant rate of 100 gauss/sec. What is the instantaneous acceleration (direction and magnitude) experienced by an electron placed at $a$, at $b$, and at $c$? Assume $r = 5.0$ cm. (The necessary fringing of the field beyond $R$ will not change your answer as long as there is axial symmetry about a perpendicular axis through $b$.)

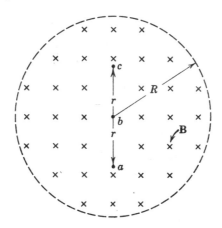

**Fig. 35-36**

18. A uniform magnetic field of induction **B** fills a cylindrical volume of radius $R$. A metal rod of length $l$ is placed as shown in Fig. 35-37. If $B$ is changing at the rate $dB/dt$,

show that the emf that is produced by the changing magnetic field and that acts between the ends of the rod is given by

$$\mathcal{E} = \frac{dB}{dt}\frac{l}{2}\sqrt{R^2 - \left(\frac{l}{2}\right)^2}.$$

**Fig. 35–37**

19. Some measurements of the maximum magnetic induction as a function of radius for the General Electric Company betatron are as follows:

| $r$, cm | $B$, gauss | $r$, cm | $B$, gauss |
|---|---|---|---|
| 0 | 4000 | 81.2 | 4090 |
| 10.2 | 9500 | 83.7 | 4000 |
| 68.2 | 9500 | 88.9 | 3810 |
| 73.2 | 5280 | 91.4 | 3720 |
| 75.2 | 4510 | 93.5 | 3600 |
| 77.3 | 4280 | 95.5 | 3400 |

Show by graphical analysis that the relation $\bar{B} = 2B_R$ is satisfied at the orbit radius, $R = 84$ cm. (Hint: Note that $\bar{B} = \dfrac{1}{\pi R^2}\displaystyle\int_0^R B(r)(2\pi r)\,dr$ and evaluate the integral graphically.)

20. Prove that the electric field $\mathbf{E}$ in a charged parallel-plate capacitor cannot drop abruptly to zero as one moves at right angles to it, as suggested by the arrow in Fig. 35–38 (see point $a$). In actual capacitors fringing of the lines of force always occurs, which means that $\mathbf{E}$ approaches zero in a continuous and gradual way. See Problem 34–28. (Hint: Apply Faraday's law to the rectangular path shown by the dashed lines.)

**Fig. 35–38**

# Inductance

## CHAPTER 36

## 36–1  Inductance

If two coils are near each other, a current $i$ in one coil will set up a flux $\Phi_B$ through the second coil. If this flux is changed by changing the current, an induced emf will appear in the second coil according to Faraday's law. However, two coils are not needed to show an inductive effect. An induced emf appears in a coil if the current *in that same coil* is changed. This is called *self-induction* and the electromotive force produced is called a *self-induced emf*. It obeys Faraday's law of induction just as other induced emfs do.

Consider first a "close-packed" coil, a toroid, or the central section of a long solenoid. In all three cases the flux $\Phi_B$ set up in each turn by a current $i$ is essentially the same for every turn. Faraday's law for such coils (Eq. 35–2)

$$\mathcal{E} = -\frac{d(N\Phi_B)}{dt} \qquad (36\text{--}1)$$

shows that the number of *flux linkages* $N\Phi_B$ ($N$ being the number of turns) is the important characteristic quantity for induction. For a given coil, provided no magnetic materials such as iron are nearby, this quantity is proportional to the current $i$, or

$$N\Phi_B = Li, \qquad (36\text{--}2)$$

in which $L$, the proportionality constant, is called the *inductance* of the device.

From Faraday's law (see Eq. 36–1) the induced emf can be written as

$$\mathcal{E} = -\frac{d(N\Phi_B)}{dt} = -L\frac{di}{dt}. \qquad (36\text{--}3a)$$

Written in the form
$$L = -\frac{\mathcal{E}}{di/dt},$$
(36-3b)

this relation may be taken as the defining equation for inductance for coils of all shapes and sizes, whether or not they are close-packed and whether or not iron or other magnetic material is nearby. It is analogous to the defining relation for capacitance, namely

$$C = \frac{q}{V}.$$

If no iron or similar materials are nearby, $L$ depends only on the geometry of the device. In an *inductor* (symbol ⌒⌒⌒⌒⌒) the presence of a *magnetic field* is the significant feature, corresponding to the presence of an *electric* field in a *capacitor*.

The unit of inductance, from Eq. 36-3b, is the volt-sec/amp. A special name, the *henry*, has been given to this combination of units, or

1 henry = 1 volt-sec/amp.

The unit of inductance is named after Joseph Henry (1797–1878), an American physicist and a contemporary of Faraday. Henry independently discovered the law of induction at about the same time Faraday did. The units *millihenry* (1 mh = $10^{-3}$ henry) and *microhenry* (1 $\mu$h = $10^{-6}$ henry) are also commonly used.

The direction of a self-induced emf can be found from Lenz's law. Suppose that a steady current $i$, produced by a battery, exists in a coil. Let us suddenly reduce the (battery) emf in the circuit to zero. The current $i$ will start to decrease at once; this *decrease* in current, in the language of Lenz's law, is the "change" which the self-induction must oppose. To oppose the falling current, the induced emf must point in the same direction as the current, as in Fig. 36-1a. When the current in a coil is increased, Lenz's law shows that the self-induced emf points in the *opposite* direction to that of the current, as in Fig. 36-1b. In each case the self-induced emf acts to op-

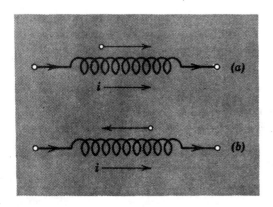

**Fig. 36–1** In (a) the current $i$ is *decreasing* and in (b) it is *increasing*. The self-induced emf $\mathcal{E}_L$ opposes the *change* in each case.

pose the *change* in the current. The minus sign in Eq. 36–3 shows that $\mathcal{E}$ and $di/dt$ are opposite in sign, since $L$ is always a positive quantity.

## 36–2  Calculation of Inductance

It has proved possible to make a direct calculation of capacitance in terms of geometrical factors for a few special cases, such as the parallel-plate capacitor. In the same way, it is possible to calculate the self-inductance $L$ for a few special cases.

For a close-packed coil with no iron nearby, we have, from Eq. 36–2,

$$L = \frac{N\Phi_B}{i}. \tag{36–4}$$

Let us apply this equation to calculate $L$ for a section of length $l$ near the center of a long solenoid. The number of flux linkages in the length $l$ of the solenoid is

$$N\Phi_B = (nl)(BA),$$

where $n$ is the number of turns per unit length, $B$ is the magnetic induction inside the solenoid, and $A$ is the cross-sectional area. From Eq. 34–7, $B$ is given by

$$B = \mu_0 ni.$$

Combining these equations gives

$$N\Phi_B = \mu_0 n^2 liA.$$

Finally, the inductance, from Eq. 36–4, is

$$L = \frac{N\Phi_B}{i} = \mu_0 n^2 lA. \tag{36–5}$$

The inductance of a length $l$ of a solenoid is proportional to its volume $(lA)$ and to the square of the number of turns per unit length. Note that it depends on geometrical factors only. The proportionality to $n^2$ is expected. If the number of turns per unit length is doubled, not only is the *total* number of turns $N$ doubled but also the flux *through each turn* $\Phi_B$ is also doubled, an over-all factor of four for the flux linkages $N\Phi_B$, hence also a factor of four for the inductance (Eq. 36–4).

▶ **Example 1.** Derive an expression for the inductance of a toroid of rectangular cross section as shown in Fig. 36–2. Evaluate for $N = 10^3$, $a = 5.0$ cm, $b = 10$ cm, and $h = 1.0$ cm.

The lines of **B** for the toroid are concentric circles. Applying Ampère's law,

$$\oint \mathbf{B} \cdot d\mathbf{l} = \mu_0 i,$$

to a circular path of radius $r$ yields

$$(B)(2\pi r) = \mu_0 i_0 N,$$

where $N$ is the number of turns and $i_0$ is the current in the toroid windings; recall that

$i$ in Ampère's law is the *total* current that passes through the path of integration. Solving for $B$ yields

$$B = \frac{\mu_0 i_0 N}{2\pi r}.$$

The flux $\Phi_B$ for the cross section of the toroid is

$$\Phi_B = \int \mathbf{B} \cdot d\mathbf{S} = \int_a^b (B)(h\,dr) = \int_a^b \frac{\mu_0 i_0 N}{2\pi r} h\,dr$$

$$= \frac{\mu_0 i_0 N h}{2\pi} \int_a^b \frac{dr}{r} = \frac{\mu_0 i_0 N h}{2\pi} \ln \frac{b}{a},$$

where $h\,dr$ is the area of the elementary strip shown in the figure. The inductance follows from Eq. 36–4, or

$$L = \frac{N\Phi_B}{i_0} = \frac{\mu_0 N^2 h}{2\pi} \ln \frac{b}{a}.$$

Substituting numerical values yields

$$L = \frac{(4\pi \times 10^{-7} \text{ weber/amp-m})(10^3)^2 (1.0 \times 10^{-2} \text{ meter})}{2\pi} \ln \frac{10 \times 10^{-2} \text{ meter}}{5 \times 10^{-2} \text{ meter}}$$

$$= 1.4 \times 10^{-3} \text{ weber/amp} = 1.4 \text{ mh.} \qquad \blacktriangleleft$$

### 36–3   An *LR* Circuit

In Section 32–8 we saw that if an emf $\mathcal{E}$ is suddenly introduced, perhaps by using a battery, into a single loop circuit containing a resistor $R$ and a capacitor $C$ the charge does not build up immediately to its final equilibrium value ($= C\mathcal{E}$) but approaches it in an exponential fashion described by Eq. 32–15, or

$$q = C\mathcal{E}\,(1 - e^{-t/\tau_c}). \tag{36–6}$$

The delay in the rise of the charge is described by the *capacitative time constant* $\tau_c$, defined from

$$\tau_c = RC. \tag{36–7}$$

If in this same circuit the battery emf $\mathcal{E}$ is suddenly removed, the charge does not immediately fall to zero but approaches zero in an exponential fashion, described by Eq. 32–18b, or

$$q = C\mathcal{E}\,e^{-t/\tau_c}. \tag{36–8}$$

The same time constant $\tau_c$ describes the fall of the charge as well as its rise.

**Fig. 36–3**   An *LR* circuit.

An analogous delay in the rise or fall of the current occurs if an emf $\mathcal{E}$ is suddenly introduced into, or removed from, a single loop circuit containing a resistor $R$ and an inductor $L$. When the switch $S$ in Fig. 36–3 is closed on $a$, for example, the current in the resistor starts to rise. If the inductor were not present, the current would rise rapidly to a steady value $\mathcal{E}/R$. Because of the inductor, however, a self-induced emf $\mathcal{E}_L$ appears in the circuit and, from Lenz's law, this emf opposes the *rise* of current, which means that it opposes the battery emf $\mathcal{E}$ in polarity. Thus the resistor responds to the difference between two emfs, a constant one $\mathcal{E}$ due to the battery and a variable one $\mathcal{E}_L$ ($= -L\,di/dt$) due to self-induction. As long as this second emf is present, the current in the resistor will be less than $\mathcal{E}/R$.

As time goes on, the rate at which the current increases becomes less rapid and the self-induced emf $\mathcal{E}_L$, which is proportional to $di/dt$, becomes smaller. Thus a time delay is introduced, and the current in the circuit approaches the value $\mathcal{E}/R$ asymptotically.

When the switch $S$ in Fig. 36–3 is thrown to $a$, the circuit reduces to that of Fig. 36–4. Let us apply the loop theorem, starting at $x$ in this figure and going clockwise around the loop. For the direction of current shown, $x$ will be higher in potential than $y$, which means that we encounter a drop in potential of $-iR$ as we traverse the resistor. Point $y$ is higher in potential than point $z$ because, for an increasing current, the induced emf will oppose the *rise* of the current by pointing as shown. Thus as we traverse the inductor from $y$ to $z$ we encounter a drop in potential of $-L(di/dt)$. We encounter a rise in potential of $+\mathcal{E}$ in traversing the battery from $z$ to $x$. The loop theorem thus gives

$$-iR - L\frac{di}{dt} + \mathcal{E} = 0$$

or

$$L\frac{di}{dt} + iR = \mathcal{E}. \qquad (36\text{–}9)$$

**Fig. 36–4**   The circuit of Fig. 36–3 just after switch $S$ is closed on $a$.

Equation 36–9 is a *differential equation* involving the variable $i$ and its first derivative $di/dt$. We seek the function $i(t)$ such that when it and its first derivative are substituted in Eq. 36–9 the equation is satisfied.

Although there are formal rules for solving various classes of differential equations (and Eq. 36–9 can, in fact, be easily solved by direct integration, after rearrangement) we often find it simpler to guess at the solution, guided by physical reasoning and by previous experience. Any proposed solution can be tested by substituting it in the differential equation and seeing whether this equation reduces to an identity.

The solution to Eq. 36–9 is, we assert,

$$i = \frac{\varepsilon}{R}(1 - e^{-Rt/L}).\tag{36–10}$$

To test this solution by substitution, we find the derivative $di/dt$, which is

$$\frac{di}{dt} = \frac{\varepsilon}{L}e^{-Rt/L}.\tag{36–11}$$

Substituting $i$ and $di/dt$ into Eq. 36–9 leads to an identity, as the student can easily verify. Thus Eq. 36–10 is a solution of Eq. 36–9. Figure 36–5 shows how the potential difference $V_R$ across the resistor ($= iR$; see Eq. 36–10) and $V_L$ across the inductor ($= L\,di/dt$; see Eq. 36–11) vary with time for particular values of $\varepsilon$, $L$, and $R$. The student should compare this figure carefully with the corresponding figure for an $RC$ circuit (Fig. 32–11).

We can rewrite Eq. 36–10 as

$$i = \frac{\varepsilon}{R}(1 - e^{-t/\tau_L}),\tag{36–12}$$

in which $\tau_L$, the *inductive time constant*, is given by

$$\tau_L = L/R.\tag{36–13}$$

The student should note the correspondence between Eqs. 36–12 and 36–6.

To show that the quantity $\tau_L$ ($= L/R$) has the dimensions of time, we put

$$\frac{1\ \text{henry}}{\text{ohm}} = \frac{1\ \text{henry}}{\text{ohm}}\left(\frac{1\ \text{volt-sec}}{1\ \text{henry-amp}}\right)\left(\frac{1\ \text{ohm-amp}}{1\ \text{volt}}\right) = 1\ \text{sec}.$$

The first quantity in parenthesis is a conversion factor based on the defining equation for inductance [$L = -\varepsilon/(di/dt)$; Eq. 36–3b]. The second conversion factor is based on the relation $V = iR$.

The physical significance of the time constant follows from Eq. 36–12. If we put $t = \tau_L = L/R$ in this equation, it reduces to

$$i = \frac{\varepsilon}{R}(1 - e^{-1}) = (1 - 0.37)\frac{\varepsilon}{R} = 0.63\frac{\varepsilon}{R}.$$

Thus the time constant $\tau_L$ is that time at which the current in the circuit

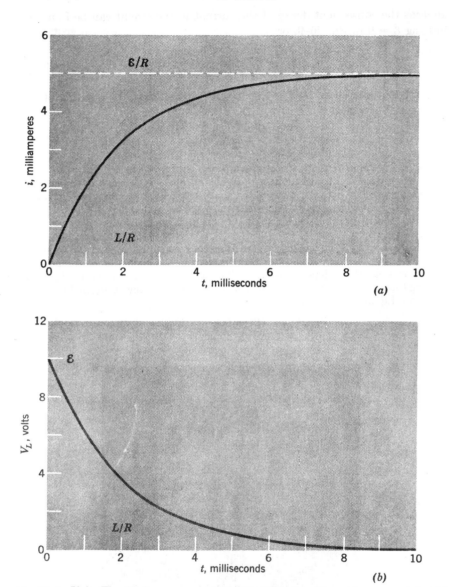

**Fig. 36–5** If in Fig. 36–3 we assume that $R$ = 2000 ohms, $L$ = 4 henrys and $\mathcal{E}$ = 10 volts, then (a) shows the variation of $i$ with $t$ during the current buildup after switch $S$ is closed on $a$, and (b) the variations of $V_L$ with $t$. The time constant is $L/R$ = 2.0 × 10⁻³ sec.

will reach a value within $1/e$ (about 37%) of its final equilibrium value (see Fig. 36–5).

If the switch $S$ in Fig. 36–3, having been left in position $a$ long enough for the equilibrium current $\mathcal{E}/R$ to be established, is thrown to $b$, the effect is to remove the battery from the circuit. The differential equation that governs the subsequent decay of the current in the circuit can be found by putting $\mathcal{E} = 0$ in Eq. 36–9, or

$$L \frac{di}{dt} + iR = 0. \tag{36–14}$$

The student can show by the test of substitution that the solution of this differential equation is

$$i = \frac{\mathcal{E}}{R} e^{-t/\tau_L}. \tag{36–15}$$

Just as for the $RC$ circuit, the behavior of the circuit of Fig. 36–3 can be investigated experimentally, using a cathode-ray oscilloscope. If switch $S$ in this figure is thrown periodically between $a$ and $b$, the applied emf alternates between the values $\mathcal{E}$ and zero. If the terminals of an oscilloscope are connected across $b$ and $c$ in Fig. 36–3, the oscilloscope will display the waveform of this applied emf on its screen, as in Fig. 36–6c.

If the terminals of the oscilloscope are connected across the resistor, the waveform displayed (Fig. 36–6a) will be that of the current in the circuit, since the potential drop across $R$, which determines the oscilloscope deflection, is given by $V_R = iR$. During the intervals marked *inc* in Fig. 36–6, the current is increasing and the waveform (see Eq. 36–12) is given by

$$V_R (= iR) = \mathcal{E}(1 - e^{-t/\tau_L}).$$

**Fig. 36–6** Oscilloscope photograph showing the variation with time of (a) the potential drop $V_R$ across the resistor, (b) the potential drop $V_L$ across the inductor, and (c) the applied emf $\mathcal{E}$. During the intervals marked *inc* the current is increasing; during those marked *dec* it is decreasing. Compare with Fig. 32–13. (Courtesy E. K. Hege.)

During the intervals marked *dec*, the current is decreasing and $V_R$ (see Eq. 36–15) is given by

$$V_R (= iR) = \mathcal{E}e^{-t/\tau_L}.$$

Note that both the growth and the decay of the current are delayed.

If the oscilloscope terminals are connected across the inductor, the screen will show a plot of the potential difference across it as a function of time (Fig. 36–6b). While the current is increasing, the equation of the trace (see Eq. 36–11) should be

$$V_L \left( = L\frac{di}{dt} \right) = \mathcal{E}e^{-t/\tau_L}.$$

When the current is decreasing, $V_L$ is given in terms of the time derivative of Eq. 36–15 and is

$$V_L \left( = L\frac{di}{dt} \right) = -\mathcal{E}e^{-t/\tau_L}.$$

Note that $V_L$ is opposite in sign when the current is increasing ($di/dt$ positive) and when it is decreasing ($di/dt$ negative), as is true also for the induced emf $\mathcal{E}_L[=-L(di/dt) = -V_L]$.

Examination of Fig. 36–6 shows that at any instant the sum of curves $a$ and $b$ always yields curve $c$. This is an expected consequence of the loop theorem, as Eq. 36–9 shows.

▶ **Example 2.** A solenoid has an inductance of 50 henrys and a resistance of 30 ohms. If it is connected to a 100-volt battery, how long will it take for the current to reach one-half its final equilibrium value?

The equilibrium value of the current is reached as $t \to \infty$; from Eq. 36–12 it is $\mathcal{E}/R$. If the current has half this value at a particular time $t_0$, this equation becomes

$$\frac{1}{2}\frac{\mathcal{E}}{R} = \frac{\mathcal{E}}{R}(1 - e^{-t_0/\tau_L}).$$

Solving for $t_0$ yields

$$t_0 = \tau_L \ln 2 = 0.69 \frac{L}{R}.$$

Putting $\tau_L = L/R$ and using the values given, this reduces to

$$t_0 = 0.69\tau_L = 0.69 \left( \frac{50 \text{ henrys}}{30 \text{ ohms}} \right) = 1.2 \text{ sec.}  \qquad ◀$$

## 36–4  Energy and the Magnetic Field

In Section 30–7 we saw that the electric field could be viewed as the site of stored energy, the energy per unit volume being given, in a vacuum, by

$$u_E = \tfrac{1}{2}\epsilon_0 E^2,$$

where $E$ is the electric field strength at the point in question. Although this formula was derived for a parallel-plate capacitor, it holds for all kinds of electric field configurations.

Energy can also be stored in a magnetic field. For example, two parallel wires carrying currents in the same direction attract each other, and to pull them further apart work must be done. It is useful to think that this expended energy is stored in the magnetic field between and around the wires. The energy can be recovered from the field if the wires are allowed to move back to their original separation. In the electrostatic case the same argument was applied to the pulling apart of two unlike charges and in the gravitational case to the pulling apart of two masses.

To derive a quantitative expression for the storage of energy in the magnetic field, consider Fig. 36–4, which shows a source of emf $\mathcal{E}$ connected to a resistor $R$ and an inductor $L$.

$$\mathcal{E} = iR + L\frac{di}{dt}, \qquad (36\text{–}9)$$

is the differential equation that describes the growth of current in this circuit. We stress that this equation follows immediately from the loop theorem and that the loop theorem in turn *is an expression of the principle of conservation of energy for single-loop circuits.* If we multiply each side of Eq. 36–9 by $i$, we obtain

$$\mathcal{E}i = i^2R + Li\frac{di}{dt}, \qquad (36\text{–}16)$$

which has the following physical interpretation in terms of work and energy:

1. If a charge $dq$ passes through the seat of emf $\mathcal{E}$ in Fig. 36–4 in time $dt$, the seat does work on it in amount $\mathcal{E}\,dq$. The *rate* of doing work is $(\mathcal{E}\,dq)/dt$, or $\mathcal{E}i$. Thus the left term in Eq. 36–16 is the *rate at which the seat of emf delivers energy to the circuit.*

2. The second term in Eq. 36–16 is the *rate at which energy appears as Joule heat in the resistor.*

3. Energy that does not appear as Joule heat must, by our hypothesis, be stored in the magnetic field. Since Eq. 36–16 represents a statement of the conservation of energy for $LR$ circuits, the last term must represent the *rate $dU_B/dt$ at which energy is stored in the magnetic field,* or

$$\frac{dU_B}{dt} = Li\frac{di}{dt}. \qquad (36\text{–}17)$$

We can write this as        $dU_B = Li\,di.$

Integrating yields

$$U_B = \int_0^{U_B} dU_B = \int_0^i Li\,di = \tfrac{1}{2}Li^2, \qquad (36\text{–}18)$$

which represents the total stored magnetic energy in an inductance $L$ carrying a current $i$.

This relation can be compared with the expression for the energy associated with a capacitor $C$ carrying a charge $q$, namely

$$U_E = \frac{1}{2}\frac{q^2}{C}.$$

Here the energy is stored in an electric field.   In each case the expression for the stored energy was derived by setting it equal to the work that must be done to set up the field.

▶ **Example 3.**   A coil has an inductance of 5.0 henrys and a resistance of 20 ohms. If a 100-volt emf is applied, what energy is stored in the magnetic field after the current has built up to its maximum value $\mathcal{E}/R$?
The maximum current is given by

$$i = \frac{\mathcal{E}}{R} = \frac{100 \text{ volts}}{20 \text{ ohms}} = 5.0 \text{ amp.}$$

The stored energy is given by Eq. 36–18:

$$U_B = \tfrac{1}{2}Li^2 = \tfrac{1}{2}(5.0 \text{ henrys})(5.0 \text{ amp})^2 = 63 \text{ joules.}$$

Note that the time constant for this coil ($= L/R$) is 0.25 sec.   After how many time constants will *half* of this equilibrium energy be stored in the field?

**Example 4.**   A 3.0-henry inductor is placed in series with a 10-ohm resistor, an emf of 3.0 volts being suddenly applied to the combination.   At 0.30 sec (which is one inductive time constant) after the contact is made, (*a*) what is the rate at which energy is being delivered by the battery?
The current is given by Eq. 36–12, or

$$i = \frac{\mathcal{E}}{R}(1 - e^{-t/\tau_L}),$$

which at $t = 0.30$ sec ($= \tau_L$) has the value

$$i = \left(\frac{3.0 \text{ volts}}{10 \text{ ohms}}\right)(1 - e^{-1}) = 0.189 \text{ amp.}$$

The rate $P_\mathcal{E}$ at which energy is delivered by the battery is

$$P_\mathcal{E} = \mathcal{E}i$$

$$= (3.0 \text{ volts})(0.189 \text{ amp})$$

$$= 0.567 \text{ watt.}$$

(*b*) At what rate does energy appear as Joule heat in the resistor?   This is given by

$$P_J = i^2 R$$

$$= (0.189 \text{ amp})^2 (10 \text{ ohms})$$

$$= 0.357 \text{ watt.}$$

(*c*) At what rate $P_B$ is energy being stored in the magnetic field?   This is given by the last term in Eq. 36–16, which requires that we know $di/dt$.   Differentiating Eq. 36–12 yields

$$\frac{di}{dt} = \left(\frac{\mathcal{E}}{R}\right)\left(\frac{R}{L}\right)e^{-t/\tau_L}$$

$$= \frac{\mathcal{E}}{L}e^{-t/\tau_L}.$$

At $t = \tau_L$ we have

$$\frac{di}{dt} = \left(\frac{3.0 \text{ volts}}{3.0 \text{ henrys}}\right)e^{-1} = 0.37 \text{ amp/sec.}$$

From Eq. 36–17, the desired rate is

$$P_B = \frac{dU_B}{dt} = Li\frac{di}{dt}$$

$$= (3.0 \text{ henrys})(0.189 \text{ amp})(0.37 \text{ amp/sec})$$

$$= 0.210 \text{ watt.}$$

Note that as required by the principle of conservation of energy (see Eq. 36–16)

$$P_\mathcal{E} = P_J + P_B,$$

or $\qquad\qquad$ 0.567 watt $= 0.357$ watt $+ 0.210$ watt

$$= 0.567 \text{ watt.} \qquad \blacktriangleleft$$

**36–5 Energy Density and the Magnetic Field**

We now derive an expression for the *density* of energy $u$ in a magnetic field. Consider a length $l$ near the center of a very long solenoid; $Al$ is the volume associated with this length. The stored energy must lie entirely within this volume because the magnetic field outside such a solenoid is essentially zero. Moreover, the stored energy must be uniformly distributed throughout the volume of the solenoid because the magnetic field is uniform everywhere inside.

Thus we can write $\qquad\qquad u_B = \dfrac{U_B}{Al}$

or, since $\qquad\qquad U_B = \tfrac{1}{2}Li^2,$

$$u_B = \frac{\tfrac{1}{2}Li^2}{Al}.$$

To express this in terms of the magnetic field, we can substitute for $L$ in this equation, using the relation $L = \mu_0 n^2 lA$ (Eq. 36–5). Also we can solve Eq. 34–7 ($B = \mu_0 in$) for $i$ and substitute in this equation. Doing so yields finally

$$u_B = \frac{1}{2}\frac{B^2}{\mu_0}. \qquad\qquad (36\text{–}19)$$

This equation gives the energy density stored at any point (in a vacuum or in a nonmagnetic substance) where the magnetic induction is **B**. The equation is true for all magnetic field configurations, even though it was derived by considering a special case, the solenoid. Equation 36–19 is to be compared with Eq. 30–27,

$$u_E = \tfrac{1}{2}\epsilon_0 E^2, \qquad (\kappa = 1) \qquad\qquad (36\text{–}20)$$

which gives the energy density (in a vacuum) at any point in an electric field. Note that both $u_B$ and $u_E$ are proportional to the square of the appropriate field quantity, $B$ or $E$.

The solenoid plays a role with relationship to magnetic fields similar to the role the parallel-plate capacitor plays with respect to electric fields. In each case we have a simple device that can be used for setting up a uniform field throughout a well-defined region of space and for deducing, in a simple way, some properties of these fields.

▶ **Example 5.**   A long *coaxial cable* (Fig. 36–7) consists of two concentric cylinders with radii $a$ and $b$. Its central conductor carries a steady current $i$, the outer conductor providing the return path.   (*a*) Calculate the energy stored in the magnetic field for a length $l$ of such a cable.

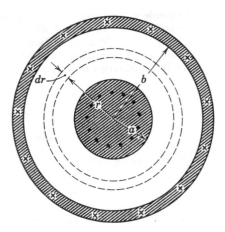

**Fig. 36–7**  Example 5.  Cross section of a coaxial cable, showing steady currents in the central and outer conductors.

In the space between the two conductors Ampère's law

$$\oint \mathbf{B} \cdot d\mathbf{l} = \mu_0 i$$

leads to

$$(B)(2\pi r) = \mu_0 i$$

or

$$B = \frac{\mu_0 i}{2\pi r}.$$

Ampère's law shows further that the magnetic field is zero for points outside the outer conductor (why?).  Magnetic fields exist *inside* each of the conductors; although their values can readily be found from Ampère's law, we choose to ignore them, on the assumption that the cable dimensions are chosen so that most of the stored magnetic energy is in the space between the conductors.

The energy density for points between the conductors, from Eq. 36–19, is

$$u = \frac{1}{2\mu_0} B^2 = \frac{1}{2\mu_0} \left( \frac{\mu_0 i}{2\pi r} \right)^2 = \frac{\mu_0 i^2}{8\pi^2 r^2}.$$

Consider a volume element $dV$ consisting of a cylindrical shell whose radii are $r$ and $r + dr$ and whose length is $l$.  The energy $dU$ contained in it is

$$dU = u \, dV = \frac{\mu_0 i^2}{8\pi^2 r^2} (2\pi r l)(dr) = \frac{\mu_0 i^2 l}{4\pi} \frac{dr}{r}.$$

The total stored magnetic energy is found by integration, or

$$U = \int dU = \frac{\mu_0 i^2 l}{4\pi} \int_a^b \frac{dr}{r} = \frac{\mu_0 i^2 l}{4\pi} \ln \frac{b}{a},$$

which is the desired expression.

(b) What is the inductance of a length $l$ of coaxial cable?
The inductance $L$ can be found from Eq. 36–18 ($U = \frac{1}{2}Li^2$), which leads to

$$L = \frac{2U}{i^2} = \frac{\mu_0 l}{2\pi}\ln\frac{b}{a}.$$

The student should also derive this expression directly from the definition of inductance, using the procedures of Example 1.

**Example 6.** Compare the energy required to set up, in a cube 10 cm on edge, (a) a uniform electric field of $10^5$ volts/meter and (b) a uniform magnetic field of 1 weber/meter$^2$ ($= 10^4$ gauss). Both these fields would be judged reasonably large but they are readily available in the laboratory.

(a) In the electric case we have, where $V_0$ is the volume of the cube,

$$U_E = u_E V_0 = \tfrac{1}{2}\epsilon_0 E^2 V_0$$

$$= (0.5)(8.9 \times 10^{-12}\ \text{coul}^2/\text{nt-m}^2)(10^5\ \text{volts/meter})^2(0.1\ \text{meter})^3$$

$$= 4.5 \times 10^{-5}\ \text{joule}.$$

(b) In the magnetic case, from Eq. 36–19, we have

$$U_B = u_B V_0 = \frac{B^2}{2\mu_0}\,V_0 = \frac{(1\ \text{weber/meter}^2)^2(0.1\ \text{meter})^3}{(2)(4\pi \times 10^{-7}\ \text{weber/amp-m})}$$

$$= 400\ \text{joules}.$$

In terms of fields normally available in the laboratory, much larger amounts of energy can be stored in a magnetic field than in an electric one, the ratio being about $10^7$ in this example. Conversely, much more energy is required to set up a magnetic field of reasonable laboratory magnitude than is required to set up an electric field of similarly reasonable magnitude. ◄

## QUESTIONS

1. Two coils are connected in series. Does their equivalent inductance depend on their geometrical relationship to each other?

2. Is the inductance per unit length for a solenoid near its center (a) the same as, (b) less than, or (c) greater than the inductance per unit length near its ends?

3. Two solenoids, $A$ and $B$, have the same diameter and length and contain only one layer of windings, with adjacent turns touching, insulation thickness being negligible. Solenoid $A$ contains many turns of fine wire and solenoid $B$ contains fewer turns of heavier wire. (a) Which solenoid has the larger inductance? (b) Which solenoid has the larger inductive time constant?

4. If the flux passing through each turn of a coil is the same, the inductance of the coil may be computed from $L = N\Phi_B/i$ (Eq. 36–4). How might one compute $L$ for a coil for which this assumption is not valid?

5. If a current in a source of emf is in the direction of the emf, the energy of the source decreases; if a current is in a direction opposite to the emf (as in charging a battery), the energy of the source increases. Do these statements apply to the inductor in Fig. 36–1a and 36–1b?

6. Show that the dimensions of the two expressions for $L$, $N\Phi_B/i$ (Eq. 36–4) and $\mathcal{E}/(di/dt)$ (Eq. 36–3b), are the same.

7. You are given $N$ turns of wire connected in series. How should the turns be arranged to obtain the maximum self-inductance?

8. Does the time required for the current in a particular $LR$ circuit to build up to any given fraction of its equilibrium value depend on the value of the applied emf?

9. A steady current is set up in a coil with a very large inductive time constant. When the current is interrupted with a switch, a heavy arc tends to appear at the switch blades. Explain. (Note: Interrupting currents in highly inductive circuits can be dangerous.)

10. In an $LR$ circuit like that of Fig. 36–4 can the self-induced emf ever be larger than the battery emf?

11. In an $LR$ circuit like that of Fig. 36–4 is the current in the resistance *always* the same as the current in the inductance?

12. In the circuit of Fig. 36–3 the self-induced emf is a maximum at the instant the switch is closed on $a$. How can this be since there is no current in the inductance at this instant?

13. Give some arguments to show that energy can be stored in a magnetic field.

14. The switch in Fig. 36–3 is thrown from $a$ to $b$. What happens to the energy stored in the inductor?

15. In a toroid is the energy density larger near the inner radius or near the outer radius?

## PROBLEMS

1. A 10-henry inductor carries a steady current of 2.0 amp. How can a 100-volt self-induced emf be made to appear in the inductor?

2. Two inductances $L_1$ and $L_2$ are connected in series and are separated by a large distance. (a) Show that the equivalent inductance $L$ is $L_1 + L_2$. (b) Why must their separation be large?

3. Show that if two inductors with equal inductance $L$ are connected in parallel the equivalent inductance of the combination is $\frac{1}{2}L$. The inductors are separated by a large distance.

4. Two parallel wires whose centers are a distance $d$ apart carry equal currents in opposite directions. Show that, neglecting the flux within the wires themselves, the inductance of a length $l$ of such a pair of wires is given by

$$L = \frac{\mu_0 l}{\pi} \ln \frac{d - a}{a},$$

where $a$ is the wire radius. See Example 4, Chapter 34.

5. A long thin solenoid can be bent into a ring to form a toroid. Show that if the solenoid is long and thin enough the equation for the inductance of a toroid (see Example 1) reduces to that for a solenoid (Eq. 36–5).

6. A solenoid is wound with a single layer of #10 copper wire (diameter, 0.10 in.). It is 4.0 cm in diameter and 2.0 meters long. What is the inductance per unit length for the solenoid near its center? Assume that adjacent wires touch and that insulation thickness is negligible.

7. The inductance of a close-packed coil of 400 turns is 8 mh. What is the magnetic flux through the coil when the current is $5 \times 10^{-3}$ amp?

8. A wooden toroidal core with a square cross section has an inner radius of 10 cm and an outer radius of 12 cm. It is wound with one layer of #18 wire (diameter, 0.040 in.; resistance, 160 ft/ohm). What are (a) the inductance and (b) the inductive time constant? Ignore the thickness of the insulation.

9. The current in an $LR$ circuit builds up to one-third of its steady-state value in 5.0 sec. What is the inductive time constant?

10. How many "time constants" must we wait for the current in an $LR$ circuit to build up to within 0.1 per cent of its equilibrium value?

11. The switch $S$ in Fig. 36–3 is thrown from $b$ to $a$. After one inductive time constant show that (a) the total energy transformed to Joule heat in the resistor is $0.168\mathcal{E}^2 \tau_L/R$

and that ($b$) the energy stored in the magnetic field is $0.200\varepsilon^2\tau_L/R$. ($c$) Show that the equilibrium energy stored in the magnetic field is $0.500\varepsilon^2\tau_L/R$.

12. Show that the inductive time constant $\tau_L$ can also be defined as the time that would be required for the current in an $LR$ circuit to reach its equilibrium value *if it continued to increase at its initial rate.*

13. A 50-volt potential difference is suddenly applied to a coil with $L = 50$ mh and $R = 180$ ohms. At what rate is the current increasing after 0.001 sec?

14. A coil with an inductance of 2.0 henrys and a resistance of 10 ohms is suddenly connected to a resistanceless battery with $\varepsilon = 100$ volts. At 0.1 sec after the connection is made, what are the rates at which ($a$) energy is being stored in the magnetic field, ($b$) Joule heat is appearing, and ($c$) energy is being delivered by the battery?

15. A coil with an inductance of 2.0 henrys and a resistance of 10 ohms is suddenly connected to a resistanceless battery with $\varepsilon = 100$ volts. ($a$) What is the equilibrium current? ($b$) How much energy is stored in the magnetic field when this current exists in the coil?

16. Prove that when switch $S$ in Fig. 36–3 is thrown from $a$ to $b$ all the energy stored in the inductor appears as Joule heat in the resistor.

17. A circular loop of wire 5.0 cm in radius carries a current of 100 amp. What is the energy density at the center of the loop?

18. What is the magnetic energy density at the center of a circulating electron in the hydrogen atom (see Example 9, Chapter 34)?

19. A long wire carries a current of uniform density. Let $i$ be the total current carried by the wire and show that the magnetic energy per unit length stored *within* the wire equals $\mu_0 i^2/16\pi$. Note that it does not depend on the wire diameter.

20. Show that the self-inductance for a length $l$ of a long wire associated with the flux *inside* the wire only is $\mu_0 l/8\pi$, independent of the wire diameter.

21. The coaxial cable of Example 5 has $a = 1.0$ mm, $b = 4.0$ mm, and $c = 5.0$ mm ($c$ is the radius of the outer surface of the outer conductor). It carries a current of 10 amp in the inner conductor and an equal but oppositely directed return current in the outer conductor. Calculate and compare the stored magnetic energy per meter of cable length ($a$) within the central conductor, ($b$) in the space between the conductors, and ($c$) within the outer conductor.

22. A length of #10 copper wire carries a current of 10 amp. Calculate ($a$) the magnetic energy density and ($b$) the electric energy density at the surface of the wire. The wire diameter is 0.10 in. and its resistance per unit length is 1.0 ohm/1000 ft.

23. What must be the strength of a uniform electric field if it is to have the same energy density as that possessed by a 5000-gauss magnetic field?

# Magnetic Properties
# of Matter

CHAPTER 37

### 37–1  Poles and Dipoles

In electricity the *isolated charge* $q$ is the simplest structure that can exist. If two such charges of opposite sign are placed near each other, they form an *electric dipole*, characterized by an electric dipole moment **p**. In magnetism isolated magnetic "poles," which would correspond to isolated electric charges, apparently do not exist. The simplest magnetic structure is the *magnetic dipole*, characterized by a magnetic dipole moment **μ**. Table 34–1 summarizes some characteristics of electric and magnetic dipoles.

A current loop, a bar magnet, and a solenoid of finite length are examples of magnetic dipoles. Their magnetic dipole moments can be measured by placing the dipole in an external magnetic field **B**, measuring the torque **τ** that acts on it, and computing **μ** from Eq. 33–11, or

$$\boldsymbol{\tau} = \boldsymbol{\mu} \times \mathbf{B}. \tag{37–1}$$

Alternatively, we can measure **B** due to the dipole at a point along its axis a (large) distance $r$ from its center and compute $\mu$ from the expression in Table 34–1, or

$$B = \frac{\mu_0}{2\pi} \frac{\mu}{r^3}. \tag{37–2}$$

Figure 37–1, which shows iron filings sprinkled on a sheet of paper under which there is a bar magnet, suggests that this dipole might be viewed as two "poles" separated by a distance $d$. However, all attempts to isolate these poles fail. If the magnet is broken, as in Fig. 37–2, the fragments prove to be dipoles and not isolated poles. If we break up a magnet into the electrons

915

**Fig. 37-1**  A bar magnet is a magnetic dipole. The iron filings suggest the pattern of lines of force in Fig. 37-4a. (Courtesy Physical Science Study Committee.)

and nuclei that make up its atoms, it will be found that even these elementary particles are magnetic dipoles.  Figure 37–3 contrasts the electric and the magnetic characters of the free electron.

All electrons have a characteristic *"spin" angular momentum* about a certain axis, which has the value of

$$L_s = 0.52723 \times 10^{-34} \text{ joule-sec.}$$

This is suggested by the vector $\mathbf{L}_s$ in Fig. 37–3b.  Such a spinning charge can be viewed classically as being made up of infinitesimal current loops.  Each such loop is a tiny magnetic dipole, its moment being given by (Eq. 33–10)

$$\mu = NiA, \tag{37-3}$$

**Fig. 37-2**  If a bar magnet is broken, each fragment becomes a small dipole.

where $i$ is the equivalent current in each infinitesimal loop and $A$ is the loop area. The number of turns, $N$, is unity for each loop. The magnetic dipole moment of the spinning charge can be found by integrating over the moments of the infinitesimal current loops that make it up; see Problem 2.

Although this model of the spinning electron is too mechanistic and is not in accord with modern quantum physics, it remains true that the magnetic dipole moments of elementary particles are closely connected with their intrinsic angular momenta, or spins. Those particles and nuclei whose spin angular momentum is zero (the $\alpha$-particle, the pion, the $O^{16}$ nucleus, etc.) have no magnetic dipole moment. The "intrinsic" or "spin" magnetic mo-

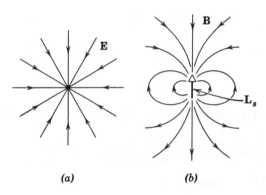

**(a)**          **(b)**

**Fig. 37-3**   (a) The lines of $\mathbf{E}$ and (b) the lines of $\mathbf{B}$ for an electron. The magnetic dipole moment of the electron, $\mu_l$, is directed opposite to the spin angular momentum vector, $\mathbf{L}_s$.

ment of the electron must be distinguished from any additional magnetic moment it may have because of its *orbital* motion in an atom; see Example 2.

▶ **Example 1.**   Devise a method for measuring $\mu$ for a bar magnet.

(a) Place the magnet in a uniform external magnetic field $\mathbf{B}$, with $\boldsymbol{\mu}$ making an angle $\theta$ with $\mathbf{B}$. The magnitude of the torque acting on the magnet (see Eq. 37-1) is given by

$$\tau = \mu B \sin \theta.$$

Clearly $\mu$ can be learned if $\tau$, $B$, and $\theta$ are measured.

(b) A second technique is to suspend the magnet from its center of mass and to allow it to oscillate about its stable equilibrium position in the external field $\mathbf{B}$. For *small* oscillations, $\sin \theta$ can be replaced by $\theta$ and the equation just given becomes

$$\tau = -(\mu B)\theta = -\kappa\theta,$$

where $\kappa$ is a constant. The minus sign has been inserted to show that $\tau$ is a *restoring torque*. Since $\tau$ is proportional to $\theta$, the condition for simple angular harmonic motion is met. The frequency $\nu$ is given by the reciprocal of Eq. 15-24, or

$$\nu = \frac{1}{2\pi} \sqrt{\frac{\kappa}{I}} = \frac{1}{2\pi} \sqrt{\frac{\mu B}{I}}.$$

With this equation $\mu$ can be found from the measured quantities $\nu$, $B$, and $I$.

**Example 2.** An electron in an atom circulating in an assumed circular orbit of radius $r$ behaves like a tiny current loop and has an *orbital magnetic dipole moment* * usually represented by $\mu_l$. Derive a connection between $\mu_l$ and the *orbital angular momentum $L_l$*.

Newton's second law ($F = ma$) yields, if we substitute Coulomb's law for $F$,

$$\frac{1}{4\pi\epsilon_0}\frac{e^2}{r^2} = ma = \frac{mv^2}{r}$$

or

$$v = \sqrt{\frac{e^2}{4\pi\epsilon_0 mr}}. \tag{37-4}$$

The angular velocity $\omega$ is given by

$$\omega = \frac{v}{r} = \sqrt{\frac{e^2}{4\pi\epsilon_0 mr^3}}.$$

The current for the orbit is the rate at which charge passes any given point, or

$$i = ev = e\left(\frac{\omega}{2\pi}\right) = \sqrt{\frac{e^4}{16\pi^3\epsilon_0 mr^3}}.$$

The orbital dipole moment $\mu_l$ is given from Eq. 37–3 if we put $N = 1$ and $A = \pi r^2$, or

$$\mu_l = NiA = (1)\sqrt{\frac{e^4}{16\pi^3\epsilon_0 mr^3}}(\pi r^2) = \frac{e^2}{4}\sqrt{\frac{r}{\pi\epsilon_0 m}}. \tag{37-5}$$

The orbital angular momentum $L_l$ is

$$L_l = (mv)r.$$

Combining with Eq. 37–4 leads to

$$L_l = \sqrt{\frac{e^2 mr}{4\pi\epsilon_0}}.$$

Finally, eliminating $r$ between this equation and Eq. 37–5 yields

$$\mu_l = L_l\left(\frac{e}{2m}\right),$$

which shows that the orbital magnetic moment of an electron is proportional to its orbital angular momentum.

For $r = 5.1 \times 10^{-11}$ meter, which corresponds to hydrogen in its normal state, we have from Eq. 37–5

$$\mu_l = \frac{e^2}{4}\sqrt{\frac{r}{\pi\epsilon_0 m}}$$

$$= \frac{(1.6 \times 10^{-19}\text{ coul})^2}{4}\sqrt{\frac{5.1 \times 10^{-11}\text{ meter}}{(\pi)(8.9 \times 10^{-12}\text{ coul}^2/\text{nt-m}^2)(9.1 \times 10^{-31}\text{ kg})}}$$

$$= 9.1 \times 10^{-24}\text{ amp-m}^2. \qquad \blacktriangleleft$$

---

* This must not be confused with the magnetic dipole moment $\mu_s$ of the electron spin, which is also present.

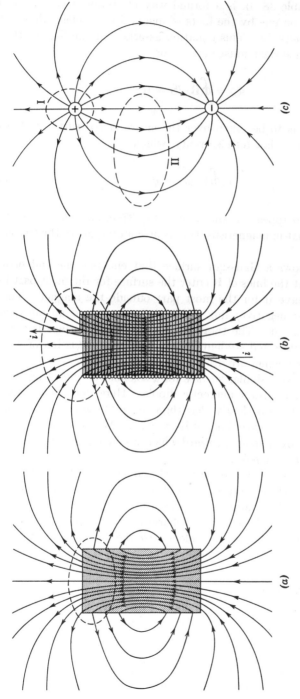

**Fig. 37-4**  Lines of **B** (*a*) for a bar magnet and (*b*) for a short solenoid.  (*c*) Lines of **E** for an electric dipole.  At large enough distances all three fields vary like those for a dipole.  The four dashed curves are intersections with the plane of the figure of closed Gaussian surfaces. Note that $\Phi_B$ equals zero for (*a*) or (*b*).  $\Phi_E$ equals zero for surfaces like II in (*c*), which do not contain any charge, but $\Phi_E$ is not zero for surfaces like I.

## 37-2 Gauss's Law for Magnetism

*Gauss's law for magnetism,* which is one of the basic equations of electromagnetism (see Table 38-3), is a formal way of stating a conclusion that seems to be forced on one by the facts of magnetism, namely, that *isolated magnetic poles do not exist.* This equation asserts that the flux $\Phi_B$ through any *closed* Gaussian surface must be zero, or

$$\Phi_B = \oint \mathbf{B} \cdot d\mathbf{S} = 0, \tag{37-6}$$

where the integral is to be taken over the entire closed surface. We contrast this with Gauss's law for electricity, which is

$$\epsilon_0 \oint \mathbf{E} \cdot d\mathbf{S} = q. \tag{37-7}$$

The fact that a zero appears at the right of Eq. 37-6, but not at the right of Eq. 37-7, means that in magnetism there is no counterpart to the free charge $q$ in electricity.

Figure 37-4a shows a Gaussian surface that encloses one end of a bar magnet. Note that the lines of **B** enter the surface for the most part inside the magnet and leave it for the most part outside the magnet. There is thus an inward (or negative) flux inside the magnet and an outward (or positive) flux outside it. The total flux for the whole surface is zero. In Section 37-7 the interested student will find a fuller discussion of why the lines of **B** for a bar magnet are drawn in the way shown.

Figure 37-4b shows a similar surface for a solenoid of finite length which, like a bar magnet, is also a magnetic dipole. Here, too, $\Phi_B$ equals zero. Figures 37-4a and b show clearly that there are no "sources" of **B**; that is, there are no points from which lines of **B** emanate. Also, there are no "sinks" of **B**; that is, there are no points toward which **B** converges. In other words, *there are no free magnetic poles.*

Figure 37-4c shows a Gaussian surface (I) surrounding the positive end of an electric dipole. Here there *is* a net flux of the lines of **E**. There is a "source" of **E**; it is the charge $q$. If $q$ is negative, we have a "sink" of **E** because the lines of **E** end on negative charges. For surfaces like surface II in Fig. 37-4c for which the charge inside is zero, the flux of **E** over the surface is also zero.

## 37-3 Paramagnetism

Magnetism as we know it in our daily experience is an important but special branch of the subject called *ferromagnetism;* we discuss this in Section 37-5. Here we discuss a weaker form of magnetism called *paramagnetism.*

For most atoms and ions, the magnetic effects of the electrons, including both their spins and orbital motions, exactly cancel so that the atom or ion is not magnetic. This is true for the rare gases such as neon and for ions * such as $Cu^+$, which makes up ordinary copper. These materials do not exhibit paramagnetism. For other atoms or ions the magnetic effects of the electrons do not cancel, so that the atom as a whole has a magnetic dipole moment **μ**. Examples are found among the so-called transition elements, such as $Mn^{++}$, the rare earths, such as $Gd^{+++}$, and the actinide elements, such as $U^{++++}$

If a sample of $N$ atoms, each of which has a magnetic dipole moment **μ**, is placed in a magnetic field, the elementary atomic dipoles tend to line up with the field. For perfect alignment, the sample as a whole would have a magnetic dipole moment of $N$**μ**. However, the aligning process is seriously interfered with by the collisions that take place between the atoms if the sample is a gas and by temperature vibrations if the sample is a solid. The importance of this thermal agitation effect may be measured by comparing two energies: one $(= \frac{3}{2}kT)$ is the mean kinetic energy of translation of a gas atom at temperature $T$; the other $(= 2\mu B)$ is the difference in energy between an atom lined up with the magnetic field and one pointing in the opposite direction. As Example 3 shows, the effect of the collisions at ordinary temperatures and fields is very great. The sample acquires a magnetic moment when placed in an external magnetic field, but this moment is usually much smaller than the maximum possible moment $N$**μ**.

▶ **Example 3.** A paramagnetic gas, whose atoms (see Example 2) have a magnetic dipole moment of about $10^{-23}$ amp-m$^2$, is placed in an external magnetic field of magnitude 1 weber/meter$^2$. At room temperature ($T = 300°K$) calculate and compare $U_T$, the mean kinetic energy of translation ($= \frac{3}{2}kT$), and $U_B$, the magnetic energy ($= 2\mu B$):

$$U_T = \tfrac{3}{2}kT = (\tfrac{3}{2})(1.38 \times 10^{-23} \text{ joule/°K})(300°K) = 6 \times 10^{-21} \text{ joule},$$

$$U_B = 2\mu B = (2)(10^{-23} \text{ amp-m}^2)(1 \text{ weber/meter}^2) = 2 \times 10^{-23} \text{ joule}.$$

Because $U_T$ equals 300 $U_B$, we see that energy exchanges in collisions can interfere seriously with the alignment of the dipoles with the external field. ◀

If a specimen of a paramagnetic substance is placed in a nonuniform magnetic field, such as that near the pole of a strong magnet, it will be attracted toward the region of higher field, that is, toward the pole. We can understand this by drawing an analogy with the corresponding electric case of Fig. 37–5, which shows a dielectric specimen (a sphere) in a nonuniform electric field. The net electric force points to the right in the figure and is

$$F_e = q(E + \Delta E) - q(E - \Delta E) = q(2\Delta E),$$

which can be written as

$$F_e = \frac{(q\,\Delta x)}{\Delta x}\,2\Delta E = p\left(\frac{2\Delta E}{\Delta x}\right) \cong p\left(\frac{dE}{dx}\right)_{\text{max}}$$

Here $p$ ($= q\,\Delta x$) is the induced electric dipole moment of the sphere. In the differential limit of a very small sphere $(2\Delta E/\Delta x)$ approaches $(dE/dx)_{\text{max}}$, the gradient of the electric field at the center of the sphere.

---

* $Cu^+$ indicates a copper atom from which one electron has been removed; $Al^{+++}$ indicates an aluminum atom from which three electrons have been removed, etc.

In the corresponding magnetic case we have, by analogy,

$$F_m = \mu \left(\frac{dB}{dx}\right)_{\text{max}} \tag{37-8}$$

Thus, by measuring the magnetic force $F_m$ that acts on a small paramagnetic specimen when it is placed in a nonuniform magnetic field whose field gradient $(dB/dx)_{\text{max}}$ is known, we can learn its magnetic dipole moment $\mu$. The *magnetization* **M** is defined as the magnetic moment per unit volume, or

$$\mathbf{M} = \frac{\mu}{V},$$

where $V$ is the volume of the specimen. It is a vector because $\mu$, the dipole moment of the specimen, is a vector.

In 1895 Pierre Curie (1859–1906) discovered experimentally that the magnetization $M$ of a paramagnetic specimen is directly proportional to $B$, the effective value of magnetic induction in which the specimen is placed, and inversely proportional to the temperature, or

$$M = C\frac{B}{T}, \tag{37-9}$$

in which $C$ is a constant. This equation is known as *Curie's law*. The law is physically reasonable in that increasing $B$ tends to align the elementary dipoles in the specimen, that is, to increase $M$, whereas increasing $T$ tends to interfere with this alignment, that is, to decrease $M$. Curie's law is well verified experimentally, provided that the ratio $B/T$ does not become too large.

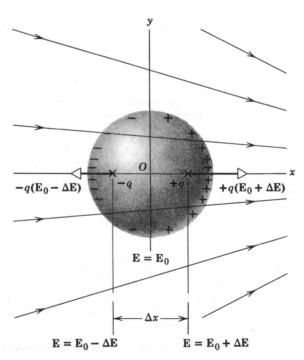

**Fig. 37-5** A dielectric sphere in a nonuniform electric field.

**Fig. 37-6** The ratio $M/M_{max}$ for a paramagnetic salt (chromium potassium alum) in various magnetic fields and at various temperatures. The curve through the experimental points is a theoretical curve calculated from modern quantum physics. (From measurements by W. E. Henry.)

$M$ cannot increase without limit, as Curie's law implies, but must approach a value $M_{max}$ ($= \mu N/V$) corresponding to the complete alignment of the $N$ dipoles contained in the volume $V$ of the specimen. Figure 37-6 shows this saturation effect for a sample of $CrK(SO_4)_2 \cdot 12H_2O$. The chromium ions are responsible for all the paramagnetism of this salt, all the other elements being paramagnetically inert. To achieve 99.5% saturation, it is necessary to use applied magnetic fields as high as 50,000 gauss and temperatures as low as 1.3°K. Note that for more readily achievable conditions, such as $B = 10,000$ gauss and $T = 10°$K, the abscissa in Fig. 37-6 is only 1.0 so that Curie's law would appear to be well obeyed for this and for all lower values of $B/T$. The curve that passes through the experimental points in this figure is calculated from a theory based on modern quantum physics; it is in excellent agreement with experiment.

### 37-4 Diamagnetism

In 1846 Michael Faraday discovered that a specimen of bismuth brought near to the pole of a strong magnet is *repelled*. He called such substances *diamagnetic*. Diamagnetism, present in all substances, is such a feeble effect that its presence is masked in substances made of atoms that have a net magnetic dipole moment, that is, in paramagnetic or ferromagnetic substances.

Figures 37-7a and b show an electron circulating in a diamagnetic atom at angular frequency $\omega_0$ in an assumed circular orbit of radius $r$. Each electron is moving under the action of a centripetal force $F_E$ of electrostatic origin where, from Newton's second law,

$$F_E = ma = m\omega_0^2 r. \qquad (37-10)$$

Each rotating electron has an orbital magnetic moment, but for the atom as a whole the orbits are randomly oriented so that there is no *net* magnetic effect. In Fig. 37-7a, for example, the magnetic dipole moment $\mu_l$ points into the page; in Fig.

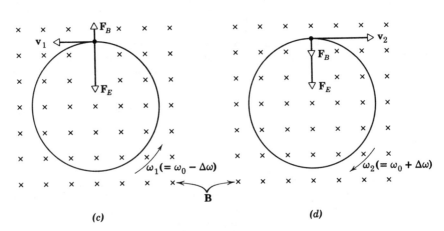

**Fig. 37-7** (a) An electron circulating in an atom. (b) An electron circulating in the opposite direction. (c) A magnetic field is introduced, *decreasing* the linear speed of the electron in (a), that is, $v_1 < v_0$. (d) The magnetic field *increases* the linear speed of the electron in (b), that is, $v_2 > v_0$.

37-7b it points out and the net effect for the two orbits shown is cancellation. This cancellation is also shown at the left in Fig. 37-8.

If an external field **B** is applied as in Fig. 37-7c and d, an *additional* force, given by $-e(\mathbf{v} \times \mathbf{B})$, acts on the electron. This magnetic force acts always at right angles to the direction of motion; its magnitude is

$$F_B = evB = e(\omega r)B. \qquad (37\text{--}11)$$

The student should show that in Fig. 37-7c $F_B$ and $F_E$ point in opposite directions and that in Fig. 37-7d they point in the same direction. Note that since the centripetal force changes when the magnetic field is applied (the radius can be shown to remain constant), the angular velocity must also change; thus $\omega$ in Eq. 37-11 differs from $\omega_0$ in Eq. 37-10.

Applying Newton's second law to Figs. 37-7c and d, and allowing for both directions of circulation, yields for the *resultant* forces on the electrons

$$F_E \pm F_B = ma = m\omega^2 r.$$

Substituting Eqs. 37-10 and 37-11 into this equation yields

$$m\omega_0^2 r \pm e\omega r B = m\omega^2 r$$

or

$$\omega^2 \mp \left(\frac{eB}{m}\right)\omega - \omega_0^2 = 0. \tag{37-12}$$

This quadratic equation can be solved for $\omega$, the new angular velocity. Rather than doing this, we take advantage of the fact (presented without proof; see Problem 7) that $\omega$ differs only slightly from $\omega_0$, even in the strongest external magnetic fields. Thus

$$\omega = \omega_0 + \Delta\omega \tag{37-13}$$

where $\Delta\omega \ll \omega_0$. Substituting this equation into Eq. 37-12 yields

$$[\omega_0^2 + 2\omega_0\,\Delta\omega + (\Delta\omega)^2] \pm [\beta\omega_0 + \beta\Delta\omega] - \omega_0^2 = 0,$$

where $\beta$ is a convenient abbreviation for $eB/m$. The two terms $\omega_0^2$ cancel each other; the terms $(\Delta\omega)^2$ and $\beta\Delta\omega$ are small compared to the remaining terms and may be set equal to zero with only small error. This leads, as an excellent approximation, to

$$\Delta\omega \cong \mp \tfrac{1}{2}\beta = \mp \frac{eB}{2m} \tag{37-14}$$

or, from Eq. 37-13,    $$\omega = \omega_0 \mp \frac{eB}{2m}.$$

Thus the effect of applying a magnetic field is to increase or decrease (depending on the direction of circulation) the angular velocity. This, in turn, increases or decreases the orbital magnetic moment of the circulating electron (see Example 2).

In Fig. 37-7c the angular velocity is reduced (because the centripetal force is reduced) so that the magnitude of the magnetic moment is reduced. In Fig. 37-7d, however, the angular velocity is increased so that the magnitude of $\mu_l$ is increased. These effects are shown on the right in Fig. 37-8, where it will be noted that the two magnetic moments *no longer cancel*.

We see that if a magnetic field $\mathbf{B}$ is applied to a diamagnetic substance (zero net magnetic moment in absence of applied field), a magnetic moment will be *induced* whose direction (out of the plane of Fig. 37-7) is *opposite* to $\mathbf{B}$; see also Fig. 37-8. This is precisely the reverse of paramagnetism, in which the (*permanent*) magnetic dipoles tend to point in the *same* direction as the applied field.

We can now understand why a diamagnetic specimen is repelled when brought near to the pole of a strong magnet. If the pole is a north pole, there exists a non-uniform magnetic field of induction with $\mathbf{B}$ pointing away from the pole. If a sphere

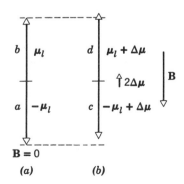

**Fig. 37-8**  The magnetic moments of the two oppositely circulating electrons in an atom cancel when there is no external magnetic field, as in (*a*), but do *not* cancel when a field is applied, as in (*b*). Note that the resultant moment in (*b*) points in the *opposite* direction to $\mathbf{B}$. Compare carefully with Fig. 37-7.

made of a diamagnetic material (bismuth, say) is brought near to this pole, the magnetization $\mathbf{M}$ that is induced in it points toward the pole, that is, *opposite to* $\mathbf{B}$. Thus the side of the sphere closest to the magnet behaves like a north pole and is *repelled* by the nearby north pole of the magnet. For a paramagnetic sphere, the vector $\mathbf{M}$ points *along the direction of* $\mathbf{B}$ and the side of the sphere nearest to the magnet is a south pole, which is *attracted* to the north pole of the magnet.

▶ **Example 4.** Calculate the *change* in magnetic moment for a circulating electron, as described in Example 2, if a magnetic field of induction $\mathbf{B}$ of 2.0 webers/meter² acts at right angles to the plane of the orbit.

We obtain $\mu$ from Eq. 37–3, or

$$\mu = NiA = (1)(e\nu)(\pi r^2) = (1)\left(\frac{e\omega}{2\pi}\right)(\pi r^2) = \tfrac{1}{2}er^2\omega.$$

The *change* in $\mu$ is      $\Delta\mu = \tfrac{1}{2}er^2\,\Delta\omega$

or, from Eq. 37–14,      $\Delta\mu = \pm\,\tfrac{1}{2}er^2\left(\dfrac{eB}{2m}\right) = \pm\,\dfrac{e^2Br^2}{4m}.$

Substituting numbers yields

$$\Delta\mu = \pm\,\frac{(1.6 \times 10^{-19}\ \text{coul})^2(2.0\ \text{webers/meter}^2)(5.1 \times 10^{-11}\ \text{meter})^2}{(4)(9.1 \times 10^{-31}\ \text{kg})}$$

$$= \pm 3.7 \times 10^{-29}\ \text{amp-m}^2.$$

In Example 2 the moment $\mu_l$ was $9.1 \times 10^{-24}$ amp-m², so that the change induced by even a strong external magnetic field is rather small, the ratio $\Delta\mu/\mu_l$ being about $4 \times 10^{-6}$.      ◀

## 37–5   Ferromagnetism

For five elements (Fe, Co, Ni, Gd, and Dy) and for a variety of alloys of these and other elements a special effect occurs which permits a specimen to achieve a high degree of magnetic alignment in spite of the randomizing tendency of the thermal motions of the atoms. In such materials, described as *ferromagnetic*, a special form of interaction called *exchange coupling* occurs between adjacent atoms, coupling their magnetic moments together in rigid parallelism.* Modern quantum physics successfully predicts that this will occur only for the five elements listed. If the temperature is raised above a certain critical value, called the *Curie temperature*, the exchange coupling suddenly disappears and the materials become simply paramagnetic. For iron the Curie temperature is 1043°K. Ferromagnetism is evidently a property not only of the individual atom or ion but also of the interaction of each atom or ion with its neighbors in the crystal lattice (see Fig. 21–5) of the solid.

Figure 37–9 shows a *magnetization curve* for a specimen of iron. To obtain such a curve, we form the specimen, assumed initially unmagnetized, into a ring and wind a toroidal coil around it as in Fig. 37–10, to form a so-called *Rowland ring*. When a current $i$ is set up in the coil, *if the iron core is not present*, a field of induction is set up within the toroid given by (Eq. 34–4)

$$B_0 = \mu_0 ni, \tag{37–15}$$

---

* Exchange coupling, a purely quantum effect, cannot be "explained" in terms of classical physics.

**Fig. 37-9** A magnetization curve for iron.

where $n$ is the number of turns per unit length for the toroid. Although this formula was derived for a long solenoid, it can be applied to a toroid if $d \ll r$ in Fig. 37-10. Because of the iron core, the actual value of **B** in the toroidal space will exceed $\mathbf{B}_0$, by a large factor in many cases, since the elementary atomic dipoles in the core line up with the applied field $\mathbf{B}_0$, thereby setting up their own field of induction. Thus we can write

$$B = B_0 + B_M \qquad (37\text{-}16)$$

where $B_M$ is the magnetic induction due to the specimen; it is proportional to the magnetization $M$ of the specimen. Often $B_M \gg B_0$.

The field $B_0$ is proportional to the current in the toroid and can be calculated readily, using Eq. 37-15; $B$ can be measured in a way that is described below. An experimental value for $B_M$ can be derived from Eq.

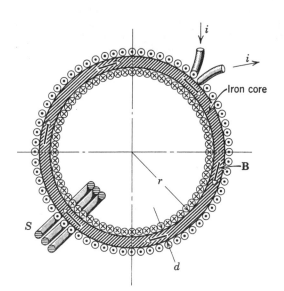

**Fig. 37-10** A Rowland ring, showing a secondary coil $S$.

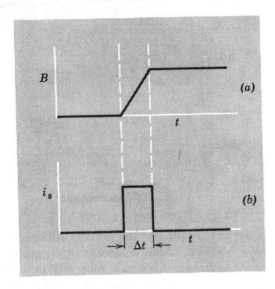

**Fig. 37-11** (a) $B$ for a Rowland ring as the current in the windings is increased from zero during an interval $\Delta t$. (b) The corresponding induced current in the secondary coil. Both curves are idealized; in practice, the sharp corners would be rounded off.

37–16. It has a maximum value $B_{M,\max}$ corresponding to complete alignment of the atomic dipoles in the iron. Thus we can plot, as in Fig. 37–9, the fractional degree of alignment ($= B_M/B_{M,\max}$) as a function of $B_0$. For this specimen a value of 96.5% saturation is achieved at $B_0 = 0.13$ weber/meter$^2$ ($= 1300$ gauss; this point is about 16 ft to the right of the origin in the figure); increasing $B_0$ to 1.0 weber/meter$^2$ ($= 10,000$ gauss; about 120 ft to the right in Fig. 37–9) increases the fractional saturation only to 97.7%.

To measure $B$ in the system of Fig. 37–10, let the current in the toroid windings be increased from zero to $i$. The flux through the secondary coil $S$ will change by $BA$, where $A$ is the area of the toroid. While the flux is changing, an induced emf will appear in coil $S$, according to Faraday's law. For simplicity, we assume that the current in the toroid is so adjusted that $B$ increases linearly with time for an interval $\Delta t$, as shown in Fig. 37–11a. The emf in coil $S$ during this interval, from Faraday's law,* will then be

$$\mathcal{E} = N\frac{\Delta\Phi_B}{\Delta t} = \frac{NBA}{\Delta t},$$

where $N$ is the number of turns in coil $S$. This emf will set up a current $i_s$ in coil $S$ given by

$$i_s = \frac{\mathcal{E}}{R} = \frac{NBA}{R\,\Delta t}$$

or

$$B = \frac{(i_s\,\Delta t)R}{NA} = \frac{qR}{NA},$$

in which $R$ is the resistance of coil $S$ and $i_s\,\Delta t$ is the charge $q$ that passes through this coil during time $\Delta t$. If a so-called *ballistic galvanometer* is connected to $S$, its deflection will be a measure of the charge $q$. Thus it is possible to find $B$ for any value of the current $i$ in the toroid windings. In practice, it is not necessary that the curve $B(t)$ in Fig. 37–11a be linear during the interval $\Delta t$.

---

* We ignore the minus sign because we are concerned only with the magnitude of $\mathcal{E}$.

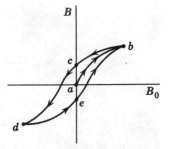

**Fig. 37-12**  A magnetization curve $(ab)$ for a specimen of iron and an associated hysteresis loop $(ebcde)$.

Magnetization curves for ferromagnetic materials *do not retrace themselves* as we increase and then decrease the toroid current. Figure 37-12 shows the following operations with a Rowland ring: (1) starting with the iron unmagnetized (point $a$), increase the toroid current until $B_0$ ($= \mu_0 n i$) has the value corresponding to point $b$; (2) reduce the current in the toroid winding back to zero (point $c$); (3) reverse the toroid current and increase it in magnitude until point $d$ is reached; (4) reduce the current to zero again (point $e$); (5) reverse the current once more until point $b$ is reached again. The lack of retraceability shown in Fig. 37-12 is called *hysteresis*. Note that at points $c$ and $e$ the iron core is magnetized, even though there is no current in the toroid windings; this is the familiar phenomenon of *permanent magnetism*.

The magnetization curve for paramagnetism (Fig. 37-6) is explained in terms of the mutually opposing tendencies of alignment with the external field and of randomization because of the temperature motions. In ferromagnetism, however, we have assumed that adjacent atomic dipoles are locked in rigid parallelism. Why, then, does the magnetic moment of the specimen not reach its saturation value for very low—even zero—values of $B_0$? The modern interpretation is to assume the existence within the specimen of *domains*, that is, of local regions within which there is essentially perfect alignment. The domains themselves, however, as Fig. 37-13 suggests, are not parallel at moderately low values of $\mathbf{B}_0$.

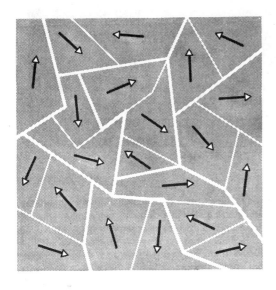

**Fig. 37-13**  The separate magnetic domains in an unmagnetized polycrystalline ferromagnetic sample are oriented to produce little external effect. Each domain, however, is made up of completely aligned atomic dipoles, as suggested by the arrows. The heavy boundaries define the crystals that make up the solid; the light boundaries define the domains within the crystals.

**Fig. 37–14** Domain patterns for a single crystal of iron containing 3.8% silicon. The white lines show the boundaries between the domains. These boundaries are regular rather than irregular, as in Fig. 37–13, because the specimen is a single crystal. In Fig. 37–13 the specimen is made up of many crystallites or grains. (Courtesy H. J. Williams, Bell Telephone Laboratories.)

Figure 37–14 shows some domain photographs, taken by sprinkling a colloidal suspension of finely powdered iron oxide on a properly etched single crystal of iron. The domain boundaries, which are thin regions in which the alignment of the elementary dipoles changes from a certain direction in one domain to an entirely different direction in the other, are the sites of intense but highly localized and nonuniform magnetic fields. The suspended colloidal particles are attracted to these regions. Although the atomic dipoles in the individual domains are completely aligned, the specimen as a whole may have a very small resultant magnetic moment. This is the state of affairs in an unmagnetized iron nail.

As we magnetize a piece of iron by placing it in an external magnetic field, two effects take place. One is a growth in size of the domains that are favorably oriented at the expense of those that are not, as in Fig. 37–15. Second, the direction of orientation of the dipoles within a domain may swing around as a unit, becoming closer to the field direction. Hysteresis comes about because the domain boundaries do not move completely back to their original positions when the external field $B_0$ is removed.

Two other types of magnetism, closely related to ferromagnetism, are *antiferromagnetism* and *ferrimagnetism* (note spelling). In antiferromagnetic substances, of

0.01 mm

(a)          (b)          (c)

**Fig. 37–15** (a) A boundary between two domains, with the magnetization in each domain as shown by the white arrows. (b) If an external magnetic field pointing from left to right is imposed on the specimen, the upper domain will grow at the expense of the lower. The domain boundary will move down as the elementary dipoles reverse themselves. (c) The process continues. The boundary has moved across a region in which there is a crystal imperfection. (Courtesy H. J. Williams, Bell Telephone Laboratories.)

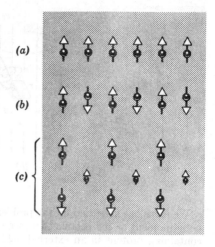

**Fig. 37-16** Showing how elementary magnetic dipoles are oriented by the interatomic exchange coupling in (a) ferromagnetism, (b) antiferromagnetism, and (c) ferrimagnetism.

which $MnO_2$ is an example, the exchange coupling to which we referred on page 834 serves to lock adjacent ions into rigid *antiparallelism* (see Fig. 37-16b). Such materials exhibit very little gross external magnetism. However, if they are heated above a certain temperature, called the *Néel temperature*, the exchange coupling ceases to act and the material becomes paramagnetic. In ferrimagnetic substances, of which iron ferrite is an example, two different kinds of magnetic ions are present. In iron ferrite the two ions are $Fe^{++}$ and $Fe^{+++}$. The exchange coupling locks the ions into a pattern like that of Fig. 37-16c, in which the external effects are intermediate between ferromagnetism and antiferromagnetism. Here, too, the exchange coupling disappears if the material is heated above a certain characteristic temperature.

## 37-6   Nuclear Magnetism

Many nuclei have magnetic dipoles, and the possibility arises that a specimen of matter may exhibit gross external magnetic effects associated with its nuclei. However, nuclear magnetic moments are several orders of magnitude smaller than those associated with the electronic motions in an atom or ion. The magnetic moment of an electron associated with its spin, for example, exceeds that of the proton (the nucleus of hydrogen) by a factor of 660.

Gross external effects for nuclear magnetism are smaller than the corresponding (electronic) paramagnetic effects by the *square* of ratios of this order of magnitude, because (a), *all else being equal*, the external magnetism is reduced by such a ratio, but (b) the very fact that the magnetic dipole moment of the nucleus is smaller means that (see Example 3) the thermal vibrations are proportionally (to a good approximation) more effective in reducing the degree of alignment of the elementary dipoles in an external magnetic field; thus all else is *not* equal and the ratio enters twice.

Techniques such as the Rowland ring (Fig. 37-10) are far too insensitive to detect nuclear magnetism. We describe here a *nuclear resonance technique* by means of which nuclear magnetism can readily reveal itself. This method is also vastly useful for studying paramagnetism, ferromagnetism, antiferromagnetism, and ferrimagnetism, in all of which cases the magnetic effects are associated not with the nuclei but with the atomic electrons. The nuclear-resonance technique was developed in 1946 by E. M. Purcell and his co-workers at Harvard. Simultaneously and independently, F. Bloch and his co-workers at Stanford discovered a very similar method. For these achievements the two physicists received a Nobel prize.

**Fig. 37-17** (a) A spinning proton precessing in an external magnetic field and (b) a spinning top precessing in an external gravitational field. $L_p$ and $L_t$ are the two angular momentum vectors.

*(a)*                        *(b)*

We focus our attention on the problem of measuring the magnitude $\mu$ of the magnetic moment of the proton. In principle, this can be done by placing a specimen containing protons in an external field of magnetic induction **B** and by measuring the energy $(= 2\mu B)$ required to turn the protons end for end. A rigorously correct description of the procedures cannot be given without using quantum physics. The description given, although based entirely on classical physics, nevertheless leads to the correct conclusions.

Figure 37–17a shows a spinning proton with its axis making an angle $\theta$ with a uniform external magnetic field **B**. Figure 37–17b shows a spinning top with its axis making an angle $\theta$ with a uniform external gravitational field **g**. In each case there is a torque that tends to align the axis of the spinning object with the field. For the proton (Eq. 33–11) it is given by

$$\tau_p = \mu B \sin \theta. \qquad (37\text{–}17a)$$

For the top it is given by    $\tau_t = mgr \sin \theta,$    (37–17b)

where $r$ locates the center of mass of the top and $m$ is its mass.

In Section 13–2, we saw that the spinning top processes about a vertical axis with an angular frequency given by

$$\omega_t = \frac{mgr}{L_t}, \qquad (37\text{–}18a)$$

in which $L_t$ is the spin angular momentum of the top.

The proton, which has a quantized spin angular momentum $L_p$, will also precess about the direction of the (magnetic) field because of the action of the (magnetic) torque. The student should derive the expression for the frequency of precession, being guided by the derivation of Section 13–2, but using the magnetic torque (Eq. 37–17a) instead of the gravitational torque (Eq. 37–17b). The relation is

$$\omega_p = \frac{\mu B}{L_p}. \qquad (37\text{–}18b)$$

▶ **Example 5.** What is the precession frequency of a proton in a magnetic field of 0.5 weber/meter²?

The quantities $\mu$ and $L_p$ in Eq. 37–18b are $1.4 \times 10^{-26}$ amp-m² and $0.53 \times 10^{-34}$ joule-sec. This equation then yields

$$\nu_p = \frac{\omega_p}{2\pi} = \frac{\mu B}{2\pi L_p} = \frac{(1.4 \times 10^{-26}\ \text{amp-m}^2)(0.50\ \text{weber/meter}^2)}{(2\pi)(0.53 \times 10^{-34}\ \text{joule-sec})} = 2.1 \times 10^7\ \text{cps}.$$

This frequency $(= 21\ \text{mc/sec})$ is in the radio-frequency range.    ◀

**Fig. 37–18**   In the nuclear magnetic resonance method a small oscillating magnetic field $B_{osc}$ is placed at right angles to a steady field $B$.

It is possible to change the energy of any system in periodic motion if we allow an external influence to act on it at the same frequency as that of its motion. This is the familiar *resonance* condition. As an "external influence" for the precessing proton, we use a small alternating magnetic field $B_{osc}$ arranged to be at right angles to the steady field $B$. This oscillating field combines vectorially with the steady field so that the *resultant* field rocks back and forth between the limits shown by the dashed lines in Fig. 37–18. Typical values for $B$ and for the amplitude of $B_{osc}$ are 5000 gauss and 1 gauss, respectively, so that the rocking angle $\alpha$ in the figure is quite small. If the angular frequency $\omega_0$ of the oscillating field is chosen equal to the angular precession frequency $\omega_p$ of the proton, it turns out that the precessing proton can absorb energy. An increase in energy means an increase in $\theta$ in Fig. 37–17$a$. The resonance condition

$$\omega_0 = \frac{\mu B}{L_p} \tag{37-19}$$

can be used to measure $\mu$. We place the spinning proton in a known field $B$, apply a "perturbing field" at right angles to it, and vary the angular frequency $\omega_0$ of this perturbing field until resonance occurs. It is possible to tell when Eq. 37–19 is satisfied because, at resonance, many spinning protons will tend to turn end for end in the field, absorbing energy which can be detected by appropriate electronic techniques.

Figure 37–19 is a schematic diagram of an experimental arrangement. The protons, present as hydrogen nuclei in a small vial $V$ of water, are immersed in a strong steady magnetic field caused by the electromagnet whose pole faces N and S are shown. A rapidly alternating current in the small coil $C$ provides the (horizontal) weak, perturbing magnetic field $B_{osc}$. This current is provided by a radio-frequency oscillator

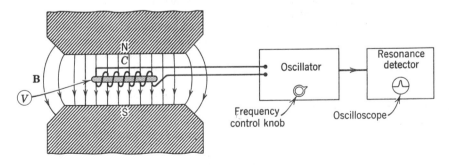

**Fig. 37–19**   An arrangement to observe nuclear resonance.   The oscillating field is horizontal within the coil.

**Fig. 37-20**  An oscilloscope photograph of a proton resonance peak showing energy absorbed from the oscillator versus oscillator frequency. (From Bloembergen et al., *Phys. Rev.*, **73**, 679.)

whose angular frequency $\omega_0$ can be varied; an electronic "resonance detector," also connected to the oscillator, serves to indicate when energy is being drained from the oscillator and used to "flip the protons." In principle, the oscillator angular frequency $\omega_0$ is varied until the resonance detector shows that Eq. 37-19 is satisfied (see Fig. 37-20). The magnetic moment $\mu$ can then be determined by measuring $B$ and $\omega_0$. Surprisingly enough, magnetic moments can be measured in this and similar ways to a much greater accuracy than we can measure $\mu$ for a bar magnet. For the proton we have

$$\mu_p = 1.41044 \times 10^{-26} \text{ amp-m}^2.$$

## 37-7   Three Magnetic Vectors

In Chapter 30 we saw that if a dielectric is placed in an electric field polarization charges will appear on its surface. These surface charges, which find their origin in the elementary electric dipoles (permanent or induced) that make up the dielectric, set up a field of their own that modifies the original field. For the simple case discussed in Chapter 30—a dielectric slab in a parallel-plate capacitor—this complication can readily be handled in terms of the electric field strength vector **E** and some knowledge of the electric properties of the slab material, such as the dielectric constant. For more complex problems we asserted that it was useful to introduce two other (subsidiary) electric vectors, the *electric polarization* **P** and the *electric displacement* **D**. Table 30-2 shows some of the characteristics of these three vectors.

In magnetism we find a similar situation. If magnetic materials are placed in a field of induction, the elementary magnetic dipoles (permanent or induced) will act to set up a field of induction of their own that will modify the original field. For the simple case discussed in this chapter—a Rowland ring with a ferromagnetic core—this complication can readily be handled in terms of the magnetic induction vector **B** and some knowledge of the magnetic properties of the ring material, such as that provided by Fig. 37-9. For more complex problems we find it useful to introduce two other (subsidiary) magnetic vectors, the *magnetization* **M** and the *magnetic field strength* **H**. We do so largely so that the student who takes a second course in electromagnetism will have some familiarity with them.

Consider a Rowland ring carrying a current $i_0$ in its windings and designed so that its core, assumed to be iron, can be removed. The magnetic induction $B$, measured by the methods of Section 37-5, will be much greater when the core is in place than when it is not, assuming that the current in the windings remains unchanged.

Physically we can understand the large value of $B$ in the iron core in terms of the alignment of the elementary dipoles in the iron. A hypothetical slice out of the iron core, as in Fig. 37-21$b$, has a magnetic moment $d\boldsymbol{\mu}$ equal to the vector sum of all of the elementary dipoles contained in it. We define our first subsidiary vector, the *magnetization* $\mathbf{M}$, as the magnetic moment per unit volume of the core material. For the slice of Fig. 37-21$b$ we have

$$d\boldsymbol{\mu} = \mathbf{M}(A\ dl),$$

where $(A\ dl)$ is the volume of the slice, $A$ being the cross section of the core.

When we discussed Ampère's law in Chapter 34, we assumed that no magnetic materials were present. If we apply this law, namely

$$\oint \mathbf{B}\cdot d\mathbf{l} = \mu_0 i, \tag{37-20}$$

to the circular path of integration shown in Fig. 37-21$a$, we obtain

$$(B)(2\pi r_0) = \mu_0(N_0 i_0), \tag{37-21}$$

in which $r_0$ is the mean radius of the core, $N_0$ is the number of turns, and $i_0$ is the current in each turn. We see at once that Ampère's law, in the form of Eq. 37-20,

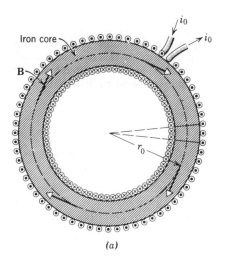

(a)

**Fig. 37-21**   ($a$) A Rowland ring with an iron core. ($b$) A slice of the core, showing its magnetic moment $d\boldsymbol{\mu}$ caused by the alignment of the elementary magnetic dipoles in the iron.

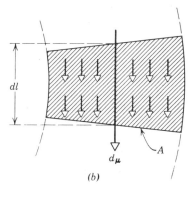

(b)

*is not valid when magnetic materials are present.* Equation 37–21 predicts that, since the right side is the same whether or not the core is in place, the induction $B$ should also be the same, a prediction not in accord with experiment.

We can increase $B$ in the absence of the iron core to the value that it has when the core is in place if we increase the current in the windings by an amount $i_{M,0}$. The magnetization of the iron core is thus *equivalent in its effect on* **B** to such a hypothetical current increase. We choose to modify Ampère's law by arbitrarily inserting a *magnetizing current* term $i_M$ on the right, obtaining

$$\oint \mathbf{B} \cdot d\mathbf{l} = \mu_0(i + i_M).$$ (37–22)

If we give $i_M$ a suitable value when the iron core is in place, it is clear that Ampère's law, in this new form, can remain valid. It remains to relate this (largely hypothetical) magnetizing current to something more physical, the magnetization **M**.*

Applying Eq. 37–22 to the iron ring of Fig. 37–21a yields

$$(B)(2\pi r_0) = \mu_0(N_0 i_0) + \mu_0(N_0 i_{M,0}).$$ (37–23)

We can relate $i_{M,0}$ to the magnetization **M** if we recall (Eq. 33–10) that the magnetic moment of a magnetic dipole in the form of a current loop is given by

$$\mu = NiA,$$

where $N$ is the number of turns in the loop, $i$ is the loop current, and $A$ is the loop area. Let us use this equation to find what increase $i_{M,0}$ in current in the windings around the slice of Fig. 37–21b would produce a magnetic moment equivalent to that actually produced by the alignment of elementary dipoles in the slice. We have

$$M(A \, dl) = \left(N_0 \frac{dl}{2\pi r_0}\right)(i_{M,0})(A),$$

the quantity in the first parentheses on the right being the number of turns associated with the slice of thickness $dl$. This reduces to

$$N_0 i_{M,0} = M(2\pi r_0).$$ (37–24)

Substituting this into Eq. 37–23 yields

$$(B)(2\pi r_0) = \mu_0(N_0 i_0) + \mu_0(M)(2\pi r_0).$$ (37–25)

We now choose to generalize from the special case of the Rowland ring by writing Eq. 37–25 as

$$\oint \mathbf{B} \cdot d\mathbf{l} = \mu_0 i + \mu_0 \oint \mathbf{M} \cdot d\mathbf{l}$$

or

$$\oint \left(\frac{\mathbf{B} - \mu_0 \mathbf{M}}{\mu_0}\right) \cdot d\mathbf{l} = i.$$

---

* It is possible to give reality to the magnetizing current by viewing it as a real current that flows around the magnet at its surface, being the resultant macroscopic effect of all the microscopic current loops that constitute the atomic electron orbits. This *Amperian current* viewpoint however does not take the magnetization due to electron spin readily into account. Since we do not attempt to measure magnetizing currents experimentally, other than through their (postulated) magnetic effects, we prefer to view the magnetizing current as a convenient formalism.

The quantity $(\mathbf{B} - \mu_0\mathbf{M})/\mu_0$ occurs so often in magnetic situations that we give it a special name, the *magnetic field strength* $\mathbf{H}$, or

$$\mathbf{H} = \frac{\mathbf{B} - \mu_0\mathbf{M}}{\mu_0}$$

which we write as

$$\mathbf{B} = \mu_0\mathbf{H} + \mu_0\mathbf{M}. \tag{37-26}$$

Ampère's law can now be written in the simple form

$$\oint \mathbf{H}\cdot d\mathbf{l} = i, \tag{37-27}$$

which holds in the presence of magnetic materials and in which $i$ is the *true current only*, that is, it does not include the magnetizing current. This reminds us that the electric displacement vector $\mathbf{D}$ permitted us to write Gauss's law for the case in which dielectric materials are present, in a form involving free charges only, that is, not polarization charges; see Table 30-2.

We state without proof (see Problems 12 and 13) that at a boundary between two media (1) the component of $\mathbf{H}$ tangential to the surface has the same value on each side of the surface * and (2) the component of $\mathbf{B}$ perpendicular to the surface has the same value on each side of the surface. These *boundary conditions* are of great value in solving complex problems.

To find $H$ in our Rowland ring, let us apply Ampère's law in the generalized form of Eq. 37-27. We have

$$(H)(2\pi r_0) = N_0 i_0,$$

where $i_0$ is the (true) current in the windings. This gives

$$H = \left(\frac{N_0}{2\pi r_0}\right) i_0 = n i_0, \tag{37-28}$$

in which $n$ is the number of turns per unit length. Since we have not introduced any information describing the core into Eq. 37-27, the value of $H$ computed from Eq. 37-28 is independent of the core material.

$B$ can be measured experimentally by the method of Section 37-5 and $M$ can then be calculated from Eq. 37-26. The student should note in passing (see Eq. 37-15) that the abscissa $B_0$ in Fig. 37-9 is proportional to $H$ ($= \mu_0 H$), the ordinate being proportional to $B$. Curves such as this and that of Fig. 37-12 are called *B-H curves*.

Let us assume that we have made measurements of $\mathbf{H}$, $\mathbf{B}$, and $\mathbf{M}$ for a wide variety of magnetic materials, using either the technique described or an equivalent one. For *paramagnetic* and *diamagnetic* materials we would find, as an experimental result, that $\mathbf{B}$ is directly proportional to $\mathbf{H}$, or

$$\mathbf{B} = \kappa_m\mu_0\mathbf{H}, \tag{37-29}$$

in which $\kappa_m$, the *permeability* of the magnetic medium, is a constant for a given temperature and density of the material. Eliminating $\mathbf{B}$ between Eqs. 37-29 and 37-26 allows us to write

$$\mathbf{M} = (\kappa_m - 1)\mathbf{H}, \tag{37-30}$$

which is another expression of the linear or proportional character of paramagnetic and diamagnetic materials.

---

* Assuming that there are no true currents at the surface, as there are in the Rowland ring of Fig. 37-21a, for example.

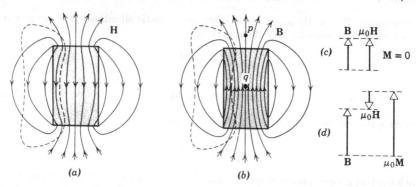

**Fig. 37–22** (a) The lines of **H** and (b) the lines of **B** for a permanent magnet. Note that the lines of **H** change direction at the boundary. The closed dashed curves are paths of integration around which Ampère's law may be applied. The relation $B = \mu_0 H + \mu_0 M$ is shown to be satisfied for (c) a particular outside point $p$ and (d) a particular inside point $q$.

For a vacuum, in which there are no magnetic dipoles present to be aligned, the magnetization **M** must be zero. Putting $M = 0$ in Eq. 37–26 leads to

$$B = \mu_0 H \qquad \text{(a vacuum)}. \qquad (37\text{–}31)$$

Comparison with Eq. 37–29 shows that a vacuum must be described by $\kappa_m = 1$. Equation 37–30 verifies that the magnetization vanishes if we put $\kappa_m$ equal to unity. For paramagnetic materials $\kappa_m$ is slightly greater than unity. For diamagnetic materials it is slightly less than unity; Eq. 37–30 shows that this requires **M** and **H** to be oppositely directed, a fact discussed at length in Section 37–4.

In ferromagnetic materials the relationship between **B** and **H** is far from linear, as Figs. 37–9 and 37–12 show. Experimentally, $\kappa_m$ proves to be a function not only of the value of H but also, because of hysteresis, of the magnetic and thermal history of the specimen.*

An interesting special case of ferromagnetism is the permanent magnet, for which **H**, **M**, and **B** all have nonvanishing values inside the magnet even though there is no true current. Figure 37–22 shows typical lines of **B** and **H** associated with such a magnet. The lines of **B** may be drawn as continuous loops, the boundary condition (2), mentioned above, being satisfied where the lines enter and leave the magnet. Equation 37–22 shows that the vector **B** is associated with the *total* current, both true and magnetizing. In Fig. 37–22a $\oint \mathbf{B} \cdot d\mathbf{l}$ around any loop such as that shown by the dashed curve is not zero and must be associated with a hypothetical magnetizing current $i_M$ imagined to circulate around the magnet at its surface; actual or true currents ($i$) do not exist in this problem. Figure 37–22b shows that **H** reverses direction at the boundary. Since **H** (see Eq. 37–27) is associated with true currents only, we must have $\oint \mathbf{H} \cdot d\mathbf{l}$ around any loop such as that shown by the dashed lines.

---

* In the dielectric case there are waxy materials, called *ferroelectrics*, for which the relationship between **D** and **E** is nonlinear, which exhibit hysteresis, and from which quasi-permanent electric dipoles (*electrets*) can be constructed. However, most commonly useful dielectric materials are linear whereas most commonly useful magnetic materials are nonlinear.

The reversal of **H** at the boundary makes this possible. Note that **M** and **H** point in opposite directions within the magnet. Table 37-1 summarizes the properties of the three vectors **B**, **H**, and **M**.

### Table 37-1

### THREE MAGNETIC VECTORS

| Name | Symbol | Associated with | Boundary Condition |
|---|---|---|---|
| Magnetic induction | **B** | All currents | Normal component continuous |
| Magnetic field strength | **H** | True currents only | Tangential component continuous † |
| Magnetization (magnetic dipole moment per unit volume) | **M** | Magnetization currents only | Vanishes in a vacuum |

| | | |
|---|---|---|
| Defining equations for **B** | $F = q\mathbf{v} \times \mathbf{B}$<br>or $= i\mathbf{l} \times \mathbf{B}$ | Eq. 33-3a<br>Eq. 33-6a |
| General relation among the three vectors | $\mathbf{B} = \mu_0 \mathbf{H} + \mu_0 \mathbf{M}$ | Eq. 37-26 |
| Ampère's law when magnetic materials are present | $\oint \mathbf{H} \cdot d\mathbf{l} = i$<br>($i$ = true current only) | Eq. 37-27 |
| Empirical relations for certain magnetic materials * | $B = \kappa_m \mu_0 H$<br>$M = (\kappa_m - 1)H$ | Eq. 37-29<br>Eq. 37-30 |

\* For paramagnetic and diamagnetic materials only, if $\kappa_m$ is to be independent of **H**.
† Assuming no true currents exist at the boundary.

▶ **Example 6.** In the Rowland ring the (true) current $i_0$ in the windings is 2.0 amp and the number of turns per unit length ($n$) in the toroid is 10 turns/cm. $B$, measured by the technique of Section 37-5, is 1.0 weber/meter². Calculate (a) $H$, (b) $M$, and (c) the magnetizing current $i_{M,0}$ both when the core is in place and when it is removed. (d) For these particular operating conditions, what is $\kappa_m$?

(a) $H$ is independent of the core material and may be found from Eq. 37-28:

$$H = ni$$

$$= (10 \text{ turns/cm})(2.0 \text{ amp})$$

$$= 2.0 \times 10^3 \text{ amp/meter}.$$

(b) $M$ is zero when the core is removed. With the core in place, we may solve Eq. 37–26 for $M$, obtaining for the magnitude of $M$,

$$M = \frac{B - \mu_0 H}{\mu_0}$$

$$= \frac{(1.0 \text{ weber/meter}^2) - (4\pi \times 10^{-7} \text{ weber/amp-m})(2.0 \times 10^3 \text{ amp/meter})}{(4\pi \times 10^{-7} \text{ weber/amp-m})}$$

$$= 7.9 \times 10^5 \text{ amp/meter}.$$

(c) The effective magnetizing current follows from Eq. 37–24:

$$i_{M,0} = M \left( \frac{2\pi r_0}{N_0} \right) = \frac{M}{n}$$

$$= \frac{7.9 \times 10^5 \text{ amp/meter}}{2.0 \times 10^3 \text{ turns/meter}}$$

$$= 390 \text{ amp}.$$

An *additional* current of this amount in the windings would produce the same value of $B$ in the absence of a core as that obtained, by alignment of the elementary dipoles, with the core in place.

(d) The permeability can be found from Eq. 37–29, or

$$\kappa_m = \frac{B}{\mu_0 H}$$

$$= \frac{1.0 \text{ weber/meter}^2}{(4\pi \times 10^{-7} \text{ weber/amp-m})(2.0 \times 10^3 \text{ amp/meter})}$$

$$= 397.$$

We emphasize that this value of $\kappa_m$ holds only for the special conditions of this experiment. ◄

## QUESTIONS

1. Two iron bars are identical in appearance. One is a magnet and one is not. How can you tell them apart? You are not permitted to suspend either bar as a compass needle or to use any other apparatus.

2. How could you reverse the magnetism of a compass needle?

3. Two iron bars always attract, no matter the combination in which their ends are brought near each other. Can you conclude that one of the bars must be unmagnetized?

4. If we sprinkle iron filings on a particular bar magnet, they cling both to the ends *and to the middle*. Sketch roughly the lines of **B**, both outside and inside the magnet.

5. The earth is a huge magnetic dipole. (a) Is the magnetic pole in the Northern Hemisphere a north or a south magnetic pole? (b) In the Northern Hemisphere do the magnetic lines of force associated with the earth's magnetic field point toward the earth's surface or away from it?

6. Cosmic rays are charged particles that strike our atmosphere from some external source. We find that more low-energy cosmic rays reach the earth at the north and south magnetic poles than at the (magnetic) equator. Why is this so?

7. How might the magnetic dipole moment of the earth be measured?

8. Give three reasons for believing that the flux $\Phi_B$ of the earth's magnetic field is greater through the boundaries of Alaska than through those of Texas.

9. The neutron, which has no charge, has a magnetic dipole moment. Is this possible on the basis of classical electromagnetism, or does this evidence alone indicate that classical electromagnetism has broken down?

10. Is the magnetization at saturation for a paramagnetic substance very much different from that for a saturated ferromagnetic substance of about the same size?

11. Explain why a magnet attracts an unmagnetized iron object such as a nail.

12. Does any net force or torque act on (a) an unmagnetized iron bar or (b) a permanent bar magnet when placed in a uniform magnetic field?

13. A nail is placed at rest on a smooth table top near a strong magnet. It is released and attracted to the magnet. What is the source of the kinetic energy it has just before it strikes the magnet?

14. The magnetization induced in a given diamagnetic sphere by a given external magnetic field does not vary with temperature, in sharp contrast to the situation in paramagnetism. Is this understandable in terms of the description that we have given of the origin of diamagnetism?

15. Compare the magnetization curves for a paramagnetic substance (Fig. 37–6) and for a ferromagnetic substance (Fig. 37–9). What would a similar curve for a diamagnetic substance look like? Do you think that it would show saturation effects in strong applied fields (say 10 weber/meter$^2$)?

16. Distinguish between the precession frequency and the cyclotron frequency of a proton in a magnetic field.

17. In our discussion of nuclear magnetism we said that energy absorption occurs because the dipoles are turned end for end. However, a given dipole might initially be lined up either with the field or against it. In the first case there would be an *absorption* of energy, but in the second case there would be a *release* of energy, each amount being $2\mu B$. Why do we observe a *net* absorption? These two events would seem to cancel.

18. Discuss similarities and differences in Tables 30–2 and 37–1.

## PROBLEMS

1. The earth has a magnetic dipole moment of $6.4 \times 10^{21}$ amp-m$^2$. (a) What current would have to be set up in a single turn of wire going around the earth at its magnetic equator if we wished to set up such a dipole? (b) Could such an arrangement be used to cancel out the earth's magnetism at points in space well above the earth's surface? (c) On the earth's surface?

2. Assume that the electron is a small sphere of radius $R$, its charge and mass being spread uniformly throughout its volume. Such an electron has a "spin" angular momentum $L$ of $0.53 \times 10^{-34}$ joule-sec and a magnetic moment $\mu$ of $9.3 \times 10^{-24}$ amp-m$^2$. Show that $e/m = 2\mu/L$. Is this prediction in agreement with experiment? (Hint: The spherical electron must be divided into infinitesimal current loops and an expression for the magnetic moment found by integration. This model of the electron is too mechanistic to be in the spirit of the modern quantum view of this particle.)

3. Calculate (a) the electric field strength and (b) the magnetic induction at a point 1.0 A (one angstrom unit) away from a proton, measured along its axis of spin. The magnetic moment of the proton is $1.4 \times 10^{-26}$ amp-m$^2$.

4. A Rowland ring is formed of ferromagnetic material. It is circular in cross section, with an inner radius of 5.0 cm and an outer radius of 6.0 cm and is wound with 400 turns of wire. (a) What current must be set up in the windings to attain $B_0 = 2 \times 10^{-4}$ weber/meter$^2$ in Fig. 37–9? (b) A secondary coil wound around the toroid has 50 turns and has a resistance of 8.0 ohms. If, for this value of $B_0$, we have $B_M = 800B_0$, how much charge moves through the secondary coil when the current in the toroid windings is turned on?

5. The dipole moment associated with an atom of iron in an iron bar is $1.8 \times 10^{-23}$ amp-m$^2$. Assume that all the atoms in the bar, which is 5 cm long and has a cross-sec-

tional area of 1 cm², have their dipole moments aligned. (a) What is the dipole moment of the bar? (b) What torque must be exerted to hold this magnet at right angles to an external field of 15,000 gauss?

6. Can you give an explanation of diamagnetism based on Faraday's law of induction? In Figs. 37–7a and b, for example, what inductive effects can be expected as the magnetic field is built up from zero to the final value **B**?

7. Prove that $\Delta\omega \ll \omega_0$ in Eq. 37–13.

8. Show that, classically, a spinning positive charge will have a spin magnetic moment that points in the same direction as its spin angular momentum.

9. Assume that the nuclei (protons) in 1 gm of water *could all be aligned.* What magnetic induction $B$ would be produced 5.0 cm from the sample, along its alignment axis?

10. It is possible to measure $e/m$ for the electron by measuring (a) the cyclotron frequency $\nu_c$ of electrons in a given magnetic field and (b) the precession frequency $\nu_p$ of protons in the same field. Show that the relation is

$$\frac{e}{m} = \frac{\nu_c}{\nu_p} \frac{\mu_s}{L_s}.$$

Since $\mu_s$ and $L_s$ for the proton are accurately known, this experiment gives us our most precise value of $e/m$ today.

11. *Dipole–dipole interaction.* The exchange coupling mentioned in Section 37–5 as being responsible for ferromagnetism is *not* the mutual magnetic interaction energy between two elementary magnetic dipoles. To show this (a) compute $B$ a distance $a$ (= 1.0 A) away from a dipole of moment $\mu$ (= $1.8 \times 10^{-23}$ amp-m²); (b) compute the energy (= $2\mu B$) required to turn a second similar dipole end for end in this field. What do you conclude about the strength of this dipole-dipole interaction? Compare with the results of Example 3. (Note: for the same distance, the field in the median plane of a dipole is only half as large as on the axis; see Eq. 37–2.)

12. *Boundary condition for* **B**. Prove that at the boundary between two media the normal component of **B** has the same value on each side of the surface. (Hint: Construct a closed Gaussian surface shaped like a flat pillbox with one face in each medium and apply Gauss's law for magnetism.)

13. *Boundary condition for* **H**. Prove that at the boundary between two media the tangential component of **H** has the same value on each side of the surface, assuming that there is no current at the surface. (Hint: Construct a closed rectangular loop, the two opposite longer sides being parallel to the surface, with one side in each medium. Use Ampère's law in the form that applies when magnetic materials are present.)

14. The magnetic energy density can be shown to be given in its most general form as

$$\mu_B = \tfrac{1}{2}\mathbf{B}\cdot\mathbf{H}.$$

Does this reduce to a familiar result for a vacuum?

# Electromagnetic Oscillations

## CHAPTER 38

### 38–1  *LC* Oscillations

The $LC$ system of Fig. 38–1 resembles a mass-spring system (see **Fig. 8–4**) in that, among other things, each system has a characteristic frequency of oscillation. To see this, we assume that initially the capacitor $C$ in Fig. 38–1$a$ carries a charge $q_m$ and the current $i$ in the inductor is zero. At this instant the energy stored in the capacitor is given by Eq. 30–25, or

$$U_E = \frac{1}{2}\frac{q_m^2}{C}. \tag{38–1}$$

The energy stored in the inductor, given by

$$U_B = \tfrac{1}{2}Li^2, \tag{38–2}$$

is zero because the current is zero. The capacitor now starts to discharge through the inductor, positive charge carriers moving counterclockwise, as shown in Fig. 38–1$b$. This means that a current $i$, given by $dq/dt$ and pointing down in the inductor, is established.

As $q$ decreases, the energy stored in the electric field in the capacitor also decreases. This energy is transferred to the magnetic field that appears around the inductor because of the current $i$ that is building up there. Thus the electric field decreases, the magnetic field builds up, and energy is transferred from the former to the latter.

At a time corresponding to Fig. 38–1$c$, all the charge on the capacitor will have disappeared. The electric field in the capacitor will be zero, the energy stored there having been transferred entirely to the magnetic field of the

**Fig. 38–1** Showing eight stages in a cycle of oscillation of an *LC* circuit. The bar graphs below each figure show the stored magnetic and electric potential energy. The vertical arrows on the inductor axis show the current. The student should compare this figure in detail with **Fig. 8–4**, to which it exactly corresponds.

inductor. According to Eq. 38–2, there must then be a current—and indeed one of maximum value—in the inductor. Note that even though $q$ equals zero the current (which is $dq/dt$) is *not* zero at this time.

The large current in the inductor in Fig. 38–1c continues to transport positive charge from the top plate of the capacitor to the bottom plate, as shown in Fig. 38–1d; energy now flows from the inductor back to the capacitor as the electric field builds up again. Eventually, the energy will have been transferred completely back to the capacitor, as in Fig. 38–1e. The situation of Fig. 38–1e is like the initial situation, except that the capacitor is charged in the opposite direction.

The capacitor will start to discharge again, the current now being clockwise, as in Fig. 38–1*f*. Reasoning as before, we see that the circuit eventually returns to its initial situation and that the process continues at a definite frequency *ν* (measured, say, in cycles/sec) to which corresponds a definite *angular* frequency *ω* (= 2*πν* and measured, say, in radians/sec). Once started, such *LC* oscillations (in the ideal case described, in which the circuit contains no resistance) continue indefinitely, energy being shuttled back and forth between the electric field in the capacitor and the magnetic field in the inductor. Any configuration in Fig. 38–1 can be set up as an initial condition. The oscillations will then continue from that point, proceeding clockwise around the figure. The student should compare these oscillations carefully with those of the mass-spring system described in Fig. 8–4.

To measure the charge *q* as a function of time, we can measure the variable potential difference $V_C(t)$ that exists across capacitor *C*. The relation

$$V_C = \left(\frac{1}{C}\right)q$$

shows that $V_C$ is proportional to *q*. To measure the current we can insert a small resistance *R* in the circuit and measure the potential difference across it. This is proportional to *i* through the relation

$$V_R = (R)i.$$

We assume here that *R* is so small that its effect on the behavior of the circuit is negligible. Both *q* and *i*, or more correctly $V_C$ and $V_R$, which are proportional to them, can be displayed on a cathode-ray oscilloscope. This instrument can plot automatically on its screen graphs proportional to $q(t)$ and $i(t)$, as in Fig. 38–2.

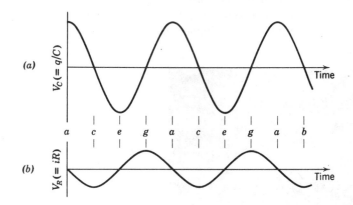

**Fig. 38-2** A drawing of an oscilloscope screen showing potential differences proportional to (*a*) the charge and (*b*) the current, in the circuit of Fig. 38–1, as a function of time. The letters indicate corresponding phases of oscillation in that figure. Note that because $i = dq/dt$ the lower curve is proportional to the derivative of the upper.

▶ **Example 1.** A 1.0-μf capacitor is charged to 50 volts. The charging battery is then disconnected and a 10-mh coil is connected across the capacitor, so that $LC$ oscillations occur. What is the maximum current in the coil? Assume that the circuit contains no resistance.

The maximum stored energy in the capacitor must equal the maximum stored energy in the inductor, from the conservation-of-energy principle. This leads, from Eqs. 38–1 and 38–2, to

$$\frac{1}{2}\frac{q_m^2}{C} = \tfrac{1}{2}Li_m^2,$$

where $i_m$ is the *maximum* current and $q_m$ is the *maximum* charge. Note that the maximum current and the maximum charge do not occur at the same time but one-fourth of a cycle apart; see Figs. 38–1 and 38–2. Solving for $i_m$ and substituting $CV_0$ for $q_m$ gives

$$i_m = V_0\sqrt{\frac{C}{L}} = (50 \text{ volts})\sqrt{\frac{1.0 \times 10^{-6} \text{ farad}}{10 \times 10^{-3} \text{ henry}}} = 0.50 \text{ amp.} \qquad \blacktriangleleft$$

In an actual $LC$ circuit the oscillations will not continue indefinitely because there is always some resistance present that will drain away energy by Joule heating. The oscillations, once started, will die away, as in Fig. 38–3. This figure should be compared to Fig. 15–19, which shows the decay of the mechanical oscillations of a mass-spring system caused by frictional damping.

It is possible to have sustained electromagnetic oscillations if arrangements are made to supply, automatically and periodically (once a cycle, say), enough energy from an outside source to compensate for that lost to Joule heat. We are reminded of a clock escapement, which is a device for feeding energy from a spring or a falling weight into an oscillating pendulum, thus compensating for frictional losses that would otherwise cause the oscillations to die away. Oscillators whose frequency $\nu$ may be varied between certain limits are commercially available as packaged units over a wide range of frequencies, extending from low audio-frequencies (lower than 10 cycles/sec) to microwave frequencies (higher than $10^{10}$ cycles/sec).

**Fig. 38–3** A photograph of an oscilloscope trace showing how the oscillations in an $LRC$ circuit die away because energy is lost to Joule heat in the resistor. The figure is a plot of the potential difference across the resistor as a function of time.

## 38–2  Analogy to Simple Harmonic Motion

Figure 8–4 shows that in a mass-spring system performing simple harmonic motion, as in an oscillating $LC$ circuit, two kinds of energy occur. One is potential energy of the compressed or extended spring; the other is kinetic energy of the moving mass. These are given by the familiar formulas in the first column of Table 38–1. The table suggests that a capacitor is in

### Table 38–1

SOME ENERGY FORMULAS

| Mechanical | Electromagnetic |
|---|---|
| spring $\quad U_P = \frac{1}{2}kx^2$ | capacitor $\quad U_E = \frac{1}{2}\frac{q^2}{C}$ |
| mass $\quad U_K = \frac{1}{2}mv^2$ | inductor $\quad U_B = \frac{1}{2}Li^2$ |
| $v = dx/dt$ | $i = dq/dt$ |

some formal way like a spring and an inductor is like a mass and that certain electromagnetic quantities "correspond" to certain mechanical ones, namely,

$q$ corresponds to $x$,
$i$ corresponds to $v$,
$C$ corresponds to $1/k$,
$L$ corresponds to $m$.

Comparison of Fig. 38–1, which shows the oscillations of the $LC$ circuit, with Fig. 8–4, which shows the oscillations in a mass-spring system, indicates how close the correspondence is. Note how $v$ and $i$ correspond in the two figures; also $x$ and $q$. Note, too, how in each case the energy alternates between two forms, magnetic and electric for the $LC$ system, and kinetic and potential for the mass-spring system.

In Section 15–3 we saw that the natural angular frequency of oscillation of an undamped mass-spring system is

$$\omega = 2\pi\nu = \sqrt{\frac{k}{m}}.$$

The method of correspondences suggests that to find the natural frequency for the $LC$ circuit $k$ should be replaced by $1/C$ and $m$ by $L$, obtaining

$$\omega = 2\pi\nu = \sqrt{\frac{1}{LC}}. \tag{38–3}$$

This formula is indeed correct, as we show in the next section.

## 38-3   Electromagnetic Oscillations—Quantitative

We now derive an expression for the frequency of oscillation of an $LC$ circuit, our derivation being based on the conservation-of-energy principle. The total energy $U$ present at any instant in an oscillating $LC$ circuit is given by

$$U = U_B + U_E = \tfrac{1}{2}Li^2 + \frac{1}{2}\frac{q^2}{C},$$

which expresses the fact that at any arbitrary time the energy is stored partly in the magnetic field in the inductor and partly in the electric field in the capacitor. If we assume the circuit resistance to be zero, there is no energy transfer to Joule heat and $U$ remains constant with time, even though $i$ and $q$ vary. In more formal language, $dU/dt$ must be zero. This leads to

$$\frac{dU}{dt} = \frac{d}{dt}\left(\tfrac{1}{2}Li^2 + \frac{1}{2C}q^2\right) = Li\frac{di}{dt} + \frac{q}{C}\frac{dq}{dt} = 0. \tag{38-4}$$

Now, $q$ and $i$ are not independent variables, being related by

$$i = \frac{dq}{dt}.$$

Differentiating yields
$$\frac{di}{dt} = \frac{d^2q}{dt^2}.$$

Substituting these two expressions into Eq. 38-4 leads to

$$L\frac{d^2q}{dt^2} + \frac{1}{C}q = 0. \tag{38-5}$$

This is the differential equation that describes the oscillations of a (resistanceless) $LC$ circuit. To solve it, the student should note that Eq. 38-5 is mathematically of exactly the same form as Eq. 15-6,

$$m\frac{d^2x}{dt^2} + kx = 0, \tag{15-3}$$

which is the differential equation for the mass-spring oscillations. Fundamentally, it is by comparing these two equations that the correspondences on p. 947 arise.

The solution of Eq. 15-6 proved to be

$$x = A\cos(\omega t + \phi), \tag{15-5}$$

where $A$ ($= x_m$) is the amplitude of the motion and $\phi$ is an arbitrary *phase angle*. Since $q$ corresponds to $x$, we can write the solution of Eq. 38-5 as

$$q = q_m\cos(\omega t + \phi), \tag{38-6}$$

where $\omega$ is the still unknown angular frequency of the electromagnetic oscillations.

We can test whether Eq. 38-6 is indeed a solution of Eq. 38-5 by substituting it and its second derivative in that equation. To find the second derivative, we write

$$\frac{dq}{dt} = i = -\omega q_m \sin (\omega t + \phi) \qquad (38\text{-}7)$$

and

$$\frac{d^2 q}{dt^2} = -\omega^2 q_m \cos (\omega t + \phi).$$

Substituting $q$ and $d^2 q/dt^2$ into Eq. 38-5 yields

$$-L\omega^2 q_m \cos (\omega t + \phi) + \frac{1}{C} q_m \cos (\omega t + \phi) = 0.$$

Canceling $q_m \cos (\omega t + \phi)$ and rearranging leads to

$$\omega = \sqrt{\frac{1}{LC}}.$$

Thus, if $\omega$ is given the constant value $1/\sqrt{LC}$, Eq. 38-6 is indeed a solution of Eq. 38-5. This expression for $\omega$ agrees with Eq. 38-3, which was arrived at by the method of correspondences.

The **phase angle** $\phi$ in Eq. 38-6 is determined by the conditions that prevail at $t = 0$. If the initial condition is as represented by Fig. 38-1a, then we put $\phi = 0$ in order that Eq. 38-6 may predict $q = q_m$ at $t = 0$. What initial condition in Fig. 38-1 is implied if we select $\phi = 90°$?

▶ **Example 2.**   (a) In an oscillating $LC$ circuit, what value of charge, expressed in terms of the maximum charge, is present on the capacitor when the energy is shared equally between the electric and the magnetic field? (b) How much time is required for this condition to arise, assuming the capacitor to be fully charged initially? Assume that $L = 10$ mh and $C = 1.0$ μf.

(a) The stored energy and the *maximum* stored energy in the capacitor are, respectively,

$$U_E = \frac{q^2}{2C} \qquad \text{and} \qquad U_{E,m} = \frac{q_m{}^2}{2C}.$$

Substituting $U_E = \frac{1}{2} U_{E,m}$ yields

$$\frac{q^2}{2C} = \frac{1}{2} \frac{q_m{}^2}{2C} \qquad \text{or} \qquad q = \frac{1}{\sqrt{2}} q_m.$$

(b) To find the time, we write, assuming $\phi = 0$ in Eq. 38-6,

$$q = q_m \cos \omega t = \frac{1}{\sqrt{2}} q_m,$$

which leads to    $\omega t = \cos^{-1} \dfrac{1}{\sqrt{2}} = \dfrac{\pi}{4}$    or    $t = \dfrac{\pi}{4\omega}.$

The angular frequency $\omega$ is found from Eq. 38-3, or

$$\omega = \sqrt{\frac{1}{LC}} = \sqrt{\frac{1}{(10 \times 10^{-3} \text{ henry})(1.0 \times 10^{-6} \text{ farad})}} = 1.0 \times 10^4 \text{ radians/sec.}$$

The time $t$ is then

$$t = \frac{\pi}{4\omega} = \frac{\pi}{(4)(1.0 \times 10^4 \text{ radians/sec})} = 7.9 \times 10^{-5} \text{ sec.}$$

What is the frequency $\nu$ in cycles/sec? ◀

The stored electric energy in the $LC$ circuit, using Eq. 38–6, is

$$U_E = \frac{1}{2}\frac{q^2}{C} = \frac{q_m{}^2}{2C} \cos^2 (\omega t + \phi), \tag{38-8}$$

and the magnetic energy, using Eq. 38–7, is

$$U_B = \tfrac{1}{2}Li^2 = \tfrac{1}{2}L\omega^2 q_m{}^2 \sin^2 (\omega t + \phi).$$

Substituting the expression for $\omega$ (Eq. 38–3) into this last equation yields

$$U_B = \frac{q_m{}^2}{2C} \sin^2 (\omega t + \phi). \tag{38-9}$$

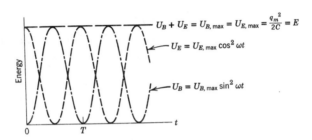

**Fig. 38–4** The stored magnetic and electric energy in the circuit of Fig. 38–1. Note that their sum is a constant. The letters indicate corresponding phases of oscillation in Fig. 38–1.

Figure 38–4 shows plots of $U_E(t)$ and $U_B(t)$ for the case of $\phi = 0$. Note that $(a)$ the maximum values of $U_E$ and $U_B$ are the same $(= q_m{}^2/2C)$; $(b)$ at any instant the sum of $U_E$ and $U_B$ is a constant $(= q_m{}^2/2C)$; and $(c)$ when $U_E$ has its maximum value, $U_B$ is zero and conversely. This analysis supports the qualitative analysis of Section 38–1. The student should compare this discussion with that given in Section 15–4 for the energy transfers in a mass-spring system.

▶ **Example 3.** *The LCR circuit.* $(a)$ Derive an expression for the quantity $q(t)$ for a single-loop circuit containing a resistance $R$ as well as an inductance $L$ and a capacitance $C$. $(b)$ After how long a time will the charge oscillations decay to half-amplitude if $L = 10$ mh, $C = 1.0$ $\mu$f, and $R = 0.1$ ohm?

$(a)$ If $U$ is the total stored field energy, we have, as before,

$$U = \tfrac{1}{2}Li^2 + \frac{1}{2}\frac{q^2}{C}.$$

$U$ is no longer constant but rather

$$\frac{dU}{dt} = -i^2R,$$

the minus sign signifying that the stored energy $U$ *decreases* with time, being converted to Joule heat at the rate $i^2R$. Combining these two equations leads to

$$Li\frac{di}{dt} + \frac{q}{C}\frac{dq}{dt} = -i^2R.$$

Substituting $dq/dt$ for $i$ and $d^2q/dt^2$ for $di/dt$ leads finally to

$$L\frac{d^2q}{dt^2} + R\frac{dq}{dt} + \frac{1}{C}q = 0,$$

which is the differential equation that describes the damped $LC$ oscillations. If we put $R = 0$, this equation reduces, as expected, to Eq. 38-5.

The student should compare this differential equation for damped $LC$ oscillations with Eq. 15-37, or

$$m\frac{d^2x}{dt^2} + b\frac{dx}{dt} + kx = 0, \tag{15-28}$$

which describes damped mass-spring oscillations. Once again the equations are mathematically identical, the resistance $R$ corresponding to the mechanical damping constant $b$.

The solution of the $LCR$ circuit follows at once, by correspondence, from the solution of Eq. 15-37. It is (see Eqs. 15-38 and 15-39) for $R$ reasonably small, and for an initial condition in which the capacitor has a maximum charge

$$q = q_m e^{-Rt/2L}\cos\omega't, \tag{38-10}$$

where

$$\omega' = \sqrt{\frac{1}{LC} - \left(\frac{R}{2L}\right)^2}. \tag{38-11}$$

Note that Eq. 38-10, which can be described as a cosine function with an exponentially decreasing amplitude, is the equation of the decay curve of Fig. 38-3. Note, too (Eq. 38-11), that the presence of resistance reduces the oscillation frequency. These two equations reduce to familiar results as $R \rightarrow 0$.

(b) The oscillation amplitude will have decreased to half when the amplitude factor $e^{-Rt/2L}$ in Eq. 38-10 has the value one-half, or

$$\tfrac{1}{2} = e^{-Rt/2L},$$

which leads readily to

$$t = \frac{2L}{R}\ln 2 = \frac{(2)(10 \times 10^{-3}\text{ henry})(0.69)}{0.10\text{ ohm}} = 0.14\text{ sec.}$$

The angular frequency, from Eq. 38-11, is

$$\omega' = \sqrt{\frac{1}{(10 \times 10^{-3}\text{ henry})(1.0 \times 10^{-6}\text{ farad})} - \left(\frac{0.10\text{ ohm}}{2 \times 10 \times 10^{-3}\text{ henry}}\right)^2}$$

$$= \sqrt{10^8\text{ radians/sec}^2 - 25\text{ radians/sec}^2} = 1.0 \times 10^4\text{ radians/sec.}$$

Note that the second term is rather small, so that in this case, as in many practical cases, the resistance has a negligible effect on the frequency. The student should show that 0.14 sec, the time at which the oscillations decrease to half-amplitude, corresponds to about 220 cycles of oscillation. The damping is much less severe than that illustrated in Fig. 38-3.   ◀

### 38–4   Forced Oscillations and Resonance

Figure 38–5 shows an $LCR$ circuit containing a sinusoidally varying emf $\mathcal{E}(t)$ given by

$$\mathcal{E} = \mathcal{E}_m \cos \omega''t,$$

in which $\omega''$ can be varied at will. The emf $\mathcal{E}(t)$ might be provided by a variable-frequency oscillator. What amplitudes of electromagnetic oscillations are set up in this circuit for various angular frequencies $\omega''$ of the "driving force"?

The problem corresponds to that of forced oscillations in the damped mass-spring system of Section 15–10. The differential equation describing that motion is

$$m \frac{d^2x}{dt^2} + b \frac{dx}{dt} + kx = F_m \cos \omega''t, \qquad (15\text{--}31)$$

where $\omega''$ is the angular frequency of the external periodic driving force applied to the system and $F_m$ is its amplitude.

For the circuit of Fig. 38–5, the differential equation that follows from the correspondences of p. 947 and the additional reasonable correspondence of $\mathcal{E}$ to $F$, is

$$L \frac{d^2q}{dt^2} + R \frac{dq}{dt} + \frac{1}{C} q = \mathcal{E}_m \cos \omega''t. \qquad (38\text{--}12)$$

This equation can also be derived by applying the energy conservation principle to the circuit of Fig. 38–5.

**Fig. 38–5**   An $LCR$ circuit containing a sinusoidal emf of angular frequency $\omega''$.

We can use the correspondences of p. 947 to write down the solution to Eq. 38–12. Starting from Eq. 15–4 and making the appropriate substitutions, we obtain

$$q = \frac{\mathcal{E}_m}{G} \sin (\omega''t - \phi), \qquad (38\text{--}13)$$

where

$$G = \sqrt{\left(\omega''^2 L - \frac{1}{C}\right)^2 + R^2 \omega''^2},$$

and $\phi$, the *phase angle* between the "driving force" and the "response," is given by

$$\phi = \cos^{-1} \frac{R\omega''}{G}.$$

As often as not, we are interested in the current $i(t)$ in the circuit, rather than the charge; the current corresponds to the velocity $v(t)$ of the moving mass in Section 15–10. We can find $i(t)$ by differentiating Eq. 38–13, or

$$i = \frac{dq}{dt} = \frac{\omega'' \mathcal{E}_m}{G} \cos (\omega''t - \alpha) = i_m \cos (\omega''t - \alpha).$$

The amplitude $i_m$ of the current oscillations is given, from these equations, by

$$i_m = \frac{\omega''\mathcal{E}_m}{G} = \frac{\mathcal{E}_m}{\sqrt{\left(\omega''L - \dfrac{1}{\omega''C}\right)^2 + R^2}}. \qquad (38\text{-}14)$$

Inspection of Eq. 38–14 shows that the current (not the charge; see Question 5) will have its maximum amplitude when

$$\omega''L = \frac{1}{\omega''C},$$

which can be written as

$$\omega'' = \sqrt{\frac{1}{LC}}. \qquad (38\text{-}15)$$

Comparison with Eq. 38–3 shows that the maximum amplitude of the current oscillations occurs when the frequency $\omega''$ of the applied emf is exactly equal to the natural (undamped) frequency $\omega$ of the system.

At *resonance* ($\omega'' = \omega$) the amplitude of the current oscillations is determined entirely by the resistance; this follows by combining Eqs. 38–14 and 38–15, or

$$i_m = \frac{\mathcal{E}_m}{R} \qquad \text{(at resonance)}.$$

Figure 38–6 shows $i_m$ as a function of $\omega''$ for an oscillating $LCR$ circuit containing three different values of resistance. Note that the smaller the resistance, the sharper the resonance curve. The sharpness of such a curve is measured by its *half-width*, which is the difference between two frequencies, each of which corresponds to a current amplitude of one-half the maximum current amplitude. The half-width of the curve for $R = 10$ ohms in Fig. 38–6 is shown in that figure by the arrow marked $\Delta\omega$.

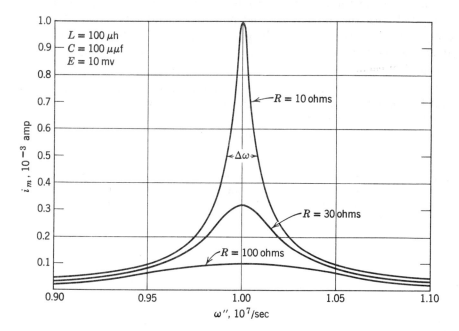

**Fig. 38–6**  The current amplitude as a function of frequency in the circuit of Fig. 38–5. The arrow marked $\Delta\omega$ on the curve for $R = 10$ ohms is the *half-width* of that curve.

### 38-5 Lumped and Distributed Elements

In the oscillating mass-spring system the two kinds of energy involved appear in separate parts of the system, the potential energy being stored in the spring and the kinetic energy in the moving mass. An *acoustic cavity resonator*, such as an organ pipe, is a mechanical oscillating system in which the two forms of energy are *not* separated in space. Kinetic energy, associated with moving air in the cavity, and potential energy, associated with compressions or rarefactions of the air, can both be present throughout the volume of the cavity. Such a cavity is an example of an oscillating system with *distributed* rather than *lumped* (as in the mass-spring system) elements.

A similar distinction exists in electromagnetic systems. The $LC$ circuit of Fig. 38-1 is an example of lumped elements, in that the two kinds of energy are stored in rather different places; the circuit is described by giving the (lumped) system parameters $L$ and $C$. Actually, in modern engineering practice and in physics research electromagnetic systems with *distributed elements* play a fundamental role.

Figure 38-7, a series of "snapshots" taken one-eighth of a cycle apart, shows the pressure and velocity variations in the fundamental mode of a particular acoustic resonator. There is a pressure node at the center and a pressure antinode at each end. There is a velocity * node at each end and a velocity antinode at the center. When the pressure variation is the greatest, the velocity is zero (Figs. 38-7a and e). When the pressure is uniform, the velocities have their maximum values (Figs. 38-7c, and g).

The energy in the acoustic resonator alternates between kinetic energy associated with the moving gas and potential energy associated with the compression and rarefaction of the gas. In Figs. 38-7c and g the energy is all kinetic and in Figs. 38-7a and e it is all potential. In intermediate phases it is part of each.

The kinetic energy of a small mass $\Delta m$ of the gas, which is moving parallel to the cylinder axis with a speed $v_g$, is $\frac{1}{2}\Delta m v_g{}^2$. The *kinetic energy density*, that is, the kinetic energy per unit volume, is

$$u_K = \frac{1}{2}\frac{\Delta m}{\Delta V} v_g{}^2 = \frac{1}{2}\rho_0 v_g{}^2,$$

in which $\Delta V$ is the volume of the gas element and $\rho_0$ is the mean density of the gas.

The potential energy per unit volume in the gas, that is, the *potential energy density*, associated with the compressions and rarefactions of the gas may be given by

$$u_P = \frac{1}{2} B \left(\frac{\Delta\rho}{\rho_0}\right)^2.$$

Here $B$ is the bulk modulus of elasticity of the gas and $\Delta\rho/\rho_0$, which is positive for a compression and negative for a rarefaction, is the fractional change in gas density.

---

* The velocity of interest here is the directed velocity $v_g$ of small volume elements of the gas which are, however, large enough to contain a great number of molecules. The thermal velocities of the molecules have no directional preference and are ignored.

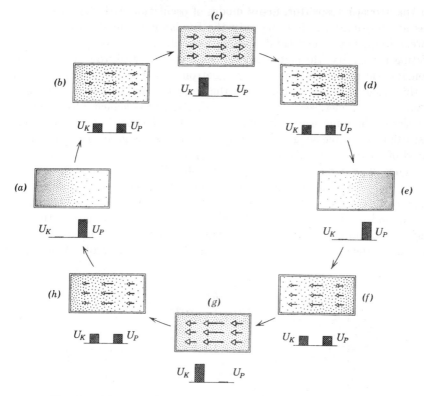

**Fig. 38–7**  Showing eight stages in a cycle of oscillation of a cylindrical acoustic resonant cavity.  The bar graphs below each figure show the kinetic and potential energy.  The arrows represent the directed velocities of small volume elements of the gas.  Compare with Fig. 38–1.

The angular frequency of oscillation for the cavity of Fig. 38–7, in the fundamental (or lowest frequency) mode shown in that figure, is found from

$$\omega_1 = 2\pi\nu = \frac{2\pi v}{\lambda} = \frac{\pi v}{l},$$

where $v$ is the speed of sound in the gas and $l$ is the length of the cavity.  From Eq. 20–1 we may write $v$ as $\sqrt{B_0/\rho_0}$.  Note that in the above we have put $\lambda = 2l$, corresponding to the fundamental mode.  What are the frequencies $\omega_2$, $\omega_3$, etc., of the higher frequency modes?

## 38–6  Electromagnetic Cavity Oscillator

Consider now a second closed cylinder, of radius $a$ and length $l$, whose walls are made of copper or some other good conductor.  A system of oscillating electric and magnetic fields can be set up in such a cavity even if, as in the common case that we consider, the cavity contains no material medium.  Such an *electromagnetic cavity resonator* is a distributed electromagnetic oscillator, in contrast to an *LC* circuit, which is a lumped system.  As for the acoustic resonator, many modes of oscillation with discrete frequencies are possible; we describe only the fundamental mode, which has the lowest frequency. The cavity oscillations can be set up by suitably connecting the cavity, through a small hole in its side wall, to a source of electromagnetic radiation such as a magnetron. If the cavity dimensions are of the order of a few centimeters, the resonant frequencies will be of the order of $10^{10}$ cycles/sec. This is far higher than the acoustic frequencies in cavities of the same size, reflecting the fact that the speed of electromagnetic disturbances in free space ($= 3 \times 10^8$ meters/sec) is much greater than the speed of sound in air (about 350 meters/sec).

Figure 38–8, which is a series of "snapshots" taken one-eighth of a cycle apart, shows, by the horizontal lines, how the electric field **E** varies with time in the cavity. The electric lines of force originate on positive charges at one end of the cylinder and terminate on negative charges at the other end. As **E** changes with time, eventually reversing itself, currents flow from one end of the cylinder to the other on the inner cylinder wall. At any point

**Fig. 38–8** Showing eight stages in a cycle of oscillation of a cylindrical electromagnetic resonant cavity. The bar graphs below each figure show the stored electric and magnetic energy. The dots and crosses represent circular lines of **B**; the horizontal lines represent **E**. Compare with Fig. 38–7.

in the cavity, energy is stored in the electric field in an amount per unit volume given by Eq. 30–27, or

$$u_E = \tfrac{1}{2}\epsilon_0 E^2. \tag{38-16}$$

Figure 38–8 also shows, by the dots and crosses, how the magnetic field **B** varies with time. The magnetic lines form circles about the cylinder axis. Note that the magnetic field has a maximum value when the electric field is zero, and conversely. At any point in the cavity energy is stored in the magnetic field in an amount per unit volume given by Eq. 36–19, or

$$u_B = \frac{1}{2\mu_0} B^2. \tag{38-17}$$

Thus, as in the $LC$ circuit, energy is shuttled back and forth between the electric and the magnetic fields. However, these fields no longer occupy completely separate regions of space.

We state without proof that the angular frequency of oscillation for the electromagnetic cavity of Fig. 38–8 is, in the fundamental mode shown in that figure,

$$\omega_1 = \frac{1.19c}{a},$$

in which $a$ is the cavity radius and $c$ is the speed of electromagnetic radiations in free space. We will see in Section 39–5 that $c$ may be written in terms of electromagnetic quantities as $1/\sqrt{\mu_0\epsilon_0}$. As the field patterns of Fig. 38–8 suggest, the resonant frequency of oscillation of the cavity, for the mode of oscillation shown, depends only on the radius of the cavity and not on its length.

Table 38–2 summarizes some characteristics of the four oscillating systems that we have discussed so far. For lumped systems it gives expressions for the two kinds

**Table 38–2**

FOUR OSCILLATING SYSTEMS

|  | Mechanical Systems | Electromagnetic Systems |
|---|---|---|
| Lumped systems | Mass + spring $U_K = \tfrac{1}{2}mv^2$ $U_P = \tfrac{1}{2}kx^2$ $\omega = \sqrt{\dfrac{k}{m}}$ | $LC$ circuit $U_B = \tfrac{1}{2}Li^2$ $U_E = \tfrac{1}{2}(1/C)q^2$ $\omega = \sqrt{\dfrac{(1/C)}{L}}$ |
| Distributed systems | Acoustic cavity $u_K = \tfrac{1}{2}\rho_0 v_g^2$ $u_P = \tfrac{1}{2}B(\Delta\rho/\rho_0)^2$ $\omega_1 = \dfrac{3.14v}{l};\quad v = \sqrt{\dfrac{B}{\rho_0}}$ | Electromagnetic cavity $u_B = \tfrac{1}{2}(1/\mu_0)B^2$ $u_E = \tfrac{1}{2}\epsilon_0 E^2$ $\omega_1 = \dfrac{1.19c}{a};\quad c = \sqrt{\dfrac{1}{\epsilon_0\mu_0}}$ |

of energy involved and for the (single) oscillation frequency. For the distributed systems it gives expressions for the two kinds of energy density involved and for the oscillation frequency in the fundamental mode. The student should study carefully all the correspondences, similarities, and differences that occur in the table.

The expression given above for the fundamental resonant angular frequency $\omega_1$ of the cavity is derived by applying the basic equations of electromagnetism (Table 38–3) to the space inside the cavity and by invoking this boundary condition: **E** *must be zero inside the cavity wall and can have no tangential component anywhere on the cavity wall.* If this were not true, an infinite current would be set up in the assumed resistanceless wall by the tangential component of **E**. This boundary condition is similar in spirit to the requirement that a clamped string must have zero amplitude of oscillation at the points at which it is clamped or that a velocity node must exist at the end walls of an acoustic cavity resonator. Granted this boundary condition, on **E**, it can be shown that, assuming a perfectly conducting wall, (a) no time-varying magnetic field can exist inside the cavity wall and (b) no time-varying currents can exist inside the wall. A tangential magnetic field can exist *on the surface,* however; surface charges can exist, and surface currents can flow.

▶ **Example 4.**  In the cavity of Fig. 38–8, what is the relationship between the "average" value of **E** throughout the cavity, measured at the instant corresponding to Fig. 38–8a, to the "average" value of **B**, measured at the instant corresponding to Fig. 38–8c?

At the first instant the energy is all electric and at the second it is all magnetic. The total energy $U$, found by integrating the energy density over the volume of the cavity, must be the same at these two instants, or

$$U = \int u_{E,m}\, dV = \int u_{B,m}\, dV,$$

where $dV$ is a volume element in the cavity and $u_{E,m}$ and $u_{B,m}$ are the *maximum* values of $u_E$ and of $u_B$ at the site of this volume element; these maximum values occur one-fourth of a cycle apart, as Fig. 38–8 shows. Substituting Eqs. 38–16 and 38–17 leads to

$$\int \frac{\epsilon_0 E_m{}^2}{2}\, dV = \int \frac{B_m{}^2}{2\mu_0}\, dV$$

or                        $$\mu_0 \epsilon_0 \int E_m{}^2\, dV = \int B_m{}^2\, dV.$$

The quantity $\int E_m{}^2\, dV$ can be written as $\overline{E_m{}^2}V$, where $V$ is the cavity volume and $\overline{E_m{}^2}$ is the average value of $E_m{}^2$ throughout the cavity. Treating $B_m$ in the same way leads to

$$\mu_0 \epsilon_0 \overline{E_m{}^2} = \overline{B_m{}^2}$$

or, taking square roots,        $$\sqrt{\overline{B_m{}^2}} = \sqrt{\mu_0 \epsilon_0}\ \sqrt{\overline{E_m{}^2}}.$$

We can represent $\sqrt{\overline{B_m{}^2}}$ by $B_{\text{rms}}$, a so-called "root-mean-square" value of $B_m$. In computing $B_{\text{rms}}$, note that the averaging is done throughout the volume of the cavity, at the instant corresponding to Fig. 38–8c. It is not a time average for a particular point in the cavity. Doing the same for **E** yields

$$B_{\text{rms}} = \sqrt{\mu_0 \epsilon_0}\ E_{\text{rms}} = \sqrt{(4\pi \times 10^{-7}\ \text{weber/amp-m})(8.9 \times 10^{-12}\ \text{coul}^2/\text{nt-m}^2)}\ E_{\text{rms}}$$

$$= (3.3 \times 10^{-9}\ \text{sec/meter}) E_{\text{rms}}.$$

If $E_{rms}$ equals $10^4$ volts/meter, a reasonable value, then

$$B_{rms} = (3.3 \times 10^{-9} \text{ sec/meter})(10^4 \text{ volts/meter})$$

$$= 3.3 \times 10^{-5} \text{ weber/meter}^2 = 0.33 \text{ gauss.}$$

What is the total stored energy in the cavity under these conditions, assuming the cavity to be 10 cm long and 3.0 cm in diameter?

The student will recall that in Example 6, Chapter 36, we showed the energy density for a magnetic field of "ordinary" laboratory magnitude (say, 1 weber/meter$^2$) to be enormously greater than that for an electric field of "ordinary" magnitude (say, $10^5$ volts/meter). This fact is consistent with the present example.        ◄

## 38-7   Induced Magnetic Fields

To understand the electromagnetic cavity oscillations in terms of electromagnetic theory, we must complete our description of the basic equations of electromagnetism by introducing a new concept, namely, that *a changing electric field produces a magnetic field*. This concept, which is the symmetrical counterpart of Faraday's law of induction, is of fundamental significance. We will develop this concept by a symmetry argument and will let the agreement with experiment of our final conclusions speak for itself. This comparison with experiment, which is worked out largely in Chapters 39 and 40, forms one of the chief experimental bases of electromagnetic theory. A central achievement was the demonstration that the experimentally measured speed $c$ of visible light in free space could be related to purely electromagnetic quantities by

$$c = \frac{1}{\sqrt{\mu_0 \epsilon_0}}. \tag{38-18}$$

This demonstration not only revealed optics as a branch of electromagnetism but led directly to the concept of the electromagnetic spectrum, which in turn resulted in the discovery of radio waves.

Figure 38-9a shows a uniform electric field **E** filling a cylindrical region of space. It might be produced by a circular parallel-plate capacitor, as suggested in Fig. 38-9b. We assume that $E$ is increasing at a steady rate $dE/dt$, which means that charge must be supplied to the capacitor plates at a steady rate; to supply this charge requires a steady current $i$ into the positive plate and an equal steady current $i$ out of the negative plate.

If a sufficiently delicate experiment could be performed, it would be found that *a magnetic field is set up by this changing electric field*. Figure 38-9a shows **B** for four arbitrary points. Figure 38-9 suggests a beautiful example of the symmetry of nature. A changing *magnetic* field induces an *electric* field (Faraday's law); now we see that a changing *electric* field induces a *magnetic* field.

To describe this new effect quantitatively, we are guided by analogy with Faraday's law of induction,

$$\oint \mathbf{E} \cdot d\mathbf{l} = -\frac{d\Phi_B}{dt}, \tag{38-19}$$

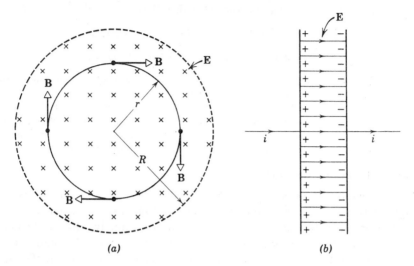

*(a)* *(b)*

**Fig. 38–9** (a) Showing the induced magnetic fields **B** at four points, produced by a changing electric field **E**. The electric field is increasing in magnitude. Compare Fig. 35–10. (b) Such a changing electric field may be produced by charging a parallel-plate capacitor as shown.

which asserts that an electric field (left term) is produced by a changing magnetic field (right term). For the symmetrical counterpart we might write *

$$\oint \mathbf{B} \cdot d\mathbf{l} = \mu_0 \epsilon_0 \frac{d\Phi_E}{dt}. \tag{38–20}$$

Equation 38–20 asserts that a magnetic field (left term) can be produced by a changing electric field (right term). The student should compare carefully Fig. 35–10, which illustrates the production of an electric field by a changing magnetic field, with Fig. 38–9a. In each case the appropriate flux $\Phi_B$ or $\Phi_E$ is *increasing*. However, experiment shows that the lines of **E** in Fig. 35–10 are *counterclockwise*, whereas those of **B** in Fig. 38–9a are *clockwise*. This difference requires that the minus sign of Eq. 38–19 be omitted from Eq. 38–20.

In Section 34–1 we saw that a magnetic field can also be set up by a current in a wire. We described this quantitatively by Ampère's law:

$$\oint \mathbf{B} \cdot d\mathbf{l} = \mu_0 i,$$

in which $i$ is the conduction current passing through the loop around which the line integral is taken. Thus there are at least two ways of setting up

---

* Our system of units requires that we insert the constants $\epsilon_0$ and $\mu_0$ in Eq. 38–20. In some unit systems they would not appear.

a magnetic field: (*a*) by a changing electric field and (*b*) by a current. In general, both possibilities must be allowed for, or *

$$\oint \mathbf{B} \cdot d\mathbf{l} = \mu_0 \epsilon_0 \frac{d\Phi_E}{dt} + \mu_0 i. \tag{38-21}$$

Maxwell is responsible for this important generalization of Ampère's law.

In Chapter 34 we assumed that no changing electric fields were present so that the term $d\Phi_E/dt$ in Eq. 38-21 is zero. In the discussion just given we assumed that there were no conduction currents in the space containing the electric field. Thus the term $i$ in Eq. 38-21 is zero. We see now that each of these situations is a special case.

▶ **Example 5.** A parallel-plate capacitor with circular plates is being charged as in Fig. 38-9. (*a*) Derive an expression for the induced magnetic field at various radii $r$. Consider both $r < R$ and $r > R$.

From Eq. 38-20,

$$\oint \mathbf{B} \cdot d\mathbf{l} = \mu_0 \epsilon_0 \frac{d\Phi_E}{dt},$$

we can write, for $r \lesssim R$,

$$(B)(2\pi r) = \mu_0 \epsilon_0 \frac{d}{dt} [(E)(\pi r^2)] = \mu_0 \epsilon_0 \pi r^2 \frac{dE}{dt}.$$

Solving for $B$ yields $\quad B = \tfrac{1}{2}\mu_0 \epsilon_0 r \dfrac{dE}{dt} \quad (r \lesssim R)$.

For $r \gtrsim R$, Eq. 38-20 yields

$$(B)(2\pi r) = \mu_0 \epsilon_0 \frac{d}{dt} [(E)(\pi R^2)] = \mu_0 \epsilon_0 \pi R^2 \left( \frac{dE}{dt} \right),$$

or $\quad\quad\quad\quad\quad B = \dfrac{\mu_0 \epsilon_0 R^2}{2r} \dfrac{dE}{dt} \quad (r \gtrsim R)$.

(*b*) Find $B$ at $r = R$ for $dE/dt = 10^{12}$ volts/m-sec and for $R = 5.0$ cm. At $r = R$ the two equations for $B$ reduce to the same expression, or

$$B = \tfrac{1}{2}\mu_0 \epsilon_0 R \frac{dE}{dt}$$

$$= (\tfrac{1}{2})(4\pi \times 10^{-7} \text{ weber/amp-m})(8.9 \times 10^{-12} \text{ coul}^2/\text{nt-m}^2)$$

$$(5.0 \times 10^{-2} \text{ meter})(10^{12} \text{ volts/m-sec})$$

$$= 2.8 \times 10^{-7} \text{ weber/meter}^2 = 0.0028 \text{ gauss}.$$

This shows that the induced magnetic fields in this example are so small that they can scarcely be measured with simple apparatus, in sharp contrast to induced *electric* fields (Faraday's law), which can be demonstrated easily. This experimental dif-

---

\* Actually, there is a third way of setting up a magnetic field, by the use of magnetized bodies. In Section 37-7 we saw that this could be accounted for by inserting a *magnetizing current* term $i_M$ on the right side of Ampère's law. This law would then read, in its full generality,

$$\oint \mathbf{B} \cdot d\mathbf{l} = \mu_0 \epsilon_0 \frac{d\Phi_E}{dt} + \mu_0 i + \mu_0 i_M.$$

In all that follows we assume that no magnetic materials are present so that $i_M = 0$.

ference is in part due to the fact that induced emfs can easily be multiplied by using a coil of many turns. No technique of comparable efficiency exists for magnetic fields. In experiments involving oscillations at very high frequencies $dE/dt$ above can be very large, resulting in significantly larger values of the induced magnetic field. ◀

## 38–8   Displacement Current

Equation 38–21 shows that the term $\epsilon_0 \, d\Phi_E/dt$ has the dimensions of a current. Even though no motion of charge is involved, there are advantages in giving this term the name *displacement * current*. Thus we can say that a magnetic field can be set up either by a conduction current $i$ or by a displacement current $i_d$ ($= \epsilon_0 \, d\Phi_E/dt$), and Eq. 38–21 can be rewritten as †

$$\oint \mathbf{B} \cdot d\mathbf{l} = \mu_0(i_d + i). \qquad (38\text{–}22)$$

The concept of displacement current permits us to retain the notion that *current is continuous*, a principle established for steady conduction currents in Section 31–1. In Fig. 38–9$b$, for example, a current $i$ enters the positive plate and leaves the negative plate. The *conduction* current is *not* continuous across the capacitor gap because no charge is transported across this gap. However, the displacement current $i_d$ in the gap will prove to be exactly $i$, thus retaining the concept of the continuity of current.       .

To calculate the displacement current, recall (see Eq. 30–5) that $E$ in the gap is given by

$$E = \frac{q}{\epsilon_0 A}.$$

Differentiating gives       $\dfrac{dE}{dt} = \dfrac{1}{\epsilon_0 A} \dfrac{dq}{dt} = \dfrac{1}{\epsilon_0 A} i.$

The displacement current $i_d$ is by definition

$$i_d = \epsilon_0 \frac{d\Phi_E}{dt} = \epsilon_0 \frac{d(EA)}{dt} = \epsilon_0 A \frac{dE}{dt}.$$

Combining these two equations leads to

$$i_d = (\epsilon_0 A)\left(\frac{1}{\epsilon_0 A} i\right) = i,$$

which shows that the displacement current in the gap is identical with the conduction current in the lead wires.

---

\* The word "displacement" was introduced for historical reasons that need not concern us here.

† We may write this more generally, taking the presence of magnetic materials into account, as

$$\oint \mathbf{B} \cdot d\mathbf{l} = \mu_0(i_d + i + i_M).$$

See the footnote on p. 961.

▶ **Example 6.** What is the displacement current for the capacitor of Example 5? From the definition of displacement current,

$$i_d = \epsilon_0 \frac{d\Phi_E}{dt} = \epsilon_0 \frac{d}{dt}[(E)(\pi R^2)] = \epsilon_0 \pi R^2 \frac{dE}{dt}$$

$$= (8.9 \times 10^{-12}\ \text{coul}^2/\text{nt-m}^2)(\pi)(5.0 \times 10^{-2}\ \text{meter})^2(10^{12}\ \text{volts/m-sec})$$

$$= 0.070\ \text{amp}.$$

Even though this displacement current is reasonably large, it produces only a small magnetic field (see Example 5) because it is spread out over a large area. ◀

## 38–9 Maxwell's Equations

Equation 38–21 completes our presentation of the basic equations of electromagnetism, called *Maxwell's equations*. They are summarized in Table 38–3. All equations of physics that serve, as these do, to correlate experiments in a vast area and to predict new results have a certain beauty about them and can be appreciated, by those who understand them, on an aesthetic level. This is true for Newton's laws of motion, for the laws of thermodynamics, for the theory of relativity, and for the theories of quantum physics. As for Maxwell's equations, the German physicist Ludwig Boltzmann (quoting a line from Goethe) wrote "Was it a god who wrote these lines. . . ." In more recent times J. R. Pierce,* in a book chapter entitled "Maxwell's Wonderful Equations" says: "To anyone who is motivated by anything beyond the most narrowly practical, it is worth while to understand Maxwell's equations simply for the good of his soul." The scope of these equations is remarkable, including as it does the fundamental operating principles of all large-scale electromagnetic devices such as motors, cyclotrons, electronic computers, television, and microwave radar.

## 38–10 Maxwell's Equations and Cavity Oscillations

In this section we show how the oscillations of an electromagnetic cavity can be understood in terms of Maxwell's equations. A completely formal treatment, which is beyond our scope here, would start from these equations and would end with mathematical expressions for the variation of **B** and **E** with time and with position in the cavity for all modes of oscillation of the cavity. We confine ourselves to the fundamental mode only, illustrated in Fig. 38–8, for which we *postulated* the variations of **B** and **E** given in that figure; we will show that these postulated fields are completely consistent with Maxwell's equations.

Figure 38–10 presents two views of the cavity of Fig. 38–8d, in which both electric and magnetic fields are present. Study of Fig. 38–8 reveals that **B** is *decreasing* in magnitude and **E** is *increasing* at this phase of the cycle of oscillation. Let us apply Faraday's law,

$$\oint \mathbf{E} \cdot d\mathbf{l} = -\frac{d\Phi_B}{dt},$$

---

* *Electrons, Waves and Messages*, Hanover House, 1956. This book is recommended as collateral reading in electromagnetism.

**Table 38-3**

THE BASIC EQUATIONS OF ELECTROMAGNETISM (MAXWELL'S EQUATIONS) *

| Name | Equation | Describes | Crucial Experiment | Text Reference |
|---|---|---|---|---|
| Gauss's law for electricity | $\epsilon_0 \oint \mathbf{E} \cdot d\mathbf{S} = q$ | Charge and the electric field | 1. Like charges repel and unlike charges attract, as the inverse square of their separation.<br>1'. A charge on an insulated conductor moves to its outer surface. | Chapter 28 |
| Gauss's law for magnetism | $\oint \mathbf{B} \cdot d\mathbf{S} = 0$ | The magnetic field | 2. It is impossible to create an isolated magnetic pole. | Section 37–2 |
| Ampère's law (as extended by Maxwell) | $\oint \mathbf{B} \cdot d\mathbf{l} = \mu_0 \left( \epsilon_0 \dfrac{d\Phi_B}{dt} + i \right)$ | The magnetic effect of a changing electric field or of a current | 3. The speed of light can be calculated from purely electromagnetic measurements.<br>3'. A current in a wire sets up a magnetic field near the wire. | Section 39–5<br>Chapter 34 |
| Faraday's law of induction | $\oint \mathbf{E} \cdot d\mathbf{l} = - \dfrac{d\Phi_B}{dt}$ | The electrical effect of a changing magnetic field | 4. A bar magnet, thrust through a closed loop of wire, will set up a current in the loop. | Chapter 35 |

* Written on the assumption that no dielectric or magnetic material is present.

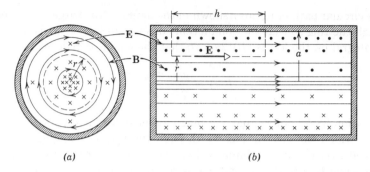

(a)                              (b)

**Fig. 38-10**   Two cross sections of an electromagnetic resonant cavity at a phase of oscillation corresponding to Fig. 38–8d.   (a) The dashed circle is a path suitable for applying Ampère's law.   (b) The dashed rectangle is a path suitable for applying Faraday's law.

to the rectangle of dimensions $h$ and $a - r$.   There is a definite flux $\Phi_B$ through the rectangular path in question, and this flux is decreasing with time because **B** is decreasing.   The line integral above is

$$\oint \mathbf{E} \cdot d\mathbf{l} = hE(r),$$

in which $E(r)$ is the value of $E$ at a radius $r$ from the center of the cavity.

Note that **E** equals zero for the upper leg of the integration path (which lies in the cavity wall) and that **E** and $d\mathbf{l}$ are at right angles on the two side legs.   Combining these equations yields

$$E(r) = -\frac{1}{h}\frac{d\Phi_B}{dt}. \tag{38-23}$$

Equation 38–23 shows that $E(r)$ depends on the rate at which $\Phi_B$ through the path shown is changing with time and that it has its maximum value when $d\Phi_B/dt$ is a maximum.   This occurs when **B** is zero, that is, when **B** is changing its direction; the student will recall that a sine or cosine is changing most rapidly, that is, it has the steepest tangent, at the instant it crosses the axis between positive and negative values.   Thus the electric field pattern in the cavity will have its *maximum* value when the magnetic field is *zero* everywhere, consistent with Figs. 38–8a and e and with the concept of the interchange of energy between electric and magnetic forms.   The student should demonstrate, by applying Lenz's law, that the electric field in Fig. 38–10b points to the right as shown, if the magnetic field is decreasing.

Figure 38–10a shows an end view of the cavity; the electric lines of force are entering the page at right angles to the page and the magnetic lines form clockwise circles.   Let us apply Ampère's law in the form

$$\oint \mathbf{B} \cdot d\mathbf{l} = \mu_0 \epsilon_0 \frac{d\Phi_E}{dt} + \mu_0 i, \tag{38-21}$$

to the circular path of radius $r$ shown in the figure. No charge is transported through the ring so that the conduction current $i$ in Eq. 38–21 is zero. The line integral on the left is $(B)(2\pi r)$ so that the equation reduces to

$$B(r) = \frac{\mu_0 \epsilon_0}{2\pi r} \frac{d\Phi_E}{dt}. \qquad (38\text{–}24)$$

Equation 38–24 shows that the magnetic field $B(r)$ is proportional to the rate at which the electric flux $\Phi_E$ through the ring is changing with time. The field $B(r)$ has its maximum value when $d\Phi_E/dt$ is at its maximum; this occurs when $\mathbf{E} = 0$, that is, when $\mathbf{E}$ is reversing its direction. Thus we see that $\mathbf{B}$ has its *maximum* value when $\mathbf{E}$ is *zero* for all points in the cavity. This is consistent with Figs. 38–8c and g and with the concept of the interchange of energy between electric and magnetic forms. A comparison with Fig. 38–9a, which, like Fig. 38–10a, corresponds to an increasing electric field, shows that the lines of $\mathbf{B}$ are indeed clockwise, as viewed along the direction of the electric field.

Comparison of Eqs. 38–23 and 38–24 suggests the complete interdependence of $\mathbf{B}$ and $\mathbf{E}$ in the cavity. As the magnetic field changes with time, it induces the electric field in a way described by Faraday's law. The electric field, which also changes with time, induces the magnetic field in a way described by Maxwell's extension of Ampère's law. The oscillations, once established, sustain each other and would continue indefinitely were it not for losses due to Joule heating in the cavity walls or leakage of energy from openings that might be present in the walls. In Chapter 39 we show that this interplay of $\mathbf{B}$ and $\mathbf{E}$ occurs not only in standing electromagnetic waves in cavities but also in traveling electromagnetic waves, such as radio waves or visible light.

Let us now analyze the currents—both conduction and displacement—that occur in the cavity and examine their connections to the electric and the magnetic fields. Figure 38–11 shows two views of the cavity, taken at an instant corresponding to that of Fig. 38–10. For simplicity the fields $\mathbf{E}$ and $\mathbf{B}$ are not shown; the arrows represent currents.

Since $\mathbf{E}$ is increasing at this instant, the positive charge on the left end cap must be increasing. Thus there must be conduction currents in the walls pointing from right to left in Fig. 38–11b. These currents are also shown by the dots (representing the tips of arrows) near the cavity walls in Fig. 38–11a.

Bearing in mind that $\epsilon_0 \, d\Phi_E/dt$ is a displacement current, we can write Eq. 38–24 as

$$B(r) = \frac{\mu_0}{2\pi r} \epsilon_0 \frac{d\Phi_E}{dt} = \frac{\mu_0}{2\pi r} i_d.$$

This equation stresses that $\mathbf{B}$ in the cavity is associated with a displacement current; compare Eq. 34–4. Applying the right-hand rule in Fig. 38–10a shows that the displacement current $i_d$ must be directed into the plane of the figure if it is to be associated with the clockwise lines of $\mathbf{B}$ that are present.

The displacement current is represented in Fig. 38–11b by the arrows that point to the right and in Fig. 38–11a by the crosses that represent arrows entering the page. Study of Fig. 38–11 shows that the current is continuous, being directed up the

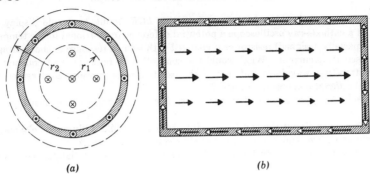

(a)                                              (b)

**Fig. 38–11** The cavity of Fig. 38–10 showing (a) the conduction current coming up the walls and displacement current going down the cavity volume and (b) the displacement current (black arrowheads) in the volume of the cavity and the conduction currents (white arrowheads) at the walls. The arrows in each case represent *current densities*. Note the continuity of current (conduction + displacement), that is, it is possible to form closed current loops. (For a *truly* resistar.eless cavity the conduction current would lie *entirely* on the surface, requiring a modification of our definition of current density; we leave this small complication for the student to consider.)

walls as a conduction current and then back down through the volume of the cavity as a displacement current. If we apply Ampère's law as extended by Maxwell,

$$\oint \mathbf{B} \cdot d\mathbf{l} = \mu_0(i_d + i), \qquad (38\text{–}25)$$

to the circular path of radius $r_1$ in Fig. 38–11a, we see that **B** at that path is due entirely to the displacement current, the conduction current $i$ *within the path* being zero.

For the path of radius $r_2$, the *net* current enclosed is zero because the conduction current in the walls is exactly equal and opposite to the displacement current in the cavity volume. Since $i$ equals $i_d$ in magnitude, but is oppositely directed, it follows from Eq. 38–25 that $B$ must be zero for all points outside the cavity, in agreement with observation.

## QUESTIONS

1. Why doesn't the $LC$ circuit of Fig. 38–1 simply stop oscillating when the capacitor has been completely discharged?

2. How might you start an $LC$ circuit into oscillation with its initial condition being represented by Fig. 38–1c? Devise a switching scheme to bring this about.

3. In an oscillating $LC$ circuit, assumed resistanceless, what determines (a) the frequency and (b) the amplitude of the oscillations?

4. Tabulate as many mechanical or electric systems as you can think of that possess a natural frequency, along with the formula for that frequency if given in the text.

5. Resonance in $LC$ circuits, judged by Eq. 38–14 and Fig. 38–6, occurs when the frequency $\omega''$ of the "driving force" is exactly equal to the (undamped) natural frequency of the $LC$ circuit. In Section 15–10 we saw that resonance for mass-spring systems, judged by Eq. 15–41 and Fig. 15–19, occurs when $\omega''$ is close to, *but not exactly equal to*, the (undamped) natural frequency of the mass-spring system. Is there a failure of the principle of correspondence here?

6. Suppose that, in a low frequency oscillating $LCR$ circuit, one could display on the screen of a cathode-ray oscilloscope a potential difference proportional to the temperature of the (specially designed) resistor as it changed with time in response to the heating effect of the oscillating current. What would the connection be between the frequency of this temperature-time waveform and that of the oscillations of current, as measured by the potential difference across the resistor?

7. Discuss the periodic flow of energy, if any, from point to point in an acoustic resonant cavity.

8. Can a given circuit element (a capacitor, say) behave like a "lumped" element under some circumstances and like a "distributed" element under others?

9. List as many (a) lumped and (b) distributed mechanical oscillating systems as you can.

10. An air-filled acoustic resonant cavity and an electromagnetic resonant cavity of the same size have resonant frequencies that are in the ratio of $10^6$ or so. Which has the higher frequency and why?

11. What constructional difficulties would you encounter if you tried to build an $LC$ circuit of the type shown in Fig. 38–1 to oscillate (a) at 0.01 cps, or (b) at $10^{10}$ cycles/sec?

12. Could an electromagnetic cavity of the type shown in Fig. 38–8 be designed to operate at 60 cycles/sec? If so, give some details of its construction.

13. The "sharpness of tuning" of a copper electromagnetic cavity can be considerably increased by immersing it in liquid air. Explain. Be guided by Fig. 38–6, which shows "tuning curves" for an $LC$ circuit.

14. Electromagnetic cavities are often silver plated on the inside. Explain.

15. Why is Faraday's law of induction more familiar than its symmetrical counterpart, Eq. 38–20?

16. Why is the quantity $\epsilon_0 \, d\Phi_E/dt$ referred to as a (displacement) *current?*

17. In Fig. 38–1c a displacement current is needed to maintain continuity of current in the capacitor. How can one exist, since there is no charge on the capacitor?

18. Discuss the symmetries that appear between (a) the first two and (b) the second two of Maxwell's equations.

19. At what parts of the cycle will (a) the conduction current and (b) the displacement current in the cavity of Fig. 38–8 be zero?

20. Discuss the time variation during one complete cycle of the charges that appear at various points on the inner walls of the oscillating electromagnetic cavity of Fig. 38–8.

## PROBLEMS

1. You are given a 10-mh inductor and two capacitors, of 5.0- and 2.0-$\mu$f capacitance. What resonant frequencies can be obtained by connecting these elements in various ways?

2. Given a 1.0-mh inductor, how would you make it oscillate at $1.0 \times 10^6$ cycles/sec?

3. An inductor is connected across a capacitor whose capacitance can be varied by turning a knob. We wish to make the frequency of the $LC$ oscillations vary linearly with the angle of rotation of the knob, going from $2 \times 10^5$ cycles/sec to $4 \times 10^5$ cycles/sec as the knob turns through 180°. If $L = 1.0$ mh, plot $C$ as a function of angle for the 180° rotation.

4. A 10-henry coil has a resistance of 180 ohms. What size of capacitor must be put in series with it if the combination is to "resonate" when connected to a 60-cycle/sec outlet?

5. Derive the differential equation for an $LC$ circuit (Eq. 38–5) using the loop theorem.

6. Derive Eq. 38–12, the differential equation for forced oscillations in an $LCR$ circuit, from the principle of conservation of energy.

7. Show that a damped $LC$ circuit (see Example 3) loses half its energy to Joule heat in a time given approximately by $0.69\tau_L$, in which $\tau_L$ is the inductive time constant.

8. A circuit has $L = 10$ mh and $C = 1.0$ $\mu$f. How much resistance must be inserted in the circuit to reduce the (undamped) resonant frequency by 0.01%?

9. Suppose that in an oscillating $LCR$ circuit the amplitude of the charge oscillations drops to one-half its initial value after $n$ cycles. Show that the fractional reduction in the frequency of resonance, caused by the presence of the resistor, is given to a close approximation by

$$\frac{\omega - \omega'}{\omega} = \frac{0.0061}{n^2},$$

which is independent of $L$, $C$, or $R$. Apply to the decay curve of Fig. 38–3.

10. Show that, for low damping, the current in a damped $LC$ circuit is given approximately by

$$i = -q_m\omega'e^{-Rt/2L}\sin(\omega't + \phi),$$

in which

$$\phi = \tan^{-1}\frac{R}{2L\omega'}.$$

Start from Eq. 38–10.

11. *"Q" for a circuit.* In the damped $LC$ circuit of Example 3 show that the fraction of the energy lost per cycle of oscillation, $\Delta U/U$, is given to a close approximation by $2\pi R/\omega L$. The quantity $\omega L/R$ is often called the "$Q$" of the circuit (for "quality"). A "high-$Q$" circuit has low resistance, low fractional energy loss per cycle ($= 2\pi/Q$) and (see Fig. 38–6) a sharp resonance or "tuning" curve.

12. Show that the amplitude of the charge oscillations in an oscillating $LCR$ circuit is given by

$$q_m = \frac{\mathcal{E}_m}{\sqrt{\left(\omega''^2L - \frac{1}{C}\right)^2 + (\omega''R)^2}}.$$

For what value of $\omega''$ will $q_m$ be a maximum?

13. An $LCR$ circuit has $L = 1.0$ henry, $C = 20$ $\mu$f, and $R = 20$ ohms. For what frequency $\omega'$ of an applied emf will it resonate with maximum response? At what frequencies will the response be one-half its maximum value?

14. Show that the fractional half-width of the resonance curves of Fig. 38–6 is given, to a close approximation, by

$$\frac{\Delta\omega}{\omega} = \frac{\sqrt{3}R}{\omega L},$$

in which $\omega$ is the resonant frequency and $\Delta\omega$ is the width of the resonance peak at $i = \frac{1}{2}i_m$. Note (see Problem 11) that this expression may be written as $\sqrt{3}/Q$ which shows clearly that a "high-$Q$" circuit has a sharp resonance peak, that is, a small $\Delta\omega/\omega$.

15. A resistor-inductor-capacitor combination $R_1$, $L_1$, $C_1$ (connected in series) exhibits resonance at the same frequency as a second combination $R_2$, $L_2$, $C_2$. If the two combinations are now connected in series, at what frequency would the whole circuit resonate?

16. In Example 5 show that the *displacement current density* $j_d$ is given, for $r < R$, by

$$j_d = \epsilon_0 \frac{dE}{dt}.$$

17. Prove that the displacement current in a parallel-plate capacitor can be written as

$$i_d = C\frac{dV}{dt}.$$

18. You are given a 1.0-$\mu$f capacitor. How would you establish an (instantaneous) displacement current of 1.0 amp in the space between its plates?

19. In Example 5 how does the displacement current through a concentric circular loop of radius $r$ vary with $r$? Consider both $r < R$ and $r > R$.

20. In microscopic terms the principle of continuity of current may be expressed as

$$\oint (\mathbf{j} + \mathbf{j}_d) \cdot d\mathbf{S} = 0,$$

in which $\mathbf{j}$ is the conduction current density and $\mathbf{j}_d$ is the displacement current density. The integral is to be taken over any closed surface; the equation essentially says that whatever current flows into the enclosed volume must also flow out. (a) Apply this equation to the surface shown by the dashed lines in Fig. 38–12 shortly after switch $S$ is closed. (b) Apply it to various surfaces that may be drawn in the cavity of Fig. 38–11, including some that cut the cavity walls.

**Fig. 38–12**

21. A cylindrical electromagnetic cavity 5.0 cm in diameter and 7.0 cm long is oscillating in the mode shown in Fig. 38–8. (a) Assume that, for points on the axis of the cavity, $E_m = 10^4$ volts/meter. For such axial points what is the maximum rate $(dE/dt)_m$ at which $E$ changes? (b) Assume that the average value of $(dE/dt)_m$, for all points over a cross section of a cavity, is about one-half the value found above for axial points. On this assumption, what is the maximum value of $B$ at the cylindrical surface of the cavity?

22. Collect and tabulate expressions for the following four quantities, considering both $r < R$ and $r > R$. Copy down the derivations side by side and study them as interesting applications of Maxwell's equations to problems having cylindrical symmetry.

(a) $B(r)$ for a current $i$ in a long wire of radius $R$ (see Section 34–2).

(b) $E(r)$ for a long uniform cylinder of charge of radius $R$ (see Section 28–6; also Problem 14, Chapter 28).

(c) $B(r)$ for a parallel-plate capacitor, with circular plates of radius $R$, in which $E$ is changing at a constant rate (see Section 38–7).

(d) $E(r)$ for a cylindrical region of radius $R$ in which a uniform magnetic field $B$ is changing at a constant rate (see Section 35–5).

# Electromagnetic Waves *

## CHAPTER 39

### 39–1 Transmission Line

In Chapter 38 we studied electromagnetic energy confined, as a standing wave, to a restricted region of space, the interior of an electromagnetic resonant cavity. Such energy can also be transferred from place to place as a traveling wave. An arrangement of conductors for facilitating such transfers is called a *transmission line*. Figure 39–1 shows one type of line, a *coaxial cable*, its input end being connected to a switch $S$. For the time being we assume that the cable is infinitely long and that the cable elements have zero resistance.

When $S$ is closed on $b$, the central and the outer conductors are at the same potential. If the switch is then thrown to $a$, a potential difference $V$ suddenly appears between these elements. This potential difference does not appear instantaneously all along the line but is propagated with a finite

**Fig. 39–1** An electromagnetic pulse can be sent along the coaxial cable by throwing switch $S$ from $b$ to $a$.

971

* This subject is treated in greater depth in Supplementary Topic V at the end of the book.

speed $c$ that will turn out to be exactly that of light, assuming a resistanceless line.  Figure 39–2a shows that the potential difference between the conductors at a distance $l$ along the line suddenly rises, at a time given by $t = l/c$, from zero to a value determined by the battery emf.  We can also consider the variation of $V$ with position $x$ along the line at a given time $t_1$ after closing the switch.  Figure 39–2b shows such an instantaneous "snapshot."  It, too, suggests a traveling "wavefront" moving along the line at speed $c$.  At $t = t_1$ the signal has not yet reached points where $x > ct_1$.

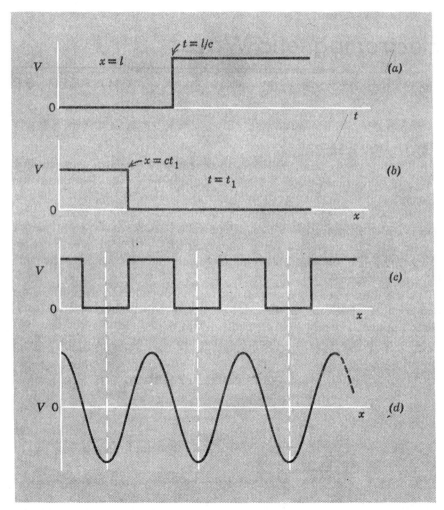

**Fig. 39–2**   (a) The variation with time of the potential difference between the conductors of a coaxial cable at a distance $l$ from the input end.  (b) An instantaneous "snapshot" of the pulse in the cable at a certain time $t_1$.  (c) The waveform if switch $S$ in Fig. 39–1 is periodically thrown between $a$ and $b$.  (d) The waveform if switch $S$ is replaced by an electromagnetic oscillator with a sinusoidal output.

If switch $S$ is periodically thrown from $b$ to $a$ and back again, a wave disturbance like that of Fig. 39–2c is propagated. This suggests that if the battery and switch arrangement is replaced by an electromagnetic oscillator with a sinusoidal output of frequency $f$ a wave like that of Fig. 39–2d will be propagated.

A traveling wave in a resistanceless transmission line will exhibit a wavelength $\lambda$ given by

$$\lambda = \frac{c}{\nu}.$$

If the oscillator frequency is 60 cycles/sec, the common commercial power frequency, the wavelength is $5 \times 10^6$ meters, which is about 3000 miles. At this low frequency traveling waves are not apparent in any line of normal length. By the time the polarity of the oscillator has changed appreciably, the energy fed into the line at the oscillator end has been delivered to the load.

Frequencies in the radio or the microwave range are much higher and the wavelengths correspondingly smaller. Commercial television frequencies as established by the Federal Communications Commission range from $54 \times 10^6$ to $980 \times 10^6$ cycles/sec. In terms of wavelength this is a range of 5.6 to 0.31 meter. At these wavelengths the patterns of potential difference in the transmission lines used to send television signals across the country can be described aptly as traveling waves. Microwaves, used in radar systems and for communication purposes, have even smaller wavelengths, in the range of about 20 cm to about 0.5 mm.

These considerations suggest another way of viewing the difference between lumped and distributed circuit elements. A system is "distributed" if the wavelength is about the same size as, or less than, the dimensions of the system. If the wavelength is much larger than the dimensions of the system, we are dealing with lumped components. A transmission line 50 meters long would be a lumped system for electromagnetic radiation at 60 cycles/sec ($\lambda = 5 \times 10^6$ meters) but a distributed system at $10^8$ cycles/sec ($\lambda = 3$ meters). In a lumped system the circuit analysis is normally carried out in terms of lumped system parameters such as $L$, $C$, and $R$; in a distributed system the analysis is often carried out in terms of the fields that are set up and the charges and currents that are related to them.

▶ **Example 1.** A potential difference given by

$$V_0 = V_m \sin \omega t$$

is applied between the terminals of a long resistanceless transmission line; the frequency $\nu$ ($= \omega/2\pi$) is $3 \times 10^9$ cycles/sec. Write an equation for $V(t)$ at a point $P$ which is 1.5 wavelengths down the line from the oscillator.

The general equation for a wave traveling in the $x$ direction (see Eq. 19–10) is

$$V = V_m \sin (\omega t - kx),$$

where $k$ ($= 2\pi/\lambda$) is the wave number. At $x = 0$ this gives correctly the time variation of the input terminal potential difference. At $x = 1.5\lambda$ we have

$$V_P = V_m \sin \left[ \omega t - \left(\frac{2\pi}{\lambda}\right)(1.5\lambda) \right] = V_m \sin (\omega t - 3\pi)$$

$$= -V_m \sin \omega t.$$

Thus $V_P$ is always equal in magnitude to $V_0$ but is opposite in sign. What is the wavelength in this example? ◀

(a)         (b)

(c)

**Fig. 39-3** (a) The electric and magnetic fields in a coaxial cable, showing a wave traveling to the right at speed $c$. (b) A cross-sectional view at a plane through $xx$ in (a); the wave is emerging from the page. (c) Conduction current (open arrows) and displacement currents (filled arrows) associated with the wave in (a); the arrows in each case represent current density vectors.

## 39-2 Coaxial Cable—Fields and Currents

Figures 39–3$a$ and $b$ are "snapshots" of the electric and magnetic field configurations in a coaxial cable. The electric field is radial and the magnetic field forms concentric lines about the central conductor. The entire pattern moves along the line, assumed resistanceless, at speed $c$.

The field patterns in this figure obey the *boundary condition* required for a line that is assumed to be resistanceless, namely, that **E** for all points on either conducting surface has no tangential component (see p. 957). The field patterns can be deduced mathematically from Maxwell's equations by imposing this requirement. The configuration shown is the simplest of many different wave patterns that can travel along the line. The coaxial cable, unlike the electromagnetic cavity of Fig. 38–8, is not a resonant device. The angular frequency $\omega$ of waves that travel along it can be varied continuously, as is the case for all traveling waves, such as transverse waves in a long stretched cord.

Figure 39–3c shows the currents in the cable at the instant corresponding to Figs. 39–3a and b. The arrows parallel to the cable axis represent conduction currents in the central and the outer conductors. The vertical arrows with filled heads represent displacement currents that exist in the space between the conductors. Note that the conduction current and the displacement current arrows form closed loops, preserving the concept of the continuity of current.

▶ **Example 2.** Verify that the displacement current represented in Fig. 39–3c is consistent with the pattern of **B** and **E** shown in Fig. 39–3a.

Consider a small surface element $\Delta S$ shown edge-on in Fig. 39–3; it is shown as viewed from above in Fig. 39–4. This hypothetical element is stationary with respect to the cable while the field configuration moves through it at speed $c$. Figure 39–4a shows the electric lines of force in the vicinity of this element. It is clear from symmetry that, at the instant shown, the net flux $\Phi_E$ through this area is zero. However, even though $\Phi_E$ is zero in magnitude, it is, at this instant, *changing at its most rapid*

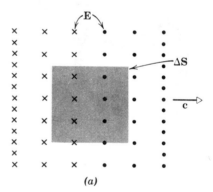

(a)

**Fig. 39–4**  The area element $S$ in Fig. 39–3 enlarged and viewed from above, showing the adjacent (a) electric and (b) magnetic fields.

(b)

*rate*, since **E** at the element $\Delta S$ is at the very moment of reversing its direction as the wave moves through. Thus the displacement current, which is given by

$$i_d = \epsilon_0 \frac{d\Phi_E}{dt},$$

also has its maximum value.

Figure 39–4b shows the magnetic field in the vicinity of the element of area. Let us apply the generalized form of Ampère's law,

$$\oint \mathbf{B} \cdot d\mathbf{l} = \mu_0 (i + i_d),$$

to the element. The conduction current $i$ is zero since no charge is transported through $\Delta S$. The displacement current $i_d$ is not zero, having, in fact, its maximum value. Thus, since the right side of this equation ($= \mu_0 i_d$) does not vanish, the left side must not vanish. Study of Fig. 39–4b shows that $\oint \mathbf{B} \cdot d\mathbf{l}$ around the boundary of this square has, indeed, a nonzero value. Thus the field and displacement current configurations of Figs. 39–3a–c are consistent. We have not discussed the direction of $i_d$; that is, does it point into the plane of Fig. 39–4, as Fig. 39–3c asserts, or out of it? We leave this as a question for the student. He may be guided by considering the direction of the displacement current in Figs. 38–9a and b.

**Example 3.** Show that the conduction currents in Fig. 39–3c are appropriately related to the magnetic field pattern.

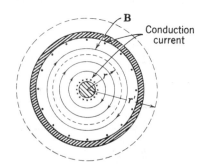

**Fig. 39–5** Example 3. The coaxial cable of Fig. 39–3b, showing the conduction currents in the central and outer conductors. The wave is emerging from the page.

Figure 39–5 shows a cross section of the cable at a plane through $xx$ in Fig. 39–3a. Let us apply Ampère's law,

$$\oint \mathbf{B} \cdot d\mathbf{l} = \mu_0 (i + i_d),$$

to the ring of radius $r$. The displacement current through this ring is zero, this current being at right angles to the central conductor. The conduction current $i$ in the central conductor, shown by the $\times$'s in the figure, does pass through this ring so that the equation becomes

$$(B)(2\pi r) = \mu_0 i,$$

or

$$B = \frac{\mu_0 i}{2\pi r}.$$

Note that **B** is related to the current in the central conductor by the usual right-hand rule and that the expression for $B$ is that found earlier (Eq. 34–4) for a long straight wire carrying a steady current.

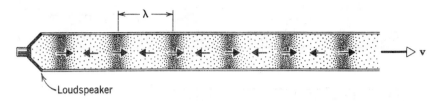

**Fig. 39–6**  An acoustic transmission line, showing a sound wave traveling to the right. The small arrows with filled heads show the directed drift velocities for small volume elements of the gas. Compare Fig. 39–3a.

If we apply Ampère's law to the large ring of radius $r'$, we must put the *net* conduction current equal to zero because the current in the outer conductor, shown by the dots, is equal and opposite to that in the inner conductor. This means that **B** must be zero for points outside the cable, in agreement with experiment.    ◄

It is interesting to compare the electromagnetic oscillations in a typical *traveling* wave, such as that of Fig. 39–3, to those in a cavity resonator, such as that of Fig. 38–8. The latter oscillations are an electromagnetic *standing* wave. In a traveling wave **E** and **B** are in phase, which means that at a given position along the transmission line they reach their maxima at the same time. However, Fig. 38–8 shows that at a given position in a cavity resonator **E** and **B** reach their maxima one-fourth of a cycle apart; they are 90° out of phase.

A complete analogy exists in mechanical systems. In the acoustic resonator of Fig. 38–7 the time variations of pressure and velocity for the standing acoustic wave are also 90° out of phase, in exact correspondence to the electromagnetic cavity oscillations of Fig. 38–8. The acoustic analogy to a transmission line (Fig. 39–6) would be an infinitely long gas-filled tube, one end being connected to an acoustic oscillator such as a loud-speaker. The entire configuration of Fig. 39–6 moves to the right with speed $v$. The pressure variations, suggested by the dots, and the instantaneous velocities, suggested by the arrows, are *in phase*, just as are **E** and **B** in the coaxial cable of Fig. 39–3.

## 39–3  Waveguide

It is possible to send electromagnetic waves through a hollow metal pipe. We assume that the inner walls of such a pipe, or *waveguide* as it is called, are resistanceless and that the cross section is rectangular.

Figure 39–7 shows a typical electric and magnetic field pattern. We imagine that a microwave oscillator is connected to the left end and sends electromagnetic energy down the guide. Figure 39–7a shows a side view of the guide and Fig. 39–7b, a top view; Fig. 39–7c shows the cross section. As for the coaxial cable, the field patterns are such that **E** has no tangential component for any point on the inner surface of the guide. The fields **E** and **B** are in phase, again like the coaxial cable.

As for all traveling waves, the angular frequency $\omega$ of electromagnetic waves traveling down a guide can be varied continuously. In a waveguide of given dimensions, however, there exists, for every mode of transmission, that is, for every pattern of **E** and **B**, a so-called *cutoff frequency* $\omega_0$. A given guide will not transmit waves in a given mode if their frequency is below the cutoff value for that mode in that guide. The field patterns of Fig. 39–7 show the *dominant mode* for a rectangular guide; this is the mode with the lowest cutoff frequency. Given the frequency $\omega$ of electromagnetic waves to be transmitted, it is common practice to select a guide whose dimensions are such that $\omega$ is larger than the cutoff frequency $\omega_0$ for the dominant mode

**Fig. 39–7**   A waveguide, showing (a) a side view of the lines of **E**, (b) a top view of the lines of **B**, and (c) a cross-sectional view of the lines of **E**. In (c) the wave is emerging from the page. For simplicity the lines of **B** are not shown in (a) and (c), nor are the lines of **E** shown in (b).

but smaller than the cutoff frequencies of all other modes. Under these conditions the dominant mode of propagation is the only one possible.

In a (resistanceless) coaxial cable the wave patterns travel at speed $c$. In the acoustic transmission line of Fig. 39–6 (assumed "resistanceless") the waves also travel at a speed $v$, which is the same as the propagation speed in an infinite medium. In a waveguide, however, the speed is *not* $c$. In waveguides we must distinguish between (a) the *phase speed* $v_{\text{ph}}$, which is the speed at which the wave patterns of Fig. 39–7 travel, and (b) the *group speed* $v_{\text{gr}}$, which is the speed at which electromagnetic energy or information-carrying "signals" travel along the guide. These speeds, which are identical for electromagnetic waves in a coaxial cable and for acoustic waves in a tube, are different for waves in a waveguide.

*The phase speed is not directly measurable.* The wave pattern is a repetitive structure, and there is no way to distinguish one wave maximum from another. The waves can be observed to enter one end of the guide and to leave at the other, but there is no way to identify a particular wave maximum so that its passage down the guide can be timed. We can put a "signal" on the wave by increasing the power level of the oscillator for a short time. This power pulse could be timed as it passes through the guide, but there is no guarantee that it travels at the same speed as the wave pattern and, indeed, it does not. The speed of such signals or markers is the speed at which *energy* is propagated, that is, the group speed.

From Maxwell's equations it can be shown that the phase speed and the group speed for the mode of Fig. 39–7 are

$$v_{\text{ph}} = \frac{c}{\sqrt{1 - \left(\dfrac{\lambda}{2a}\right)^2}} \tag{39–1}$$

and

$$v_{\text{gr}} = c\,\sqrt{1 - \left(\dfrac{\lambda}{2a}\right)^2}, \tag{39–2}$$

in which $a$ is the width of the guide and $\lambda$ the free-space wavelength. Note that as $a \to \infty$, which corresponds to free-space conditions, $v_{\text{ph}} = v_{\text{gr}} = c$.

The phase speed $v_{\text{ph}}$ is *greater* than the velocity of light, the group speed $v_{\text{gr}}$ being correspondingly less. In relativity theory we learn that no speed at which signals or energy travel can be faster than that of light. However, signals or energy cannot be transmitted down a guide at speeds exceeding $c$; they travel with speed $v_{\text{gr}}$ which is always less than $c$ so there is no conflict with the theory of relativity.

The wavelength $\lambda$ in Eqs. 39-1 and 39-2 is the wavelength that would be measured for the oscillations in free space, that is,

$$\lambda = \frac{c}{\nu}, \tag{39-3}$$

where $c$ is the speed in free space and $\nu$ is the frequency. For waves of a given frequency, the wavelength exhibited in a guide ($\lambda_g$) must differ from the free-space wavelength $\lambda$ because the speed $v_{ph}$ has changed. The so-called *guide wavelength* $\lambda_g$ is given by

$$\lambda_g = \frac{v_{ph}}{\nu} = \frac{v_{ph}}{c/\lambda} = \lambda \frac{v_{ph}}{c}.$$

From Eq. 39-1 this yields

$$\lambda_g = \frac{\lambda}{\sqrt{1 - \left(\dfrac{\lambda}{2a}\right)^2}}. \tag{39-4}$$

Thus the guide wavelength, which is the wavelength exhibited by the field patterns in Fig. 39-7, is larger than the free-space wavelength.

▶ **Example 4.** What must be the width $a$ of a rectangular guide such that the energy of electromagnetic radiation whose free-space wavelength is 3.0 cm travels down the guide (*a*) at 95% of the speed of light? (*b*) At 50% of the speed of light? From Eq. 39-2 we have

$$v_{gr} = 0.95c = c \sqrt{1 - \left(\frac{\lambda}{2a}\right)^2}.$$

Solving for $a$ yields $a = 4.8$ cm; repeating for $v_{gr} = 0.50c$ yields $a = 1.7$ cm.

This formula illustrates the cutoff phenomenon described above. If $\lambda = 2a$, then $v_{gr} = 0$ and energy cannot travel down the guide. For the radiation considered in this example $\lambda = 3.0$ cm, so that the guide must have a width $a$ of *at least* $\frac{1}{2} \times 3.0$ cm = 1.5 cm if it is to transmit this wave. The guide whose width we calculated in (*a*) above can transmit radiations whose free-space wavelength is $2 \times 4.8$ cm = 9.6 cm *or less*. ◀

## 39-4 Radiation

The acoustic transmission line of Fig. 39-6 cannot be infinitely long. Its far end may be sealed by a solid cap or left open, or it may have a flange, a horn, or some similar device mounted on it. If the far end is not sealed, energy will escape into the medium beyond. This is called *acoustic radiation*. In general, some energy will also be reflected back down the transmission line. If acoustic radiation is desirable, the designer's task is to fashion a termination (that is, an "acoustic antenna") for the transmission line such that the smallest possible fraction of the incident energy will be reflected back down the line. Such a termination might take the form of a flared horn. Acoustic radiation, of course, requires a medium such as air in order to be propagated.

An electromagnetic transmission line such as a coaxial cable or a waveguide can also be terminated in many ways, and energy can escape from the end of the line into the space beyond. In contrast to sound waves, a physical

**Fig. 39–8** An electric dipole antenna on the end of a coaxial cable.

medium is not required. Thus electromagnetic energy can be radiated from the end of the transmission line, to form a traveling electromagnetic wave in free space.

Figure 39–8 shows an effective termination for a coaxial cable; it consists of two wires arranged as shown and is called an *electric dipole antenna*. The potential difference between the two conductors alternates sinusoidally as the wave reaches them, the effect being that of an electric dipole whose dipole moment **p** varies with time.

Figure 39–9 shows such a dipole, represented by two equal and opposite charges. Its dipole moment, represented by the arrows marked **p** in the

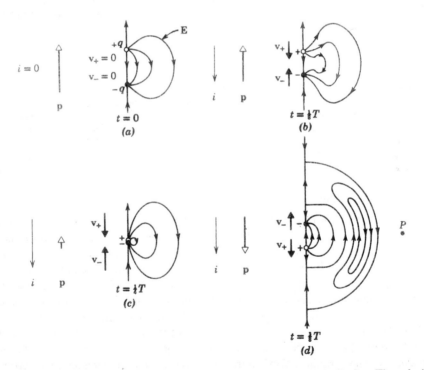

**Fig. 39–9** Showing how radiation escapes from an oscillating electric dipole. The velocities of the charges, the electric dipole moment, the equivalent current, and the lines of **E** are shown at four stages of oscillation, one-eighth of a period apart. The lines of **B** are not shown. (Adapted from Attwood, *Electric and Magnetic Fields*, John Wiley and Sons, third edition, 1949.)

figure, oscillates sinusoidally as the charges oscillate; in Fig. 39–9c it is on the verge of reversing its direction. The four views, one-eighth of a cycle apart, show how the electric lines of force break away from the dipole and form closed loops that travel through free space with speed c. The oscillating charges constitute a current, which is represented by the arrows marked i in Fig. 39–9. These oscillating currents generate a field of **B** which, for simplicity, is not represented in the figure. The lines of **B** as well as those of **E** also form closed loops that move away from the dipole with speed c. These traveling electric and magnetic fields, which, as we shall see, are strongly interdependent, constitute *electromagnetic radiation*.

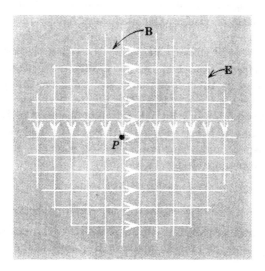

**Fig. 39–10** An instantaneous view of an electromagnetic wave as seen by an observer at P in Fig. 39–9d.

Figure 39–10 shows a part of the wavefront as it would appear to an observer at point P in Fig. 39–9d. The wave is moving directly out of the page. One-half a period later the observer at P will see a field pattern like that of Fig. 39–10, except that the directions of both the electric and the magnetic fields will be reversed. The speed c of the wave in free space is given by c = νλ, which can be written as

$$c = \frac{\omega}{k},\qquad(39\text{–}5)$$

where ω, the angular frequency, and k, the wave number, are related to the frequency ν and the wavelength λ by

$$\omega = 2\pi\nu \quad\text{and}\quad k = 2\pi/\lambda.$$

## 39-5   Traveling Waves and Maxwell's Equations

In earlier sections we have postulated the existence of certain magnetic and electric field distributions, in resonant cavities, coaxial cables, and waveguides, and we have shown that these postulated distributions are consistent with Maxwell's equations, as are the distributions of conduction and displacement currents associated with the fields. The student who pursues his studies of electromagnetism will learn how to derive mathematical expressions for **E** and **B** by subjecting Maxwell's equations to the boundary conditions appropriate to the problem at hand. In this section we continue our program by showing that the postulated patterns of **E** and **B** for a traveling electromagnetic wave are completely consistent with Maxwell's equations. In doing so, we will be able to show that the speed of such waves in free space is that of visible light and thus that visible light is itself an electromagnetic wave.

If the observer at $P$ in Fig. 39–9d is a considerable distance from the source, the *wavefronts* described by the electric and magnetic fields that reach him (see Fig. 39–10) will be planes and the wave that moves past him will be a *plane wave* (see Section 19–2). Figure 39–11 shows a "snapshot" of a plane wave traveling in the $x$ direction. The lines of **E** are parallel to the $z$ axis and those of **B** are parallel to the $y$ axis. The values of **B** and **E** for this wave depend only on $x$ and $t$ (not on $y$ or $z$). We postulate that they are given in magnitude by

$$B = B_m \sin (kx - \omega t) \qquad (39\text{-}6)$$

and

$$E = E_m \sin (kx - \omega t). \qquad (39\text{-}7)$$

Figure 39–12 shows two sections through the three-dimensional diagram of Fig. 39–11. In Fig. 39–12a the plane of the page is the $xz$ plane and in

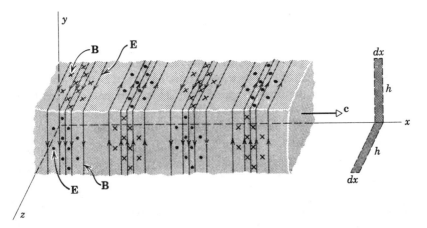

**Fig. 39–11**   A plane electromagnetic wave traveling to the right at speed $c$. Lines of **B** are parallel to the $y$ axis; those of **E** are parallel to the $z$ axis. The shaded rectangles on the right refer to Fig. 39–12.

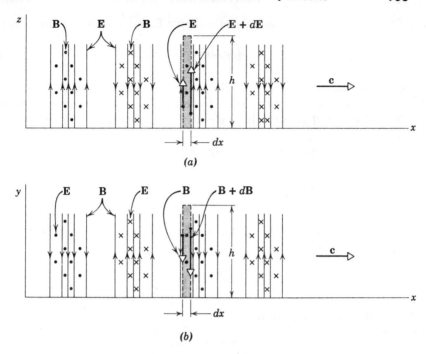

**Fig. 39-12**   The wave of Fig. 39-11 viewed (a) in the xz plane and (b) in the xy plane.

Fig. 39-12b it is the xy plane.   Note that, as for the traveling waves in a coaxial cable (Fig. 39-3a) and in a waveguide (Fig. 39-7), E and B are in phase, that is, at any point through which the wave is moving they reach their maximum values at the same time.

The shaded rectangle of dimensions $dx$ and $h$ in Fig. 39-12a is fixed in space.   As the wave passes over it, the magnetic flux $\Phi_B$ through the rectangle will change, which will give rise to induced electric fields around the rectangle, according to Faraday's law of induction.   These induced electric fields are, in fact, simply the electric component of the traveling wave.

Let us apply Lenz's law to this induction process.   The flux $\Phi_B$ for the shaded rectangle of Fig. 39-12a is *decreasing* with time because the wave is moving through the rectangle to the right and a region of weaker magnetic fields is moving into the rectangle.   The induced field will act to oppose this change, which means that if we imagine that the boundary of the rectangle is a conducting loop a *counterclockwise* induced current would appear in it. This current would produce a field of B that, within the rectangle, would point out of the page, thus opposing the decrease in $\Phi_B$.   There is, of course, no conducting loop, but the net induced electric field E does indeed act counterclockwise around the rectangle because $E + dE$, the magnitude of E at the right edge of the rectangle, is greater than $E$, the magnitude of E at the left edge.   Thus the electric field configuration is entirely consistent with the concept that it is induced by the changing magnetic field.

For a more detailed analysis let us apply Faraday's law of induction, or

$$\oint \mathbf{E} \cdot d\mathbf{l} = -\frac{d\Phi_B}{dt}, \tag{39-8}$$

going counterclockwise around the shaded rectangle of Fig. 39–12a. There is no contribution to the integral from the top or bottom of the rectangle because $\mathbf{E}$ and $d\mathbf{l}$ are at right angles here. The integral then becomes

$$\oint \mathbf{E} \cdot d\mathbf{l} = [(E + dE)(h)] - [(E)(h)] = dE\, h.$$

The flux $\Phi_B$ for the rectangle is

$$\Phi_B = (B)(dx\, h),$$

where $B$ is the magnitude of $\mathbf{B}$ at the rectangular strip and $dx\, h$ is the area of the strip. Differentiating gives

$$\frac{d\Phi_B}{dt} = h\, dx\, \frac{dB}{dt}.$$

From Eq. 39–8 we have then

$$dE\, h = -h\, dx\, \frac{dB}{dt},$$

or
$$\frac{dE}{dx} = -\frac{dB}{dt}. \tag{39-9}$$

Actually, both $B$ and $E$ are functions of $x$ and $t$; see Eqs. 39–6 and 39–7. In evaluating $dE/dx$, it is assumed that $t$ is constant because Fig. 39–12a is an "instantaneous snapshot." Also, in evaluating $dB/dt$ it is assumed that $x$ is constant since what is required is the time rate of change of $B$ at a particular place, the strip in Fig. 39–12a. The derivatives under these circumstances are called *partial derivatives*, and a somewhat different notation is used for them; see the footnote on p. 725. In this notation Eq. 39–9 becomes

$$\frac{\partial E}{\partial x} = -\frac{\partial B}{\partial t}. \tag{39-10}$$

The minus sign in this equation is appropriate and necessary, for, although $E$ is increasing with $x$ at the site of the shaded rectangle in Fig. 39–12a, $B$ is decreasing with $t$. Since $E(x,t)$ and $B(x,t)$ are known (see Eqs. 39–6 and 39–7), Eq. 39–10 reduces to

$$kE_m \cos(kx - \omega t) = \omega B_m \cos(kx - \omega t),$$

or (see Eq. 39–5)
$$\frac{\omega}{k} = \frac{E_m}{B_m} = c. \tag{39-11a}$$

Thus the speed of the wave $c$ is the ratio of the amplitudes of the electric and the magnetic components of the wave. From Eqs. 39–6 and 39–7 we see that the ratio of amplitudes is the same as the ratio of instantaneous values, or

$$E = cB. \tag{39-11b}$$

This important result will be useful in later sections.

We now turn our attention to Fig. 39–12b, in which the flux $\Phi_E$ for the shaded rectangle is decreasing with time as the wave moves through it. According to Maxwell's third equation (with $i = 0$, because there are no conduction currents in a traveling electromagnetic wave),

$$\oint \mathbf{B} \cdot d\mathbf{l} = \mu_0 \epsilon_0 \frac{d\Phi_E}{dt}, \tag{39-12}$$

this changing flux will induce a magnetic field at points around the periphery of the rectangle. This induced magnetic field is simply the magnetic component of the electromagnetic wave. Thus, as in the cavity resonator of Section 38–10, the electric and the magnetic components of the wave are intimately connected with each other, each depending on the time rate of change of the other.

Comparison of the shaded rectangles in Fig. 39–12 shows that for each the appropriate flux, $\Phi_B$ or $\Phi_E$, is *decreasing* with time. However, if we proceed counterclockwise around the upper and lower shaded rectangles, we see that $\oint \mathbf{E} \cdot d\mathbf{l}$ is *positive*, whereas $\oint \mathbf{B} \cdot d\mathbf{l}$ is *negative*. This is as it should be. If the student will compare Figs. 35–10 and 38–9a, he will be reminded that although the fluxes $\Phi_B$ and $\Phi_E$ in those figures are changing with time in the same way (both are increasing) the lines of the induced fields, $\mathbf{E}$ and $\mathbf{B}$, respectively, circulate in opposite directions.

The integral in Eq. 39–12, evaluated by proceeding counterclockwise around the shaded rectangle of Fig. 39–12b, is

$$\oint \mathbf{B} \cdot d\mathbf{l} = [-(B + dB)(h)] + [(B)(h)] = -h \, dB,$$

where $B$ is the magnitude of $\mathbf{B}$ at the left edge of the strip and $B + dB$ is its magnitude at the right edge.

The flux $\Phi_E$ through the rectangle of Fig. 39–12b is

$$\Phi_E = (E)(h \, dx).$$

Differentiating gives
$$\frac{d\Phi_E}{dt} = h \, dx \, \frac{dE}{dt}.$$

Equation 39–12 can thus be written

$$-h \, dB = \mu_0 \epsilon_0 \left( h \, dx \, \frac{dE}{dt} \right)$$

or, substituting partial derivatives,

$$-\frac{\partial B}{\partial x} = \mu_0 \epsilon_0 \frac{\partial E}{\partial t}. \tag{39-13}$$

Again, the minus sign in this equation is appropriate and necessary, for, although $B$ is increasing with $x$ at the site of the shaded rectangle in Fig. 39–12b, $E$ is decreasing with $t$.

Combining this equation with Eqs. 39–6 and 39–7 yields

$$-kB_m \cos (kx - \omega t) = -\mu_0 \epsilon_0 \omega E_m \cos (kx - \omega t),$$

or (see Eq. 39–5)
$$\frac{E_m}{B_m} = \frac{k}{\mu_0 \epsilon_0 \omega} = \frac{1}{\mu_0 \epsilon_0 c}. \tag{39–14}$$

Eliminating $E_m/B_m$ between Eqs. 39–11a and 39–14 yields

$$c = \frac{1}{\sqrt{\mu_0 \epsilon_0}}. \tag{39–15}$$

Substituting numerical values yields

$$c = \frac{1}{\sqrt{(4\pi \times 10^{-7} \text{ weber/amp-m})(8.9 \times 10^{-12} \text{ coul}^2/\text{nt-m}^2)}}$$

$$= 3.0 \times 10^8 \text{ meters/sec}, \tag{39–16}$$

which is the speed of light in free space! This emergence of the speed of light from purely electromagnetic considerations is the crowning achievement of Maxwell's electromagnetic theory. Maxwell made this prediction before radio waves were known and before it was realized that light was electromagnetic in nature. His prediction led to the concept of the electromagnetic spectrum, which we discuss in Chapter 40, and to the discovery of radio waves by Heinrich Hertz in 1890. It made it possible to discuss optics as a branch of electromagnetism and to derive its fundamental laws from Maxwell's equations.

A conclusion as fundamental as Eq. 39–15 must be subject to rigorous experimental verification. Of the three quantities in that equation, one, $\mu_0$, has an assigned value, namely, $4\pi \times 10^{-7}$ weber/amp-m. The speed of light $c$ is one of the most precisely measured physical constants, having the presently accepted value of $2.997924 \times 10^8$ meters/sec. The remaining quantity, $\epsilon_0$, can be measured by making measurements on an accurately constructed parallel-plate capacitor, as described in Section 30–2. The best measured value, by Rosa and Dorsey of the National Bureau of Standards (U.S.A.) in 1906, is $8.84025 \times 10^{-12}$ coul$^2$/nt-m$^2$. To this accuracy Eq. 39–15 is completely verified. Our confidence in electromagnetic theory, bolstered by numerous successful predictions and agreements with experiment, is now such that we reverse the foregoing procedure and calculate our presently accepted value of $\epsilon_0$ (see Appendix $A$) from the measured speed of light, using Eq. 39–15.

### 39–6 The Poynting Vector

One of the important characteristics of an electromagnetic wave is that it can transport energy from point to point. As we show below, the rate of energy flow per unit area in a plane electromagnetic wave can be described by a vector **S**, called the *Poynting vector* after John Henry Poynting (1852–1914), who first pointed out its properties. We define **S** from

$$S = \frac{1}{\mu_0} E \times B. \qquad (39\text{--}17)$$

In the mks system **S** is expressed in watts/meter$^2$; the direction of **S** gives the direction in which the energy moves. The vectors **E** and **B** refer to their instantaneous values at the point in question. If Eq. 39–17 is applied to the traveling plane electromagnetic wave of Fig. 39–11, it is clear that **E × B**, hence **S**, point in the direction of propagation. Note, too, that **S** points parallel to the axis for all points in the coaxial cable of Fig. 39–3.

We get meaningful results if we extend the Poynting vector concept to other electromagnetic situations involving either traveling or standing electromagnetic waves, as we will see in Examples 5 and 6. If we extend it to circuit situations involving steady or almost steady currents and lumped circuit elements, we are led to some interesting conclusions, which we explore in Problems 11, 17, and 18.

▶ **Example 5.** Analyze energy flow in the cavity of Fig. 38–8, using the Poynting vector.

Study of Fig. 39–13 shows that when the energy is all electric (Figs. 39–13a and e) it is concentrated along the axis, because this is the region in which **E** has its maximum

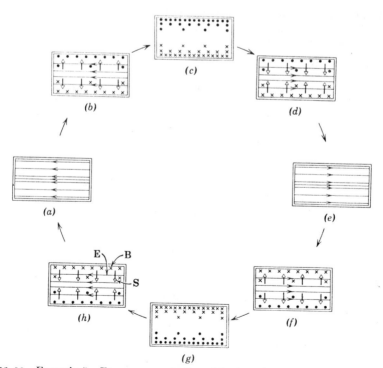

**(g)**

**Fig. 39–13** Example 5. Energy surges back and forth periodically between the central region of the cavity and the region near the walls, as indicated by the Poynting vector **S**.

value. When the energy is all magnetic (Figs. 39–13c and g), it is concentrated near the walls. Thus the energy surges back and forth periodically between the central region and the region near the walls. The figure shows, by the open arrows, the direction of S at various points in the cavity and at various times in the cycle. Note that S equals zero for Figs. 39–13a, c, e, and g, which is appropriate because at those instants of time the field configurations are momentarily stationary and energy is not flowing. A pendulum bob at the end of its swing and at the bottom of its trajectory forms a mechanical analogy. The student should verify from Eq. 39–17 that these arrows point in the correct directions. ◀

Figure 39–14 can be used to derive the Poynting relation for the special case of a traveling plane electromagnetic wave. It shows a cross section of a traveling plane wave, along with a thin "box" of thickness $dx$ and area $A$. The box, a mathematical construction, is fixed with respect to the axes while the wave moves through it.

**Fig. 39–14** A plane wave is traveling to the right at speed $c$; compare Fig. 39–12b. The dashed rectangle in this figure represents a three-dimensional box, of area $A$ and thickness $dx$, that extends at right angles to the plane of the figure.

At any instant the energy stored in the box, from Eqs. 30–27 and 36–19, is

$$dU = dU_E + dU_B = (u_E + u_B)(A\,dx)$$

$$= \left(\tfrac{1}{2}\epsilon_0 E^2 + \frac{1}{2\mu_0} B^2\right) A\,dx, \qquad (39\text{–}18)$$

where $A\,dx$ is the volume of the box and $E$ and $B$ are the instantaneous values of the field vectors in the box.

Using Eq. 39–11b ($E = cB$) to eliminate *one* of the $E$'s in the first term in Eq. 39–18 and *one* of the $B$'s in the second term leads to

$$dU = \left[\tfrac{1}{2}\epsilon_0 E(cB) + \frac{1}{2\mu_0} B\left(\frac{E}{c}\right)\right] A\,dx$$

$$= \frac{(\mu_0\epsilon_0 c^2 + 1)(EBA\,dx)}{2\mu_0 c}.$$

From Eq. 39–15, however, $\mu_0\epsilon_0 c^2 = 1$, so that

$$dU = \frac{EBA\,dx}{\mu_0 c}.$$

This energy $dU$ will pass through the right face of the box in a time $dt$ equal to $dx/c$. Thus the energy per unit area per unit time, which is $S$, is given by

$$S = \frac{dU}{dt\,A} = \frac{EBA\,dx}{\mu_0 c\,(dx/c)\,A} = \frac{1}{\mu_0} EB.$$

This is exactly the prediction of the more general relation Eq. 39–17 for a traveling plane wave.

This relation refers to values of $S$, $E$, and $B$ at any instant of time. We are usually more interested in the *average* value of $S$, taken over one or more cycles of the wave. An observer making intensity measurements on a wave moving past him would measure this average value $\bar{S}$. We can easily show (see Example 6) that $\bar{S}$ is related to the *maximum* values of $E$ and $B$ by

$$\bar{S} = \frac{1}{2\mu_0} E_m B_m.$$

▶ **Example 6.** An observer is at a great distance $r$ from a point light source whose power output is $P_0$. Calculate the magnitudes of the electric and the magnetic fields. Assume that the source is monochromatic, that it radiates uniformly in all directions, and that at distant points it behaves like the traveling plane wave of Fig. 39–11.

The power that passes through a sphere of radius $r$ is $(\bar{S})(4\pi r^2)$, where $\bar{S}$ is the *average* value of the Poynting vector at the surface of the sphere. This power must equal $P_0$, or

$$P_0 = \bar{S} 4\pi r^2.$$

From the definition of $S$ (Eq. 39–17), we have

$$\bar{S} = \overline{\left( \frac{1}{\mu_0} EB \right)}.$$

Using the relation $E = cB$ (Eq. 39–11b) to eliminate $B$ leads to

$$\bar{S} = \frac{1}{\mu_0 c} \overline{E^2}.$$

The average value of $E^2$ over one cycle is $\frac{1}{2} E_m{}^2$, since $E$ varies sinusoidally (see Eq. 39–7). This leads to

$$P_0 = \left( \frac{E_m{}^2}{2\mu_0 c} \right) (4\pi r^2),$$

or

$$E_m = \frac{1}{r} \sqrt{\frac{P_0 \mu_0 c}{2\pi}}.$$

For $P_0 = 10^3$ watts and $r = 1.0$ meter this yields

$$E_m = \frac{1}{(1.0m)} \sqrt{\frac{(10^3 \text{ watts})(4\pi \times 10^{-7} \text{ weber/amp-m})(3 \times 10^8 \text{ meters/sec})}{2\pi}}$$

$$= 240 \text{ volts/meter.}$$

The relationship $E_m = cB_m$ (Eq. 39–11a) leads to

$$B_m = \frac{E_m}{c} = \frac{240 \text{ volts/meter}}{3 \times 10^8 \text{ meters/sec}} = 8 \times 10^{-7} \text{ weber/meter}^2.$$

Note that $E_m$ is appreciable as judged by ordinary laboratory standards but that $B_m$ (= 0.008 gauss) is quite small.                                                        ◀

## QUESTIONS

1. In the coaxial cable of Fig. 39–1, what are the directions of the conduction current (a) in the central conductor and (b) in the outer conductor, shortly after the switch is thrown to position a? Consider points that have been reached by the wavefront of Fig. 39–2a and b and those that have not.

2. Compare a coaxial cable and a waveguide, used as a transmission line. Point out both similarities and differences.

3. What is the relation between the wavelength in the cable and that in free space for a coaxial cable?

4. Can traveling waves with a continuous range of wavelengths be sent down (a) a coaxial cable and (b) a waveguide? Can standing waves with a continuous range of wavelengths be set up in a resonant cavity? Develop mechanical or acoustical analogies to support your answers.

5. If a certain wavelength is larger than the cutoff wavelength for a guide in its dominant mode, can energy be sent down it in any other mode?

6. Explain why the term $\epsilon_0 \, d\Phi_E/dt$ is needed in Ampère's equation to understand the propagation of electromagnetic waves.

7. In the equation $c = 1/\sqrt{\mu_0 \epsilon_0}$ (Eq. 39–15), how can $c$ always have the same value if $\mu_0$ is arbitrarily assigned and $\epsilon_0$ is measured?

8. Is it conceivable that electromagnetic theory might some day be able to predict the value of $c$ ($3 \times 10^8$ meters/sec), not in terms of $\mu_0$ and $\epsilon_0$, but directly and numerically without recourse to any measurements?

9. What is the direction of the displacement current in Fig. 39–4? Give an argument to support your answer.

10. In a coaxial cable is the energy transported in the conductors, through the agency of the currents, or in the space between them, through the agency of the fields?

## PROBLEMS

1. Using Gauss's law, sketch the instantaneous charges that appear on the conductors of the coaxial cable of Fig. 39–3 and show that this pattern of charges is appropriately related to the conduction currents shown in Fig. 39–3c.

2. For a rectangular guide of width 3.0 cm, plot the phase speed, the group speed, and the guide wavelength as a function of the free-space wavelength. Assume the dominant mode.

3. For a rectangular guide of width 3.0 cm, what must the free-space wavelength of radiation be if it is to require 1.0 $\mu$sec (= $10^{-6}$ sec) for energy to traverse a 100-meter length of guide? What is the phase speed under these circumstances?

4. Under what conditions will the guide wavelength in the guide of Fig. 39–7 be double the free-space wavelength?

5. How does the displacement current vary with space and time in a traveling plane electromagnetic wave?

6. Prove that for any point in an electromagnetic wave such as that of Fig. 39–11 the density of energy stored in the electric field equals that stored in the magnetic field.

7. A resonant cavity is constructed by closing each end of the coaxial cable of Fig. 39–3 with a metal cap. The cavity contains three half-waves. Describe the patterns of **E** and **B**

that occur, assuming the same mode of oscillation as that shown in Fig. 39–3. (Hint: Remember that **E** can have no tangential component at a conducting surface and that **B** and **E** must be 90° out of phase.)

8. If a coaxial cable has resistance, energy must flow from the fields into the conducting surfaces to provide the Joule heating. How must the electric lines of force of Fig. 39–3*a* be modified in this case? (Hint: The Poynting vector near the surface must have a component pointing toward the surface.)

9. What guide wavelength does 10-cm radiation (free-space wavelength) exhibit in a rectangular guide whose width is 6.0 cm? Assume the dominant mode. What is the cutoff wavelength for this guide?

10. Sketch five more figures to complete the sequence of Fig. 39–9, showing radiation from an oscillating dipole. Include an indication of the lines of **B** in your drawings.

11. Figure 39–15 shows a long resistanceless transmission line, delivering power from a battery to a resistive load. A steady current $i$ exists as shown. (*a*) Sketch qualitatively the electric and magnetic fields around the line, and (*b*) show that, according to the Poynting vector point of view, energy travels from the battery to the resistor through the space around the line and not through the line itself. (Hint: Each conductor in the line is an equipotential surface, since the line has been assumed to have no resistance.)

**Fig. 39–15**

12. Analyze the flow of energy in the waveguide of Fig. 39–7, using the Poynting vector.

13. A cube of edge $a$ has its edges parallel to the $x$-, $y$-, and $z$-axes of a rectangular coordinate system. A uniform electric field **E** is parallel to the $y$-axis and a uniform magnetic field **B** is parallel to the $x$-axis. Calculate (*a*) the rate at which, according to the Poynting vector point of view, energy may be said to pass through each face of the cube and (*b*) the net rate at which the energy stored in the cube may be said to change.

14. A #10 copper wire (diameter, 0.10 in.; resistance per 1000 ft, 1.00 ohm) carries a current of 25 amp. Calculate **E**, **B**, and **S** for a point on the surface of the wire.

15. Sunlight strikes the earth, outside its atmosphere, with an intensity of 2.0 cal/cm²-min. Calculate $E_m$ and $B_m$ for sunlight, assuming it to be a wave like that of Fig. 39–10.

16. A plane radio wave has $E_m \cong 10^{-4}$ volt/meter. Calculate (*a*) $B_m$ and (*b*) the intensity of the wave, as measured by $\overline{S}$.

17. Figure 39–16 shows a cylindrical resistor of length $l$, radius $a$, and resistivity $\rho$, carrying a current $i$. (*a*) Show that the Poynting vector **S** at the surface of the resistor is everywhere directed normal to the surface, as shown. (*b*) Show that the rate $P$ at which energy flows into the resistor through its cylindrical surface, calculated by integrating the Poynting vector over this surface, is equal to the rate at which Joule heat is produced; that is,

$$\int \mathbf{S} \cdot d\mathbf{A} = i^2 R,$$

where $d\mathbf{A}$ is an element of area of the cylindrical surface. This shows that, according to the Poynting vector point of view, the energy that appears in a resistor as Joule heat does not enter it through the connecting wires but through the space around the wires and the resistor. (Hint: **E** is parallel to the axis of the cylinder, in the direction of the current; **B** forms concentric circles around the cylinder, in a direction given by the right-hand rule.)

**Fig. 39-16**                  **Fig. 39-17**

18. Figure 39-17 shows a parallel-plate capacitor being charged. (a) Show that the Poynting vector S points everywhere radially into the cylindrical volume. (b) Show that the rate $P$ at which energy flows into this volume, calculated by integrating the Poynting vector over the cylindrical boundary of this volume, is equal to the rate at which the stored electrostatic energy increases; that is, that

$$\int \mathbf{S} \cdot d\mathbf{A} = \alpha d \frac{d}{dt} (\tfrac{1}{2} \epsilon_0 E^2),$$

where $\alpha d$ is the volume of the capacitor and $\tfrac{1}{2} \epsilon_0 E^2$ is the energy density for all points within that volume. This analysis shows that, according to the Poynting vector point of view, the energy stored in a capacitor does not enter it through the wires but through the space around the wires and the plates. (Hint: To find S we must first find $\mathbf{B}$, which is the magnetic field set up by the displacement current during the charging process; see Fig. 38-9. Ignore fringing of the lines of $\mathbf{E}$.)

# Nature and Propagation of Light

## CHAPTER 40

### 40–1 Light and the Electromagnetic Spectrum

Light was shown by Maxwell to be a component of the *electromagnetic spectrum* of Fig. 40–1. All these waves are electromagnetic in nature and have the same speed $c$ in free space. They differ in wavelength (and thus in frequency) only, which means that the sources that give rise to them and the instruments used to make measurements with them are rather different.* The electromagnetic spectrum has no definite upper or lower limit. The labeled regions in Fig. 40–1 represent frequency intervals within which a common body of experimental technique, such as common sources and common detectors, exists. All such regions overlap. For example, we can produce radiation of wavelength $10^{-3}$ meter either by microwave techniques (microwave oscillators) or by infrared techniques (incandescent sources).

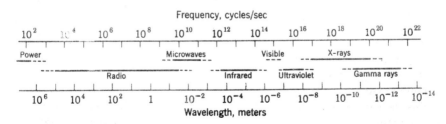

**Fig. 40–1** The electromagnetic spectrum. Note that the wavelength and frequency scales are logarithmic.

---

* For a report of electromagnetic waves with wavelengths as long as $1.9 \times 10^7$ miles the student should consult an article by James Heirtzler in the *Scientific American* for March 1962.

**Fig. 40–2**   The relative eye sensitivity of an assumed *standard observer* at different wavelengths for normal levels of illumination.   The shaded areas represent the (continuously graded) color sensations for normal vision.

"Light" is defined here as radiation that can affect the eye.   Figure 40–2, which shows the relative eye sensitivity of an assumed *standard observer* to radiations of various wavelengths, shows that the center of the visible region is about $5.55 \times 10^{-7}$ meter.   Light of this wavelength produces the sensation of yellow-green.*

In optics we often use the micron (abbr. $\mu$) the millimicron (abbr. $m\mu$), and the Angstrom (abbr. A) as units of wavelength.   They are defined from

$$1 \ \mu = 10^{-6} \ \text{meter}$$

$$1 \ m\mu = 10^{-9} \ \text{meter}$$

$$1 \ A = 10^{-10} \ \text{meter}.$$

Thus the center of the visible region can be expressed as 0.555 $\mu$, 555 $m\mu$, or 5550 A.

The limits of the visible spectrum are not well defined because the eye sensitivity curve approaches the axis asymptotically at both long and short wavelengths.   If the limits are taken, arbitrarily, as the wavelengths at which the eye sensitivity has dropped to 1% of its maximum value, these limits are about 4300 A and 6900 A, less than a factor of two in wavelength. The eye can detect radiation beyond these limits if it is intense enough.   In many experiments in physics one can use photographic plates or light-sensitive electronic detectors in place of the human eye.

---

* See "Experiments in Color Vision" by Edwin H. Land, *Scientific American*, May 1959, and especially "Color and Perception: the Work of Edwin Land in the Light of Current Concepts" by M. H. Wilson and R. W. Brocklebank, *Contemporary Physics*, December 1961, for a fascinating discussion of the problems of perception and the distinction between color as a characteristic of light and color as a perceived property of objects.

### 40–2   Energy and Momentum

Energy is carried by electromagnetic waves from the sun to the earth or from an open fire to a hand placed nearby. The transport of energy by such a wave in free space was described in Section 39–6 by the Poynting vector **S**, or

$$\mathbf{S} = \frac{1}{\mu_0} \, \mathbf{E} \times \mathbf{B}, \tag{40–1}$$

where **E** and **B** are the instantaneous values of the electric and magnetic field vectors.

Less familiar is the fact that electromagnetic waves may also transport linear momentum. In other words, it is possible to exert a pressure (a *radiation pressure* *) on an object by shining a light on it. Such forces must be small in relation to forces of our daily experience because we do not ordinarily notice them. The first measurement of radiation pressure was made in 1901–1903 by Nichols and Hull in this country and by Lebedev in Russia, about thirty years after the existence of such effects had been predicted theoretically by Maxwell.

Let a parallel beam of light fall on an object for a time $t$, the incident light being *entirely absorbed* by the object. If energy $U$ is absorbed during this time, the momentum $p$ delivered to the object is given, according to Maxwell's prediction, by

$$p = \frac{U}{c} \quad \text{(total absorption)}, \tag{40–2a}$$

where $c$ is the speed of light. The direction of **p** is the direction of the incident beam. If the light energy $U$ is *entirely reflected*, the momentum delivered will be twice that given above, or

$$p = \frac{2U}{c} \quad \text{(total reflection)}. \tag{40–2b}$$

In the same way, twice as much momentum is delivered to an object when a perfectly elastic tennis ball is bounced from it as when it is struck by a perfectly inelastic ball of the same mass and speed. If the light energy $U$ is partly reflected and partly absorbed, the delivered momentum will lie between $U/c$ and $2U/c$.

▶ **Example 1.** A parallel beam of light with an energy flux $S$ of 10 watts/cm² falls for 1 hr on a perfectly reflecting plane mirror of 1.0-cm² area. (*a*) What momentum is delivered to the mirror in this time and (*b*) what force acts on the mirror?

(*a*) The energy that is reflected from the mirror is

$$U = (10 \text{ watts/cm}^2)(1.0 \text{ cm}^2)(3600 \text{ sec}) = 3.6 \times 10^4 \text{ joules.}$$

The momentum delivered after 1 hr's illumination is

$$p = \frac{2U}{c} = \frac{(2)(3.6 \times 10^4 \text{ joules})}{3 \times 10^8 \text{ meters/sec}} = 2.4 \times 10^{-4} \text{ kg-m/sec.}$$

---

* See "Radiation Pressure," G. E. Henry, *Scientific American*, p. 99, June 1957.

(b) From Newton's second law, the average force on the mirror is equal to the average rate at which momentum is delivered to the mirror, or

$$F = \frac{p}{t} = \frac{2.4 \times 10^{-4} \text{ kg-m/sec}}{3600 \text{ sec}} = 6.7 \times 10^{-8} \text{ nt}.$$

This is a small force.                                                          ◀

Nichols and Hull, in 1903, measured radiation pressures and verified Eq. 40–2, using a torsion balance technique. They allowed light to fall on mirror $M$ in Fig. 40–3; the radiation pressure caused the balance arm to turn through a measured angle $\theta$, twisting the torsion fiber $F$. Assuming a suitable calibration for their torsion fiber, the experimenters could arrive at a numerical value for this pressure. Nichols and Hull measured the intensity of their light beam by allowing it to fall on a blackened metal disk of known absorptivity and by measuring the temperature rise of this disk. In a particular run these experimenters measured a radiation pressure of $7.01 \times 10^{-6}$ nt/meter$^2$; for their light beam, the value predicted, using Eq. 40–2, was $7.05 \times 10^{-6}$ nt/meter$^2$, in excellent agreement. Assuming a mirror area of 1 cm$^2$, this represents a force on the mirror of only $7 \times 10^{-10}$ nt, about 100 times smaller than the force calculated in Example 1.

The success of the experiment of Nichols and Hull was the result in large part of the care they took to eliminate spurious deflecting effects caused by changes in the speed distribution of the molecules in the gas surrounding the mirror. These changes were brought about by the small rise in the temperature of the mirror as it absorbed light energy from the incident beam. This "radiometer effect" is responsible for the spinning action of the familiar toy radiometers when placed in a beam of sunlight. In a perfect vacuum such effects would not occur, but in the best vacuums available in 1903 radiometer effects were present and had to be taken specifically into account in the design of the experiment.

To demonstrate the transport of momentum from Maxwell's equations in a particular case, let a plane electromagnetic wave traveling in the $z$ direction fall on a

**Fig. 40-3**

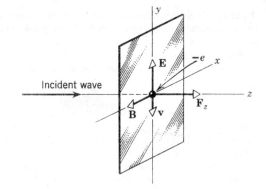

**Fig. 40–4**  An incident plane light wave falls on an electron in a thin resistive sheet. Instantaneous values of **E**, **B**, the electron velocity **v**, and the radiation force $\mathbf{F}_z$ are shown.

large thin sheet of a material of high resistivity as in Fig. 40–4. A small part of the incident energy will be absorbed within the sheet, but most of it will be transmitted if the sheet is thin enough.*

The incident wave **E** and **B** vary with time at the sheet as

$$\mathbf{E} = \mathbf{E}_m \sin \omega t \qquad (40\text{–}3)$$

and

$$\mathbf{B} = \mathbf{B}_m \sin \omega t \qquad (40\text{–}4)$$

where **E** is parallel to the $\pm y$ axis and **B** is parallel to the $\pm x$ axis.

In Section 31–4 we saw that the effect of a (constant) electric force ($= -e\mathbf{E}$) on a conduction electron in a metal was to make it move with a (constant) drift speed $v_d$. The electron behaves as if it is immersed in a viscous fluid, the electric force acting on it being counterbalanced by a "viscous" force, which may be taken as proportional to the electron speed. Thus for a constant field $E$, after equilibrium is established,

$$eE = bv_d, \qquad (40\text{–}5)$$

where $b$ is a resistive damping coefficient. The electron equilibrium speed, dropping the subscript $d$, is thus

$$v = \frac{eE}{b}. \qquad (40\text{–}6)$$

If the applied electric field varies with time and if the variation is slow enough, the electron speed can continually readjust itself to the changing value of $E$ so that its speed continues to be given essentially by its equilibrium value (Eq. 40–6) at all times. These readjustments are more rapidly made the more viscous the medium, just as a stone falling in air reaches a constant equilibrium rate of descent only relatively slowly but one falling in a viscous oil does so quite rapidly. We assume that the sheet in Fig. 40–4 is so viscous, that is, that its resistivity is so high, that Eq. 40–6 remains valid even for the rapid oscillations of $E$ in the incident light beam.

As the electron vibrates parallel to the $y$ axis, it experiences a *second* force due to the *magnetic* component of the wave. This force $\mathbf{F}_z$ ($= -e\mathbf{v} \times \mathbf{B}$) points in the $z$ direction, being at right angles to the plane formed by **v** and **B**, that is, the $xy$ plane. The instantaneous magnitude of $\mathbf{F}_z$ is given by

$$F_z = evB = \frac{e^2 EB}{b}. \qquad (40\text{–}7)$$

---

* Some of the incident energy will also be reflected, but the reflected wave is of such low intensity that it can be ignored in the derivation that follows; see *Optics* by B. Rossi, Addison-Wesley Publishing Company, p. 411, 1957, from which this derivation is adapted.

$\mathbf{F}_z$ always points in the positive $z$ direction because $\mathbf{v}$ and $\mathbf{B}$ reverse their directions simultaneously; this force is, in fact, the mechanism by which the radiation pressure acts on the sheet of Fig. 40–4.

From Newton's second law, $F_z$ is the rate $dp_e/dt$ at which the incident wave delivers momentum to each electron in the sheet, or

$$\frac{dp_e}{dt} = \frac{e^2 EB}{b}. \tag{40–8}$$

Momentum is delivered at this rate to every electron in the sheet and thus to the sheet itself. It remains to relate the momentum transfer to the sheet to the absorption of energy within the sheet.

The electric field component of the incident wave does work on each oscillating electron at an instantaneous rate (see Eq. 40–6) given by

$$\frac{dU_e}{dt} = F_E v = (eE)\left(\frac{eE}{b}\right) = \frac{e^2 E^2}{b}.$$

Note that the magnetic force $\mathbf{F}_z$, always being at right angles to the velocity $\mathbf{v}$, does no work on the oscillating electron. Equation 39–11$b$ shows that for a plane wave in free space $B$ and $E$ are related by

$$E = Bc.$$

Substituting above for *one* of the $E$'s leads to

$$\frac{dU_e}{dt} = \frac{e^2 EBc}{b}. \tag{40–9}$$

This equation represents the rate, per electron, at which energy is absorbed from the incident wave.

Comparing Eqs. 40–8 and 40–9 shows that

$$\frac{dp_e}{dt} = \frac{1}{c}\frac{dU_e}{dt}.$$

Integrating yields
$$\int_0^t \frac{dp_e}{dt}\,dt = \frac{1}{c}\int_0^t \frac{dU_e}{dt}\,dt,$$

or
$$p_e = \frac{U_e}{c}, \tag{40–10}$$

where $p_e$ is the momentum delivered to a single electron in any given time $t$ and $U_e$ is the energy absorbed by that electron in the same time interval. Multiplying each side by the number of free electrons in the sheet leads to Eq. 40–2$a$.

Although we derived this relation (Eq. 40–10) for a particular kind of absorber, no characteristics of the absorber—for example, the resistive damping coefficient $b$—remain in the final expression. This is as it should be because Eq. 40–10 is a general property of radiation absorbed by *any* material.

### 40–3   The Speed of Light *

Light travels so fast that there is nothing in our daily experience to suggest that its speed is not infinite. It calls for considerable insight even to ask "How fast does light travel?" Galileo asked himself this question and tried to answer it experimentally. His chief work, *Two New Sciences*, published

---

* See "The Speed of Light," J. H. Rush, *Scientific American*, p. 67, August 1955.

in the Netherlands in 1638, is written in the form of a conversation among three fictitious persons called Salviati, Sagredo, and Simplicio. Here is part of what they say about the speed of light.

*Simplicio:* Everyday experience shows that the propagation of light is instantaneous; for when we see a piece of artillery fired, at a great distance, the flash reaches our eyes without lapse of time; but the sound reaches the ear only after a noticeable interval.

*Sagredo:* Well, Simplicio, the only thing I am able to infer from this familiar bit of experience is that sound, in reaching our ear, travels more slowly than light; it does not inform me whether the coming of the light is instantaneous or whether, although extremely rapid, it still occupies time. . . .

Sagredo, who evidently is Galileo himself, then describes a possible method for measuring the speed of light. He and an assistant stand facing each other some distance apart, at night. Each carries a lantern which can be covered or uncovered at will. Galileo started the experiment by uncovering his lantern. When the light reached the assistant he uncovered his own lantern, whose light was then seen by Galileo. Galileo tried to measure the time between the instant at which he uncovered his own lantern and the instant at which the light from his assistant's lantern reached him. For a 1-mile separation we now know that the round trip travel time would be only $11 \times 10^{-6}$ sec. This is much less than human reaction times, so the method fails.

To measure a large velocity directly, we must either measure a small time interval or use a long base line. This situation suggests that astronomy, which deals with great distances, might be able to provide an experimental value for the speed of light; this proved to be true. Although it would be desirable to time the light from the sun as it travels to the earth, there is no way of knowing when the light that reaches us at any instant left the sun; we must use subtler astronomical methods.

Note, however, that microwave pulses are quite regularly reflected from the moon; this gives a $7.68 \times 10^8$-meter base line (there and back) for timing purposes. The speed of light (and of microwaves) is so well known now from other experiments that these measurements are used to measure the lunar distance accurately. Microwave signals have also been reflected from Venus.

In 1675 Ole Roemer, a Danish astronomer working in Paris, made some observations of the moons of Jupiter (see Problem 9) from which a speed of light of $2 \times 10^8$ meters/sec may be deduced. About fifty years later James Bradley, an English astronomer, made some astronomical observations of an entirely different kind from which a value of $3.0 \times 10^8$ meters/sec may be deduced.

In 1849 Hippolyte Louis Fizeau (1819–1896), a French physicist, first measured the speed of light by a nonastronomical method, obtaining a value of $3.13 \times 10^8$ meters/sec. Figure 40–5 shows Fizeau's apparatus. Let us first ignore the toothed wheel. Light from source $S$ is made to converge by lens $L_1$, is reflected from mirror $M_1$, and forms in space at $F$ an image of the source. Mirror $M_1$ is a so-called "half-silvered mirror"; its reflecting coating is so thin that only half the light that falls on it is reflected, the other half being transmitted.

Light from the image at $F$ enters lens $L_2$ and emerges as a parallel beam; after passing through lens $L_3$ it is reflected back along its original direction by mirror $M_2$. In Fizeau's experiment the distance $l$ between $M_2$ and $F$ was

**Fig. 40–5**  Fizeau's apparatus for measuring the speed of light.

8630 meters or 5.36 miles.  When the light strikes mirror $M_1$ again, some will be transmitted, entering the eye of the observer through lens $L_4$.

The observer will see an image of the source formed by light that has traveled a distance $2l$ between the wheel and mirror $M_2$ and back again.  To time the light beam a marker of some sort must be put on it.  This is done by "chopping" it with a rapidly rotating toothed wheel.  Suppose that during the round-trip travel time of $2l/c$ the wheel has turned just enough so that, when the light from a given "burst" returns to the wheel, point $F$ is covered by a tooth.  The light will hit the face of the tooth that is toward $M_2$ and will not reach the observer's eye.

If the speed of the wheel is exactly right, the observer will not see any of the bursts because each will be screened by a tooth.  The observer measures $c$ by increasing the angular speed $\omega$ of the wheel from zero until the image of source $S$ disappears.  Let $\theta$ be the angular distance from the center of a gap to the center of a tooth.  The time needed for the wheel to rotate a distance $\theta$ is the round-trip travel time $2l/c$.  In equation form,

$$\frac{\theta}{\omega} = \frac{2l}{c} \quad \text{or} \quad c = \frac{2\omega l}{\theta}. \tag{40–11}$$

This "chopped beam" technique, suitably modified, is used today to measure the speeds of neutrons and other particles.

▶ **Example 2.**  The wheel used by Fizeau had 720 teeth.  What is the smallest angular speed at which the image of the source will vanish?

The angle $\theta$ is $1/1440$ rev; solving Eq. 40–11 for $\omega$ gives

$$\omega = \frac{c\theta}{2l} = \frac{(3.00 \times 10^8 \text{ meters/sec})(1/1440 \text{ rev})}{(2)(8630 \text{ meters})} = 12.1 \text{ rev/sec.} \quad ◀$$

The French physicist Foucault (1819–1868) greatly improved Fizeau's method by substituting a rotating mirror for the toothed wheel.  The American physicist Albert A. Michelson (1852–1931) conducted an extensive series of measurements of $c$, extending over a fifty-year period, using this technique.

**Table 40–1**

THE SPEED OF ELECTROMAGNETIC RADIATION IN FREE SPACE
(Some selected measurements)

| Date | Experimenter | Country | Method | Speed, km/sec | Uncertainty, km/sec |
|------|-------------|---------|--------|---------------|---------------------|
| 1600(?) | Galileo | Italy | Lanterns and shutters | "If not instantaneous, it is extraordinarily rapid" | |
| 1675 | Roemer | France | Astronomical | 200,000 | |
| 1729 | Bradley | England | Astronomical | 304,000 | |
| 1849 | Fizeau | France | Toothed wheel | 313,300 | |
| 1862 | Foucault | France | Rotating mirror | 298,000 | 500 |
| 1876 | Cornu | France | Toothed wheel | 299,990 | 200 |
| 1880 | Michelson | U.S.A. | Rotating mirror | 299,910 | 50 |
| 1883 | Newcomb | England | Rotating mirror | 299,860 | 30 |
| 1883 | Michelson | U.S.A. | Rotating mirror | 299,853 | 60 |
| 1906 | Rosa and Dorsey | U.S.A. | Electromagnetic theory | 299,781 | 10 |
| 1923 | Mercier | France | Standing waves on wires | 299,782 | 15 |
| 1926 | Michelson | U.S.A. | Rotating mirror | 299,796 | 4 |
| 1928 | Karolus and Mittelstaedt | Germany | Kerr cell | 299,778 | 10 |
| 1932 | Michelson, Pease, and Pearson | U.S.A. | Rotating mirror | 299,774 | 11 |
| 1940 | Huettel | Germany | Kerr cell | 299,768 | 10 |
| 1941 | Anderson | U.S.A. | Kerr cell | 299,776 | 14 |
| 1950 | Bergstrand | Sweden | Geodimeter | 299,792.7 | 0.25 |
| 1950 | Essen | England | Microwave cavity | 299,792.5 | 3 |
| 1950 | Houston | Scotland | Vibrating crystal | 299,775 | 9 |
| 1950 | Bol and Hansen | U.S.A. | Microwave cavity | 299,789.3 | 0.4 |
| 1951 | Aslakson | U.S.A. | Shoran radar | 299,794.2 | 1.9 |
| 1952 | Rank, Ruth, and Ven der Sluis | U.S.A. | Molecular spectra | 299,776 | 7 |
| 1952 | Froome | England | Microwave interferometer | 299,792.6 | 0.7 |
| 1954 | Florman | U.S.A. | Radio interferometer | 299,795.1 | 3.1 |
| 1954 | Rank, Shearer, and Wiggins | U.S.A. | Molecular spectra | 299,789.8 | 3.0 |
| 1956 | Edge | Sweden | Geodimeter | 299,792.9 | 0.2 |

We must view the speed of light within the larger framework of the speed of electromagnetic radiation in general. It is a significant experimental confirmation of Maxwell's theory of electromagnetism that the speed in free space of waves in all parts of the electromagnetic spectrum has the same value $c$. Table 40–1 shows some selected measurements that have been made of the speed of electromagnetic radiation since Galileo's day. It stands as a monument to man's persistence and ingenuity. Note in the last column how the uncertainty in the measurement has improved through the years. Note also the international character of the effort and the variety of methods.

The task of arriving at a single "best" value of $c$ from the many listed in the table is difficult, for it involves a careful study of each reported measurement and a selection from among them, based on the reported uncertainty and the selector's judgment of the probable presence or absence of hidden error. In the final averaging measurements with small uncertainties will be given more weight than those with large ones. By careful analysis of such measurements the "best" value, as of 1964, is

$$c = 2.997925 \times 10^8 \text{ meters/sec.}$$

The uncertainty of measurement is less than $0.000003 \times 10^8$ meters/sec or $0.0001\%$.

Since about 1940, nearly all precise measurements of $c$ have been made in the microwave or the short radio wave region of the electromagnetic spectrum. We describe here the "microwave cavity method" used by Essen in England and by Bol and Hansen in the U.S.A. It employs standing electromagnetic waves confined to a cavity rather than traveling waves in free space.

It is possible to convert a section of waveguide such as that of Fig. 39–7 into a resonant cavity by closing it with two metal caps; see Fig. 40–6. The pattern of oscillations in the cavity is closely related to that in the guide and exhibits the same "guide wavelength" $\lambda_g$. The guide wavelength is related to the cavity length $l$ by

$$\lambda_g = \frac{2l}{n} \qquad n = 1, 2, 3, \cdots, \qquad (40-12)$$

which is the same relationship used for acoustic waves in closed pipes; $n$ ( $= 3$ for Fig. 40–6) gives the number of half-waves contained in the cavity.

(a)

(b)

**Fig. 40–6** A resonant cavity constructed from a section of waveguide; compare Fig. 39–7. For simplicity the lines of **E** are not shown in (a) and those of **B** are not shown in (b).

The procedure is to measure $\lambda_g$ for such a cavity, which has been tuned to resonance, and then, using Eq. 39–4,

$$\lambda_g = \frac{\lambda}{\sqrt{1 - \left(\frac{\lambda}{2a}\right)^2}},$$

(40–13)

calculate the free-space wavelength $\lambda$. From the measured resonant frequency, the speed $c$ can be found from $c = \lambda\nu$.

▶ **Example 3.** Essen of the National Physical Laboratory in England made a resonant cavity measurement of the speed of electromagnetic waves. His cavity was made of a circular waveguide rather than a rectangular one; it can be shown that, for the oscillation pattern used by him, the geometrical factor $2a$ in Eq. 40–13 must be replaced by $1.64062R$, where $R$ is the guide radius. The cavity radius was 3.25876 cm; the cavity length was 15.64574 cm and it proved to resonate at $9.498300 \times 10^9$ cycles/sec. At resonance it was determined that there were eight half-waves in the cavity. What value of $c$ results?

From Eq. 40–12, computing only an approximate result,

$$\lambda_g = \frac{2l}{n} = \frac{(2)(15.6 \text{ cm})}{8} = 3.90 \text{ cm}.$$

Substituting into Eq. 40–13, suitably modified for a circular waveguide, yields

$$3.90 \text{ cm} = \frac{\lambda}{\sqrt{1 - \left(\frac{\lambda}{(1.64)(3.26 \text{ cm})}\right)^2}}.$$

Solving this equation for $\lambda$ yields $\lambda = 3.15$ cm. Finally, we have

$$c = \lambda\nu = (3.15 \text{ cm})(9.50 \times 10^9 \text{ cycles/sec}) = 2.99 \times 10^8 \text{ meters/sec}.$$

For practical reasons Essen analyzed his data in a more roundabout way than that given. His final result, based on many measurements under different conditions and carried to much greater accuracy than that illustrated in the above example, was $2.997925 \times 10^8$ meters/sec with an uncertainty of $0.000030 \times 10^8$ meters/sec.     ◀

## 40–4  Moving Sources and Observers

When we say that the speed of sound in dry air at 0°C is 331.7 meters/sec, we imply a reference frame fixed with respect to the air mass. When we say that the speed of light in free space is $2.997925 \times 10^8$ meters/sec, what reference frame is implied? It cannot be the medium through which the light wave travels because, in contrast to sound, no medium is required.

The concept of a wave requiring no medium was abhorrent to the physicists of the nineteenth century, influenced as they then were by a false analogy between light waves and sound waves or other purely mechanical disturbances. These physicists postulated the existence of an *ether*, which was a tenuous substance that filled all space and served as a medium of transmission for light. The ether was required to have a vanishingly small density to account for the fact that it could not be observed by any known means in an evacuated space.

The ether concept, although it proved useful for many years, did not survive the test of experiment. In particular, careful attempts to measure

**Fig. 40-7**   Observers $S$ and $S'$, who are in relative motion, each observe a light pulse $P$. The pulse is emitted from a source, not shown, that is at rest in the $S'$ frame of reference.

the speed of the earth through the ether always gave the result of zero.* Physicists were not willing to believe that the earth was permanently at rest in the ether and that all other bodies in the universe were in motion through it. Other hypotheses about the nature of the propagation of light also proved unsatisfactory for one reason or another.

Einstein in 1905 resolved the difficulty of understanding the propagation of light by making a bold postulate: If a number of observers are moving (at uniform velocity) with respect to each other and to a source of light and if each observer measures the speed of the light emerging from the source, *they will all obtain the same value.* This is the fundamental assumption of Einstein's theory of relativity. It does away with the need for an ether by asserting that the speed of light is the same in *all* reference frames; none is singled out as fundamental. The theory of relativity, derived from this postulate, has been subject to many experimental tests, from which agreement with the predictions of theory has always emerged. These agreements, extending over half a century, lend strong support to Einstein's basic postulate about light propagation.

Figure 40-7 focuses specifically on the fundamental problem of light propagation. A source of light, at rest in reference frame $S'$, emits a light pulse $P$ whose speed $v'$ is measured by an observer at rest in this same frame. From the point of view of an observer in reference frame $S$, frame $S'$ and its associated observer are moving in the positive $x$ direction at speed $u$. Question: What speed $v$ would observer $S$ measure for the light pulse $P$? Einstein's hypothesis asserts that *each* observer would measure the same speed $c$, or that

$$v = v' = c.$$

This hypothesis contradicts the classical law of addition of velocities (see Section 4-6), which asserts that

$$v = v' + u. \tag{40-14}$$

This law, which is so familiar that it seems (incorrectly) to be intuitively true, is in fact based on observations of gross moving objects in the world about us. Even the fastest of these—an earth satellite, say—is moving at

---

* See Section 43-7, which describes the crucial experiment of Michelson and Morley.

a speed that is quite small compared to that of light. The body of experimental evidence that underlies Eq. 40-14 thus represents a severely restricted area of experience, namely, experiences in which $v' \ll c$ and $u \ll c$. If we assume that Eq. 40-14 holds for all particles regardless of speed, we are making a gross extrapolation. Einstein's theory of relativity predicts that this extrapolation is indeed not valid and that Eq. 40-14 is a limiting case of a more general relationship that holds for light pulses and for material particles, whatever their speed, or

$$v = \frac{v' + u}{1 + v'u/c^2}. \tag{40-15}$$

Equation 40-15 is quite indistinguishable from Eq. 40-14 at low speeds, that is, when $v' \ll c$ and $u \ll c$; see Example 4.

If we apply Eq. 40-15 to the case in which the moving object is a light pulse, and if we put $v' = c$, we obtain

$$v = \frac{c + u}{1 + cu/c^2} = c.$$

This is consistent, as it must be, with the fundamental assumption on which the derivation of Eq. 40-15 is based; it shows that *both* observers measure the same speed $c$ for light. Equation 40-14 predicts (incorrectly) that the speed measured by $S$ will be $c + u$. Figure 40-8 shows that the (correct) Eq. 40-15 and the (approximate) Eq. 40-14 cannot be distinguished from each other at speeds that are small compared to the speed of light.

**Fig. 40-8**   The speed of a particle $P$, as seen by observer $S$ in Fig. 40-7, for the special case of $v' = u$. All speeds are expressed as a ratio to $c$, the speed of light. The vertical arrow corresponds to $5 \times 10^7$ miles/hr.

▶ **Example 4.**  Suppose that $v' = u = 25,000$ miles/hr.  What per cent error is made in using Eq. 40–14 rather than Eq. 40–15 to calculate $v$?  The speed of light is $6.7 \times 10^8$ miles/hr.

Equation 40–14 gives

$$v = v' + u = 25,000 \text{ miles/hr} + 25,000 \text{ miles/hr} = 50,000 \text{ miles/hr}.$$

Equation 40–15 gives

$$v = \frac{v' + u}{1 + v'u/c^2}$$

$$= \frac{25,000 \text{ miles/hr} + 25,000 \text{ miles/hr}}{1 + \dfrac{(25,000 \text{ miles/hr})^2}{(6.7 \times 10^8 \text{ miles/hr})^2}}$$

$$= \frac{50,000 \text{ miles/hr}}{1.0000000014}.$$

Even at 25,000 miles/hr the error in Eq. 40–14 is immeasurably small.

**Example 5.**  Two electrons are ejected in opposite directions from radioactive atoms in a sample of radioactive material.  Let each electron have a speed, as measured by a laboratory observer, of $0.6c$ (this corresponds to a kinetic energy of 130 kev).  What is the speed of one electron as seen from the other?

Equation 40–14 gives

$$v = v' + u = 0.6c + 0.6c = 1.2c.$$

Equation 40–15 gives

$$v = \frac{v' + u}{1 + v'u/c^2} = \frac{0.6c + 0.6c}{1 + (0.6c)^2/c^2} = 0.88c.$$

This example shows that for speeds that are comparable to $c$, Eqs. 40–14 and 40–15 yield rather different results.  A wealth of indirect experimental evidence points to the latter result as being correct.     ◀

## 40–5  Doppler Effect

We have seen that the same speed is measured for light no matter what the relative speeds of the light source and the observer are.  The measured frequency and wavelength will change, but always in such a way that their product, which is the velocity of light, remains constant.  Such frequency shifts are called *Doppler shifts*, after Johann Doppler (1803–1853), who first predicted them.

In Section 20–7 we showed that if a source of *sound* is moving away from an observer at a speed $u$, the frequency heard by the observer (see Eq. 20–10, which has been rearranged with $u$ substituted for $v_s$) is

$$\nu' = \nu \, \frac{1}{1 + u/v} \cdot \qquad \left\{ \begin{array}{l} 1. \text{ sound wave} \\ 2. \text{ observer fixed in medium} \\ 3. \text{ source receding from observer} \end{array} \right. \qquad (40\text{--}16)$$

In this equation $\nu$ is the frequency heard when the source is at rest and $v$ is the speed of sound.

If the source is at rest in the transmitting medium but the observer is moving away from the source at speed $u$, the observed frequency (see Eq. 20–9b, in which $u$ has been substituted for $v_0$) is

$$\nu' = \nu\left(1 - \frac{u}{v}\right). \quad \begin{cases} 1.\ \text{sound wave} \\ 2.\ \text{source fixed in medium} \\ 3.\ \text{observer receding from source} \end{cases} \quad (40\text{-}17)$$

Even if the relative separation speeds $u$ of the source and the observer are the same, the frequencies predicted by Eqs. 40–16 and 40–17 are different. This is not surprising, because a sound source moving through a medium in which the observer is at rest is physically different from an observer moving through that medium with the source at rest, as comparison of Figs. 20–10 and 20–11 shows.

We might be tempted to apply Eqs. 40–16 and 40–17 to light, substituting $c$, the speed of light, for $v$, the speed of sound. For light, as contrasted with sound, however, it has proved impossible to identify a medium of transmission relative to which the source and the observer are moving. This means that "source receding from observer" and "observer receding from source" are physically identical situations and must exhibit *exactly the same* Doppler frequency. As applied to light, either Eq. 40–16 or Eq. 40–17 or both must be incorrect. The Doppler frequency predicted by the theory of relativity is, in fact,

$$\nu' = \nu\,\frac{1 - u/c}{\sqrt{1 - (u/c)^2}}. \quad \begin{cases} 1.\ \text{light wave} \\ 2.\ \text{source and observer} \\ \quad\ \text{separating} \end{cases} \quad (40\text{-}18)$$

In all three of the foregoing equations we obtain the appropriate relations for the source and the observer *approaching* each other if we replace $u$ by $-u$.

Equations 40–16, 40–17, and 40–18 are not so different as they seem if the ratio $u/c$ is small enough. This was made clear in Example 3, Chapter 20, for the first two of these equations. Let us expand Eqs. 40–16, 40–17 and 40–18 by the binomial theorem, as in the example referred to. The equations then become, substituting $c$ for $v$,

$$\nu' = \nu\left[1 - \frac{u}{c} + \left(\frac{u}{c}\right)^2 + \cdots\right], \quad (40\text{-}16a)$$

$$\nu' = \nu\left(1 - \frac{u}{c}\right), \quad (40\text{-}17a)$$

and

$$\nu' = \nu\left[1 - \frac{u}{c} + \frac{1}{2}\left(\frac{u}{c}\right)^2 + \cdots\right]. \quad (40\text{-}18a)$$

The ratio $u/c$ for all available monochromatic light sources, even those of atomic dimensions, is small. This means that successive terms in these equations become small rapidly and, depending on the accuracy required, only a limited number of terms need be retained.

Under nearly all circumstances the differences among these three equations are not important. Nevertheless, it is of extreme interest to carry out at least one experiment precisely enough to serve as a test of Eq. 40–18a and thus, in part, of the theory of relativity.

H. E. Ives and G. R. Stilwell carried out such a precision experiment in 1938. They sent a beam of hydrogen atoms, generated in a gas discharge, down a tube at speed $u$, as in Fig. 40–9a. They could observe light emitted by these atoms in a direction opposite to **u** (atom 1, for example) using a mirror, and also in a direction parallel to **u** (atom 2, for example). With a precision spectrograph, they could photograph a particular characteristic spectrum line in this light, obtaining, on a frequency scale, the lines marked $v_1'$ and $v_2'$ in Fig. 40–9b. It is also possible to photograph, on the same photographic plate, a line corresponding to light emitted from *resting* atoms; such a line appears as $v$ in Fig. 40–9b. A fundamental measured quantity in this experiment is $\Delta v/v$, defined from

$$\frac{\Delta v}{v} = \frac{\Delta v_2 - \Delta v_1}{v},\qquad(40\text{–}19)$$

(see Fig. 40–9b). It measures the extent to which the frequency of the light from resting atoms fails to lie halfway between the frequencies $v_1'$ and $v_2'$. Table 40–2 shows that the measured results agree with the formula predicted by the theory of relativity (Eq. 40–18a) and not with the classical formula borrowed from the theory of sound propagation in a material medium (Eq. 40–16a).

Ives and Stilwell did not present their experimental results as evidence for the support of Einstein's theory of relativity but rather gave them an alternative theoretical explanation. Modern observers, looking not only at their excellent experiment but at the whole range of experimental evidence, now give the Ives-Stilwell experiment the interpretation we have described for it above.

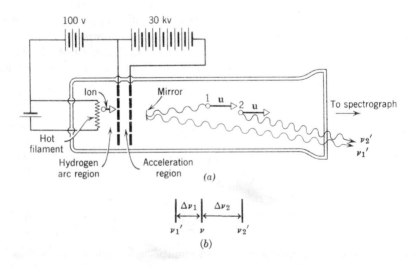

**Fig. 40–9**  The Ives-Stilwell experiment.

**Table 40–2**

THE IVES-STILWELL EXPERIMENT *

| $\frac{\Delta \nu}{\nu}$, $10^{-5}$ | Speed of moving atoms ($= u$), $10^6$ meters/sec | | | |
|---|---|---|---|---|
| | 0.865 | 1.01 | 1.15 | 1.33 |
| Theoretical value according to classical theory (Eq. 40–16a) | 1.67 | 2.26 | 2.90 | 3.94 |
| Theoretical value according to the theory of relativity (Eq. 40–18a) | 0.835 | 1.13 | 1.45 | 1.97 |
| Experimental value | 0.762 | 1.1 | 1.42 | 1.9 |

* See Eq. 40–19; the table shows only part of the data taken by Ives and Stilwell.

The Doppler effect for light finds many applications in astronomy, where it is used to determine the speeds at which luminous heavenly bodies are moving toward us or receding from us. Such Doppler shifts measure only the radial or line-of-sight components of the relative velocity. All galaxies * for which such measurements have been made (Fig. 40–10) appear to be receding from us, the recession velocity being greater for the more distant galaxies; these observations are the basis of the expanding-universe concept.

*(a)*

*(b)*

**Fig. 40–10** *(a)* The central spot is a nebula in the constellation Corona Borealis; it is 130,000,000 light years distant. *(b)* The central streak shows the distribution in wavelength of the light emitted from this nebula. The two vertical dark bands show the presence of calcium. The horizontal arrow shows that these calcium lines occur at longer wavelengths than those for terrestrial light sources containing calcium, the length of the arrow representing the wavelength shift. Measurement of this shift shows that the galaxy is receding from us at 13,400 miles/sec. The lines above and below the central streak represent light from a terrestrial source, used to establish a wavelength scale. (Courtesy Mount Wilson and Mount Palomar Observatories.)

* See "The Red-Shift," Allen R. Sandage, *Scientific American*, p. 171, September 1956.

▶ **Example 6.** Certain characteristic wavelengths in the light from a galaxy in the constellation Virgo are observed to be increased in wavelength, as compared with terrestrial sources, by about 0.4%. What is the radial speed of this galaxy with respect to the earth? Is it approaching or receding?

If $\lambda$ is the wavelength for a terrestrial source, then

$$\lambda' = 1.004\lambda.$$

Since we must have $\lambda'\nu' = \lambda\nu = c$, we can write this as

$$\nu' = 0.996\nu.$$

This frequency shift is so small that, in calculating the source velocity, it makes no practical difference whether we use Eq. 40–16, 40–17, or 40–18. Using Eq. 40–17 we obtain

$$\nu' = 0.996\nu = \nu\left(1 - \frac{u}{c}\right).$$

Solving yields $u/c = 0.004$, or $u = (0.004)(3 \times 10^8$ meters/sec$) = 1.2 \times 10^6$ meters/ sec or $2.7 \times 10^6$ miles/hr. The galaxy is *receding;* had $u$ turned out to be negative, the galaxy would have been moving toward us. ◀

## QUESTIONS

1. How might an eye-sensitivity curve like that of Fig. 40–2 be measured?
2. Why are danger signals in red, when the eye is most sensitive to yellow-green?
3. Comment on this definition of the limits of the spectrum of visible light given by a physiologist: "The limits of the visible spectrum occur when the eye is no better adapted than any other organ of the body to serve as a detector."
4. How can an object absorb light energy without absorbing momentum?
5. A searchlight sends out a parallel beam of light. Does the searchlight experience any force associated with the emission of light?
6. Name two historic experiments, in addition to the radiation pressure measurements of Nichols and Hull, in which a torsion balance was used. Both are described in this book, one in Part 1 and one in Part 2.
7. Show that for complete absorption of a parallel beam of light the radiation pressure on the absorbing object is given by $p = S/c$, where $S$ is the magnitude of the Poynting vector and $c$ is the speed of light in free space.
8. How could Galileo test experimentally that reaction times were an overwhelming source of error in his attempt to measure the speed of light, described on p. 999?
9. It has been suggested that the velocity of light may change slightly in value as time goes on. Can you find any evidence for this in Table 40–1?
10. A friend asserts that Einstein's postulate (that the speed of light is not affected by the uniform motion of the source or the observer) must be discarded because it violates "common sense." How would you answer him?
11. In a vacuum, does the speed of light depend on (a) the wavelength, (b) the frequency, (c) the intensity, (d) the speed of the source, or (e) the speed of the observer?
12. Can a galaxy be so distant that its recession speed equals $c$? If so, how can we see the galaxy? That is, will its light ever reach us?

# PROBLEMS

1. (a) At what wavelengths does the eye sensitivity have half its maximum value? (b) What are the frequency and the period of the light for which the eye is most sensitive?

2. It has been proposed that a spaceship might propel itself in the solar system by radiation pressure, using a large sail made of aluminum foil. How large must the sail be if the radiation force is to be equal in magnitude to the sun's gravitational attraction? Assume that the mass of the *ship* + *sail* is 100 slugs, that the sail is perfectly reflecting, and that the sail is oriented at right angles to the sun's rays. The sun's mass is $1.97 \times 10^{30}$ kg.

3. Radiation from the sun striking the earth has an intensity of 1400 watts/meter². Assuming that the earth behaves like a flat disk at right angles to the sun's rays and that all the incident energy is absorbed, calculate the force on the earth due to radiation pressure. Compare it with the force due to the sun's gravitational attraction.

4. Prove, for a plane wave at normal incidence on a plane surface, that the radiation pressure on the surface is equal to the energy density in the beam outside the surface. This relation holds no matter what fraction of the incident energy is reflected.

5. Prove, for a stream of bullets striking a plane surface at right angles, that the "pressure" is *twice* the (kinetic) energy density in the stream above the surface; assume that the bullets are completely "absorbed" by the surface. Contrast this with the behavior of light (Problem 4).

6. A small spaceship whose mass, with occupant, is 100 slugs is drifting in outer space, where no gravitational field exists. If it shines a searchlight, which radiates $10^4$ watts, into space, what speed would the ship attain in one day because of the reaction force associated with the momentum carried away by the light beam?

7. What is the radiation pressure 1.0 meter away from a 500-watt light bulb? Assume that the surface on which the pressure is exerted faces the bulb and is perfectly absorbing and that the bulb radiates uniformly in all directions.

8. The uncertainty of the distance to the moon, as measured by the reflection of radar waves from it, is about 0.5 mile. Assuming that this uncertainty is associated only with the measurement of the elapsed time, what uncertainty in this time is implied?

9. Roemer's method for measuring the speed of light consisted in observing the apparent times of revolution of one of the moons of Jupiter. The true period of revolution is 42.5 hr. (a) Taking into account the finite speed of light, how would you expect the apparent time of revolution to alter as the earth moves in its orbit from point $x$ to point $y$ in Fig. 40–11? (b) What observations would be needed to compute the speed of light? Neglect the motion of Jupiter in its orbit. Figure 40–11 is not drawn to scale.

**Fig. 40–11**

10. Suppose that light is timed over a 1-mile base line and its speed is measured to the accuracy quoted on p. 1002. How large an error in the length of the base line could be tolerated, assuming other sources of error to be negligible?

11. For what value of $u/c$ does Eq. 40–17 differ from Eq. 40–18 by 1%?

12. The "red shift" of radiation from a distant nebula consists of the light ($H_\gamma$), known to have a wavelength of $4340 \times 10^{-8}$ cm when observed in the laboratory, appearing to have a wavelength of $6562 \times 10^{-8}$ cm. What is the speed of the nebula in the line of sight relative to the earth? (b) Is it approaching or receding?

13. The difference in wavelength between an incident microwave beam and one reflected from an approaching or receding car is used to determine automobile speeds on the highway. (a) Show that if $v$ is the speed of the car and $\nu$ the frequency of the incident beam, the change of frequency is approximately $2v\nu/c$, where $c$ is the speed of the electromagnetic radiation. (b) For microwaves of frequency 2450 megacycles/sec, what is the change of frequency per mile/hr of speed?

14. Show that, for slow speeds, the Doppler shift can be written in the approximate form

$$\frac{\Delta\lambda}{\lambda} = \frac{u}{c},$$

where $\Delta\lambda$ is the change in wavelength.

15. The period of rotation of the sun at its equator is 24.7 days; its radius is $7.0 \times 10^8$ meters. What Doppler wavelength shifts are expected for characteristic wavelengths in the vicinity of 5500 A emitted from the edge of the sun's disk?

16. An earth satellite, transmitting on a frequency of $40 \times 10^6$ cycles/sec (exactly), passes directly over a radio receiving station at an altitude of 250 miles and at a speed of 18,000 miles/hr. Plot the change in frequency, attributable to the Doppler effect, as a function of time, counting $t = 0$ as the instant the satellite is over the station. (Hint: The speed $u$ in the Doppler formula is not the actual velocity of the satellite but its component in the direction of the station. Use the nonrelativistic formula (Eq. 40–16a) and neglect the curvature of the earth and of the satellite orbit.)

17. A rocketship is receding from the earth at a speed of $0.2c$. A light in the rocketship appears blue to passengers on the ship. What color would it appear to be to an observer on the earth? See Fig. 40–2.

18. In the experiment of Ives and Stilwell the speed $u$ of the hydrogen atoms in a particular run was $8.61 \times 10^5$ meters/sec. Calculate $\Delta\nu_1$, $\Delta\nu_2$, and $\Delta\nu/\nu$, on the assumptions that (a) Eq. 40–18a is correct and (b) that Eq. 40–16a is correct; compare your results with those given in Table 40–2 for this speed. Retain the first three terms only in Eqs. 40–18a and 40–16a.

# Reflection and Refraction—
# Plane Waves
# and Plane Surfaces

## CHAPTER 41

### 41–1 Reflection and Refraction

In Fig. 41–1a a light beam falling on a water surface is both reflected from the surface and bent (that is, *refracted*) as it enters the water. The incident beam is represented in Fig. 41–1b by a single line, the *incident ray*, parallel to the direction of propagation. The incident beam is assumed in Fig. 41–1b to be a *plane wave*, the wavefronts being normal to the incident ray. The reflected and refracted beams are also represented by rays. The angles of *incidence* ($\theta_1$), of *reflection* ($\theta_1'$), and of *refraction* ($\theta_2$) are measured between the normal to the surface and the appropriate ray, as shown in the figure.

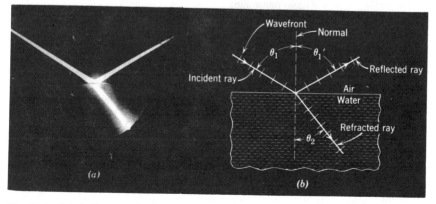

**Fig. 41–1**  (a) A photograph showing reflection and refraction at an air-water interface. (b) A representation using rays.

The laws governing reflection and refraction can easily be found from experiment:

1. The reflected and the refracted rays lie in the plane formed by the incident ray and the normal to the surface at the point of incidence, that is, the plane of Fig. 41–1b.

2. For reflection:

$$\theta_1' = \theta_1. \tag{41-1}$$

3. For refraction:

$$\frac{\sin \theta_1}{\sin \theta_2} = n_{21}, \tag{41-2}$$

where $n_{21}$ is a constant called the *index of refraction* of medium 2 with respect to medium 1. Table 41–1 shows the indices of refraction for some common

### Table 41–1

SOME INDICES OF REFRACTION *

(For $\lambda = 5890$ A)

| Medium | Index of Refraction |
|---|---|
| Water | 1.33 |
| Ethyl alcohol | 1.36 |
| Carbon bisulfide | 1.63 |
| Air (1 atm and 20°C) | 1.0003 |
| Methylene iodide | 1.74 |
| Fused quartz | 1.46 |
| Glass, crown | 1.52 |
| Glass, dense flint | 1.66 |
| Sodium chloride | 1.53 |
| Polyethylene | 1.50–1.54 |
| Fluorite | 1.43 |

* Measured with respect to a vacuum. The index with respect to air (except, of course, the index of air itself—see item 4) will be negligibly different in most cases.

substances with respect to a vacuum for a wavelength of 5890 A (sodium light).

The index of refraction of one medium with respect to another generally varies with wavelength, as Fig. 41–2 shows. Because of this fact refraction, unlike reflection, can be used to analyze a beam of light into its component wavelengths. Figure 41–3, taken from Newton's *Opticks*, shows how Newton, using glass prism $ABC$, formed a spectrum of sunlight entering his window through a small hole at $F$.

**Fig. 41-2** The index of refraction of fused quartz at 18°C, with respect to a vacuum.

The law of reflection was known to Euclid. That of refraction was discovered experimentally by Willebrod Snell (1591–1626) and deduced from the early corpuscular theory of light by René Descartes (1596–1650). The law of refraction is known as Snell's law or (in France) as Descartes' law.

The laws of reflection and refraction can be derived from Maxwell's equations, which means that these laws should hold for all regions of the electromagnetic spectrum. Figure 41–4a shows an experimental setup for investigating the reflection of microwaves from a large metal sheet. Figure 41–4b shows the reading of the detector as a function of the angular position of the mirror. The existence of a reflected beam at the proper angle confirms the law of reflection for microwaves. There is ample experimental evidence that Eqs. 41–1 and 41–2 correctly describe the behavior of reflected and refracted beams in all parts of the electromagnetic spectrum.

It is common knowledge that a polished steel surface will form a well-defined reflected beam if an incident beam falls on it, but a sheet of paper will reflect light more or less in all directions (*diffuse reflection*). It is largely by diffuse reflection that we see nonluminous objects around us. The difference between diffuse and *specular* (that is, mirror-like) reflection is a matter of surface roughness; a reflected beam will

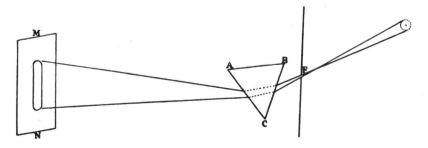

**Fig. 41-3** Sunlight from a hole $F$ in a screen is refracted by prism $ABC$, forming a spectrum on screen $MN$; from Newton's *Opticks* (1704).

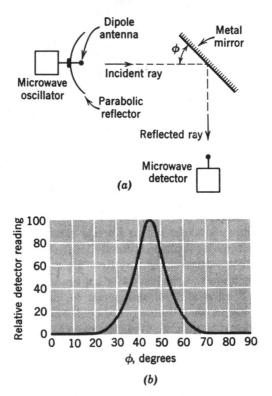

**Fig. 41–4**  (a) An apparatus to test the law of reflection for microwaves.  (b) A reflected beam (for $\lambda \cong 10$ cm) appears for the expected orientation of the mirror.

be formed only if the average depth of the surface irregularities of the reflector is substantially less than the wavelength of the incident light. This criterion of surface roughness has different implications in different regions of the electromagnetic spectrum. The bottom of a cast-iron skillet for example is a good reflector for microwaves of wavelength 0.5 cm but it is not a good reflector for visible light (that is, one cannot shave by it).

A second requirement for the existence of a reflected beam is that the transverse dimensions of the reflector must be substantially larger than the wavelength of the incident beam. If a beam of visible light falls on a polished metal disk the size of a dime, a reflected beam will be formed. However, if the same disk is placed in a beam of short radio waves with, say, $\lambda = 1.0$ meter, radiation will be scattered in all directions from it, and no well-defined unidirectional beam will appear. We investigate this phenomenon of *diffraction* in Chapter 44. The requirements that surfaces be "smooth" and "large" also apply to the formation of refracted beams. If these two requirements are not met the description of reflection and refraction in terms of rays, whose behavior is governed by Eqs. 41–1 and 41–2, is not valid.

▶ **Example 1.**  Figure 41–5 shows an incident ray $i$ striking a plane mirror $MM'$ at angle of incidence $\theta$. Trace this ray.

The reflected ray makes an angle $\theta$ with the normal at $b$ and falls as an incident ray on mirror $M'M''$. Its angle of incidence $\theta'$ on this mirror is $\pi/2 - \theta$. A second reflected ray $r'$ makes an angle $\theta'$ with the normal erected at $b'$. Rays $i$ and $r'$ are antiparallel for any value of $\theta$. To see this, note that

$$\phi = \pi - 2\theta' = \pi - 2\left(\frac{\pi}{2} - \theta\right) = 2\theta.$$

Two lines are parallel if their opposite interior angles for an intersecting line ($\phi$ and $2\theta$) are equal.

Repeat the problem if the angle between the mirrors is 120° rather than 90°.

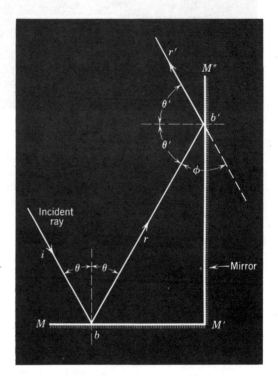

**Fig. 41–5**    Example 1.

**Example 2.**  An incident ray in air falls on the plane surface of a block of quartz and makes an angle of 30° with the normal. This beam contains two wavelengths, 4000 and 5000 A. The indices of refraction for quartz with respect to air ($n_{qa}$) at these wavelengths are 1.4702 and 1.4624, respectively. What is the angle between the two refracted beams?

From Eq. 41–2 we have, for the 4000-A beam,

$$\sin\theta_1 = n_{qa}\sin\theta_2,$$

or

$$\sin 30° = (1.4702)\sin\theta_2,$$

which leads to

$$\theta_2 = 19.88°.$$

For the 5000-A beam we have

$$\sin 30° = (1.4624)\sin\theta_2',$$

or

$$\theta_2' = 19.99°.$$

The angle $\Delta\theta$ between the beams is 0.11°, the shorter wavelength component being bent through the larger angle, that is, having the smaller angle of refraction.

**Fig. 41–6**   Example 3.

**Example 3.**   An incident ray falls on one face of a glass prism in air as in Fig. 41–6. The angle $\theta$ is so chosen that the emerging ray also makes an angle $\theta$ with the normal to the other face. Derive an expression for the index of refraction of the prism material with respect to air.

Note that $\angle\ abc = \alpha$, the two angles having their sides mutually perpendicular. Therefore

$$\alpha = \tfrac{1}{2}\phi. \qquad (41\text{--}3)$$

The *deviation angle* $\psi$ is the sum of the two opposite interior angles in triangle *aed*, or

$$\psi = 2(\theta - \alpha).$$

Substituting $\tfrac{1}{2}\phi$ for $\alpha$ and solving for $\theta$ yields

$$\theta = \tfrac{1}{2}(\psi + \phi). \qquad (41\text{--}4)$$

At point $a$, $\theta$ is the angle of incidence and $\alpha$ the angle of refraction. The law of refraction (see Eq. 41–2) is

$$\sin \theta = n_{ga} \sin \alpha,$$

in which $n_{ga}$ is the index of refraction of the glass with respect to air.

From Eqs. 41–3 and 41–4 this yields

$$\sin \frac{\psi + \phi}{2} = n_{ga} \sin \frac{\phi}{2}$$

or

$$n_{ga} = \frac{\sin \tfrac{1}{2}(\psi + \phi)}{\sin (\phi/2)},$$

which is the desired relation. This equation holds only for $\theta$ so chosen that the light ray passes symmetrically through the prism. For this condition the deviation angle $\psi$ is a minimum; if $\theta$ is either increased or decreased, a larger deviation will be produced.   ◄

### 41–2   Huygens' Principle

A theory of light would not be accepted if it were not able to predict the well-established laws of reflection and refraction. These laws can be derived from Maxwell's equations, but mathematical complexity prevents us from doing so.  Fortunately, these and several other laws of optics can be derived on the basis of a simpler but less comprehensive theory of light, put forward by the Dutch physicist Christian Huygens in 1678.  This theory simply assumes that light is a wave rather than, say, a stream of particles.  It says nothing about the nature of the wave and, in particular—since Maxwell's theory of electromagnetism appeared only after the lapse of a century— gives no hint of the electromagnetic character of light.  Huygens did not know whether light was a transverse wave or a longitudinal one; he did not know the wavelengths of visible light; he had little knowledge of the speed of light.  Nevertheless, his theory was a useful guide to experiment for many years and remains useful today for pedagogic and certain other practical purposes.  We must not expect it to yield the same wealth of detailed information that Maxwell's more complete electromagnetic theory does.

Huygens' theory is based on a geometrical construction, called *Huygens' principle*, that allows us to tell where a given wavefront will be at any time in the future if we know its present position; it is: *All points on a wavefront can be considered as point sources for the production of spherical secondary wavelets.  After a time t the new position of the wavefront will be the surface of tangency to these secondary wavelets.*

We illustrate this by a trivial example: Given a wavefront (*ab* in Fig. 41–7) in a plane wave in free space, where will the wavefront be a time *t* later? Following Huygens' principle, we let several points on this plane (see dots) serve as centers for secondary spherical wavelets.  In a time *t* the radius of these spherical waves is *ct*, where *c* is the speed of light in free space.  The plane of tangency to these spheres at time *t* is represented by *de*.  As we

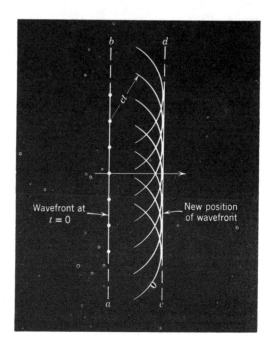

**Fig. 41–7**  The propagation of a plane wave in free space is described by the Huygens construction.  Note that the ray (horizontal arrow) representing the wave is perpendicular to the wavefronts.

Wavefront at
$t = 0$

New position
of wavefront

expect, it is parallel to plane $ab$ and a perpendicular distance $ct$ from it. Thus plane wavefronts are propagated as planes and with speed $c$. Note that the Huygens method involves a three-dimensional construction and that Fig. 41–7 is the intersection of this construction with the plane of the page.

We might expect that, contrary to observation, a wave should be radiated backward as well as forward from the dots in Fig. 41–7. This result is avoided by assuming that the *intensity* of the spherical wavelets is not uniform in all directions but varies continuously from a maximum in the forward direction to a minimum of zero in the back direction. This is suggested by the shading of the circular arcs in Fig. 41–7. Huygens' method can be applied quantitatively to *all* wave phenomena; see Problem 1. The method was put on a firm mathematical footing by Augustin Fresnel (1788–1827).

### 41–3　Huygens' Principle and the Law of Reflection

Figure 41–8$a$ shows three wavefronts in a plane wave falling on mirror $MM'$. For convenience they are chosen to be one wavelength apart. Note that $\theta_1$, the angle between the wavefronts and the mirror, is the same as the angle between the incident ray and the normal to the mirror. In other

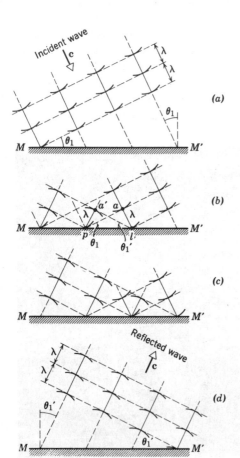

**Fig. 41–8** The reflection of a plane wave as described by the Huygens construction.

words, $\theta_1$ is the *angle of incidence*. The three wavefronts are related to each other by the Huygens construction, as in Fig. 41-7.

In Fig. 41-8b a Huygens wavelet centered on point $a$ will expand to include point $l$ after a time $\lambda/c$. Light from point $p$ in this same wavefront cannot move beyond the mirror but must expand upward as a spherical Huygens wavelet. Setting a compass to radius $\lambda$ and swinging an arc about $p$ provides a semicircle to which the reflected wavefront must be tangent. Since point $l$ must lie on the new wavefront, this tangent must pass through $l$. Note that the angle $\theta_1'$ between the wavefront and the mirror is the same as the angle between the reflected ray and the normal to the mirror. In other words, $\theta_1'$ is the *angle of reflection*.

Consider right triangles $alp$ and $a'lp$. They have side $lp$ in common and side $al$ $(= \lambda)$ is equal to side $a'p$. The two right triangles are thus congruent and we may conclude that

$$\theta_1 = \theta_1',$$

as required by the law of reflection. If the student recalls that the Huygens construction is three-dimensional and that the arcs shown represent segments of spherical surfaces, he will be able to convince himself that the reflected ray lies in the plane formed by the incident ray and the normal to the mirror, that is, the plane of Fig. 41-8. This is also a requirement of the law of reflection; see p. 1014.

### 41-4  Huygens' Principle and the Law of Refraction

Figure 41-9 shows four stages in the refraction of three successive wavefronts in a plane wave falling on an interface between air (medium 1) and glass (medium 2). For convenience, we assume that the incident wavefronts are separated by $\lambda_1$, the wavelength as measured in medium 1. Let the speed of light in air be $v_1$ and that in glass be $v_2$. We assume that

$$v_2 < v_1. \tag{41-5}$$

This assumption about the speeds is vital to the derivation that follows. It was not possible to test it experimentally because of technical difficulties until 1850, when the assumption was shown by Foucault to be correct.

The wavefronts in Fig. 41-9a are related to each other by the Huygens construction of Fig. 41-7. As in Fig. 41-8, $\theta_1$ is the angle of incidence. In Fig. 41-9b consider the time $(= \lambda_1/v_1)$ during which a Huygens wavelet from point $e$ moves to include point $c$. Light from point $h$, traveling through glass at a reduced speed (recall the assumption of Eq. 41-5) will move a shorter distance

$$\lambda_2 = \lambda_1 \frac{v_2}{v_1} \tag{41-6}$$

during this time. The refracted wavefront must be tangent to an arc of this radius centered on $h$. Since $c$ lies on the new wavefront, the tangent must pass through this point, as shown. Note that $\theta_2$, the angle between the refracted wavefront and the air-glass interface, is the same as the angle

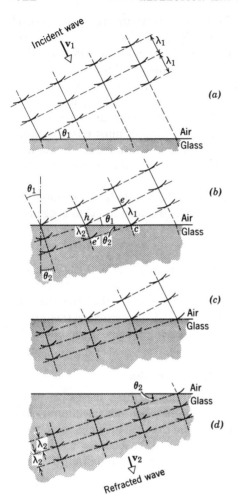

**Fig. 41–9**  The refraction of a plane wave as described by the Huygens construction; the reflected wave is omitted for simplicity.  Note the change in wavelength on refraction.

between the refracted ray and the normal to this interface.  In other words, $\theta_2$ is the *angle of refraction*.  Note, too, that the wavelength in glass ($\lambda_2$) is less than the wavelength in air ($\lambda_1$).

For the right triangles $hce$ and $hce'$ we may write

$$\sin \theta_1 = \frac{\lambda_1}{hc} \qquad \text{(for } hce\text{)}$$

and

$$\sin \theta_2 = \frac{\lambda_2}{hc} \qquad \text{(for } hce'\text{)}.$$

Dividing and using Eq. 41–6 yields

$$\frac{\sin \theta_1}{\sin \theta_2} = \frac{\lambda_1}{\lambda_2} = \frac{v_1}{v_2} = \text{a constant.} \qquad (41\text{–}7)$$

The law of refraction, as stated in Eq. 41–2, is

$$\frac{\sin \theta_1}{\sin \theta_2} = n_{21}, \tag{41–2}$$

so that $n_{21}$ is now revealed as the ratio of the speeds of light in the two media, or

$$n_{21} = \frac{v_1}{v_2}. \tag{41–8}$$

We may rewrite Eq. 41–7 as

$$\left(\frac{c}{v_1}\right) \sin \theta_1 = \left(\frac{c}{v_2}\right) \sin \theta_2, \tag{41–9}$$

in which $c$ is the speed of light in free space. The quantities $(c/v_1)$ and $(c/v_2)$ (see Eq. 41–8) are the indices of refraction of medium 1 and of medium 2, respectively, with respect to a vacuum. Introducing the symbols $n_1$ and $n_2$ for these quantities allows us to write the law of refraction as

$$n_1 \sin \theta_1 = n_2 \sin \theta_2. \tag{41–10}$$

If we assume that the medium above the glass in Fig. 41–9 is a vacuum rather than air, the speed $v_1$ becomes $c$ and the wavelength, called $\lambda_1$ in Fig. 41–9, assumes a value $\lambda$ that is characteristic of the wave in free space. Equation 41–6 may thus be written

$$\lambda_2 = \lambda \frac{v_2}{c} = \frac{\lambda}{n_2}. \tag{41–11}$$

This shows specifically that the wavelength of light in a material medium is less than the wavelength of the same wave in a vacuum. Figure 41–9 shows clearly the difference in wavelength in the two media.

The application of Huygens' principle to refraction requires that if a light ray is bent toward the normal in passing from air to an optically dense medium then the speed of light in that optically dense medium (glass, say) must be *less* than that in air; see Eq. 41–5. This requirement holds for all wave theories of light. For the early particle theory of light put forward by Newton, refraction can be explained only if the speed of light in the medium in which light is bent toward the normal (the optically dense medium) is *greater* than that in air. The dense medium was thought to exert attractive forces on the light "corpuscles" as they neared the surface, speeding them up and changing their direction to cause them to make a smaller angle with the normal. Figure 41–10 shows a figure from a 1637 work of René Descartes, in which he makes an analogy between the refraction of light and the motion of a tennis ball on entering a medium in which it moves more slowly.

An experimental comparison of the speed of light in water and in air is decisive, therefore, between the wave and corpuscular theories of light. Such a measurement was first carried out by Foucault in 1850; he showed conclusively that *light travels more slowly in water than in air*, thus ruling out the corpuscular theory of Newton.

**Fig. 41–10**  According to the early (incorrect) corpuscular theory of light, $ABI$ is the path of a ray on entering a medium in which its speed is *less*. The (correct) wave theory predicts that for the ray shown the speed in the lower medium (below $BE$) must be *greater;* from Descartes' *La Dioptrique* (1637).

### 41-5  Total Internal Reflection

Let light rays in an optically dense medium (glass, say) fall on a surface on the other side of which is a less optically dense medium (air, say); see Fig. 41–11.  As the angle of incidence $\theta$ is increased, a situation is reached (see ray $e$) at which the refracted ray points along the surface, the angle of refraction being 90°.  For angles of incidence larger than this *critical angle* $\theta_c$ no refracted ray exists, giving rise to a phenomenon called *total internal reflection.*

The critical angle is found by putting $\theta_2 = 90°$ in the law of refraction (see Eq. 41–10):

$$n_1 \sin \theta_c = n_2 \sin 90°,$$

or
$$\sin \theta_c = \frac{n_2}{n_1}. \qquad (41\text{–}12)$$

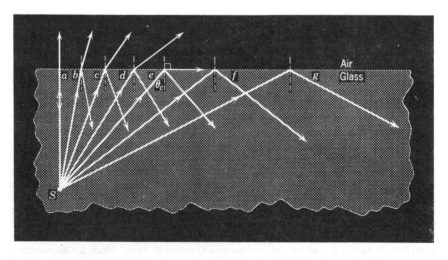

**Fig. 41–11**  Showing the total internal reflection of light from a source $S$; the *critical angle* is $\theta_c$.

For glass and air $\sin \theta_c = (1.00/1.50) = 0.667$, which yields $\theta_c = 41.8°$. Total internal reflection does not occur when light originates in the medium of lower index of refraction.

Light can be "piped" from one point to another with little loss by allowing it to enter one end of a rod of transparent plastic. The light will undergo total internal

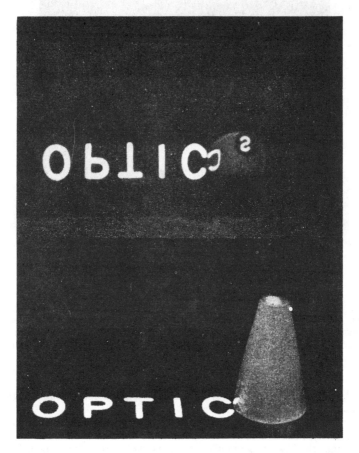

**Fig. 41-12**   A bundle of tapered fibers (*below*) is placed over the letter $S$. Above, with the aid of a mirror, we see that the image, reduced in size, is transmitted to the top of the bundle by total internal reflection in the individual fibers. (Courtesy Dr. N. S. Kapany, Optics Technology, Inc.)

reflection at the boundary of the rod and will follow its contour, emerging at its far end. Images may be transferred from one location to another, using a bundle of fine glass fibers, each fiber transmitting a small fraction of the image.* Such bundles can be made in which a (flexible) seven-foot length delivers half the energy entering it at the far end. In a fiber in such a bundle a typical ray may undergo 48,000 reflections. Most of the energy loss is due to absorption within the glass, reflection being almost

---

* See "Fiber Optics," by N. S. Kapany, *Scientific American*, November 1960.

**Fig. 41–13**   A photomicrograph of light emerging from the end of a bundle of fibers. The fiber diameters approach the wavelength of light so that each fiber acts like an "optical waveguide." We have here convincing visual evidence that light is an electromagnetic wave. (Courtesy of Dr. N. S. Kapany, Optics Technology, Inc.)

truly total. Measurable amounts of light can be transmitted through single fibers 150 feet long.

Fiber optics techniques make possible many useful optical devices for transmitting and transforming luminous images. Figure 41–12 shows a short fiber bundle constructed so that the fibers taper in diameter along its length. The wide end is shown placed over the letter $S$ in the printed word "OPTICS." We see, with the aid of a mirror placed above the bundle, that a letter $S$, reduced in size, has been transmitted by total internal reflection through the bundle to its narrow end.

Figure 41–13 is an enlarged view of a cross section of such a fiber bundle in which the diameters of the individual fibers are made so small that they are of the order of magnitude of the wavelength of light. This condition violates the spirit of our assumption of p. 1016, namely that the transverse dimensions of reflecting and refracting surfaces would be large compared to the wavelength of light. Consequently, a description of the reflection and refraction of light in terms of rays, as in Figs. 41–1b and 41–11, is not possible. Figure 41–13 is readily interpreted, however, on the basis of the electromagnetic wave theory of light and provides convincing pictorial supporting evidence for that theory. The fibers behave like waveguides *

---

* A dielectric rod can serve as a waveguide in the same way that a hollow metal pipe can, and it has similar properties.

(see Section 39–3), and the patterns of darkness and light represent the distribution of the **E** and **B** vectors for various modes of oscillation of the electromagnetic waves traveling down the "guides."

▶ **Example 4.**  Figure 41–14*a* shows a triangular prism of glass, a ray incident normal to one face being totally reflected.  If $\theta_1$ is 45°, what can you conclude about the index of refraction $n$ of the glass?

**Fig. 41–14**  Example 4.

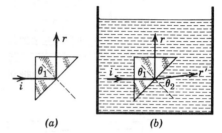

(a)                    (b)

The angle $\theta_1$ must be equal to or greater than the critical angle $\theta_c$ where $\theta_c$ is given by Eq. 41–12:

$$\sin \theta_c = \frac{n_2}{n_1} = \frac{1}{n},$$

in which, for all practical purposes, the index of refraction of air ($= n_2$) is set equal to unity.  Suppose that the index of refraction of the glass is such that total internal reflection just occurs, that is, that $\theta_c = 45°$.  This would mean

$$n = \frac{1}{\sin 45°} = 1.41.$$

Thus the index of refraction of the glass must be *equal to or larger than* 1.41.  If it were less, total internal reflection would not occur.

**Example 5.**  What happens if the prism in Example 4 (assume that $n = 1.50$) is immersed in water ($n = 1.33$)?  See Fig. 41–14*b*.

The new critical angle, given by Eq. 41–12, is

$$\sin \theta_c = \frac{n_2}{n_1} = \frac{1.33}{1.50} = 0.887,$$

which corresponds to $\theta_c = 62.5°$.  The actual angle of incidence ($= 45°$) is less than this so that we do *not* have total internal reflection.

There is a reflected ray, with an angle of reflection of 45°, as Fig. 41–14*b* shows. There is also a refracted ray, with an angle of refraction given by

$$n_1 \sin \theta_1 = n_2 \sin \theta_2$$

$$(1.50)(\sin 45°) = (1.33) \sin \theta_2,$$

which yields $\theta_2 = 52.9°$.  ◀

Maxwell's equations permit us to calculate how the incident energy is divided between the reflected and the refracted beams.  Figure 41–15 shows the theoretical

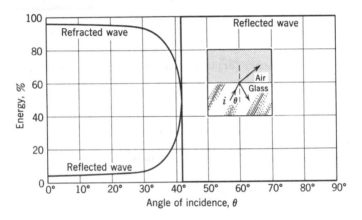

**Fig. 41–15**   (a) The per cent of the energy reflected and refracted when an incident wave in air falls on glass ($n = 1.50$).   (b) The same for the incident wave in glass, showing total internal reflection.

prediction for (a) a light beam in air falling on a glass-air interface and (b) a light beam in glass falling on such an interface.   Figure 41–15a shows that for angles of incidence up to about 50°, less than 10% of the light energy is reflected.   At grazing incidence, however (that is, angles of incidence near 90°), the surface becomes an excellent reflector.   We are all familiar with the high reflecting power of a wet road for light from automobile headlights that strikes near grazing incidence.

Figure 41–15b shows clearly that at a certain critical angle (41.8° in this case; see Eq. 41–12) *all* the light is reflected.   For angles of incidence appreciably below this value, about 4% of the energy is reflected.

### 41–6   Fermat's Principle

In 1650 Pierre Fermat discovered a remarkable principle which we often express today in these terms: *A light ray traveling from one point to another will follow a path such that, compared with nearby paths, the time required is either a minimum or a maximum or will remain unchanged (that is, it will be stationary).*

The laws of reflection and refraction can readily be derived from this principle.

**Fig. 41–16**   A ray from $A$ passes through $B$ after reflection at $P$.

Figure 41–16 shows two fixed points $A$ and $B$ and a ray $APB$ connecting them.*
The total length $l$ of this ray is

$$l = \sqrt{a^2 + x^2} + \sqrt{b^2 + (d - x)^2},$$

where $x$ locates the point $P$ at which the ray touches the mirror.

According to Fermat's principle, $P$ will have a position such that the time of travel
of the light must be a minimum (or a maximum or must remain unchanged).  Expressed in another way, the total length $l$ of the ray must be a minimum (or a maximum or must remain unchanged).  In either case, the methods of the calculus require that $dl/dx$ be zero.  Taking this derivative yields

$$\frac{dl}{dx} = (\tfrac{1}{2})(a^2 + x^2)^{-1/2}(2x) + \tfrac{1}{2}[b^2 + (d - x)^2]^{-1/2}(2)(d - x)(-1) = 0,$$

which can be rewritten as

$$\frac{x}{\sqrt{a^2 + x^2}} = \frac{d - x}{\sqrt{b^2 + (d - x)^2}}.$$

Comparison with Fig. 41–16 shows that this can be written as

$$\sin \theta_1 = \sin \theta_1',$$

or                                         $$\theta_1 = \theta_1',$$

which is the law of reflection.

To prove the law of refraction from Fermat's principle, consider Fig. 41–17, which
shows two points $A$ and $B$ in two different media and a ray $APB$ connecting them.
The time $t$ is given by

$$t = \frac{l_1}{v_1} + \frac{l_2}{v_2}.$$

Using the relation $n = c/v$ this can be written as

$$t = \frac{n_1 l_1 + n_2 l_2}{c} = \frac{l}{c}.$$

The quantity $l$ $(= n_1 l_1 + n_2 l_2)$ is called the *optical path length* of the ray.  Equation
41–11 (written as $\lambda = n\lambda_n$) shows that the optical path length is equal to the length

---

* We assume that ray $APB$ lies in the plane of the figure; see Problem 20.

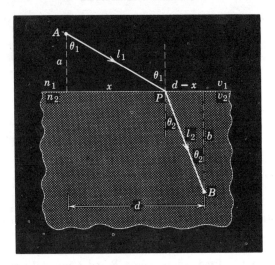

that this same number of waves would have if the medium were a vacuum. The optical path length must not be confused with the geometrical path length, which is $l_1 + l_2$.

Fermat's principle requires that $l$ be a minimum (or a maximum or must remain unchanged) which, in turn, requires that $x$ be so chosen that $dl/dx = 0$. The optical path length is

$$l = n_1 l_1 + n_2 l_2 = n_1 \sqrt{a^2 + x^2} + n_2 \sqrt{b^2 + (d - x)^2}.$$

Differentiating yields

$$\frac{dl}{dx} = n_1(\tfrac{1}{2})(a^2 + x^2)^{-1/2}(2x) + n_2(\tfrac{1}{2})[b^2 + (d - x)^2]^{-1/2}(2)(d - x)(-1) = 0,$$

which can be rewritten as

$$n_1 \frac{x}{\sqrt{a^2 + x^2}} = n_2 \frac{d - x}{\sqrt{b^2 + (d - x)^2}}.$$

Comparison with Fig. 41-17 shows that this, in turn, can be written as

$$n_1 \sin \theta_1 = n_2 \sin \theta_2,$$

which is the law of refraction.

In each of the examples of this section the time required, or, what is equivalent, the optical path length, proves to be a *minimum*. Problem 22 describes a case in which it may be a maximum, a minimum, or stationary.

## QUESTIONS

1. Discuss the propagation of spherical and of cylindrical waves, using Huygens' principle.

2. Does Huygens' principle apply to sound waves in air?

3. If Huygens' principle predicts the laws of reflection and refraction, why is it necessary or desirable to view light as an electromagnetic wave, with all its attendant complexity?

4. Would you expect sound waves to obey the laws of reflection and of refraction obeyed by light waves?

5. A street light, viewed by reflection across a body of water in which there are ripples, appears very elongated. Explain.

6. The light beam in Fig. 41–1a is broadened on entering the water. Explain.

7. By what per cent does the speed of blue light in fused quartz differ from that of red light?

8. Can (a) reflection phenomena or (b) refraction phenomena be used to determine the wavelength of light?

9. How did Foucault's measurement of the speed of light in water decide between the wave and the particle theories of light?

10. Why does a diamond "sparkle" more than a glass imitation cut to the same shape?

11. Is it plausible that the wavelength of light should change in passing from air into glass but that its frequency should not? Explain.

12. How can one determine the indices of refraction of the media in Table 41–1 relative to water, given the data in that table?

13. You are given a cube of glass. How can you find the speed of light (from a sodium light source) in this cube?

14. Describe and explain what a fish sees as he looks in various directions above his "horizon."

15. Design a periscope, taking advantage of total internal reflection. What are the advantages compared with silvered mirrors?

16. What characteristics must a material have in order to serve as an efficient "light pipe"?

17. Can the optical path length between two points ever be less than the geometrical path length between those points?

## PROBLEMS

1. One end of a stick is dragged through water at a speed $v$ which is greater than the speed $u$ of water waves. Applying Huygens' construction to the water waves, show that a conical wavefront is set up and that its half-angle $\alpha$ is given by

$$\sin \alpha = u/v.$$

This is familiar as the bow wave of a ship or the shock wave caused by an object moving through air with a speed exceeding that of sound, as in Fig. 20–12.

2. Prove that if a mirror is rotated through an angle $\alpha$, the reflected beam is rotated through an angle $2\alpha$. Is this result reasonable for $\alpha = 45°$?

3. What is the speed in fused quartz of light of wavelength 5500 A; see Fig. 41–2?

4. The wavelength of yellow sodium light in air is 5890 A. (a) What is its frequency? (b) What is its wavelength in glass whose index of refraction is 1.52? (c) From the results of (a) and (b) find its speed in this glass.

5. The speed of yellow sodium light in a certain liquid is measured to be $1.92 \times 10^8$ meters/sec. What is the index of refraction of this liquid, with respect to air, for sodium light?

6. Suppose that the speed of light in air has been measured with an uncertainty of, say, 1 km/sec. In calculating the speed in vacuum, suppose that it is not certain whether $n$ for air is 1.00029 or 1.00030. (a) How much extra uncertainty is introduced into the calculated value for $c$? (b) Estimate how accurately $n$ should be known for this purpose.

7. In Fig. 41–6 show by graphical ray tracing, using a protractor, that if $\theta$ for the incident ray is *either* increased *or* decreased, the deviation angle $\psi$ is increased. The symmetrical situation shown in this figure is called the *position of minimum deviation*.

8. A ray of light is incident normally on the face $ab$ of a glass prism ($n = 1.52$), as shown in Fig. 41–18. (a) Assuming that the prism is immersed in air, find the largest value

for the angle $\phi$ so that the ray is totally reflected at face $ac$. (b) Find $\phi$ if the prism is immersed in water.

9. Show that for a thin prism ($\phi$ small) and light not far from normal incidence ($\theta_1$ small) the deviation angle is independent of the angle of incidence and is equal to $(n - 1)\,\phi$ (see Fig. 41–6).

**Fig. 41–18**

10. A glass prism with an apex angle of 60° has $n = 1.60$. (a) What is the smallest angle of incidence for which a ray can enter one face of the prism and emerge from the other? (b) What angle of incidence would be required for the ray to pass through the prism symmetrically, as in Fig. 41–6?

11. A 60° prism is made of fused quartz. A ray of light falls on one face, making an angle of 45° with the normal. Trace the ray through the prism graphically with some care, showing the paths traversed by rays representing (a) blue light, (b) yellow-green light, and (c) red light. See Figs. 40–2 and 41–2.

12. Ptolemy, who lived at Alexandria toward the end of the first century A.D., gave the following measured values for the angle of incidence $\theta_1$ and the angle of refraction $\theta_2$ for a light beam passing from air to water:

| $\theta_1$ | $\theta_2$ | $\theta_1$ | $\theta_2$ |
|---|---|---|---|
| 10° | 7°45′ | 50° | 35°0′ |
| 20° | 15°30′ | 60° | 40°30′ |
| 30° | 22°30′ | 70° | 45°30′ |
| 40° | 29°0′ | 80° | 50°0′ |

Are these data consistent with Snell's law; if so, what index of refraction results? These data are interesting as the oldest recorded physical measurements.

13. Prove that a ray of light incident on the surface of a sheet of plate glass of thickness $t$ emerges from the opposite face parallel to its initial direction but displaced sideways, as in Fig. 41–19. Show that, for small angles of incidence $\theta$, this displacement is given by

$$x = t\theta\,\frac{n - 1}{n}$$

where $n$ is the index of refraction and $\theta$ is measured in radians.

14. A plane wave of white light traveling in fused quartz strikes a plane surface of the quartz, making an angle of incidence $\theta$. Is it possible for the internally reflected beam to appear (a) bluish or (b)

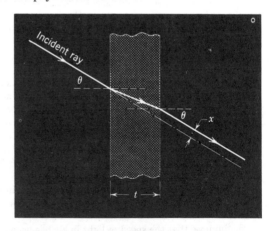

**Fig. 41–19**

reddish? Roughly what value of $\theta$ must be used? (Hint: White light will appear bluish if wavelengths corresponding to red are removed from the spectrum.)

15. A point source of light is placed a distance $h$ below the surface of a large deep lake. (a) Show that the fraction $f$ of the light energy that escapes directly from the water surface

ıs independent of $h$ and is given by

$$f = \frac{1}{2} - \frac{1}{2n} \sqrt{n^2 - 1}$$

where $n$ is the index of refraction of water. (Note: Absorption within the water and reflection at the surface—except where it is total—have been neglected.) (b) Evaluate this fraction for $n = 1.33$.

16. Figure 41-20 shows a *constant-deviation prism*. Although made of one piece of glass, it is equivalent to two 30°–60°–90° prisms and one 45°–45°–90° prism. White light is incident in the direction $i$. $\theta_1$ is changed by rotating the prism so that, in turn, light of any desired wavelength may be made to follow the path shown, emerging at $r$. Show that, if $\sin \theta_1 = \frac{1}{2}n$, then $\theta_2 = \theta_1$ and beams $i$ and $r$ are at right angles.

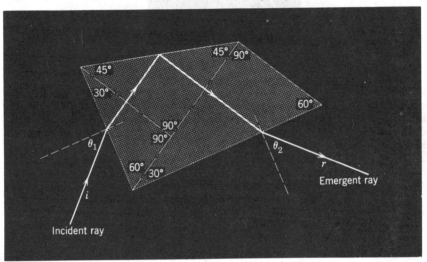

**Fig. 41–20**

17. A drop of liquid may be placed on a semicircular slab of glass as in Fig. 41-21. Show how to determine the index of refraction of the liquid by observing total internal reflection. The index of refraction of the glass is unknown and must also be determined. Is the range of indices of refraction that can be measured in this way restricted in any sense?

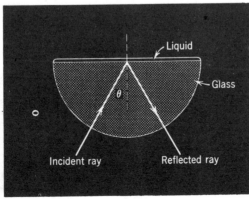

**Fig. 41–21**

18. A light ray falls on a square glass slab as in Fig. 41–22. What must the index of refraction of the glass be if total internal reflection occurs at the vertical face?

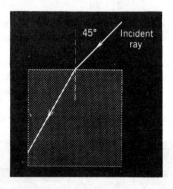

**Fig. 41–22**

19. A glass cube has a small spot at its center. What parts of the cube face must be covered to prevent the spot from being seen, no matter what the direction of viewing? What fraction of the cube surface must be so covered? Assume a cube edge of 1.0 cm and an index of refraction of 1.50. (Neglect the subsequent behavior of an internally reflected ray.)

20. Using Fermat's principle, prove that the reflected ray, the incident ray, and the normal lie in one plane.

21. Prove that the optical path lengths for reflection and refraction in Figs. 41–16 and 41–17 are minima when compared with other nearby paths connecting the same two points.

22. Figure 41–23 shows two points $A$ and $B$ connected by a light ray $AvB$. Show that, by comparison with nearby rays, such as $AcB$, the ray $AvB$ represents a minimum, a stationary, or a maximum optical path, depending on whether the distance $a$ is respectively less than, equal to, or greater than, the quantity

$$R \frac{n+1}{n-1}.$$

$R$ is the radius of curvature of the spherical surface and $n$ is the index of refraction of the medium to the right of this surface. (Hint: Express the optical path length $l$ of the arbitrary path $AcB$ in terms of the angle $\phi$ in Fig. 41–23. Use approximations that are appropriate when $\phi$ is small, since $AcB$ must be a *nearby* path. Take the first and second derivatives of $l$ with respect to $\phi$.)

**Fig. 41–23**

# Reflection and Refraction— Spherical Waves and Spherical Surfaces

## CHAPTER 42

### 42-1 Geometrical Optics and Wave Optics

In Chapter 41 we described the reflection and refraction of plane waves at plane surfaces. In this chapter we consider the more general case of spherical waves falling on spherical reflecting and refracting surfaces. All of the results of Chapter 41 will emerge as special cases of the results of this chapter, since a plane can be viewed as a spherical surface with an infinite radius of curvature.

Both in Chapter 41 and in this chapter we make extensive use of *rays*. Although a ray is a convenient construction, it proves impossible to isolate one physically. Figure 42-1a shows schematically a plane wave of wavelength $\lambda$ falling on a slit of width $a = 5\lambda$. We find that the light flares out into the geometrical shadow of the slit, a phenomenon called *diffraction*. Figures 42-1b ($a = 3\lambda$) and 42-1c ($a = \lambda$) show that diffraction becomes more pronounced as $a/\lambda \to 0$ and that attempts to isolate a single ray from the incident plane wave are futile.

Figure 42-2 shows water waves in a shallow *ripple tank*, produced by tapping the water surface periodically and automatically with the edge of a flat stick. We see that the plane wave so generated flares out by diffraction when it encounters a gap in a barrier placed across it. Diffraction is characteristic of waves of all types. We can hear around corners, for example, because of the diffraction of sound waves.

The diffraction of waves at a slit (or at an obstacle such as a wire) is expected from Huygens' principle. Consider the portion of the wavefront that arrives at the position of the slit in Fig. 42-1 Every point on it can be

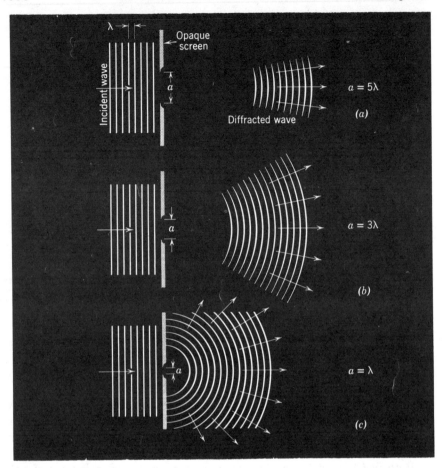

**Fig. 42–1** An attempt to isolate a ray by reducing the slit width $a$ fails because of diffraction, which becomes more pronounced as $a/\lambda$ approaches zero.

viewed as the site of an expanding spherical Huygens' wavelet. The "bending" of light into the region of the geometrical shadow is associated with the blocking off of Huygens' wavelets from those parts of the incident wavefront that lie behind the slit edges.

Figure 42–3 was made by allowing parallel light to fall on a slit placed 50 cm in front of a photographic plate. In Fig. 42–3a the slit width was about $6 \times 10^{-3}$ mm. The central band of light is much wider than this, showing that light has "flared out" into the geometric shadow of the slit. In addition, many secondary maxima, omitted from Fig. 42–1 for simplicity, appear. Figure 42–3b shows what happens when the slit width is *reduced* by a factor of two. The central maximum becomes *wider*, in agreement with Fig. 42–1. Figure 42–3c shows the effect of reducing the slit width by an additional factor of 7, to $4 \times 10^{-4}$ mm. The central maximum is now much wider and the secondary maxima, whose intensities relative to the central

**Fig. 42–2**   Diffraction of water waves at a slit in a ripple tank.   Note that the slit width is about the same size as the wavelength.   (Courtesy of Educational Services Incorporated.)

maximum have been deliberately overemphasized by long exposure, are very evident.

Diffraction can be ignored if the ratio $a/\lambda$ is large enough, $a$ being a measure of the smallest sideways dimension of the slit or obstacle.   If $a \gg \lambda$, light appears to travel in straight lines which can be represented by rays that obey the laws of reflection (Eq. 41–1) and refraction (Eq. 41–2).   In Chapter 41 this condition, called *geometrical optics*, prevailed, the lateral dimensions of all mirrors, prisms, etc., being much greater than the wavelength.   We assume in this chapter also that the conditions for geometrical optics are satisfied.

**Fig. 42–3**   (*a*) The intensity of light diffracted from a slit of width $a \cong 6 \times 10^{-3}$ mm and falling on a screen 50 cm beyond.   (*b*) The slit width is reduced by a factor of two. (*c*) The slit width is further reduced by an additional factor of seven.   Note that secondary maxima, made prominent in this case by deliberate overexposure, appear on either side of the central maximum.   These secondary maxima have been omitted from Fig. 42–1 for simplicity.

If the requirement for geometrical optics is not met, we cannot describe the behavior of light by rays but must take its wave nature specifically into account. This subject is called *wave optics;* it includes geometrical optics as an important limiting case. We will treat wave optics in succeeding chapters.

### 42–2 Spherical Waves—Plane Mirror

Figure 42–4 shows a point source of light $O$, the *object*, placed a distance $o$ in front of a plane mirror. The light falls on the mirror as a spherical wave represented in the figure by rays emanating from $O$.* At the point at which each ray strikes the mirror we construct a reflected ray. If the reflected rays are extended backward, they intersect in a point $I$ which is the same distance

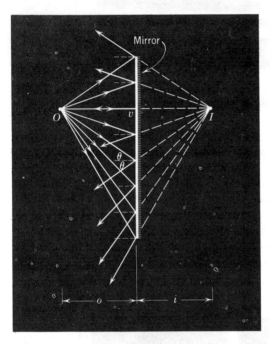

**Fig. 42–4** A point object $O$ forms a virtual image $I$ in a plane mirror. The rays appear to emanate from $I$, but actually light energy does not pass through this point.

behind the mirror that the object $O$ is in front of it; $I$ is called the *image* of $O$.

Images may be *real* or *virtual*. In a real image light energy actually passes through the image point; in a virtual image the light behaves as though it diverges from the image point, although, in fact, it does not pass through this point; see Fig. 42–4. Images in plane mirrors are always virtual. We know from daily experience how "real" such a virtual image appears to be and how definite is its location in the space behind the mirror, even though this space may, in fact, be occupied by a brick wall.

Figure 42–5 shows two rays from Fig. 42–4. One strikes the mirror at $v$, along a perpendicular line. The other strikes it at an arbitrary point $a$, making an angle of incidence $\theta$ with the normal at that point. Elementary

---

* In our discussion of reflection from mirrors in Chapter 41 (see Fig. 41–8) we assumed an incident *plane* wave; the incident rays are parallel to each other in that case.

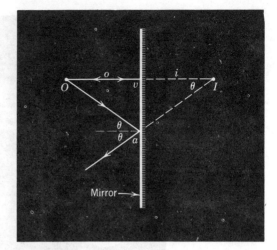

**Fig. 42–5** Two rays from Fig. 42–4; ray $Oa$ makes an arbitrary angle $\theta$ with the normal.

geometry shows that the angles $aOv$ and $aIv$ are also equal to $\theta$. Thus the right triangles $aOva$ and $aIva$ are congruent and

$$o = -i, \qquad (42\text{-}1)$$

in which the minus sign is arbitrarily introduced to show that $I$ and $O$ are on opposite sides of the mirror. Equation 42–1 does not involve $\theta$, which means that *all* rays striking the mirror pass through $I$ when extended backward, as we have seen above. Beyond assuming that the mirror is truly plane and that the conditions for geometrical optics hold, we have made no approximations in deriving Eq. 42–1. A point object produces a point image in a plane mirror, with $o = -i$, no matter how large the angle $\theta$ in Fig. 42–5.

Because of the finite diameter of the pupil of the eye, only rays that lie fairly close together can enter the eye after reflection at a mirror. For the eye position shown in Fig. 42–6 only a small patch of the mirror near point $a$ is effective in forming the image; the rest of the mirror may be covered up or removed. If the eye is moved to another location, a different patch of the mirror will be effective; the location of the virtual image $I$ will remain unchanged, however, as long as the object remains fixed.

If the object is an extended source such as the head of a person, a virtual image is also formed. From Eq. 42–1, every point of the source has an image point that lies an equal distance directly behind the plane of the mirror. Thus the image reproduces the object point by point.

Images in plane mirrors differ from objects in that left and right are interchanged. The image of a printed page is different from the page itself. Similarly, if a top is made to spin clockwise, the image, viewed in a vertical mirror, will seem to spin counterclockwise. Figure 42–7 shows an image of a left hand, constructed by using point-by-point application of Eq. 42–1; the image has the symmetry of a right hand.*

---

* See "The Overthrow of Parity" by Philip Morrison, *Scientific American*, April, 1957, for a discussion of the distinction in nature between right and left.

**Fig. 42–6**   A pencil of rays from $O$ enters the eye after reflection at the mirror.   Only a small portion of the mirror near $a$ is effective.   The small arcs represent portions of spherical wavefronts.

**Fig. 42–7**   A plane mirror reverses right and left.

▶ **Example 1.**  How tall must a vertical mirror be if a person 6 ft high is to be able to see his entire length?  Assume that his eyes are 4 in. below the top of his head.

Figure 42–8 shows the paths followed by light rays leaving the top of the man's head and the tips of his toes.  These rays, chosen so that they will enter the eye $e$ after reflection, strike the vertical mirror at points $a$ and $b$, respectively.  The mirror need occupy only the region between these two points.  Calculation shows that $b$ is 2 ft, 10 in. and $a$ is 5 ft, 10 in. above the floor.  The length of the mirror is thus 3 ft, or half the height of the person.  Note that this height is independent of the distance between the person and the mirror.  Mirrors that extend below point $b$ show reflections of the floor between the person and the mirror.

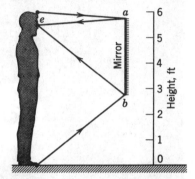

**Fig. 42–8**  Example 1.  A person can view his full-length image in a mirror that is only half his height.

**Example 2.**  Two plane mirrors are placed at right angles, and a point object $O$ is located on the perpendicular bisector, as shown in Fig. 42–9$a$.  Locate the images. Images $I_1$ and $I_2$ are formed in mirrors $ab$ and $cd$, respectively.  There is also a third image; it may be considered to be the image of $I_1$ in mirror $cd$ or the image of $I_2$ in mirror $ab$.  The three images and the object $O$ lie on a circle whose center is on the line of intersection of the mirrors and whose plane is at right angles to that line.

In viewing $I_3$ the light entering the observer's eye is reflected *twice* after leaving the source.  Figure 42–9$b$ shows a typical bundle of rays.  In viewing $I_1$ or $I_2$, the light is reflected only once, as in Fig. 42–6.  ◀

### 42–3  Spherical Waves—Spherical Mirror

In Fig. 42–10 a spherical light wave from a point object $O$ falls on a concave spherical mirror whose radius of curvature is $r$.*  A line through $O$ and the center of curvature $C$ makes a convenient reference axis.

A ray from $O$ that makes an arbitrary angle $\alpha$ with this axis intersects the axis at $I$ after reflection from the mirror at $a$.  A ray that leaves $O$ along the axis will be reflected back along itself at $v$ and will also pass through $I$.  Thus, for these two rays at least, $I$ is the image of $O$; it is a *real* image because light energy actually passes through $I$.  Let us find the location of $I$.

A useful theorem is that the exterior angle of a triangle is equal to the sum of the two opposite interior angles.  Applying this to triangles $OaCO$ and

---

* A spherical shell, viewed from inside, is everywhere *concave;* viewed from outside it is everywhere *convex.*  In this chapter concave and convex will always be judged from the point of view of an observer sighting along the direction of the incident light.

**Fig. 42–9** Example 2. (a) Object $O$ has three virtual images. (b) A typical bundle of rays used to view $I_3$.

**Fig. 42–10** Two rays from $O$ converge after reflection in a spherical concave mirror, forming a real image at $I$.

$OaIO$ in Fig. 42–10 yields

$$\beta = \alpha + \theta$$

and

$$\gamma = \alpha + 2\theta.$$

Eliminating $\theta$ between these equations leads to

$$\alpha + \gamma = 2\beta. \tag{42–2}$$

In radian measure we can write angles $\alpha$, $\beta$, and $\gamma$ as

$$\alpha \cong \frac{av}{vO} = \frac{av}{o}$$

$$\beta = \frac{av}{vC} = \frac{av}{r} \tag{42–3}$$

$$\gamma \cong \frac{av}{vI} = \frac{av}{i}.$$

Note that only the equation for $\beta$ is exact, for the reason that the center of curvature of arc $av$ is at $C$ and not at $O$ or $I$. However, the equations for $\alpha$ and for $\gamma$ are approximately correct if these angles are sufficiently small. *In all that follows we assume that the rays diverging from the object make only a small angle $\alpha$ with the axis of the mirror.* Such rays, which lie close to the mirror axis, are called *paraxial rays*. We did not find it necessary to make such an assumption for plane mirrors. Substituting these equations into Eq. 42–2 and canceling $av$ yields

$$\frac{1}{o} + \frac{1}{i} = \frac{2}{r}, \tag{42–4}$$

in which $o$ is the *object distance* and $i$ is the *image distance*. Both these distances are measured from the *vertex* of the mirror, which is the point $v$ at which the axis intercepts the mirror.

Significantly, Eq. 42–4 does not contain $\alpha$ (or $\beta$, $\gamma$, or $\theta$), so that it holds for all rays that strike the mirror provided that they are sufficiently paraxial. In an actual case the rays can be made as paraxial as one likes by putting a circular diaphragm in front of the mirror, centered about the vertex $v$; this will impose a certain maximum value of $\alpha$.

As $\alpha$ in Fig. 42–10 is permitted to become larger, it will become less true that a point object will form a point image; the image will become extended and fuzzy. No sharp criterion for deciding whether a given ray is paraxial can be laid down. If the maximum permitted value of $\alpha$ is reduced, the rays will become more paraxial and the image will become sharper. Unfortunately, the image will also become fainter because less total light energy will be reflected from the mirror. A compromise must often be made between image brightness and image quality.

As for plane mirrors, the image (real or virtual) in a spherical mirror can be seen only if the eye is located so that light rays from the object can enter

**Fig. 42–11**  The eye must be properly located to see image $I$.

it after reflection.  In Fig. 42–11 a bundle of light rays is shown entering the eye in position $x$; only the small patch of mirror near $a$ is effective for this eye position.  If the observer moves his eye to position $y$, the image will vanish for him because the mirror does not exist near point $a'$.

Although Eq. 42–4 was derived for the special case in which the object is located beyond the center of curvature, it is generally true, no matter where the object is located.  It is also true for convex mirrors, as in Fig. 42–12.

In applying Eq. 42–4, we must be careful to follow a consistent convention of signs for $o$, $i$, and $r$.  As the basis for the sign conventions to be used in this book, we start from this statement:

> In Fig. 42–10, in which light *diverges* from a *real* object, falls on a *concave* mirror, and *converges* after reflection to form a *real* image, the quantities $o$, $i$, and $r$ in Eq. 42–4 are given positive numerical values.

Figure 42–10 was used to derive Eq. 42–4 and the student should associate them in his mind as an aid in getting the signs correct.

Let us fix our minds on the side of the mirror from which incident light comes.  Because mirrors are opaque, the light, after reflection, must remain on this side, and if an image is formed here it will be a *real* image.  There-

**Fig. 42–12**  Two rays from $O$ diverge after reflection in a spherical convex mirror, forming a virtual image at $I$, the point from which they appear to originate.  Compare Fig. 42–10.

fore, we call the side of the mirror from which the light comes the *R-side* (for *real image*). We call the back of the mirror the *V-side* (for *virtual image*), because images formed on this side of the mirror must be virtual, no light energy being present on this side.*

In the indented statement above we associated real images with positive image distances. This suggests our first sign convention:

1. The image distance *i* is positive if the image (real) lies on the R-side of the mirror, as in Fig. 42–10; *i* is negative if the image (virtual) lies on the V-side, as in Fig. 42–12.

If the mirror in Fig. 42–10, which is concave as viewed from the direction of the incident light, is made convex, the rays will *diverge* after reflection and will form a *virtual* image, as Fig. 42–12 shows. Thus the indented statement above suggests our second sign convention:

2. The radius of curvature *r* is positive if the center of curvature of the mirror lies on the R-side, as in Fig. 42–10; *r* is negative if the center of curvature lies on the V-side, as in Fig. 42–12.

The student should not commit these sign conventions to memory but should deduce them in each case from the basic statement on p. 1044, using Fig. 42–10 as a mnemonic aid.

For all cases in this book the object distance *o* is to be taken as positive. In systems of two or more mirrors (or combinations of mirrors and refracting surfaces) it is possible to arrange that *converging* light falls on the mirror. In such cases the object is called *virtual* and the object distance *o* is negative; we limit our discussion here to real objects.

▶ **Example 3.** A convex mirror has a radius of curvature of 20 cm. If a point source is placed 14 cm away from the mirror, as in Fig. 42–12, where is the image?

A rough graphical construction, applying the law of reflection at *a* in the figure, shows that the image will be on the V-side of the mirror and thus will be virtual. We may verify this quantitatively and analytically from Eq. 42–4, noting that *r* is negative here because the center of curvature of the mirror is on its V-side. We have

$$\frac{1}{o} + \frac{1}{i} = \frac{2}{r}$$

or

$$\frac{1}{+14 \text{ cm}} + \frac{1}{i} = \frac{2}{-20 \text{ cm}},$$

which yields $i = -5.8$ cm, in agreement with the graphical prediction. The negative sign for *i* reminds us that the image is on the V-side of the mirror and thus is virtual.     ◀

When *parallel* light falls on a mirror (Fig. 42–13), the image point (real or virtual) is called the *focal point F* of the mirror. The focal length *f* is the distance between *F* and the vertex. If we put $o \to \infty$ in Eq. 42–4, thus insuring parallel incident light, we have

$$i = \tfrac{1}{2}r = f.$$

---

* This nomenclature may seem unnecessarily cumbersome at this point. We adopt it because of the later extension of these ideas to refracting surfaces and lenses.

**Fig. 42–13** (*a*) The focal point for a concave spherical mirror, showing both the rays and the wavefronts. *F* and *C* lie on the R-side, the focal point is real, and the focal length *f* of the mirror is positive (as is *r*). (*b*) The same, except that the incident light makes an angle $\alpha$ with the mirror axis; the rays are focused at a point in the *focal plane* *F'F''*. (*c*) Same as (*a*) except that the mirror is convex; *F* and *C* lie on the V-side of the mirror. The focal point is virtual and the focal length *f* is negative (as is *r*).

Equation 42-4 can then be rewritten

$$\frac{1}{o} + \frac{1}{i} = \frac{1}{f},\tag{42-5}$$

where $f$, like $r$, is taken as positive for mirrors whose centers of curvature are on the R-side (that is, for *concave*, or *converging* mirrors; see Fig. 42-13a) and negative for those whose centers of curvature are on the V-side (that is, for *convex*, or *diverging* mirrors; see Fig. 42-13c). Figure 42-13b shows an incident plane wave that makes a small angle $\alpha$ with the mirror axis. The rays are focused at a point in the *focal plane* of the mirror. This is a plane at right angles to the mirror axis at the focal point.

**Fig. 42-14** The image of an extended object in (a) a concave mirror and (b) a convex mirror is located graphically. Any two of the three special rays shown are sufficient.

We now consider objects that are not points. Figure 42-14 shows a candle in front of (a) a concave mirror and (b) a convex mirror. We choose to draw the mirror axis through the foot of the candle and, of course, through the center of curvature. The image of any off-axis point, such as the tip of the candle, can be found graphically, using the following facts:

1. A ray that strikes the mirror after passing (either directly or upon being extended) through the center of curvature $C$ returns along itself (ray $x$ in Fig. 42-13). Such rays strike the mirror at right angles.

2. A ray that strikes the mirror parallel to its axis passes (or will pass when extended) through the focal point (ray $y$).

3. A ray that strikes the mirror after passing (either directly or upon being extended) through the focal point emerges parallel to the axis (ray $z$).

Figure 42–15 shows a ray ($dve$) that originates on the tip of the object candle of Fig. 42–14$a$, is reflected from the mirror at point $v$, and passes through the tip of the image candle. The law of reflection demands that this ray make equal angles $\theta$ with the mirror axis as shown. For the two similar right triangles in the figure we can write

$$\frac{ce}{bd} = \frac{vc}{vb}.$$

The quantity on the left (apart from a question of sign) is the *lateral magnification* $m$ of the mirror. Since we want to represent an *inverted* image by a *negative* magnification, we arbitrarily define $m$ for this case as $-(ce/bd)$. Since $vc = i$ and $vb = o$, we have at once

$$m = -\frac{i}{o}. \tag{42–6}$$

This equation gives the magnification for spherical and plane mirrors under all circumstances. For a plane mirror, $o = -i$ and the predicted magnification is $+1$ which, in agreement with experience, indicates an *erect* image the same size as the object.

Images in spherical mirrors suffer from several "defects" that arise because the assumption of paraxial rays is never completely justified. In general, a point source will not produce a point image; see Problem 5. Apart from this, distortion arises because the magnification varies somewhat with distance from the mirror axis, Eq. 42–6 being strictly correct only for paraxial rays. Superimposed on these defects are *diffraction effects* which come about because the basic assumption of geometrical optics, that light travels in straight lines, must always be considered an approximation.

**Fig. 42–15**  A particular ray for the arrangement of Fig. 42–14, used to show that the *lateral magnification* $m$ is given by $-i/o$.

**Fig. 42-16**  A graphical representation of the mirror formula (Eq. 42-5). The numbers on the curves give the lateral magnifications (Eq. 42-6).

Figure 42-16 summarizes the predictions of the mirror equation (Eq. 42-5) and of the lateral magnification equation (Eq. 42-6). For convex mirrors the image is always virtual. For concave mirrors the image is virtual if the object is inside the focal point ($o/f < 1$) and real otherwise ($o/f > 1$). As $o \rightarrow \infty$ for both types of mirror, the image approaches the focal point ($i/f \rightarrow 1$). A plane mirror ($m = +1$) is represented in the figure by a point at the origin. It is appropriate that this point form the central point of the lower-left branch of Fig. 42-16 because both convex and concave mirrors approach plane mirrors as $r$ is increased in magnitude, that is, as $f \rightarrow \infty$ (or as $o/f \rightarrow 0$ in Fig. 42-16, assuming a fixed object distance).

## 42-4  Spherical Refracting Surface

Figure 42-17 shows a point source $O$ near a convex spherical *refracting* surface of radius of curvature $r$. The surface separates two media whose indices of refraction differ, *that of the medium in which the incident light falls on the surface being $n_1$ and that on the other side of the surface being $n_2$.*

From $O$ we draw a line through the center of curvature $C$ of the refracting surface, thus establishing a convenient axis which intercepts the surface at vertex $v$. From $O$ we draw a ray that makes a small but arbitrary angle $\alpha$ with the axis and strikes the refracting surface at $a$, being refracted according to

$$n_1 \sin \theta_1 = n_2 \sin \theta_2.$$

**Fig. 42–17** Two rays from $O$ converge after refraction at a spherical surface, forming a real image at $I$.

The refracted ray intersects the axis at $I$. A ray from $O$ that travels along the axis will not be bent on entering the surface and will also pass through $I$. Thus, for these two rays at least, $I$ is the image of $O$.

As in the derivation of the mirror equation, we use the theorem that the exterior angle of a triangle is equal to the sum of the two opposite interior angles. Applying this to triangles $COaC$ and $ICaI$ yields

$$\theta_1 = \alpha + \beta \qquad (42\text{–}7)$$

and

$$\beta = \theta_2 + \gamma. \qquad (42\text{–}8)$$

As $\alpha$ is made small, angles $\beta$, $\gamma$, $\theta_1$, and $\theta_2$ in Fig. 42–17 also become small. *We at once assume that $\alpha$, hence all these angles, are arbitrarily small,* this paraxial ray assumption was also made for spherical mirrors. Replacing the sines of the angles by the angles themselves—since the angles are required to be small—permits us to write the law of refraction as

$$n_1\theta_1 \cong n_2\theta_2. \qquad (42\text{–}9)$$

Combining Eqs. 42–8 and 42–9 leads to

$$\beta = \frac{n_1}{n_2}\theta_1 + \gamma.$$

Eliminating $\theta_1$ between this equation and Eq. 42–7 leads, after rearrangement, to

$$n_1\alpha + n_2\gamma = (n_2 - n_1)\beta. \qquad (42\text{–}10)$$

In radian measure the angles $\alpha$, $\beta$, and $\gamma$ in Fig. 42–17 are

$$\alpha \cong \frac{av}{o}$$

$$\beta = \frac{av}{r} \qquad (42\text{–}11)$$

$$\gamma \cong \frac{av}{i}.$$

Only the second of these equations is exact. The other two are approximate because $I$ and $O$ are *not* the centers of circles of which $av$ is an arc. However, for paraxial rays ($\alpha$ small enough) the inaccuracies in Eq. 42–11 can be made as small as desired.

Substituting Eqs. 42–11 into Eq. 42–10 leads readily to

$$\frac{n_1}{o} + \frac{n_2}{i} = \frac{n_2 - n_1}{r}. \qquad (42\text{–}12)$$

This equation holds whenever light is refracted from point objects at spherical surfaces, assuming only that the rays are paraxial. As with the mirror formula, care must be taken to use Eq. 42–12 with consistent signs for $o$, $i$, and $r$. Once again we establish our sign conventions by physical reasoning from a particular case, that of Fig. 42–17:

> In Fig. 42–17, in which light *diverges* from a *real* object, falls on a *convex* refracting surface, and *converges* after refraction to form a *real* image, the quantities $o$, $i$, and $r$ in Eq. 42–12 have positive numerical values.

Figure 42–17 was used to derive Eq. 42–12, and the student should associate them in his mind as an aid in getting the signs correct. This basic statement is quite similar to that which we made for mirrors on p. 1044.

We fix our attention on the side of the refracting surface from which the incident light falls on the surface. In contrast to mirrors, the light energy *passes through* a refracting surface to the other side, and if a real image is formed it must appear on the far side, which we call the R-side. The side from which the incident light comes is called the V-side because virtual images must appear here. Figure 42–18 suggests this import nt distinction between reflection and refraction.

In the indented statement above we associated real images with positive-image distances. Thus we are led to the sign convention:

1. The image distance $i$ is positive if the image (real) is on the R-side of the refracting surface, as in Fig. 42–17; $i$ is negative if the image (virtual) lies on the V-side, as in Fig. 42–19.

The refracting surface in Fig. 42–17 is convex. If it is made concave (still assuming that $n_2 > n_1$), the rays will *diverge* after refraction and form

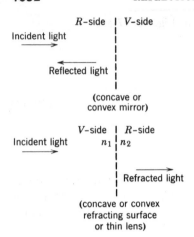

R-side | V-side

Incident light
$\longrightarrow$

$\longleftarrow$
Reflected light

(concave or
convex mirror)

V-side | R-side
Incident light   $n_1$ | $n_2$
$\longrightarrow$

$\longrightarrow$
Refracted light

(concave or convex
refracting surface
or thin lens)

**Fig. 42–18**  Real images are formed on the same side as the incident light for mirrors but on the opposite side for refracting surfaces and thin lenses. This is so because the incident light is reflected back by mirrors but is transmitted through by refracting surfaces.

a *virtual* image, as Fig. 42–19 shows. Thus we are led to our second sign convention:

2. The radius of curvature $r$ is positive if the center of curvature of the refracting surface lies on the R-side, as in Fig. 42–17; $r$ is negative if the center of curvature is on the V-side, as in Fig. 42–19.

The sign conventions for refracting surfaces are the same as for mirrors (p. 1045), the fundamental difference between the two situations being absorbed in the definitions of R-side and V-side in Fig. 42–18. This difference is easily remembered on physical grounds.

For all cases in this book the object distance $o$ is to be taken as positive. In systems of two or more refracting surfaces (or combinations of refracting surfaces and mirrors) it is possible to arrange that *converging* light falls on the refracting surface. In such cases the object is called *virtual* and the object distance $o$ is negative; we limit our discussions here to real objects.

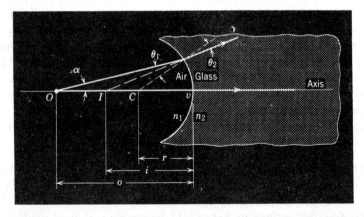

**Fig. 42–19**  Two rays from $O$ diverge after refraction at a spherical surface, forming a virtual image at $I$.

▶ **Example 4.** Locate the image for the geometry shown in Fig. 42–17, assuming the radius of curvature to be 10 cm, $n_2$ to be 2.0, and $n_1$ to be 1.0. Let the object be 20 cm to the left of $v$.
From Eq. 42–12,

$$\frac{n_1}{o} + \frac{n_2}{i} = \frac{n_2 - n_1}{r},$$

we have

$$\frac{1.0}{+20 \text{ cm}} + \frac{2.0}{i} = \frac{2.0 - 1.0}{+10 \text{ cm}}.$$

Note that $r$ is positive because the center of curvature of the surface lies on the R-side. This relation yields $i = +40$ cm in agreement with the graphical construction. The light energy actually passes through $I$ so that the image is real, as indicated by the positive sign for $i$.

**Example 5.** An object is immersed in a medium with $n_1 = 2.0$, being 15 cm from the spherical surface whose radius of curvature is $-10$ cm, as in Fig. 42–20; $r$ is negative because $C$ lies on the V-side. Locate the image.

**Fig. 42–20** Two rays from $O$ appear to originate from $I$ (virtual image) after refraction at a spherical surface.

Figure 42–20 shows a ray traced through the surface by applying the law of refraction at point $a$. A second ray from $O$ along the axis emerges undeflected at $v$. The image $I$ is found by extending these two rays backward; it is virtual.
From Eq. 42–12,

$$\frac{n_1}{o} + \frac{n_2}{i} = \frac{n_2 - n_1}{r},$$

we have

$$\frac{2.0}{+15 \text{ cm}} + \frac{1.0}{i} = \frac{1.0 - 2.0}{-10 \text{ cm}},$$

which yields $i = -30$ cm, in agreement with Fig. 42–20 and with the sign conventions. Note that $n_1$ always refers to the medium on the side of the surface from which the light comes.

**Example 6.** What is the relationship between $i$ and $o$ if the refracting surface is plane?
A plane surface has an infinite radius of curvature. Putting $r \to \infty$ in Eq. 42–12 leads to

$$i = -o\frac{n_2}{n_1}.$$

(a)

(b)

**Fig. 42–21** Refraction at a plane surface at near-normal incidence, showing a pencil of rays and the corresponding wavefronts entering the pupil. (a) Source in air and (b) source in water.

Figure 42–21 illustrates the situation graphically (a) for an object in air as seen from below water and (b) for an object in water with air above. This shows that a diver, looking upward at, say, an overhanging tree branch, will think it higher than it is by the factor 1.33/1.00. Similarly, an observer in air will think that objects on the bottom of a water tank are closer to the surface than they actually are, in the ratio 1.00/1.33. These considerations, being based on Eq. 42–12, hold only for paraxial rays, which means that the incident rays can make only a small angle with the normal; this angle has been exaggerated in the figure for clarity. Note again that $n_1$ is always identified with the medium that lies on the side of the surface containing the incident light. ◄

### 42–5  Thin Lenses

In most refraction situations there is more than one refracting surface. This is true even for a spectacle lens, the light passing from air into glass and then from glass into air. In microscopes, telescopes, cameras, etc., there are often many more than two surfaces.

Figure 42–22a shows a thick glass "lens" of length $l$ whose surfaces are ground to radii $r'$ and $r''$. A point object $O'$ is placed near the left surface as shown. A ray leaving $O'$ along the axis is not deflected on entering or leaving the lens because it falls on each surface along a normal.

A second ray leaving $O'$, at an arbitrary angle $\alpha$ with the axis, strikes the surface at point $a'$, is refracted, and strikes the second surface at point $a''$. The ray is again refracted and crosses the axis at $I''$, which, being the intersection of two rays from $O''$, is the image of point $O'$, formed after refraction at two surfaces.

Figure 42–22b shows the first surface, which forms a virtual image of $O'$ at $I'$. To locate $I'$, we use Eq. 42–12,

$$\frac{n_1}{o} + \frac{n_2}{i} = \frac{n_2 - n_1}{r}.$$

Putting $n_1 = 1.0$ and $n_2 = n$ and bearing in mind that the image distance is negative (that is, $i = -i'$ in Fig. 42–22b), we obtain

$$\frac{1}{o'} - \frac{n}{i'} = \frac{n-1}{r'}. \qquad (42\text{–}13)$$

In this equation $i'$ will be a positive number because we have arbitrarily introduced the minus sign appropriate to a virtual image.

Figure 42–22c shows the second surface. Unless an observer at point $a''$ were aware of the existence of the first surface, he would think that the light striking that point originated at point $I'$ in Fig. 42–22b and that the region to the left of the surface was filled with glass. Thus the (virtual) image $I'$ formed by the first surface serves as a real object $O''$ for the second surface. The distance of this object from the second surface is

$$o'' = i' + l. \qquad (42\text{–}14)$$

In applying Eq. 42–12 to the second surface, we insert $n_1 = n$ and $n_2 = 1.0$ because the object behaves as if it were imbedded in glass. If we use

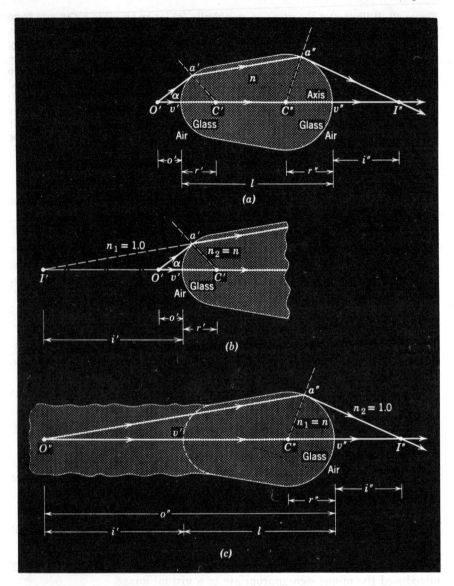

**Fig. 42–22** (a) Two rays from $O'$ intersect at $I''$ (real image) after refraction at two spherical surfaces. (b) The first surface and (c) the second surface shown separately. The quantities $\alpha$ and $n$ have been exaggerated for clarity.

Eq. 42–14, Eq. 42–12 becomes

$$\frac{n}{i' + l} + \frac{1}{i''} = \frac{1 - n}{r''}. \tag{42–15}$$

Let us now assume that the thickness $l$ of the "lens" in Fig. 42–22 is so small that it can be neglected in comparison with other linear quantities in this figure (such as $o'$, $i'$, $o''$, $i''$, $r'$, and $r''$). In all that follows we make this *thin-lens approximation.* Putting $l = 0$ in Eq. 42–15 leads to

$$\frac{n}{i'} + \frac{1}{i''} = -\frac{n-1}{r''}. \qquad (42\text{–}16)$$

Adding Eqs. 42–13 and 42–16 leads to

$$\frac{1}{o'} + \frac{1}{i''} = (n-1)\left(\frac{1}{r'} - \frac{1}{r''}\right).$$

Finally, calling the original object distance simply $o$ and the final image distance simply $i$ leads to

$$\frac{1}{o} + \frac{1}{i} = (n-1)\left(\frac{1}{r'} - \frac{1}{r''}\right). \qquad (42\text{–}17)$$

This equation holds only for paraxial rays and only if the lens is so thin that it essentially makes no difference from which surface of the lens the quantities $o$ and $i$ are measured. In Eq. 42–17 $r'$ refers to the first surface struck by the light as it traverses the lens and $r''$ to the second surface.

The sign conventions for Eq. 42–17 are the same as those for mirrors and for single refracting surfaces. Because the lens is assumed to be thin, we refer to the R-side and the V-side of the lens itself (see Fig. 42–18) rather than those of its separate surfaces. The sign conventions then are the following:

1. The image distance $i$ is positive if the image (real) lies on the R-side of the lens, as in Fig. 42–23$a$; $i$ is negative if the image (virtual) lies on the V-side of the lens, as in Fig. 42–23$b$.

2. The radii of curvature $r'$ and $r''$ are positive if their respective centers

**Fig. 42–23**   Illustrations used to establish sign conventions for thin lenses.

of curvature lie on the R-side of the lens. They are negative if their centers lie on the V-side. In Fig. 42–23a, $r'$ is positive and $r''$ is negative; in Fig. 42–23b, $r'$ is negative and $r''$ is positive.

Figure 42–24a and c shows parallel light from a distant object falling on a thin lens. The image location is called the *second focal point* $F_2$ of the lens. The distance from $F_2$ to the lens is called the *focal length f*. The *first focal point* for a thin lens ($F_1$ in figure) is the object position for which the image

**Fig. 42–24**   (a) Parallel light passes through the second focal point $F_2$ of a converging lens.   (b) The incident light makes an angle $\alpha$ with the lens axis, the rays being focused in the focal plane $F'F''$.   (c) Parallel light, passing through a diverging lens, seems to originate at the second focal point $F_2$. $C'$ and $C''$ are centers of curvature for the lens surfaces; $F_1$ is the first focal point.

is at infinity.   For thin lenses the first and second focal points are on opposite sides of the lens and are equidistant from it.

The focal length can be computed from Eq. 42–17 by inserting $o \to \infty$ and $i = f$.   This yields

$$\frac{1}{f} = (n - 1)\left(\frac{1}{r'} - \frac{1}{r''}\right). \tag{42-18}$$

This relation is called the *lens maker's equation* because it allows us to compute the focal length of a lens in terms of the radii of curvature and the index of refraction of the material.   Combining Eqs. 42–17 and 42–18 allows us to write the thin-lens equation as

$$\frac{1}{o} + \frac{1}{i} = \frac{1}{f}. \tag{42-19}$$

Figure 42–24b shows parallel incident rays that make a small angle $\alpha$ with the lens axis; they are brought to a focus in the *focal plane F'F''*, as shown. This is a plane normal to the lens axis at the focal point.

In Fig. 42–24a we note that all rays in the figure contain the same number of wavelengths; in other words, they have the same *optical path lengths;* see Section 41–6.   The optical path lengths are the same because the wavefronts are surfaces over which the wave disturbance has the same constant value and because all the rays shown pass through the same number of wavefronts.

▶ **Example 7.**  The lenses of Fig. 42–24 have radii of curvature of magnitude 40 cm and are made of glass with $n = 1.65$.   Compute their focal lengths.

Since $C'$ lies on the R-side of the lens in Fig. 42–24a, $r'$ is positive ($= +40$ cm). Since $C'''$ lies on the V-side, $r''$ is negative ($= -40$ cm).   Substituting in Eq. 42–18 yields

$$\frac{1}{f} = (n - 1)\left(\frac{1}{r'} - \frac{1}{r''}\right) = (1.65 - 1)\left(\frac{1}{+40 \text{ cm}} - \frac{1}{-40 \text{ cm}}\right),$$

or                                         $f = +31$ cm.

A positive focal length indicates that in agreement with Fig. 42–24a the focal point $F_2$ is on the R-side of the lens and parallel incident light converges after refraction to form a real image.

In Fig. 42–24c $C'$ lies on the V-side of the lens so that $r'$ is negative ($= -40$ cm). Since $r''$ is positive ($= +40$ cm), Eq. 42–17 yields

$$f = -31 \text{ cm.}$$

A negative focal length indicates that in agreement with Fig. 42–24c the focal point $F_2$ is on the V-side of the lens and incident light diverges after refraction to form a virtual image.                                         ◀

The location of the image of an extended object such as a candle (Fig. 42–25) can be found graphically by using the following three facts:

1. A ray parallel to the axis and falling on the lens passes, either directly or when extended, through the second focal point (ray $x$ in Fig. 42–25).

2. A ray falling on a lens after passing, either directly or when extended,

through the first focal point will emerge from the lens parallel to the axis (ray $y$).

3. A ray falling on the lens at its center will pass through undeflected. There is no deflection because the lens, near its center, behaves like a thin piece of glass with parallel sides. The direction of the light rays is not changed and the sideways displacement can be neglected because the lens thickness has been assumed to be negligible (ray $z$; see also Problem 13, Chapter 41).

Figure 42-26, which represents part of Fig. 42-25a, shows a ray passing from the tip of the object through the center of curvature to the tip of the image. For the similar triangles $abc$ and $dec$ we may write

$$\frac{de}{ab} = \frac{dc}{ac}.$$

The right side of this equation is $i/o$ and the left side is $-m$, where $m$ is the

Fig. 42-25  Showing the graphical location of images for three thin lenses.

**Fig. 42-26**   Two rays for the situation of Fig. 42-25a.

*lateral magnification.* The minus sign is required because we wish $m$ to be negative for an inverted image. This yields

$$m = -\frac{i}{o},\qquad (42\text{-}20)$$

which holds for all types of thin lenses and for all object distances.

▶ **Example 8.** A converging thin lens has a focal length of $+24$ cm. An object is placed 9.0 cm from the lens as in Fig. 42-25b; describe the image.

From Eq. 42-19,

$$\frac{1}{o} + \frac{1}{i} = \frac{1}{f},$$

we have

$$\frac{1}{+9.0 \text{ cm}} + \frac{1}{i} = \frac{1}{+24 \text{ cm}},$$

which yields $i = -14.4$ cm, in agreement with the figure. The minus sign means that the image is on the V-side of the lens and is thus virtual.

The lateral magnification is given by

$$m = -\frac{i}{o} = -\frac{-14.4 \text{ cm}}{+9.0 \text{ cm}} = +1.6,$$

again in agreement with the figure. The plus signifies an erect image.    ◀

Images formed by lenses suffer from defects similar to those discussed for mirrors on p. 1048. There are effects connected with the failure of a point object to form a point image, with the variation of magnification with distance from the lens axis, and with diffraction. For lenses, but not for mirrors, there are also *chromatic aberrations* associated with the fact that the refracting properties of the lens vary with wavelength because the index of refraction of the lens material does. If a point object on the lens axis emits white light, the image, neglecting other lens defects, will be a series of colored points spread out along the axis. We have all seen the colored images produced by inexpensive lenses. A great deal of ingenious optical engineering goes into the design of lenses (more commonly lens systems) in which the various lens defects are minimized. The lens surfaces are normally not spherical.

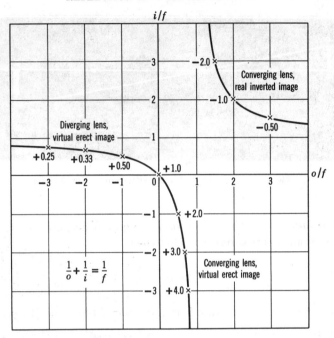

**Fig. 42-27**  A graphical representation of the thin-lens formula (Eq. 42-19). The numbers on the curves give the lateral magnifications (Eq. 42-20). Compare Fig. 42-16.

Figure 42-27 is a graphical representation of the object-image relationships for thin lenses; see Eqs. 42-19 and 42-20. The fact that it is identical in form with Fig. 42-16, which holds for mirrors, is not surprising because the basic equations for mirrors and thin lenses (Eqs. 42-19 and 42-5; Eqs. 42-20 and 42-6) are identical. A converging lens of a given focal length is quantitatively similar to a concave mirror of the same focal length, the difference being that the lens forms real images on the opposite side from the (real) object and the mirror forms them on the same side.

## QUESTIONS

1. If a mirror reverses right and left, why doesn't it reverse up and down?

2. Is it possible to photograph a virtual image?

3. What approximations were made in deriving the mirror equation (Eq. 42-4):

$$\frac{1}{o} + \frac{1}{i} = \frac{2}{r}?$$

4. Can you think of a simple test or observation to prove that the law of reflection is the same for all wavelengths, under conditions in which geometrical optics prevails?

5. Under what conditions will a spherical mirror, which may be concave or convex, form (a) a real image, (b) an inverted image, and (c) an image smaller than the object?

6. An unsymmetrical thin lens forms an image of a point object on its axis. Is the image location changed if the lens is reversed?

7. Why has a lens two focal points and a mirror only one?

8. Under what conditions will a thin lens, which may be converging or diverging, form (a) a real image, (b) an inverted image, and (c) an image smaller than the object?

9. Does the apparent depth of an object below water depend on the angle of view of the observer in air? Explain and illustrate with ray diagrams.

10. A skin diver wants to use an air-filled plastic bag as a converging lens for underwater use. Sketch a suitable cross section for the bag.

11. What approximations were made in deriving the thin lens equation (Eq. 42–19):

$$\frac{1}{o} + \frac{1}{i} = \frac{1}{f}?$$

12. Under what conditions will a thin lens have a lateral magnification (a) of $-1$ and (b) of $+1$?

13. How does the focal length of a glass lens for blue light compare with that for red light, assuming the lens is (a) diverging and (b) converging?

14. Does the focal length of a lens depend on the medium in which the lens is immersed? Is it possible for a given lens to act as a converging lens in one medium and a diverging lens in another medium?

15. Are the following statements true for a glass lens in air? (a) A lens that is thicker at the center than at the edges is a converging lens for parallel light. (b) A lens that is thicker at the edges than at the center is a diverging lens for parallel light. Explain and illustrate, using wavefronts.

16. Under what conditions would the lateral magnification, $(m = -i/o)$ for lenses and mirrors become infinite? Is there any practical significance to such a condition?

17. Light rays are reversible. Discuss the situation in terms of objects and images if all rays in Figs. 42–10, 42–14, 42–17, 42–19, 42–23, and 42–25 are reversed in direction.

18. What significance can be given to the origin of coordinates in the graphical representation of the thin-lens formula (Fig. 42–27)?

19. In connection with Fig. 42–24a, we pointed out that all rays originating on the same wavefront in the incident wave have the same optical path length to the image point. Discuss this in connection with Fermat's principle (Section 41–6).

## PROBLEMS

1. Solve Example 2 if the angle between the mirrors is (a) 45°, (b) 60°, (c) 120°, the object always being placed on the bisector of the mirrors.

2. Two plane mirrors make an angle of 90° with each other. What is the largest number of images of an object placed between them that can be seen by a properly placed eye? The object need *not* lie on the mirror bisector.

3. A small object is 10 cm in front of a plane mirror. If you stand behind the object, 30 cm from the mirror, and look at its image, for what distance must you focus your eyes?

4. A small object $O$ is placed one-third of the way between two parallel plane mirrors as in Fig. 42–28. Trace appropriate bundles of rays for viewing the four images that lie closest to the object.

**Fig. 42–28**

5. Redraw Fig. 42–29 on a large sheet of paper and trace carefully the reflected rays, using the law of reflection. Is a point focus formed? Discuss.

**Fig. 42–29**

6. Fill in this table, each column of which refers to a spherical mirror. Check your results by graphical analysis. Distances are in centimeters; if a number has no plus or minus sign in front of it, it may have either sign.

|  | $a$ | $b$ | $c$ | $d$ | $e$ | $f$ | $g$ | $h$ |
|---|---|---|---|---|---|---|---|---|
| Type | concave |  |  |  |  |  | convex |  |
| $f$ | 20 |  | +20 |  |  | 20 |  |  |
| $r$ |  |  |  | −40 |  |  | 40 |  |
| $i$ |  |  |  | −10 |  |  | 4 |  |
| $o$ | +10 | +10 | +30 | +60 |  |  |  | +24 |
| $m$ |  | +1 |  | −0.5 |  | +0.10 |  | 0.50 |
| Real image? |  | no |  |  |  |  |  |  |
| Erect image? |  |  |  |  |  |  |  | no |

7. A short linear object of length $l$ lies on the axis of a spherical mirror, a distance $o$ from the mirror. (a) Show that its image will have a length $l'$ where

$$l' = l \left( \frac{f}{o-f} \right)^2.$$

(b) Show that the *longitudinal magnification* $m'(= l'/l)$ is equal to $m^2$ where $m$ is the lateral magnification discussed in Section 42–3. (c) Is there any condition such that, neglecting all mirror defects, the image of a small cube would also be a cube?

8. As an example of the effect of relaxing the paraxial ray assumption find, analytically,

the apparent depth of a swimming pool having water ($n = 1.33$) of actual depth 8.0 ft (*a*) when viewed at normal incidence and (*b*) when viewed at an angle of 30° from the normal.

9. A layer of water ($n = 1.33$) 2.0 cm thick floats on carbon tetrachloride ($n = 1.46$) 4.0 cm thick. How far below the water surface, viewed at normal incidence, does the bottom of the tank seem to be?

10. Fill out the following table, each column of which refers to a spherical surface separating two media with different indices of refraction. Distances are measured in centimeters.

| | *a* | *b* | *c* | *d* | *e* | *f* | *g* | *h* |
|---|---|---|---|---|---|---|---|---|
| $n_1$ | 1.0 | 1.0 | 1.0 | 1.0 | 1.5 | 1.5 | 1.5 | 1.5 |
| $n_2$ | 1.5 | 1.5 | 1.5 | | 1.0 | 1.0 | 1.0 | |
| *o* | +10 | +10 | | +20 | +10 | | +70 | +100 |
| *i* | | −13 | +600 | −20 | −6 | −7.5 | | +600 |
| *r* | +30 | | +30 | −20 | | −30 | +30 | −30 |
| Real image? | | | | | | | | |

Draw a figure for each situation and construct the appropriate rays graphically. Assume a point object.

11. Fill in this table, each column of which refers to a thin lens, to the extent possible. Check your results by graphical analysis. Distances are in centimeters; if a number (except in row *n*) has no plus sign or minus sign in front of it, it may have either sign.

| | *a* | *b* | *c* | *d* | *e* | *f* | *g* | *h* | *i* |
|---|---|---|---|---|---|---|---|---|---|
| Type | converging | | | | | | | | |
| *f* | 10 | +10 | 10 | 10 | | | | | |
| *r'* | | | | | +30 | −30 | −30 | | |
| *r''* | | | | | −30 | +30 | −60 | | |
| *i* | | | | | | | | | |
| *o* | +20 | +5 | +5 | +5 | +10 | +10 | +10 | +10 | +10 |
| *n* | | | | | 1.5 | 1.5 | 1.5 | | |
| *m* | | >1 | <1 | | | | | 0.5 | 0.5 |
| Real image? | | | | | | | | | yes |
| Erect image? | | | | | | | | yes | |

Draw a figure for each situation and construct the appropriate rays graphically. Assume a finite object.

12. Define and locate the first and second focal points (see p. 966) for a single spherical refracting surface such as that of Fig. 42–17.

13. A luminous object and a screen are a fixed distance $D$ apart. (a) Show that a converging lens of focal length $f$ will form a real image on the screen for two positions that are separated by

$$d = \sqrt{D(D - 4f)}.$$

(b) Show that the ratio of the two image sizes for these two positions is

$$\left(\frac{D - d}{D + d}\right)^2.$$

14. Using the lens maker's equation (Eq. 42–18), decide which of the thin lenses in Fig. 42–30 is converging and which diverging for parallel incident light.

**Fig. 42–30**

15. Two thin lenses of focal length $f_1$ and $f_2$ are in contact. Show that they are equivalent to a single thin lens with a focal length given by

$$f = \frac{f_1 f_2}{f_1 + f_2}.$$

16. Show that the distance between an object and its real image formed by a thin converging lens is always greater than four times the focal length of the lens.

17. A double-convex lens is to be made of glass with an index of refraction of 1.50. One surface is to have twice the radius of curvature of the other and the focal length is to be 6.0 cm. What are the radii?

18. The formula

$$\frac{1}{o} + \frac{1}{i} = \frac{1}{f}$$

is called the *Gaussian form* of the thin lens formula. Another form of this formula, the *Newtonian* form, is obtained by considering the distance $x$ from the object to the first focal point and the distance $x'$ from the second focal point to the image. Show that

$$xx' = f^2.$$

19. A parallel incident beam falls on a solid glass sphere at normal incidence. Locate the image in terms of the index of refraction $n$ and the sphere radius $r$.

20. An erect object is placed a distance in front of a converging lens equal to twice the focal length $f_1$ of the lens. On the other side of the lens is a converging mirror of focal length $f_2$ separated from the lens by a distance $2(f_1 + f_2)$. (a) Find the location, nature and relative size of the final image. (b) Draw the appropriate ray diagram. See Fig. 42–31.

**Fig. 42–31**

21. An object is placed at a center of curvature of a double-concave lens, both of whose radii of curvature are the same. (a) According to the convention used in this book, what are the signs of the two radii of curvature? (b) Find the location of the image in terms of the radius of curvature $r$ and the index of refraction, $n$, of the glass. (c) Describe the nature of the image. (d) Verify your result with a ray diagram.

22. Two lenses with their focal points are shown in Fig. 42–32. With the given object, find the image formed by lens 1 and, using this as an object for lens 2, find the final image. Discuss the nature of the two images. Verify your conclusions by copying the figure to scale and drawing a ray diagram.

**Fig. 42–32**

23. An object is 20 cm to the left of a lens with a focal length of +10 cm. A second lens of focal length +12.5 cm is 30 cm to the right of the first lens. (a) Using the image formed by the first lens as the object for the second, find the location and relative size of the final image. (b) Verify your conclusions by drawing the lens system to scale and constructing a ray diagram. (c) Describe the final image.

# Interference

## CHAPTER 43

### 43-1 Young's Experiment

In Section 19–7 we saw that if two waves of the same frequency travel in approximately the same direction and have a phase difference that remains constant with time, they may combine so that their energy is not distributed uniformly in space but is a maximum at certain points and a minimum (possibly even zero) at others. The demonstration of such *interference* effects for light by Thomas Young in 1801 first established the wave theory of light on a firm experimental basis. Young was able to deduce the wavelength of light from his experiments, the first measurement of this important quantity.

Young allowed sunlight to fall on a pinhole $S_0$ punched in a screen $A$ in Fig. 43–1. The emerging light spreads out by diffraction (see Section 42–1) and falls on pinholes $S_1$ and $S_2$ punched into screen $B$. Again diffraction occurs and two overlapping spherical waves expand into the space to the right of screen $B$.

The condition for geometric optics, namely that $a \gg \lambda$ where $a$ is the diameter of the pinholes, is definitely *not* met in this experiment. The pinholes do not cast geometrical shadows but act as sources of expanding Huygens' wavelets. We are dealing here (and in succeeding chapters) with *wave optics* rather than with geometrical optics.

Figure 43–2, taken from an 1803 paper of Young, shows the region between screens $B$ and $C$. The blackening represents the minima of the wave disturbance; the white space between represents the maxima. If you hold the page with your eye close to the left edge and look at a grazing angle along the figure, you will see that along lines marked by $x$'s there is cancella-

**Fig. 43–1** Showing how Thomas Young produced an interference pattern by allowing diffracted waves from pinholes $S_1$ and $S_2$ to overlap on screen $C$.

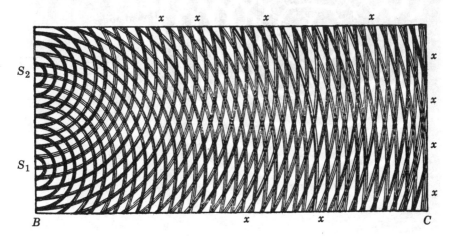

**Fig. 43–2** Thomas Young's original drawing showing interference effects in overlapping waves. Place the eye near the left edge and sight at a grazing angle along the figure. (From Thomas Young, *Phil. Transactions*, 1803.)

tion of the wave; between them there is reinforcement. If a screen is placed anywhere across the superimposed waves, we expect to find alternate bright and dark spots on it. Figure 43–3 shows a photograph of such *interference*

**Fig. 43–3** Interference fringes for monochromatic light, made with an arrangement like that of Fig. 43–1, using long narrow slits rather than pinholes.

*fringes;* in keeping with modern technique, long narrow slits rather than pinholes were used in preparing this figure.

Interference is not limited to light waves but is a characteristic of all wave phenomena. Figure 43–4, for example, shows the interference pattern of

**Fig. 43–4** The interference of water waves in a ripple tank. There is destructive interference along the lines marked "Line of nodes" and constructive interference between these lines. (Courtesy Physical Science Study Committee.)

**Fig. 43–5**   Rays from $S_1$ and $S_2$ combine at $P$.   The light falling on screen $B$ has been taken as parallel.   Actually, $D \gg d$, the figure being distorted for clarity.

water waves in a shallow *ripple tank.*   The waves are generated by two vibrators that tap the water surface in synchronism, producing two expanding spherical waves.

Let us analyze Young's experiment quantitatively, assuming that the incident light consists of a single wavelength only.   In Fig. 43–5 $P$ is an arbitrary point on the screen, a distance $r_1$ and $r_2$ from the narrow slits $S_1$ and $S_2$, respectively.   Let us draw a line from $S_2$ to $b$ in such a way that the lines $PS_2$ and $Pb$ are equal.   If $d$, the slit spacing, is much smaller than the distance $D$ between the two screens (the ratio $d/D$ in the figure has been exaggerated for clarity), $S_2b$ is then almost perpendicular to both $r_1$ and $r_2$. This means that angle $S_1S_2b$ is almost equal to angle $PaO$, both angles being marked $\theta$ in the figure.   This is equivalent to saying that the lines $r_1$ and $r_2$ may be taken as parallel.

We often put a lens in front of the two slits, as in Fig. 43–6, the screen $C$ being in the focal plane of the lens.   Under these conditions light focused at $P$ must have struck the lens parallel to the line $Px$, drawn from $P$ through the center of the (thin) lens.   Under these conditions rays $r_1$ and $r_2$ are strictly parallel even though the requirement $D \gg d$ is not met.   The lens $L$ may in practice be the lens and cornea of the eye, screen $C$ being the retina.

The two rays arriving at $P$ in Figs. 43–5 or 43–6 from $S_1$ and $S_2$ are in phase at the source slits, both being derived from the same wavefront in the incident plane wave.   Because the rays have different optical path lengths,

**Fig. 43–6** A lens is normally used to produce interference fringes; compare with Fig. 43–5. The figure is again distorted for clarity in that $f \gg d$ in practice.

they arrive at $P$ with a phase difference. The number of wavelengths contained in $S_1 b$, which is the path difference, determines the nature of the interference at $P$.

To have a *maximum* at $P$, $S_1 b$ ($= d \sin \theta$) must contain an integral number of wavelengths, or

$$S_1 b = m\lambda \qquad m = 0, 1, 2, \ldots,$$

which can be written as

$$d \sin \theta = m\lambda \qquad m = 0, 1, 2, \ldots \text{ (maxima)}. \qquad (43\text{–}1)$$

Note that each maximum above $O$ in Figs. 43–5 and 43–6 has a symmetrically located maximum below $O$. There is a central maximum described by $m = 0$.

For a *minimum* at $P$, $S_1 b$ ($= d \sin \theta$) must contain a half-integral number of wavelengths, or

$$d \sin \theta = (m + \tfrac{1}{2})\lambda \qquad m = 0, 1, 2, \ldots \text{ (minima)}. \qquad (43\text{–}2)$$

If a lens is used as in Fig. 43–6, it may seem that a phase difference should develop between the rays beyond the plane represented by $S_2 b$, the path lengths between this plane and $P$ being clearly different. In Section 42–5, however, we saw that for such parallel rays focused by a lens the *optical path lengths* are identical. Two rays with the same optical path lengths contain the same number of wavelengths, so that no phase difference will result because of the light passing through the lens.

▶ **Example 1.**   The double-slit arrangement in Fig. 43–5 is illuminated with light from a mercury vapor lamp so filtered that only the strong green line ($\lambda = 5460$ A) is effective.   The slits are 0.10 mm apart, and the screen on which the interference pattern appears is 20 cm away.   What is the angular position of the first minimum? Of the tenth maximum?

At the first minimum we put $m = 0$ in Eq. 43–2, or

$$\sin \theta = \frac{(m + \frac{1}{2})\lambda}{d} = \frac{(\frac{1}{2})(546 \times 10^{-9} \text{ meter})}{0.10 \times 10^{-3} \text{ meter}} = 0.0027.$$

This value for $\sin \theta$ is so small that we can take it to be the value of $\theta$, expressed in radians; expressed in degrees it is 0.16°.

At the tenth maximum (not counting the central maximum) we must put $m = 10$ in Eq. 43–1.   Doing so and calculating as before leads to an angular position of 3.8°. For these conditions we see that the angular spread of the first dozen or so fringes is small.

**Example 2.**   In Example 1 what is the linear distance on screen $C$ between adjacent maxima?

If $\theta$ is small enough, we can use the approximation

$$\sin \theta \cong \tan \theta \cong \theta.$$

From Fig. 43–5 we see that     $\tan \theta = \dfrac{y}{D} \cdot$

Substituting this into Eq. 43–1 for $\sin \theta$ leads to

$$y = m \frac{\lambda D}{d} \qquad m = 0, 1, 2, \ldots \text{ (maxima)}.$$

The positions of any two adjacent maxima are given by

$$y_m = m \frac{\lambda D}{d}$$

and

$$y_{m+1} = (m + 1) \frac{\lambda D}{d} \cdot$$

Their separation $\Delta y$ is found by subtracting:

$$\Delta y = y_{m+1} - y_m = \frac{\lambda D}{d}$$

$$= \frac{(546 \times 10^{-9} \text{ meter})(20 \times 10^{-2} \text{ meter})}{0.10 \times 10^{-3} \text{ meter}} = 1.09 \text{ mm.}$$

As long as $\theta$ in Figs. 43–5 and 43–6 is small, the separation of the interference fringes is independent of $m$; that is, the fringes are evenly spaced.   Note that if the incident light contains more than one wavelength the separate interference patterns, which will have different fringe spacings, will be superimposed.     ◀

Equation 43–1 can be used to determine the wavelength of light; to quote Thomas Young:

From a comparison of various experiments, it appears that the breadth of the undulations [that is, the wavelength] constituting the extreme red light must be supposed to be, in air, about one 36 thousandth of an inch, and those of the extreme violet about one 60 thousandth; the mean of the whole spectrum, with respect to the intensity of light, being one 45 thousandth.

Young's value for the average effective wavelength present in sunlight (1/45,000 in.) can be written as 5700 A, which agrees rather well with the wavelength at which the eye sensitivity is a maximum, 5550 A (see Fig. 40–2). It must not be supposed that Young's work was received without criticism. One of his contemporaries, evidently a firm believer in the corpuscular theory of light, wrote:

> We wish to raise our feeble voice against innovations that can have no other effect than to check the progress of science, and renew all those wild phantoms of the imagination which Bacon and Newton put to flight from her temple. This paper contains nothing that deserves the name of either experiment or discovery.

Needless to say, posterity has decided in favor of Young.

### 43–2 Coherence

Analysis of the derivation of Eqs. 43–1 and 43–2 shows that a fundamental requirement for the existence of well-defined interference fringes on screen $C$ in Fig. 43–1 is that the light waves that travel from $S_1$ and $S_2$ to any point $P$ on this screen must have a sharply defined phase difference $\phi$ that remains constant with time. If this condition is satisfied, a stable, well-defined fringe pattern will appear. At certain points $P$, $\phi$ will be given, independent of time, by $n\pi$ where $n = 1, 3, 5, \ldots$ so that the resultant intensity will be strictly zero and will remain so throughout the time of observation. At other points $\phi$ will be given by $n\pi$ where $n = 0, 2, 4 \ldots$ and the resultant intensity will be a maximum. Under these conditions the two beams emerging from slit $S_1$ and $S_2$ are said to be completely *coherent*.

Let the source in Fig. 43–1 be removed and let slits $S_1$ and $S_2$ be replaced by two completely independent light sources, such as two fine incandescent wires placed side by side in a glass envelope. No interference fringes will appear on screen $C$ but only a relatively uniform illumination. We can interpret this if we make the reasonable assumption that for completely independent light sources the phase difference between the two beams arriving at $P$ will vary with time in a random way. At a certain instant conditions may be right for cancellation and a short time later (perhaps $10^{-8}$ sec) they may be right for re-enforcement. This same random phase behavior holds for all points on screen $C$ with the result that this screen is uniformly illuminated. The intensity at any point is equal to the sum of the intensities that each source $S_1$ and $S_2$ produces separately at that point. Under these conditions the two beams emerging from $S_1$ and $S_2$ are said to be completely *incoherent*.

Note that for completely coherent light beams one (1) combines the amplitudes vectorially, taking the (constant) phase difference properly into account, and then (2) squares this resultant amplitude to obtain a quantity proportional to the resultant intensity. For completely incoherent light beams, on the other hand, one (1) squares the individual amplitudes to obtain quantities proportional to the individual intensities and then (2) adds the individual intensities to obtain the resultant intensity. This procedure is in agreement with the experimental fact that for completely independent light sources the resultant intensity at every point is always greater than the intensity produced at that point by either light source acting alone.

It remains to investigate under what experimental conditions coherent or incoherent beams may be produced and to give an explanation for coherence in terms of the mode of production of the radiation. Consider first a parallel beam of microwave radiation emerging from an antenna connected by a coaxial cable to an oscillator based on an electromagnetic resonant cavity. The cavity oscillations (see Section 38-6) are completely periodic with time and produce, at the antenna, a completely periodic variation of $E$ and $B$ with time. The radiated wave at large enough distances from the antenna is well represented by Fig. 39-11. Note that (1) the wave has essentially infinite extent in time, including both future times ($t > 0$, say) and past times ($t < 0$); see Fig. 43-7a. At any point, as the wave passes by, the wave disturbance (i.e., $E$ or $B$) varies with time in a perfectly periodic way. (2) The wavefronts at points far removed from the antenna are parallel planes of essentially infinite extent at right angles to the propagation direction. At any instant of time the wave disturbance varies with distance along the propagation direction in a perfectly periodic way.

Two beams generated from a single traveling wave like that of Fig. 39-11 will be completely coherent. One way to generate two such beams is to put an opaque screen containing two slits in the path of the beam. The waves emerging from the slits will always have a constant phase difference at any point in the region in which they overlap and interference fringes will be produced. Coherent radio beams can also be readily established, as can coherent elastic waves in solids, liquids and gases. The two prongs of the vibrating tapper in Fig. 43-4, for example, generate two coherent waves in the water of the ripple tank.

The technique of producing two beams from a single beam (and thus from a single source) tests specifically whether the wavefronts in the single parallel beam are truly planes, that is, whether all points in a plane at right angles to the direction of propagation have the same phase at any given instant. By dividing the beam in another way it is possible to test whether the beam is truly periodic over a large number of cycles of oscillation. This can be done, as we show in detail in Section 43-6, by inserting in the beam at 45° to it a thin sheet of material possessing the property that two beams are produced, one (which will be at right angles to the incident beam) by reflection and a second (which will be in the direction of the incident beam) by transmission. In the visible region such a sheet, called a half-silvered mirror, may be formed from a glass plate by depositing on it an appropriately thin film of silver. By appropriate use of mirrors (see Section 43-7) these two sub-beams can be recombined into a single beam traveling in a chosen direction. If the beams travel different distances before they are recombined, we are comparing in the combined beam a sample of the original beam with another sample an arbitrarily large number of cycles away. If the original beam is truly periodic in space and time, the two sub-beams will be completely coherent and interference fringes will be produced when they are recombined.

If we turn from microwave sources to common sources of visible light, such as incandescent wires or an electric discharge passing through a gas, we become aware of a fundamental difference. In both of these sources the fundamental light emission processes occur in individual atoms and these atoms do not act together in a cooperative (i.e., coherent) way. The act of light emission by a single atom takes, in a typical case, about $10^{-8}$ sec and the emitted light is properly described as a *wavetrain* (Fig. 43–7b) rather than as a wave (Fig. 43–7a). For emission times such as these the wavetrains are a few meters long.

Interference effects from ordinary light sources may be produced by putting a very narrow slit ($S_0$ in Fig. 43–1) directly in front of the source. This insures that the wavetrains that strike slits $S_1$ and $S_2$ in screen $B$ in this figure originate from the same small region of the source. The diffracted beams emerging from $S_1$ and $S_2$ thus represent the same population of wavetrains and are coherent with respect to each other. If the phase of the light emitted from $S_0$ changes, this change is transmitted simultaneously to $S_1$ and $S_2$. Thus, at any point on screen $C$, a constant phase difference is maintained between the beams from these two slits and a stationary interference pattern occurs.

If the width of slit $S_0$ in Fig. 43–1 is gradually increased it will be observed experimentally that the maxima of the interference fringes become reduced in intensity and that the intensity in the fringe minima is no longer strictly zero. In other words, the fringes become less distinct. If $S_0$ is opened extremely wide, the lowering of the maximum intensity and the raising of the minimum intensity will be such that the fringes disappear, leaving only a uniform illumination. Under these conditions we say that the beams from $S_1$ and $S_2$ pass continuously from a condition of complete coherence to one of complete incoherence. When not at either of these two limits the beams are said to be partially coherent.

Partial coherence can also be demonstrated in two beams that are produced, as described on p. 1090 by inserting a "half-silvered mirror" in a beam at an angle of 45° to the direction of propagation. The two beams so produced, by reflection and transmission, traverse paths of different lengths before they are recombined. If the path difference is small compared to the average length of a wavetrain, the interference fringes will be sharply defined and will go essentially to zero at their minima. If the path difference is deliberately made longer, the fringes will become less distinct, and finally, when the path difference is larger than the average length of a wavetrain, the fringes will disappear altogether. Thus it is possible once again to progress smoothly in an experimental arrangement from complete coherence, through partial coherence, to complete incoherence.

The lack of coherence of the light from ordinary sources such as glowing wires is due to the fact that the emitting atoms do not act cooperatively

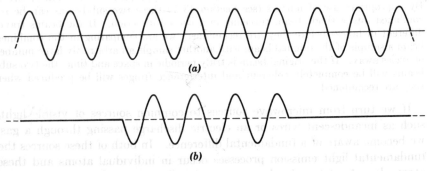

(a)

(b)

**Fig. 43–7** (a) A section of an infinite wave and (b) a wavetrain.

**Fig. 43-8** A screen with two small holes is placed against the end of an optical maser. (a) The light passing through the holes forms an interference pattern on a strip of photographic film placed at (b). The fact that the pattern is formed shows that the light emitted from the maser is coherent across the beam cross section. At (b) is shown the image as formed on a photographic strip exposed in this manner. At (c) is an intensity plot of the film made by measuring the degree to which the film has been exposed. (Courtesy of D. F. Nelson and R. J. Collins, Bell Telephone Laboratories.)

(i.e., *coherently*). Since 1960 it has proved possible to construct sources of visible light in which the atoms *do* act cooperatively and in which the emitted light is highly coherent. Such devices are called *optical masers* or *lasers*; * their light output is extremely monochromatic, intense, and highly collimated. The coherence of the emitted light can be demonstrated by placing a screen with two holes in it in the beam emerging from the laser. An interference pattern results, as Fig. 43-8 shows. These methods permit, for the first time, a degree of control of visible light approaching that possible for radio and for microwaves. The practical applications of lasers, which include the amplification of weak light signals, the use of light beams as highly efficient carriers of information from point to point (see problem 13), and the production of high temperatures by intense local heating, remain to be fully exploited.

## 43-3   Intensity in Young's Experiment

Let us assume that the electric field components of the two waves in Fig. 43-5 vary with time at point $P$ as

$$E_1 = E_0 \sin \omega t \qquad (43\text{-}3)$$

and $$E_2 = E_0 \sin (\omega t + \phi) \qquad (43\text{-}4)$$

where $\omega$ ($= 2\pi\nu$) is the angular frequency of the waves and $\phi$ is the phase difference between them. Note that $\phi$ depends on the location of point $P$,

---

* Laser, like maser, is a coined word, meaning "*l*ight *a*mplification through *s*timulated *e*mission of *r*adiation." The interested student is referred to an article called "Optical Masers" by Arthur L. Schawlow, *Scientific American*, June 1961.

which, in turn, for a fixed geometrical arrangement, is described by the angle $\theta$ in Figs. 43–5 and 43–6. We assume that the slits are so narrow that the diffracted light from each slit illuminates the central portion of the screen uniformly. This means that near the center of the screen $E_0$ is independent of the position of $P$, that is, of the value of $\theta$.

The resultant wave disturbance * at $P$ is found from

$$E = E_1 + E_2 \tag{43–5}$$

and (see Eq. 19–17) proves to be

$$E = E_\theta \sin (\omega t + \beta), \tag{43–6a}$$

where $$\beta = \tfrac{1}{2}\phi \tag{43–6b}$$

and $$E_\theta = 2E_0 \cos \beta = E_m \cos \beta. \tag{43–6c}$$

$E_m$, the maximum possible amplitude for $E_\theta$, is equal to twice the amplitude of the combining waves ( $= 2E_0$), corresponding to complete reinforcement. The student should verify Eq. 43–6 carefully. The amplitude $E_\theta$ of the resultant wave disturbance, which determines the intensity of the interference fringes, will turn out to depend strongly on the value of $\theta$, that is, on the location of point $P$ in Figs. 43–5 and 43–6.

In Section 19–6 we showed that the intensity of a wave $I$, measured perhaps in watts/meter$^2$, is proportional to the square of its amplitude. For the resultant wave then, ignoring the proportionality constant,

$$I_\theta \propto E_\theta^2. \tag{43–7}$$

This relationship seems reasonable if we recall (Eq. 30–27) that the energy density in an electric field is proportional to the *square* of the electric field strength. This is true for rapidly varying electric fields, such as those in a light wave, as well as for static fields.

The ratio of the intensities of two light waves is the ratio of the squares of the amplitudes of their electric fields. If $I_\theta$ is the intensity of the resultant wave at $P$ and $I_0$ is the intensity that a single wave acting alone would produce, then

$$\frac{I_\theta}{I_0} = \left(\frac{E_\theta}{E_0}\right)^2. \tag{43–8}$$

Combining with Eq. 43–6c leads to

$$I_\theta = 4I_0 \cos^2 \beta = I_m \cos^2 \beta. \tag{43–9}$$

---

* The electric field **E** in the light wave rather than the magnetic field **B** is normally identified with the "wave disturbance" because the effects of **B** on the human eye and on various light detectors are exceedingly small. Radiation pressure (Section 40–2) is one such effect. Note too that, although Eq. 43–5 should be a vector equation, in most cases of interest the **E** vectors in the two interfering waves are closely parallel so that an algebraic equation suffices.

Note that the intensity of the resultant wave at any point $P$ varies from zero [for a point at which $\phi \ (= 2\beta) = \pi$, say] to $I_m$, which is four times the intensity $I_0$ of each individual wave [for a point at which $\phi \ (= 2\beta) = 0$, say]. Let us compute $I_\theta$ as a function of the angle $\theta$ in Figs. 43–5 or 43–6.

The phase difference $\phi$ in Eq. 43–4 is associated with the path difference $S_1b$ in Fig. 43–5 or 43–6. If $S_1b$ is $\frac{1}{2}\lambda$, $\phi$ will be $\pi$; if $S_1b$ is $\lambda$, $\phi$ will be $2\pi$, etc. This suggests that

$$\frac{\text{phase difference}}{2\pi} = \frac{\text{path difference}}{\lambda},$$

$$\phi = \frac{2\pi}{\lambda} (d \sin \theta),$$

or, finally, from Eq. 43–6b,

$$\beta = \tfrac{1}{2}\phi = \frac{\pi d}{\lambda} \sin \theta. \tag{43–10}$$

This expression for $\beta$ can be substituted into Eq. 43–9 for $I_\theta$, yielding the latter quantity as a function of $\theta$. For convenience we collect here the expressions for the amplitude and the intensity in double-slit interference.

[Eq. 43–6c]    $E_\theta = E_m \cos \beta$      interference      (43–11a)

[Eq. 43–9]    $I_\theta = I_m \cos^2 \beta$      from narrow      (43–11b)

slits (that is,

[Eq. 43–10]    $\beta \ (= \tfrac{1}{2}\phi) = \dfrac{\pi d}{\lambda} \sin \theta$    $a \ll \lambda$)      (43–11c)

To find the positions of the intensity maxima, we put

$$\beta = m\pi \qquad m = 0, 1, 2, \ldots$$

in Eq. 43–11b. From Eq. 43–11c this reduces to

$$d \sin \theta = m\lambda \qquad m = 0, 1, 2, \ldots \text{ (maxima)},$$

which is the equation derived in Section 43–1 (Eq. 43–1). To find the intensity minima we write

$$\frac{\pi d \sin \theta}{\lambda} = (m + \tfrac{1}{2})\pi \qquad m = 0, 1, 2, \ldots \text{ (minima)},$$

which reduces to the previously derived Eq. 43–2.

Figure 43–9 shows the intensity pattern for double-slit interference. The horizontal solid line is $I_0$; this describes the (uniform) intensity pattern on the screen if one of the slits is covered up. If the two sources were incoherent the intensity would be uniform over the screen and would be $2I_0$; see the horizontal dashed line in Fig. 43–9. For coherent sources we expect the

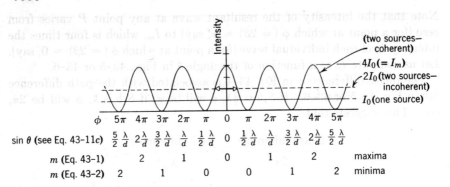

| $\phi$ | $5\pi$ | $4\pi$ | $3\pi$ | $2\pi$ | $\pi$ | 0 | $\pi$ | $2\pi$ | $3\pi$ | $4\pi$ | $5\pi$ | |
|---|---|---|---|---|---|---|---|---|---|---|---|---|
| $\sin\theta$ (see Eq. 43-11c) | $\frac{5}{2}\frac{\lambda}{d}$ | $2\frac{\lambda}{d}$ | $\frac{3}{2}\frac{\lambda}{d}$ | $\frac{\lambda}{d}$ | $\frac{1}{2}\frac{\lambda}{d}$ | 0 | $\frac{1}{2}\frac{\lambda}{d}$ | $\frac{\lambda}{d}$ | $\frac{3}{2}\frac{\lambda}{d}$ | $2\frac{\lambda}{d}$ | $\frac{5}{2}\frac{\lambda}{d}$ | |
| $m$ (Eq. 43-1) | 2 | | 1 | | 0 | | 1 | | 2 | | | maxima |
| $m$ (Eq. 43-2) | 2 | | 1 | | 0 | | 0 | | 1 | | 2 | minima |

**Fig. 43–9** The intensity pattern for double-slit interference. The heavy arrow in the central peak represents the half-width of the peak. This figure is constructed on the assumption that the two interfering waves each illuminate the central portion of the screen uniformly, that is, $I_0$ is independent of position as shown.

energy to be merely redistributed over the screen, since energy is neither created nor destroyed by the interference process. Thus the *average* intensity in the interference pattern should be $2I_0$, as for incoherent sources. This follows at once if, in Eq. 43–11*b*, we substitute one-half for the cosine-squared term and if we recall that $I_m = 4I_0$. We have seen several times that the average value of the square of a sine or a cosine term over one or more half-cycles is one-half.

### 43–4 Adding Wave Disturbances

In Section 43–3 we combined two time-varying wave disturbances, namely

$$E_1 = E_0 \sin \omega t \qquad (43\text{--}3)$$

and

$$E_2 = E_0 \sin (\omega t + \phi), \qquad (43\text{--}4)$$

which have the same angular frequency $\omega$ and amplitude $E_0$ but which have a phase difference $\phi$ between them. In this case the result (Eqs. 43–11*a* and *c*) is easily obtained algebraically.

In later chapters we will want to add larger numbers of wave disturbances, often an infinite number, with infinitesimal individual amplitudes. Since analytic methods become more difficult in such cases we describe a graphical method, illustrating it by rederiving Eq. 43–11*a*.

A sinusoidal wave disturbance such as that represented by Eq. 43–3 can be represented graphically, using a rotating vector. In Fig. 43–10*a* a vector of magnitude $E_0$ is allowed to rotate about the origin in a counterclockwise direction with an angular frequency $\omega$. Following electrical engineering practice we call such a rotating vector a *phasor*. The alternating wave disturbance $E_1$ (Eq. 43–3) is represented by the projection of this phasor on the vertical axis.

A second wave disturbance $E_2$, which has the same amplitude $E_0$ but a phase difference $\phi$ with respect to $E_1$,

$$E_2 = E_0 \sin (\omega t + \phi), \qquad (43\text{–}4)$$

can be represented graphically (Fig. 43–10$b$) as the projection on the vertical axis of a second phasor of magnitude $E_0$ which makes an angle $\phi$ with the first phasor. As this figure shows, the sum $E$ of $E_1$ and $E_2$ is the sum of the projections of the two phasors on the vertical axis. This is revealed more clearly if the phasors are redrawn, as in Fig. 43–10$c$, placing the foot of one arrow at the head of the other, maintaining the proper phase difference, and letting the whole assembly rotate counterclockwise about the origin.

In Fig. 43–10$c$ $E$ can also be regarded as the projection on the vertical axis of a phasor of length $E_\theta$, which is the vector sum of the two phasors of magnitude $E_0$. Note that the (algebraic) sum of the projections of the two phasors is equal to the projection of the (vector) sum of the two phasors.

In most problems in optics we are concerned only with the *amplitude* $E_\theta$ of the resultant wave disturbance and not with its time variation. This is because the eye and other common measuring instruments respond to the resultant intensity of the light (that is, to the square of the amplitude) and cannot detect the rapid time variations that characterize visible light. For sodium light, for example ($\lambda = 5890$ A), the frequency $\nu$ ($= \omega/2\pi$) is 5.1 $\times$ $10^{14}$ cycles/sec. Often, then, we need not consider the rotation of the phasors but can confine our attention to finding the magnitude of the resultant phasor.

*(a)*

*(b)*

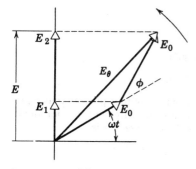

*(c)*

**Fig. 43–10**   (*a*) A wave disturbance $E_1$ is represented by a rotating vector or *phasor*. (*b*) Two wave disturbances $E_1$ and $E_2$, with a phase difference $\phi$ between them, are so represented. These two phasors can represent the two wave disturbances in the double-slit problem; see Eqs. 43–3 and 43–4. (*c*) Another way of drawing (*b*).

(a)

(b)

**Fig. 43–11**   (a) A construction to find the amplitude $E_\theta$ of two wave disturbances of amplitude $E_0$ and phase difference $\phi$.   (b) The maximum possible amplitude for these wave disturbances occurs for $\phi = 0$ and has the value $E_m = 2E_0$.

Figure 43–11a shows the phasors for double-slit interference at time $t = 0$; compare Fig. 43–10c.  We see that

$$E_\theta = 2E_0 \cos \beta = E_m \cos \beta,$$

in which, from the theorem that the exterior angle of a triangle ($\phi$) is equal to the sum of its two opposite interior angles ($\beta + \beta$),

$$\beta = \tfrac{1}{2}\phi.$$

This is exactly the result arrived at earlier algebraically; compare Eqs. 43–11a and c.

In a more general case we might want to find the resultant of a number ($>2$) of sinusoidally varying wave disturbances.  The general procedure is the following:

1. Construct a series of phasors representing the functions to be added. Draw them end to end, maintaining the proper phase relationships between adjacent phasors.

2. Construct the vector sum of this array.  Its length gives the amplitude of the resultant.  The angle between it and the first phasor is the phase of the resultant with respect to this first phasor.  The projection of this phasor on the vertical axis gives the time variation of the resultant wave disturbance.

▶ **Example 3.**   Find graphically the resultant $E(t)$ of the following wave disturbances:

$$E_1 = 10 \sin \omega t$$

$$E_2 = 10 \sin (\omega t + 15°)$$

$$E_3 = 10 \sin (\omega t + 30°)$$

$$E_4 = 10 \sin (\omega t + 45°).$$

Figure 43–12 in which $E_0$ equals 10, shows the assembly of four phasors that represents these functions.  Their vector sum, by graphical measurement, has an amplitude $E_R$ of 38 and a phase $\phi_0$ with respect to $E_1$ of 23°.  In other words

$$E(t) = E_1 + E_2 + E_3 + E_4 = 38 \sin (\omega t + 23°).$$

Check this result by trigonometric calculation.   ◀

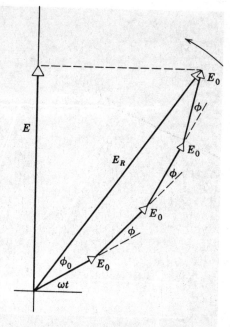

**Fig. 43-12** Example 3. Four wave disturbances are added graphically, using the method of phasors.

## 43-5  Interference from Thin Films

The colors of soap bubbles, oil slicks, and other thin films are the result of interference. Figure 43-13 shows interference effects in a thin vertical film of soapy water illuminated by monochromatic light.

Figure 43-14 shows a film of uniform thickness $d$ and index of refraction $n$, the eye being focused on spot $a$. The film is illuminated by a broad source of monochromatic light $S$. There exists on this source a point $P$ such that two rays, identified by the single and double arrows, respectively, can leave $P$ and enter the eye as shown, after passing through point $a$. These two rays follow

**Fig. 43-13** A soapy water film on a wire loop, viewed by reflected light. The black segment at the top is not a tear. It arises because the film, by drainage, is so thin here that there is destructive interference between the light reflected from its front surface and that reflected from its back surface. Recall that these two waves differ in phase by 180°

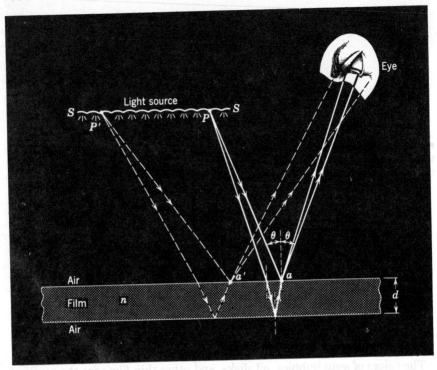

Eye

Light source

**Fig. 43–14** Interference by reflection from a thin film, assuming an extended source $S$.

different paths in going from $P$ to the eye, one being reflected from the upper surface of the film, the other from the lower surface. Whether point $a$ appears bright or dark depends on the nature of the interference between the two waves that diverge from $a$. These waves are coherent because they both originate from the same point $P$ on the light source.

If the eye looks at another part of the film, say $a'$, the light that enters the eye must originate from a different point $P'$ of the extended source, as suggested by the dashed lines in Fig. 43–14.

For near-normal incidence ($\theta \cong 0$ in Fig. 43–14) the geometrical path difference for the two rays from $P$ will be close to $2d$. We might expect the resultant wave reflected from the film near $a$ to be an interference maximum if the distance $2d$ is an integral number of wavelengths. This statement must be modified for two reasons.

First, the wavelength must refer to the wavelength of the light in the film $\lambda_n$ and not to its wavelength in air $\lambda$; that is, we are concerned with optical path lengths rather than geometrical path lengths. The wavelengths $\lambda$ and $\lambda_n$ (see Eq. 41–11) are related by

$$\lambda_n = \lambda/n. \qquad (43\text{–}12)$$

To bring out the second point, let us assume that the film is so thin that $2d$ is very much less than a wavelength. The phase difference between the two waves would be close to zero on our assumption, and we would expect such a film to appear bright on reflection. However, it appears dark. This is clear from Fig. 43–13, in which the action of gravity produces a wedge-shaped film, extremely thin at its top edge. As drainage continues, the dark area increases in size. To explain this and many similar phenomena, we assume that one or the other of the two rays of Fig. 43–14 suffers an abrupt phase change of $\pi$ ($= 180°$) associated either with reflection at the air-film interface or transmission through it. As it turns out, the ray reflected from the upper surface suffers this phase change. The other ray is not changed abruptly in phase, either on transmission through the upper surface or on reflection at the lower surface.

In Section 19–9 we discussed phase changes on reflection for transverse waves in strings. To extend these ideas, consider the composite string of Fig. 43–15, which consists of two parts with different masses per unit length, stretched to a given tension. If a pulse moves to the right in Fig. 43–15a, approaching the junction, there will be a reflected and a transmitted pulse,

**Fig. 43–15** Phase changes on reflection at a junction between two stretched composite strings. (a) Incident pulse in heavy string and (b) incident pulse in light string.

the reflected pulse being *in phase* with the incident pulse. In Fig. 43–15b the situation is reversed, the incident pulse now being in the less massive string. In this case the reflected pulse will differ in phase from the incident pulse by $\pi$ ($= 180°$). In each case the transmitted pulse will be in phase with the incident pulse.

Figure 43–15a suggests a light wave in glass, say, approaching a surface beyond which there is a less optically dense medium (one of lower index of refraction) such as air. Figure 43–15b suggests a light wave in air approaching glass. To sum up the optical situation, when reflection occurs from an interface beyond which the medium has a *lower* index of refraction, the reflected wave undergoes *no phase change;* when the medium beyond the interface has a *higher* index, there is a phase change of $\pi$.* The transmitted wave does not experience a change of phase in either case.

---

* These statements, which can be proved rigorously from Maxwell's equations (see also Section 43–6), must be modified for light falling on a less dense medium at an angle such that total internal reflection occurs. They must also be modified for reflection from metallic surfaces.

We are now able to take into account both factors that determine the nature of the interference, namely, differences in optical path length and phase changes on reflection. For the two rays of Fig. 43–14 to combine to give a *maximum* intensity, assuming normal incidence, we must have

$$2d = (m + \tfrac{1}{2})\lambda_n \qquad m = 0, 1, 2, \ldots .$$

The term $\tfrac{1}{2}\lambda_n$ is introduced because of the phase change on reflection, a phase change of 180° being equivalent to half a wavelength. Substituting $\lambda/n$ for $\lambda_n$ yields finally

$$2dn = (m + \tfrac{1}{2})\lambda \qquad m = 0, 1, 2, \ldots \text{(maxima)}. \qquad (43\text{--}13)$$

The condition for a *minimum* intensity is

$$2dn = m\lambda \qquad m = 0, 1, 2, \ldots \text{(minima)}. \qquad (43\text{--}14)$$

These equations hold when the index of refraction of the film is either greater or less than the indices of the media on *each* side of the film. Only in these cases will there be a relative phase change of 180° for reflections at the two surfaces. A water film in air and an air film in the space between two glass plates provide examples of cases to which Eqs. 43–13 and 43–14 apply. Example 5 provides a case in which they do not apply.

If the film thickness is not uniform, as in Fig. 43–13, where the film is wedge-shaped, constructive interference will occur in certain parts of the film and destructive interference will occur in others. Lines of maximum and of minimum intensity will appear—these are the interference fringes. They are called *fringes of constant thickness*, each fringe being the locus of points for which the film thickness $d$ is a constant. If the film is illuminated with white light rather than monochromatic light, the light reflected from various parts of the film will be modified by the various constructive or destructive interferences that occur. This accounts for the brilliant colors of soap bubbles and oil slicks.

Only if the film is "thin," which implies that $d$ is no more than a few wavelengths of light, will fringes of the type described, that is, fringes that appear localized on the film and associated with a variable film thickness, be possible. For very thick films (say $d \cong 1$ cm), the path difference between the two rays of Fig. 43–14 will be many wavelengths and the phase difference at a given point on the film will change rapidly as we move even a small distance away from $a$. For "thin" films, however, the phase difference at $a$ also holds for reasonably nearby points; there is a characteristic "patch brightness" for any point on the film, as Fig. 43–13 shows. Interference fringes can be produced for thick films; they are not localized on the film but are at infinity. See Section 43–7.

▶ **Example 4.** A water film ($n = 1.33$) in air is 3200 A thick. If it is illuminated with white light at normal incidence, what color will it appear to be in reflected light?
By solving Eq. 43–13 for $\lambda$,

$$\lambda = \frac{2dn}{m + \tfrac{1}{2}} = \frac{(2)(3200 \text{ A})(1.33)}{m + \tfrac{1}{2}} = \frac{8500 \text{ A}}{m + \tfrac{1}{2}} \qquad \text{(maxima)}.$$

From Eq. 43-14 the minima are given by

$$\lambda = \frac{8500 \text{ A}}{m} \quad \text{(minima)}.$$

Maxima and minima occur for the following wavelengths:

| $m$ | 0 (max) | 1 (min) | 1 (max) | 2 (min) | 2 (max) |
|---|---|---|---|---|---|
| $\lambda$, A | 17000 | 8500 | 5700 | 4250 | 3400 |

Only the maximum corresponding to $m = 1$ lies in the visible region (see Fig. 40–2); light of this wavelength appears yellow-green. If white light is used to illuminate the film, the yellow-green component will be enhanced when viewed by reflection.

**Example 5.** *Nonreflecting glass.* Lenses are often coated with thin films of transparent substances like $MgF_2$ ($n = 1.38$) in order to reduce the reflection from the glass surface, using interference. How thick a coating is needed to produce a minimum reflection at the center of the visible spectrum (5500 A)?

We assume that the light strikes the lens at near-normal incidence ($\theta$ is exaggerated for clarity in Fig. 43–16), and we seek destructive interference between rays $r$ and $r_1$. Equation 43–14 does not apply because in this case a phase change of 180° is associated with *each* ray, for at *both* the upper and lower surfaces of the $MgF_2$ film the reflection is from a medium of greater index of refraction.

There is no net change in phase produced by the two reflections, which means that the optical path difference for destructive interference is $(m + \frac{1}{2})\lambda$ (compare Eq. 43–13), leading to

$$2dn = (m + \tfrac{1}{2})\lambda \quad m = 0, 1, 2, \ldots \text{ (minima)}.$$

Solving for $d$ and putting $m = 0$ yields

$$d = \frac{(m + \frac{1}{2})\lambda}{2n} = \frac{\lambda}{4n} = \frac{5500 \text{ A}}{(4)(1.38)} = 1000 \text{ A}.$$

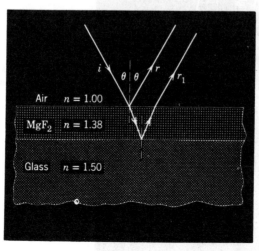

**Fig. 43–16**   Example 5.  Unwanted reflections from glass can be reduced by coating the glass with a thin transparent film.

**Example 6.** *Newton's rings.* Figure 43–17 shows a lens of radius of curvature $R$ resting on an accurately plane glass plate and illuminated from above by light of wavelength $\lambda$. Figure 43–18 shows that circular interference fringes (Newton's rings) appear, associated with the variable thickness air film between the lens and the plate. Find the radii of the circular interference maxima.

Here it is the ray from the *bottom* of the (air) film rather than from the top that undergoes a phase change of 180°, for it is the one reflected from a medium of higher refractive index. The condition for a maximum remains unchanged, however (Eq. 43–13), and is

$$2d = (m + \tfrac{1}{2})\lambda \qquad m = 0, 1, 2, \ldots, \qquad (43\text{–}15)$$

the index of refraction of the air film being assumed to be unity. From Fig. 43–17 we can write

$$d = R - \sqrt{R^2 - r^2} = R - R\left[1 - \left(\frac{r}{R}\right)^2\right]^{\frac{1}{2}}.$$

If $r/R \ll 1$, the square bracket can be expanded by the binomial theorem, keeping only two terms, or

$$d = R - R\left[1 - \frac{1}{2}\left(\frac{r}{R}\right)^2 + \cdots\right] \cong \frac{r^2}{2R}.$$

Combining with Eq. 43–15 yields

$$r = \sqrt{(m + \tfrac{1}{2})\lambda R} \qquad m = 0, 1, 2, \ldots,$$

**Fig. 43–17** Example 6. Apparatus for observing Newton's rings.

**Fig. 43-18**   Example 6.   Newton's rings.   (Courtesy of Bausch and Lomb Optical Co.)

which gives the radii of the bright rings.  If white light is used, each spectrum component will produce its own set of circular fringes, the sets all overlapping.     ◄

### 43-6   Phase Changes on Reflection

G. G. Stokes (1819–1903) used the principle of optical reversibility to investigate the reflection of light at an interface between two media.  The principle states that if there is no absorption of light a light ray that is reflected or refracted will retrace its original path if its direction is reversed.  This reminds us that any mechanical system can run backward as well as forward, provided there is no absorption of energy because of friction, etc.

Figure 43-19a shows a wave of amplitude $E$ reflected and refracted at a surface separating media 1 and 2, where $n_2 > n_1$.  The amplitude of the reflected wave is $r_{12}E$, in which $r_{12}$ is an *amplitude reflection coefficient*.  The amplitude of the refracted wave is $t_{12}E$, where $t_{12}$ is an *amplitude transmission coefficient*.

We consider only the possibility of phase changes of 0 or 180°.  If $r_{12} = +0.5$, for example, we have a reduction in amplitude on reflection by one-half and no change in phase.  For $r_{12} = -0.5$ we have a phase change of 180° because

$$E \sin (\omega t + 180°) = -E \sin \omega t.$$

Figure 43-19b suggests that if we reverse these two rays they should combine to produce the original ray reversed in direction.  Ray $r_{12}E$, identified by the single arrows in the figure, is reflected and refracted, producing the rays of amplitudes

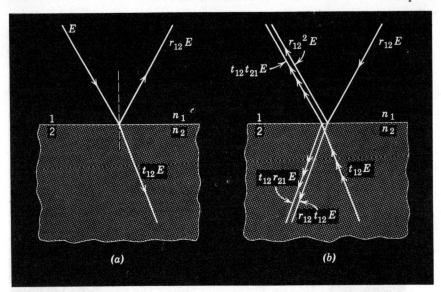

**Fig. 43–19** (a) A ray is reflected and refracted at an air-glass interface. (b) The optically reversed situation; the two rays in the lower left must cancel.

$r_{12}{}^2E$ and $r_{12}t_{12}E$. Ray $t_{12}E$, identified by the triple arrows, is also reflected and refracted, producing the rays of amplitudes $t_{12}t_{21}E$ and $t_{12}r_{21}E$ as shown. Note that $r_{12}$ describes a ray in medium 1 reflected from medium 2, and $r_{21}$ describes a ray in medium 2 reflected from medium 1. Similarly, $t_{12}$ describes a ray that passes from medium 1 to medium 2; $t_{21}$ describes a ray that passes from medium 2 to medium 1.

The two rays in the upper left of Fig. 43–19b must be equivalent to the incident ray of Fig. 43–19a, reversed; the two rays in the lower left of Fig. 43–19b must cancel. This second requirement leads to

$$r_{12}t_{12}E + t_{12}r_{21}E = 0,$$

or $$r_{12} = -r_{21}.$$

This result tells us that if we compare a wave reflected from medium one with one reflected from medium 2, they behave differently in that one or the other undergoes a phase change of 180°. We must rely on experiment to show that, as we pointed out earlier, the ray reflected from the more optically dense medium is the one that experiences the phase change of 180°.

### 43–7 Michelson's Interferometer

An interferometer is a device that can be used to measure lengths or changes in length with great accuracy by means of interference fringes. We describe the form originally built by Michelson in 1881.

Consider light that leaves point $P$ on extended source $S$ (Fig. 43–20) and falls on half-silvered mirror $M$. This mirror has a silver coating just thick enough to transmit half the incident light and to reflect half; in the figure we have assumed that this mirror, for convenience, possesses negligible thickness. At $M$ the light divides into two waves. One proceeds by transmission toward mirror $M_1$; the other proceeds by reflection toward $M_2$. The waves are reflected at each of these mirrors and are sent back along their directions of incidence, each wave eventually entering the eye $E$. Since the waves are coherent, being derived from the same point on the source, they will interfere.

If the mirrors $M_1$ and $M_2$ are exactly perpendicular to each other, the effect is that of light from an extended source $S$ falling on a uniformly thick slab of air, between glass, whose thickness is equal to $d_2 - d_1$. Interference fringes appear, caused by small changes in the angle of incidence of the light from different points on the extended source as it strikes the equivalent air film. For *thick* films a path difference of one wavelength can be brought about by a very small change in the angle of incidence.

If $M_2$ is moved backward or forward, the effect is to change the thickness of the equivalent air film. Suppose that the center of the (circular) fringe pattern appears bright and that $M_2$ is moved just enough to cause the first bright circular fringe to move to the center of the pattern. The path of the light beam striking $M_2$ has been changed by one wavelength. This means (because the light passes twice through the equivalent air film) that the mirror must have moved one-half a wavelength.

The interferometer is used to measure changes in length by counting the number of interference fringes that pass the field of view as mirror $M_2$ is moved. Length measurements made in this way can be accurate if large numbers of fringes are counted.

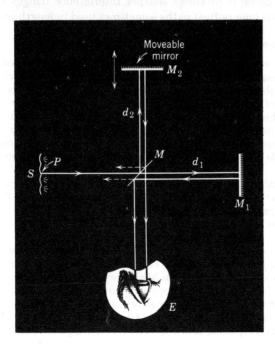

**Fig. 43–20**  Michelson's interferometer, showing the path of a particular ray originating at point $P$ of an extended source $S$.

Michelson measured the length of the standard meter, kept in Paris, in terms of the wavelength of certain monochromatic red light emitted from a light source containing cadmium. He showed that the standard meter was equivalent to 1,553,163.5 wavelengths of the red cadmium light.

Physicists have long speculated on the advantages of discarding the standard meter bar as the basic standard of length and of *defining* the meter in terms of the wavelength of some carefully chosen monochromatic radiation. This would make the primary length standard readily available in laboratories all over the world. It would improve the accuracy of length measurements, since one would no longer need to compare an unknown object with a standard object (the meter bar), using interferometer techniques, but could measure the unknown object *directly* and in an absolute sense, using these techniques. There is the additional advantage that if the standard meter bar were destroyed it could never be replaced, whereas light sources and interferometers will (presumably) always be available.

In 1961 such an atomic standard of length was adopted by international agreement. Quoting from an article * describing the event:

> The wavelength of the orange-red light of krypton-86 has replaced the platinum iridium bar as the world standard of length. Formerly the wavelength of this light was defined as a function of the length of the meter bar. Now the meter is defined as a multiple (1,650,763.73) of the wavelength of the light.

The light from krypton-86 was used in preference to that from cadmium or other sources because it produces sharper interference fringes in the interferometer over the long optical paths sometimes used in length measurement.

### 43–8   Michelson's Interferometer and Light Propagation

In Section 40–4 we presented Einstein's hypothesis, now well verified, that in free space light is propagated with the same speed $c$ no matter what the relative velocity of the source and the observer may be. We pointed out that this hypothesis contradicted the views of nineteenth-century physicists regarding wave propagation. It was difficult for these physicists, trained as they were in the classical physics of the time, to believe that a wave could be propagated without a medium. If such a medium could be established, the speed $c$ of light would naturally be construed as the speed *with respect to that medium,* just as the speed of sound always refers to a medium such as air.

Although no medium for light propagation was obvious, the physicists postulated one, called the *ether* † and hypothesized that its properties were such that it was undetectable by ordinary means such as weighing.

In 1881 (24 years before Einstein's hypothesis) A. A. Michelson set himself the task of forcing the ether, assuming that it existed, to submit to direct physical verification. In particular, Michelson, later joined by E. W. Morley, tried to measure the speed $u$ with which the earth moves through the ether. Michelson's interferometer was their instrument of choice for this now-famous Michelson-Morley experiment.

The earth together with the interferometer moving with velocity **u** through the ether is equivalent to the interferometer at rest with the ether streaming through it with velocity $-$**u**, as shown in Fig. 43–21. Consider a wave moving along the path $MM_1M$ and one moving along $MM_2M$. The first corresponds classically to a man

---

* *Scientific American,* p.75, December 1960.

† More fully, the *luminiferous* (or light-carrying) *ether.*

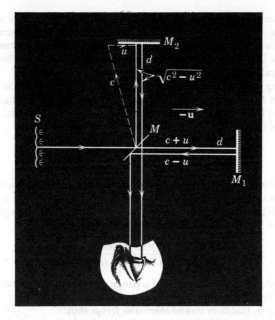

**Fig. 43–21** The "ether" is streaming with velocity $-\mathbf{u}$ through Michelson's interferometer. The wave speeds shown are on the basis of the (incorrect) ether hypothesis.

rowing a boat a distance $d$ downstream and the same distance upstream; the second corresponds to rowing a boat a distance $d$ across a stream and back.

*On the ether hypothesis* the speed of light on the path $MM_1$ is $c + u$; on the return path $M_1M$ it is $c - u$. The time required for the complete trip is

$$t_1 = \frac{d}{c + u} + \frac{d}{c - u} = d\,\frac{2c}{c^2 - u^2} = \frac{2d}{c}\,\frac{1}{1 - (u/c)^2}.$$

The speed of light, *on the ether hypothesis*, for path $MM_2$ is $\sqrt{c^2 - u^2}$, as Fig. 43–21 suggests. This same speed holds for the return path $M_2M$, so that the time required for this complete path is

$$t_2 = \frac{2d}{\sqrt{c^2 - u^2}} = \frac{2d}{c}\,\frac{1}{\sqrt{1 - (u/c)^2}}.$$

The difference of time for the two paths is

$$\Delta t = t_1 - t_2$$

$$= \frac{2d}{c}\left\{\left[1 - \left(\frac{u}{c}\right)^2\right]^{-1} - \left[1 - \left(\frac{u}{c}\right)^2\right]^{-\frac{1}{2}}\right\}.$$

Assuming $u/c \ll 1$, we can expand the quantities in the square brackets by using the binomial theorem, retaining only the first two terms. This leads to

$$\Delta t = \frac{2d}{c}\left\{\left[1 + \left(\frac{u}{c}\right)^2 + \cdots\right] - \left[1 + \frac{1}{2}\left(\frac{u}{c}\right)^2 + \cdots\right]\right\}$$

$$= \frac{2d}{c}\left\{\frac{1}{2}\left(\frac{u}{c}\right)^2\right\} = \frac{du^2}{c^3}. \tag{43–16}$$

Now let the entire interferometer be rotated through 90°. This will interchange the roles of the two light paths, $MM_1M$ now being the "cross-stream" path and $MM_2M$ the "down- and upstream" path. The time difference between the two waves entering the eye is also reversed; this changes the phase difference between the combining waves and alters the positions of the interference maxima. *The experiment consists of looking for a shift of the interference fringes as the apparatus is rotated.*

The *change* in time difference is $2\Delta t$, which corresponds to a fringe shift of $2\Delta t/T$ where $T$ ($= \lambda/c$) is the period of vibration of the light. The expected maximum shift in the number of fringes on a 90° rotation (see Eq. 43–16) is

$$\Delta N = \frac{2\Delta t}{T} = \frac{2\Delta t c}{\lambda} = \frac{2d}{\lambda}\left(\frac{u}{c}\right)^2. \tag{43–17}$$

In the Michelson-Morley interferometer let $d = 11$ meters (obtained by multiple reflection in the interferometer) and $\lambda = 5.9 \times 10^{-7}$ meter. If $u$ is assumed to be roughly the orbital speed of the earth, then $u/c \cong 10^{-4}$. The expected maximum fringe shift when the interferometer is rotated through 90° is then

$$\Delta N = \frac{2d}{\lambda}\left(\frac{u}{c}\right)^2 = \frac{(2)(11 \text{ meters})}{5.9 \times 10^{-7} \text{ meter}}(10^{-4})^2 = 0.4.$$

Even though a shift of only about 0.4 of a fringe was expected, Michelson and Morley were confident that they could observe a shift of 0.01 fringe. *They found from their experiment, however, that there was no observable fringe shift!*

The analogy between a light wave in the supposed ether and a boat moving in water, which seemed so evident in 1881, is simply incorrect. The derivation based on this analogy is incorrect for light waves. When the analysis is carried through on Einstein's hypothesis, the observed negative result is clearly predicted, the speed of light being $c$ for all paths. The motion of the earth around the sun and the rotation of the interferometer have, in Einstein's view, no effect whatever on the speed of the light waves in the interferometer.

It should be made clear that although Einstein's hypothesis is completely consistent with the negative result of the Michelson-Morley experiment this experiment standing alone cannot serve as a proof for Einstein's hypothesis. Einstein said that no number of experiments, however large, could prove him right but that a single experiment could prove him wrong. Our present-day belief in Einstein's hypothesis rests on consistent agreement in a large number of experiments designed to test it. The "single experiment" that might prove Einstein wrong has never been found.

# QUESTIONS

1. Is Young's experiment an interference experiment or a diffraction experiment, or both?

2. Do interference effects occur for sound waves? Recall that sound is a longitudinal wave and that light is a transverse wave.

3. In Young's double-slit interference experiment, using a monochromatic laboratory light source, why is screen $A$ in Fig. 43-1 necessary? What would happen if one gradually enlarged the hole in this screen?

4. Describe the pattern of light intensity on screen $C$ in Fig. 43-5 if one slit is covered with a red filter and the other with a blue filter, the incident light being white.

5. Is coherence important in reflection and refraction?

6. Define carefully, and distinguish between, the angles $\theta$ and $\phi$ that appear in Eq. 43-10.

7. If one slit in Fig. 43-5 is covered, what change occurs in the intensity of light in the center of the screen?

8. What changes occur in the pattern of interference fringes if the apparatus of Fig. 43-5 is placed under water?

9. What are the requirements for a maximum intensity when viewing a thin film by *transmitted* light?

10. In a Newton's rings experiment, is the central spot, as seen by reflection, dark or light? Explain.

11. Why must the film of Fig. 43-14 be "thin" for us to see an interference pattern of the type described?

12. Why do coated lenses (see Example 5) look purple by reflected light?

13. A person wets his eyeglasses to clean them. As the water evaporates he notices that for a short time the glasses become markedly more nonreflecting. Explain.

14. A lens is coated to reduce reflection, as in Example 5. What happens to the energy that had previously been reflected? Is it absorbed by the coating?

15. Very small changes in the angle of incidence do not change the interference conditions much for "thin" films but they do change them for "thick" films. Why?

16. The directional characteristics of a certain radar antenna as a receiver of radiation are known. What can be said about its directional characteristics as a transmitter?

17. A person in a dark room, looking through a small window, can see a second person standing outside in bright sunlight. The second person cannot see the first person. Is this a failure of the principle of optical reversibility? Assume no absorption of light.

18. Why is it necessary to rotate the interferometer in the Michelson-Morley experiment?

19. How is the negative result of the Michelson-Morley experiment interpreted according to Einstein's theory of relativity?

20. If interference between light waves of different frequencies is possible, one should observe light beats, just as one obtains sound beats from two sources of sound with slightly different frequencies. Discuss how one might experimentally look for this possibility.

21. In Young's double-slit experiment suppose that screen $A$ in Fig. 43-1 contained *two* very narrow parallel slits instead of one. (a) Show that if the spacing between these slits is properly chosen the interference fringes can be made to disappear. (b) Under these conditions, would you call the beams emerging from slits $S_1$ and $S_2$ in screen $B$ coherent? They do not produce interference fringes. (c) Discuss what would happen to the interference fringes in the case of a single slit in screen $A$ if the slit width were gradually increased.

## PROBLEMS

1. Design a double-slit arrangement that will produce interference fringes 1° apart on a distant screen. Assume sodium light ($\lambda = 5890$ A).
2. Two point sources in Fig. 43–22 emit coherent waves. Show that curves, such as that given, over which the phase difference for rays $r_1$ and $r_2$ is a constant are hyperbolas. Extend the analysis to three dimensions. (Hint: A constant phase difference implies a constant difference in length between $r_1$ and $r_2$.)

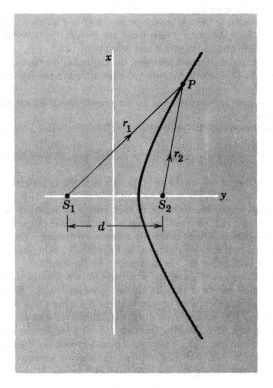

**Fig. 43–22**

3. A double-slit arrangement produces interference fringes for sodium light ($\lambda = 5890$ A) that are 0.20° apart. What is the angular fringe separation if the entire arrangement is immersed in water?
4. A double-slit arrangement produces interference fringes for sodium light ($\lambda = 5890$ A) that are 0.20° apart. For what wavelength would the angular separation be 10% greater?
5. A thin flake of mica ($n = 1.58$) is used to cover one slit of a double-slit arrangement. The central point on the screen is occupied by what used to be the seventh bright fringe. If $\lambda = 5500$ A, what is the thickness of the mica?
6. Sodium light ($\lambda = 5890$ A) falls on a double slit of separation $d = 2.0$ mm. $D$ in Fig. 43–5 is 4 cm. What per cent error is made in locating the tenth bright fringe if it is *not* assumed that $D \gg d$?
7. Sodium light ($\lambda = 5890$ A) falls on a double slit of separation $d = 0.20$ mm. A thin lens ($f = +1.0$ meter) is placed near the slit as in Fig. 43–6. What is the linear fringe separation on a screen placed in the focal plane of the lens?

8. $S_1$ and $S_2$ in Fig. 43–23 are effective point sources of radiation, excited by the same oscillator. They are coherent and in phase with each other. Placed 4.0 meters apart, they emit equal amounts of power in the form of 1.0-meter wavelength electromagnetic waves. (a) Find the positions of the first (that is, the nearest), the second, and the third maxima of the received signal, as the detector is moved out along $Ox$. (b) Is the intensity at the nearest minimum equal to zero? Justify your answer.

**Fig. 43–23**

9. One of the slits of a double-slit system is wider than the other, so that the amplitude of the light reaching the central part of the screen from one slit, acting alone, is twice that from the other slit, acting alone. Derive an expression for $I_\theta$ in terms of $\theta$, corresponding to Eqs. 43–11b and c.

10. Show that the half-width $\Delta\theta$ of the double-slit interference fringes (see arrow in Fig. 43–9) is given by

$$\Delta\theta = \frac{\lambda}{2d}$$

if $\theta$ is small enough so that $\sin\theta \cong \theta$.

11. Find the sum of the following quantities (a) by the vector method and (b) analytically:

$$y_1 = 10 \sin \omega t$$

$$y_2 = 8 \sin (\omega t + 30°).$$

12. Add the following quantities graphically, using the vector method:

$$y_1 = 10 \sin \omega t$$

$$y_2 = 15 \sin (\omega t + 30°)$$

$$y_3 = 5 \sin (\omega t - 45°).$$

13. The frequency width of a standard television channel is $4 \times 10^6$ cycles/sec. If it were possible to transmit television signals in the visible portion of the electromagnetic spectrum, possibly by using optical maser or laser techniques, how many such standard channels would be available for allocation in the visible spectrum? Assume that this spectrum extends from 4000 to 7000 A.

14. In a Newton's rings experiment the radius of curvature $R$ of the lens is 5.0 meters and its diameter is 2.0 cm. (a) How many rings are produced? (b) How many rings would be seen if the arrangement were immersed in water ($n = 1.33$)? Assume that $\lambda = 5890$ A.

15. The diameter of the tenth bright ring in a Newton's rings apparatus changes from 1.40 to 1.27 cm as a liquid is introduced between the lens and the plate. Find the index of refraction of the liquid.

16. A broad source of light ($\lambda$ = 6800 A) illuminates normally two glass plates 12 cm long that touch at one end and are separated by a wire 0.048 mm in diameter at the other (Fig. 43–24). How many bright fringes appear over the 12-cm distance?

**Fig. 43–24**

17. A thin film $4 \times 10^{-5}$ cm thick is illuminated by white light normal to its surface. Its index of refraction is 1.5. What wavelengths within the visible spectrum will be intensified in the reflected beam?

18. White light reflected at perpendicular incidence from a soap film has, in the visible spectrum, an interference maximum at 6000 A and a minimum at 4500 A, with no minimum in between. If $n$ = 1.33 for the film, what is the film thickness, assumed uniform?

19. A plane wave of monochromatic light falls normally on a uniformly thin film of oil which covers a glass plate. The wavelength of the source can be varied continuously. Complete destructive interference of the reflected light is observed for wavelengths of 5000 and 7000 A and for no other wavelengths in between. If the index of refraction of the oil is 1.30 and that of the glass is 1.50, find the thickness of the oil film.

20. In Example 5 assume that there is zero reflection for light of wavelength 5500 A at normal incidence. Calculate the factor by which the reflection is diminished by the coating at 4500 and at 6500 A.

21. A plane monochromatic light wave in air falls at normal incidence on a thin film of oil which covers a glass plate. The wavelength of the source may be varied continuously. Complete destructive interference in the reflected beam is observed for wavelengths of 5000 and 7000 A and for no other wavelength in between. The index of refraction of glass is 1.50. Show that the index of refraction of the oil must be less than 1.50.

22. White light reflected at perpendicular incidence from a soap bubble has, in the visible spectrum, a single interference maximum (at $\lambda$ = 6000 A) and a single minimum at the violet end of the spectrum. If $n$ = 1.33 for the film, calculate its thickness.

23. If mirror $M_2$ in Michelson's interferometer is moved through 0.233 mm, 792 fringes are counted. What is the wavelength of the light?

24. A thin film with $n$ = 1.40 for light of wavelength 5890 A is placed in one arm of a Michelson interferometer. If a shift of 7.0 fringes occurs, what is the film thickness?

25. (a) What is the wavelength of the orange-red line of krypton-86 in angstrom units? Take 1 A = $10^{-10}$ meter exactly. (b) Does this question really make sense, in view of the fact that the meter is defined in terms of this wavelength? Explain.

26. A Michelson interferometer is used with a sodium discharge tube as a light source. The yellow sodium light consists of two wavelengths, 5890 and 5896 A. It is observed that the interference pattern disappears and reappears periodically as one moves mirror $M_2$ in Fig. 43–20. (a) Explain this effect. (b) Calculate the change in path difference between two successive reappearances of the interference pattern.

# Diffraction

## CHAPTER 44

## 44–1  Introduction

Diffraction, which is illustrated in Fig. 42–3, is the bending of light around an obstacle such as the edge of a slit. We can see the diffraction of light by looking through a crack between two fingers at a distant light source such as a tubular neon sign or by looking at a street light through a cloth umbrella. Usually diffraction effects are small and must be looked for carefully. Also, most sources of light have an extended area so that a diffraction pattern produced by one point of the source will overlap that produced by another. Finally, common sources of light are not monochromatic. The patterns for the various wavelengths overlap and again the effect is less apparent.

Diffraction was discovered by Francesco Maria Grimaldi (1618–1663), and the phenomenon was known both to Huygens (1629–1695) and to Newton (1642–1727). Newton did not see in it any justification for a wave theory for light. Huygens, although he believed in a wave theory, did not believe in diffraction! He imagined his secondary wavelets to be effective only at the point of tangency to their common envelope, thus denying the possibility of diffraction. In his words:

> And thus we see the reasons why light . . . proceeds only in straight lines in such a way that it does not illuminate any object except when the path from the source to the object is open along such a line.

Fresnel (1788–1827) correctly applied Huygens' principle (which is called the Huygens-Fresnel principle in Europe) to explain diffraction. In these early days the light waves were believed to be mechanical waves in an all-

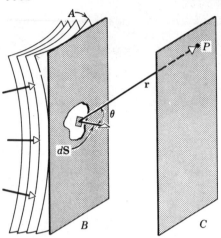

**Fig. 44–1** Light is diffracted at the aperture in screen $B$ and illuminates screen $C$. The intensity at $P$ is found by dividing the wavefront at $B$ into elementary radiators $d\mathbf{S}$ and combining their effects at $P$.

pervading ether. We have seen (Section 39–5) how Maxwell (1831–1879) showed that light waves were not mechanical in nature but electromagnetic. Einstein (1879–1955) rounded out our modern view of light waves by eliminating the need to postulate an ether (see Section 40–4).

Figure 44–1 shows a general diffraction situation. Surface $A$ is a wavefront that falls on $B$, which is an opaque screen containing an aperture of arbitrary shape; $C$ is a diffusing screen that receives the light that passes through this aperture. This pattern of light intensity on $C$ can be calculated by subdividing the wavefront into elementary areas $d\mathbf{S}$, each of which becomes a source of an expanding Huygens' wavelet. The light intensity at an arbitrary point $P$ is found by superimposing the wave disturbances (that is, the **E** vectors) caused by the wavelets reaching $P$ from all these elementary radiators.

The wave disturbances reaching $P$ differ in amplitude and in phase because (a) the elementary radiators are at varying distances from $P$, (b) the light leaves the radiators at various angles to the normal to the wavefront (see p. 1020), and (c) some radiators are blocked by screen $B$; others are not. Diffraction calculations—simple in principle—may become difficult in practice. The calculation must be repeated for every point on screen $C$ at which we wish to know the light intensity. We followed exactly this program in calculating the double-slit intensity pattern in Section 43–3. The calculation there was simple because we assumed only two elementary radiators, the two narrow slits.

Figure 44–2a shows the general case of *Fresnel diffraction*, in which the light source and/or the screen on which the diffraction pattern is displayed are a finite distance from the diffracting aperture; the wavefronts that fall on the diffracting aperture in this case and that leave it to illuminate any point $P$ of the diffusing screen are not planes; the corresponding rays are not parallel.

A simplification results if source $S$ and screen $C$ are moved to a large distance from the diffraction aperture, as in Fig. 44-2$b$. This limiting case is called *Fraunhofer diffraction*. The wavefronts arriving at the diffracting aperture from the distant source $S$ are planes, and the rays associated with these wavefronts are parallel to each other. Similarly, the wavefronts arriving at any point $P$ on the distant screen $C$ are planes, the corresponding rays

**Fig. 44-2**   (a) Fresnel diffraction.   (b) Source $S$ and screen $C$ are moved to a large distance, resulting in Fraunhofer diffraction.   (c) Fraunhofer diffraction conditions produced by lenses, leaving source $S$ and screen $C$ in their original positions.

also being parallel. Fraunhofer conditions can be established in the laboratory by using two converging lenses, as in Fig. 44–2c. The first of these
converts the diverging wave from the source into a plane wave. The second
lens causes plane waves leaving the diffracting aperture to converge to point
$P$. All rays that illuminate $P$ will leave the diffracting aperture parallel to
the dashed line $Px$ drawn from $P$ through the center of this second (thin) lens.
We assumed Fraunhofer conditions for Young's double-slit experiment in
Section 43–1 (see Fig. 43–5).

Although Fraunhofer diffraction is a limiting case of the more general
Fresnel diffraction, it is an important limiting case and is easier to handle
mathematically. This book deals only with Fraunhofer diffraction.

### 44–2   Single Slit

Figure 44–3 shows a plane wave falling at normal incidence on a long
narrow slit of width $a$. Let us focus our attention on the central point $P_0$ of
screen $C$. The rays extending from the slit to $P_0$ all have the same optical
path lengths, as we saw in Section 42–5. Since they are in phase at the
plane of the slit, they will still be in phase at $P_0$, and the central point of
the diffraction pattern that appears on screen $C$ has a maximum intensity.

**Fig. 44–3**   Conditions at the central maximum of the diffraction pattern. The slit extends
a distance above and below the figure, this distance being much greater than the slit
width $a$.

**Fig. 44–4**    Conditions at the first minimum of the diffraction pattern.

We now consider another point on the screen. Light rays which reach $P_1$ in Fig. 44–4 leave the slit at an angle $\theta$ as shown. Ray $r_1$ originates at the top of the slit and ray $r_2$ at its center. If $\theta$ is chosen so that the distance $bb'$ in the figure is one-half a wavelength, $r_1$ and $r_2$ will be out of phase and will produce no effect at $P_1$.* In fact, every ray from the upper half of the slit will be canceled by a ray from the lower half, originating at a point $a/2$ below the first ray. The point $P_1$, the first minimum of the diffraction pattern, will have zero intensity (compare Fig. 42–3).

The condition shown in Fig. 44–4 is

$$\frac{a}{2}\sin\theta = \frac{\lambda}{2},$$

or                       $a\sin\theta = \lambda.$           (44–1)

As we stated earlier (see Fig. 42–1), the central maximum becomes wider as the slit is made narrower. If the slit width is as small as one wavelength $(a = \lambda)$, the first minimum occurs at $\theta = 90°$, which implies that the central maximum fills the entire forward hemisphere. We assumed a condition ap-

---

* Whatever phase relation exists between $r_1$ and $r_2$ at the plane represented by the sloping dashed line in Fig. 44–4 that passes through $b'$ also exists at $P_1$, not being affected by the lens (see Section 42–5).

**Fig. 44–5**  Conditions at the second minimum of the diffraction pattern.

proaching this in our discussion of Young's double-slit interference experiment in Section 43–1.

In Fig. 44–5 the slit is divided into four equal zones, with a ray leaving the top of each zone. Let $\theta$ be chosen so that the distance $bb'$ is one-half a wavelength. Rays $r_1$ and $r_2$ will then cancel at $P_2$. Rays $r_3$ and $r_4$ will also be half a wavelength out of phase and will also cancel. Consider four other rays, emerging from the slit a given distance below the four rays above. The two rays below $r_1$ and $r_2$ will cancel uniquely, as will the two rays below $r_3$ and $r_4$. We can proceed across the entire slit and conclude again that no light reaches $P_2$; we have located a second point of zero intensity.

The condition described (see Fig. 44–5) requires that

$$\frac{a}{4}\sin\theta = \frac{\lambda}{2},$$

or                                          $a\sin\theta = 2\lambda.$

By extension, the general formula for the minima in the diffraction pattern on screen $C$ is

$$a\sin\theta = m\lambda \qquad m = 1, 2, 3, \ldots \text{(minima)}. \qquad (44\text{–}2)$$

There is a maximum approximately halfway between each adjacent pair of minima. The student should consider the simplification that has resulted in this analysis by examining Fraunhofer (Fig. 44-2c) rather than Fresnel conditions (Fig. 44-2a).

▶ **Example 1.** A slit of width $a$ is illuminated by white light. For what value of $a$ will the first minimum for red light ($\lambda = 6500$ A) fall at $\theta = 30°$?

At the first minimum we put $m = 1$ in Eq. 44-2. Doing so and solving for $a$ yields

$$a = \frac{m\lambda}{\sin \theta} = \frac{(1)(6500 \text{ A})}{\sin 30°} = 13,000 \text{ A}.$$

Note that the slit width must be twice the wavelength in this case.

**Example 2.** In Example 1 what is the wavelength $\lambda'$ of the light whose first diffraction maximum (not counting the central maximum) falls at $\theta = 30°$, thus coinciding with the first minimum for red light?

This maximum is about halfway between the first and second minima. It can be found without too much error by putting $m = 1.5$ in Eq. 44-2, or

$$a \sin \theta \cong 1.5\lambda'.$$

From Example 1, however,     $a \sin \theta = \lambda.$

Dividing gives     $\lambda' = \dfrac{\lambda}{1.5} = \dfrac{6500 \text{ A}}{1.5} = 4300 \text{ A}.$

Light of this color is violet. The second maximum for light of wavelength 4300 A will *always* coincide with the first minimum for light of wavelength 6500 A, no matter what the slit width. If the slit is relatively narrow, the angle $\theta$ at which this overlap occurs will be relatively large.     ◀

## 44-3  Single Slit—Qualitative

Figure 44-6 shows a slit of width $a$ divided into $N$ parallel strips of width $\Delta x$. Each strip acts as a radiator of Huygens' wavelets and produces a characteristic wave disturbance at point $P$, whose position on the screen, for a particular arrangement of apparatus, can be described by the angle $\theta$.

If the strips are narrow enough—which we assume—all points on a given strip have essentially the same optical path length to $P$, and therefore all the light from the strip will have the same phase when it arrives at $P$. The amplitudes $\Delta E_0$ of the wave disturbances at $P$ from the various strips may be taken as equal if $\theta$ in Fig. 44-6 is not too large.

We limit our considerations to points that lie in, or infinitely close to, the plane of Fig. 44-6. It can be shown that this procedure is valid for a slit whose length is much greater than its width $a$. We made this same assumption tacitly both earlier in this chapter and in Chapter 43; see Figs. 43-5 and 44-3, for example.

The wave disturbances from adjacent strips have a constant phase difference $\Delta\phi$ between them at $P$ given by

$$\frac{\text{phase difference}}{2\pi} = \frac{\text{path difference}}{\lambda},$$

or     $\Delta\phi = \left(\dfrac{2\pi}{\lambda}\right)(\Delta x \sin \theta),$     (44-3)

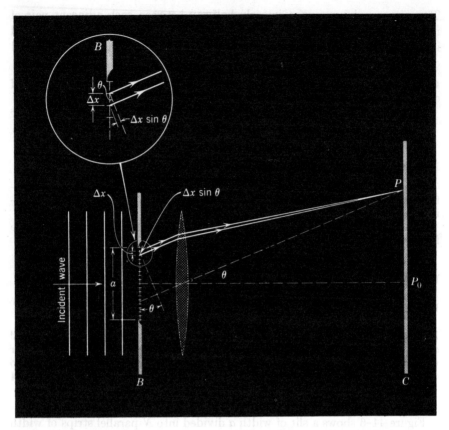

**Fig. 44–6**  A slit of width $a$ is divided into $N$ strips of width $\Delta x$. The insert shows conditions at the second strip more clearly.  In the differential limit the slit is divided into an infinite number of strips (that is, $N \to \infty$) of differential width $dx$.  For clarity in this and the following figure, we take $N = 18$.

where $\Delta x \sin \theta$ is, as the figure insert shows, the path difference for rays originating at the top edges of adjacent strips.  Thus, at $P$, $N$ vectors with the same amplitude $\Delta E_0$, the same frequency, and the same phase difference $\Delta \phi$ between adjacent members combine to produce a resultant disturbance.  We ask, for various values of $\Delta \phi$ [that is, for various points $P$ on the screen, corresponding to various values of $\theta$ (see Eq. 44–3)], what is the amplitude $E_\theta$ of the resultant wave disturbance?  We find the answer by representing the individual wave disturbances $\Delta E_0$ by phasors and calculating the resultant phasor amplitude, as described in Section 43–4.

At the center of the diffraction pattern $\theta$ equals zero, and the phase shift between adjacent strips (see Eq. 44–3) is also zero.  As Fig. 44–7a shows, the phasor arrows in this case are laid end to end and the amplitude of the resultant has its maximum value $E_m$.  This corresponds to the center of the central maximum.

As we move to a value of $\theta$ other than zero, $\Delta\phi$ assumes a definite nonzero value (again see Eq. 44–3), and the array of arrows is now as shown in Fig. 44–7b. The resultant amplitude $E_\theta$ is less than before. Note that the length of the "arc" of small arrows is the same for both figures and indeed for all figures of this series. As $\theta$ increases further, a situation is reached (Fig. 44–7c) in which the chain of arrows curls around through 360°, the tip of the last arrow touching the foot of the first arrow. This corresponds to $E_\theta = 0$, that is, to the first minimum. For this condition the ray from the top of the slit (1 in Fig. 44–7c) is 180° out of phase with the ray from the center of the slit ($\frac{1}{2}N$ in Fig. 44–7c). These phase relations are consistent with Fig. 44–4, which also represents the first minimum.

As $\theta$ increases further, the phase shift continues to increase, and the chain of arrows coils around through an angular distance greater than 360°, as in Fig. 44–7d, which corresponds to the first maximum beyond the central maximum. This maximum is much smaller than the central maximum. In making this comparison, recall that the arrows marked $E_\theta$ in Fig. 44–7 correspond to the *amplitudes* of the wave disturbance and not to the *in-*

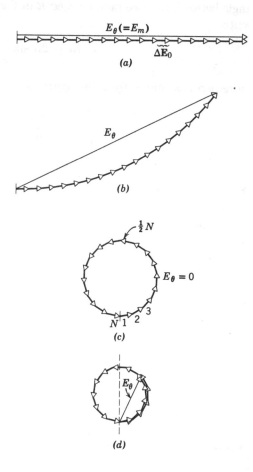

**Fig. 44–7** Conditions at (a) the central maximum, (b) a direction slightly removed from the central maximum, (c) the first minimum, and (d) the first maximum beyond the central maximum for single-slit diffraction. This figure corresponds to $N = 18$ in Fig. 44–6.

*tensity.* The amplitudes must be squared to obtain the corresponding relative intensities (see Eq. 43–7).

### 44–4   Single Slit—Quantitative

The "arc" of small arrows in Fig. 44–8 shows the phasors representing, in amplitude and phase, the wave disturbances that reach an arbitrary point $P$ on the screen of Fig. 44–6, corresponding to a particular angle $\theta$. The resultant amplitude at $P$ is $E_\theta$. If we divide the slit of Fig. 44–6 into infinitesimal strips of width $dx$, the arc of arrows in Fig. 44–8 approaches the arc of a circle, its radius $R$ being indicated in that figure. The length of the arc is $E_m$, the amplitude at the center of the diffraction pattern, for at the center of the pattern the wave disturbances are all in phase and this "arc" becomes a straight line as in Fig. 44–7a.

The angle $\phi$ in the lower part of Fig. 44–8 is revealed as the difference in phase between the infinitesimal vectors at the left and right ends of the arc $E_m$. This means that $\phi$ is the phase difference between rays from the top and the bottom of the slit of Fig. 44–6. From geometry we see that $\phi$ is also the angle between the two radii marked $R$ in Fig. 44–8. From this figure we can write

$$E_\theta = 2R \sin \frac{\phi}{2}.$$

In radian measure $\phi$, from the figure, is

$$\phi = \frac{E_m}{R}.$$

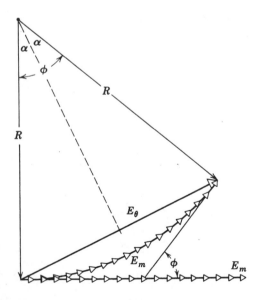

**Fig. 44–8**  A construction used to calculate the intensity in single-slit diffraction. The situation corresponds to that of Fig. 44–7.

Combining yields
$$E_\theta = \frac{E_m}{\phi/2} \sin \frac{\phi}{2},$$

or
$$E_\theta = E_m \frac{\sin \alpha}{\alpha}, \tag{44–4}$$

in which
$$\alpha = \frac{\phi}{2}. \tag{44–5}$$

From Fig. 44–6, recalling that $\phi$ is the phase difference between rays from the top and the bottom of the slit and that the path difference for these rays is $a \sin \theta$, we have

$$\frac{\text{phase difference}}{2\pi} = \frac{\text{path difference}}{\lambda},$$

or
$$\phi = \left(\frac{2\pi}{\lambda}\right)(a \sin \theta).$$

Combining with Eq. 44–5 yields

$$\alpha = \frac{\phi}{2} = \frac{\pi a}{\lambda} \sin \theta. \tag{44–6}$$

Equation 44–4, taken together with the definition of Eq. 44–6, gives the amplitude of the wave disturbance for a single-slit diffraction pattern at any angle $\theta$. The intensity $I_\theta$ for the pattern is proportional to the square of the amplitude, or

$$I_\theta = I_m \left(\frac{\sin \alpha}{\alpha}\right)^2. \tag{44–7}$$

For convenience we display together, and renumber, the formulas for the amplitude and the intensity in single-slit diffraction.

[Eq. 44–4]
$$E_\theta = E_m \frac{\sin \alpha}{\alpha} \tag{44–8a}$$

[Eq. 44–7]
$$I_\theta = I_m \left(\frac{\sin \alpha}{\alpha}\right)^2 \tag{44–8b}$$

single-slit diffraction

[Eq. 44–6]
$$\alpha \,(= \tfrac{1}{2}\phi) = \frac{\pi a}{\lambda} \sin \theta \tag{44–8c}$$

Figure 44–9 shows plots of $I_\theta$ for several values of the ratio $a/\lambda$. Note that the pattern becomes narrower as $a/\lambda$ is increased; compare this figure with Figs. 42–1 and 42–3.

Minima occur in Eq. 44–8b when

$$\alpha = m\pi \qquad m = 1, 2, 3, \ldots. \tag{44–9}$$

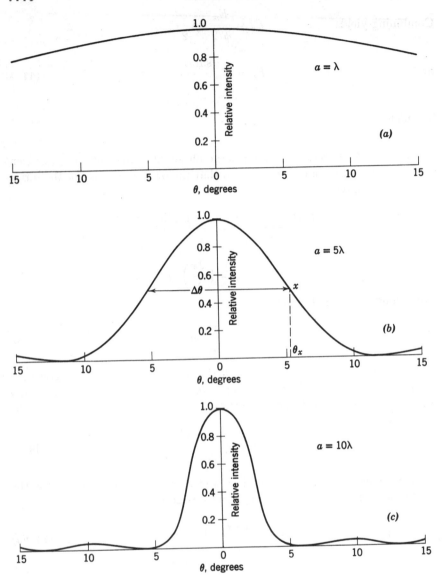

**Fig. 44–9** The relative intensity in single-slit diffraction for three values of the ratio $a/\lambda$. The arrow in (b) shows the half-width $\Delta\theta$ of the central maximum.

Combining with Eq. 44–8c leads to

$$a \sin \theta = m\lambda \qquad m = 1, 2, 3, \ldots \text{ (minima)},$$

which is the result derived in the preceding section (Eq. 44–2). In that section, however, we derived *only* this result, obtaining no quantitative information about the intensity of the diffraction pattern at places in which it was not zero. Here (Eqs. 44–8) we have complete intensity information.

▶ **Example 3.** *Intensities of the secondary diffraction maxima.* Calculate, approximately, the relative intensities of the secondary maxima in the single-slit Fraunhofer diffraction pattern.

The secondary maxima lie approximately halfway between the minima and are found (compare Eq. 44–9) from

$$\alpha \cong (m + \tfrac{1}{2})\pi \qquad m = 1, 2, 3, \ldots.$$

Substituting into Eq. 44–8b yields

$$I_\theta = I_m \left[ \frac{\sin (m + \tfrac{1}{2})\pi}{(m + \tfrac{1}{2})\pi} \right]^2,$$

which reduces to

$$\frac{I_\theta}{I_m} = \frac{1}{(m+\tfrac{1}{2})^2\pi^2}.$$

This yields, for $m = 1, 2, 3, \ldots, I_\theta/I_m = 0.045, 0.016, 0.0083$, etc. The successive maxima decrease rapidly in intensity.

**Example 4.** *Width of the central diffraction maximum.* Derive the *half-width* $\Delta\theta$ of the central maximum in a single-slit Fraunhofer diffraction (see Fig. 44–9b). The half-width is the angle between the two points in the pattern where the intensity is one-half that at the center of the pattern.

Point $x$ in Fig. 44–9b is so chosen that $I_\theta = \tfrac{1}{2}I_m$, or, from Eq. 44–8b,

$$\frac{1}{2} = \left( \frac{\sin \alpha_x}{\alpha_x} \right)^2.$$

This equation cannot be solved analytically for $\alpha_x$. It can be solved graphically, as accurately as one wishes, by plotting the quantity $(\sin \alpha_x/\alpha_x)^2$ as ordinate versus $\alpha_x$ as abscissa and noting the value of $\alpha_x$ at which the curve intersects the line "one-half" on the ordinate scale (see Problem 5). However, if only an approximate answer is desired, it is often quicker to use trial-and-error methods.

We know that $\alpha$ equals $\pi$ at the first minimum; we guess that $\alpha_x$ is perhaps $\pi/2$ ($= 90° = 1.57$ radians). Trying this in Eq. 44–8b yields

$$\frac{I_\theta}{I_m} = \left[ \frac{\sin (\pi/2)}{\pi/2} \right]^2 = 0.4.$$

This intensity ratio is *less* than 0.5, so that $\alpha_x$ must be *less* than 90°. After a few more trials we find easily enough that

$$\alpha_x = 1.40 \text{ radians} = 80°$$

does yield a ratio close to the correct value of 0.5.

We now use Eq. 44–8c to find the corresponding angle $\theta$:

$$\alpha_x = \frac{\pi a}{\lambda} \sin \theta_x = 1.40,$$

or, noting that $a/\lambda = 5$ for Fig. 44–9b,

$$\sin \theta_x = \frac{1.40\lambda}{\pi a} = \frac{1.40}{5\pi} = 0.0892.$$

The half-width $\Delta\theta$ of the central maximum (see Fig. 44–9b) is given by

$$\Delta\theta = 2\theta_x = 2 \sin^{-1} 0.0892 = 2 \times 5.1° = 10.2°,$$

which is in agreement with the figure.    ◀

### 44–5  Diffraction at a Circular Aperture

Diffraction will occur when a wavefront is partially blocked off by an opaque object such as a metal disk or an opaque screen containing an aperture. Here we consider diffraction at a circular aperture of diameter $d$, the aperture constituting the boundary of a circular lens.

Our previous treatment of lenses was based on geometrical optics, diffraction being specifically assumed not to occur. A rigorous analysis would be based from the beginning on wave optics, since geometrical optics is always an approximation, although often a good one. Diffraction phenomena would emerge in a natural way from such a wave-optical analysis.

Figure 44–10 shows the image of a distant point source of light (a star) formed on a photographic film placed in the focal plane of a converging lens. It is not a point, as the (approximate) geometrical optics treatment suggests, but a circular disk surrounded by several progressively fainter secondary rings. Comparison with Fig. 42–3c leaves little doubt that we are dealing with a diffraction phenomenon in which, however, the aperture is a circle rather than a long narrow slit. The ratio $d/\lambda$, where $d$ is the diameter of the lens (or of a circular aperture placed in front of the lens), determines the scale of the diffraction pattern, just as the ratio $a/\lambda$ does for a slit.

Analysis shows that the first minimum for the diffraction pattern of a circular aperture of diameter $d$, assuming Fraunhofer conditions, is given by

$$\sin \theta = 1.22 \frac{\lambda}{d}. \qquad (44\text{–}10)$$

This is to be compared with Eq. 44–1, or

$$\sin \theta = \frac{\lambda}{a},$$

which locates the first minimum for a long narrow slit of width $a$. The factor 1.22 emerges from the mathematical analysis when we integrate over the elementary radiators into which the circular aperture may be divided.

**Fig. 44–10**  The image of a star formed by a converging lens is a diffraction pattern. Note the central maximum, sometimes called the Airy disk (after Sir George Airy, who first solved the problem of diffraction at a circular aperture in 1835), and the circular secondary maximum. Other secondary maxima occur at larger radii but are too faint to be seen.

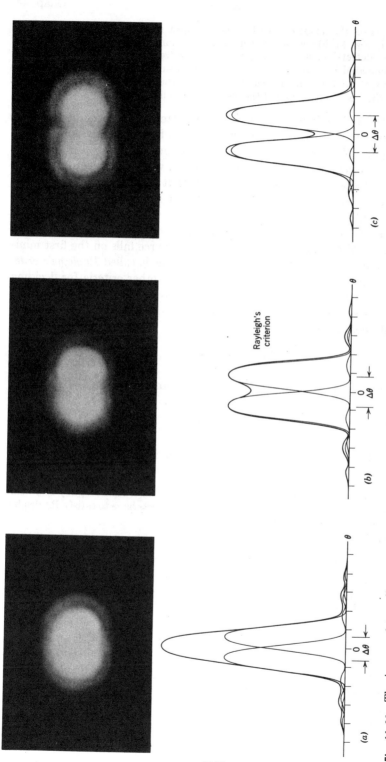

**Fig. 44–11** The images of two distant point objects are formed by a converging lens whose diameter ( = 10 cm) is 200,000 times the effective wavelength ( = 5000 Å). Sketches of the images as they appear in the focal plane of the lens are shown with the corresponding intensity plots below them. (a) The angular separation of the objects (see vertical ticks) is so small that the images are not resolved. (b) The objects are still farther apart and the images meet Rayleigh's criterion for resolution. (c) The objects are farther apart and the images are well resolved.

In actual lenses the image of a distant point object will be somewhat larger than that shown in Fig. 44-10 and may not have radial symmetry. This is caused by the various lens "defects" mentioned on p. 1061. However, even if all of these defects could be eliminated by suitable shaping of the lens surfaces or by introducing correcting lenses, the diffraction pattern of Fig. 44-10 would remain. It is an inherent property of the lens aperture and of the wavelength of light used.

The fact that lens images are diffraction patterns is important when we wish to distinguish two distant point objects whose angular separation is small. Figure 44-11 shows the visual appearances and the corresponding intensity patterns for two distant point objects with small angular separations. In (a) the objects are not resolved; that is, they cannot be distinguished from a single point object. In (b) they are barely resolved and in (c) they are fully resolved.

In Fig. 44-11b the angular separation of the two point sources is such that the maximum of the diffraction pattern of one source falls on the first minimum of the diffraction pattern of the other. This is called *Rayleigh's criterion*. This criterion, though useful, is arbitrary; other criteria for deciding when two objects are resolved are sometimes used. From Eq. 44-10, two objects that are barely resolvable by Rayleigh's criterion must have an angular separation $\theta_R$ of

$$\theta_R = \sin^{-1}\frac{1.22\lambda}{d}.$$

Since the angles involved are rather small, we can replace $\sin\theta_R$ by $\theta_R$, or

$$\theta_R = 1.22\frac{\lambda}{d}. \tag{44-11}$$

If the angular separation $\theta$ between the objects is greater than $\theta_R$, we can resolve the two objects; if it is less, we cannot.

▶ **Example 5.** A converging lens 3.0 cm in diameter has a focal length $f$ of 20 cm. (a) What angular separation must two distant point objects have to satisfy Rayleigh's criterion? Assume that $\lambda = 5500$ A.

From Eq. 44-11,

$$\theta_R = 1.22\frac{\lambda}{d} = \frac{(1.22)(5.5 \times 10^{-7} \text{ meter})}{3.0 \times 10^{-2} \text{ meter}} = 2.2 \times 10^{-5} \text{ radian.}$$

(b) How far apart are the centers of the diffraction patterns in the focal plane of the lens? The linear separation is

$$x = f\theta = (20 \text{ cm})(2.2 \times 10^{-5} \text{ radian}) = 44,000 \text{ A.}$$

This is 8.0 wavelengths of the light employed.                    ◀

When one wishes to use a lens to resolve objects of small angular separation, it is desirable to make the central disk of the diffraction pattern as small as possible. This can be done (see Eq. 44-11) by increasing the lens diameter or by using a shorter wavelength. One reason for constructing energy is concentrated into a smaller diffraction disk but because the larger lens collects more light. Thus fainter objects, for example, more distant stars, can be seen.

To reduce diffraction effects in *microscopes* we often use ultraviolet light, which, because of its shorter wavelength, permits finer detail to be examined than would be possible for the same microscope operated with visible light. We shall see in Chapter 48 that beams of electrons behave like waves under some circumstances. In the *electron microscope* such beams may have an effective wavelength of 0.04 A, of the order of $10^5$ times shorter than visible light ($\lambda \cong 5000$ A). This permits the detailed examination of tiny objects like viruses. If a virus were examined with an optical microscope, its structure would be hopelessly concealed by diffraction.

### 44–6  Double Slit

In Young's double-slit experiment (Section 43–1) we assume that the slits are arbitrarily narrow (that is, $a \ll \lambda$), which means that the central part of the diffusing screen was uniformly illuminated by the diffracted waves from each slit. When such waves interfere, they produce fringes of uniform intensity, as in Fig. 43–9. This idealized situation cannot occur with actual slits because the condition $a \ll \lambda$ cannot usually be met. Waves from the two actual slits combining at different points of the screen will have intensities that are *not* uniform but are governed by the diffraction pattern of a single slit. The effect of relaxing the assumption that $a \ll \lambda$ in Young's experiment is to leave the fringes relatively unchanged in location but to alter their intensities.

The interference pattern for infinitesimally narrow slits is given by Eq. 43–11$b$ and $c$ or, with a small change in nomenclature,

$$I_{\theta,\text{int}} = I_{m,\text{int}} \cos^2 \beta, \qquad (44\text{–}12)$$

where

$$\beta = \frac{\pi d}{\lambda} \sin \theta. \qquad (44\text{–}13)$$

The intensity for the diffracted wave from either slit is given by Eqs. 44–8$b$ and $c$, or, with a small change in nomenclature,

$$I_{\theta,\text{dif}} = I_{m,\text{dif}} \left( \frac{\sin \alpha}{\alpha} \right)^2, \qquad (44\text{–}14)$$

where

$$\alpha = \frac{\pi a}{\lambda} \sin \theta. \qquad (44\text{–}15)$$

The combined effect is found by regarding $I_{m,\text{int}}$ in Eq. 44–12 as a variable amplitude, given in fact by $I_{\theta,\text{dif}}$ of Eq. 44–14. This assumption, for the combined pattern, leads to

$$I_{\theta} = I_m \, (\cos \beta)^2 \left( \frac{\sin \alpha}{\alpha} \right)^2, \qquad (44\text{–}16)$$

in which we have dropped all subscripts referring separately to interference and diffraction.

Let us express this result in words. At any point on the screen the available light intensity from each slit, considered separately, is given by the diffraction pattern of that slit (Eq. 44–14). The diffraction patterns for the two slits, again considered separately, coincide because parallel rays in

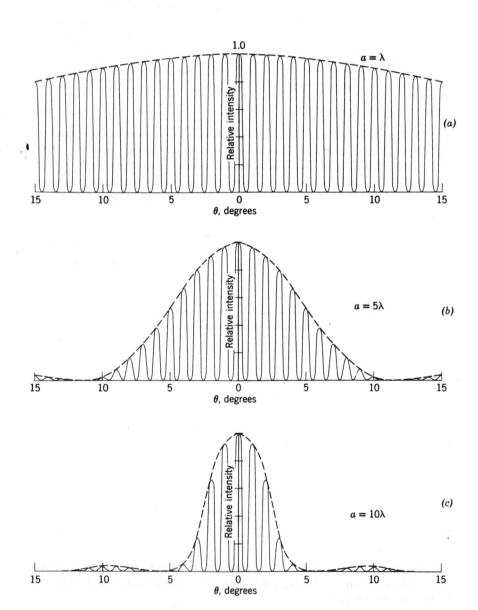

**Fig. 44–12** Interference fringes for a double slit with slit separation $d = 50\lambda$. Three different slit widths, described by $a/\lambda = 1$, 5, and 10 are shown.

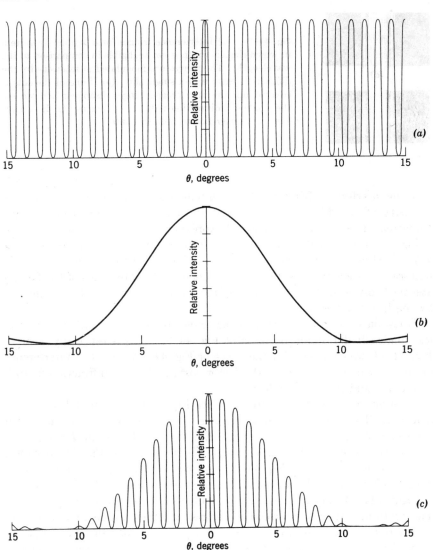

**Fig. 44–13** (*a*) The "interference factor" and (*b*) the "diffraction factor" in Eq. 44–16 and (*c*) their product; compare Fig. 44–12*b*.

Fraunhofer diffraction are focused at the same spot (see Fig. 44–5). Because the two diffracted waves are coherent, they will interfere.

The effect of interference is to redistribute the available energy over the screen, producing a set of fringes. In Section 43–1, where we assumed $a \ll \lambda$, the available energy was virtually the same at all points on the screen so that the interference fringes had virtually the same intensities (see Fig. 43–9). If we relax the assumption $a \ll \lambda$, the available energy is *not* uniform over the screen but is given by the diffraction pattern of a slit of width $a$. In this

**Fig. 44-14** (a) Interference fringes for a double-slit system in which the slit width is *not* negligible in comparison to the wavelength. The fringes are modulated in intensity by the diffraction pattern of a single slit. (b) If one of the slits is covered up, the interference fringes disappear and we see the single slit diffraction pattern. (Courtesy G. H. Carragan, Rensselaer Polytechnic Institute.)

case the interference fringes will have intensities that are determined by the intensity of the diffraction pattern at the location of a particular fringe. Equation 44-16 is the mathematical expression of this argument.

Figure 44-12 is a plot of Eq. 44-16 for $d = 50\lambda$ and for three values of $a/\lambda$. It shows clearly that for narrow slits ($a = \lambda$) the fringes are nearly uniform in intensity. As the slits are widened, the intensities of the fringes are markedly modulated by the "diffraction factor" in Eq. 44-16, that is, by the factor $(\sin \alpha/\alpha)^2$.

Equation 44-16 shows that the fringe envelopes of Fig. 44-12 are precisely the single-slit diffraction patterns of Fig. 44-9. This is especially clear in Fig. 44-13, which shows, for the curve of Fig. 44-12b, (a) the "interference factor" in Eq. 44-16 (that is, the factor $\cos^2 \beta$), (b) the "diffraction factor" $(\sin \alpha/\alpha)^2$, and (c) their product.

If we put $a = 0$ in Eq. 44-16, then (see Eq. 44-15) $\alpha = 0$ and $\sin \alpha/\alpha \cong \alpha/\alpha = 1$. Thus this equation reduces, as it must, to the intensity equation for a pair of vanishingly narrow slits (Eq. 44-12). If we put $d = 0$ in Eq. 44-16, the two slits coalesce into a single slit of width $a$, as Fig. 44-15 shows; $d = 0$ implies $\beta = 0$ (see Eq. 44-13) and $\cos^2 \beta = 1$. Thus Eq. 44-16 reduces, as it must, to the diffraction equation for a single slit (Eq. 44-14).

Figure 44-14 shows some actual double-slit interference photographs. The uniformly spaced interference fringes and their intensity modulation by the diffraction pattern of a single slit is clear. If one slit is covered up, as in Fig. 44-14b, the interference fringes disappear and we see the diffraction pattern of a single slit.

▶ **Example 6.** Starting from the curve of Fig. 44-12b, what is the effect of (a) increasing the slit width, (b) increasing the slit separation, and (c) increasing the wavelength?

(a) If we increase the slit width $a$, the envelope of the fringe pattern changes so that its central peak is sharper (compare Fig. 44-12c). The fringe spacing, which depends on $d/\lambda$, does not change.

(b) If we increase $d$, the fringes become closer together, the envelope of the pattern remaining unchanged.

(c) If we increase $\lambda$, the envelope becomes broader and the fringes move further apart. Increasing $\lambda$ is equivalent to decreasing both of the ratios $a/\lambda$ and $d/\lambda$. The general relationship of the envelope to the fringes, which depends only on $d/a$, does not change with wavelength.

**Example 7.** In double-slit Fraunhofer diffraction what is the fringe spacing on a screen 50 cm away from the slits if they are illuminated with blue light ($\lambda$ = 4800 A), if $d$ = 0.10 mm, and if the slit width $a$ = 0.02 mm? What is the linear distance from the central maximum to the first minimum of the fringe envelope?

The intensity pattern is given by Eq. 44–16, the fringe spacing being determined by the interference factor $\cos^2 \beta$. From Example 2, Chapter 43, we have

$$\Delta y = \frac{\lambda D}{d},$$

where $D$ is the distance of the screen from the slits. Substituting yields

$$\Delta y = \frac{(480 \times 10^{-9} \text{ meter})(50 \times 10^{-2} \text{ meter})}{0.10 \times 10^{-3} \text{ meter}} = 2.4 \times 10^{-3} \text{ meter} = 2.4 \text{ mm.}$$

The distance to the first minimum of the envelope is determined by the diffraction factor $(\sin \alpha / \alpha)^2$ in Eq. 44–16. The first minimum in this factor occurs for $\alpha = \pi$. From Eq. 44–15,

$$\sin \theta = \frac{\alpha \lambda}{\pi a} = \frac{\lambda}{a} = \frac{480 \times 10^{-9} \text{ meter}}{0.02 \times 10^{-3} \text{ meter}} = 0.024.$$

This is so small that we can assume that $\theta \cong \sin \theta \cong \tan \theta$, or

$$y = D \tan \theta \cong D \sin \theta = (50 \text{ cm})(0.024) = 1.2 \text{ cm.}$$

There are about ten fringes in the central peak of the fringe envelope.

**Example 8.** What requirements must be met for the central maximum of the envelope of the double-slit Fraunhofer pattern to contain exactly eleven fringes?

The required condition will be met if the sixth minimum of the interference factor $(\cos^2 \beta)$ in Eq. 44–16 coincides with the first minimum of the diffraction factor $(\sin \alpha / \alpha)^2$.

The sixth minimum of the interference factor occurs when

$$\beta = \tfrac{11}{2}\pi$$

in Eq. 44–12.

The first minimum in the diffraction term occurs for

$$\alpha = \pi.$$

Dividing (see Eqs. 44–13 and 44–15) yields

$$\frac{\beta}{\alpha} = \frac{d}{a} = \frac{11}{2}.$$

This condition depends only on the slit geometry and not on the wavelength. For long waves the pattern will be broader than for short waves, but there will always be eleven fringes in the central peak of the envelope.  ◀

The double-slit problem as illustrated in Fig. 44–12 combines interference and diffraction in an intimate way. At root both are superposition effects and depend on adding wave disturbances at a given point, taking phase differences properly into account. If the waves to be combined originate from a *finite* (and usually small) number of elementary coherent radiators, as in Young's double-slit experiment, we call the effect *interference*. If the waves to be combined originate by subdividing a wave into *infinitesimal* coherent radiators, as in our treatment of a single slit (Fig. 44–6), we call the effect *diffraction*. This distinction between interference and diffraction is convenient and useful. However, it should not cause us to lose sight of the fact that both are superposition effects and that often both are present simultaneously, as in Young's experiment.

## QUESTIONS

1. Why is the diffraction of sound waves more evident in daily experience than that of light waves?

2. Why do radio waves diffract around buildings, although light waves do not?

3. A loud-speaker horn has a rectangular aperture 4 ft high and 1 ft wide. Will the pattern of sound intensity be broader in the horizontal plane or in the vertical?

4. A radar antenna is designed to give accurate measurements of the height of an aircraft but only reasonably good measurements of its direction in a horizontal plane. Must the height-to-width ratio of the radar reflector be less than, equal to, or greater than unity?

5. A person holds a single narrow vertical slit in front of the pupil of his eye and looks at a distant light source in the form of a long heated filament. Is the diffraction pattern that he sees a Fresnel or a Fraunhofer pattern?

6. In a single-slit Fraunhofer diffraction, what is the effect of increasing ($a$) the wavelength and ($b$) the slit width?

7. Sunlight falls on a single slit of width $10^4$ A. Describe qualitatively what the resulting diffraction pattern looks like.

8. In Fig. 44–5 rays $r_1$ and $r_3$ are in phase; so are $r_2$ and $r_4$. Why isn't there a *maximum* intensity at $P_2$ rather than a minimum?

9. Describe what happens to a Fraunhofer single-slit diffraction pattern if the whole apparatus is immersed in water.

10. Distinguish clearly between $\theta$, $\alpha$, and $\phi$ in Eq. 44–8c.

11. Do diffraction effects occur for virtual images as well as for real images? Explain.

12. Do diffraction effects occur for images formed by ($a$) plane mirrors and ($b$) spherical mirrors? Explain.

13. If we were to redo our analysis of the properties of lenses in Section 42–5 by the methods of geometrical optics but *without* restricting our considerations to paraxial rays and to "thin" lenses, would diffraction phenomena, such as that of Fig. 44–10, emerge from the analysis? Discuss.

14. Distinguish carefully between interference and diffraction in Young's double-slit experiment.

15. In what way are interference and diffraction similar? In what way are they different?

16. In double-slit interference patterns such as that of Fig. 44–14a we said that the interference fringes were modulated in intensity by the diffraction pattern of a single slit. Could we reverse this statement and say that the diffraction pattern of a single slit is intensity-modulated by the interference fringes? Discuss.

## PROBLEMS

1. In a single-slit diffraction pattern the distance between the first minimum on the right and the first minimum on the left is 5.2 mm. The screen on which the pattern is displayed is 80 cm from the slit and the wavelength is 5460 A. Calculate the slit width.

2. A plane wave ($\lambda$ = 5900 A) falls on a slit with $a$ = 0.40 mm. A converging lens ($f$ = +70 cm) is placed behind the slit and focuses the light on a screen. What is the linear distance on the screen from the center of the pattern to (a) the first minimum and (b) the second minimum?

3. A single slit is illuminated by light whose wavelengths are $\lambda_a$ and $\lambda_b$, so chosen that the first diffraction minimum of $\lambda_a$ coincides with the second minimum of $\lambda_b$. (a) What relationship exists between the two wavelengths? (b) Do any other minima in the two patterns coincide?

4. (a) Show that the values of $\alpha$ at which intensity maxima for single-slit diffraction occur can be found exactly by differentiating Eq. 44–8b with respect to $\alpha$ and equating to zero, obtaining the condition

$$\tan \alpha = \alpha.$$

(b) Find the values of $\alpha$ satisfying this relation by plotting graphically the curve $y = \tan \alpha$ and the straight line $y = \alpha$ and finding their intersections. (c) Find the (nonintegral) values of $m$ corresponding to successive maxima in the single-slit pattern. Note that the secondary maxima do not lie exactly halfway between minima.

5. In Example 4 solve the transcendental equation

$$\frac{1}{2} = \left(\frac{\sin \alpha_x}{\alpha_x}\right)^2$$

graphically for $\alpha_x$, to an accuracy of three significant figures.

6. (a) In Fig. 44–7d, why is $E_\theta$, which represents the first maximum beyond the central maximum, not vertical? (b) Calculate the angle it makes with the vertical, assuming the slit to be divided into infinitesimal strips of width $dx$.

7. What is the half-width of a diffracted beam for a slit whose width is (a) 1, (b) 5, and (c) 10 wavelengths?

8. (a) A circular diaphragm 0.60 meter in diameter oscillates at a frequency of 25,000 cycles/sec in an underwater source of sound for submarine detection. Far from the source the sound intensity is distributed as a Fraunhofer diffraction pattern for a circular hole whose diameter equals that of the diaphragm. Take the speed of sound in water to be 1450 meters/sec and find the angle between the normal to the diaphragm and the direction of the first minimum. (b) Repeat for a source having an (audible) frequency of 1000 cycles/sec.

9. The two headlights of an approaching automobile are 4 ft apart. At what maximum distance will the eye resolve them? Assume a pupil diameter of 5.0 mm and $\lambda$ = 5500 A. Assume also that this distance is determined only by diffraction effects at the circular pupil aperture.

10. The wall of a large room is covered with acoustic tile in which small holes are drilled 5.0 mm from center to center. How far can a person be from such a tile and still distinguish the individual holes, assuming ideal conditions? Assume the diameter of the pupil to be 4.0 mm and $\lambda$ to be 5500 A.

11. (a) How small is the angular separation of two stars if their images are barely resolved by the Thaw refracting telescope at the Allegheny Observatory in Pittsburgh? The lens diameter is 30 in. and its focal length is 46 ft. Assume $\lambda$ = 5000 A. (b) Find the distance between these barely resolved stars if each of them is 10 light years distant from the earth. (c) For the image of a single star in this telescope, find the diameter of the first dark ring in the diffraction pattern, as measured on a photographic plate placed at the

focal plane. Assume that the star image structure is associated entirely with diffraction at the lens aperture and not with (small) lens "errors."

12. Find the separation of two points on the moon's surface that can just be resolved by the 200-in. telescope at Mount Palomar, assuming that this distance is determined by diffraction effects. The distance from the earth to the moon is 240,000 miles.

13. Construct qualitative vector diagrams like those of Fig. 44–7 for the double-slit interference pattern. For simplicity, consider $d = 2a$ (see Fig. 44–15). Can you interpret the main features of the intensity pattern this way?

**Fig. 44–15**

14. Suppose that, as in Example 8, the envelope of the central peak contains eleven fringes. How many fringes lie between the first and second minima of the envelope?

15. For $d = 2a$ in Fig. 44–15, how many interference fringes lie in the central diffraction envelope?

16. If we put $d = a$ in Fig. 44–15, the two slits coalesce into a single slit of width $2a$. Show that Eq. 44–16 reduces to the diffraction pattern for such a slit.

17. (a) Design a double-slit system in which the fourth fringe, not counting the central maximum, is missing. (b) What other fringes, if any, are also missing?

# Gratings and Spectra

## CHAPTER 45

## 45–1  Introduction

In connection with Young's experiment (Sections 43–1 and 43–3) we discussed the interference of two coherent waves formed by diffraction at two elementary radiators (pinholes or slits).  In our first treatment we assumed that the slit width was much less than the wavelength, so that light diffracted from each slit illuminated the observation screen essentially uniformly.  Later, in Section 44–6, we took the slit width into account and showed that the intensity pattern of the interference fringes is modulated by a "diffraction factor" $(\sin \alpha/\alpha)^2$ (see Eq. 44–16).

Here we extend our treatment to cases in which the number $N$ of radiators or diffracting centers is larger—and usually much larger—than two. We consider two situations:

1. An array of $N$ parallel equidistant slits, called a *diffraction grating*.

2. A three-dimensional array of periodically arranged radiators—the atoms in a crystalline solid such as NaCl.  In this case the average spacing between the elementary radiators is so small that interference effects must be sought at wavelengths much smaller than those of visible light.  We speak of *X-ray diffraction*.

In each case we distinguish carefully between the diffracting properties of a single radiator (slit or atom) and the interference of the waves diffracted, coherently, from the assembly of radiators.

## 45–2  Multiple Slits

A logical extension of Young's double-slit interference experiment is to increase the number of slits from two to a larger number $N$.  An arrangement like that of Fig. 45–1, usually involving many more slits, is called a *diffrac-*

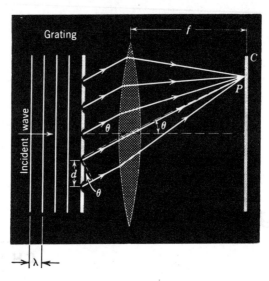

**Fig. 45–1** An idealized diffraction grating containing five slits. The slit width $a$ is shown for convenience to be considerably smaller than $\lambda$, although this condition is not realized in practice. The figure is distorted in that $f$ is much greater than $d$ in practice.

*tion grating.* As for a double slit, the intensity pattern that results when monochromatic light of wavelength $\lambda$ falls on a grating consists of a series of interference fringes. The *angular separations* of these fringes are determined by the ratio $\lambda/d$, where $d$ is the spacing between the centers of adjacent slits. The relative *intensities* of these fringes are determined by the diffraction pattern of a single grating slit, which depends on the ratio $\lambda/a$, where $a$ is the slit width.

Figure 45–2, which compares the intensity patterns for $N = 2$ and $N = 5$, shows clearly that the "interference" fringes are modulated in intensity by a "diffraction" envelope, as in Fig. 44–14. Figure 45–3 presents a theoretical calculation of the intensity patterns for a few fringes near the centers of the patterns of Fig. 45–2. These two figures show that increasing $N$ $(a)$ does not change the spacing between the (principal) interference fringe maxima,

*(a)*                $N = 2$

*(b)*                $N = 5$

**Fig. 45–2** Intensity patterns for "gratings" with $(a)$ $N = 2$ and $(b)$ $N = 5$ for the same value of $d$ and $\lambda$. Note how the intensities of the fringes are modulated by a diffraction envelope as in Fig. 44–14; thus the assumption $a \ll \lambda$ is not realized in these actual "gratings." For $N = 5$ three very faint secondary maxima, not visible in this photograph, appear between each pair of adjacent primary maxima.

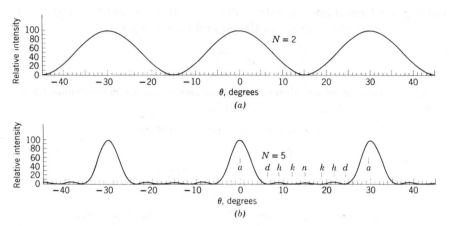

**Fig. 45–3** Calculated intensity patterns for (a) a two-slit and (b) a five-slit grating for the same value of d and λ. This figure shows the sharpening of the principal maxima and the appearance of faint secondary maxima for $N > 2$. The letters on the five-slit pattern refer to Fig. 45–5. The figure assumes slits with $a \ll \lambda$ so that the principal maxima are of uniform intensity.

provided $d$ and $\lambda$ remain unchanged, (b) sharpens the (principal) maxima, and (c) introduces small secondary maxima between the principal maxima. Three such secondaries are present (but not readily visible) between each pair of adjacent principal maxima in Fig. 45–2b.

A principal maximum in Fig. 45–1 will occur when the path difference between rays from adjacent slits ($= d \sin \theta$) is given by

$$d \sin \theta = m\lambda \qquad m = 0, 1, 2, \ldots \qquad \text{(principal maxima)}, \qquad (45\text{–}1)$$

where $m$ is called the *order number*. This equation is identical with Eq. 43–1, which locates the intensity maxima for a double slit. The *locations* of the (principal) maxima are thus determined only by the ratio $\lambda/d$ and are independent of $N$. As for the double slit, the ratio $a/\lambda$ determines the relative *intensities* of the principal maxima but does not alter their locations appreciably.

The sharpening of the principal maxima as $N$ is increased can be understood by a graphical argument, using phasors. Figures 45–4a and b show conditions at any of the principal maxima for a two-slit and a nine-slit grating. The small arrows represent the amplitudes of the wave disturbances arriving at the screen at the position of each principal maximum. For simplicity we consider the central principal maximum only, for which $m = 0$, and thus $\theta = 0$, in Eq. 45–1.

Consider the angle $\Delta\theta_0$ corresponding to the position of zero intensity that lies on either side of the central principal maximum. Figures 45–4c and d show the phasors at this point. The phase difference between waves from adjacent slits, which is zero at the central principal maximum, must increase by an amount $\Delta\phi$ chosen so that the array of phasors just closes on itself, yielding zero resultant intensity. For $N = 2$, $\Delta\phi = 2\pi/2$ ($= 180°$); for $N = 9$, $\Delta\phi = 2\pi/9$ ($= 40°$). In the general case it is given by

$$\Delta\phi = \frac{2\pi}{N}.$$

This increase in phase difference for adjacent waves corresponds to an increase in the path difference $\Delta l$ given by

$$\frac{\text{phase difference}}{2\pi} = \frac{\text{path difference}}{\lambda},$$

or

$$\Delta l = \left(\frac{\lambda}{2\pi}\right)\Delta\phi = \left(\frac{\lambda}{2\pi}\right)\left(\frac{2\pi}{N}\right) = \frac{\lambda}{N}.$$

From Fig. 45–1, however, the path difference $\Delta l$ at the first minimum is also given by $d \sin \Delta\theta_0$, so that we can write

$$d \sin \Delta\theta_0 = \frac{\lambda}{N},$$

or

$$\sin \Delta\theta_0 = \frac{\lambda}{Nd}.$$

Since $N \gg 1$ for actual gratings, $\sin \Delta\theta_0$ will ordinarily be quite small (that is, the lines will be sharp), and we may replace it by $\Delta\theta_0$ to good approximation, or

$$\Delta\theta_0 = \frac{\lambda}{Nd} \qquad \text{(central principal maximum).} \qquad (45\text{–}2)$$

This equation shows specifically that if we increase $N$ for a given $\lambda$ and $d$,

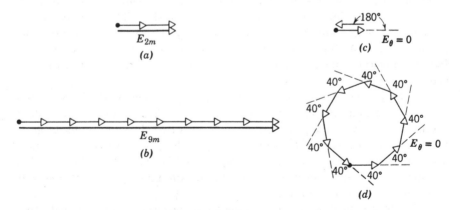

**Fig. 45–4** Drawings ($a$) and ($b$) show conditions at the central principal maximum for a two-slit and a nine-slit grating, respectively. Drawings ($c$) and ($d$) show conditions at the minimum of zero intensity that lies on either side of this central principal maximum. In going from ($a$) to ($c$) the phase shift between waves from adjacent slits changes by 180° ($\Delta\phi = 2\pi/2$); in going from ($b$) to ($d$) it changes by 40° ($\Delta\phi = 2\pi/9$).

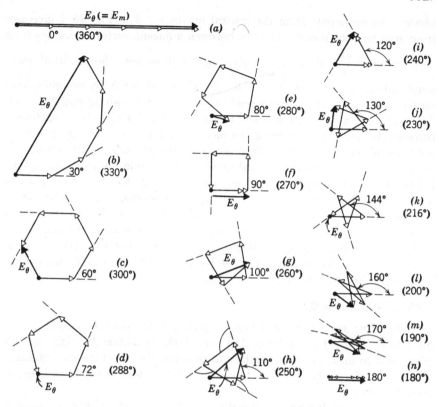

**Fig. 45-5** The figures taken in sequence from (a) to (n) and then from (n) to (a) show conditions as the intensity pattern of a five-slit grating is traversed from the central principal maximum to an adjacent principal maximum. Phase differences between waves from adjacent slits are shown directly or, when going from (n) to (a), in parentheses. Principal maxima occur at (a), secondary maxima at, or near, (h) and (n), and points of zero intensity at (d) and (k). Compare Fig. 45-3b.

$\Delta\theta_0$ will decrease, which means that the central principal maximum becomes sharper.

We state without proof,* and for later use, that for principal maxima other than the central one (that is, for $m \neq 0$) the angular distance between the position $\theta_m$ of the principal maximum of order $m$ and the minimum that lies on either side is given by

$$\Delta\theta_m = \frac{\lambda}{Nd \cos\theta_m} \qquad \text{(any principal maximum).} \qquad (45\text{-}3)$$

For the central principal maximum we have $m = 0$, $\theta_m = 0$, and $\Delta\theta_m = \Delta\theta_0$, so that Eq. 45-3 reduces, as it must, to Eq. 45-2.

The origin of the secondary maxima that appear for $N > 2$ can also be understood using the phasor method. Figure 45-5a shows conditions at the central principal maximum for a five-slit grating. The vectors are in

_____

* See Problem 15.

phase. As we depart from the central maximum, $\theta$ in Fig. 45–1 increases from zero and the phase difference between adjacent vectors increases from zero to $\Delta\phi = \dfrac{2\pi}{\lambda} d \sin \theta$. Successive figures show how the resultant wave amplitude $E_\theta$ varies with $\Delta\phi$. The student should verify by graphical construction that a given figure represents conditions for both $\Delta\phi$ and $2\pi - \Delta\phi$. Thus we start at $\Delta\phi = 0$, proceed to $\Delta\phi = 180°$, and then trace backward through the sequence, following the phase differences shown in parentheses, until we reach $\Delta\phi = 360°$. This sequence corresponds to traversing the intensity pattern from the central principal maximum to an adjacent one. Figure 45–5, which should be compared with Fig. 45–3b, shows that for $N = 5$ there are three secondary maxima, corresponding to $\Delta\phi = 110°, 180°$, and $250°$. The student should make a similar analysis for $N = 3$ and should show that only one secondary maximum occurs. In actual gratings, which commonly contain 10,000 to 50,000 "slits," the secondary maxima lie so close to the principal maxima or are so reduced in intensity that they cannot be distinguished from them experimentally.

### 45–3 Diffraction Gratings

The *grating spacing d* for a typical grating that contains 12,000 "slits" distributed over a 1-in. width is 2.54 cm/12,000, or 21,000 A. Gratings are often used to measure wavelengths and to study the structure and intensity of spectrum lines. Few devices have contributed more to our knowledge of modern physics.

Gratings are made by ruling equally spaced parallel grooves on a glass or a metal * plate, using a diamond cutting point whose motion is automatically controlled by an elaborate ruling engine. Once such a master grating has been prepared, replicas can be formed by pouring a collodion solution on the grating, allowing it to harden, and stripping it off. The stripped collodion, fastened to a flat piece of glass or other backing, forms a good grating.

Figure 45–6 shows a cross section of a common type of grating ruled on glass. In the rudimentary grating of Fig. 45–1 open slits were separated by opaque strips; the *amplitude* of the wave disturbance varied in a periodic way as the grating was crossed, dropping to zero on the opaque strips. The grating of Fig. 45–6 is transparent everywhere, so that there is little periodic change in amplitude as the grating is crossed. The effect of the rulings is to change the *optical thickness* of the grating in a periodic way, rays traversing the grating between the rulings (b in Fig. 45–6) containing more wavelengths than rays traversing the grating in the center of the rulings (a in Fig. 45–6). This results in a periodic change of *phase* as one crosses the grating at right angles to the rulings. Reflection gratings also depend for their operation on a periodic change in phase of the reflected wave as one crosses the grating, the change in amplitude under these conditions being negligible. The principal maxima for *phase gratings*, assuming that the incident light falls on the grating at right angles, can be given by the same formula derived earlier for idealized amplitude or slit gratings,

---

* Gratings ruled on metal are called *reflection gratings* because the interference effects are viewed in reflected rather than in transmitted light. Many research gratings are the reflection type; commonly they are ruled on the surface of a concave mirror, which eliminates the need for lenses.

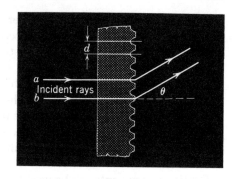

**Fig. 45–6** An enlarged cross section of a diffraction grating ruled on glass. Such gratings, in which the phase of the emerging wave changes as one crosses the grating, are called *phase gratings*.

namely

$$d \sin \theta = m\lambda \qquad m = 0, 1, 2 \ldots,$$

where $d$ is the distance between the rulings and the integer $m$ is called the *order* of the particular principal maximum. Essentially all gratings used in the visible spectrum, whether of the transmission type, as in Fig. 45–6, or the reflection type, are phase gratings.

Figure 45–7 shows a simple grating spectroscope, used for viewing the spectrum of a light source, assumed to emit a number of discrete wavelengths, or *spectrum lines*. The light from source $S$ is focused by lens $L_1$ on a slit $S_1$ placed in the focal plane of lens $L_2$. The parallel light emerging from collimator $C$ falls on grating $G$. Parallel rays associated with a particular interference maximum occurring at angle $\theta$ fall on lens $L_3$, being brought to a focus in plane $F$-$F'$. The image formed in this plane is examined, using a magnifying lens arrangement $E$, called an eyepiece. A symmetrical inter-

**Fig. 45–7** A simple type of grating spectroscope used to analyze the wavelengths of the light emitted by source $S$.

ference pattern is formed on the other side of the central position, as shown by the dotted lines. The entire spectrum can be viewed by rotating telescope $T$ through various angles. Instruments used for scientific research or in industry are more complex than the simple arrangement of Fig. 45–7. They invariably employ photographic or photoelectric recording and are called *spectrographs*. Figure 47–12 shows a small portion of the spectrum of iron, produced by examining the light produced in an arc struck between iron electrodes, using a research type spectrograph with photographic recording. Each line in the figure represents a different wavelength that is emitted from the source.

Grating instruments can be used to make absolute measurements of wavelength, since the grating spacing $d$ in Eq. 45–1 can be measured accurately with a traveling microscope. Several spectra are normally produced in such instruments, corresponding to $m = \pm 1, \pm 2$, etc., in Eq. 45–1 (see Fig. 45–8). This may cause some confusion if the spectra overlap. Further, this multiplicity of spectra reduces the recorded intensity of any given spectrum line because the available energy is divided among a number of spectra.

This disadvantage of the grating instrument can be overcome by shaping the profile of the grating grooves so that a large fraction of the light is thrown into a particular order on a particular side (for a given wavelength). This technique, called *blazing*, so alters the diffracting properties of the individual grooves (by controlling their profiles) that the light of wavelength $\lambda$ diffracted by a single groove has a sharp peak of maximum intensity at a selected angle $\theta$ ($\neq 0$).

Light can also be analyzed into its component wavelengths if the grating in Fig. 45–7 is replaced by a prism. In a *prism spectrograph* each wavelength

**Fig. 45–8**  Example 1. The spectrum of white light as viewed in a grating instrument like that of Fig. 45–7. The different orders, identified by the order number $m$, are shown separated vertically for clarity. As actually viewed, they would not be so displaced. The central line in each order corresponds to $\lambda = 5500$ A.

in the incident beam is deflected through a definite angle $\theta$, determined by the index of refraction of the prism material for that wavelength. Curves such as Fig. 41–2, which gives the index of refraction of fused quartz as a function of wavelength, show that the shorter the wavelength, the larger the angle of deflection $\theta$. Such curves vary from substance to substance and must be found by measurement. Prism instruments are not adequate for accurate *absolute* measurements of wavelength because the index of refraction of the prism material at the wavelength in question is usually not known precisely enough. Both prism and grating instruments make accurate *comparisons* of wavelength, using a suitable comparison spectrum such as that shown in Fig. 47–12, in which careful absolute determinations have been made of the wavelengths of the spectrum lines. The prism instrument has an advantage over a grating instrument (unblazed) in that its light energy is concentrated into a single spectrum so that brighter lines may be produced.

▶ **Example 1.**  A grating with 8000 rulings/in. is illuminated with white light at perpendicular incidence. Describe the diffraction pattern. Assume that the wavelength of the light extends from 4000 to 7000 A.

The grating spacing $d$ is 2.54 cm/8000, or 31,700 A. The central or zero-order maximum corresponds to $m = 0$ in Eq. 45–1. All wavelengths present in the incident light are superimposed at $\theta = 0$, as Fig. 45–8 shows.

The first-order diffraction pattern corresponds to $m = 1$ in Eq. 45–1. The 4000-A line occurs at an angle given by

$$\theta = \sin^{-1}\frac{m\lambda}{d} = \sin^{-1}\frac{(1)(4000\ A)}{31{,}700\ A} = \sin^{-1} 0.126 = 7.3°.$$

In the same way the angle for the 7000-A line is found to be 12.8°, and the entire pattern of Fig. 45–8 can be calculated. Note that the *first-order spectrum* ($m = 1$) is isolated but that the second-, third-, and fourth-order spectra overlap.

**Example 2.**  A diffraction grating has $10^4$ rulings uniformly spaced over 1 in. It is illuminated at normal incidence by yellow light from a sodium vapor lamp. This light contains two closely spaced lines (the well-known *sodium doublet*) of wavelengths 5890.0 and 5895.9 A. (*a*) At what angle will the first-order maximum occur for the first of these wavelengths?

The grating spacing $d$ is $10^{-4}$ in., or 25,400 A. The first-order maximum corresponds to $m = 1$ in Eq. 45–1. We thus have

$$\theta = \sin^{-1}\frac{m\lambda}{d} = \sin^{-1}\frac{(1)(5890\ A)}{25{,}400\ A} = \sin^{-1} 0.232 = 13.3°.$$

(*b*) What is the angular separation between the first-order maxima for these lines?

The straightforward way to find this separation is to repeat this calculation for $\lambda = 5895.9$ A and to subtract the two angles. A difficulty, which can best be appreciated by carrying out the calculation, is that we must carry a large number of significant figures to obtain a meaningful value for the difference between the angles. To calculate the difference in angular positions *directly*, let us write down Eq. 45–1, solved for $\sin\theta$, and differentiate it, treating $\theta$ and $\lambda$ as variables:

$$\sin\theta = \frac{m\lambda}{d}$$

If the wavelengths are close enough together, as in this case, $d\lambda$ can be replaced by $\Delta\lambda$, the actual wavelength difference; $d\theta$ then becomes $\Delta\theta$, the quantity we seek. This gives

$$\Delta\theta = \frac{m\,\Delta\lambda}{d\cos\theta} = \frac{(1)(5.9\text{ A})}{(25{,}400\text{ A})(\cos 13.3°)} = 2.4 \times 10^{-4}\text{ radian} = 0.014°.$$

Note that although the wavelengths involve five significant figures our calculation, done this way, involves only two or three, with consequent reduction in numerical manipulation.          ◄

The quantity $d\theta/d\lambda$, called the *dispersion D* of a grating, is a measure of the angular separation produced between two incident monochromatic waves whose wavelengths differ by a small wavelength interval. From this example we see that

$$D = \frac{d\theta}{d\lambda} = \frac{m}{d\cos\theta}. \tag{45–4}$$

### 45–4  Resolving Power of a Grating

To distinguish light waves whose wavelengths are close together, the principal maxima of these wavelengths formed by the grating should be as narrow as possible. Expressed otherwise, the grating should have a high *resolving power R*, defined from

$$R = \frac{\lambda}{\Delta\lambda}. \tag{45–5}$$

Here $\lambda$ is the mean wavelength of two spectrum lines that can barely be recognized as separate and $\Delta\lambda$ is the wavelength difference between them. The smaller $\Delta\lambda$ is, the closer the lines can be and still be resolved; hence the greater the resolving power $R$ of the grating. It is to achieve a high resolving power that gratings with many rulings are constructed.

The resolving power of a grating is usually determined by the same consideration (that is, the Rayleigh criterion) that we used in Section 44–5 to determine the resolving power of a lens. If two principal maxima are to be barely resolved, they must, according to this criterion, have an angular separation $\Delta\theta$ such that the maximum of one line coincides with the first minimum of the other; see Fig. 44–11. If we apply this criterion, we can show that

$$R = Nm, \tag{45–6}$$

where $N$ is the total number of rulings in the grating and $m$ is the order. As expected, the resolving power is zero for the central principal maximum ($m = 0$), all wavelengths being undeflected in this order.

Let us derive Eq. 45–6. The angular separation between two principal maxima whose wavelengths differ by $\Delta\lambda$ is found from Eq. 45–4, which we recast as

$$\Delta\theta = \frac{m\,\Delta\lambda}{d\cos\theta}. \tag{45–4}$$

The Rayleigh criterion (Section 44–5) requires that this be equal to the angular separation between a principal maximum and its adjacent minimum. This is given from Eq. 45–3, dropping the subscript $m$ in $\cos\theta_m$, as

$$\Delta\theta_m = \frac{\lambda}{dN \cos\theta}. \qquad (45\text{–}3)$$

Equating Eqs. 45–4 and 45–3 leads to

$$R \; (= \lambda/\Delta\lambda) = Nm,$$

which is the desired relation.

▶ **Example 3.** In Example 2 how many rulings must a grating have if it is barely to resolve the sodium doublet in the third order?

From Eq. 45–5 the required resolving power is

$$R = \frac{\lambda}{\Delta\lambda} = \frac{5890\ \text{A}}{(5895.9 - 5890.0)\text{A}} = 1000.$$

From Eq. 45–6 the number of rulings needed is

$$N = \frac{R}{m} = \frac{1000}{3} = 330.$$

This is a modest requirement.      ◀

The resolving power of a grating must not be confused with its dispersion. Table 45–1 shows the characteristics of three gratings, each illuminated with light of $\lambda = 5890$ A, the diffracted light being viewed in the first order ($m = 1$ in Eq. 45–1).

**Table 45–1**

SOME CHARACTERISTICS OF THREE GRATINGS

($\lambda = 5890$ A, $m = 1$)

| Grating | $N$ | $d,$ A | $\theta$ | $R$ | $D$ $10^{-3}$ degrees/A |
|---------|-----|--------|----------|-----|--------------------------|
| $A$ | 10,000 | 25,400 | 13.3° | 10,000 | 2.32 |
| $B$ | 20,000 | 25,400 | 13.3° | 20,000 | 2.32 |
| $C$ | 10,000 | 13,700 | 25.5° | 10,000 | 4.64 |

The student should verify that the values of $D$ and $R$ given in the table can be calculated from Eqs. 45–4 and 45–6, respectively.

For the conditions of use noted in Table 45–1, gratings $A$ and $B$ have the same *dispersion* and $A$ and $C$ have the same *resolving power*. Figure 45–9 shows the intensity patterns that would be produced by these gratings for two incident waves of wavelengths $\lambda_1$ and $\lambda_2$, in the vicinity of $\lambda = 5890$ A. Grating $B$, which has high resolving power, has narrow intensity maxima and is inherently capable of distinguishing lines that are much closer together in wavelength than those of Fig. 45–9. Grating $C$, which has high dispersion, produces twice the angular separation between rays $\lambda_1$ and $\lambda_2$ that grating $B$ does.

**Fig. 45–9** The intensity patterns for light of wavelengths $\lambda_1$ and $\lambda_2$ near 5890 A, incident on the gratings of Table 45–1. Grating $B$ has the highest resolving power and grating $C$ the highest dispersion.

▶ **Example 4.** The grating of Example 1 has 8000 lines illuminated by light from a mercury vapor discharge. (a) What is the expected dispersion, in the third order, in the vicinity of the intense green line ($\lambda = 5460$ A)? Noting that $d = 31{,}700$ A, we have, from Eq. 45–1,

$$\theta = \sin^{-1}\frac{m\lambda}{d} = \sin^{-1}\frac{(3)(5460 \text{ A})}{31{,}700 \text{ A}} = \sin^{-1} 0.517 = 31.1°.$$

From Eq. 45–4 we have

$$D = \frac{m}{d\cos\theta} = \frac{3}{(31{,}700 \text{ A})(\cos 31.1°)} = 1.1 \times 10^{-4} \text{ radian/A} = 6.3 \times 10^{-3} \text{ deg/A}.$$

(b) What is the expected resolving power of this grating in the fifth order? Equation 45–6 gives

$$R = Nm = (8000)(5) = 40{,}000.$$

Thus near $\lambda = 5460$ A a wavelength difference $\Delta\lambda$ given by Eq. 45–5, or

$$\Delta\lambda = \frac{\lambda}{R} = \frac{5460 \text{ A}}{40{,}000} = 0.14 \text{ A},$$

can be distinguished. ◀

### 45–5  X-ray Diffraction

Figure 45–10 shows how X-rays are produced when electrons from a heated filament $F$ are accelerated by a potential difference $V$ and strike a metal target $T$. X-rays are electromagnetic radiation with wavelengths of the order of 1 A. This value is to be compared to 5500 A for the center of the visible spectrum. For such small wavelengths a standard optical diffraction grating, as normally employed, cannot be used. For $\lambda = 1$ A and $d = 30{,}000$ A,

**Fig. 45-10**  X-rays are generated when electrons from heated filament $F$, accelerated by potential difference $V$, are brought to rest on striking metallic target $T$. $W$ is a "window" —transparent to X-rays—in the evacuated metal container $C$.

for example, Eq. 45-1 shows that the first-order maximum occurs at

$$\theta = \sin^{-1}\frac{m\lambda}{d} = \sin^{-1}\frac{(1)(1\ \text{A})}{3 \times 10^4\ \text{A}} = \sin^{-1} 0.33 \times 10^{-4} = 0.002°.$$

This is too close to the central maximum to be practical. A grating with $d \cong \lambda$ is desirable, but, since X-ray wavelengths are about equal to atomic diameters, such gratings cannot be constructed mechanically.

In 1912 it occurred to the German physicist Max von Laue that a crystalline solid, consisting as it does of a regular array of atoms, might form a natural three-dimensional "diffraction grating" for X-rays. Figure 45-11 shows that if a collimated beam of X-rays, continuously distributed in wavelength, is allowed to fall on a crystal, such as sodium chloride, intense beams corresponding to constructive interference from the many diffracting centers

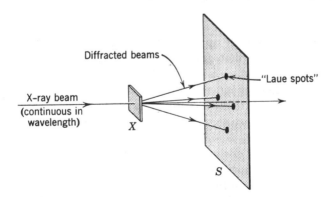

**Fig. 45-11**  A nonmonochromatic beam of X-rays falls on a crystal $X$, which may be NaCl. Strong diffracted beams appear in certain directions, forming a so-called Laue pattern on a photographic film $S$.

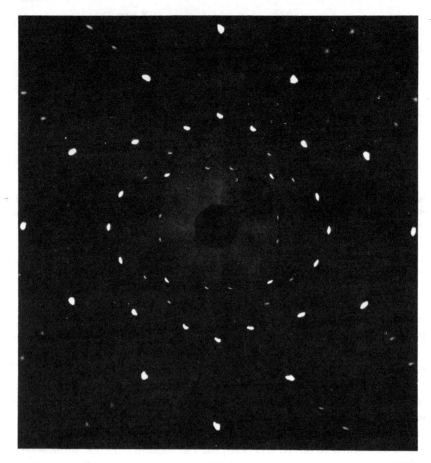

**Fig. 45–12**   Laue X-ray diffraction pattern from sodium chloride.   A crystal of ordinary table salt was used in making this plate.   (Courtesy of W. Arrington and J. L. Katz, X-ray Laboratory, Rensselaer Polytechnic Institute.)

of which the crystal is made up appear in certain sharply defined directions. If these beams fall on a photographic film, they form an assembly of "Laue spots."   Figure 45–12, which is an actual example of these spots, shows that the hypothesis of Laue is indeed correct.   The atomic arrangements in the crystal can be deduced from a careful study of the positions and intensities of the Laue spots * in much the same way that we might deduce the structure of an optical grating (that is, the detailed profile of its slits) by a study of the positions and intensities of the lines in the interference pattern.

Figure 45–13 shows how sodium and chlorine atoms (strictly, $Na^+$ and $Cl^-$ ions) are stacked to form a crystal of sodium chloride.   This pattern, which has *cubic* symmetry, is one of the many atomic arrangements exhibited

---

* Other experimental arrangements have supplanted the Laue technique to a considerable extent today; the principle remains unchanged, however.

by solids. The model represents the *unit cell* for sodium chloride. This is the smallest unit from which the crystal may be built up by repetition in three dimensions. The student should verify that no smaller assembly of atoms possesses this property. For sodium chloride the length of the cube edge of the unit cell is 5.62737 A.

Each unit cell in sodium chloride has four sodium ions and four chlorine ions associated with it. In Fig. 45–13 the sodium ion in the center belongs entirely to the cell shown. Each of the other twelve sodium ions shown is shared with three adjacent unit cells so that each contributes one-fourth of an ion to the cell under consideration. The total number of sodium ions is then $1 + \frac{1}{4}(12) = 4$. By similar reasoning the student can show that although there are fourteen chlorine ions in Fig. 45–13 only four are associated with the unit cell shown.

The unit cell is the fundamental repetitive diffracting unit in the crystal, corresponding to the slit (and its adjacent opaque strip) in the optical dif-

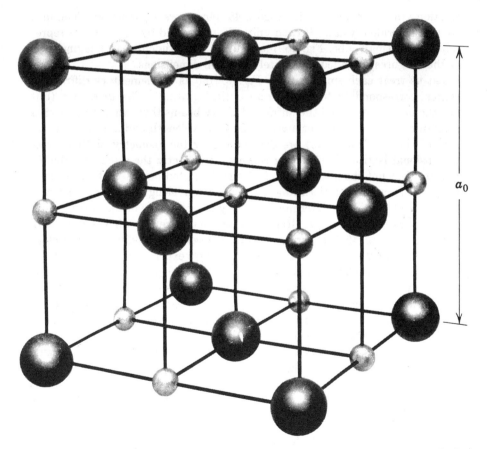

**Fig. 45–13**　A model showing how $Na^+$ and $Cl^-$ ions are stacked to form a unit cell of NaCl. The small spheres represent sodium ions, the large ones chlorine. The edge $a_0$ of the (cubical) unit cell is 5.62737 A.

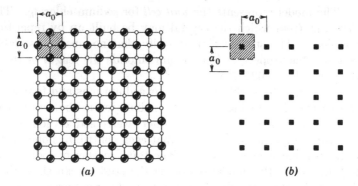

(a)                              (b)

**Fig. 45-14**   (a) A section through a crystal of sodium chloride, showing the sodium and chlorine ions.   (b) The corresponding unit cells in this section, each cell being represented by a small black square.

fraction grating of Fig. 45-1.   Figure 45-14a shows a particular plane in a sodium chloride crystal.   If each unit cell intersected by this plane is represented by a small cube, Fig. 45-14b results.   The student may imagine each of these figures extended indefinitely in three dimensions.

Let us treat each small cube in Fig. 45-14b as an elementary diffracting center, corresponding to a slit in an optical grating.   The *directions* (but not the intensities) of all the diffracted X-ray beams that can emerge from a sodium chloride crystal (for a given X-ray wavelength and a given orientation of the incident beam) are determined by the geometry of this three-dimensional lattice of diffracting centers.   In exactly the same way the *directions* (but not the intensities) of all the diffracted beams that can emerge from a particular optical grating (for a given wavelength and orientation of the incident beam) are determined only by the geometry of the grating, that is, by the grating spacing $d$.   Representing the unit cell by what is essentially a point, as in Fig. 45-14b, corresponds to representing the slits in a diffraction grating by lines, as we did in discussing Young's experiment in Section 43-1.

The *intensities* of the lines from an optical diffraction grating are determined by the diffracting characteristics of a single slit, as Fig. 44-14 shows.   In the idealized case of Fig. 45-1 these characteristics depend on the slit width $a$.   In practical optical gratings these characteristics depend on the detailed shape of the profile of the grating rulings.

In exactly the same way the *intensities* of the diffracted beams emerging from a crystal depend on the diffracting characteristics of the unit cell.*   Fundamentally the X-rays are diffracted by electrons, diffraction by nuclei being negligible in most cases.   Thus the diffracting characteristics of a

---

* For some directions in which a beam might be expected to emerge, from interference considerations, no beam will be found because the diffracting characteristics of the unit cell are such that no energy is diffracted in that direction.   Similarly, in optical gratings some lines, permitted by interference considerations, may not appear if their predicted positions coincide with a null in the single-slit diffraction pattern (see Fig. 44-12).

*(a)*

*(b)*

**Fig. 45–15** (*a*) A photograph of an oscilloscope screen arranged to display projected electron density contours for phthalocyanine ($C_{32}H_{18}N_8$). Such plots, constructed electronically from X-ray diffraction data by an analog computer, provide a vivid picture of the structure of molecules. (Courtesy of Ray Pepinsky.) (*b*) A structural representation of the molecule phthalocyanine. The student should make a detailed comparison with (*a*), locating the various atoms identified in (*b*). Note that hydrogen atoms, which contain only a single electron, are not prominent in (*a*).

unit cell depend on how the electrons are distributed throughout the volume of the cell. By studying the *directions* of diffracted X-ray beams, we can learn the basic symmetry of the crystal. By also studying the *intensities* we can learn how electrons are distributed in the unit cell. Figure 45–15 shows the average density of electrons projected onto a particular plane through a unit cell of a crystal of phthalocyanine. This remarkable figure suggests something of the full power of X-ray methods for studying the structure of solids.

### 45–6 Bragg's Law

Bragg's law predicts the conditions under which diffracted X-ray beams from a crystal are possible. In deriving it, we ignore the structure of the unit cell, which is related only to the intensities of these beams. The dashed sloping lines in Fig. 45–16a represent the intersection with the plane of the figure of an arbitrary set of planes passing through the elementary diffracting centers. The perpendicular distance between adjacent planes is $d$. Many other such families of planes, with different *interplanar spacings*, can be defined.

Figure 45–16b shows a plane wave that lies in the plane of the figure falling on one member of the family of planes defined in Fig. 45–16a, the incident rays making an angle $\theta$ with the plane.* Consider a family of diffracted rays lying in the plane of Fig. 45–16b and making an angle $\beta$ with the plane containing the elementary diffracting centers. The diffracted rays will combine to produce maximum intensity if the path difference between adjacent rays is an integral number of wavelengths or

$$ae - bd = h(\cos \beta - \cos \theta) = l\lambda \qquad l = 0, 1, 2, \ldots. \qquad (45\text{–}7)$$

For $l = 0$ this leads to $\qquad\qquad \beta = \theta,$

and the plane of atoms acts like a mirror for the incident wave, no matter what the value of $\theta$.

For other values of $l$, $\beta$ does not equal $\theta$, but the diffracted beam can always be regarded as being "reflected" from a *different* set of planes than that shown in Fig. 45–16a with a different interplanar spacing $d$. Since we wish to describe each diffracted beam as a "reflection" from a particular set of planes and since we are dealing in the present argument only with the particular set of planes shown in Fig. 45–16a we ignore all values of $l$ other than $l = 0$ in Eq. 45–7. It can also be shown that a plane of diffracting centers acts like a mirror (that is, $\beta = \theta$) whether or not the incident wave lies in the plane of Fig. 45–16b.

Figure 45–16c shows an incident wave striking the *family* of planes, a single member of which was considered in Fig. 45–16b. For a single plane, mirror-like "reflection" occurs for *any* value of $\theta$, as we have seen. To have a constructive interference in the beam diffracted from the entire family of planes

---

* In X-ray diffraction it is customary to specify the direction of a wave by giving the angle between the ray and the plane (the *glancing angle*) rather than the angle between the ray and the normal.

in the direction). This means that the adjacent planes must reinforce each other.
This means that the path difference for rays from adjacent planes (see Fig. 45–16c) must be an integral number of wave lengths or

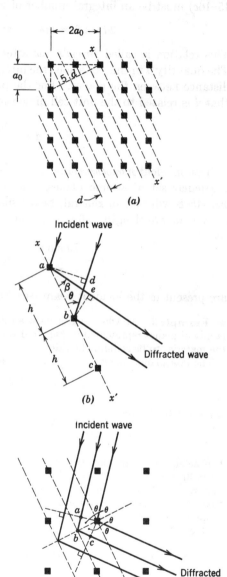

**Fig. 45–16** (a) A section through the NaCl unit cell lattice of Fig. 45–14b. The dashed sloping lines represent an arbitrary family of planes, with interplanar spacing d. (b) An incident wave falls, at grazing angle θ, on one of the planes, xx′, shown in (a). (c) An incident wave falls on the entire family of planes shown in (a). A strong diffracted wave is formed.

in the direction $\theta$, the rays from the separate planes must reinforce each other. This means that the path difference for rays from adjacent planes ($abc$ in Fig. 45–16c) must be an integral number of wavelengths or

$$2d \sin \theta = m\lambda \qquad m = 1, 2, 3, \ldots . \qquad (45\text{–}8)$$

This relation is called *Bragg's law* after W. L. Bragg who first derived it. The quantity $d$ in this equation (the interplanar spacing) is the perpendicular distance between the planes. For the planes of Fig. 45–16a analysis shows that $d$ is related to the unit cell dimension $a_0$ by

$$d = \frac{a_0}{\sqrt{5}}. \qquad (45\text{–}9)$$

If an incident *monochromatic* X-ray beam falls at an *arbitrary* angle $\theta$ on a particular set of atomic planes, a diffracted beam will *not* result because Eq. 45–8 will not, in general, be satisfied. If the incident X-rays are *continuous* in wavelength, diffracted beams will result when wavelengths given by

$$\lambda = \frac{2d \sin \theta}{m} \qquad m = 1, 2, 3, \ldots$$

are present in the incident beam (see Eq. 45–8).

▶ **Example 5.** At what angles must an X-ray beam with $\lambda = 1.10$ A fall on the family of planes represented in Fig. 45–16c if a diffracted beam is to exist? Assume the material to be sodium chloride.

The interplanar spacing $d$ for these planes is given by Eq. 45–9 or

$$d = \frac{a_0}{\sqrt{5}} = \frac{5.63 \text{ A}}{2.24} = 2.52 \text{ A}.$$

Equation 45–8 gives

$$\sin \theta = \frac{m\lambda}{2d} = \frac{(m)(1.10 \text{ A})}{(2)(2.52 \text{ A})} = 0.218m.$$

Diffracted beams are possible at $\theta = 12.6°$ ($m = 1$), $\theta = 25.9°$ ($m = 2$), $\theta = 40.9°$ ($m = 3$), and $\theta = 60.7°$ ($m = 4$). Higher-order beams cannot exist because they require $\sin \theta$ to exceed unity. Actually, the odd-order beams ($m = 1, 3$) prove to have zero intensity because the unit cell in cubic crystals such as NaCl has diffracting properties such that the intensity of the light scattered in these orders is zero (see Problem 26).                                                                        ◀

X-ray diffraction is a powerful tool for studying the arrangements of atoms in crystals. To do so quantitatively requires that the wavelength of the X-rays be known. In one of several approaches to this problem the unit cell dimension for NaCl * is determined by a method that does not involve X-rays. X-ray diffraction measurements on NaCl can then be used to determine the wavelength of the X-ray beam which in turn can be used to determine the structures of solids other than NaCl.

---

* In practice, calcite ($CaCO_3$) proves to be more useful as a standard crystal for a number of technical reasons.

If $\rho$ is the measured density of NaCl, we have, for the unit cell of Fig. 45-13,* recalling that each unit cell contains four NaCl "molecules,"

$$\rho = \frac{m}{V} = \frac{4m_{\text{NaCl}}}{a_0{}^3}.$$

Here $m_{\text{NaCl}}$, the mass of a NaCl molecule, is given by

$$m_{\text{NaCl}} = \frac{M}{N_0},$$

where $M$ is the molecular weight of NaCl and $N_0$ is Avogadro's number. Combining these two equations and solving for $a_0$ yields

$$a_0 = \left(\frac{4M}{N_0\rho}\right)^{\frac{1}{3}}$$

which permits us to calculate $a_0$. Once $a_0$ is known, the wavelengths of monochromatic X-ray beams can be found, using Bragg's law (Eq. 45–8).

## QUESTIONS

1. Discuss this statement: "A diffraction grating can just as well be called an interference grating."

2. For the simple spectroscope of Fig. 45–7, show (a) that $\theta$ increases with $\lambda$ for a grating and (b) that $\theta$ decreases with $\lambda$ for a prism.

3. You are given a photograph of a spectrum on which the angular positions and the wavelengths of the spectrum lines are marked. (a) How can you tell whether the spectrum was taken with a prism or a grating instrument? (b) What information could you gather about either the prism or the grating from studying such a spectrum?

4. Assume that the limits of the visible spectrum are 4300 and 6800 A. Is it possible to design a grating, assuming that the incident light falls normally on it, such that the first-order spectrum *barely overlaps* the second-order spectrum?

5. (a) Why does a diffraction grating have closely spaced rulings? (b) Why does it have a large number of rulings?

6. The relation $R = Nm$ suggests that the resolving power of a given grating can be made as large as desired by choosing an arbitrarily high order of diffraction. Discuss.

7. Show that at a given wavelength and a given angle of diffraction the resolving power of a grating depends only on its width $W$ ($= Nd$).

8. According to Eq. 45–3 the principal maxima become wider (that is, $\Delta\theta_m$ increases) the higher the order $m$ (that is, the larger $\theta_m$ becomes). According to Eq. 45–6 the resolving power becomes greater the higher the order $m$. Explain this apparent paradox.

9. Is the pattern of Fig. 45–12 more properly described as a diffraction pattern or as an interference pattern?

10. For a given family of planes in a crystal, can the wavelength of incident X-rays be (a) too large or (b) too small to form a diffracted beam?

11. If a parallel beam of X-rays of wavelength $\lambda$ is allowed to fall on a randomly oriented crystal of any material, generally no intense diffracted beams will occur. Such beams

* This relation cannot be written down unless it is known that the structure of NaCl is cubic. This can be determined, however, by inspection of the symmetry of the spots in Fig. 45–12; the wavelength of the X-rays need not be known.

appear if (a) the X-ray beam consists of a continuous distribution of wavelengths rather than a single wavelength or (b) the specimen is not a single crystal but a finely divided powder. Explain.

12. Why cannot a simple cube of edge $a_0/2$ in Fig. 45–13 be used as a unit cell for sodium chloride?

13. How would you *measure* (a) the dispersion $D$ and (b) the resolving power $R$ for either a prism or a grating spectrograph.

## PROBLEMS

1. Given a grating with 4000 lines/cm, how many orders of entire visible spectrum (4000–7000 A) can be produced?

2. Derive this expression for the intensity pattern for a three-slit "grating":

$$I_\theta = \tfrac{1}{9}I_m(1 + 4 \cos \phi + 4 \cos^2 \phi),$$

where

$$\phi = \frac{2\pi d \sin \theta}{\lambda}.$$

Assume that $a \ll \lambda$ and be guided by the derivation of the corresponding double-slit formula (Eq. 43–9).

3. (a) Using the result of Problem 2, show that the half-width of the fringes for a three-slit diffraction pattern, assuming $\theta$ small enough so that $\sin \theta \cong \theta$, is

$$\Delta\theta \cong \frac{\lambda}{3.2d}.$$

(b) Compare this with the expression derived for the two-slit pattern in Problem 10, Chapter 43. (c) Do these results support the conclusion that for a fixed slit spacing the interference maxima become sharper as the number of slits is increased?

4. Using the result of Problem 2, show that a three-slit "grating" has only one secondary maximum. Find its location and its relative intensity.

5. A grating designed for use in the infrared region of the electromagnetic spectrum is "blazed" to concentrate all its intensity in the first order ($m = 1$) for $\lambda = 80,000$ A. If visible light (4000 A $< \lambda <$ 7000 A) were allowed to fall on this grating, what visual appearance would the diffracted beams present?

6. The central intensity maximum formed by a grating, along with its subsidiary secondary maxima, can be viewed as the diffraction pattern of a single "slit" whose width is that of the entire grating. Treating the grating as a single wide slit, assuming that $m = 0$, and using the methods of Section 44–4, show that Eq. 45–2 can be derived.

7. A grating has 8000 rulings/in. For what wavelengths in the visible spectrum can fifth-order diffraction be observed?

8. A diffraction grating has 5000 rulings/in., and a strong diffracted beam is noted at $\theta = 30°$. (a) What are the possible wavelengths of the incident light? (b) How could you identify them in an actual case?

9. A diffraction grating 2.0 cm wide has 6000 rulings. At what angles will maximum-intensity beams occur if the incident radiation has a wavelength of 5890 A?

10. Assume that the limits of the visible spectrum are arbitrarily chosen as 4300 and 6800 A. Design a grating that will spread the first-order spectrum through an angular range of 20°.

11. A grating has 8000 rulings/in. and is illuminated at normal incidence by white light. A spectrum is formed on a screen 30 cm from the grating. If a 1.0-cm square hole is cut in the screen, its inner edge being 5.0 cm from the central maximum, what range of wavelengths passes through the hole?

12. Assume that light is incident on a grating at an angle $\psi$ as shown in Fig. 45–17. Show that the condition for a diffraction maximum is

$$d(\sin \psi + \sin \theta) = m\lambda \qquad m = 0, 1, 2, \ldots$$

Only the special case $\psi = 0$ has been treated in this chapter (compare Eq. 45–1).

**Fig. 45–17**

13. Show that in a grating with alternately transparent and opaque strips of *equal* width all the even orders (except $m = 0$) are absent.

14. A transmission grating with $d = 1.50 \times 10^{-4}$ cm is illuminated at various angles of incidence by light of wavelength 6000 A. Plot as a function of angle of incidence (0 to 90°) the angular deviation of the first-order diffracted beam from the incident direction.

15. Derive Eq. 45–3, that is, the expression for $\Delta\theta_m$, the angular distance between a principal maximum of order $m$ and either adjacent minimum.

16. A three-slit grating has separation $d$ between adjacent slits. If the middle slit is covered up, will the half-width of the intensity maxima become broader or narrower? See Problem 3 and also Problem 10, Chapter 43.

17. A grating has 40,000 rulings spread over 3.0 in. (*a*) What is its expected dispersion $D$ for sodium light ($\lambda = 5890$ A) in the first three orders? (*b*) What is its resolving power in these orders?

18. In a particular grating the sodium doublet (see Example 2) is viewed in third order at 80° to the normal and is barely resolved. Find (*a*) the grating spacing and (*b*) the total width of the rulings.

19. A source containing a mixture of hydrogen and deuterium atoms emits a red doublet at $\lambda = 6563$ A whose separation is 1.8 A. Find the minimum number of lines needed in a diffraction grating which can resolve these lines in the first order.

20. Show that the dispersion of a grating can be written as

$$D = \frac{\tan \theta}{\lambda}.$$

21. A grating has 6000 rulings/cm and is 6.0 cm wide. (*a*) What is the smallest wavelength interval that can be resolved in the third order at $\lambda = 5000$ A? (*b*) For this wavelength and this grating, can the resolution be improved? How?

22. Light containing a mixture of two wavelengths, 5000 A and 6000 A, is incident normally on a diffraction grating. It is desired (1) that the first and second principal maxima for each wavelength appear at $\theta \leq 30°$, (2) that the dispersion be as high as possible, *and* (3) that the third order for 6000 A be a missing order. (*a*) What is the separation

between adjacent slits? (b) What is the smallest possible individual slit width? (c) Name *all* orders for 6000 A that actually appear on the screen with the values chosen in (a) and (b).

23. Light of wavelength 6000 A is incident normally on a diffraction grating. Two *adjacent* principal maxima occur at $\sin \theta = 0.2$ and $\sin \theta = 0.3$, respectively. The fourth order is a missing order. (a) What is the separation between adjacent slits? (b) What is the smallest possible individual slit width? (c) Name *all* orders actually appearing on the screen with the values chosen in (a) and (b).

24. An optical grating with a spacing $d = 15,000$ A is used to analyze soft X-rays of wavelength $\lambda = 5.0$ A. The angle of incidence $\theta$ is $90° - \gamma$, where $\gamma$ is a *small* angle. The first order maximum is found at an angle $\theta = 90° - 2\beta$. Find the value of $\beta$.

25. Monochromatic X-rays ($\lambda = 1.20$ A) fall on a crystal of sodium chloride, making an angle of 45° with a reference line as shown in Fig. 45–18. Through what angles must the crystal be turned to give a diffracted beam associated with the planes shown? Assume that the crystal is turned about an axis that is perpendicular to the plane of the page. Ignore the possibility (see Problem 26) that some of these beams may be of zero intensity.

**Fig. 45–18**

26. *Missing orders in X-ray diffraction.* In Problem 25 the $m = 1$ beam, permitted by interference considerations, has zero intensity because of the diffracting properties of the unit cell for this geometry of beams and crystal. Prove this. (Hint: Show that the "reflection" from an atomic plane through the top of a layer of unit cells is canceled by a "reflection" from a plane through the middle of this layer of cells. All odd-order beams prove to have zero intensity.)

27. Assume that the incident X-ray beam in Fig. 45–18 is not monochromatic but contains wavelengths in a band from 0.95 to 1.30 A. Will diffracted beams, associated with the planes shown, occur? Assume $a_0 = 2.75$ A.

28. In comparing the wavelengths of two monochromatic X-ray lines, it is noted that line A gives a first-order reflection maximum at a glancing angle of 30° to the smooth face of a crystal. Line B, known to have a wavelength of 0.97 angstroms, gives a third-order reflection maximum at an angle of 60° from the same face of the same crystal. Find the wavelength of line A.

# Polarization

## CHAPTER 46

### 46–1  Polarization

Light, like all electromagnetic radiation, is predicted by electromagnetic theory to be a *transverse wave*, the directions of the vibrating electric and magnetic vectors being at right angles to the direction of propagation instead of parallel to it as in a longitudinal wave.  The transverse waves of Figs. 46–1 and 39–11 have the additional characteristic that they are *plane-polarized*. This means that the vibrations of the E vector are parallel to each other for all points in the wave.  At any such point the vibrating E vector and the direction of propagation form a plane, called the *plane of vibration;* in a plane-polarized wave all such planes are parallel.

**Fig. 46–1**  An instantaneous "snapshot" of a plane-polarized wave showing the vectors E and B along a particular ray.  The wave is moving to the right with speed *c*.  The plane containing the vibrating E vector and the direction of propagation is a *plane of vibration.*

The transverse nature of light waves cannot be deduced from the interference or diffraction experiments so far described because longitudinal waves such as sound waves also show these effects. An experimental basis for believing that light waves are transverse was provided by Thomas Young in 1817. Two of his contemporaries, Dominique-François Arago (1786–1853) and Augustin Jean Fresnel (1788–1827), were able, by allowing a light beam to fall on a crystal of calcite, to produce two separate beams (see Section 46–4). Astonishingly, these beams, although coherent, produced no interference fringes but only a uniform illumination. Young deduced from this that light must be a transverse wave and that the planes of vibration in the two beams must be at right angles to each other. Wave disturbances that act at right angles to each other cannot show interference effects; the student is asked to prove this in Problem 9. Young's words to Arago were these:

> I have been reflecting on the possibility of giving an imperfect explanation of the affection of light which constitutes polarization without departing from the genuine doctrine of undulations. It is a principle in this theory that all undulations are simply propagated through homogeneous mediums in concentric spherical surfaces like the undulations of sound, consisting simply in the direct and retrograde motions of the particles in the direction of the radius with their concomitant condensation and rarefactions [that is, longitudinal waves]. And yet, it is possible to explain in this theory a transverse vibration, propagated also in the direction of the radius, and with equal velocity, the motions of the particles being in a certain constant direction with respect to that radius; and this is a *polarization*.

Note how Young presents the possibility of a transverse vibration as a novel idea, light having been generally—but incorrectly—assumed to be a longitudinal vibration.

In a plane-polarized transverse wave it is necessary to specify two directions, that of the wave disturbance ($E$, say) and that of propagation. In a longitudinal wave these directions are identical. In plane-polarized transverse waves, but not in longitudinal waves, we may thus expect a lack of symmetry about the direction of propagation. Electromagnetic waves in the radio and microwave range exhibit this lack of symmetry readily. Such a wave, generated by the surging of charge up and down in the dipole that forms the transmitting antenna of Fig. 46–2, has (at large distances from the dipole and at right angles to it) an electric field vector parallel to the dipole axis. When this plane-polarized wave falls on a second dipole connected to a microwave detector, the alternating electric component of the wave will cause electrons to surge back and forth in the receiving antenna, producing a reading on the detector. If we turn the receiving antenna through 90° about the direction of propagation, the detector reading drops to zero. In this orientation the electric field vector is not able to cause charge to move along the dipole axis because it points at right angles to this axis. We can reproduce the experiment of Fig. 46–2 by turning the receiving antenna of a television set (assumed an electric dipole type) through 90° about an axis that points toward the transmitting station.

Common sources of visible light differ from radio and microwave sources

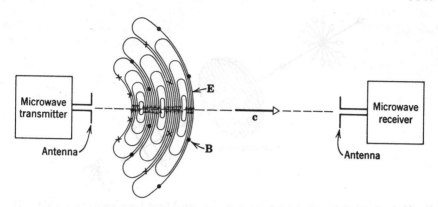

**Fig. 46–2**　The vectors **E** in the transmitted wave are parallel to the axis of the receiving antenna so that the wave will be detected.  If the receiving antenna is rotated through 90° about the direction of propagation, no signal will be detected.

in that the elementary radiators, that is, the atoms and molecules, act independently.  The light propagated in a given direction consists of independent wavetrains whose planes of vibration are randomly oriented about the direction of propagation, as in Fig. 46–3b.  Such light, though still transverse, is *unpolarized*.  The random orientation of the planes of vibration produces symmetry about the propagation direction, which, on casual study, conceals the true transverse nature of the waves.  To study this transverse nature, a way must be found to unsort the different planes of vibration.

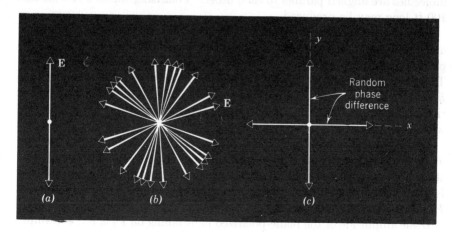

**Fig. 46–3**　(a) A plane-polarized transverse wave moving toward the reader, showing only the electric vector.  (b) An unpolarized transverse wave viewed as a random superposition of many plane-polarized wavetrains.  (c) A second, completely equivalent, description of an unpolarized transverse wave; here the unpolarized wave is viewed as two plane-polarized waves *with a random phase difference*.  The orientation of the x and y axes about the propagation direction is completely arbitrary.

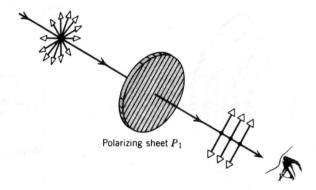

.Polarizing sheet $P_1$

**Fig. 46–4** A polarizing sheet produces plane-polarized light from unpolarized light. The parallel lines, which are not actually visible on the sheet, suggest the characteristic polarizing direction of the sheet.

## 46–2  Polarizing Sheets

Figure 46–4 shows unpolarized light falling on a sheet of commercial polarizing material called *Polaroid.** There exists in the sheet a certain characteristic polarizing direction, shown by the parallel lines. *The sheet will transmit only those wave-train components whose electric vectors vibrate parallel to this direction and will absorb those that vibrate at right angles to this direction.* The emerging light will be plane-polarized. This polarizing direction is established during the manufacturing process by embedding certain long-chain molecules in a flexible plastic sheet and then stretching the sheet so that the molecules are aligned parallel to each other. Polarizing sheets 2 ft wide and 100 ft long may be produced.

In Fig. 46–5 the polarizing sheet or *polarizer* lies in the plane of the page and the direction of propagation is into the page. The arrow **E** shows the plane of vibration of a randomly selected wavetrain falling on the sheet. Two vector components, $\mathbf{E}_x$ (of magnitude $E \sin \theta$) and $\mathbf{E}_y$ (of magnitude $E \cos \theta$), can replace **E**, one parallel to the polarizing direction and one at right angles to it. Only the former will be transmitted; the other is absorbed within the sheet.

Let us place a second polarizing sheet $P_2$ (usually called, when so used, an *analyzer*) as in Fig. 46–6. If $P_2$ is rotated about the direction of propagation, there are two positions, 180° apart, at which the transmitted light intensity is almost zero; these are the positions in which the polarizing directions of $P_1$ and $P_2$ are at right angles.

If the amplitude of the plane-polarized light falling on $P_2$ is $E_m$, the amplitude of the light that emerges is $E_m \cos \theta$, where $\theta$ is the angle between the polarizing directions of $P_1$ and $P_2$. Recalling that the intensity of the light

---

*There are other ways of producing polarized light without using this well-known commercial product. We mention some of them below.

**Fig. 46–5**  A wavetrain **E** is equivalent to two component wavetrains $\mathbf{E}_y$ and $\mathbf{E}_x$. Only the former is transmitted by the polarizer.

beam is proportional to the square of the amplitude, we see that the transmitted intensity $I$ varies with $\theta$ according to

$$I = I_m \cos^2 \theta, \qquad (46\text{–}1)$$

in which $I_m$ is the maximum value of the transmitted intensity. It occurs when the polarizing directions of $P_1$ and $P_2$ are parallel, that is, when $\theta = 0$ or $180°$. Figure 46–7$a$, in which two overlapping polarizing sheets are in the parallel position ($\theta = 0$ or $180°$ in Eq. 46–1) shows that the light transmitted through the region of overlap has its maximum value. In Fig. 46–7$b$ one or the other of the sheets has been rotated through $90°$ so that $\theta$ in Eq. 46–1 has the value 90 or $270°$; the light transmitted through the region of overlap is now a minimum.

Equation 46–1, called the law of Malus, was discovered by Étienne Louis Malus (1775–1812) experimentally in 1809, using polarizing techniques other

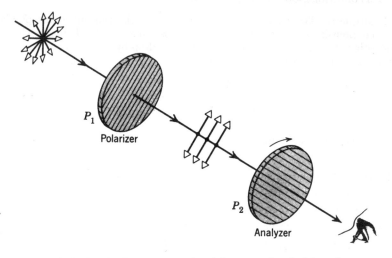

**Fig. 46–6**  Unpolarized light is not transmitted by crossed polarizing sheets.

**Fig. 46-7** Two square sheets of Polaroid are laid over a book. In (a) the axes of polarization of the two sheets are parallel and light passes through both sheets. In (b) one sheet has been rotated 90° and no light passes through. The book is opened to an illustration of the Luxembourg Palace in Paris. Malus discovered the phenomenon of polarization by reflection while looking at sunlight reflected off the palace windows through a calcite crystal.

than those so far described (see Section 46–3). Equation 46–1 describes precisely the lack of symmetry about the propagation direction that must be exhibited by plane-polarized transverse waves. Longitudinal waves could not possibly show such effects. Interestingly enough the human eye, under certain conditions, can detect polarized light.*

▶ **Example 1.** Two polarizing sheets have their polarizing directions parallel so that the intensity $I_m$ of the transmitted light is a maximum. Through what angle must either sheet be turned if the intensity is to drop by one-half?

From Eq. 46–1, since $I = \frac{1}{2}I_m$, we have

$$\tfrac{1}{2}I_m = I_m \cos^2 \theta$$

or

$$\theta = \cos^{-1} \pm \frac{1}{\sqrt{2}} = \pm 45°, \ \pm 135°.$$

The same effect is obtained no matter which sheet is rotated or in which direction.                                                                    ◀

Historically polarization studies were made to investigate the nature of light. Today we reverse the procedure and deduce something about the nature of an object from the polarization state of the light emitted by or scattered from that object. It has been possible to deduce, from studies of

---

* The so-called *Haidinger's brushes*; the interested student is referred to *Concepts of Classical Optics*, John Strong, W. H. Freeman & Co., 1958.

the polarization of light reflected from them, that the grains of cosmic dust present in our galaxy have been oriented in the weak galactic magnetic field ($\sim 2 \times 10^{-4}$ gauss) so that their long dimension is parallel to this field. Polarization studies have shown that Saturn's rings consist of ice crystals. The size and shape of virus particles can be determined by the polarization of ultraviolet light scattered from them. Much useful information about the structure of atoms and nuclei is gained from polarization studies of their emitted radiations in all parts of the electromagnetic spectrum. Thus we have a useful research technique for structures ranging in size from a galaxy ($\sim 10^{+20}$ meters) to a nucleus ($\sim 10^{-14}$ meter). Polarized light also has many practical applications in industry and in engineering science.

### 46–3    Polarization by Reflection

Malus discovered in 1809 that light can be partially or completely polarized by reflection. Anyone who has watched the sun's reflection in water, while wearing a pair of sunglasses made of polarizing sheet, has probably noticed the effect. It is necessary only to tilt the head from side to side, thus rotating the polarizing sheets, to observe that the intensity of the reflected sunlight passes through a minimum.

Figure 46–8 shows an unpolarized beam falling on a glass surface. The E vector for each wavetrain in the beam can be resolved into two components, one perpendicular to the plane of incidence—which is the plane of Fig. 46–8—and one lying in this plane. The first component, represented by the dots, is called the $\sigma$-component, from the German *senkrecht*, meaning perpendicular. The second component, represented by the arrows, is called the $\pi$-component (for *parallel*). On the average, for completely unpolarized incident light, these two components are of equal amplitude.

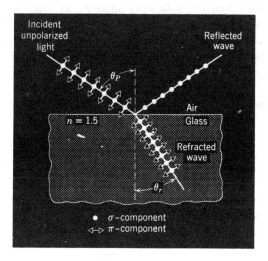

**Fig. 46–8**  For a particular angle of incidence $\theta_p$, the reflected light is completely polarized, as shown. The transmitted light is partially polarized.

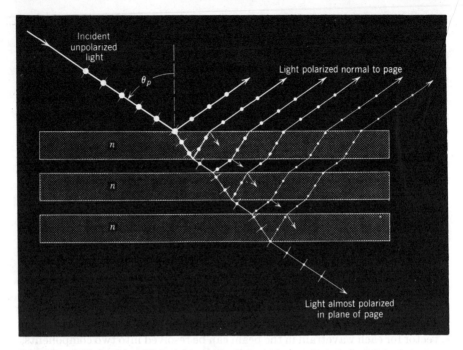

**Fig. 46–9**    Polarization of light by a stack of glass plates.    Unpolarized light is incident on a stack of glass plates at Brewster's angle $\theta_p$.    (Polarization in the plane of the page is shown by the short lines and polarization normal to the page by the dots.)    All light reflected out of the original ray is polarized normal to the page.    After passing through several reflecting interfaces, the light in the original ray no longer contains any appreciable component polarized normal to the page.

Experimentally, for glass or other dielectric materials, there is a particular angle of incidence, called the *polarizing angle* $\theta_p$, at which the reflection coefficient for the $\pi$-component is zero.    This means that the beam reflected from the glass, although of low intensity, is plane-polarized, with its plane of vibration at right angles to the plane of incidence.    This polarization of the reflected beam can easily be verified by analyzing it with a polarizing sheet.

The $\pi$-component at the polarizing angle is entirely refracted; the $\sigma$-component is only partially refracted.    Thus the transmitted beam, which is of high intensity, is only partially polarized.    By using a stack of glass plates rather than a single plate, reflections from successive surfaces occur and the intensity of the emerging reflected ($\sigma$-component) beam can be increased (see Fig. 46–9).    By the same token, the $\sigma$-components are progressively removed from the transmitted beam, making it more completely $\pi$-polarized.

At the polarizing angle it is found experimentally that the reflected and the refracted beams are at right angles, or (Fig. 46–8)

$$\theta_p + \theta_r = 90°.$$

From Snell's law,    $n_1 \sin \theta_p = n_2 \sin \theta_r.$

Combining these equations leads to

$$n_1 \sin \theta_p = n_2 \sin (90° - \theta_p) = n_2 \cos \theta_p$$

or $\qquad\qquad \tan \theta_p = \dfrac{n_2}{n_1},$ $\qquad\qquad\qquad$ (46-2)

where the incident ray is in medium one and the refracted ray in medium two. This can be written as

$$\tan \theta_p = n, \qquad\qquad (46\text{-}3)$$

where $n$ $(= n_2/n_1)$ is the index of refraction of medium two with respect to medium one. Equation 46-3 is known as *Brewster's law* after Sir David Brewster (1781-1868), who deduced it empirically in 1812. It is possible to prove this law rigorously from Maxwell's equations.

▶ **Example 2.** We wish to use a plate of glass ($n = 1.50$) as a polarizer. What is the polarizing angle? What is the angle of refraction?
From Eq. 46-3,

$$\theta_p = \tan^{-1} 1.50 = 56.3°.$$

The angle of refraction follows from Snell's law:

$$(1) \sin \theta_p = n \sin \theta_r$$

or $\qquad\qquad \sin \theta_r = \dfrac{\sin 56.3°}{1.50} = 0.555 \qquad \theta_r = 33.7°.$ ◀

### 46-4  Double Refraction

In earlier chapters we assumed that the speed of light, and thus the index of refraction, is independent of the direction of propagation in the medium and of the state of polarization of the light. Liquids, amorphous solids such as glass, and crystalline solids having cubic symmetry normally show this behavior and are said to be *optically isotropic*. Many other crystalline solids are optically *anisotropic* (that is, not isotropic).*

Solids may be anisotropic in many properties. Mica cleaves readily in one plane only; a cube of crystalline graphite does not have the same electric resistance between all pairs of opposite faces; a cube of crystalline nickel magnetizes more readily in certain directions than in others, etc. If a solid is a mixture of a large number of tiny crystallites, it may appear to be isotropic because of the random orientations of the crystallites. Powdered

---

* Many transparent amorphous solids such as glasses and plastics become optically anisotropic when they are mechanically stressed. This fact is useful in engineering design studies in that strains in gears, bridge structures, etc., can be studied quantitatively by building plastic models, stressing them appropriately, and examining the optical anisotropy that results, using polarization techniques. The interested student should consult "Photo-elasticity," a chapter by H. T. Jessop in Vol. 6 of the *Encyclopedia of Physics*, edited by H. Flugge (1958), Springer Verlag, Berlin.

**Fig. 46–10**  Two images, one polarized 90° relative to the other, are formed by a calcite crystal. The book on which the crystal is lying is Huygens' *Opera Reliqua*, wherein the phenomenon of birefringence is discussed.

mica, for example, compacted to a solid mass with a binder, does not exhibit the cleavage properties that characterize the crystallites making it up.

Figure 46–10, in which a polished crystal of calcite ($CaCO_3$) is laid over some printed letters, shows the optical anisotropy of this material; *the image appears double*. Figure 46–11 shows a beam of unpolarized light falling on a calcite crystal at right angles to one of its faces. The single beam splits into two at the crystal surface. The "double-bending" of a beam transmitted through calcite, exhibited in Figs. 46–10 and 46–11, is called *double refraction*.

If the two emerging beams in Fig. 46–11 are analyzed with a polarizing sheet they are found to be plane-polarized with their planes of vibration at right angles to each other, a fact discovered by Huygens in 1678. Huygens used a second calcite crystal to investigate the polarization states of the beams labeled *o* and *e* in the figure.

If experiments are carried out at various angles of incidence, one of the beams in Fig. 46–11 (represented by the *ordinary ray*, or *o*-ray) will be found to obey Snell's law of refraction at the crystal surface, just like a ray passing from one isotropic medium into another. The second beam (represented by the *extraordinary ray*, or *e*-ray) will not. In Fig. 46–11, for example, the angle of incidence for the incident light is zero but the angle of refraction of the *e*-ray, contrary to the prediction of Snell's law, is not. In general, the *e*-ray does not even lie in the plane of incidence.

This difference between the waves represented by the *o*- and *e*-rays with respect to Snell's law can be explained in these terms:

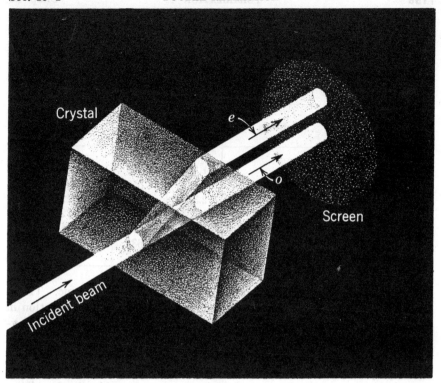

**Fig. 46–11**  A beam of unpolarized light falling on a calcite crystal is split into two beams which are polarized at right angles to each other.

1. The $o$-wave travels in the crystal with the same speed $v_o$ in all directions. In other words, the crystal has, for this wave, a single index of refraction $n_o$, just like an isotropic solid.

2. The $e$-wave travels in the crystal with a speed that varies with direction from $v_o$ to a larger value (for calcite) $v_e$. In other words, the index of refraction, defined as $c/v$, varies with direction from $n_o$ to a smaller value (for calcite) $n_e$.

The quantities $n_o$ and $n_e$ are called the *principal indices of refraction* for the crystal. Problem 7 suggests how to measure them. Table 46–1 shows these indices for six doubly refracting crystals. For three of them the $e$-wave is slower; for the other three it is faster. Some doubly refracting crystals (mica, topaz, etc.) are more complex optically than calcite and require *three* principal indices of refraction for a complete description of their optical properties. Crystals whose basic crystal structure is cubic (see Fig. 45–13) are optically isotropic, requiring only *one* index of refraction.

The behavior for the speeds of the two waves traveling in calcite is summarized by Fig. 46–12, which shows two wave surfaces spreading out from an imaginary point light source $S$ imbedded in the crystal. The $o$-wave sur-

**Table 46–1**

PRINCIPAL INDICES OF REFRACTION OF
SEVERAL DOUBLY REFRACTING CRYSTALS
(For sodium light, $\lambda = 5890$ A)

| Crystal | Formula | $n_o$ | $n_e$ | $n_e - n_o$ |
|---------|---------|-------|-------|-------------|
| Ice | $H_2O$ | 1.309 | 1.313 | $+0.004$ |
| Quartz | $SiO_2$ | 1.544 | 1.553 | $+0.009$ |
| Wurzite | ZnS | 2.356 | 2.378 | $+0.022$ |
| Calcite | $CaCO_3$ | 1.658 | 1.486 | $-0.172$ |
| Dolomite | $CaO \cdot MgO \cdot 2CO_2$ | 1.681 | 1.500 | $-0.181$ |
| Siderite | $FeO \cdot CO_2$ | 1.875 | 1.635 | $-0.240$ |

face is a sphere, as we would expect if the medium were isotropic. The $e$-wave surface is an ellipsoid of revolution about a characteristic direction in the crystal called the *optic axis*. The two wave surfaces represent light having two different polarization states. If we consider for the present only rays lying in the plane of Fig. 46–12, then (*a*) the plane of polarization for the $o$-rays is perpendicular to the figure, as suggested by the dots, and (*b*) that for the $e$-rays coincides with the plane of the figure, as suggested by the short lines. We describe the polarization states more fully at the end of this section.

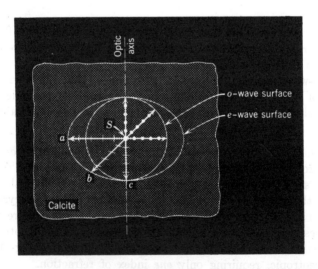

**Fig. 46–12** Huygens' wave surfaces generated by a point source $S$ imbedded in calcite. The polarization states for three $o$-rays and three $e$-rays are shown by the dots and lines, respectively. Note that in general (ray $Sb$) the bars representing the polarization direction are not perpendicular to the $e$-rays.

**Fig. 46–13** A calcite crystal; $\alpha$ is 78° 13'; $\beta$ is 102° 21'.

Figure 46–13, which shows a typical calcite crystal that may be obtained by cleavage from a naturally occurring crystal, shows how to locate the optic axis. The edges of calcite crystals may have any lengths but the angles at which the edges intersect always have one or another of two values, 78° 13' or 102° 21'. The optic axis is found by erecting a line at either of the two corners where three obtuse angles meet (the "blunt" corners), making equal angles with the crystal edges. *Any line in the crystal parallel to this line is also an optic axis.*

We can use Huygens' principle to study the propagation of light waves in doubly refracting crystals. Figure 46–14a shows the special case in which unpolarized light falls at normal incidence on a calcite slab cut from a crystal in such a way that the optic axis is normal to the surface. Consider a wavefront that, at time $t = 0$, coincides with the crystal surface. Following Huygens, we may let any point on this surface serve as a radiating center for a double set of Huygens' wavelets, such as those in Fig. 46–12. The plane of tangency to these wavelets represents the new position of this wavefront at a later time $t$. The incident beam in Fig. 46–14a is propagated through the crystal without deviation at speed $v_o$. The beam emerging from the slab will have the same polarization character as the incident beam. The calcite slab, in these special circumstances only, behaves like an isotropic material, and no distinction can be made between the $o$- and the $e$-waves.

Figure 46–14b shows two views of another special case, namely, unpolarized incident light falling at right angles on a slab cut so that the optic axis is parallel to its surface. In this case also the incident beam is propagated without deviation. However, we can now identify $o$- and $e$-waves that travel through the crystal with different speeds, $v_o$ and $v_e$, respectively. These waves are polarized at right angles to each other.

Some doubly refracting crystals have the interesting property, called *dichroism*, in which one of the polarization components is strongly absorbed within the crystal, the other being transmitted with little loss. Dichroism, illustrated in Fig. 46–15, is the basic operating principle of the commercial Polaroid sheet. The many small crystallites, imbedded in a plastic sheet with their optic axes parallel, have a polarizing action equivalent to that of a single large crystal slab.

Figure 46–14c shows unpolarized light falling at normal incidence on a calcite slab cut so that its optic axis makes an arbitrary angle with the crystal surface. Two spatially separated beams are produced, as in Fig. 46–11. They travel through the crystal at different speeds, that for the $o$-wave being $v_o$ and that for the $e$-wave being intermediate between $v_o$ and $v_e$.

**Fig. 46–14** Unpolarized light falls at normal incidence on slabs cut from a calcite crystal. The Huygens' wavelets are appropriate sections of the figure of revolution about the optic axis represented by Fig. 46–15. (a) No double refraction or speed difference occurs. (b) No double refraction occurs but there is a speed difference. (c) Both double refraction and a speed difference occur. (d) Same as (c) but showing the polarization states and the emerging rays.

**Fig. 46–15** Showing the absorption of one polarization component inside a dichroic crystal of the type used in Polaroid sheets.

Note that ray $xa$ represents the shortest *optical* path for the transfer of light energy from point $x$ to the $e$-wavefront. Energy transferred along any other ray, in particular along ray $xb$, would have a longer transit time, a consequence of the fact that the speed of $e$-waves varies with direction.* Figure 46–14$d$ represents the same case as Fig. 46–14$c$. It shows the rays emerging from the slab, as in Fig. 46–11, and makes clear that the emerging beams are polarized at right angles to each other, that is, they are *cross-polarized*.

We now seek to understand, in terms of the atomic structure of optically anisotropic crystals, how cross-polarized light waves with different speeds can exist. Light is propagated through a crystal by the action of the vibrating **E** vectors of the wave on the electrons in the crystal. These electrons, which experience electrostatic restoring forces if they are moved from their equilibrium positions, are set into forced periodic oscillation about these positions and pass along the transverse wave disturbance that constitutes the light wave. The strength of the restoring forces may be measured by a force constant $k$, as for the simple harmonic oscillator discussed in Chapter 15 (see Eq. 15–4).

In optically isotropic materials the force constant $k$ is the same for all directions of displacement of the electrons from their equilibrium positions. In doubly refracting crystals, however, $k$ varies with direction. For electron displacements that lie in a plane at right angles to the optic axis $k$ has the constant value $k_o$, no matter how the displacement is oriented in this plane. For displacements parallel to the

---

* The student who has not previously read Section 41–6 on Fermat's principle may care to do so now.

**Fig. 46–16**  Two views of a one-dimensional mechanical model for double refraction.

optic axis, $k$ has the larger value (for calcite) $k_e$.*  Note carefully that the speed of a wave in a crystal is determined by the direction in which the **E** vectors vibrate and *not* by the direction of propagation.  It is the transverse **E**-vector vibrations that call the restoring forces into play and thus determine the wave speed.  Note too that the stronger the restoring force, that is, the larger $k$, the faster the wave.  For waves traveling along a stretched cord, for example, the restoring force for the transverse displacements is determined by the tension $F$ in the cord.  Equation 19–12 shows that an increase in $F$ means an increase in the wave speed $v$.

Figure 46–16, a long weighted "tire chain" supported at its upper end, provides a one-dimensional mechanical analogy for double refraction.  It applies specifically to $o$- and $e$-waves traveling at right angles to the optic axis, as in Fig. 46–14b.  If the supporting block is oscillated, as in Fig. 46–16a, a transverse wave travels along the chain with a certain speed.  If the block is oscillated lengthwise, as in Fig. 46–16b, another transverse wave is also propagated.  The restoring force for the second wave is greater than for the first, the chain being more rigid in the plane of Fig. 46–16b than in the plane of Fig. 46–16a.  Thus the second wave travels along the chain with a greater speed.

In the language of optics we would say that the speed of a transverse wave in the chain depends on the orientation of the plane of vibration of the wave.  If we oscillate the top of the chain in a random way, the wave disturbance at a point along the chain can be described as the sum of two waves, polarized at right angles and traveling with different speeds.  This corresponds exactly to the optical situation of Fig. 46–14b.

---

* For doubly refracting crystals with $n_e > n_o$ (see Table 46–1) $k$ for displacements parallel to the optic axis is *smaller* than for those at right angles to it.  Also, for crystals with three principal indices of refraction, there will be three principal force constants.  Such crystals have two optic axes and are called *biaxial*.  The crystals listed in Table 46–1 have only a single optic axis and are called *uniaxial*.

For waves traveling parallel to the optic axis, as in Fig. 46–14a, or for waves in optically isotropic materials, the appropriate mechanical analogy is a single weighted hanging chain. Here there is only one speed of propagation, no matter how the upper end is oscillated. The restoring forces are the same for all orientations of the plane of polarization of waves traveling along such a chain.

These considerations allow us to understand more clearly the polarization states of the light represented by the double-wave surface of Fig. 46–12. For the (spherical) o-wave surface, the E-vector vibrations must be everywhere at right angles to the optic axis. If this is so, the same force constant $k_o$ will always be operative, and the o-waves will travel with the same speed in all directions. More specifically, if we draw a ray in Fig. 46–12 from $S$ to the o-wave surface, considered three-dimensionally (that is, as a sphere), the E-vector vibrations will always be at right angles to the plane defined by this ray and the optic axis. Thus these vibrations will always be at right angles to the optic axis.

For the (ellipsoidal) e-wave surface, the E-vector vibrations in general have a component parallel to the optic axis. For rays such as $Sa$ in Fig. 46–12 or for the e-rays of Fig. 46–14b, the vibrations are completely parallel to this axis. Thus a relatively strong force constant (in calcite) $k_e$ is operative, and the wave speed $v_e$ will be relatively high. For e-rays, such as $Sb$ in Fig. 46–12, the parallel component of the E-vector vibrations is less than 100%, so that the corresponding wave speed will be less than $v_e$. For ray $Sc$, in Fig. 46–12, the parallel component is zero, and the distinction between o- and e-rays disappears.

## 46–5 Circular Polarization

Let plane-polarized light of angular frequency $\omega$ ($= 2\pi\nu$) fall at normal incidence on a slab of calcite cut so that the optic axis is parallel to the face of the slab, as in Fig. 46–17. The two waves that emerge will be plane-polarized at right angles to each other, and, if the incident plane of vibration is at 45° to the optic axis, they will have equal amplitudes. Since the waves travel through the crystal at different speeds, there will be a phase difference $\phi$ between them when they emerge from the crystal. If the crystal thickness is chosen so that (for a given frequency of light) $\phi = 90°$, the slab is called a *quarter-wave plate*. The emerging light is said to be *circularly polarized*.

In Section 15–7 we saw that the two emerging plane-polarized waves just described (vibrating at right angles with a 90° phase difference) can be represented as the projections on two perpendicular axes of a vector rotating with

**Fig. 46–17**  Plane-polarized light falls on a doubly refracting slab of thickness $x$ cut with its optic axis parallel to the surface. The plane of vibration of the incident light is oriented to make an angle of 45° with the optic axis.

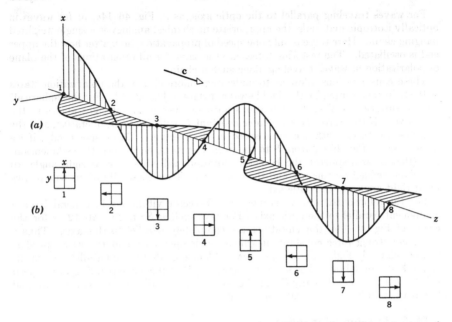

**Fig. 46–18** (a) Two plane-polarized waves of equal amplitude and at right angles to each other are moving in the z direction. They differ in phase by 90°; where one wave has maximum values, the other is zero. (b) Views of the resultant amplitude of the approaching wave as seen by observers located at the positions shown on the z axis. Note that each observer will see the resultant vector rotate clockwise with time.

angular frequency $\omega$ about the propagation direction. These two descriptions of circularly polarized light are completely equivalent. Figure 46–18 clarifies the relationship between these two descriptions.

▶ **Example 3.** A quartz quarter-wave plate is to be used with sodium light ($\lambda = 5890$ A). What must its thickness be?

Two waves travel through the slab at speeds corresponding to the two principal indices of refraction given in Table 46–1 ($n_e = 1.553$ and $n_o = 1.544$). If the crystal thickness is $x$, the number of wavelengths of the first wave contained in the crystal is

$$N_e = \frac{x}{\lambda_e} = \frac{x n_e}{\lambda},$$

where $\lambda_e$ is the wavelength of the $e$-wave in the crystal and $\lambda$ is the wavelength in air. For the second wave the number of wavelengths is

$$N_o = \frac{x}{\lambda_o} = \frac{x n_o}{\lambda},$$

where $\lambda_o$ is the wavelength of the $o$-wave in the crystal. The difference $N_e - N_o$ must be one-fourth, or

$$\frac{1}{4} = \frac{x}{\lambda}(n_e - n_o).$$

This equation yields

$$x = \frac{\lambda}{4(n_e - n_o)} = \frac{5890\ \text{A}}{(4)(1.553 - 1.544)} = 0.016\ \text{mm}.$$

This plate is rather thin; most quarter-wave plates are made from mica, splitting the sheet to the correct thickness by trial and error.

**Example 4.** A beam of circularly polarized light falls on a polarizing sheet. Describe the emerging beam.

The circularly polarized light, as it enters the sheet, can be represented by

$$E_x = E_m \sin \omega t$$

and
$$E_y = E_m \cos \omega t,$$

where $x$ and $y$ represent arbitrary perpendicular axes. These equations correctly represent the fact that a circularly polarized wave is equivalent to two plane-polarized waves with equal amplitude and a 90° phase difference.

The resultant amplitude in the incident circularly polarized wave is

$$E_{\text{cp}} = \sqrt{E_x{}^2 + E_y{}^2} = \sqrt{E_m{}^2 (\sin^2 \omega t + \cos^2 \omega t)} = E_m,$$

an expected result if the circularly polarized wave is represented as a rotating vector. The resultant intensity in the incident circularly polarized wave is proportional to $E_m{}^2$, or

$$I_{\text{cp}} \propto E_m{}^2. \tag{46–4}$$

Let the polarizing direction of the sheet make an arbitrary angle $\theta$ with the $x$ axis as shown in Fig. 46–19. The instantaneous value of the plane-polarized wave transmitted by the sheet is

$$E = E_y \sin \theta + E_x \cos \theta$$
$$= E_m \cos \omega t \sin \theta + E_m \sin \omega t \cos \theta$$
$$= E_m \sin (\omega t + \theta).$$

The intensity of the wave transmitted by the sheet is proportional to $E^2$, or

$$I \propto E_m{}^2 \sin^2 (\omega t + \theta).$$

The eye and other measuring instruments respond only to the average intensity $\bar{I}$, which is found by replacing $\sin^2 (\omega t + \theta)$ by its average value over one or more cycles $(= \frac{1}{2})$, or

$$\bar{I} \propto \tfrac{1}{2} E_m{}^2.$$

Comparison with Eq. 46–4 shows that inserting the polarizing sheet reduces the intensity by one-half. The orientation of the sheet makes no difference, since $\theta$ does not

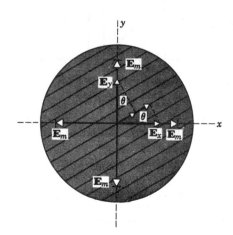

**Fig. 46–19** Circularly polarized light falls on a polarizing sheet. $\mathbf{E}_x$ and $\mathbf{E}_y$ are instantaneous values of the two components, their maximum values being $\mathbf{E}_m$.

appear in this equation; this is to be expected if circularly polarized light is represented by a rotating vector, all azimuths about the propagation direction being equivalent. Inserting a polarizing sheet in an *unpolarized* beam has just the same effect, so that a simple polarizing sheet cannot be used to distinguish between unpolarized and circularly polarized light.

**Example 5.** A beam of light is thought to be circularly polarized. How may this be verified?

Insert a quarter-wave plate. If the beam is circularly polarized, the two components will have a phase difference of 90° between them. The quarter-wave plate will introduce a further phase difference of $\pm 90°$ so that the emerging light will have a phase difference of either zero or 180°. In either case the light will now be *plane-polarized* and can be made to suffer complete extinction by rotating a polarizer in its path.

Does the quarter-wave plate have to be oriented in any particular way to carry out this test?

**Example 6.** A plane-polarized light wave of amplitude $E_0$ falls on a calcite quarter-wave plate with its plane of vibration at 45° to the optic axis of the plate, which is taken as the $y$ axis; see Fig. 46–20. The emerging light will be circularly polarized. In what direction will the rotating electric vector appear to rotate? The direction of propagation is out of the page.

The wave component whose vibrations are parallel to the optic axis (the $e$-wave) can be represented as it emerges from the plate as

$$E_y = (E_0 \cos 45°) \sin \omega t = \frac{1}{\sqrt{2}} E_0 \sin \omega t = E_m \sin \omega t.$$

The wave component whose vibrations are at right angles to the optic axis (the $o$-wave) can be represented as

$$E_x = (E_0 \sin 45°) \sin (\omega t - 90°) = -\frac{1}{\sqrt{2}} E_0 \cos \omega t = -E_m \cos \omega t,$$

the 90° phase shift representing the action of the quarter-wave plate. Note that $E_x$

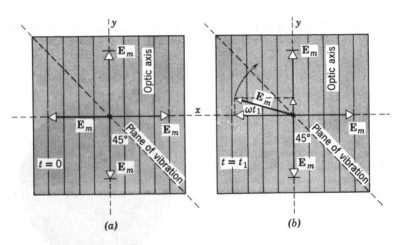

*(a)*                    *(b)*

**Fig. 46–20** Plane-polarized light falls from behind on a quarter-plate oriented so that the light emerging from the page is circularly polarized. In this case the electric vector $E_m$ rotates clockwise as seen by an observer facing the light source.

reaches its maximum value one-fourth of a cycle *later* than $E_y$ does, for, in calcite, wave $E_x$ (the *o*-wave) travels *more slowly* than wave $E_y$ (the *e*-wave).

To decide the direction of rotation, let us locate the tip of the rotating electric vector at two instants of time, (a) $t = 0$ and (b) a short time $t_1$ later chosen so that $\omega t_1$ is a small angle. At $t = 0$ the coordinates of the tip of the rotating vector (see Fig. 46–20a) are

$$E_y = 0 \quad \text{and} \quad E_x = -E_m.$$

At $t = t_1$ these coordinates become, approximately,

$$E_y = E_m \sin \omega t_1 \cong E_m(\omega t_1)$$

$$E_x = -E_m \cos \omega t_1 \cong -E_m.$$

Figure 46–20b shows that the vector that represents the emerging circular polarized light is rotating clockwise; by convention such light is called *right-circularly polarized*, the observer always being considered to face the light source.

If the plane of vibration of the incident light in Fig. 46–20 is rotated through $\pm 90°$, the emerging light will be *left-circularly polarized*.     ◀

## 46–6   Angular Momentum of Light

That light waves can deliver *linear momentum* to an absorbing screen or to a mirror is in accord with classical electromagnetism, with quantum physics, and with experiment. The facts of circular polarization suggest that light so polarized might also have *angular* momentum associated with it. This is indeed the case; once again the prediction is in accord with classical electromagnetism and with quantum physics. Experimental proof was provided in 1936 by Beth, who showed that when circularly polarized light is produced in a doubly refracting slab the slab experiences a reaction torque.

The angular momentum carried by light plays a vital role in understanding the emission of light from atoms and of $\gamma$-rays from nuclei. If light carries away angular momentum as it leaves the atom, the angular momentum of the residual atom must change by exactly the amount carried away; otherwise the angular momentum of the isolated system *atom plus light* will not be conserved.

Classical and quantum theory both predict that if a beam of circularly polarized light is completely absorbed by an object on which it falls, an angular momentum given by

$$L = \frac{U}{\omega} \tag{46–5}$$

is transferred to the object, where $U$ is the amount of absorbed energy and $\omega$ the angular frequency of the light. The student should verify that the dimensions in Eq. 46–5 are consistent.

## 46–7   Scattering of Light

A light wave, falling on a transparent solid, causes the electrons in the solid to oscillate periodically in response to the time-varying electric vector of the incident wave. The wave that travels through the medium is the resultant of the incident wave and of the radiations from the oscillating electrons. The resultant wave has a maximum intensity in the direction of the incident beam, falling off rapidly on either side. The lack of sideways scattering, which would be essentially complete in a large "perfect" crystal, comes about because the oscillating charges in the medium act cooperatively or coherently.

When light passes through a gas, we find much more sideways scattering. The oscillating electrons in this case, being separated by relatively large distances and not being bound together in a rigid structure, act independently rather than cooperatively. Thus the rigid cancellation of wave disturbances that are not in the forward direction is less likely to occur; there is more sideways scattering.

Light scattered sideways from a gas can be wholly or partially polarized, even though the incident light is unpolarized. Figure 46–21 shows an unpolarized beam moving upward on the page and striking a gas atom at $a$. The electrons at $a$ will oscillate in response to the electric components of the incident wave, their motion being equivalent to two oscillating dipoles whose axes are represented by the arrow and the dot at $a$. An oscillating dipole does not radiate along its own line of action. Thus an observer at $b$ would receive no radiation from the dipole represented by the arrow at $a$. The radiation reaching him would come entirely from the dipole represented by the dot at $a$; thus this radiation would be plane-polarized, the plane of vibration passing through the line $ab$ and being normal to the page.

Observers at $c$ and $d$ would detect partially polarized light, since the dipole represented by the arrow at $a$ would radiate somewhat in these directions. Observers viewing the transmitted or the back-scattered light would not detect any polarization effects because both dipoles at $a$ would radiate equally in these two directions.

A familiar example is the scattering of sunlight by the molecules of the earth's atmosphere. If the atmosphere were not present, the sky would appear black except when we looked directly at the sun. This has been verified

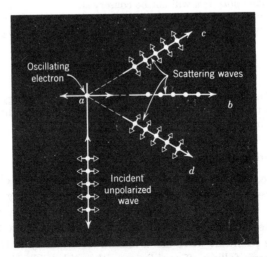

**Fig. 46–21**  Light is polarized either partially ($c$ and $d$) or completely ($b$) by scattering from a gas molecule at $a$.

by measurements made in rockets and satellites above the atmosphere. We can easily check with a polarizer that the light from the cloudless sky is at least partially polarized. This fact is used in polar exploration in the so-called *solar compass*. In this device we establish direction by noting the nature of the polarization of the scattered sunlight. As is well known, magnetic compasses are not useful in these regions. It has been learned * that bees orient themselves in their flights between their hive and the pollen sources by means of polarization of the light from the sky; bees' eyes contain built-in polarization-sensing devices.

It still remains to be explained why the light scattered from the sky is predominantly blue and why the light received directly from the sun—particularly at sunset when the length of the atmosphere that it must traverse is greatest—is red. The cross section of an atom or molecule for light scattering depends on the wavelength, blue light being scattered more effectively than red light. Since the blue light is largely scattered, the transmitted light will have the color of normal sunlight with the blues largely removed; it is therefore more reddish in appearance.

The fact that the scattering cross section for blue light is higher than that for red light can be made reasonable. An electron in an atom or molecule is bound there by strong restoring forces. It has a definite natural frequency, like a small mass suspended in space by an assembly of springs. The natural frequency for electrons in atoms and molecules is usually in a region corresponding to violet or ultraviolet light.

When light is allowed to fall on such bound electrons, it sets up forced oscillations at the frequency of the incident light beam. In mechanical resonant systems it is possible to "drive" the system most effectively if we impress on it an external force whose frequency is as close as possible to that of the natural resonant frequency. In the case of light the blue is closer to the natural resonant frequency of the bound electron than is the red light. Therefore, we would expect the blue light to be more effective in causing the electron to oscillate, and thus it will be more effectively scattered.

### 46-8   Double Scattering

When X-rays were discovered in 1898, there was much speculation whether they were waves or particles. In 1906 they were established as transverse waves by Charles Glover Barkla (1877–1944) by means of a polarization experiment.

When the unpolarized X-rays strike scattering block $S_1$ in Fig. 46–22, they set the electrons into oscillatory motion. The considerations of the preceding section require that the X-rays scattered toward the second block be plane-polarized as shown in the figure. Let this wave be scattered from the second scattering block, and let us examine the radiation scattered from it by rotating a detector $D$ in a plane at right angles to the line joining the blocks. The electrons will oscillate parallel to each other, and the positions of maximum and zero intensity will be as shown. A plot of detector reading as a function of the angle $\phi$ supports the hypothesis that X-rays are transverse waves. If the X-rays were a stream of particles or a longitudinal wave, these effects could by no means be so readily understood. Thus Barkla's important experiment established that X-rays are a part of the electromagnetic spectrum.

---

* See *Scientific American*, July 1955, and *Bees: Their Vision, Chemical Sense, and Language*, K. von Frisch, Cornell University Press, 1950.

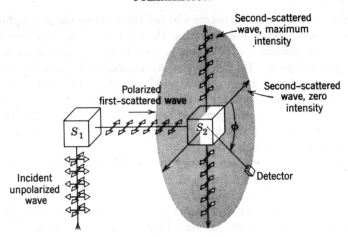

**Fig. 46–22**   A double-scattering experiment used by Barkla to show that X-rays are transverse waves.

In his later studies the student will learn that beams of particles such as electrons, protons, and pions can be viewed as waves. Scattering (including double scattering) techniques are often used to investigate the polarization characteristics of such beams.

## QUESTIONS

1. Why do sunglasses made of polarizing materials have a marked advantage over those that simply depend on absorption effects?

2. Unpolarized light falls on two polarizing sheets so oriented that no light is transmitted. If a third polarizing sheet is placed between them, can light be transmitted?

3. Can polarization by reflection occur if the light is incident on the interface from the side with the higher index of refraction (glass to air, for example)?

4. Is the optic axis of a doubly refracting crystal simply a line or a direction in space? Has it a direction sense, like an arrow? What about the characteristic direction of a polarizing sheet?

5. Devise a way to identify the polarizing direction of a sheet of Polaroid.

6. If ice is doubly refracting (see Table 46–1), why don't we see two images of objects viewed through an ice cube?

7. From Table 46–1, would you expect a quarter-wave plate made from calcite to be thicker than one made from quartz?

8. Does the $e$-wave in doubly refracting crystals always travel at a speed given by $c/n_e$?

9. In Fig. 46–14$a$ and $b$ describe qualitatively what happens if the incident beam falls on the crystal with an angle of incidence that is not zero. Assume in each case that the incident beam remains in the plane of the figure.

10. Devise a way to identify the direction of the optic axis in a quarter-wave plate.

11. If plane-polarized light falls on a quarter-wave plate with its plane of vibration making an angle of ($a$) 0° or ($b$) 90° with the axis of the plate, describe the transmitted light. ($c$) If this angle is arbitrarily chosen, the transmitted light is called *elliptically polarized;* describe such light.

12. What would be the action of a *half-wave plate* (that is, a plate twice as thick as a

quarter-wave plate) on (a) plane-polarized light (assume the plane of vibration to be at 45° to the optic axis of the plate), (b) circularly polarized light, and (c) unpolarized light?

13. You are given an object which may be (a) a disk of grey glass, (b) a polarizing sheet, (c) a quarter-wave plate, or (d) a half-wave plate (see Question 12). How could you identify it?

14. Can a plane-polarized light beam be represented as a sum of two circularly polarized light beams of opposite rotation? What effect has changing the phase of one of the circular components on the resultant beam?

15. How can a right-circularly polarized light beam be transformed into a left-circularly polarized beam?

16. Could (a) a radar beam and (b) a sound wave in air be circularly polarized?

17. A beam of light is said to be unpolarized, plane-polarized, or circularly polarized. How could you choose among them experimentally?

18. A parallel beam of light is absorbed by an object placed in its path. Under what circumstances will (a) linear momentum and (b) angular momentum be transferred to the object?

19. When observing a clear sky through a polarizing sheet, one finds that the intensity varies by a factor of two on rotating the sheet. This does not happen when one views a cloud through the sheet. Can you devise an explanation?

## PROBLEMS

1. Unpolarized light falls on two polarizing sheets placed one on top of the other. What must be the angle between the characteristic directions of the sheets if the intensity of the transmitted light is (a) one-third the maximum intensity of the transmitted beam or (b) one-third the intensity of the incident beam? Assume that the polarizing sheet is ideal, that is, that it reduces the intensity of unpolarized light by exactly 50%.

2. An unpolarized beam of light is incident on a group of four polarizing sheets which are lined up so that the characteristic direction of each is rotated by 30° clockwise with respect to the preceding sheet. What fraction of the incident intensity is transmitted?

3. Describe the state of polarization represented by these sets of equations:

$$(a) \ E_x = E \sin (kz - \omega t)$$

$$E_y = E \cos (kz - \omega t),$$

$$(b) \ E_x = E \cos (kz - \omega t)$$

$$E_y = E \cos \left( kz - \omega t + \frac{\pi}{4} \right),$$

$$(c) \ E_x = E \sin (kz - \omega t)$$

$$E_y = -E \sin (kz - \omega t).$$

4. (a) At what angle of incidence will the light reflected from water be completely polarized? (b) Does this angle depend on the wavelength of the light?

5. Calculate the range of polarizing angles for white light incident on fused quartz. Assume that the wavelength limits are 4000 and 7000 A and use the dispersion curve of Fig. 41–2.

6. A narrow beam of unpolarized light falls on a calcite crystal cut with its optic axis as shown in Fig. 46–23. (a) For $t = 1.0$ cm and for $\theta_i = 45°$, calculate the perpendicular distance between the two emerging rays $x$ and $y$. (b) Which is the o-ray and which the e-ray? (c) What are the states of polarization of the emerging rays? (d) Describe what

happens if a polarizer is placed in the incident beam and rotated. (Hint: Inside the crystal the E-vector vibrations for one ray are always perpendicular to the optic axis and for the other ray they are always parallel. The two rays are described by the indices $n_o$ and $n_e$; *in this plane* each ray obeys Snell's law.)

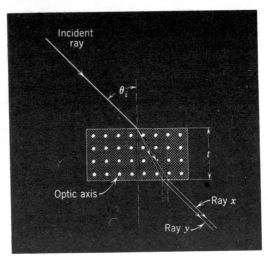

**Fig. 46–23**

7. A prism is cut from calcite so that the optic axis is parallel to the prism edge as shown in Fig. 46–24. Describe how such a prism might be used to measure the two principal indices of refraction for calcite. (Hint: See hint in Problem 6; see also Example 3, Chapter 41.)

**Fig. 46–24**

8. How thick must a sheet of mica be if it is to form a quarter-wave plate for yellow light ($\lambda = 5890$ A)? Mica cleaves in such a way that the appropriate indices of refraction, for transmission at right angles to the cleavage plane, are 1.6049 and 1.6117.

9. Prove that two plane-polarized light waves of equal amplitude, their planes of vibration being at right angles to each other, cannot produce interference effects. (Hint: Prove that the intensity of the resultant light wave, averaged over one or more cycles of oscillation, is the same no matter what phase difference exists between the two waves.)

10. Show that in a parallel beam of circularly polarized light the angular momentum per unit volume $L_v$ is given by

$$L_v = \frac{P}{\omega c},$$

where $P$ is the power per unit area (watts/cm$^2$, say) of the beam. Start from Eq. 46–5.

11. Assume that a parallel beam of circularly polarized light whose intensity is 100 watts is absorbed by an object. At what rate is angular momentum transferred to the object? If the object is a flat disk of diameter 5.0 mm and mass $1.0 \times 10^{-2}$ gm, after how long a time (assuming it is free to rotate about its axis) would it attain an angular speed of 1.0 rev/sec? Assume a wavelength of 5000 A.

# Light and Quantum Physics

## CHAPTER 47

## 47–1 Sources of Light

We have studied the propagation, reflection, refraction, diffraction, polarization, scattering, and interference of light. This chapter deals in part with the *production* of light and with the way that such studies led, in 1900, to the birth of modern quantum physics.

The most common light sources are heated solids and gases through which an electric discharge is passing. The tungsten filament of an incandescent lamp and the familiar neon sign are examples in each category. By analyzing the light from a source with a spectrometer, we can learn how strongly it radiates at various wavelengths. Figure 47–1, which is typical of spectra for heated solids, shows the results of such measurements for a heated tungsten ribbon at 2000° K.

The ordinate $\mathcal{R}_\lambda$ in Fig. 47–1 is called the *spectral radiancy*, defined so that the quantity $\mathcal{R}_\lambda\, d\lambda$ is the rate at which energy is radiated per unit area of surface for wavelengths lying in the interval $\lambda$ to $\lambda + d\lambda$. Typical units for $\mathcal{R}_\lambda$ are watts/cm$^2$-$\mu$; the corresponding units of $\mathcal{R}_\lambda\, d\lambda$ are watts/cm$^2$. In measuring $\mathcal{R}_\lambda$, all radiation emerging into the forward hemisphere is included.

Sometimes we wish to discuss the radiated energy without regard to its wavelength. An appropriate quantity here is the *radiancy* $\mathcal{R}$, defined as the rate per unit surface area at which energy is radiated into the forward hemisphere, appropriate units being watts/cm$^2$. It can be found by integrating the radiation present in all wavelength intervals:

$$\mathcal{R} = \int_0^\infty \mathcal{R}_\lambda\, d\lambda. \qquad (47\text{–}1)$$

**Fig. 47–1** The spectral radiancy of tungsten at 2000°K. The dashed curve refers to a cavity radiator at the same temperature. One micron $(1 \mu) = 10^{-6}$ meter $= 10^4$ A.

The radiancy $\mathfrak{R}$ can be interpreted as the area under the plot of $\mathfrak{R}_\lambda$ against $\lambda$. In Fig. 47–1 this area—and thus $\mathfrak{R}$—is 23.5 watts/cm². The student should note the formal similarity between such curves and the Maxwell speed distribution curve of Section 24–2.

For every material there exists a family of spectral radiancy curves like that of Fig. 47–1, one curve for every temperature. If such families of curves are compared, no obvious regularities stand out. A quantitative understanding in terms of a basic theory presents serious difficulties. Fortunately, it is possible to work with an *idealized heated solid*, called a *cavity radiator*. Its light-emitting properties prove to be independent of any particular material and to vary in a simple way with temperature. In much the same way it proved convenient earlier to deal with an ideal gas rather than to analyze the properties of the infinite variety of real gases. The cavity radiator is the *ideal solid* as far as its light-emitting characteristics are concerned. We shall describe in the next two sections how the theoretical study of cavity radiation in 1900 by the German physicist Max Planck (1858–1947) laid the foundations of modern quantum physics.

### 47–2   Cavity Radiators

Let us construct a cavity in each of three metal blocks through the walls of which a small hole is drilled. Let the blocks be made of any suitable materials; for example, tungsten, tantalum, and molybdenum. Let each block be raised to the same uniform temperature (say 2000°K) as determined by a suitable thermometer. Finally, let us observe the blocks by their emitted light in a dark room. Measurements of ℛ and ℛλ show the following:

1. The radiation from the cavity interior is always more intense than the radiation from the outside wall. Comparison of the two curves in Fig. 47–1 makes this clear for tungsten. For the three materials given, at 2000°K the ratio of the radiancy for the outside surface to that for the cavity is 0.259 (tungsten), 0.212 (molybdenum), and 0.232 (tantalum).

2. At a given temperature the radiancy of the hole is *identical for all three radiators*, in spite of the fact that the radiancies of the outer surfaces are different. At 2000°K the cavity radiancy (that is, the hole radiancy) is 90.0 watts/cm².

3. In contrast to the radiancy of the outer surfaces, the cavity radiancy ℛ_c varies with temperature in a simple way, namely as

$$\mathcal{R}_c = \sigma T^4, \tag{47–2}$$

where $\sigma$ is a universal constant (the Stefan-Boltzmann constant) whose measured value is $5.67 \times 10^{-8}$ watt/(meter²)(°K⁴). The radiancy of the outer surfaces varies with temperature in a more complicated way and is different for different materials. It is often written as

$$\mathcal{R} = e\mathcal{R}_c = e\sigma T^4, \tag{47–3}$$

where $e$, the *emissivity*, depends on the material and the temperature.

4. ℛλ for the cavity radiation varies with temperature in the way shown in Fig. 47–2. These curves depend only on the temperature and are quite independent of the material and of the shape and size of the cavity.

Figure 47–3 shows an actual cavity, consisting of a hollow thin-walled cylinder of tungsten heated by sending an electric current through it. The cylinder is mounted in an evacuated glass bulb, and a tiny hole is drilled

**Fig. 47–2**   The spectral radiancy for cavity radiation at three different temperatures.

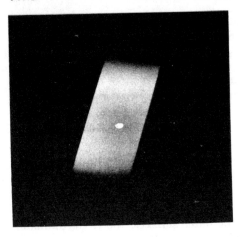

**Fig. 47-3** Photograph of an incandescent tungsten tube with a small hole drilled in its wall. The radiation emerging from the hole is cavity radiation.

through the cylinder wall. It is clear from the photograph that the radiancy of the cavity interior is greater than that of the cavity walls.

Many of the facts just given about cavity radiation can be deduced from Fig. 47-4, which shows two cavities made of different materials, of arbitrary shapes, and with the same wall temperature $T$. Radiation, described by $\mathfrak{R}_A$, goes from cavity $A$ to cavity $B$ and radiation described by $\mathfrak{R}_B$ moves in the opposite direction. If these two rates of energy transfer are not equal, one end of the composite block will start to heat up and the other end will start to cool down, which is a violation of the second law of thermodynamics. (Why?) Thus we must have

$$\mathfrak{R}_A = \mathfrak{R}_B = \mathfrak{R}_c, \qquad (47\text{-}4)$$

where $\mathfrak{R}_c$ describes the total radiation for *all* cavities.

Not only the total radiation but also the distribution of radiant energy with wavelength must be the same for each cavity in Fig. 47-4. This can be shown by placing a filter between the two cavity openings, so chosen that it permits only a selected narrow band of wavelengths to pass. Applying the same argument, we can show that we must have

$$\mathfrak{R}_{\lambda A} = \mathfrak{R}_{\lambda B} = \mathfrak{R}_{\lambda c}, \qquad (47\text{-}5)$$

where $\mathfrak{R}_{\lambda c}$ is a spectral radiancy characteristic of all cavities.

**Fig. 47-4** Two radiant cavities initially at the same temperature are placed together as shown.

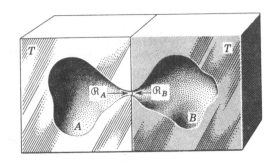

## 47-3  Planck's Radiation Formula

A theoretical explanation for the cavity radiation was the outstanding unsolved problem in physics during the years before the turn of the present century.  A number of capable physicists advanced theories based on classical physics, which, however, had only limited success.  Figure 47-5, for example, shows the theory of Wien; the fit to the experimental points is reasonably good, within the experimental error of the data, but definitely not exact.  Wien's formula is

$$\mathfrak{R}_\lambda = \frac{c_1}{\lambda^5} \frac{1}{e^{c_2/\lambda T}},$$

where $c_1$ and $c_2$ are constants that must be determined empirically by fitting the theoretical formula to the experimental data.

**Fig. 47-5**  The circles show the experimental spectral radiancy data of Coblentz for cavity radiation.  The theoretical formulas of Wien and Planck are also shown, Planck's providing an excellent fit to the data.

In 1900 Max Planck pointed out that if Wien's formula were modified in a simple way it would prove to fit the data precisely.  Planck's formula, announced to the Berlin Physical Society on October 19, 1900, was

$$\mathfrak{R}_\lambda = \frac{c_1}{\lambda^5} \frac{1}{e^{c_2/\lambda T} - 1}. \tag{47-6}$$

This formula, though interesting and important, was still empirical at that stage and did not constitute a theory.

Planck sought such a theory in terms of a detailed model of the atomic processes taking place at the cavity walls.  He assumed that the atoms that make up these walls behave like tiny electromagnetic oscillators, each with a characteristic frequency of oscillation. The oscillators emit electromagnetic energy into the cavity and absorb electromagnetic energy from it. Thus it should be possible to deduce the characteristics of the cavity radiation from those of the oscillators with which it is in equilibrium.

Planck was led to make two radical assumptions about the atomic oscillators. As eventually formulated, these assumptions are the following:

1. An oscillator cannot have *any* energy but only energies given by *

$$E = nh\nu, \qquad (47\text{--}7)$$

where $\nu$ is the oscillator frequency, $h$ is a constant (now called *Planck's constant*), and $n$ is a number (now called a *quantum number*) that can take on only integral values. Equation 47–7 asserts that the oscillator energy is *quantized*.

2. The oscillators do not radiate energy continuously, but only in "jumps," or *quanta*. These quanta of energy are emitted when an oscillator changes from one to another of its quantized energy states. Thus, if $n$ changes by one unit, Eq. 47–7 shows that an amount of energy given by

$$\Delta E = \Delta nh\nu = h\nu \qquad (47\text{--}8)$$

is radiated. As long as an oscillator remains in one of its quantized states (or *stationary states* as they are called), it neither emits nor absorbs energy.

These assumptions were radical ones and, indeed, Planck himself resisted accepting them wholeheartedly for many years. In his words, "My futile attempts to fit the elementary quantum of action [that is, the quantity $h$] somehow into the classical theory continued for a number of years, and they cost me a great deal of effort."

Consider the application of Planck's hypotheses to a large-scale oscillator such as a mass-spring system or an $LC$ circuit. It would be a stoutly defended common belief that oscillations in such systems could take place with *any* value of total energy and not with only certain discrete values. In the decay of such oscillations (by friction in the mass-spring system or by resistance and radiation in the $LC$ circuit), it would seem that the mechanical or electromagnetic energy would decrease in a perfectly continuous way and not by "jumps." There is no basis in everyday experience, however, to dismiss Planck's assumptions as violations of "common sense," for Planck's constant proves to have a very small value, namely

$$h = 6.625 \times 10^{-34} \text{ joule-sec.}$$

The following example makes this clear.

---

* Later developments show that the correct formula for a harmonic oscillator is

$$E = (n + \tfrac{1}{2})h\nu.$$

This change makes no difference to Planck's conclusions, however.

▶ **Example 1.** A mass-spring system has a mass $m = 1.0$ kg and a spring constant $k = 20$ nt/meter and is oscillating with an amplitude of 1.0 cm. (a) If its energy is quantized according to Eq. 47–7, what is the quantum number $n$? (b) If $n$ changes by unity, what fractional change in energy occurs?

(a) From Eq. 15–8 the frequency is

$$\nu = \frac{1}{2\pi}\sqrt{\frac{k}{m}} = \frac{1}{2\pi}\sqrt{\frac{20 \text{ nt/meter}}{1.0 \text{ kg}}} = 0.71 \text{ cycles/sec.}$$

From Eq. 8–8 the mechanical energy is

$$E = \tfrac{1}{2}kx_{max}^2 = \tfrac{1}{2}(20 \text{ nt/meter})(10^{-2} \text{ meter})^2 = 1.0 \times 10^{-3} \text{ joule.}$$

From Eq. 47–7 the quantum number is

$$n = \frac{E}{h\nu} = \frac{1.0 \times 10^{-3} \text{ joule}}{(6.6 \times 10^{-34} \text{ joule-sec})(0.71 \text{ cycles/sec})} = 2.1 \times 10^{30}.$$

(b) If $n$ changes by unity, the fractional change in energy is given by dividing Eq. 47–8 by Eq. 47–7, or

$$\frac{\Delta E}{E} = \frac{h\nu}{nh\nu} = \frac{1}{n} = \sim 10^{-30}.$$

Thus for large-scale oscillators the quantum numbers are enormous and the quantized nature of the energy of the oscillations will not be apparent. Similarly, we are not aware in large-scale experiments of the discrete nature of mass and the quantized nature of charge, that is, of the existence of atoms and electrons.     ◀

On the basis of his two assumptions, Planck was able to derive his radiation law (Eq. 47–6) entirely from theory, receiving a Nobel prize for this accomplishment in 1918. His theoretical expressions for the hitherto empirical constants $c_1$ and $c_2$ were

$$c_1 = 2\pi c^2 h \qquad \text{and} \qquad c_2 = \frac{hc}{k},$$

where $k$ is Boltzmann's constant (see Section 23–5) and $c$ is the speed of light. By inserting the experimental values for $c_1$ and $c_2$, Planck was able to derive the values of both $h$ and $k$. Planck described his theory to the Berlin Physical Society on December 14, 1900. Quantum physics dates from that day. Planck's ideas soon received re-enforcement from Einstein, who, in 1905, applied the concepts of energy quantization to a new area of physics, the photoelectric effect.

Before discussing this effect, it is important to realize that although Planck had quantized the energies of the oscillators in the cavity walls he *still treated the radiation within the cavity* as an electromagnetic wave. Einstein's analysis of the photoelectric effect first pointed out the inadequacy of the wave picture of light in certain situations.

### 47–4 Photoelectric Effect

Figure 47–6 shows an apparatus used to study the photoelectric effect. Monochromatic light, falling on metal plate $A$, will liberate *photoelectrons*, which can be detected as a current if they are attracted to metal cup $B$ by

**Fig. 47-6**   An apparatus used to study the photoelectric effect. $V$ cannot only be varied continuously but can be reversed in sign by a switching arrangement not shown.

means of a potential difference $V$ applied between $A$ and $B$.   Galvanometer $G$ serves to measure this *photoelectric current.*

Figure 47–7 (curve $a$) is a plot of the photoelectric current in an apparatus like that of Fig. 47–6, as a function of the potential difference $V$.   If $V$ is made large enough, the photoelectric current reaches a certain limiting value at which *all* photoelectrons ejected from plate $A$ are collected by cup $B$.

If $V$ is reversed in sign, the photoelectric current does not immediately drop to zero, which proves that the electrons are emitted from $A$ with a finite velocity.   Some will reach cup $B$ in spite of the fact that the electric field opposes their motion.   However, if this reversed potential difference is made large enough, a value $V_0$ (the *stopping potential*) is reached at which the photoelectric current does drop to zero.   This potential difference $V_0$, multiplied by electron charge, measures the kinetic energy $K_{max}$ of the *fastest* ejected photoelectron.   In other words,

$$K_{max} = eV_0. \tag{47–9}$$

Here $K_{max}$ turns out to be independent of the intensity of the light as shown by curve $b$ in Fig. 47–7, in which the light intensity has been reduced to one-half.

Figure 47–8 shows the stopping potential $V_0$ as a function of the frequency of the incident light for sodium.   Note that there is a definite cutoff frequency

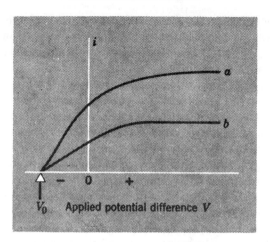

**Fig. 47–7** Some data taken with the apparatus of Fig. 47–6. The applied potential difference $V$ is called positive when the cup $B$ in Fig. 47–6 is positive with respect to the photoelectric surface $A$. In curve $b$ the incident light intensity has been reduced to one-half that of curve $a$.

$\nu_0$, below which no photoelectric effect occurs. These data were taken by R. A. Millikan (1868–1953), whose painstaking work on the photoelectric effect won him the Nobel prize in 1923. Because the photoelectric effect is largely a surface phenomenon, it is necessary to avoid oxide films, grease, or other surface contaminants. Millikan devised a technique to cut shavings from the metal surface under vacuum conditions, a "machine shop *in vacuo*" as he called it.

Three major features of the photoelectric effect cannot be explained in terms of the wave theory of light:

**Fig. 47–8** A plot of Millikan's measurements of the stopping potential at various frequencies for sodium. The cutoff frequency $\nu_0$ is $4.39 \times 10^{14}$ cycles/sec.

1. Wave theory suggests that the kinetic energy of the photoelectrons should increase as the light beam is made more intense. However, Fig. 47–7 shows that $K_{max}$ ($= eV_0$) *is independent of the light intensity;* this has been tested over a range of intensities of $10^7$.

2. According to the wave theory, the photoelectric effect should occur for *any* frequency of the light, provided only that the light is intense enough. However, Fig. 47–8 shows that there exists, for each surface, *a characteristic cutoff frequency* $\nu_0$. For frequencies less than this, the photoelectric effect disappears, no matter how intense the illumination.

3. If the energy of the photoelectrons is "soaked up" from the incident wave by the metal plate, it is not likely that the "effective target area" for an electron in the metal is much more than a few atomic diameters. Thus, if the light is feeble enough, there should be a measurable time lag (see Example 2) between the impinging of the light on the surface and the ejection of the photoelectron. During this interval the electron should be "soaking up" energy from the beam until it had accumulated enough energy to escape. However, *no detectable time lag has ever been measured.* This disagreement is particularly striking when the photoelectric substance is a gas; under these circumstances the energy of the emitted photoelectron must certainly be "soaked out of the beam" by a single atom.

▶ **Example 2.** A metal plate is placed 5 meters from a monochromatic light source whose power output is $10^{-3}$ watt. Consider that a given ejected photoelectron may collect its energy from a circular area of the plate as large as ten atomic diameters ($10^{-9}$ meter) in radius. The energy required to remove an electron through the metal surface is about 5.0 ev. *Assuming light to be a wave,* how long would it take for such a "target" to soak up this much energy from such a light source?

The target area is $\pi$ $(10^{-9}$ meter$)^2$ or $3 \times 10^{-18}$ meter$^2$; the area of a 5-meter sphere centered on the light source is $4\pi$ (5 meters$)^2 \cong 300$ meters$^2$. Thus, if the light source radiates uniformly in all directions, the rate $P$ at which energy falls on the target is given by

$$P = (10^{-3} \text{ watt}) \left( \frac{3 \times 10^{-18} \text{ meter}^2}{300 \text{ meters}^2} \right) = 10^{-23} \text{ joule/sec.}$$

Assuming that all this power is absorbed, we may calculate the time required from

$$t = \left( \frac{5 \text{ ev}}{10^{-23} \text{ joule/sec}} \right) \left( \frac{1.6 \times 10^{-19} \text{ joule}}{1 \text{ ev}} \right) \cong 20 \text{ hr.}$$

However, *no detectable time lag can be measured under any circumstances.*     ◀

### 47–5   Einstein's Photon Theory

Einstein succeeded in explaining the photoelectric effect by making a remarkable assumption, namely, that the energy in a light beam travels through space in concentrated bundles, called *photons.* The energy $E$ of a single photon (see Eq. 47–8) is given by

$$E = h\nu. \tag{47–10}$$

Recall that Planck believed that light, although emitted from its source discontinuously, travels through space as an electromagnetic wave. Einstein's hypothesis suggests that light traveling through space behaves not like a wave at all but like a particle. Millikan, whose experiments verified Einstein's ideas in every detail, spoke of Einstein's "bold, not to say reckless, hypothesis."

Applying the photon concept to the photoelectric effect, Einstein wrote

$$h\nu = E_0 + K_{max} \qquad (47–11)$$

where $h\nu$ is the energy of the photon. Equation 47–11 says that a photon carries an energy $h\nu$ into the surface. Part of this energy ($E_0$) is used in causing the electron to pass through the metal surface. The excess energy ($h\nu - E_0$) is given to the electron in the form of kinetic energy; if the electron does not lose energy by internal collisions as it escapes from the metal, it will exhibit it all as kinetic energy after it emerges. Thus $K_{max}$ represents the *maximum* kinetic energy that the photoelectron can have outside the surface; in nearly all cases it will have less energy than this because of internal losses.

Consider how Einstein's photon hypothesis meets the three objections raised against the wave-theory interpretation of the photoelectric effect. As for objection 1 (the lack of dependence of $K_{max}$ on the intensity of illumination), there is complete agreement of the photon theory with experiment. Doubling the light intensity merely doubles the number of photons and thus doubles the photoelectric current; it does not change the energy ($= h\nu$) of the individual photons or the nature of the individual photoelectric processes described by Eq. 47–11.

Objection 2 (the existence of a cutoff frequency) follows from Eq. 47–11. If $K_{max}$ equals zero, we have

$$h\nu_0 = E_0,$$

which asserts that the photon has just enough energy to eject the photoelectrons and none extra to appear as kinetic energy. This quantity $E_0$ is called the work function of the substance. If $\nu$ is reduced below $\nu_0$, the individual photons, no matter how many of them there are (that is, no matter how intense the illumination), will not have enough energy to eject photoelectrons.

Objection 3 (the absence of a time lag) follows from the photon theory because the required energy is supplied in a concentrated bundle. It is *not* spread uniformly over a large area, as in the wave theory.

Although the photon hypothesis certainly fits the facts of photoelectricity, it seems to be in direct conflict with the wave theory of light which, as we have seen in earlier chapters, has been verified in many experiments. Our modern view of the nature of light is that *it has a dual character, behaving like a wave under some circumstances and like a particle, or photon, under others.* We discuss the wave-particle duality at length in Chapter 48. Meanwhile, let us continue our studies of the firm experimental foundation on which the photon concept rests.

Let us rewrite Einstein's photoelectric equation (Eq. 47–11) by substituting $eV_0$ for $K_{max}$ (see Eq. 47–9). This yields, after rearrangement,

$$V_0 = \frac{h}{e} \nu - \frac{E_0}{e}. \tag{47-12}$$

Thus Einstein's theory predicts a linear relationship between $V_0$ and $\nu$, in complete agreement with experiment; see Fig. 47–8. The slope of the experimental curve in this figure should be $h/e$, or

$$\frac{h}{e} = \frac{ab}{bc} = \frac{2.20 \text{ volt} - 0.65 \text{ volt}}{(10 \times 10^{14} - 6 \times 10^{14}) \text{ cycles/sec}} = 3.9 \times 10^{-15} \text{ volt-sec.}$$

We can find $h$ by multiplying this ratio by the electron charge $e$,

$$h = (3.9 \times 10^{-15} \text{ volt-sec})(1.6 \times 10^{-19} \text{ coul}) = 6.2 \times 10^{-34} \text{ joule-sec.}$$

From a more careful analysis of this and other data, including data taken with lithium surfaces, Millikan found the value $h = 6.57 \times 10^{-34}$ joule-sec, with an accuracy of about 0.5%. This agreement with the value of $h$ derived from Planck's radiation formula is a striking confirmation of Einstein's photon concept.

▶ **Example 3.**   Deduce the work function for sodium from Fig. 47–8.
    The intersection of the straight line in Fig. 47–8 with the horizontal axis is the cutoff frequency $\nu_0$. Substituting these values yields

$$E_0 = h\nu_0 = (6.63 \times 10^{-34} \text{ joule-sec})(4.39 \times 10^{14} \text{ cycles/sec})$$

$$= 2.92 \times 10^{-19} \text{ joule} = 1.82 \text{ ev.} \qquad ◀$$

### 47–6   The Compton Effect

Compelling confirmation of the concept of the photon as a concentrated bundle of energy was provided in 1923 by A. H. Compton (1892–1962) who earned a Nobel prize for this work in 1927.* Compton allowed a beam of X-rays of sharply defined wavelength $\lambda$ to fall on a graphite block, as in Fig. 47–9, and he measured, for various angles of scattering, the intensity of the scattered X-rays as a function of their wavelength. Figure 47–10 shows his experimental results. We see that although the incident beam consists essentially of a single wavelength $\lambda$ the scattered X-rays have intensity peaks at *two* wavelengths; one of them is the same as the incident wavelength, the other, $\lambda'$, being larger by an amount $\Delta\lambda$. This so-called *Compton shift* $\Delta\lambda$ varies with the angle at which the scattered X-rays are observed.

The presence of a scattered wave of wavelength $\lambda'$ cannot be understood if the incident X-rays are regarded as an electromagnetic wave like that of Fig. 39–11. On this picture the incident wave of frequency $\nu$ causes electrons in the scattering block to oscillate at that same frequency. These oscillating electrons, like charges surging back and forth in a small radio transmitting

---

* For an historical account of Compton's researches read "The Scattering of X Rays as Particles," A. H. Compton, p. 817, *Am. J. Phys.*, December 1961.

**Fig. 47–9**  Compton's experimental arrangement.  Monochromatic X-rays of wavelength λ fall on a graphite scatterer.  The distribution of intensity with wavelength is measured for X-rays scattered at any selected angle φ.  The scattered wavelengths are measured by observing Bragg reflections from a crystal; see Eq. 45–8.  Their intensities are measured by a detector, such as a ionization chamber.

antenna, radiate electromagnetic waves that again have this same frequency ν.  Thus, on the wave picture the scattered wave should have the same frequency ν and the same wavelength λ as the incident wave.

Compton * was able to explain his experimental results by postulating that the incoming X-ray beam was not a wave but an assembly of photons of energy E ( = hν) and that these photons experienced billiard-ball-like collisions with the free electrons in the scattering block.  The "recoil" photons emerging from the block constitute, on this view, the scattered radiation.  Since the incident photon transfers some of its energy to the electron with

---

* P. W. Debye simultaneously and independently offered the same interpretation.

**Fig. 47–10**  Compton's experimental results.  The solid vertical line on the left corresponds to the wavelength λ, that on the right to λ'.  Results are shown for four different angles of scattering φ.  Note that the Compton shift Δλ for φ = 90° is $h/m_0c$ = 0.242 A.

**Fig. 47–11**   A photon of wavelength $\lambda$ is incident on an electron at rest. On collision, the photon is scattered at an angle $\varphi$ with increased wavelength $\lambda'$, while the electron moves off with speed $v$ in direction $\theta$.

which it collides, the scattered photon must have a lower energy $E'$; it must therefore have a lower frequency $\nu'(= E'/h)$, which implies a larger wavelength $\lambda'(= c/\nu')$. This point of view accounts, at least qualitatively, for the wavelength shift $\Delta\lambda$. Notice how different this particle model of X-ray scattering is from that based on the wave picture. Now let us analyze a single photon-electron collision quantitatively.

Figure 47–11 shows a collision between a photon and an electron, the electron assumed to be initially at rest and essentially free, that is, not bound to the atoms of the scatterer. Let us apply the law of conservation of energy to this collision. Since the recoil electrons may have a speed $v$ that is comparable with that of light, we must use the relativistic expression for the kinetic energy of the electron. From Eqs. 47–10 and 8–21 we may write

$$h\nu = h\nu' + (m - m_0)c^2,$$

in which the second term on the right is the relativistic expression for the kinetic energy of the recoiling electron, $m$ being the relativistic mass and $m_0$ the rest mass of that particle. Substituting $c/\lambda$ for $\nu$ (and $c/\lambda'$ for $\nu'$) and using Eq. 8–20 to eliminate the relativistic mass $m$ leads us to

$$\frac{hc}{\lambda} = \frac{hc}{\lambda'} + m_0 c^2 \left( \frac{1}{\sqrt{1 - (v/c)^2}} - 1 \right). \tag{47–13}$$

Now let us apply the (vector) law of conservation of linear momentum to the collision of Fig. 47–11. We first need an expression for the momentum of a photon. In Section 40–2 we saw that if an object completely absorbs an energy $U$ from a parallel light beam that falls on it the light beam, according to the wave theory of light, will simultaneously transfer to the object a linear momentum given by $U/c$. On the photon picture we imagine this momentum to be carried along by the individual photons, each photon transporting linear momentum in amount $p = h\nu/c$, where $h\nu$ is the photon energy. Thus, if we substitute $\lambda$ for $c/\nu$, we can write

$$p = \frac{E}{c} = \frac{h\nu}{c} = \frac{h}{\lambda}. \tag{47–14}$$

This conclusion, that the momentum of a photon is given by $h/\lambda$, may also be deduced from the theory of relativity.

For the electron, the relativistic expression for the linear momentum is given by Eq. 9–13, or

$$\mathbf{p}_e = \frac{m_0 \mathbf{v}}{\sqrt{1 - (v/c)^2}}.$$

We can then write for the conservation of the $x$ component of linear momentum

$$\frac{h}{\lambda} = \frac{h}{\lambda'} \cos \varphi + \frac{m_0 v}{\sqrt{1 - (v/c)^2}} \cos \theta \qquad (47\text{–}15)$$

and for the $y$ component

$$0 = \frac{h}{\lambda'} \sin \varphi - \frac{m_0 v}{\sqrt{1 - (v/c)^2}} \sin \theta. \qquad (47\text{–}16)$$

Our immediate aim is to find $\Delta\lambda$ ($= \lambda' - \lambda$), the wavelength shift of the scattered photons, so that we may compare it with the experimental results of Fig. 47–10. Compton's experiment did not involve observations of the recoil electron in the scattering block. Of the five collision variables ($\lambda$, $\lambda'$, $v$, $\varphi$, and $\theta$) that appear in the three equations (47–13, 47–15, and 47–16) we may eliminate two. We chose to eliminate $v$ and $\theta$, which deal only with the electron, thereby reducing the three equations to a single relation among the variables.

Carrying out the necessary algebraic steps (see Problem 15) leads to this simple result:

$$\Delta\lambda \ (= \lambda' - \lambda) = \frac{h}{m_0 c} (1 - \cos \varphi). \qquad (47\text{–}17)$$

Thus the Compton shift $\Delta\lambda$ depends only on the scattering angle $\varphi$ and *not* on the initial wavelength $\lambda$. Equation 47–17 predicts within experimental error the experimentally observed Compton shifts of Fig. 47–10. Note from the equation that $\Delta\lambda$ varies from zero (for $\varphi = 0$, corresponding to a "grazing" collision in Fig. 47–11, the incident photon being scarely deflected) to $2h/m_0 c$ (for $\varphi = 180°$, corresponding to a "head-on" collision, the incident photon being reversed in direction).

It remains to explain the presence of the peak in Fig. 47–10 for which the wavelength does *not* change on scattering. This peak can be understood as resulting from a collision between a photon and electrons bound in an ionic core in the scattering block. During photon collisions the bound electrons behave like the free electrons that we considered in Fig. 47–11, with the exception that their effective mass is much greater. This is because the ionic core as a whole recoils during the collision. The effective mass $M$ for a carbon scatterer is approximately the mass of a carbon nucleus. Since this nucleus contains 6 protons and 6 neutrons, we have approximately that $M = 12 \times 1840 m_0 = 22{,}000 m_0$. If we replace $m_0$ by $M$ in Eq. 47–17, we see that the Compton shift for collisions with tightly bound electrons is immeasurably small.

As in the cavity radiation problem (see Eq. 47–7) and the photoelectric effect (see Eq. 47–11), Planck's constant $h$ is centrally involved in the Compton effect. The quantity $h$ is the central constant of quantum physics. In a universe in which $h = 0$ there would be no quantum physics and classical physics would be valid in the subatomic domain. In particular, as Eq. 47–17 shows, there would be no Compton effect (that is, $\Delta\lambda = 0$) in such a universe.

▶ **Example 4.** X-rays with $\lambda = 1.00$ A are scattered from a carbon block. The scattered radiation is viewed at 90° to the incident beam. (a) What is the Compton shift $\Delta\lambda$? (b) What kinetic energy is imparted to the recoiling electron?

(a) Putting $\varphi = 90°$ in Eq. 47–17, we have, for the Compton shift,

$$\Delta\lambda = \frac{h}{m_0 c}(1 - \cos\varphi)$$

$$= \frac{6.63 \times 10^{-34} \text{ joule-sec}}{(9.11 \times 10^{-31} \text{ kg})(3.00 \times 10^{8} \text{ meters/sec})}(1 - \cos 90°)$$

$$= 2.43 \times 10^{-12} \text{ meter} = 0.0243 \text{ A.}$$

(b) If we put $K$ for the kinetic energy of the electron, we can write Eq. 47–13 as

$$\frac{hc}{\lambda} = \frac{hc}{\lambda'} + K.$$

Since $\lambda' = \lambda + \Delta\lambda$, we obtain

$$\frac{hc}{\lambda} = \frac{hc}{\lambda + \Delta\lambda} + K,$$

which reduces to

$$K = \frac{hc\,\Delta\lambda}{\lambda(\lambda + \Delta\lambda)}$$

$$= \frac{(6.63 \times 10^{-34} \text{ joule-sec})(3.00 \times 10^{8} \text{ meters/sec})(2.43 \times 10^{-12} \text{ meter})}{(1.00 \times 10^{-10} \text{ meter})(1.00 + 0.024) \times 10^{-10} \text{ meter}}$$

$$= 4.73 \times 10^{-17} \text{ joule} = 295 \text{ ev.}$$

The student may show that the initial photon energy $E$ in this case ($= h\nu = hc/\lambda$) is 12,400 ev so that the photon lost about 2.3% of its energy in this collision. A photon whose energy was ten times as large ($= 124{,}000$ ev) can be shown to lose 23% of its energy in a similar collision. This follows from the fact that $\Delta\lambda$ does not depend on the initial wavelength. Hence more energetic X-rays, which have smaller wavelengths, will experience a larger *per cent* increase in wavelength and thus a larger per cent loss in energy.    ◀

### 47–7  Line Spectra

We have seen how Planck successfully explained the nature of the radiation from heated solid objects of which the cavity radiator formed the prototype. Such radiations form *continuous spectra* and are contrasted with *line spectra* such as that of Fig. 47–12, which shows the radiation emitted from iron ions

**Fig. 47-12** A small portion of the spectrum of iron, in the region 3400 to 3500 A.

and atoms in an electric arc struck between iron electrodes. We shall see that Planck's quantization ideas, suitably extended, lead to an understanding of line spectra also. The prototype for the study of line spectra is that of atomic hydrogen; being the simplest atom it has the simplest spectrum.

Line spectra are common in all parts of the electromagnetic spectrum. Figure 47-13 shows a spectrum of the $\gamma$-rays ($\lambda \cong 10^{-12}$ meter) emitted from a particular radioactive nucleus, an isotope of mercury. Figure 47-14 shows a spectrum of X-rays ($\lambda \cong 10^{-10}$ meter) emitted from a molybdenum target when struck by a 35-kev electron beam. The sharp emission lines are superimposed on a continuous background.

Figure 47-15 shows a spectrum associated with the molecule HCl. It occurs in the infrared, with $\lambda \cong 10^{-6}$ meter. This is an *absorption* spectrum rather than an emission spectrum, as in Fig. 47-12. Experiment shows that isolated atoms and molecules absorb radiation, as well as emit it, at discrete wavelengths.

Figure 47-16 shows a portion of the absorption spectrum of ammonia ($NH_3$) in the microwave region ($\lambda \cong 10^{-2}$ meter). Finally, Fig. 47-17 shows how radiation in the radio-frequency region ($\lambda \cong 43$ meters) is absorbed by hydrogen molecules placed in a magnetic field.

**Fig. 47-13** A wavelength plot for a gamma ray emitted by the nucleus $Hg^{198}$. (From data by Du-Mond and co-workers.)

**Fig. 47–14** X-rays from a molybdenum target struck by 35-kev electrons. Note the two sharp lines rising above a broad continuous base. The wavelength of the most intense line is $7.1 \times 10^{-11}$ meter or 0.71 A. (From data by Ulrey.)

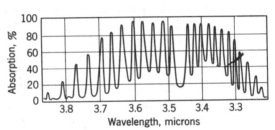

**Fig. 47–15** An absorption spectrum of the HCl molecule near $\lambda = 3.5 \times 10^{-6}$ meter = $3.5 \mu$. (From data by E. S. Imes.)

**Fig. 47–16** An oscilloscope trace showing one strong line and four weak lines in the absorption spectrum of ammonia at microwave frequencies.

**Fig. 47–17** A portion of the absorption spectrum of the protons in molecular hydrogen at $\lambda \cong 43$ meters. In this technique the frequency is left fixed and the sample is placed in a magnetic field, which is varied to scan the spectrum. (From data by Kellogg, Rabi, and Zacharias.)

### 47–8   The Hydrogen Atom

Figure 47–18 shows the spectrum of hydrogen. A theoretical interpretation of the hydrogen spectrum, based on quantum ideas, was first given by Niels Bohr in 1913.

We might wish to associate the frequency of an emitted spectrum line with the frequency of an electron revolving in an orbit inside the atom. Classical electromagnetism predicts that charges will radiate energy when they are accelerated. In this way electromagnetic waves are emitted from a radio transmitting antenna in which electrons are caused to surge back and forth. This radiation represents a loss of energy for the moving electrons which, in a radio antenna, is compensated for by supplying energy from an oscillator. In an isolated atom, however, no energy is supplied from external sources. We would expect the frequency of the electron and thus that of the emitted radiation to change continuously as the energy drains away. This prediction of classical theory cannot be reconciled with the existence of sharp spectrum lines. Thus classical physics cannot explain the hydrogen, or any other, spectrum.

Bohr circumvented this difficulty by assuming that, like Planck's oscillators, the hydrogen atom exists in certain *stationary states* in which it does not radiate. Radiation occurs *only* when the atom makes a transition from one state, with energy $E_k$, to a state with lower energy $E_j$. In equation form

$$h\nu = E_k - E_j, \tag{47–18}$$

where $h\nu$ is the quantum of energy carried away by the photon that is emitted from the atom during the transition.

To learn the allowed frequencies predicted by Eq. 47–18, it is necessary to know the energies of the various stationary states in which a hydrogen atom can exist. This calculation was first carried out by Bohr on the basis of a specific model for the hydrogen atom put forward by him. Bohr's model was highly successful for hydrogen and had a tremendous influence on the

**Fig. 47–18**   The spectrum of hydrogen. It consists of a number of series of lines, three of which are shown. Within each series the spectrum lines follow a regular pattern, approaching a so-called *series limit* at the short-wave end of the series.

further development of the subject; it is now regarded as an important preliminary stage in the development of a more complete theory of quantum physics.

Let us assume that the electron in the hydrogen atom moves in a circular orbit of radius $r$ centered on its nucleus. We assume that the nucleus, which is a single proton, is so massive that the center of mass of the system is essentially at the position of the proton. Let us calculate the energy $E$ of such an atom.

Writing Newton's second law for the motion of the electron, we have (using Coulomb's law)

$$F = ma,$$

or

$$\frac{e^2}{4\pi\epsilon_0 r^2} = m\frac{v^2}{r}.$$

This allows us to calculate the kinetic energy of the electron, which is

$$K = \tfrac{1}{2}mv^2 = \frac{e^2}{8\pi\epsilon_0 r}. \tag{47-19}$$

The potential energy $U$ of the proton-electron system is given by

$$U = V(-e) = -\frac{e^2}{4\pi\epsilon_0 r}, \tag{47-20}$$

where $V$ ($= e/4\pi\epsilon_0 r$) is the potential of the proton at the radius of the electron.

The total energy $E$ of the system is

$$E = K + U = -\frac{e^2}{8\pi\epsilon_0 r}. \tag{47-21}$$

Since the orbit radius can apparently take on any value, so can the energy $E$. The problem of quantizing $E$ reduces to that of quantizing $r$.

Every property of the orbit is fixed if the radius is given. Equations 47-19, 47-20, and 47-21 show this specifically for the energies $K$, $U$, and $E$. From Eq. 47-19 we can show that the *linear speed* $v$ for the electron is also given in terms of $r$ by

$$v = \sqrt{\frac{e^2}{4\pi\epsilon_0 mr}}. \tag{47-22}$$

The *rotational frequency* $\nu_0$ follows at once from

$$\nu_0 = \frac{v}{2\pi r} = \sqrt{\frac{e^2}{16\pi^3\epsilon_0 mr^3}}. \tag{47-23}$$

The *linear momentum* $p$ follows from Eq. 47–22:

$$p = mv = \sqrt{\frac{me^2}{4\pi\epsilon_0 r}}. \tag{47-24}$$

The *angular momentum* $L$ is given by

$$L = pr = \sqrt{\frac{me^2 r}{4\pi\epsilon_0}}. \tag{47-25}$$

Thus if $r$ is known, the orbit parameters $K$, $U$, $E$, $v$, $v_o$, $p$, and $L$ are also known. If any one of these quantities is quantized, all of them must be.

At this stage Bohr had no rules to guide him and so made (after some indirect reasoning which we do not reproduce) a bold hypothesis, namely, that the necessary quantization of the orbit parameters shows up most simply when applied to the angular momentum and that, specifically, $L$ can take on only values given by

$$L = n\frac{h}{2\pi} \qquad n = 1, 2, 3, \ldots. \tag{47-26}$$

Planck's constant appears again in a fundamental way; the integer $n$ is a *quantum number*.

Combining Eqs. 47–25 and 47–26 leads to

$$r = n^2 \frac{h^2\epsilon_0}{\pi me^2} \qquad n = 1, 2, 3, \ldots, \tag{47-27}$$

which tells how $r$ is quantized. Substituting Eq. 47–27 into Eq. 47–21 produces

$$E = -\frac{me^4}{8\epsilon_0^2 h^2}\frac{1}{n^2} \qquad n = 1, 2, 3, \ldots, \tag{47-28}$$

which gives directly the energy values of the allowed stationary states.

Figure 47–19 shows the energies of the stationary states and their associated quantum numbers. Equation 47–27 shows that the orbit radius increases as $n^2$. The upper level in Fig. 47–19, marked $n = \infty$, corresponds to a state in which the electron is completely removed from the atom (that is, $E = 0$ and $r = \infty$). Figure 47–19 also shows some of the quantum jumps that take place between the different stationary states.

Combining Eqs. 47–18 and 47–28 allows us to write a completely theoretical formula for the frequencies of the lines in the hydrogen spectrum. It is

$$\nu = \frac{me^4}{8\epsilon_0^2 h^3}\left(\frac{1}{j^2} - \frac{1}{k^2}\right) \tag{47-29}$$

in which $j$ and $k$ are integers describing, respectively, the lower and the upper stationary states. The corresponding wavelengths can easily be

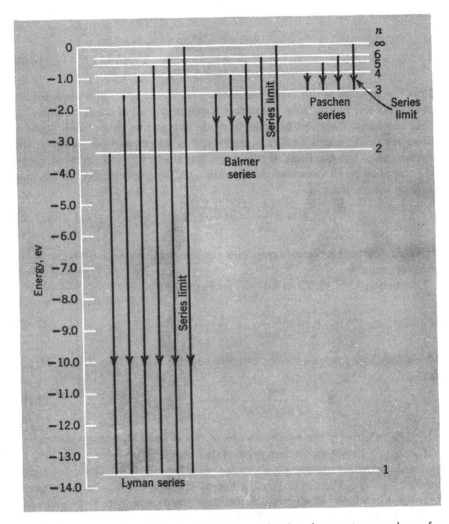

**Fig. 47-19** An energy level diagram for hydrogen showing the quantum number $n$ for each level and some of the transitions that appear in the spectrum. An infinite number of levels is crowded in between the levels marked $n = 6$ and $n = \infty$. Compare this figure carefully with Fig. 47-18.

found from $\lambda = c/\nu$. Table 47–1 shows some wavelengths so calculated; it should be compared carefully with Figs. 47–18 and 47–19.

**Table 47–1**

THE HYDROGEN SPECTRUM

(Some selected lines)

| Name of series | Quantum Number | | Wavelength, A |
|---|---|---|---|
| | $j$ (lower state) | $k$ (upper state) | |
| Lyman | 1 | 2 | 1216 |
| | 1 | 3 | 1026 |
| | 1 | 4 | 970 |
| | 1 | 5 | 949 |
| | 1 | 6 | 940 |
| | 1 | ∞ | 912 |
| Balmer | 2 | 3 | 6563 |
| | 2 | 4 | 4861 |
| | 2 | 5 | 4341 |
| | 2 | 6 | 4102 |
| | 2 | 7 | 3970 |
| | 2 | ∞ | 3650 |
| Paschen | 3 | 4 | 18751 |
| | 3 | 5 | 12818 |
| | 3 | 6 | 10938 |
| | 3 | 7 | 10050 |
| | 3 | 8 | 9546 |
| | 3 | ∞ | 8220 |

▶ **Example 5.** Calculate the binding energy of the hydrogen atom (the energy binding the electron to the nucleus) from Eq. 47–28.

The binding energy is numerically equal to the energy of the lowest state in Fig. 47–19. The largest negative value of $E$ in Eq. 47–28 is found for $n = 1$. This yields

$$E = -\frac{me^4}{8\epsilon_0^2 h^2}$$

$$= -\frac{(9.11 \times 10^{-31} \text{ kg})(1.60 \times 10^{-19} \text{ coul})^4}{(8)(8.85 \times 10^{-12} \text{ coul}^2/\text{nt-m}^2)^2(6.63 \times 10^{-34} \text{ joule-sec})^2}$$

$$= -2.17 \times 10^{-18} \text{ joule} = -13.6 \text{ ev},$$

which agrees with the experimentally observed binding energy for hydrogen.   ◀

### 47–9   The Correspondence Principle

Although all theories in physics have limitations, they usually do not break down abruptly but in a continuous way, yielding results that agree less and less well with experiment. Thus the predictions of Newtonian mechanics become less and less accurate as the speed is made to approach that of light. A similar relationship must exist between quantum physics and classical physics; it remains to find the circumstances under which the latter theory is revealed as a special case of the former.

The radius of the lowest energy state in hydrogen (the so-called *ground state*) is found by putting $n = 1$ in Eq. 47–27; it turns out to be $5.3 \times 10^{-11}$ meter. If $n = 10{,}000$, however, the radius is $(10{,}000)^2$ times as large or 5.3 mm. This "atom" is so large that we suspect that its behavior should be accurately described by classical physics. Let us test this by computing the frequency of the emitted light on the basis of both classical and quantum assumptions. These calculations should differ at small quantum numbers but should agree at large quantum numbers. The fact that *quantum physics reduces to classical physics at large quantum numbers* is called the *correspondence principle*. This principle, credited to Niels Bohr, was very useful during the years in which quantum physics was being developed. Bohr, in fact, based his theory of the hydrogen atom on correspondence principle arguments.

Classically, the frequency of the light emitted from an atom is equal to $\nu_0$, its frequency of revolution * in its orbit. This can be expressed in terms of a quantum number $n$ by combining Eqs. 47–23 and 47–27 to obtain

$$\nu_0 = \frac{me^4}{8\epsilon_0^2 h^3} \frac{2}{n^3}. \tag{47–30}$$

Quantum physics predicts that the frequency $\nu$ of the emitted light is given by Eq. 47–29. Considering a transition between an orbit with quantum number $k = n$ and one with $j = n - 1$ leads to

$$\nu = \frac{me^4}{8\epsilon_0^2 h^3} \left[ \frac{1}{(n-1)^2} - \frac{1}{n^2} \right]$$

$$= \frac{me^4}{8\epsilon_0^2 h^3} \left[ \frac{2n-1}{(n-1)^2 n^2} \right]. \tag{47–31}$$

As $n \to \infty$ the expression in the square brackets above approaches $2/n^3$ so that $\nu \to \nu_0$ as $n \to \infty$. Table 47–2 illustrates this example of the correspondence principle.

---

* Integral multiples of the frequency also exist but may be ignored without affecting the present argument.

## Table 47–2

THE CORRESPONDENCE PRINCIPLE AS APPLIED TO THE
HYDROGEN ATOM

| Quantum Number, $n$ | Frequency of Revolution in Orbit (Eq. 47–30) cycles/sec | Frequency of Transition to Next Lowest State (Eq. 47–31) cycles/sec | Difference, % |
|---|---|---|---|
| 2 | $8.20 \times 10^{14}$ | $24.6 \times 10^{14}$ | 67 |
| 5 | $5.26 \times 10^{13}$ | $7.38 \times 10^{13}$ | 29 |
| 10 | $6.57 \times 10^{12}$ | $7.72 \times 10^{12}$ | 14 |
| 50 | $5.25 \times 10^{10}$ | $5.42 \times 10^{10}$ | 3 |
| 100 | $6.578 \times 10^{9}$ | $6.677 \times 10^{9}$ | 1.5 |
| 1,000 | $6.5779 \times 10^{6}$ | $6.5878 \times 10^{6}$ | 0.15 |
| 10,000 | $6.5779 \times 10^{3}$ | $6.5789 \times 10^{3}$ | 0.015 |

## QUESTIONS

1. "Pockets" formed by the coals in a coal fire seem brighter than the coals themselves. Is the temperature in such pockets appreciably higher than the surface temperature of an exposed glowing coal?

2. The relation $R = \sigma T^4$ (Eq. 47–2) is exact for true cavities and holds for all temperatures. Why don't we use this relation as the basis of a definition of temperature at, say, 100°C?

3. Do all incandescent solids obey the fourth-power law of temperature, as Eq. 47–3 seems to suggest?

4. A hole in the wall of a cavity radiator is sometimes called a *black body*. Why?

5. It is stated that if we look into a cavity whose walls are maintained at a constant temperature no details of the interior are visible. Does this seem reasonable?

6. How can a *photon* energy be given by $E = h\nu$ (Eq. 47–10) when the very presence of the frequency $\nu$ in the formula implies that light is a *wave*?

7. In the photoelectric effect, why does the existence of a cutoff frequency speak in favor of the photon theory and against the wave theory?

8. Why are photoelectric measurements so sensitive to the nature of the photoelectric surface?

9. Does Einstein's theory of photoelectricity, in which light is postulated to be a photon, invalidate Young's interference experiment?

10. List and discuss carefully the assumptions made by Planck in connection with the cavity radiation problem, by Einstein in connection with the photoelectric effect, and by Bohr in connection with the hydrogen atom problem.

11. In Bohr's theory for the hydrogen atom orbits, what is the implication of the fact that the potential energy is negative and is greater in magnitude than the kinetic energy?

12. Can a hydrogen atom absorb a photon whose energy exceeds its binding energy (13.6 ev)?

13. Discuss Example 1 in terms of the correspondence principle.

14. According to classical mechanics, an electron moving in an orbit should be able to do so with any angular momentum whatever. According to Bohr's theory of the hydrogen atom, however, the angular momentum is quantized according to $L = nh/2\pi$. Reconcile these two statements, using the correspondence principle.

## PROBLEMS

1. At what wavelength does a cavity radiator at 6000°K radiate most per unit wavelength? Solve either analytically or graphically.

2. Using Fig. 47–1, verify that the emissivity of tungsten at 2000°K is 0.259.

3. A cavity radiator at 6000°K has a hole 0.10 mm in diameter drilled in its wall. At what rate do photons in the range 5500 to 5510 A escape from this hole?

4. A cavity whose walls are held at 4000°K has a circular aperture 5.0 mm in diameter. (a) At what rate does energy in the visible range (defined to extend from 0.40 to 0.70 μ) escape from this hole? (b) What fraction of the total radiation escaping from the cavity does this represent? Solve either analytically or graphically.

5. Show that Wien's law (p. 1085) is a special case of Planck's law (Eq. 47–6) for short wavelengths or low temperatures.

6. Solar radiation falls on the earth at a rate of 2.0 cal/cm²-min. How many photons/cm²-min is this, assuming an average wavelength of 5500 A?

7. A spectral emission line, important in radioastronomy, has a wavelength of 21 cm. To what photon energy does this correspond?

8. The energy required to remove an electron from sodium is 2.3 ev. Does sodium show a photoelectric effect for orange light, with λ = 6800 A?

9. Light of a wavelength 2000 A falls on an aluminum surface. In aluminum 4.2 ev are required to remove an electron. What is the kinetic energy of (a) the fastest and (b) the slowest emitted photoelectrons? (c) What is the stopping potential? (d) What is the cutoff wavelength for aluminum?

10. The work function for a clean lithium surface is 2.3 ev. Make a rough plot of the stopping potential $V_0$ versus the frequency of the incident light for such a surface.

11. In Example 2 suppose that the "target" is a single gas atom of 1.0 A radius and that the intensity of the light source is reduced to $10^{-5}$ watt. If the binding energy of the most loosely bound electron in the atom is 20 ev, what time lag for the photoelectric effect is expected on the basis of the wave theory of light?

12. A 100-watt sodium vapor lamp radiates uniformly in all directions. (a) At what distance from the lamp will the average density of photons be 10/cm³? (b) What is the average density of photons 2.0 meters from the lamp? Assume the light to be monochromatic, with λ = 5890 A.

13. Show, by analyzing a collision between a photon and a free electron (using relativistic mechanics), that it is impossible for a photon to give all of its energy to the free electron. In other terms, the photoelectric effect cannot occur for completely free electrons; the electrons must be bound in a solid or in an atom.

14. Calculate the per cent change in photon energy for a Compton collision with φ in Fig. 47–11 equal to 90° for radiation in (a) the microwave range, with λ = 3.0 cm, (b) the visible range, with λ = 5000 A, (c) the X-ray range, with λ = 1.00 A, and (d) the gamma ray range, the energy of the gamma-ray photons being 1.0 Mev. What are your conclusions about the importance of the Compton effect in these various regions of the electromagnetic spectrum, judged solely by the criterion of energy loss in a single Compton encounter?

15. Carry out the necessary algebra to eliminate $v$ and $\theta$ from Eqs. 47–13, 47–15, and 47–16 to obtain the Compton shift relation (Eq. 47–17).

16. (a) Using Bohr's formula, calculate the three longest wavelengths in the Balmer series. (b) Between what wavelength limits does the Balmer series lie?

17. In the ground state of the hydrogen atom, according to Bohr's theory, what are (a) the quantum number, (b) the orbit radius, (c) the angular momentum, (d) the linear momentum, (e) the angular velocity, (f) the linear speed, (g) the force on the electron, (h) the acceleration of the electron, (i) the kinetic energy, (j) the potential energy, and (k) the total energy?

18. How do the quantities (b) to (k) in Problem 17 vary with the quantum number?

19. How much energy is required to remove an electron from a hydrogen atom in a state with $n = 8$?

20. A hydrogen atom is excited from a state with $n = 1$ to one with $n = 4$. (a) Calculate the energy that must be absorbed by the atom. (b) Calculate and display on an energy-level diagram the different photon energies that may be emitted if the atom returns to its $n = 1$ state. (c) Calculate the recoil speed of the hydrogen atom, assumed initially at rest, if it makes the transition from $n = 4$ to $n = 1$ in a single quantum jump.

21. A hydrogen atom in a state having a *binding energy* (this is the energy required to remove an electron) of 0.85 ev makes a transition to a state with an *excitation energy* (this is the difference in energy between the state and the ground state) of 10.2 ev. (a) Find the energy of the emitted photon. (b) Show this transition on an energy-level diagram for hydrogen, labeling the appropriate quantum numbers.

22. Show on an energy-level diagram for hydrogen the quantum numbers corresponding to a transition in which the wavelength of the emitted photon is 1216 A.

23. A neutron, with kinetic energy of 6.0 ev, collides with a resting hydrogen atom in its ground state. Apply the laws of conservation of momentum and of energy to this collision and show that it must be elastic (that is, *kinetic* energy must be conserved).

24. Apply Bohr's theory to singly ionized helium, that is, to a helium atom with one electron removed. What relationship exists between this spectrum and the hydrogen spectrum?

25. Using Bohr's theory, calculate the energy required to remove the electron from singly ionized helium.

26. *Positronium.* Apply Bohr's theory to the positronium atom. This consists of a positive and a negative electron revolving around their center of mass, which lies halfway between them. (a) What relationship exists between this spectrum and the hydrogen spectrum? (b) What is the radius of the ground state orbit? (Hint: It will be necessary to analyze this problem from first principles because this "atom" has no nucleus; both particles revolve about a point halfway between them.)

27. *Muonic atoms.* Apply Bohr's theory to a muonic atom, which consists of a nucleus of charge $Ze$ with a negative muon (an elementary particle with a charge of $-e$ and a mass $m$ that is 207 times as large as the electron mass; see Appendix $F$) circulating about it. Calculate (a) the radius of the first Bohr orbit, (b) the ionization energy, and (c) the wavelength of the most energetic photon that can be emitted. Assume that the muon is circulating about a hydrogen nucleus ($Z = 1$).

28. If an electron is rotating in an orbit at frequency $\nu_0$, classical electromagnetism predicts that it will radiate energy not only at this frequency but also at $2\nu_0$, $3\nu_0$, $4\nu_0$, etc.; see footnote on p. 1104. Show that this is also predicted by Bohr's theory of the hydrogen atom in the limiting case of large quantum numbers.

29. In Table 47–2 show that the quantity in the last column is given by

$$\frac{100(\nu - \nu_0)}{\nu} \cong \frac{150}{n}$$

for large quantum numbers.

30. If the angular momentum of the earth due to its motion around the sun were quantized according to Bohr's relation $L = nh/2\pi$, what would the quantum number be? Could such quantization be detected if it existed?

# Waves and Particles

## CHAPTER 48

### 48–1 Matter Waves

In 1924 Louis de Broglie of France reasoned that (a) nature is strikingly symmetrical in many ways; (b) our observable universe is composed entirely of light and matter; (c) if light has a dual, wave-particle nature, perhaps matter has also. Since matter was then regarded as being composed of particles, de Broglie's reasoning suggested that one should search for a wave-like behavior for matter.

De Broglie's suggestion might not have received serious attention had he not predicted what the expected wavelength of the so-called matter waves would be. We recall that about 1680 Huygens put forward a wave theory of light that did not receive general acceptance, in part because Huygens was not able to state what the wavelength of the light was. When Thomas Young rectified this defect in 1800, the wave theory of light started on its way to acceptance.

De Broglie assumed that the wavelength of the predicted matter waves was given by the same relationship that held for light namely, Eq. 47–14, or

$$\lambda = \frac{h}{p}, \tag{48–1}$$

which connects the wavelength of a light wave with the momentum of the associated photons. The dual nature of light shows up strikingly in this equation and also in Eq. 47–10 ($E = h\nu$). Each equation contains within its structure both a wave concept ($\nu$ and $\lambda$) and a particle concept ($E$ and $p$) *De Broglie predicted that the wavelength of matter waves would also be given by Eq. 48–1, where p would now be the momentum of the particle of matter.*

▶ **Example 1.** What wavelength is predicted by Eq. 48–1 for a beam of electrons whose kinetic energy is 100 ev?

The velocity of the electrons is found from $K = \frac{1}{2}mv^2$, or

$$v = \sqrt{\frac{2K}{m}} = \sqrt{\frac{(2)(100 \text{ ev})(1.6 \times 10^{-19} \text{ joule/ev})}{9.1 \times 10^{-31} \text{ kg}}}$$

$$= 5.9 \times 10^6 \text{ meters/sec.}$$

The momentum follows from

$$p = mv = (9.1 \times 10^{-31} \text{ kg})(5.9 \times 10^6 \text{ meters/sec}) = 5.4 \times 10^{-24} \text{ kg-m/sec.}$$

The wavelength (called the *de Broglie wavelength*) is found from Eq. 48–1 or

$$\lambda = \frac{h}{p} = \frac{6.6 \times 10^{-34} \text{ joule-sec}}{5.4 \times 10^{-24} \text{ kg-m/sec}} = 1.2 \text{ A.}$$

This is the same order of magnitude as the size of an atom or the spacing between adjacent planes of atoms in a solid. ◀

**Fig. 48–1** The apparatus of Davisson and Germer. Electrons from filament $F$ are accelerated by a variable potential difference $V$. After "reflection" from crystal $C$ they are collected by detector $D$.

In 1926 Elsasser pointed out that the wave nature of matter might be tested in the same way that the wave nature of X-rays was first tested, namely, by allowing a beam of electrons of the appropriate energy to fall on a crystalline solid. The atoms of the crystal serve as a three-dimensional array of diffracting centers for the electron "wave"; we should look for strong diffracted peaks in certain characteristic directions, just as for X-ray diffraction.

This idea was tested by C. J. Davisson and L. H. Germer in this country and by G. P. Thomson in Scotland.* Figure 48–1 shows the apparatus of

---

* For an historical account of Thomson's researches see "Early Work in Electron Diffraction," Sir George Thomson, p. 821, *Am. J Phys.*, December, 1961.

**Fig. 48-2**   The collector current in
detector $D$ in Fig. 48-1 as a function of the kinetic energy of the
incident electrons, showing a diffraction maximum.   The angle $\phi$
in Fig. 48-1 is adjusted to 50°.   If
an appreciably smaller or larger
value is used, the diffraction maximum disappears.

Davisson and Germer.   Electrons from a heated filament are accelerated
by a variable potential difference $V$ and emerge from the "electron gun" $G$
with kinetic energy $eV$.   This electron beam is allowed to fall at normal
incidence on a single crystal of nickel at $C$.   Detector $D$ is set at a particular
angle $\phi$ and readings of the intensity of the "reflected" beam are taken at
various values of the accelerating potential $V$.   Figure 48-2 shows that a
strong beam occurs at $\phi = 50°$ for $V = 54$ volts.

All such strong "reflected" beams can be accounted for by assuming that
the electron beam has a wavelength, given by $\lambda = h/p$, and that "Bragg
reflections" occur from certain families of atomic planes precisely as described for X-rays in Section 45-5.

Figure 48-3 shows such a Bragg reflection, obeying the Bragg relationship

$$m\lambda = 2d \sin \theta \qquad m = 1, 2, 3, \ldots . \tag{48-2}$$

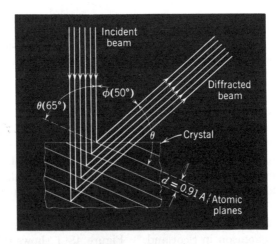

**Fig. 48-3**   The strong diffracted beam at $\phi = 50°$ and $V = 54$ volts arises from wave-like
"reflection" from the family of atomic planes shown, for $d = 0.91$ A.   The Bragg angle
$\theta$ is 65°.   For simplicity, refraction of the diffracted wave as it leaves the surface is ignored.

For the conditions of Fig. 48–3 the effective interplanar spacing $d$ can be shown by X-ray analysis to be 0.91 A.  Since $\phi$ equals $50°$, it follows that $\theta$ equals $90° - \frac{1}{2} \times 50°$ or $65°$.  The wavelength to be calculated from Eq. 48–2, if we assume $m = 1$, is

$$\lambda = 2d \sin \theta = 2(0.91 \text{ A})(\sin 65°) = 1.65 \text{ A}.$$

The wavelength calculated from the de Broglie relationship $\lambda = h/p$ is, for 54-ev electrons (see Example 1), 1.64 A.  This excellent agreement, combined with much similar evidence, is a convincing argument for believing that electrons are wave-like in some circumstances.

Not only electrons but all other particles, charged or uncharged, show wave-like characteristics.  Beams of slow neutrons from nuclear reactors are routinely used to investigate the atomic structure of solids.  Figure 48–4 shows a "neutron diffraction pattern" for finely powdered lead.

The evidence for the existence of matter waves with wavelengths given by Eq. 48–1 is strong indeed.  Nevertheless, the evidence that matter is

**Fig. 48–4**  A diffraction pattern for powdered lead, using a monochromatic neutron beam from a nuclear reactor.  The peaks represent "Bragg reflections" from the various atomic planes, $\theta$ being the corresponding "Bragg angle."

composed of particles remains equally strong; see Fig. 10–10.  Thus, for matter as for light, we must face up to the existence of a dual character; *matter behaves in some circumstances like a particle and in others like a wave.*

## 48–2  Atomic Structure and Standing Waves

The motion of electrons in beams is not bounded or limited in the beam direction.  We can make an analogy to a sound wave in a long gas-filled tube, a wave traveling down a long string, or an electromagnetic wave in a long waveguide.  All four cases can be described by appropriate traveling waves and, significantly, waves of *any* wavelength (within a certain range) can be propagated.

Let these last three waves be *bounded* by imposing physical restrictions. For the sound wave this corresponds to inserting end walls on a section of the long gas-filled pipe, thus forming an acoustic resonant cavity (Section 38–5).  For the waves in the string it corresponds to removing a finite section of string and clamping it at each end, as a violin string (Section 20–5).

**Fig. 48–5** Showing how an electron wave can be adjusted in wavelength to fit an integral number of times around the circumference of a Bohr orbit of radius $r$. This concept, like the Bohr orbit concept, is now regarded as oversimplified.

For the electromagnetic wave it corresponds to inserting end caps on a finite length of waveguide, thus forming an electromagnetic resonant cavity (Section 38–6).

Two important changes occur: (*a*) the motions are now represented by *standing* rather than traveling waves and (*b*) *only certain wavelengths (or frequencies) can now exist*. This *quantization* of the wavelength is a direct result of bounding or limiting the wave. We expect that if electrons are limited in their motions by being localized in an atom that (*a*) the electron motion can be represented by a standing matter wave, and (*b*) the electron motion will become quantized, that is, its energy can take on only certain discrete values.

De Broglie was able to derive the Bohr quantization condition for angular momentum by applying proper *boundary conditions* to matter waves in the hydrogen atom. Figure 48–5 suggests an instantaneous "snapshot" of a standing matter wave associated with an orbit of radius $r$. The de Broglie wavelength ($\lambda = h/p$) has been chosen so that the orbit of radius $r$ contains an integral number $n$ of the matter waves, or

$$\frac{2\pi r}{\lambda} = \frac{2\pi r}{(h/p)} = n \qquad n = 1, 2, 3, \ldots.$$

This leads at once to

$$L = pr = n\frac{h}{2\pi} \qquad n = 1, 2, 3, \ldots,$$

which is the Bohr quantization condition for $L$.

### 48–3  Wave Mechanics

The idea that the stationary states in atoms correspond to standing matter waves was taken up by Erwin Schrödinger in 1926 and used by him as the foundation of *wave mechanics*, one of several equivalent formulations of quantum physics.

An important quantity in wave mechanics is the *wave function* $\Psi$, which measures the "wave disturbance" of matter waves. For waves on strings the "wave disturbance" may be measured by a transverse displacement $y$; for sound waves it may be measured by a pressure variation $p$; for electromagnetic waves it may be measured by the electric field vector **E**.

We make the physical meaning of the wave disturbance $\Psi$ clear in Section 48–4. Meanwhile, let us study the wave function $\Psi(x, t)$ for a simple, one-dimensional problem, that of the possible motions a particle of mass $m$ confined between rigid walls of separation $l$ as in Fig. 48–6$b$. The wave function can be obtained by analogy with a known mechanical problem, that of the natural modes of vibration of a string of length $l$, clamped at each end as in Fig. 48–6$a$.

In the vibrating string the boundary conditions require that nodes exist at each end. This means that the wavelength $\lambda$ must be chosen so that

$$l = n\frac{\lambda}{2} \quad n = 1, 2, 3, \ldots,$$

or that the wavelength $\lambda$ is "quantized" by the requirement that

$$\lambda = \frac{2l}{n} \quad n = 1, 2, 3, \ldots. \tag{48-3}$$

The wave disturbance for the string is represented by a standing wave whose equation was shown in Section 19–9 to be

$$y = 2y_m \sin kx \cos \omega t,$$

where $\omega (= 2\pi\nu)$ is the angular frequency of the wave and $k (= 2\pi/\lambda)$ is the wave number. Since $\lambda$ is quantized, $k$ must be also, or

$$k = \frac{2\pi}{\lambda} = \frac{n\pi}{l} \quad n = 1, 2, 3, \ldots.$$

which leads to

$$y = \left[2y_m \sin \frac{n\pi x}{l}\right] \cos \omega t \quad n = 1, 2, 3, \ldots. \tag{48-4}$$

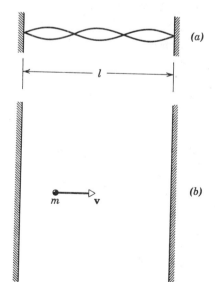

(a)

(b)

**Fig. 48–6** (a) A stretched string of length $l$ clamped between rigid supports. (b) A particle of mass $m$ and velocity $v$ confined to move between rigid walls a distance $l$ apart.

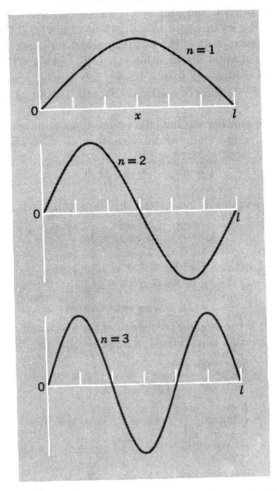

**Fig. 48–7** Three quantized modes of vibration for the string of Fig. 48–6a. The figure also represents three of the quantized wave functions for the particle of Fig. 48–6b. The ordinate is a displacement amplitude in the first case and a wave-function amplitude in the second.

Inspection of Eq. 48–4 shows that no matter what value of $n$ is selected nodes exist at $x = 0$ and at $x = l$, as required by the boundary conditions. Figure 48–7 shows plots of the quantity in the square brackets in this equation (the amplitude of the standing wave) for the modes of vibration of the string corresponding to $n = 1$, 2, and 3.

Consider now the particle confined between rigid walls. Since the walls are assumed to be perfectly rigid, the particle cannot penetrate them so that $\Psi$, which represents the particle motion in some way not yet clearly specified (see Section 48–4), must vanish at $x = 0$ and at $x = l$. The allowed wavelengths of the matter waves must be given by Eq. 48–3, or

$$\lambda = \frac{2l}{n}.$$

Replacing $\lambda$ by $h/p$ (see Eq. 48–1) leads to

$$p = \frac{nh}{2l}, \qquad (48\text{–}5)$$

which shows that the *linear momentum* of the particle is quantized. The momentum $p$ ($= mv$) is related to the energy $E$ (which is entirely kinetic and is equal to $\frac{1}{2}mv^2$) by

$$p = \sqrt{2mE}. \qquad (48\text{–}6)$$

Combining Eqs. 48–5 and 48–6 leads to the quantization condition for $E$, or

$$E = n^2 \frac{h^2}{8ml^2} \qquad n = 1, 2, 3, \ldots . \qquad (48\text{–}7)$$

The particle cannot have any energy, as we would expect classically, but only energies given by Eq. 48–7.

The matter wave is described, in strict analogy with Eq. 48–4, by

$$\Psi = \left[ \Psi_m \sin \frac{n\pi x}{l} \right] \cos \omega t \qquad n = 1, 2, 3, \ldots . \qquad (48\text{–}8)$$

Figure 48–7 can serve equally well to show how the amplitude of the standing matter waves for the states of motion corresponding to $n = 1, 2$, and 3 varies throughout the box. We see clearly in this problem how the act of localizing or bounding a particle leads to energy quantization.

▶ **Example 2.** Consider an electron ($m = 9.1 \times 10^{-31}$ kg) confined by electrical forces to move between two rigid "walls" separated by $1.0 \times 10^{-9}$ meter, which is about five atomic diameters. Find the quantized energy values for the three lowest stationary states.

From Eq. 48–7, for $n = 1$, we have

$$E = n^2 \frac{h^2}{8ml^2} = (1)^2 \frac{(6.6 \times 10^{-34} \text{ joule-sec})^2}{(8)(9.1 \times 10^{-31} \text{ kg})(1.0 \times 10^{-9} \text{ meter})^2}$$

$$= 6.0 \times 10^{-20} \text{ joule} = 0.38 \text{ ev}.$$

The energies for the next two states ($n = 2$ and $n = 3$) are $2^2 \times 0.38$ ev $= 1.5$ ev and $3^2 \times 0.38$ ev $= 3.4$ ev.

**Example 3.** Consider a grain of dust ($m = 1.0$ μgm $= 1.0 \times 10^{-9}$ kg) confined to move between two rigid walls separated by 0.1 mm ($= 10^{-4}$ meter). Its speed is only $10^{-6}$ meter/sec, so that it requires 100 sec to cross the gap. What quantum number describes this motion?

The energy is

$$E \,(= K) = \tfrac{1}{2}mv^2 = \tfrac{1}{2}(10^{-9} \text{ kg})(10^{-6} \text{ meter/sec})^2$$

$$= 5 \times 10^{-22} \text{ joule}.$$

Solving Eq. 48–7 for $n$ yields

$$n = \sqrt{8mE}\,\frac{l}{h} = \sqrt{(8)(10^{-9}\text{ kg})(5 \times 10^{-22}\text{ joule})}\left(\frac{10^{-4}\text{ meter}}{6.6 \times 10^{-34}\text{ joule-sec}}\right)$$

$$= 3 \times 10^{14}.$$

Even in these extreme conditions the quantized nature of the motion would never be apparent; we cannot distinguish experimentally between $n = 3 \times 10^{14}$ and $n = 3 \times 10^{14} + 1$. Classical physics, which fails completely for the problem of Example 2, works extremely well for this problem.  ◀

### 48–4  Meaning of $\Psi$

Max Born first suggested that the quantity $\Psi^2$ at any particular point is a measure of *the probability that the particle will be near that point.*  More exactly, if a volume element $dV$ is constructed at that point, the probability that the particle will be found in the volume element at a given instant is $\Psi^2\,dV$. This interpretation of $\Psi$ provides a statistical connection between

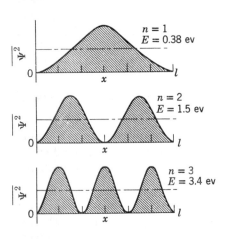

**Fig. 48–8**  The "probability functions" for three states of motion of the particle of Fig. 48–6b, along with the corresponding quantized energies for the conditions of Example 2. The horizontal lines show the predictions of classical mechanics, in which the probability function is constant for all positions of the particle.

the wave and the associated particle; it tells us where the particle is *likely to be*, not where it *is*.

For the particle confined between rigid walls the probability that the particle will lie between two planes that are distance $x$ and $x + dx$ from one wall (see Fig. 48–8) is given by

$$\Psi^2\,dx = \Psi_m{}^2\,\sin^2\frac{n\pi}{l}\,x\,\cos^2\omega t\,dx.$$

Since we are more interested in the particle's spatial location than in its time behavior, we average $\Psi^2$ over one cycle of the motion. This is equivalent to replacing $\cos^2\omega t$ by its average value for one cycle, namely one-half, or

$$\overline{\Psi^2} = \tfrac{1}{2}\Psi_m{}^2\,\sin^2\frac{n\pi x}{l} \qquad n = 1, 2, 3, \ldots. \tag{48–9}$$

Figure 48–8 shows $\overline{\Psi^2}$ for the three stationary states corresponding to $n = 1, 2$, and 3. Note that for $n = 1$ the particle is more likely to be near the center than the ends. This is in sharp contradiction to the results of classical physics, according to which the particle has the same probability of being located anywhere between the walls, as shown by the horizontal line in Fig. 48-8.

The problem of a particle confined between rigid walls has little real application in physics. We would prefer to illustrate the wave mechanics of Schrödinger by applying it to a more experimentally realizable situation, such as the hydrogen atom. Only mathematical complexity prevents us from doing this. We state without proof that when this problem is solved by wave mechanics the motion of the electron in the ground state of the atom, defined by putting $n = 1$ in Eq. 47-28, is described by the following wave function,

$$\Psi = \frac{1}{\sqrt{\pi a^3}}\, e^{-r/a} \cos \omega t, \qquad (48\text{-}10)$$

where

$$a = \frac{h^2 \epsilon_0}{\pi m e^2}.$$

Putting $n = 1$ in Eq. 47-27 shows that $a$ is the radius of the ground-state orbit in Bohr's theory. This special interpretation has little meaning in wave mechanics; $a$ is taken here merely as a convenient unit of length when dealing with atomic problems, having the value 0.529 A.

▶ **Example 4.** Consider two hypothetical spherical shells centered on the nucleus of a hydrogen atom with radii $r$ and $r + dr$. What is the probability $P(r)$ that the electron will lie between these shells, as a function of $r$?

This probability is $\Psi^2\, dV$, where $dV$ is the volume between the shells, or $4\pi r^2\, dr$. Thus

$$\Psi^2\, dV = \left(\frac{1}{\sqrt{\pi a^3}}\, e^{-r/a} \cos \omega t\right)^{2} (4\pi r^2\, dr) = P(r)\, dr.$$

Averaging over the time (that is, replacing $\cos^2 \omega t$ by $\tfrac{1}{2}$) yields for the probability $\overline{P(r)}$

$$\overline{P(r)} = \frac{2r^2}{a^3}\, e^{-2r/a}.$$

Figure 48-9 shows a plot of this function. Note that the most probable location for the electron corresponds to the first Bohr radius. Thus in wave mechanics we do not say that the electron in the $n = 1$ state in hydrogen goes around the nucleus in a circular orbit of 0.529 A radius but only that the electron is more likely to be found at this distance from the nucleus than at any other distance, either larger or smaller. ◀

**Fig. 48-9**  The probability function for the ground state of the hydrogen atom, as calculated from wave mechanics. The separation between the nucleus and the electron is $r$; $a$ is the radius of the first Bohr orbit $(0.529 \times 10^{-10}$ meter), used here merely as a convenient unit of distance.

### 48–5   The Uncertainty Principle

Only those quantities that can be measured have any real meaning in physics. If we could focus a "super" microscope on an electron in an atom and see it moving around in an orbit, we would declare that such orbits have meaning. However, we shall show that *it is fundamentally impossible to make such an observation*—even with the most ideal instruments that could conceivably be constructed. Therefore, we declare that such orbits have no physical meaning.

We observe the moon traveling around the earth by means of the sunlight that it reflects in our direction. Now light transfers linear momentum to an object from which it is reflected. In principle, this reflected light would disturb the course of the moon in its orbit, although a little thought shows that this disturbing effect is negligible.

For electrons the situation is quite different. Here, too, we can hope to "see" the electron only if we reflect light, or another particle, from it. In this case the recoil that the electron experiences when the light (photon) bounces from it completely alters the electron's motion in a way that cannot be avoided or even corrected for.

It is not surprising that the probability curve of Fig. 48–9 is the most detailed information that we can hope to obtain, by measurement, about the distribution of negative charge in the hydrogen atom. If orbits such as those envisaged by Bohr existed, they would be broken up completely in our attempts to verify their existence. Under these circumstances, we prefer to say that it is the probability function, and not the orbits, that represents physical reality.

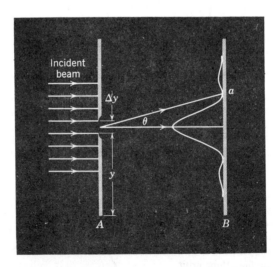

**Fig. 48–10**  An incident beam of electrons is diffracted at the slit in screen $A$, forming a typical diffraction pattern on screen $B$. If the slit is made narrower, the pattern becomes wider.

Our inherent inability to describe the motions of electrons in a classical way finds expression in the *uncertainty principle,* enunciated by Werner Heisenberg in 1927. To formulate this principle, consider a beam of monoenergetic electrons of speed $v_0$ moving from left to right in Fig. 48–10. Let us set ourselves the task of measuring the position of a particular electron in the vertical ($y$) direction and also its velocity component $v_y$ in this direction. If we succeed in carrying out these measurements with unlimited accuracy, we can then claim to have established the position and motion of the electron (or one component of it at least) with precision. However, we shall see that *it is impossible to make these two measurements simultaneously with unlimited accuracy.*

To measure $y$ we block the beam with an absorbing screen $A$ in which we put a slit of width $\Delta y$. If an electron gets through the slit, its vertical position must be known to this accuracy. By making the slit narrower, we can improve the accuracy of this vertical position measurement as much as we wish.

Since the electron is a wave, it will undergo diffraction at the slit, and a photographic plate placed at $B$ in Fig. 48–10 will reveal a typical *diffraction pattern.* The existence of this diffraction pattern means that there is an uncertainty in the values of $v_y$ possessed by the electrons emerging from the slit. Let $v_{ya}$ be the value of $v_y$ that corresponds to an electron landing at the first minimum on the screen, marked by point $a$ and described by a characteristic angle $\theta_a$. We take $v_{ya}$ as a *rough* measure of the uncertainty $\Delta v_y$ in $v_y$ for electrons emerging from the slit.

The first minimum in the diffraction pattern is given by Eq. 44–2, or

$$\sin \theta_a = \frac{\lambda}{\Delta y}.$$

If we assume that $\theta_a$ is small enough, we can write this equation as

$$\theta_a \cong \frac{\lambda}{\Delta y}. \tag{48–11}$$

To reach point $a$, $v_{ya}$ ($= \Delta v_y$) must be such that

$$\theta_a \cong \frac{\Delta v_y}{v_0}. \tag{48–12}$$

Combining Eqs. 48–11 and 48–12 leads to

$$\frac{\Delta v_y}{v_0} = \frac{\lambda}{\Delta y},$$

which we rewrite as     $$\Delta v_y \, \Delta y \cong \lambda v_0. \tag{48–13}$$

Now $\lambda$, the wavelength of the electron beam, is given by $h/p$ or $h/mv_0$; substituting this into Eq. 48–13 yields

$$\Delta v_y \, \Delta y \cong \frac{h v_0}{m v_0}.$$

We rewrite this as     $$\Delta p_y \, \Delta y \cong h. \tag{48–14}$$

In Eq. 48–14 $\Delta p_y$ ($= m \, \Delta v_y$) is the uncertainty in our knowledge of the vertical momentum of the electrons; $\Delta y$ is the uncertainty in our knowledge of their vertical position. The equation tells us that, since the product of these uncertainties is a constant, *we cannot measure $p_y$ and $y$ simultaneously with unlimited accuracy.*

If we want to improve our measurement of $y$ (that is, if we want to reduce $\Delta y$), we use a finer slit. However (see Eq. 48–11), this will produce a wider diffraction pattern. A wider pattern means that our knowledge of the vertical momentum component of the electron has deteriorated, or, in other words, $\Delta p_y$ has increased; this is exactly what Eq. 48–14 predicts.

The limits on measurement imposed by Eq. 48–14 have nothing to do with the crudity of our measuring instruments. We are permitted to postulate the existence of the finest conceivable measuring equipment. Equation 48–14 represents a *fundamental* limitation, imposed by nature.

Equation 48–14 is a derivation, for a special case, of a general principle known as the *uncertainty principle*. As applied to position and momentum measurements, it asserts that

$$\Delta p_x \, \Delta x \gtrless h$$

$$\Delta p_y \, \Delta y \gtrless h$$

$$\Delta p_z \, \Delta z \gtrless h. \tag{48–15}$$

*Thus no component of the motion of an electron, free or bound, can be described with unlimited precision.*

Planck's constant $h$ probably appears nowhere that has more deep-seated significance than in Eq. 48–15. If this product had been zero instead of $h$, the classical ideas about particles and orbits would be correct; it would then be possible to measure both momentum and position with unlimited precision. The fact that $h$ appears means that the classical ideas are wrong; the magnitude of $h$ tells us under what circumstances these classical ideas must be replaced by quantum ideas. Gamow * has speculated, in an interesting and readable fantasy, what our world would be like if the constant $h$ were much larger than it is, so that nonclassical ideas would be apparent to our sense perceptions.

▶ **Example 5.** An electron has a speed of 300 meters/sec, accurate to 0.01%. With what fundamental accuracy can we locate the position of this electron?

The electron momentum is

$$p = mv = (9.1 \times 10^{-31} \text{ kg})(300 \text{ meters/sec}) = 2.7 \times 10^{-28} \text{ kg-m/sec}.$$

The uncertainty in momentum is given to be 0.01% of this, or

$$\Delta p = (0.0001)(2.7 \times 10^{-28} \text{ kg-m/sec}) = 2.7 \times 10^{-32} \text{ kg-m/sec}.$$

The minimum uncertainty in position, from Eq. 48–15, is

$$\Delta x = \frac{h}{\Delta p} = \frac{6.6 \times 10^{-34} \text{ joule-sec}}{2.7 \times 10^{-32} \text{ kg-m/sec}}$$

$$= 2.4 \text{ cm}.$$

If the electron momentum has really been determined by measurer⎯ �842o have the accuracy stated, there is no hope whatever that its position can be known to any better accuracy than that stated, namely about 1 in. The concept of the electron as a tiny dot is not very valid under these circumstances.

▶ **Example 6.** A bullet has a speed of 300 meters/sec, accurate to 0.01%. With what fundamental accuracy can we locate its position? Its mass is 50 gm ( = 0.05 kg).

This example is the same as Example 5 in every respect save the mass of the particle involved. The momentum is

$$p = mv = (0.05 \text{ kg})(300 \text{ meters/sec}) = 15 \text{ kg-m/sec}$$

and $$\Delta p = (0.0001)(15 \text{ kg-m/sec}) = 1.5 \times 10^{-3} \text{ kg-m/sec}.$$

Equation 48–15 yields

$$\Delta x = \frac{6.6 \times 10^{-34} \text{ joule-sec}}{1.5 \times 10^{-3} \text{ kg-m/sec}} = 4.4 \times 10^{-31} \text{ meter}.$$

---

* *Mr. Tompkins in Wonderland*, Macmillan, 1940.

This is so far beyond the possibility of measurement (a nucleus is only about $10^{-15}$ meter in diameter) that we can assert that for heavy objects like bullets the uncertainty principle sets no limits whatever on our measuring procedures. Once again the correspondence principle shows us how quantum physics reduces to classical physics under the appropriate circumstances. ◀

The uncertainty relation shows us why it is possible for both light and matter to have a dual, wave-particle, nature. It is because these two views, so obviously opposite to each other, can never be brought face to face in the same experimental situation. If we devise an experiment that forces the electron to reveal its wave character strongly, its particle character will always be inherently fuzzy. If we modify the experiment to bring out the particle character more strongly, the wave character necessarily becomes fuzzy. Matter and light are like coins that can be made to display either face at will but not both simultaneously. Niels Bohr first pointed out in his *principle of complementarity* how the ideas of wave and of particle complement rather than contradict each other.

## QUESTIONS

1. How can the *wavelength* of an electron be given by $\lambda = h/p$ when the very presence of the momentum $p$ in this formula implies that the electron is a particle?

2. How could Davisson and Germer be sure that the "54-volt" peak of Fig. 48–2 was a first-order diffraction peak, that is, that $m = 1$ in Eq. 48–2?

3. In a repetition of Thomson's experiment for measuring $e/m$ for the electron (see Section 33–8), a beam of $10^4$-ev electrons is collimated by passage through a slit of width 0.50 mm. Why is the beam-like character of the emerging electrons not destroyed by diffraction of the electron wave at this slit?

4. Why is the wave nature of matter not more apparent to our daily observations?

5. Apply the correspondence principle to the problem of a particle confined between rigid walls, showing that those features which seem "strange" (that is, the quantization of energy and the nonuniformity of the probability functions of Fig. 48–8) become undetectable experimentally at large quantum numbers.

6. In the $n = 1$ mode, for a particle confined between rigid walls, what is the probability that the particle will be found in a small volume element at the surface of either wall?

7. A standing wave can be viewed as the superposition of two traveling waves. Can you apply this to the problem of a particle confined between rigid walls, giving an interpretation in terms of the motion of the electron?

8. What is the physical significance of the wave function $\Psi$?

9. Why does the concept of Bohr orbits violate the uncertainty principle?

10. How can the predictions of wave mechanics be so exact if the only information we have about the positions of the electrons is statistical?

11. Make up some numerical examples to show the difficulty of getting the uncertainty principle to reveal itself during experiments with an object whose mass is about 1 gm.

12. Figure 48–8 shows that for $n = 3$ the probability function for a particle confined between rigid walls is zero at two points between the walls. How can the particle ever move across these positions? (Hint: Consider the implications of the uncertainty principle.)

13. The uncertainty principle can be stated in terms of angular quantities (compare Eq. 48–15) as

$$\Delta L \, \Delta\phi \gtrsim h$$

where $\Delta L$ is the uncertainty in the *angular* momentum and $\Delta\phi$ the uncertainty in the *angular* position. For electrons in atoms the angular momentum has definite quantized values, with no uncertainty whatever. What can we conclude about the uncertainty in the angular position and about the validity of the orbit concept?

## PROBLEMS

1. A bullet of mass 40 gm travels at 1000 meters/sec. (a) What wavelength can we associate with it? (b) Why does the wave nature of the bullet not reveal itself through diffraction effects?

2. What wavelength do we associate with a beam of neutrons whose energy is 0.025 ev?

3. An electron and a photon each have a wavelength of 2.0 A. What are their (a) momenta and (b) energies?

4. The 50-Bev electron accelerator to be built at Stanford will provide an electron beam of small wavelength, suitable for probing the fine details of nuclear structure by scattering experiments. What will this wavelength be and how does it compare to the size of an average nucleus? (Hint: At these energies it is necessary to use the extreme relativistic relationship between momentum and energy, namely $p = E/c$. This is the same relationship used for light (Section 40–2) and is justified whenever the kinetic energy of a particle is very much greater than its rest energy $m_0 c^2$, as in this case.)

5. In the experiment of Davisson and Germer (a) at what angles would the second- and third-order diffracted beams corresponding to the strong maximum of Fig. 48–2 occur, provided they are present, and (b) at what angle would the first-order diffracted beam occur if the accelerating potential were changed from 54 to 60 volts?

6. Make a plot of de Broglie wavelength against kinetic energy for (a) electrons and (b) protons. Restrict the range of energy values to those in which classical mechanics applies reasonably well. A convenient criterion is that the maximum kinetic energy on each plot be only about, say, 5% of the rest energy $m_0 c^2$ for the particular particle.

7. What is the wavelength of a hydrogen atom moving with a velocity corresponding to the mean kinetic energy for thermal equilibrium at 20°C?

8. If an electron moves from a state represented by $n = 3$ in Fig. 48–8 to one represented by $n = 2$ in that figure, emitting electromagnetic radiation in the process, what are (a) the energy of the emitted single photon and (b) the corresponding wavelength?

9. A particle is confined between rigid walls separated by a distance $l$. What is the probability that it will be found within a distance $l/3$ of one wall (a) for $n = 1$, (b) for $n = 2$, (c) for $n = 3$, and (d) under the assumptions of classical physics?

10. In the ground state of the hydrogen atom show that the probability $P_r$ that the electron lies *within* a sphere of radius $r$ is given by

$$P_r = 1 - e^{-2r/a}\left(\frac{2r^2}{a^2} + \frac{2r}{a} + 1\right).$$

Does this yield expected values for (a) $r = 0$ and (b) $r = \infty$? (c) State clearly the difference in meaning between this expression and that given on p. 1117.

11. In the ground state of the hydrogen atom, what is the probability that the electron will lie within a sphere whose radius is that of the first Bohr orbit?

12. The uncertainty in the position of an electron is given as about 0.5 A, which is the radius of the first Bohr orbit in hydrogen. What is the uncertainty in the linear momentum of the electron?

13. Show that if the uncertainty in the location of a particle is equal to its de Broglie wavelength the uncertainty in its velocity is equal to its velocity.

14. The highest achievable resolving power of a microscope is limited only by the wavelength used; that is, the smallest detail that can be separated is about equal to the wavelength. Suppose one wishes to "see" inside an atom. Assuming the atom to have a diameter of 1.0 A, this means that we wish to resolve detail of separation about 0.1 A. (a) If an electron microscope is used, what minimum energy of electrons is needed? (b) If a light microscope is used, what minimum energy of photons is needed? (c) Which microscope seems more practical for this purpose? Explain.

15. A microscope using photons is employed to locate an electron in an atom to within a distance of 0.1 A. What is the uncertainty in the momentum of the electron located in this way?

# Relation between Linear and Angular Kinematics for a Particle Moving in a Plane

In Section 11–6 we discussed the relations between the linear and angular kinematic variables for a particle moving in a plane but confined to move in a circle about an axis at right angles to the plane. Such a particle might be any particle in a rigid body rotating about a fixed axis. Here we relax the restriction and allow the particle to move freely in the plane. A planet moving in an elliptical orbit about the sun is an example.

We start from Eq. 11–11, $\mathbf{r} = \mathbf{u}_r r$, in which, however, we now take *both* $\mathbf{u}_r$ and $r$ to be variables; the particle is no longer confined to a circle of constant radius. We find the velocity by differentiation, or

$$\mathbf{v} = \frac{d\mathbf{r}}{dt} = \mathbf{u}_r \frac{dr}{dt} + r \frac{d\mathbf{u}_r}{dt}.$$

Equation 11–13 shows us that $d\mathbf{u}_r/dt = \mathbf{u}_\theta \omega$. Thus we can write

$$\mathbf{v} = \mathbf{u}_r \frac{dr}{dt} + \mathbf{u}_\theta \omega r, \tag{I–1}$$

which shows that $\mathbf{v}$ has two components, a radial component $v_r = dr/dt$ and a component at right angles, $v_\theta = \omega r$. If we hold $r$ constant, then $dr/dt = 0$ and Eq. I–1 reduces to Eq. 11–14a as it must.

To find the acceleration we differentiate Eq. I–1, remembering that *all five* quantities on the right are variables. We obtain

$$\mathbf{a} = \frac{d\mathbf{v}}{dt} = \mathbf{u}_r \frac{d^2 r}{dt^2} + \frac{dr}{dt} \frac{d\mathbf{u}_r}{dt} + (\mathbf{u}_\theta)\left(\omega \frac{dr}{dt} + r \frac{d\omega}{dt}\right) + (\omega r)\left(\frac{d\mathbf{u}_\theta}{dt}\right).$$

Now $du_r/dt = \mathbf{u}_\theta\omega$, $du_\theta/dt = -\mathbf{u}_r\omega$ (see Eq. 11–16), and $d\omega/dt = \alpha$. Substituting and rearranging leads us finally to

$$\mathbf{a} = \mathbf{u}_r\left(\frac{d^2r}{dt^2} - \omega^2 r\right) + \mathbf{u}_\theta\left(\alpha r + 2\omega\frac{dr}{dt}\right). \tag{I-2}$$

Once again, if $r =$ a constant, then $dr/dt = d^2r/dt^2 = 0$ and Eq. I–2 reduces to Eq. 11–17, which we derived especially for this case.

The two new terms in Eq. I–2, $\mathbf{u}_r d^2r/dt^2$ and $\mathbf{u}_\theta 2\omega\, dr/dt$, need a little explanation. The first of these terms is simple and we can understand it by imagining that the particle moving in the plane is *not* rotating about the axis. If we put $\omega = \alpha = 0$ in Eq. I–2 this equation reduces to

$$\mathbf{a} = \mathbf{u}_r\frac{d^2r}{dt^2},$$

which is just the familiar acceleration of a particle moving along a straight line. Hence this term in Eq. I–2 gives the radial acceleration due to the change in the *magnitude* of $\mathbf{r}$, the other radial acceleration term arising from the changing *direction* of $\mathbf{r}$ as the particle rotates.

There are also two $\theta$-directed acceleration terms. The first one, $\mathbf{u}_\theta\alpha r$, arises simply from the angular acceleration $\alpha$ of a particle in circular motion ($r =$ constant) and is the tangential acceleration of Section 11–5. To understand the second term, $\mathbf{u}_\theta 2\omega\, dr/dt$, consider a man walking outward along a radial line painted on the floor of a merry-go-round. The merry-go-round is rotating with constant angular velocity $\omega$ so that its angular acceleration $\alpha$ is now zero. If the man were simply to stand still on the merry-go-round, ($dr/dt = 0$, and $r =$ constant) his acceleration, as seen by an observer in a reference frame on the ground (see Eq. I–2), would be simply the familiar centripetal acceleration $-\mathbf{u}_r\omega^2 r$, directed radially inward. If he walks outward, however, $dr/dt \neq 0$ and then Eq. I–2 predicts that the ground observer would also measure a $\theta$-directed acceleration given by $\mathbf{u}_\theta 2\omega v_r$, where $v_r = dr/dt$. This is called a *Coriolis acceleration*. It arises from the fact that even though the angular velocity of the man is constant his speed increases as $r$ increases. Let us convince ourselves that this effect really exists.[*]

Figure I–1a shows the walking man (point $P$) as he appears to the ground observer at times $t$ and $t + \Delta t$. We show at time $t$ his radially directed velocity $\mathbf{v}_r (= \mathbf{u}_r\, dr/dt)$ and also a $\theta$-directed velocity caused by the rotation of the merry-go-round and given by $\mathbf{v}_\theta (= \mathbf{u}_\theta\omega r)$. At a time $\Delta t$ later each of these velocities has changed. The radial velocity has changed in direction, although its magnitude remains $dr/dt$. The $\theta$-directed velocity has not only changed direction (we have learned to account for this as a centripetal acceleration), but, because the man has moved outward to a point at which the floor is moving faster, its *magnitude* has also changed, from $\omega r$ to $\omega(r + \Delta r)$.

Figure I–1b shows the change in velocity caused by the change in direction of the radial line along which the man is walking. If $\Delta\theta$ in the triangle shown is small enough, we have

$$\Delta v_r = v_r\,\Delta\theta.$$

Dividing by $\Delta t$ and letting $\Delta t$ approach zero yields

$$a' = \frac{dv_r}{dt} = v_r\frac{d\theta}{dt} = v_r\omega.$$

The change in tangential velocity caused by the fact that the man is moving radially outward is

$$\Delta v_\theta = \omega(r + \Delta r) - \omega r = \omega\Delta r.$$

---

[*] See "The Coriolis Effect," James E. McDonald, *Scientific American*, May 1952.

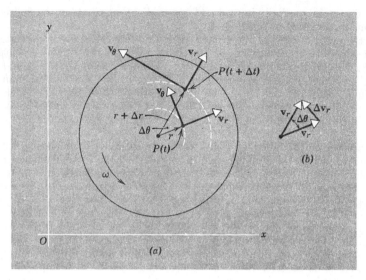

**Fig. I–1** (a) A merry-go-round, rotating about a fixed axis, is observed by an observer in inertial reference frame $x$, $y$. A man walks along a radial line at constant speed $v$. In a time interval $\Delta t$ this line, as seen by the ground observer, sweeps through an angle $\Delta \theta$ and the man moves between the positions shown. His $r$- and $\theta$-directed velocities are shown for each position. (b) Showing the change $\Delta v_r$ in the walking man's $r$-directed velocity. Note that, as $\Delta t \rightarrow 0$, $\Delta v_r$ points in the $\theta$-direction at $P$.

Dividing by $\Delta t$ and letting $\Delta t$ approach zero yields

$$a'' = \frac{dv_\theta}{dt} = \omega \frac{dr}{dt} = \omega v_r.$$

Now both $a'$ and $a''$ are magnitudes of vectors that point in the same direction, namely the direction of increasing $\theta$ at point $P(t)$. The total acceleration in this direction is then

$$a' + a'' = v_r\omega + \omega v_r = 2\omega v_r,$$

which is just what we set out to prove.

If there is indeed an acceleration in the $\theta$-direction in Fig. I–1, there must be a force in this direction. For a man walking outward along a radial line on a rotating merry-go-round this force can only be provided by the friction between his feet and the floor.

We remember that we can interpret classical mechanics most simply if we always view events from an inertial frame. If we do so we can always associate accelerations with forces exerted by bodies that we can point to in the environment. We can still apply classical mechanics, however, if we select a noninertial reference frame, such as a rotating frame. The small penalty that we must pay is that we must introduce *pseudo-forces*, that is, forces that we cannot associate with objects in the environment and which cannot be detected by an observer in an inertial frame. In Section 6–4 we saw that centrifugal force is such a pseudo-force.

Consider an observer on the rotating merry-go-round watching a man walk along a radial line at a constant speed $v_r = dr/dt$. He would say that the man is in equilibrium because he has no acceleration. Yet the floor is exerting a (very real) frictional force on the soles of the man's feet. This force has one component

$(-\mathbf{u}_r F_r)$ that points radially inward and one $(\mathbf{u}_\theta F_\theta)$ that points in the $\theta$-direction, that is, in the direction of rotation.

From the point of view of the ground observer these forces are understandable and, indeed, quite necessary. $F_r$ is associated with the centripetal acceleration $\omega^2 r$ and $F_\theta$ with the Coriolis acceleration $2\omega v_r$. The observer on the merry-go-round does not see either of these accelerations however; to him the walking man is in equilibrium. How can this be, in view of the frictional forces that act on the soles of the walking man's shoes? The man himself is well aware of these forces; if he did not lean to compensate for their turning effect, they would knock him off his feet!

The observer on the merry-go-round saves the situation by declaring that two pseudo-forces act on the walking man, just canceling the (real) frictional forces. One of these pseudo-forces, called the *centrifugal force*, has magnitude $F_r$ and acts radially *outward*. The other, called the *Coriolis force*, has magnitude $F_\theta$ and acts in the negative $\theta$-direction, that is, *opposite* to the direction of rotation. By introducing these forces, which seem quite "real" to him although he cannot point to any body in the environment that is causing them, the observer in the rotating (noninertial) reference frame can apply classical mechanics in the usual way. The ground observer, who is in an inertial frame, cannot detect these pseudo-forces. Indeed there is no need for them—and no room for them—in his applications of classical mechanics.

Equations I–1 and I–2 are general kinematical descriptions for the motion of a particle in two dimensions. An obvious extension, which we will not attempt here, is to derive corresponding descriptions for motion in three dimensions; this will require us to introduce a third unit vector to define the third dimension.*

---

* See, for example, *Mechanics*, Section 3–5, by Keith R. Symon, Addison-Wesley Publishing Co., 2nd ed., 1960.

# Polar Vectors and Axial Vectors

## SUPPLEMENTARY TOPIC II

Some vectors called *axial vectors*, such as $\boldsymbol{\omega}$, $\boldsymbol{\alpha}$, $\boldsymbol{\tau}$, and $\mathbf{l}$, differ in a rather important way from other vectors called *polar vectors*, of which $\mathbf{r}$, $\mathbf{v}$, $\mathbf{a}$, $\mathbf{F}$, and $\mathbf{p}$ are examples. Although we shall not need to take this difference into account in this book, it may prove to be instructive and interesting to the student to examine briefly what the difference is.

Consider a typical polar vector such as $\mathbf{r}$. If a student leaves his dormitory and goes to a classroom, his displacement vector $\mathbf{r}$ points *from* the dormitory *to* the classroom; there is no question as to our choice of direction. This direction is both "physical" and "natural." Similar remarks apply to the other typical polar vectors listed, namely, $\mathbf{v}$, $\mathbf{a}$, $\mathbf{F}$, and $\mathbf{p}$.

If a student sees a wheel rotating about a fixed axis, he can assign an angular velocity $\boldsymbol{\omega}$ to the wheel and can give direction to $\boldsymbol{\omega}$ by the right-hand rule (see Section 11–4). This direction, however, *is a convention only*, based on this arbitrary rule. A left-hand rule would have given the opposite direction. The things that are "physical" and "natural" about the wheel are the axis of rotation and the sense of rotation, that is, is it going clockwise or counterclockwise as the student looks at it from a particular end of the axis? Whether $\boldsymbol{\omega}$ is chosen to point in one way or the other along the axis does not really matter as long as we are consistent. The same remarks apply to the angular acceleration $\boldsymbol{\alpha}$ and to the other axial vectors listed, namely $\boldsymbol{\tau}(= \mathbf{r} \times \mathbf{F})$ and $\mathbf{l}(= \mathbf{r} \times \mathbf{p})$. It is for this reason that we sometimes find it more comfortable to say "torque *around* an axis" than "torque *along* an axis" although they mean the same thing. All vectors defined as the vector product of two *polar* vectors are axial vectors because they all depend for their direction assignment on the (arbitrary) right-hand rule.

We have stressed that the laws of physics remain the same no matter how we change the inertial reference frame in which they are expressed. In Section 2–5 we discussed this for translations and rotations of the reference frame and noted that laws expressed in vector form remained unchanged (that is, *invariant*) under such transformations. We also noted that something special may occur when we change the reference frame in another way, namely, by substituting a left-handed

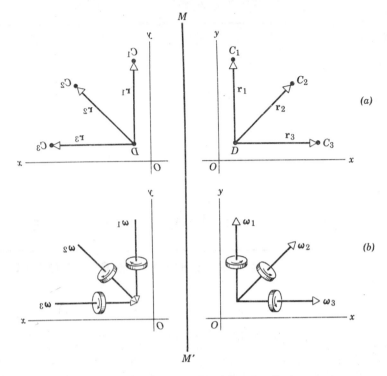

**Fig. II–1** (a) *Polar vectors*, showing, on the right, the displacements $r_1$, $r_2$, and $r_3$ between a dormitory $D$ and three classrooms $C_1$, $C_2$, and $C_3$. On the left we have the mirror images of $D$, $C_1$, $C_2$, and $C_3$, along with the corresponding displacements. (b) *Axial vectors*, showing, on the right, the angular velocities $\omega_1$, $\omega_2$, and $\omega_3$ of three wheels rotating as shown. On the left we have the mirror images of these wheels, along with the angular velocities assigned using the usual right hand rule.

frame for a right-handed one. There is an easy way to make such a transforma-tion: Build a right-handed frame and look at its image in a mirror; it will be con-verted to a left-handed frame (see Fig. II–1) because of the well-known property of a mirror to reverse right and left.

Figure II–1a shows the vector displacement of a student from his dormitory to each of three classrooms. In the mirror each displacement is *still* from the dormi-tory $D$ to a classroom $C$. In Fig. II–1b, however, we show a rotating wheel in three orientations. If we establish the directions of $\omega$ for both the wheels and their mirror images by the right-hand rule, we see that the image vectors are reversed in comparison to the corresponding image vectors in Fig. II–1a (toward the origin rather than away from the origin). Polar vectors and axial vectors behave differently when we transform reference frames by mirror reflection! This behavior of axial vectors under mirror reflection is not hard to understand. If we imagine ourselves physically applying the right-hand rule to a real rotating wheel, in the mirror, we shall *seem* to be applying a left-hand rule because the image of our right hand is our left hand. A left-hand rule, of course, will give us the opposite direction for $\omega$.

Hence an axial vector is a vector whose sense of direction depends on the handed-ness of the reference frame. It is sometimes called a *pseudovector*. A polar vector is a vector that has a direction independent of the reference frame. We mention these facts (1) to stress the arbitrary character of the direction assigned to axial vectors and (2) to stress the importance of testing experiments and physical laws for invariance under translation, rotation, and mirror reflection of the inertial reference frame. In Section 2–5 we referred briefly to some experiments that were *not* invariant under a reflection transformation. This fact, which constituted a violation under certain circumstances of a law of physics previously thought to be well founded (the law of *conservation of parity*), has posed some challenging problems and is leading us to an understanding of the physical world at a deeper level.*

---

* See "The Overthrow of Parity," by Philip Morrison, *Scientific American*, April 1957.

# The Wave Equation for
# a Stretched String

Figure III-1 shows a section of a long string which is under tension $F$. The string has been pulled transversely in the $y$-direction so that a displacement wave travels along the string in the $x$-direction. We consider a differential element of the string $dx$ and apply Newton's second law of motion to it in order to find how the wave moves along the string.

Let $\mu$ be the mass per unit length of the string, so that the mass of element $dx$ is $\mu\,dx$. The net force in the $y$-direction acting on this element is

$$F \sin \theta_{x+dx} - F \sin \theta_x.$$

We consider only small transverse displacements of the string, so that the restoring force will vary linearly with displacement and the principle of superposition will hold (see Section 19–4). This means that $\theta$ in Fig. III–1 will be small, so that we may replace $\sin \theta$ by $\tan \theta$. Now $\tan \theta$ is simply the slope of the string, that is, it equals $\partial y/\partial x$. We must use partial derivatives because the transverse displacement $y$ depends not only on $x$ but also on $t$. The net force in the $y$-direction is then

$$F \left(\frac{\partial y}{\partial x}\right)_{x+dx} - F \left(\frac{\partial y}{\partial x}\right)_x,$$

which we may write as

$$F \frac{\partial}{\partial x} \left(\frac{\partial y}{\partial x}\right) dx$$

or

$$F \frac{\partial^2 y}{\partial x^2}\, dx.$$

**8**

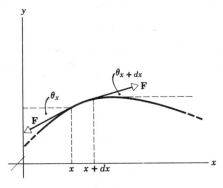

**Fig. III–1**

The mass of the element of the string is $\mu\,dx$ and its transverse acceleration is simply $\partial^2 y/\partial t^2$. Hence, Newton's second law, applied to the transverse motion of the string, is

$$F\frac{\partial^2 y}{\partial x^2}\,dx = (\mu\,dx)\frac{\partial^2 y}{\partial t^2}$$

or

$$\frac{\partial^2 y}{\partial t^2} = \frac{\mu}{F}\frac{\partial^2 y}{\partial t^2}. \tag{III–1}$$

Equation III–1, called the *wave equation*, is the differential equation that describes wave propagation in a string of mass per unit length $\mu$ and tension $F$.

To prove this we show that Eqs. 19–2 and 19–3

$$y = f(x \pm vt), \tag{III–2}$$

which is the general equation representing a wave of any shape traveling along $x$, is a solution of Eq. III–1. Recall that $v$ in Eq. III–2 is the speed of the wave disturbance and $f$ is *any* function of $(x \pm vt)$.

Let us see whether Eq. III–2 is indeed a solution of Eq. III–1 by substituting the former equation into the latter. To do so we note that the two second partial derivatives of $y$ are

$$\frac{\partial^2 y}{\partial x^2} = f'' \quad \text{and} \quad \frac{\partial^2 y}{\partial t^2} = v^2 f''$$

in which $f''$ is the second derivative of the function $f$ of Eq. III–2 with respect to $(x \pm vt)$. Substitution of these derivatives into Eq. III–1 yields

$$f'' = \frac{\mu}{F}v^2 f'',$$

which we may write as (see Eq. 19–12)

$$v = \sqrt{\frac{F}{\mu}}. \tag{III–3}$$

Thus we conclude that Eq. III–2 is indeed a solution of the partial differential equation Eq. IIi–1 if the speed of the wave disturbance described by this equation is given by Eq. III–3.

In particular, let us check that Eq. 19–10

$$y = y_m \sin (kx \pm \omega t) \tag{19-10}$$

is a solution of Eq. III–1. We know that it must be because Eq. 19–10 is simply a special case of the general relation Eq. III–2, which we have just shown to be a solution. Even so it is instructive to test this important specific function of $(x \pm vt)$ by substitution into Eq. III–1.

The second derivatives of Eq. 19–10 are

$$\frac{\partial^2 y}{\partial x^2} = -k^2 y_m \sin (kx \pm \omega t)$$

and

$$\frac{\partial^2 y}{\partial t^2} = -\omega^2 y_m \sin (kx \pm \omega t).$$

Substitution into Eq. III–1 yields

$$-k^2 y_m \sin. (kx \pm \omega t) = \left(\frac{\mu}{F}\right) [-\omega^2 y_m \sin (kx \pm \omega t)]$$

or

$$\frac{\omega}{k} = \sqrt{\frac{F}{\mu}}.$$

Since $\omega/k = v$ (see Eq. 19–11), this relation is identical with Eq. III–3, and Eq. 19–10, as we expect, is indeed a solution of Eq. III–1.

# Derivation of Maxwell's Speed Distribution Law

Boltzmann, in 1876, derived the Maxwell speed distribution law from this line of argument: Let a uniform gravitational field $\mathbf{g}$ act on an ideal gas maintained at a fixed temperature $T$. The number of molecules per unit volume $n$ will then decrease with altitude $z$ according to the law of atmospheres (see Example 1, Chapter 17). From what we know about the statistical-mechanical interpretation of temperature, however, the speed distribution law—whose form we assume that we do not yet know—must remain the same at all altitudes because it depends only on the temperature. However this law determines the rate at which molecules move vertically in the atmosphere at any altitude and must thus be intimately related to the decrease of $n$ with $z$. By exploring this relationship in detail we can, in fact, deduce the speed distribution law.

The weight of gas per unit area between the levels $z$ and $z + dz$ in Fig. IV-1 is $nmg\,dz$ in which $m$ is the mass of a single molecule. For equilibrium, this weight per unit area must equal the difference in pressure between $z$ and $z + dz$, or

$$nmg\,dz = -dp \qquad\qquad \text{(IV–1)}$$

in which we have inserted a minus sign because $p$ decreases as $z$ increases.

We can write the equation of state of an ideal gas, $pV = \mu RT$, as

$$p = nkT \qquad\qquad \text{(IV–2)}$$

because $\mu = nV/N_0$, where $N_0 \ (= R/k)$ is Avogadro's number, the number of molecules per mole, and $k$ is Boltzmann's constant. Combining Eqs. IV–1 and IV–2 yields

$$\frac{dp}{p} = \frac{dn}{n} = -\frac{mg}{kT}\,dz.$$

For a constant temperature, we can integrate this relation to yield

$$n = \text{constant }e^{-mgz/kT} \tag{IV–3}$$

which, in view of Eq. IV–2, agrees with the result of Example 1, Chapter 17.

We can find the change in $n$ as we go from $z$ to $z + dz$ by differentiating Eq. IV–3, or

$$dn = -\text{ constant }e^{-mgz/kT}\,dz. \tag{IV–4}$$

**Fig. IV–1**

We associate this decrease in $n$ over the interval $dz$ with the fact that, at $z = 0$ (which can be any level we choose) there are some upward-directed molecules—we call them "special molecules" temporarily for convenience—whose vertical velocity components lie in a particular range $v_z$ to $v_z + dv_z$ such that (neglecting collisions; see below) they can rise as high as $z$ but not as high as $z + dz$. Such molecules pass upward through the level $z$, reverse their direction and pass downward again, as Fig. IV–1 shows. At this point we see more clearly the relationship between Eq. IV–3 and the speed distribution law. Molecules that pass through the interval $dz$ (from above or below) or molecules that never reach the interval cannot contribute to the decrease $dn$ of Eq. IV–4.

The rate per unit area at which "special molecules" leave level $z = 0$ (and arrive at level $z$) is $v_z n(v_z)\,dv_z$. Here $n(v_z)\,dv_z$ is the number of molecules per unit volume whose vertical velocity components lie between $v_z$ and $v_z + dv_z$;

Now the rate per unit area at which the "special molecules" arrive at level $z$, but not as high as level $z + dz$, is proportional to the magnitude of the density difference $dn$ between $z$ and $z + dz$, or, from Eq. IV–4,

$$v_z n(v_z)\,dv_z = \text{constant }e^{-mgz/kT}\,dz, \tag{IV–5}$$

in which the constant is independent of $z$. Equation IV–5, which requires that the change $dn$ be accounted for by the "special molecules" is, in fact, the defining equation for $n(v_z)$.

From conservation of energy the special molecules have the property that[*]

$$\tfrac{1}{2}mv_z{}^2 = mgz$$

or

$$mv_z\,dv_z = mg\,dz.$$

We use these two relations to eliminate $z$ and $dz$ from Eq. IV–5, obtaining, as the student should verify,

$$n(v_z)\,dv_z = \text{constant }e^{-mv_z{}^2/2kT}\,dv_z \tag{IV–6a}$$

---

[*] If we consider collisions this result is still true *on the average* for the many molecules that start at $z = 0$ with a given value of $v_z$ and move to the interval $z$ to $z + dz$, having $v_z = 0$ there, even though such molecules would follow very erratic paths because of the collisions.

in which $n(v_z)\, dv_z$ is the number of molecules per unit volume whose vertical velocity components lie between $v_z$ and $v_z + dv_z$. Note that Eq. IV–6a does not contain $g$ or $z$. The gravitational field of Fig. IV–1, introduced to allow us to calculate the speed distribution, has served its purpose. We may apply Eq. IV–6a to a gas for which $g = 0$ or in which gravitational effects are negligible. In such a case the vertical direction, which we have identified as the $z$-direction, no longer has any special meaning. That is, the speed distribution for one component of velocity should be the same for another component of velocity since there is no special or preferred direction in a gas in equilibrium free of external forces. Thus we can write

$$n(v_x)\, dv_x = \text{constant } e^{-mv_x{}^2/2kT}\, dv_x \qquad (IV–6b)$$

and

$$n(v_y)\, dv_y = \text{constant } e^{-mv_y{}^2/2kT}\, dv_y, \qquad (IV–6c)$$

for the other two velocity components.

We now seek to find Maxwell's speed distribution (Eq. 24–2); it is expressed in terms of the speed $v$, rather than in terms of the separate components $v_x$, $v_y$, and $v_z$. We are not concerned here with the direction of $\mathbf{v}$, because we assume it to be completely random. We can represent any velocity $\mathbf{v}$ as a vector extending from the origin in Fig. IV–2; the projections of the vector in the $x$-$y$- and $z$-directions are $v_x$, $v_y$, and $v_z$, respectively. We commonly say that the axes of Fig. IV–2 define a "velocity space," which has many formal similarities to ordinary (or coordinate) space, in which the axes are $x$, $y$, and $z$.

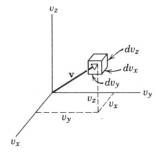

**Fig. IV–2**

We also show in Fig. IV–2a small "volume" element, whose sides are $dv_x$, $dv_y$, and $dv_z$; we say that this element has a volume $dv_x\, dv_y\, dv_z$ in velocity space. A point in this element corresponds to a particle whose velocity components lie between $v_x$ and $v_x + dv_x$; $v_y$ and $v_y + dv_y$; and $v_z$ and $v_z + dv_z$. We can regard $n(v_z)$ in Eq. IV–6a as giving the *probability* that a given molecule will have a velocity component in the specified range $v_z$ to $v_z + dv_z$, with similar interpretations for $n(v_x)$ and $n(v_y)$. The probability that a given molecule will have *all three* of its velocity components in the specified ranges, that is, the probability that the tip of the velocity vector $\mathbf{v}$ will lie inside the volume element of Fig. IV–2, is the *product* of the three (independent) probabilities given in Eq. IV–6, or

$$\text{constant } e^{-mv_x{}^2/2kT}e^{-mv_y{}^2/2kT}e^{-mv_z{}^2/2kT}\, dv_x\, dv_y\, dv_z$$

which, since

$$v^2 = v_x{}^2 + v_y{}^2 + v_z{}^2,$$

we may write as

$$\text{constant } e^{-mv^2/2kT}(dv_x\, dv_y\, dv_z). \qquad (IV–7)$$

The quantity in parentheses above is a volume element in velocity space. Since in Maxwell's speed distribution law we are not concerned with the direction of molecular velocities but only with their speeds, it is more convenient to substitute a different volume element for the above, namely one corresponding to all molecules whose speeds lie between $v$ and $v + dv$, *regardless of direction*. This volume element is not a "cube" but is the space between two concentric spheres, one of radius $v$ and one of radius $v + dv$. The volume of this element in velocity space is $(4\pi v^2)(dv)$. Substituting this for the quantity enclosed in parentheses in Eq. IV–7 yields for the number of molecules per unit volume whose speeds lie between $v$ and $v + dv$,

$$n(v) \, dv = \text{constant } e^{-mv^2/2kT}(4\pi v^2 \, dv)$$

or

$$n(v) = Cv^2 e^{-mv^2/2kT}$$

in which $C$ is a constant. If we sum up over all possible speeds we simply obtain the total number of molecules per unit volume, regardless of speed. Hence, we can find $C$ by requiring that

$$\int_0^\infty n(v) \, dv = n,$$

where $n$ is the total number of particles per unit volume, regardless of speed. The student, guided by the methods of Example 3 (Chapter 24), should show that

$$C = 4\pi n(m/2\pi kT)^{3/2}$$

so that

$$n(v) = 4\pi n(m/2\pi kT)^{3/2}v^2 e^{-mv^2/2kT}. \qquad (IV\text{–}8)$$

Let us consider a finite number $N$ of molecules contained in a box of volume $V$. If we multiply each side of the above equation by $V$, we can replace $nV$ on the right by $N$ and $n(v)V$ on the left by $N(v)$, which gives us Eq. 24–2.

# The Differential Form of Maxwell's Equations and the Electromagnetic Wave Equation

## SUPPLEMENTARY TOPIC V

### V–1 Introduction

In Chapter 39 we sought to make the existence of electromagnetic waves plausible by showing that such waves are consistent with Maxwell's equations as expressed in Table 38–3. Here we seek to start from Maxwell's equations and derive from them a differential equation whose solutions will describe electromagnetic waves. We will show directly that the speed $c$ of such waves is given by Eq. 39–15, or $c = 1/\sqrt{\epsilon_0 \mu_0}$.

We followed a similar program in Supplementary Topic III for mechanical waves on a stretched string. Starting from Newton's laws of motion we derived a differential equation (Eq. III–1) whose solutions (Eq. III–2) described such waves. We showed further that the speed $v$ of these waves is given by Eq. III–3, or $v = \sqrt{F/\mu}$.

In Table 38–3 we wrote Maxwell's equations as

$$\epsilon_0 \oint \mathbf{E} \cdot d\mathbf{S} = q, \tag{V–1}$$

$$\oint \mathbf{B} \cdot d\mathbf{S} = 0, \tag{V–2}$$

$$\oint \mathbf{B} \cdot d\mathbf{l} = \mu_0(i + \epsilon_0 \, d\Phi_E/dt), \tag{V–3}$$

and
$$\oint \mathbf{E} \cdot d\mathbf{l} = -d\Phi_B/dt. \tag{V–4}$$

These equations are said to be written in integral form.   The field variables **E** and **B**, which are usually the unknown quantities, appear in the integrands.   Only in a few symmetric cases (see Sections 28–6 and 34–2, for example) can we "factor them out."   In more general problems we cannot do so.

The situation is somewhat analogous to computing the density $\rho$ of a body if we know its mass $m$ and volume $\tau$.   In general these are related by the integral equation

$$m = \int \rho \, d\tau.$$

Only if $\rho$ is a constant over all parts of the volume can we factor it out and write $\rho = m/\tau$.

To carry out our program it is desirable to recast Maxwell's equations in the form of equalities that apply at each *point* in space rather than as integrals that apply to various *regions* of space.   In other words, we wish to convert Maxwell's equations from the integral form of Eqs. V–1 to 4 into *differential form*.   We will then be able to relate **E** and **B** at a point to the charge density and current density at that point.

## V–2   The Operator $\nabla$

To transform Maxwell's equations into differential form we must deepen our understanding of vector methods and, in particular, become familiar with the vector operator $\nabla$.

In Section 29–7 we saw how to obtain the components of the (vector) electrostatic field **E** at any point from the (scalar) potential function $V(x,y,z)$ by partial differentiation.   Thus,

$$E_x = -\frac{\partial V}{\partial x}, \quad E_y = -\frac{\partial V}{\partial y}, \quad \text{and} \quad E_z = -\frac{\partial V}{\partial z}$$

so that the electrostatic field

$$\mathbf{E} = \mathbf{i}E_x + \mathbf{j}E_y + \mathbf{k}E_z$$

can be written as

$$\mathbf{E} = -\left( \mathbf{i}\frac{\partial V}{\partial x} + \mathbf{j}\frac{\partial V}{\partial y} + \mathbf{k}\frac{\partial V}{\partial z} \right). \tag{V–5}$$

We can write Eq. V–5 in compact vector notation as

$$\mathbf{E} = -\nabla V,$$

where $\nabla$ ("del") is a vector operator defined as

$$\nabla = \mathbf{i}\frac{\partial}{\partial x} + \mathbf{j}\frac{\partial}{\partial y} + \mathbf{k}\frac{\partial}{\partial z}. \tag{V–6}$$

This operator is useful in dealing with scalar and vector fields (see Sections 16–8 and 18–7 for examples of such fields).   Given any scalar field $\psi$ we may form a vector field, called the gradient of $\psi$ and written as grad $\psi$ or $\nabla\psi$, simply by applying the operator $\nabla$ to $\psi$.   Given a vector field $\mathbf{U} = U_x\mathbf{i} + U_y\mathbf{j} + U_z\mathbf{k}$ we may apply the operator $\nabla$ to it in two different ways.   One way is to take the dot product of $\nabla$ and **U**, yielding the scalar field called the divergence of **U** and written as div **U** or $\nabla \cdot \mathbf{U}$. The other way is to take the cross product of $\nabla$ and **U**, yielding the vector field called the curl of **U** and written curl **U** or $\nabla \times \mathbf{U}$. These operations may be summarized as

$$\text{grad } \psi \equiv \nabla \psi = \mathbf{i} \frac{\partial \psi}{\partial x} + \mathbf{j} \frac{\partial \psi}{\partial y} + \mathbf{k} \frac{\partial \psi}{\partial z}$$

$$\text{div } \mathbf{U} \equiv \nabla \cdot \mathbf{U} = \frac{\partial U_x}{\partial x} + \frac{\partial U_y}{\partial y} + \frac{\partial U_z}{\partial z}$$

$$\text{curl } \mathbf{U} \equiv \nabla \times \mathbf{U} = \mathbf{i} \left( \frac{\partial U_z}{\partial y} - \frac{\partial U_y}{\partial z} \right)$$

$$+ \mathbf{j} \left( \frac{\partial U_x}{\partial z} - \frac{\partial U_z}{\partial x} \right)$$

$$+ \mathbf{k} \left( \frac{\partial U_y}{\partial x} - \frac{\partial U_x}{\partial y} \right)$$

Note that grad $\psi$ and curl **U** are vectors, whereas div **U** is a scalar. The student can gain some familiarity with these operations by the following exercises: (1) prove that curl (grad $\psi$) = 0 and (2) prove that div (curl **U**) = 0.

Another frequently occuring operator is $\nabla^2$ ("del squared"). It is simply $\nabla \cdot \nabla$, or, as the student can show from Eq. V–6,

$$\nabla^2 = \nabla \cdot \nabla = \frac{\partial^2}{\partial x^2} + \frac{\partial^2}{\partial y^2} + \frac{\partial^2}{\partial z^2}.$$

When we apply $\nabla^2$ to a scalar field $\psi$, we obtain

$$\nabla^2 \psi = \frac{\partial^2 \psi}{\partial x^2} + \frac{\partial^2 \psi}{\partial y^2} + \frac{\partial^2 \psi}{\partial z^2} \tag{V–10}$$

For a vector field **U**, the operation $\nabla^2 \mathbf{U}$ is defined as

$$\nabla^2 \mathbf{U} = \mathbf{i} \frac{\partial^2 U_x}{\partial x^2} + \mathbf{j} \frac{\partial^2 U_y}{\partial y^2} + \mathbf{k} \frac{\partial^2 U_z}{\partial z^2}. \tag{V–11}$$

As an exercise the student can show that curl (curl **U**) $= -\nabla^2 \mathbf{U} + \text{grad (div } \mathbf{U})$.

## V–3  Maxwell's Equations in Differential Form—I

In this section we show how to cast the first two of Maxwell's equations (Eqs. V–1, 2) into differential form. Let us apply Eq. V–1 to a differential volume element shaped like a rectangular parallelepiped and containing a point $P$ at (and near) which an electric field exists (see Fig. V–1$a$). Point $P$ is located at $x$, $y$, $z$ in the reference frame of Fig. V–1$b$ and the edges of the parallelepiped have lengths $dx$, $dy$, and $dz$.

We can write the surface area vector for the rear face of the parallelepiped as $d\mathbf{S} = -\mathbf{i} \, dy \, dz$. The minus sign enters because $d\mathbf{S}$ is defined to point in the direction of the *outward* normal, which is defined by $-\mathbf{i}$. For the front face we have $d\mathbf{S} = +\mathbf{i} \, dy \, dz$.

**Fig. V–1**

If the electric field at the rear face is $\mathbf{E}$, that at the front face, which is a distance $dx$ away from the rear face, is $\mathbf{E} + (\partial\mathbf{E}/\partial x)\,dx$, the latter term representing the change in $\mathbf{E}$ associated with the change $dx$ in $x$.

The flux through the entire surface of the parallelepiped is $\oint \mathbf{E} \cdot d\mathbf{S}$ and the contribution to this flux due to these two faces alone is

$$(\mathbf{E}) \cdot (-\mathbf{i}\,dy\,dz) + \left(\mathbf{E} + \frac{\partial\mathbf{E}}{\partial x}\,dx\right) \cdot (+\mathbf{i}\,dy\,dz)$$

$$= dx\,dy\,dz\left(\frac{\partial\mathbf{E}}{\partial x} \cdot \mathbf{i}\right) = dx\,dy\,dz\frac{\partial}{\partial x}(\mathbf{E} \cdot \mathbf{i})$$

$$= dx\,dy\,dz\frac{\partial E_x}{\partial x}.$$

With similar contributions from the other four faces the total electric flux becomes

$$\oint \mathbf{E} \cdot d\mathbf{S} = dx\,dy\,dz\left(\frac{\partial E_x}{\partial x} + \frac{\partial E_y}{\partial y} + \frac{\partial E_z}{\partial z}\right).$$

From Eq. V–8 we may write this as

$$\oint \mathbf{E} \cdot d\mathbf{S} = dx\,dy\,dz \text{ div } \mathbf{E}. \tag{V–12}$$

Now the right-hand side of Eq. V–1, which gives the charge enclosed by the surface, may be written in general as $q = \int\rho\,d\tau$ and, in particular, for the differential volume element at $P$, as

$$q = \rho\,dx\,dy\,dz, \tag{V–13}$$

where $\rho$ is the charge per unit volume at $P$. Substituting Eqs. V–12 and 13 into Eq. V–1 and canceling the common factor $dx\,dy\,dz$, we have finally

$$\epsilon_0 \text{ div } \mathbf{E} = \rho, \tag{V–14}$$

which is Maxwell's first equation (Eq. V–1) in differential form.

Using the same technique, we can express Maxwell's second equation (Eq. V–2) in differential form as

$$\text{div } \mathbf{B} = 0. \tag{V–15}$$

## V–4   Maxwell's Equations in Differential Form—II

We now seek to transform Maxwell's third and fourth equations (Eqs. V–3, 4) into differential form. We start by applying Eq. V–3 to a differential surface element of rectangular shape at a point $P$ in some region of a magnetic field, as shown in Fig. V–2a. The point $P$ is located at $x$, $y$, $z$ in the reference frame of Fig.

(a)                              (b)

**Fig. V–2**

V–2b and the sides of the rectangle, which is parallel to the $x$-$y$ plane, have lengths $dx$ and $dy$. Going around the path, as shown by the arrows, we have

$$\oint \mathbf{B} \cdot d\mathbf{l} = \mathbf{B} \cdot (-\mathbf{j}\, dy) \qquad \text{(rear side)}$$

$$+ \mathbf{B} \cdot (+\mathbf{i}\, dx) \qquad \text{(left side)}$$

$$+ \left(\mathbf{B} + \frac{\partial \mathbf{B}}{\partial x}\, dx\right) \cdot (+\mathbf{j}\, dy) \qquad \text{(front side)}$$

$$+ \left(\mathbf{B} + \frac{\partial \mathbf{B}}{\partial y}\, dy\right) \cdot (-\mathbf{i}\, dx), \qquad \text{(right side)}$$

where $\mathbf{B}$ is the magnetic induction at $P$.

Collecting terms we obtain

$$\oint \mathbf{B} \cdot d\mathbf{l} = dx\, dy \left(\frac{\partial \mathbf{B}}{\partial x} \cdot \mathbf{j} - \frac{\partial \mathbf{B}}{\partial y} \cdot \mathbf{i}\right)$$

$$= dx\, dy \left[\frac{\partial}{\partial x}(\mathbf{B} \cdot \mathbf{j}) - \frac{\partial}{\partial y}(\mathbf{B} \cdot \mathbf{i})\right]$$

$$= dx\, dy \left(\frac{\partial B_y}{\partial x} - \frac{\partial B_x}{\partial y}\right). \qquad (V–16)$$

Now in the right-hand side of Eq. V–3 $i$ is the current enclosed by the path and $d\Phi_E/dt$ is the change in electric flux through the enclosed surface. Hence, if $\mathbf{J}$ is taken to represent the current density and $d\mathbf{S}(= \mathbf{k}\, dx\, dy)$ the surface area vector, we can write

$$i = \mathbf{J} \cdot d\mathbf{S} = \mathbf{J} \cdot (\mathbf{k}\, dx\, dy) = dx\, dy\, J_z \qquad (V–17)$$

and

$$\frac{d\Phi_E}{dt} = \frac{\partial \mathbf{E}}{\partial t} \cdot d\mathbf{S} = \frac{\partial \mathbf{E}}{\partial t} \cdot (\mathbf{k}\, dx\, dy)$$

or

$$\frac{d\Phi_E}{dt} = \frac{\partial E_z}{\partial t}\, dx\, dy. \qquad (V–18)$$

Substituting Eqs. V–16, 17, and 18 into Eq. V–3 and canceling the common factor $dx\,dy$, we get

$$\frac{1}{\mu_0}\left(\frac{\partial B_y}{\partial x} - \frac{\partial B_x}{\partial y}\right) = J_z + \epsilon_0 \frac{\partial E_z}{\partial t} \tag{V–19}$$

We could have proceeded exactly as above if we had started with a rectangle parallel to the $y$-$z$ plane or one parallel to the $z$-$x$ plane. Each rectangle would have given us a different component of an arbitrarily oriented differential surface at $P$. Equation V–19 is obviously the $z$-component equation corresponding to Eq. V–3. If we multiply it by $\mathbf{k}$ and add to it the two similar vector equations, which may be obtained by cyclically permuting $x$, $y$, $z$ and $\mathbf{i}$, $\mathbf{j}$, $\mathbf{k}$, corresponding to the $x$-component and $y$-component equations, we obtain

$$\text{curl } \mathbf{B} = \mu_0(\mathbf{J} + \epsilon_0\,\partial \mathbf{E}/\partial t), \tag{V–20}$$

which is the third Maxwell equation in differential form.

Similarly, starting with Eq. V–4, we may show that

$$\text{curl } \mathbf{E} = -\partial \mathbf{B}/\partial t, \tag{V–21}$$

which is the fourth Maxwell equation in differential form.

We have derived four differential equations (see V-22 to V-25 below) from the four integral equations (V-1 to V-4). It can be shown that the integral equations can be derived from the differential equations, that is, the two sets of equations are *equivalent*

## V–5 The Wave Equation

We have now obtained from their integral form the four basic equations of electromagnetism, Maxwell's equations, in differential form. Corresponding to the integral equations, Eqs. V–1, 2, 3, and 4 respectively, we have

$$\epsilon_0 \text{ div } \mathbf{E} = \rho, \tag{V–22}$$

$$\text{div } \mathbf{B} = 0, \tag{V–23}$$

$$\text{curl } \mathbf{B} = \mu_0(\mathbf{J} + \epsilon_0\,\partial \mathbf{E}/\partial t), \tag{V–24}$$

$$\text{curl } \mathbf{E} = -\partial \mathbf{B}/\partial t, \tag{V–25}$$

which are four coupled partial differential equations. They apply at each point of space in an electromagnetic field.

We will now derive the wave equation for electromagnetic waves in free space. In free space, the charge density $\rho$ and the current density $\mathbf{J}$ are zero, so that the Maxwell equations there become

$$\text{div } \mathbf{E} = 0,$$

$$\text{div } \mathbf{B} = 0,$$

$$\text{curl } \mathbf{E} = -\,\partial \mathbf{B}/\partial t,$$

and
$$\text{curl } \mathbf{B} = \mu_0\epsilon_0\,\partial \mathbf{E}/\partial t.$$

Let us take the curl of the equation for curl $\mathbf{E}$; we obtain

$$\text{curl curl } \mathbf{E} = -\text{ curl }\frac{\partial \mathbf{B}}{\partial t} = -\frac{\partial}{\partial t}\text{ curl } \mathbf{B}.$$

But, from above, curl $\mathbf{B} = \mu_0\epsilon_0(\partial\mathbf{E}/\partial t)$, so that

$$\text{curl curl } \mathbf{E} = -\mu_0\epsilon_0 \frac{\partial^2\mathbf{E}}{\partial t^2} \qquad (V\text{-}26)$$

From the exercise in V–2, we know that curl curl $\mathbf{E} = -\nabla^2 E + \text{grad div } \mathbf{E}$ and from above that div $\mathbf{E} = 0$. Thus,

$$\text{curl curl } \mathbf{E} = -\nabla^2\mathbf{E}. \qquad (V\text{-}27)$$

Combining Eqs. V–26 and V–27, we obtain finally

$$\nabla^2\mathbf{E} = \mu_0\epsilon_0 \frac{\partial^2\mathbf{E}}{\partial t^2}. \qquad (V\text{-}28a)$$

The student, proceeding as above, should be able to show that $\mathbf{B}$ satisfies the same equation, or

$$\nabla^2\mathbf{B} = \mu_0\epsilon_0 \frac{\partial^2\mathbf{B}}{\partial t^2}. \qquad (V\text{-}28b)$$

Equations V–28 are the equations of electromagnetic wave motion. Being vector equations, they are equivalent to six scalar equations, one for each component of $\mathbf{E}$ and of $\mathbf{B}$.

There are many solutions of Eqs. V–28, corresponding to different kinds of electromagnetic waves—plane, spherical, and cylindrical waves being three examples. Let us consider a solution in which two components of $\mathbf{E}$ and two of $\mathbf{B}$ vanish, that is, in which

$$E_x = E_z = 0 \qquad \text{and} \qquad B_x = B_y = 0.$$

Equations V–28 are satsified for these assumptions. For the nonvanishing components, $E_y$ and $B_z$, Eqs. V–28 reduce to (see Eq. V–11)

$$\frac{\partial^2 E_y}{\partial x^2} + \frac{\partial^2 E_y}{\partial y^2} + \frac{\partial^2 E_y}{\partial z^2} = \mu_0\epsilon_0 \frac{\partial^2 E_y}{\partial t^2} \qquad (V\text{-}29a)$$

and

$$\frac{\partial^2 B_z}{\partial x^2} + \frac{\partial^2 B_z}{\partial y^2} + \frac{\partial^2 B_z}{\partial z^2} = \mu_0\epsilon_0 \frac{\partial^2 B_z}{\partial t^2} \qquad (V\text{-}29b)$$

If we make the additional assumption that $E_y$ and $B_z$ are functions of $x$ and $t$ only, the simplified wave equation that results, namely

$$\frac{\partial^2 E_y}{\partial x^2} = \mu_0\epsilon_0 \frac{\partial^2 E_y}{\partial t^2} \qquad \text{and} \qquad \frac{\partial^2 B_z}{\partial x^2} = \mu_0\epsilon_0 \frac{\partial^2 B_z}{\partial t^2}, \qquad (V\text{-}29c)$$

is similar to Eq. III-1 for the vibrating string.

A solution to these equations, as the student may verify by substitution, is

$$E_y = E_m \sin(kx - \omega t) \qquad (V\text{-}30a)$$

and

$$B_z = B_m \sin(kx - \omega t). \qquad (V\text{-}30b)$$

We interpret Eqs. V–30 as an electromagnetic wave traveling in the positive $x$-direction, as in Fig. 39–11, with a speed $c = \omega/k$. The student can show that substituting Eq. V–30a into Eq. V–29a (or Eq. V–30b into Eq. V–29b) yields

$$c = \omega/k = 1/\sqrt{\epsilon_0\mu_0},$$

which (see Eq. 39–15) gives the speed of electromagnetic waves in free space.

# Supplementary Problems

1. Two free point charges $+q$ and $+4q$ are a distance $l$ apart. A third charge is so placed that the entire system is in equilibrium. Find the location, magnitude, and sign of the third charge.

2. If the balls of Fig. 26-7 are conducting, what happens to them after one is discharged? Find the new equilibrium separation.

3. Two identical conducting spheres, having charges of opposite sign, attract each other with a force of 0.108 nt when separated by 0.5 meter. The spheres are connected by a conducting wire, which is then removed, and thereafter repel each other with a force of 0.036 nt. What were the initial charges on the spheres?

4. A particle of charge $-q$ and mass $m$ moves in a circular orbit about a fixed charge $+Q$. (a) Show that the "distance cubed $\propto$ period squared" law,

$$r^3 = \frac{Qq}{16\pi^3\epsilon_0 m} T^2$$

is satisfied. Note that the proportionality constant depends on the property $(q/m)$ of the orbiting particle. (b) What is the corresponding situation when the force is gravitational rather than electrical?

5. An electron is projected with an initial speed of $3.24 \times 10^5$ meter/sec directly toward a proton which is essentially at rest. If the electron is initially a very great distance from the proton, at what distance from the proton is its speed instantaneously equal to twice its initial value? (*Hint:* Use the work-energy theorem.)

6. A "dipole" is formed from a rod of length $2a$ and two charges, $+q$ and $-q$. Two such dipoles are oriented as shown in Fig. 26-9, their centers being separated by the

Fig. 26-9

23

distance $R$. (a) Calculate the force exerted on the left dipole. (b) For $R \gg a$, show that the magnitude of the force exerted on the left dipole is approximately given by

$$F = \frac{3p^2}{2\pi\epsilon_0 R^4}$$

where $p = 2qa$ is the "dipole moment."

## Chapter 27

1. A uniform vertical field **E** is established in the space between two large parallel plates. In this field one suspends a small conducting sphere of mass $m$ from a string of length $l$. Find the period of this pendulum when the sphere is given a charge $+q$ if the lower plate is charged positively; is charged negatively.

2. A charge $q = 3.0 \times 10^{-6}$ coul is 30 cm from a small dipole along its perpendicular bisector. The magnitude of the force on the charge is $5.0 \times 10^{-6}$ nt. Show on a diagram (a) the direction of the force on the charge, (b) the direction of the force on the dipole, and (c) determine the magnitude of the force on the dipole.

3. A thin glass rod is bent into a semicircle of radius $R$. A charge $+Q$ is uniformly distributed along the upper half and a charge $-Q$ is uniformly distributed along the lower half, as shown in Fig. 27–25. Find the electric field **E** at $P$, the center of the semicircle.

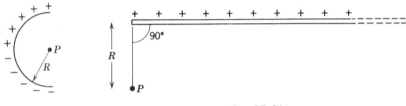

Fig. 27–25          Fig. 27–26

4. A "semi-infinite" insulating rod (Fig. 27–26) carries a constant charge per unit length of $\lambda$. Show that the electric field at the point $P$ makes an angle of 45° with the rod. This result is independent of the distance $R$.

5. Find the frequency of oscillation of an electric dipole, of moment $p$ and rotational inertia $I$, for small amplitudes of oscillation about its equilibrium position in a uniform electric field of strength $E$.

6. An electric dipole of moment **p** is placed parallel to an electric field line along the $y$-axis in a nonuniform electric field (Fig. 27–27). The magnitude of the field **E** varies uniformly along the $y$-direction as shown. (a) Show that the magnitude of the force on the dipole is $p\, dE/dy$. (b) What is the direction of the force?

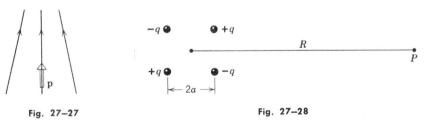

Fig. 27–27          Fig. 27–28

7. One type of "electric quadrupole" is formed by four charges located at the vertices of a square of side $2a$. Point $P$ lies a distance $R$ from the center of the quadrupole on a line parallel to two of sides of the square as shown in Fig. 27–28. For $R \gg a$, show that

the electric field at $P$ is approximately given by

$$E = \frac{3(2qa^2)}{4\pi\epsilon_0 R^4}.$$

(*Hint:* Treat the quadrupole as two dipoles.)

## Chapter 28

**1.** It is found experimentally that the electric field in a large region of the earth's atmosphere is directed vertically down. At an altitude of 300 meters the field is 60 volts/meter and at an altitude of 200 meters it is 100 volts/meter. Find the net amount of charge contained in a cube 100 meters on edge located between 200 and 300 meters altitude. Neglect the curvature of the earth.

**2.** Suppose that an electric field in some region is found to have a constant direction but to be decreasing in strength in that direction. What do you conclude about the charge in the region?

**3.** Two concentric conducting spherical shells have radii $R_1 = 0.145$ meter and $R_2 = 0.207$ meter. The inner sphere bears a charge $-6.00 \times 10^{-2}$ coul. An electron escapes from the inner sphere with negligible speed. Assuming that the region between the spheres is a vacuum, compute the speed with which the electron strikes the outer sphere.

**4.** (*a*) Two identical nonconducting spheres have radius $r$ and are fixed with their centers a distance $R > 2r$ apart. If each sphere has a total charge $q$ *uniformly distributed* on its surface, what is the magnitude of the electric force that either sphere exerts on the other? (*b*) Suppose instead that the spheres are conductors, the same total charge on each still being $q$. Will the electric force that either sphere exerts on the other in this case be greater than, less than, or equal to the force in case (*a*)? Explain.

**5.** The spherical region $a < r < b$ carries a charge per unit volume of $\rho = A/r$, where $A$ is constant. At the center ($r = 0$) of the enclosed cavity is a point charge $Q$. What should the value of $A$ be so that the electric field in the region $a < r < b$ has constant magnitude?

**6.** A solid insulating sphere carries a uniform charge per unit volume of $\rho$. Let $\mathbf{r}$ be the vector from the center of the sphere to a general point $P$ within the sphere. (*a*) Show that the electric field at $P$ is given by $\mathbf{E} = \rho\mathbf{r}/3\epsilon_0$. (*b*) A spherical "cavity" is removed from the above sphere, as shown in Fig. 28–25. Using superposition concepts show that the electric field at all points within the cavity is $\mathbf{E} = \rho\mathbf{a}/3\epsilon_0$ (uniform field), where $\mathbf{a}$ is the vector connecting the center of the sphere with the center of the cavity. Note that both these results are independent of the radii of the sphere and the cavity.

Fig. 28–25

## Chapter 29

**1.** What is the charge density on the surface of a conducting sphere of radius 0.15 meter whose potential is 200 volts?

**2.** Two identical conducting spheres of radius $r = 0.15$ meter are separated by a distance $a = 10.0$ meters. What is the charge on each sphere if the potential of one is $+1500$ volts and if the other is $-1500$ volts?

**3.** Two conducting spheres, one of radius 6.0 cm and the other of radius 12.0 cm, each have a charge of $3 \times 10^{-8}$ coul and are very far apart. If the spheres are connected by a conducting wire, find (*a*) the direction of motion and the magnitude of the charge transferred and (*b*) the final charge on and potential of each sphere.

**4.** In the rectangle shown in Fig. 29–29, the sides have lengths 5.0 cm and 15.0 cm, $q_1 = -5.0 \times 10^{-6}$ coul and $q_2 = +2.0 \times 10^{-6}$ coul. (a) What is the electric potential at corner $B$? At corner $A$? (b) How much work is involved in moving a third charge $q_3 = +3.0 \times 10^{-6}$ coul *from B to A* along a diagonal of the rectangle? (c) In this process, is external work converted into electrostatic potential energy or vice versa? Explain.

**Fig. 29–29**

**5.** Show that the potential energy of an assembly of four charges, each of charge $q$, in the configuration of a triangular pyramid, $a_0$ on an edge, is $6 \times (q^2/a_0)/4\pi\epsilon_0$.

**6.** Three charges of $+0.1$ coul each are placed on the corner of an equilateral triangle, 1.0 meter on a side. If energy is supplied at the rate of 1.0 kw, how many days would be required to move one of the charges onto the midpoint of the line joining the other two?

**7.** Show, using the fact that an electrostatic field is a conservative field, that one cannot create an electric field in which all the lines of force are straight parallel lines whose density (number per unit cross-sectional area) changes in a direction at right angles to the lines of force.

**8.** Two line charges are parallel to the $z$-axis; one, of charge per unit length $+\lambda$, is a distance $a$ to the right of this axis, and the other, of charge per unit length $-\lambda$, is a distance $a$ to the left of this axis (the lines and $z$-axis being in the same plane). Sketch some of the surfaces of equipotential.

**9.** A particle of (positive) charge $Q$ is assumed to have a fixed position at $P$. A second particle of mass $m$ and (negative) charge $-q$ moves at constant speed in a circle of radius $r_1$, centered at $P$. Derive an expression for the work $W$ that must be done by an external agent on the second particle in order to increase the radius of the circle of motion, centered at $P$, to $r_2$. Express $W$ in terms of quantities chosen from among $m$, $r_1$, $r_2$, $q$, $Q$, and $\epsilon_0$ only.

**10.** A particle of charge $Q$ is kept in a fixed position at a point $P$ and a second particle of mass $m$, having the same charge $Q$, is initially held at rest a distance $r_1$ from $P$. The second particle is then released and is repelled from the first one. Determine its velocity at the instant it is a distance $r_2$ from $P$. Let $Q = 3.1 \times 10^{-6}$ coul, $m = 2.0 \times 10^{-5}$ kg, $r_1 = 9.0 \times 10^{-4}$ meter, and $r_2 = 25 \times 10^{-4}$ meter.

**11.** A particle of mass $m$, charge $q > 0$, and initial kinetic energy $K$ is projected (from "infinity") toward a heavy nucleus of charge $Q$, assumed to have a fixed position

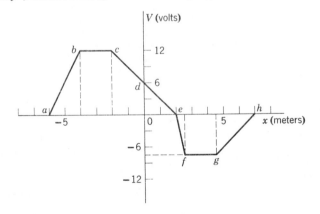

**Fig. 29–30**

in our reference frame.  (a) If the "aim is perfect," how close to the center of the nucleus is the particle when it comes instantaneously to rest?  (b) With a particular imperfect aim the particle's closest approach to the nucleus is *twice* the distance determined in part (a).  Determine the *speed* of the particle at this closest distance of approach.

**12.** The electric potential varies along the $x$-axis as shown in the graph of Fig. 29–30. For each of the intervals shown (ignore the behavior at the end points of the intervals) determine the $x$-component of the electric field and plot $E_x$ vs. $x$.

**13.** A charge per unit length $\lambda$ is distributed uniformly along a straight-line segment of length $L$.  (a) Determine the electrostatic potential (chosen to be zero at infinity) at a point $P$ a distance $y$ from one end of the charged segment and in line with it (see Fig. 29–31).  (b) Use the result of (a) to compute the component of the electric field intensity at $P$ in the $y$-direction (along the line).  (c) Determine the component of the electric field intensity at $P$ in a direction perpendicular to the straight line.

Fig. 29–31                     Fig. 29–32

**14.** On a thin rod of length $L$ lying along the $x$-axis with one end at the origin ($x = 0$), as in Fig. 29–32, there is distributed a charge per unit length given by $\lambda = kx$, where $k$ is a constant.  (a) Taking the electrostatic potential at infinity to be zero, find $V$ at the point $P$ on the $y$-axis.  (b) Determine the vertical component, $E_y$, of the electric field intensity at $P$ from the result of part (a) and also by direct calculation.  (c) Why cannot $E_x$, the horizontal component of the electric field at $P$, be found using the result of part (a)?

## Chapter 30

**1.** Show that the capacitance of two oppositely charged metal spheres of the same radius, when far apart, is one-half the capacitance of one isolated sphere.

**2.** Two metallic spheres, radii $a$ and $b$, are connected by a thin wire.  Their separation is large compared with their dimensions.  A charge $Q$ is put onto this system. (a) How much charge resides on each sphere?  (b) Apply the definition of capacitance to show that the capacitance of this system is $C = 4\pi\epsilon_0 (a + b)$.

**3.** $N$ identical spherical drops of liquid are charged to the same potential $V$.  One large drop is formed by combining these.  Show that the potential of the large drop is $N^{2/3} V$.

**4.** Charges $q_1$, $q_2$, $q_3$ are placed on capacitors of capacitance $C_1$, $C_2$, $C_3$ respectively, arranged in series as shown in Fig. 30–28.  Switch $S$ is then closed.  What are the final charges $q_1'$, $q_2'$, $q_3'$ on the capacitors?

**5.** When switch $S$ is thrown to the left in Fig. 30–29, the plates of the capacitor of capacitance $C_1$ acquire a potential difference $V_0$.  $C_2$ and $C_3$ are initially uncharged.

The switch is now thrown to the right.   What are the final charges $q_1$, $q_2$, $q_3$ on the corresponding capacitors?

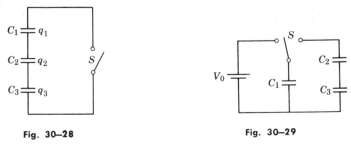

**Fig. 30–28**          **Fig. 30–29**

**6.** A geiger tube is made of two long concentric metal cylinders with a gas of dielectric constant $\kappa$ between them.   Neglecting end effects, use Gauss' law to calculate the capacitance of this configuration.   The center rod has a radius $a$, the surrounding tube a radius $b$, and the length $l \gg b$.

**7.** A parallel plate capacitor has plates of area 0.12 $m^2$ and a separation of 1.2 cm. A battery charges the plates to a potential difference of 120 volts and is then disconnected.   A dielectric slab of thickness 0.4 cm and dielectric constant 4.8 is then placed symmetrically between the plates. In terms of $\epsilon_0$ (a) find the capacitance before the slab is inserted. (b) what is the capacitance with the slab in place? (c) what is the free charge $q$ before and after the slab is inserted? (d) determine the electric field strength in the space between the plates and dielectric. (e) what is the electric field strength in the dielectric? (f) with the slab in place what is the potential difference across the plates? (g) how much external work is involved in the process of inserting the slab?

**Chapter 31**

**1.** A steady beam of alpha particles ($q = 2e$) traveling with constant kinetic energy 20 MeV carries a current $0.25 \times 10^{-6}$ ampere.   (a) If the beam is directed perpendicular to a plane surface, how many alpha particles strike the surface in 3.0 sec?   (b) At any instant, how many alpha particles are there in a given 20-cm length of the beam?

(c) Through what potential difference was it necessary to accelerate each alpha particle from rest to bring it to an energy of 20 MeV?

**2.** List similarities and differences between the flow of charge and the flow of a fluid; between the flow of charge and the conduction of heat.

**3.** Explain why the momentum which conduction electrons transfer to the ions in a metal conductor does not give rise to a resultant force on the conductor.

**4.** A resistor is in the shape of a truncated right circular cone (Fig. 31–10).   The end

**Fig. 31–10**

radii are $a$ and $b$, the altitude is $l$.   If the taper is small, we may assume that the current density is uniform across any cross section.   (a) Calculate the resistance of this object. (b) Show that your answer reduces to $\rho(l/A)$ for the special case of zero taper ($a = b$).

**5.** Conductors $A$ and $B$, having equal lengths of 40 meters and a cross-sectional area of 0.10 $m^2$, are connected in series.   A potential of 60 volts is applied across the terminal points of the connected wires.   The resistances of the wires are 40 and 20 ohms respectively.   Determine: (a) the resistivities of the two wires: (b) the magnitude of the electric field in each wire; (c) the current density in each wire; (d) the potential difference applied to each conductor.

**6.** A 1250-watt radiant heater is constructed to operate at 115 volts. (a) What will be the current in the heater? (b) What is the resistance of the heating coil? (c) How many kilocalories are created in our hour by the heater?

**7.** An iron wire (diameter 1 mm, length 10 cm) is placed in an evacuated chamber. Estimate the equilibrium temperature of the wire if it carries a current of 10 amp. Assume that all heat transfer is by radiation and that the surface of the wire radiates according to Eq. 47–2. Take the temperature of the chamber walls to be 27° C. List any additional assumptions that you use.

## Chapter 32

**1.** Two batteries having the same emf $\varepsilon$ but different internal resistances $r_1$ and $r_2$ are connected in series to an external resistance $R$. Find the value of $R$ that makes the potential difference zero between the terminals of the first battery.

**2.** The section of circuit $AB$ (see Fig. 32–26) absorbs power $P = 50.0$ watts and a current $i = 1.0$ amp passes through it in the indicated direction. (a) What is the potential difference between $A$ and $B$? (b) If the element $C$ does not have internal resistance, what is its emf? (c) What is its polarity?

**Fig. 32–26**

**3.** Two light bulbs, one of resistance $R$ and the other of resistance $r(< R)$, are connected (a) in parallel and (b) in series. Which bulb is brighter?

**4.** $N$ identical batteries of emf $\varepsilon$ and internal resistance $r$ may be connected all in series or all in parallel. Show that each arrangement will give the same current in an external resistor $R$ if $R = r$.

**5.** Twelve resistors, each of resistance $R$ ohms, form a cube (see Fig. 32–27). (a) Find $R_{AB}$, the resistance of an edge. (b) Find $R_{BC}$, the equivalent resistance of a face. (c) Find $R_{AC}$, the equivalent resistance of the body diagonal.

**Fig. 32–27**

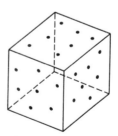

**Fig. 32–28**

**6.** What internal connections (resistors only) can account for the fact that there are 2 ohms resistance between any pair of the terminals on a box with $N$ terminals? (See Fig. 32–28.)

**7.** A voltmeter and an ammeter are used to determine two unknown resistances $R_1$ and $R_2$, one determination by each of the two methods shown in Fig. 32–29. The voltmeter resistance is 307 ohms and the ammeter resistance is 3.62 ohms; in method (a) the ammeter reads 0.317 amp and the voltmeter reads 28.1 volts, whereas in method (b) the ammeter reads 0.356 amp and the voltmeter 23.7 volts. Compute $R_1$ and $R_2$.

(a)          (b)

**Fig. 32–29**          **Fig. 32–30**

**8.** An $RC$ circuit is discharged by closing a switch at time $t = 0$. The initial potential difference across the capacitor is 100 volts. If the potential difference has decreased to 1.0 volt after 10 sec, (a) what will the potential difference be 20 sec after $t = 0$? (b) What is the time constant of the circuit?

**9.** A capacitor with capacitance $C = 1.0$ μf and initial stored energy $U_0 = 0.5$ joule is discharged through a resistance $R = 1.0 \times 10^6$ ohms. (a) What is the initial charge on the capacitor? (b) What is the current through the resistor when the discharge starts? (c) Determine $V_c$, the voltage across the capacitor, and $V_R$, the voltage across the resistor, as a function of time. (d) Express the rate of joule heating in the resistor as a function of time.

**10.** In the circuit of Fig. 32–30, ε $= 1200$ volts, $C = 6.50$ μf, $R_1 = R_2 = R_3 = 7.30 \times 10^5$ ohms. With $C$ completely uncharged, the switch $S$ is suddenly closed $(t = 0)$. (a) Determine, for $t = 0$ and $t = \infty$, the currents through each resistor. (b) Draw qualitatively a graph of the potential drop $V_2$ across $R_2$ from $t = 0$ to $t = \infty$. (c) What are the numerical values of $V_2$ at $t = 0$ and $t = \infty$? (d) Give the physical meaning of "$t = \infty$" and state a rough, but significant, numerical lower bound, in seconds, for "$t = \infty$" in this case.

## Chapter 33

**1.** Particles 1, 2, and 3 follow the paths shown in Fig. 33–25 as they pass through the magnetic field there. What can one conclude about each particle?

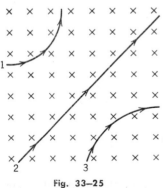

**Fig. 33–25**

**2.** (a) What speed would a proton need to circle the earth at the equator, if the earth's magnetic field is everywhere horizontal there and directed along longitudinal lines. Take the magnitude of the earth's magnetic field to be $0.41 \times 10^{-4}$ weber/meter$^2$ at the equator. (b) Draw the velocity and magnetic induction vectors corresponding to this situation.

**3.** An electron is accelerated through a potential difference of 1000 volts and directed into a region between two parallel plates separated by 0.02 meter with a voltage difference of 100 volts between them. If the electron enters moving perpendicular to the electric field between the plates, what magnetic field is necessary perpendicular to both the electron path and the electric field so that the electron travels in a straight line?

**4.** A positive point charge $Q$ travels in a straight line with constant speed through an evacuated region in which there is a uniform electric field **E** and a uniform magnetic field **B**. (*a*) If **E** is directed vertically up and the charge travels horizontally from north to south with speed $v$, determine the least value of the magnitude of **B** and the corresponding direction of **B**. (*b*) Explain why **B** is not uniquely determined when **E** and **v** alone are given. (*c*) Suppose the charge is a proton which enters the region after having been accelerated through a potential difference of $3.10 \times 10^5$ volts. If $E = 1.90 \times 10^5$ volt/meter, compute the value of $B$ in part (*a*). (*d*) If in part (*c*) the electric field **E** is turned off, determine the radius $r$ of the circle in which the proton now moves.

**5.** A certain galvanometer has a resistance of 75.3 ohms; its needle experiences a full-scale deflection when a current $1.62 \times 10^{-3}$ amp passes through its coil. (*a*) Determine the value of the auxiliary resistance required to convert the galvanometer into a voltmeter that reads 1.000 volt at full-scale deflection. How is it to be connected? (*b*) Determine the value of the auxiliary resistance required to convert the galvanometer into an ammeter that reads 0.0500 amp at full-scale deflection. How is it to be connected?

**6.** In a Hall effect experiment a current of 3.0 amp lengthwise in a conductor 1.0 cm wide, 4.0 cm long, and $10^{-3}$ cm thick produced a transverse Hall voltage (across the width) of $1.0 \times 10^{-5}$ volt when a magnetic field of 1.5 weber/meter² passed perpendicularly through the thin conductor. From these data, find (*a*) the drift velocity of the charge carriers and (*b*) the number of carriers per cubic centimeter. (*c*) Show on a diagram the polarity of the Hall voltage with a given current and magnetic field direction, assuming the charge carriers are (negative) electrons.

**7.** (*a*) What is the cyclotron frequency of an electron with an energy of 100 ev in the earth's magnetic field of $1.0 \times 10^{-4}$ webers/meters²? (*b*) What is the radius of curvature of the path of this electron if its velocity is perpendicular to the magnetic field?

## Chapter 34

**1.** Eight wires cut the page perpendicularly at the points shown in Fig. 34–32. A wire labeled with the integer $k$ ($k = 1, 2, \ldots 8$) bears the current $ki_0$. For those with odd $k$, the current flows up out of the page; for those with even $k$ it flows down into the page. Evaluate $\oint \mathbf{B} \cdot d\mathbf{l}$ along the closed path shown in the direction indicated by the single arrowhead.

**2.** Two long straight wires pass near one another at right angles. If the wires are free to move, describe what happens when currents are sent through them.

**3.** Suppose, in Fig. 34–25, that the currents are all in the same direction. What is the force per meter (magnitude and direction) on any one wire? In the analogous case of parallel motion of charged particles in a plasma this is known as the pinch effect.

**Fig. 34–32**

**4.** A long straight conductor has a circular cross section of radius $R$ and carries a current $i$. Inside the conductor there is a cylindrical hole of radius $a$ whose axis is parallel to the conductor axis at a distance $b$ from it. Use superposition ideas, and obtain an expression for the magnetic induction $B$ inside the hole.

**Fig. 34–33**

**5.** A straight conductor is split into identical semicircular turns as shown in Fig. 34–33. What is the magnetic field at the center $C$ of the circular loop so-formed?

**6.** (*a*) A current $i$ flows in a straight wire of length $L$ in the direction shown in Fig. 34–34*a*. Starting from the Biot-Savart law, determine the resulting magnetic induction ($\mathbf{B}_P$, $\mathbf{B}_Q$, $\mathbf{B}_R$, $\mathbf{B}_S$, respectively-direction and magnitude in each case) at each of the four points $P$, $Q$, $R$, $S$ (all coplanar with the wire). (b) Using the results of part (a), compute the magnetic induction $\mathbf{B}$ (magnitude and direction) resulting at the point $T$

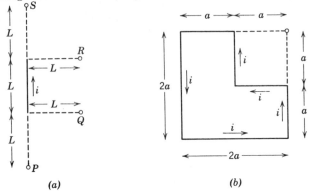

(a)  (b)

Fig. 34-34

from the current flowing as indicated in the six-sided rectilinear closed loop shown in Fig. 34-34b. (Everything drawn is meant to lie in the same plane and all angles are 90°.)

**7.** Use the Biot-Savort law to calculate the magnetic induction $\mathbf{B}$ at $C$, the common center of the semicircular arcs $AD$ and $HJ$, of radii $R_2$ and $R_1$ respectively, forming part of the circuit $ADJHA$ carrying current $i$, as shown in Fig. 34-35.

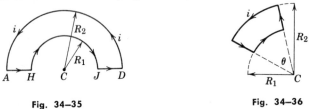

Fig. 34-35  Fig. 34-36

**8.** Compute the magnetic induction $\mathbf{B}$ at $C$, the common center of the circular arcs of the circuit carrying current $i$, the arcs cutting a sector of angle $\theta$, as shown in Fig. 34-36.

**9.** (a) A long wire is bent into the shape shown in Fig. 34-37, without cross-contact

at $P$. Determine the magnitude and direction of $\mathbf{B}$ at the center $C$ of the circular portion when the current $i$ flows as indicated. (b) The circular part of the wire is rotated without distortion about its (dashed) diameter perpendicular to the straight portion of the wire. The magnetic moment associated with the circular loop is now in the direction of the current in the straight part of the wire. Determine $\mathbf{B}$ at $C$ in this case.

Fig. 34-37

## Chapter 35

**1.** Show that emf has the same dimensions as time rate of change of magnetic flux.

**2.** In Fig. 35-39, $l = 2.0$ meters and $v = 50$ cm/sec. $\mathbf{B}$ is the earth's magnetic field, directed perpendicularly out of the page and having a magnitude $6.0 \times 10^{-5}$ webers/m$^2$ at that place. The resistance of the circuit $ADCB$, assumed constant (explain how this may be achieved approximately), is $R = 1.2 \times 10^{-5}$ ohms. (a) What is the emf induced in the circuit? (b) What is the electric field strength in the wire $AB$? (c) What force does each electron in the wire experience due to the motion of the wire in the magnetic field? (d) What is the magnitude and direction of the current in the wire? (e) What force must an external agency exert in order to keep the wire moving with this constant velocity? (f) Compute the rate at which the external agency is doing work. (g) Compute the rate at which electrical energy is being converted into heat energy.

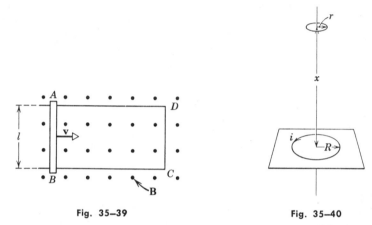

Fig. 35–39                          Fig. 35–40

3. Figure 35–40 shows two loops of wire having the same axis. The smaller loop is above the larger one, a distance $x$ which is large compared to the radius $R$ of the larger loop. Hence, with current $i$ flowing as indicated in the larger loop, the consequent magnetic induction is nearly constant throughout the plane area $\pi r^2$ bounded by the smaller loop. Suppose now that $x$ is not constant but is changing at the constant rate $dx/dt = v$. (a) Determine the magnetic flux across the area bounded by the smaller loop as a function of $x$. (b) Compute the emf generated in the smaller loop at the instant when $x = NR$. (c) Determine the direction of the induced current flowing in the smaller loop if $v > 0$.

4. A closed loop of wire consists of a pair of equal semicircles, radius 3.70 cm, lying in mutually perpendicular planes. The loop was formed by folding a circular loop along a diameter until the two halves became perpendicular. A uniform magnetic field $B$ of magnitude 760 gauss is directed perpendicular to the fold diameter and makes equal angles (45°) with the planes of the semicircles as shown in Fig. 35–41a. (a) The magnetic field is reduced at a uniform rate to zero during a time interval $4.50 \times 10^{-3}$ sec. Determine the magnitude of the induced emf and the sense of the induced current in the loop during this interval. (b) How would the answers change if $B$ is directed as shown in Fig. 35–41b, perpendicular to the direction first given for it but still perpendicular to the "fold-diameter?"

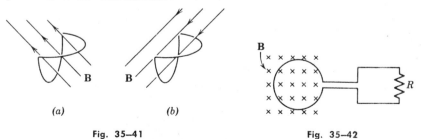

(a)                          (b)

Fig. 35–41                          Fig. 35–42

5. A loop of wire of area $A$ is connected to a resistance $R$. The loop is exposed to a time varying $B$ field (see Fig. 35–42). (a) Derive an expression for the *net* charge

transferred through the resistor between $t = t_1$ and $t = t_2$. Show that your answer is proportional to the difference $\Phi_B(t_2) - \Phi_B(t_1)$, and is otherwise independent of the manner in which **B** is changing.    (b) Suppose the change in flux, $\Phi_B(t_2) - \Phi_B(t_1)$ is zero.

**Fig. 35–43**

Does it then follow that no joule-heating occurred during this time interval?

**6.** An electromagnetic "eddy current" brake consists of a disk of conductivity $\sigma$ and thickness $t$ rotating about an axis through its center with a magnetic field **B** applied perpendicular to the plane of the disk over a small area $a^2$ (see Fig. 35–43). If the area $a^2$ is at a distance $r$ from the axis, find an approximate expression for the torque tending to slow down the disk at the instant its angular velocity equals $\omega$.

## Chapter 36

**1.** Two equal solenoids (inductance $L$) are wired in series.    (a) If they are far apart, show that the equivalent inductance is $2L$.    (b) If they are "close wound," show that the equivalent inductance is either zero or $4L$ depending on the direction of the windings. (*Hint:* They form a single solenoid.)

**2.** In the circuit shown in Fig. 36–8, $\varepsilon = 10$ volts, $R_1 = 5.0$ ohms, $R_2 = 10$ ohms, and $L = 5.0$ henries. For the two separate conditions (I) switch $S$ just closed and (II) switch $S$ closed for a very long time, calculate (a) the current $i_1$ through $R_1$, (b) the current $L_2$ through $R_2$, (c) the current $i$ through the switch, (d) the voltage across $R_2$, (e) the voltage across $L$, and (f) $di_2/dt$.

**Fig. 36–8**

**Fig. 36–9**

**3.** In Fig. 36–9, $\varepsilon = 100$ volts, $R_1 = 10\,\Omega$, $R_2 = 20\,\Omega$, $R_3 = 30\,\Omega$ and $L = 2$ h. Find the value of $i_1$ and $i_2$ (a) immediately after $S$ is closed; (b) a long time later; (c) immediately after $S$ is opened again; (d) a long time later.

**4.** A coaxial cable (inner radius $a$, outer radius $b$) is used as a transmission line between a battery $\varepsilon$ and a resistor $R$. The cable acts as both a capacitor and an inductor. If the stored electric and magnetic energies are equal, show that $R$ must be

$$R = \frac{377}{2\pi} \ln\left(\frac{b}{a}\right) \text{ ohms.}$$

(The quantity 377 ohms is sometimes called *the impedance of free space.*)

**5.** Each item (a) coulomb-ohm-meter/weber, (b) volt-second, (c) coulomb-ampere/ farad, (d) kilogram-volt-meter$^2$/(henry-ampere)$^2$, (e) (henry/farad)$^{1/2}$ is equal to one of the items in the following list: meter, second, kilogram, dimensionless number, newton, joule, volt, ohm, watt, coulomb, ampere, weber, henry, farad. Give the equalities.

### Chapter 37

**1.** A total charge $q$ is distributed uniformly on a dielectric ring of radius $r$. If the ring is rotated about an axis perpendicular to its plane and through its center at an angular speed $\omega$, find the magnitude and direction of its resulting magnetic moment.

**2.** (a) What is the magnetic moment due to the orbital motion of an electron in an atom when the orbital angular momentum is one quantum unit ($= \hbar = 1.05 \times 10^{-34}$ joule-sec). (b) The intrinsic spin magnetic moment of an electron is $0.928 \times 10^{-23}$ amp-meter$^2$. What is the difference in the magnetic potential energy $U$ between the states in which the magnetic moment is aligned with and aligned in the opposite direction to an external magnetic field of 1.2 weber/meter$^2$? (c) What absolute temperature would be required so that the energy difference in (b) would equal the mean thermal energy $kT/2$?

**3.** An electron travels in a circular orbit about a fixed positive point charge in the presence of a uniform magnetic field $\mathbf{B}$ directed normal to the plane of its motion. The electric force has precisely $N$ times the magnitude of the magnetic force on the electron. (a) Determine the two possible angular speeds of the electron's motion. (b) Evaluate these speeds numerically if $B = 4.27 \times 10^3$ gauss and $N = 100$.

**4.** A simple bar magnet is suspended by a string as shown in Fig. 37–23. If a uniform magnetic field $\mathbf{B}$ directed parallel to the ceiling is then established, show the resulting orientation of string and magnet.

**5.** An iron magnet containing iron of relative permeability 5000 has a flux path 1.0 meter long in the iron and an air gap 0.01 meter long each with cross-sectional areas of 0.02 meter.$^2$ What current is neces-

**Fig. 37–23**

sary in a 500 turn coil wrapped around the iron to give a flux density in the air gap of 1.8 webers/meter$^2$?

### Chapter 38

**1.** Initially the 900 $\mu$f capacitor is charged to 100 volts, and the 100 $\mu$f capacitor is uncharged in Fig. 38–13. (a) Describe in detail how one may charge the 100 $\mu$f capaci-

tor to 300 volts using $S_1$ and $S_2$ appropriately. (b) Describe in detail the mass + spring mechanical analogy of this problem.

**Fig. 38–13**

**2.** A self-consistency property of two of the Maxwell equations. Two adjacent parallelepipeds share a common face as shown in Fig. 38–14. (a) We may apply $\epsilon_0 \oint \mathbf{E} \cdot d\mathbf{S} = q$ to each of the two closed surfaces separately. Show that, from this alone, it follows that $\epsilon_0 \oint \mathbf{E} \cdot d\mathbf{S} = q$ is automatically satisfied for the composite closed surface. (b) Repeat using $\oint \mathbf{B} \cdot d\mathbf{S} = 0$.

**Fig. 38–14**

**Fig. 38–15**

**3.** A self-consistency property of two of the Maxwell equations. Two adjacent closed paths $abcda$ and $efcbe$ share the common edge $bc$ as shown in Fig. 38–15. (a) We may apply $\oint \mathbf{E} \cdot d\mathbf{l} = -d\Phi_B/dt$ to each of these closed paths separately. Show that from this alone, $\oint \mathbf{E} \cdot d\mathbf{l} = -d\Phi_B/dt$ is *automatically* satisfied for the composite closed path *abefcda.*   (b) Repeat using $\dfrac{1}{\mu_0} \oint \mathbf{B} \cdot d\mathbf{l} = i + \epsilon_0 \dfrac{d\Phi_E}{dt}.$

**4.** Using the definitions of flux, volume charge density $\rho$, and current density $\mathbf{j}$, write the four Maxwell equations in such a manner that all the fluxes, currents, and charges appear as volume or surface integrals.

## Chapter 39

**1.** A coaxial cable is made of a center wire of radius $a$ surrounded by a thin metal tube of radius $b$.   The substance between the conductors is air.   (a) Find the capacitance per unit length of this coaxial cable (*Hint:* Imagine equal but opposite charges to be on the wire and the tube).   (b) Find the inductance per unit length of this coaxial cable (*Hint:* Imagine a current $i$ flowing down the center wire and back along the tube.)

**2.** Starting with Eqs. 39-10 and 39-13, show that $E$ satisfies the "wave equation"

$$\frac{\partial^2 E}{\partial x^2} = \mu_0 \epsilon_0 \frac{\partial^2 E}{\partial t^2}.$$

Does $B$ also satisfy the wave equation?

**3.** Show that (a) through (d) below satisfy Eqs. 39-10 and 39-13.   In each of these, $A$ is a constant.   (a) $E = Ac(x - ct)$, $B = A(x - ct)$.   (b) $E = Ac(x + ct)^{15}$, $B = -A(x + ct)^{15}$.   (c) $E = Ace^{(x-ct)}$, $B = Ae^{(x-ct)}$.   (d) $E = Ac \ln (x + ct)$, $B = -A \ln (x + ct)$.   (e) Generalize these examples to show that $E = Acf(x - ct)$, $B = Af(x - ct)$ is a solution where $f$ is *any* function of $(x - ct)$.   What is the corresponding situation for functions of $(x + ct)$?

**4.** Consider the possibility of "standing waves":

$$E = E_m(\sin \omega t)(\sin kx)$$
$$B = B_m(\cos \omega t)(\cos kx)$$

(a) Show that these satisfy Eqs. 39–10 and 39–13 if $E_m$ is suitably related to $B_m$ and $\omega$ suitably related to $k$.   What are these relationships?   (b) Find the (instantaneous) Poynting vector.   (c) Show that the time average power flow across any area is zero. (d) Describe the flow of energy in this problem.

**5.** An airplane flying at a distance of 10 km from a radio transmitter receives a signal of power 10.0 microwatts/meter$^2$.   Calculate (a) the (average) electric field at the airplane due to this signal; (b) the (average) magnetic field at the airplane; (c) the total power radiated by the transmitter, assuming the transmitter to radiate isotropically and the earth to be a perfect absorber.

**6.** A coaxial cable (inner radius $a$, outer radius $b$) is used as a transmission line between a battery $\varepsilon$ and a resistor $R$, as shown in Fig. 39–18.   (a) Calculate $\mathbf{E}$, $\mathbf{B}$ for

**Fig. 39–18**

$a < r < b$.  (b) Calculate the Poynting vector **S** for $a < r < b$.  (c) By suitably integrating the Poynting vector, show that the total power flowing across the annular cross section $a < r < b$ is $\mathcal{E}^2/R$.  Is this reasonable?  (d) Show that the direction of **S** is always from the battery to the resistor, no matter which way the battery is connected.

**7.** A long hollow cylinder (radius $R$, length $l$) carries a uniform charge per unit area of $\sigma$ on its surface.  An externally applied torque causes the cylinder to rotate at constant acceleration $\omega(t) = \alpha t$.  (a) Find **B** within the cylinder (treat it as a solenoid).  (b) Find **E** at the inner surface of the cylinder.  (c) Find **S** at the inner surface of the cylinder.  (d) Show that the flux of **S** entering the interior volume of the cylinder is equal to $\dfrac{d}{dt}\left(\dfrac{\pi R^2 l}{2\mu_0} B^2\right)$.  (Compare with Problem 18.)

## Chapter 40

**1.** A plane electromagnetic wave, with wavelength 3.0 meters, travels in free space in the $+x$-direction with its electric vector **E**, of amplitude 300 volts/meter, directed along the $y$-axis.  (a) What is the frequency $\nu$ of the wave?  (b) What is the direction and amplitude of the **B** field associated with the wave?  (c) If $E = E_m \sin (kx - \omega t)$, what are the values of $k$ and $\omega$ for this wave?  (d) What is the time averaged rate of energy flow per unit area associated with this wave?  (e) If the wave fell upon a perfectly absorbing sheet of area $A$, what momentum would be delivered to the sheet per second and what is the radiation pressure exerted on the sheet?

**2.** Show that $\epsilon_0 \mathbf{E} \times \mathbf{B}$ has the dimensions of $\dfrac{\text{momentum}}{\text{area-time}}$, whereas $\dfrac{1}{\mu_0} \mathbf{E} \times \mathbf{B}$ has the dimensions of $\dfrac{\text{energy}}{\text{area-time}}$.  (The vector $\epsilon_0 \mathbf{E} \times \mathbf{B}$ may be used for computing momentum flow in the same manner that $\mathbf{S} = \dfrac{1}{\mu_0} \mathbf{E} \times \mathbf{B}$ is used to compute energy flow.)

**3.** A particle in the solar system is under the combined influence of the sun's gravitational attraction and the radiation force due to the sun's rays.  Assume that the particle is a sphere of density $1.0 \text{ gm/cm}^3$ and that all of the incident light is absorbed.  (a) Show that all particles with radius less than some critical radius, $R_0$, will be blown out of the solar system.  (b) Calculate $R_0$.  (c) Does $R_0$ depend on the distance from the earth to the sun?  (See the appendices for the necessary constants.)

## Chapter 41

**1.** When an electron moves through a medium at a speed exceeding the speed of light in that medium, it radiates electromagnetic energy (the Cerenkov effect, see Section 20–7).  What minimum speed must an electron have in a liquid of refractive index 1.54 in order to radiate?

**2.** Assume that the index of refraction of the earth's atmosphere varies, with altitude only, from the value one at the edge of the atmosphere to some larger value at the surface of the earth.  (a) Neglecting the earth's curvature, show that the apparent angle of a star from the zenith direction is independent of how the refractive index of the atmosphere varies with altitude and depends only on the value of $n$ at the earth's surface.  (*Hint:* Compare a uniform atmosphere with one consisting of layers of increasing refractive index.)  (b) How does the earth's curvature affect the analysis?

**3.** A point source is 80 cm below the surface of a body of water.  Find the diameter of the largest circle at the surface through which light can emerge from the water.

**4.** A pole extends 2.0 meters above the bottom of a swimming pool and 0.5 meters above the water.  Sunlight is incident at 45°.  What is the length of the shadow of the pole on the bottom of the pool?

**5.** A given monochromatic light ray, initially in air, strikes the 90° prism at $P$ (see Fig. 41–24) and is refracted there and at $Q$ to such an extent that it just grazes the right-hand prism surface after it emerges into air at $Q$.  (a) Determine the index of

Fig. 41–24                                              Fig. 41–25

refraction, relative to air, of the prism for this wavelength in terms of the angle of incidence $\theta_1$ which gives rise to this situation. (b) Give a numerical upper bound for the index of refraction of the prism. (c) Show, by a ray diagram, what happens if the angle of incidence at $P$ is slightly greater than $\theta_1$, is slightly less than $\theta_1$.

**6.** Two perpendicular mirrors form the sides of a vessel filled with water, as shown in Fig. 41–25. A light ray is incident from above, normal to the water surface. (a) Show that the emerging ray is parallel to the incident ray. Assume that there are two reflections at the mirror surfaces. (b) Repeat the analysis for the case of oblique incidence, the ray lying in the plane of the figure. (c) Using three mirrors, state and prove the three-dimensional analog to this problem.

## Chapter 42

**1.** How many images of himself can an observer see in a room whose ceiling and two adjacent walls are mirrors? Explain.

**2.** A thin flat plate of glass is a distance $b$ from a convex mirror. A point source of light $S$ is placed a distance $a$ in front of the plate (see Fig. 42–33) so that its image in the partially reflecting plate coincides with its image in the mirror. If $b = 7.5$ cm and the focal length of the mirror is $f = -30$ cm, find $a$ and draw the ray diagram.

**3.** (a) A simple magnifier (a converging lens) is used directly in front of the eye to examine an object. Draw a ray diagram showing the final image on the retina of the eye. (b) The smallest distance at which a normal eye can focus upon an object is 25 cm. Use this result with your ray diagram to prove that the (angular) magnification of a simple magnifier is $25/f + 1$, where $f$ is the focal length of the magnifier lens.

Fig. 42–33

**4.** Two thin lens, one having $f = +12.0$ cm and the other $f = -10.0$ cm, are separated by 7.0 cm. A small object is placed 43.5 cm from the center of the lens system on the principal axis first on one side and next on the other side. Find the location of the final image in each case.

**5.** Show that a thin converging lens of focal length $f$ followed by a thin diverging lens of focal length $-f$ will bring parallel light to a focus beyond the second lens provided that the separation of the lenses $L$ satisfies $0 < L < f$. (b) Does this property change if the lenses are interchanged? (c) What happens when $L = 0$?

**6.** A concave and a convex lens are cut out of a plane parallel block of glass as shown in Fig. 42–34. Discuss the geometry of a beam of parallel rays incident (a) on the concave lens and (b) on the convex lens as the distance between lenses is increased from contact to a large separation.

**7.** An object is placed 1.0 meter in front of a convergent lens, of focal length 0.5 meter, which is 2.0 meters in front of a plane mirror. (a) Where is the final image, measured from the lens,

Fig. 42–34

that would be seen by an eye looking toward the mirror through the lens? (*b*) Is the final image real or virtual? (*c*) Is the final image erect or inverted? (*d*) What is the lateral magnification?

## Chapter 43

**1.** In a double-slit arrangement the distance between slits is 5.0 mm and the slits are 1.0 meter from the screen. Two interference patterns can be seen on the screen, one due to light of 4800 A and the other 6000 A. What is the separation on the screen between the third-order interference fringes of the two different patterns?

**2.** In Young's interference experiment in a large ripple tank (see Fig. 43–4) the coherent vibrating sources are placed 12.0 cm apart. The distance between maxima 2.0 meters away is 18.0 cm. If the speed of ripples is 25.0 cm/sec, find the frequency of the vibrators.

**3.** One slit of a double-slit arrangement is covered by a thin glass plate of refractive index 1.4, and the other by a thin glass plate of refractive index 1.7. The point on the screen where the central maximum fell before the glass plates were inserted is now occupied by what had been the fifth bright fringe before. Assume $\lambda$ = 4800 A and that the plates have the same thickness $t$ and find the value of $t$.

**4.** In Fig. 43–25, the source emits monochromatic light of wavelength $\lambda$. $S$ is a very narrow slit in an otherwise opaque screen I. A plane mirror, whose surface includes the axis of the lens shown, is located a distance $h$ below $S$. Screen II is at the focal plane of the lens. (*a*) Find the condition for maxima and minima brightness of fringes

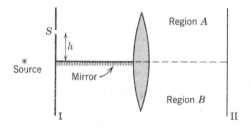

**Fig. 43–25**

on screen II in terms of the usual angle $\theta$, the wavelength $\lambda$, and the distance $h$. (*b*) Do fringes appear only in region $A$ (above the axis of the lens), only in region $B$ (below the axis of the lens), or in both regions $A$ and $B$? Explain. (*Hint:* Consider the image of $S$ formed by the mirror.)

**5.** Let $f_1(t) = A_1 \sin (\omega t + \phi_1)$ and $f_2(t) = A_2 \sin (\omega t + \phi_2)$. Suppose we want to calculate the time average of their product:

$$\frac{1}{T} \int_{t=0}^{T} f_1(t)f_2(t) \, dt, \qquad T = \frac{2\pi}{\omega}.$$

(Such a problem might arise if $f_1$ represents a current and $f_2$ a voltage; $f_1 f_2$ would then be the *instantaneous* power.) Show that this average is equal to one-half the dot product of the corresponding phasors.

**6.** Consider the problem of determining the sum

$$A_1 \sin (\omega t + \phi_1) + A_2 \sin (\omega t + \phi_2) + \cdots + A_n \sin (\omega t + \phi_n)$$

from the phasor diagram.

(a) Show that the sum may always be written in the form

$$B \sin \omega t + C \cos \omega t.$$

(b) Show that $B^2 + C^2 \le (A_1 + A_2 + \cdots + A_n)^2$.

(c) When does the equality sign in (b) hold?

**7.** A thin film of acetone (refractive index 1.25) is floated on a thick glass plate (refractive index 1.50). Plane light waves of variable wavelength are incident normal to the film. When one views the reflected wave it is noted that complete destructive interference occurs at 6000 A and constructive interference at 7000 A. Calculate the thickness of the acetone film.

**8.** We wish to coat a flat piece of glass ($n = 1.50$) with a transparent material ($n = 1.25$) so that light of wavelength 6000 A (in vacuum) incident normally is not reflected. How can this be done?

**9.** Light of wavelength 6300 A is incident normally on a thin wedge-shaped film of index of refraction 1.5. There are ten bright and nine dark fringes over the length of film. By how much does the film thickness change over this length?

**10.** An oil drop ($n = 1.20$) floats on a water ($n = 1.33$) surface and is observed from above by reflected light (see Fig. 43–26). (a) Will the outer (thinnest) regions of the drop correspond to a bright or a dark region? (b) Approximately how thick is the oil

Fig. 43–26

film where one observes the third blue region from the outside of the drop? (c) Why do the colors gradually disappear as the oil thickness becomes larger?

## Chapter 44

**1.** It can be shown that, except for $\theta = 0$, a circular obstacle produces the same diffraction pattern as a circular hole of the same diameter. Furthermore, if there are many such obstacles located randomly, then the interference effects vanish leaving only the diffraction associated with a *single* obstacle. (a) Explain why one sees a "ring" around the moon on a foggy day. (b) Calculate the size of the water droplet in the air if the bright ring around the moon appears to have a diameter 1.5 times that of the moon.

**2.** A monochromatic beam of parallel light is incident on a "collimating" hole of diameter $x \gg \lambda$. Point $P$ lies in the geometrical shadow region on a distance screen, as shown in Fig. 44–15a. Two obstacles, shown in Fig. 44–15b, are placed in turn over the collimating hole. $A$ is an opaque circle with a hole in it and $B$ is the "photographic negative" of $A$. Using superposition concepts, show that the intensity at $P$ is identical for each of the two diffracting objects $A$ and $B$ (*Babinet's principle*).

**3.** An astronaut in a satellite claims he can just barely resolve two point sources on the earth, 100 miles below him. What is their separation, assuming ideal conditions? Take $\lambda = 5500$ A, and the pupil diameter to be 5.0 mm.

**4.** Under ideal conditions, estimate the linear separation of two objects on the planet Mars which can just be resolved by an observer on earth (a) using the naked eye,

Fig. 44–15

(b) using the 200-in. Mt. Palomar telescope. Use the following data: distance to Mars = 50 million miles; diameter of pupil = 5.0 mm; wavelength of light = 5500 A.

5. A double-slit system (slit separation $d$, slit width $a$) is driven by two loudspeakers as shown in Fig. 44–16. By use of a variable delay line, the phase of one of the speakers

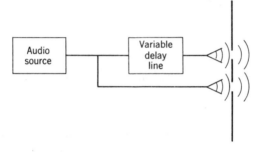

Fig. 44–16

may be varied. Describe in detail what changes occur in the intensity pattern at large distances as this phase difference is varied from zero to $2\pi$. Take both the interference and diffraction effects into account.

## Chapter 45

1. A diffraction grating has a large number $N$ of slits, each of width $d$. Let $I_{\max}$ denote the intensity at some principal maximum, and let $I_k$ denote the intensity of the $k$th adjacent secondary maxima. (a) If $k \ll N$, show from the phasor diagram that, approximately, $I_k/I_{\max} = 1/(k + \frac{1}{2})^2 \pi^2$. (Compare this with the single-slit formula.) (b) For those secondary maxima which lie roughly midway between two adjacent principal maxima, show that roughly $I_k/I_{\max} = 1/N^2$. (c) Consider the central principal maximum and those adjacent secondary maxima for which $k \ll N$. Show that this part of the diffraction pattern quantitatively resembles that of one single slit of width $Nd$.

2. With light from a gaseous discharge tube incident normally on a grating with a distance $1.732 \times 10^{-4}$ cm between adjacent slit centers, a green line appears with sharp maxima at measured transmission angles $\theta = \pm 17.6°, 37.3°, -37.1°, 65.2°$, and $-65.0°$. (a) Compute the wavelength of the green line that best fits the data.

3. A narrow beam of monochromatic light strikes a grating at normal incidence and produces sharp maxima at the following angles from the normal: 6°40′, 13°30′, 20°20′, 35°40′. No other maxima appear at any angle between 0° and 35°40′. The separation between adjacent slit centers in the grating is $5.04 \times 10^{-4}$ cm. (a) Compute the wavelength of the light used. (b) Make the most complete *quantitative* statement that can be inferred from the above data concerning the width of each slit.

**4.** Two spectral lines have wavelengths $\lambda$ and $\lambda + \Delta\lambda$, respectively, where $\Delta\lambda \ll \lambda$. Show that their angular separation $\Delta\theta$ in a grating spectrometer is given approximately by $\Delta\theta = \Delta\lambda/\sqrt{(d/m)^2 - \lambda^2}$, where $d$ is the separation of adjacent slit centers and $m$ is the order at which lines are observed. Notice that the angular separation is greater in the higher orders.

**5.** A diffraction grating is made up of slits of width 3000 A with a 9000 A separation between centers. The grating is illuminated by monochromatic plane waves, $\lambda = 6000$ A, the angle of incidence being zero. (a) How many diffracted lines are there? (b) What is the angular width of the spectral lines observed, if the grating has 1000 slits? (c) How is the angular width of the spectral lines related to the resolving power of the grating?

**6.** A diffraction grating has a resolving power $R = \lambda/\Delta\lambda = Nm$. (a) Show that the corresponding frequency range, $\Delta\nu$, that can just be resolved is given by $\Delta\nu = c/Nm\lambda$. (b) From Fig. 45-1, show that the "times of flight" of the two extreme rays differ by an amount $\Delta t = Nd \sin\theta/c$. (c) Show that $(\Delta\nu)(\Delta t) = 1$, this relation being independent of the various grating parameters.

**7.** Consider an infinite two-dimensional square lattice as in Fig. 45-14b. One interplanar spacing is obviously $a_0$ itself. (a) Calculate the next five smaller interplanar spacings by sketching figures similar to Figure 45-16a. (b) Show that your answers obey the general formula

$$d = a_0/\sqrt{h^2 + k^2}$$

where $h$, $k$ are both relatively prime integers (no common integer factor other than unity).

## Chapter 46

**1.** A beam of light is a mixture of plane polarized light and randomly polarized light. When it is sent through a Polaroid sheet, it is found that the transmitted intensity can be varied by a factor of five depending on the orientation of the Polaroid. Find the relative intensities of these two components of the incident beam.

**2.** It is desired to rotate the plane of polarization of a beam of plane polarized light by 90°. (a) How might this be done using only Polaroid sheets? (b) How many sheets are required in order that the total intensity loss is less than 5%? Assume that each Polaroid sheet is ideal.

**3.** A sheet of Polaroid and a quarter-wave plate are glued together in such a way that, if the combination is placed with face $A$ against a shiny coin, the face of the coin can be seen when illuminated with light of appropriate wavelength. When the combination is placed with face $A$ away from the coin, the coin cannot be seen. Which component is on face $A$ and what is the relative orientation of the components?

**4.** A beam of right circularly polarized light is reflected from a mirror. (a) Is the reflected beam right or left circularly polarized? (b) Has the direction of the associated linear momentum of the light changed? (c) Has the direction of the associated angular momentum of light changed? (d) Describe the reaction "felt" by the mirror.

# Definition of Standards and Fundamental and Derived Physical Constants*

The definition of primary standards is by agreement within the International Conference of Weights and Measures whose most recent general meeting was October, 1964 in Paris. Measured and derived values of the fundamental physical constants summarize hundreds of physical measurements made over the years by scientists in all parts of the world. They have been subjected to exhaustive statistical analysis and, with their accompanying error limits (which are given as three standard deviations), represent the best values to date (1963). For most problem work three significant figures suffice, and the "computational" (rounded) values may be used. The data presented are based largely on values given in the *National Bureau of Standards Technical News Bulletin*, Vol. 47, No. 10 (October 1963).

---

* See "A Pilgrim's Progress in Search of the Fundamental Constants," by J. W. M. Du Mond, *Physics Today*, October 1965.

## DEFINITION OF STANDARDS AND EQUIVALENTS

| Standard | Abbreviation | Equivalent |
|---|---|---|
| Meter | m | 1,650,763.73 wavelengths in vacuo of the unperturbed transition $2p_{10}$—$5d_5$ in $Kr^{86}$ |
| Kilogram | kg | mass of the international kilogram at Sèvres, France |
| Second | sec | 9,192,631,770 vibrations of the unperturbed hyperfine transition 4,0—3,0 of the fundamental state $^2S_{\frac{1}{2}}$ in $Cs^{133}$[a] |
| Degree Kelvin | °K | defined in the thermodynamic scale by assigning 273.16 °K to the triple point of water |
| Unified atomic mass unit | amu | $\frac{1}{12}$ the mass of an atom of the $C^{12}$ nuclide |
| Mole | mol | amount of substance containing the same number of atoms as 12 gm (exactly) of pure $C^{12}$ |
| Standard acceleration of free fall | $g_n$ | 9.80665 meter/sec$^2$ |
| Normal atmospheric pressure | atm | 101,325 nt/meter$^2$ |
| Thermochemical calorie | cal | 4.1840 joules |
| Liter | $l$ | 0.001,000,028 meter$^3$ |
| Inch | in. | 0.0254 meter |
| Pound (avdp.) | lb | 0.453,592,37 kg |

[a] There is no measurable difference between this and the previous standard of time, 1/31,556,925.9747 of the tropical year at 12$^h$ ET, 0 January 1900. For this reason and because even more accurate maser standards may soon be available, the Cs standard was adopted provisionally rather than "permanently."

## FUNDAMENTAL AND DERIVED CONSTANTS

| Name | Symbol | Computational Value | Best Experimental Value[b] |
|------|--------|---------------------|----------------------------|
| Speed of light | $c$ | $3.00 \times 10^8$ meters/sec | $2.997925 \pm 0.000003$ |
| Permeability constant | $\mu_0$ | $1.26 \times 10^{-6}$ henry/meter | $4\pi \times 10^{-7}$ exactly |
| Permittivity constant | $\epsilon_0$ | $8.85 \times 10^{-12}$ farad/meter | $8.85418 \pm 0.00002$ |
| Elementary charge | $e$ | $1.60 \times 10^{-19}$ coul | $1.60210 \pm 0.00007$ |
| Avogadro constant | $N_0$ | $6.02 \times 10^{23}$/mole | $6.02252 \pm 0.00028$ |
| Electron rest mass | $m_e$ | $9.11 \times 10^{-31}$ kg | $9.1091 \pm 0.0004$ |
| Proton rest mass | $m_p$ | $1.67 \times 10^{-27}$ kg | $1.67252 \pm 0.00008$ |
| Neutron rest mass | $m_n$ | $1.67 \times 10^{-27}$ kg | $1.67482 \pm 0.00008$ |
| Faraday constant | $F$ | $9.65 \times 10^4$ coul/mole | $9.64870 \pm 0.00016$ |
| Planck constant | $h$ | $6.63 \times 10^{-34}$ joule sec | $6.6256 \pm 0.0005$ |
| Fine structure constant | $\alpha$ | $7.30 \times 10^{-3}$ | $7.29720 \pm 0.00010$ |
| Electron charge/mass ratio | $e/m_e$ | $1.76 \times 10^{11}$ coul/kg | $1.758796 \pm 0.000019$ |
| Quantum/charge ratio | $h/e$ | $4.14 \times 10^{-15}$ joule sec/coul | $4.13556 \pm 0.00012$ |
| Electron Compton wavelength | $\lambda_C$ | $2.43 \times 10^{-12}$ meter | $2.42621 \pm 0.00006$ |
| Proton Compton wavelength | $\lambda_{Cp}$ | $1.32 \times 10^{-15}$ meter | $1.32140 \pm 0.00004$ |
| Rydberg constant | $R_\infty$ | $1.10 \times 10^7$/meter | $1.0973731 \pm 0.0000003$ |
| Bohr radius | $a_0$ | $5.29 \times 10^{-11}$ meter | $5.29167 \pm 0.00007$ |
| Bohr magneton | $\mu_B$ | $9.27 \times 10^{-24}$ joule/tesla[a] | $9.2732 \pm 0.0006$ |
| Nuclear magneton | $\mu_N$ | $5.05 \times 10^{-27}$ joule/tesla[a] | $5.0505 \pm 0.0004$ |
| Proton magnetic moment | $\mu_p$ | $1.41 \times 10^{-26}$ joule/tesla[a] | $1.41049 \pm 0.00013$ |
| Universal gas constant | $R$ | $8.31$ joule/°K mole | $8.3143 \pm 0.0012$ |
| Standard volume of ideal gas | — | $2.24 \times 10^{-2}$ meter³/mole | $2.24136 \pm 0.00030$ |
| Boltzmann constant | $k$ | $1.38 \times 10^{-23}$ joule/°K | $1.38054 \pm 0.00018$ |
| First radiation constant $\pi 2\ hc^2$ | $c_1$ | $3.74 \times 10^{-16}$ watt/meter² | $3.7405 \pm 0.0003$ |
| Second radiation constant $hc/k$ | $c_2$ | $1.44 \times 10^{-2}$ meter °K | $1.43879 \pm 0.00019$ |
| Wien displacement constant | $b$ | $2.90 \times 10^{-3}$ meter °K | $2.8978 \pm 0.0004$ |
| Stefan-Boltzmann constant | $\sigma$ | $5.67 \times 10^{-8}$ watt/meter² °K⁴ | $5.6697 \pm 0.0029$ |
| Gravitational constant | $G$ | $6.67 \times 10^{-11}$ nt meter²/kg² | $6.670 \pm 0.015$ |

[a] Tesla $\equiv$ weber/meter².
[b] Same units and power of ten as the computational value.

# Miscellaneous Terrestrial Data

| | |
|---|---|
| Standard atmosphere | $1.013 \times 10^5$ nt/meter$^2$ |
| | 14.70 lb/in$^2$ |
| | 760.0 mm-Hg |
| Density of dry air at STP[a] | 1.293 kg/meter$^3$ |
| | $2.458 \times 10^{-3}$ slug/ft$^3$ |
| Speed of sound in dry air at STP | 331.4 meters/sec |
| | 1089 ft/sec |
| | 742.5 miles/hr |
| Acceleration of gravity, $g$ (standard value)[b] | 9.80665 meters/sec$^2$ |
| | 32.1740 ft/sec$^2$ |
| Solar constant[c] | 1340 watts/m$^2$ |
| | 1.92 cal/cm$^2$-min |
| Mean total solar radiation | $3.92 \times 10^{26}$ watts |
| Equatorial radius of earth | $6.378 \times 10^6$ meters |
| | 3963 miles |
| Polar radius of earth | $6.357 \times 10^6$ meters |
| | 3950 miles |
| Volume of earth | $1.087 \times 10^{21}$ meter$^3$ |
| | $3.838 \times 10^{22}$ ft$^3$ |
| Radius of sphere having same volume | $6.371 \times 10^6$ meters |
| | 3959 miles |
| | $2.090 \times 10^7$ ft |

| | |
|---|---|
| Mean density of earth | $5522 \ \text{kg/meter}^3$ |
| Mass of earth | $5.983 \times 10^{24} \ \text{kg}$ |
| Mean orbital speed of earth | 29,770 meters/sec |
| | 18.50 miles/sec |
| Mean angular speed of rotation of earth | $7.29 \times 10^{-5} \ \text{radians/sec}$ |
| Earth's magnetic field, $B$ (at Washington, D. C.) | $5.7 \times 10^{-5} \ \text{tesla}$[d] |
| Earth's magnetic dipole moment | $6.4 \times 10^{21} \ \text{amp-m}^2$ |

[a] STP = standard temperature and pressure = 0° C and 1 atm.

[b] This value, used for barometer corrections, legal weights, etc., was adopted by the International Committee on Weights and Measures in 1901.   It approximates 45° latitude at sea level.

[c] The solar constant is the solar energy falling per unit time at normal incidence on unit area of the earth's surface.

[d] Tesla ≡ weber/meter².

# The Solar System [a]

| Planet | Mercury ☿ | Venus ♀ | Earth ⊕, ♁, ♁ | Mars ♂ | Jupier ♃ | Saturn ♄ | Uranus ♅, ♅ | Neptune ♆ | Pluto ♇ |
|---|---|---|---|---|---|---|---|---|---|
| Mean diameter km | 5,000 | 12,400 | 12,742 | 6,870 | 139,760 | 115,100 | 51,000 | 50,000 | 12,700? |
| Earth diameters | 0.39 | 0.973 | 1.000 | 0.532 | 10.97 | 9.03 | 4.00 | 3.90 | 0.46 |
| Volume (earth volumes) | 0.06 | 0.92 | 1.00 | 0.15 | 1,318 | 736 | 64 | 39 | 0.10 |
| Mass (earth masses) | 0.04 | 0.82 | 1.00 | 0.11 | 318.3 | 95.3 | 14.7 | 17.3 | 1.0? |
| Density (earth densities) | 0.69 | 0.89 | 1.00 | 0.70 | 0.24 | 0.13 | 0.23 | 0.29 | ? |
| Mean density gm/cm$^3$ | 3.8 | 4.86 | 5.52 | 3.96 | 1.33 | 0.71 | 1.26 | 1.6 | ? |
| Surface gravity (earth's) | 0.27 | 0.86 | 1.00 | 0.37 | 2.64 | 1.17 | 0.92 | 1.44 | ? |
| Velocity of escape, km/sec | 3.6 | 10.2 | 11.2 | 5.0 | 60 | 36 | 21 | 23 | 11? |
| Length of day (earth days) | 58.6$^d$ | 30$^d$? | 1$^d$ | 1$^d$37$^m$23$^s$ | 9$^h$55$^m$ | 10$^h$38$^m$ | 10.7$^h$ | 15.8$^h$ | ? |

48

| Planet | Mercury ☿ | Venus ♀ | Earth ⊕, ♁, ⊖ | Mars ♂ | Jupiter ♃ | Saturn ♄ | Uranus ♅, ⛢ | Neptune ♆ | Pluto ♇ |
|---|---|---|---|---|---|---|---|---|---|
| Period, siderial days | 87.97 | 224.70 | 365.26 | 686.98 | 4,332.59 | 10,759.20 | 30,685.93 | 60,187.64 | 90,885 |
| Inclination of equator to orbit | — | 0°? | 23°27' | 25°12' | 3°7' | 26°45' | 98.0° | 29° | ? |
| Oblateness | 0.00 | 0.00 | 1/296 | 1/192 | 1/15.4 | 1/9.5 | 1/14 | 1/45 | ? |
| Atmosphere, main constituents | none | $N_2$, $CO_2$, A | $N_2$, $O_2$ | $N_2$, $CO_2$, $H_2O$ | $CH_4$, $NH_3$ | $CH_4$, $NH_3$ | $CH_4$, $NH_3$ | $CH_4$, $NH_3$ | none |
| Maximum surface temperature, °K | 700 | 700 | 350 | 320 | 153 | 138 | 110? | 90? | 80? |
| Distance from Sun, $10^6$ km | 58 | 108 | 149 | 228 | 778 | 1426 | 2869 | 4495 | 5900 |

The Sun ☉ 329,390 earth masses, mean density 1.42, mean diameter 1,390,600 km, surface gravity 28 (earth's).

The Moon ☽ 0.01228 earth masses, mean density 3.36, mean diameter 3,476 km, surface gravity 0.17 (earth's), distance from earth 38 × 10⁴ km.

ª Adapted from Payne-Gaposchkin and *Handbook of Chemistry and Physics.*

# Periodic Table of the Elements

Atomic weights are expressed in *atomic mass units* (amu), one atom of the isotope $C^{12}$ being defined to have a mass of (exactly) 12 amu. For unstable elements the mass number of the most stable or best known isotope is given in brackets.

| Period | Series | I | II | III | IV | V | VI | VII | VIII | | | 0 |
|---|---|---|---|---|---|---|---|---|---|---|---|---|
| 1 | 1 | 1 H 1.00797 | | | | | | | | | | 2 He 4.0026 |
| 2 | 2 | 3 Li 6.939 | 4 Be 9.0122 | 5 B 10.811 | 6 C 12.01115 | 7 N 14.0067 | 8 O 15.9994 | 9 F 18.9984 | | | | 10 Ne 20.183 |
| 3 | 3 | 11 Na 22.9898 | 12 Mg 24.312 | 13 Al 26.9815 | 14 Si 28.086 | 15 P 30.9738 | 16 S 32.064 | 17 Cl 35.453 | | | | 18 A 39.948 |
| 4 | 4 | 19 K 39.102 | 20 Ca 40.08 | 21 Sc 44.956 | 22 Ti 47.90 | 23 V 50.942 | 24 Cr 51.996 | 25 Mn 54.9380 | 26 Fe 55.847 | 27 Co 58.9332 | 28 Ni 58.71 | |
| | 5 | 29 Cu 63.54 | 30 Zn 65.37 | 31 Ga 69.72 | 32 Ge 72.59 | 33 As 74.9216 | 34 Se 78.96 | 35 Br 79.909 | | | | 36 Kr 83.80 |
| 5 | 6 | 37 Rb 85.47 | 38 Sr 87.62 | 39 Y 88.905 | 40 Zr 91.22 | 41 Nb 92.906 | 42 Mo 95.94 | 43 Tc [99] | 44 Ru 101.07 | 45 Rh 102.905 | 46 Pd 106.4 | |
| | 7 | 47 Ag 107.870 | 48 Cd 112.40 | 49 In 114.82 | 50 Sn 118.69 | 51 Sb 121.75 | 52 Te 127.60 | 53 I 126.9044 | | | | 54 Xe 131.30 |
| 6 | 8 | 55 Cs 132.905 | 56 Ba 137.34 | 57-71 Lanthanide series[a] | 72 Hf 178.49 | 73 Ta 180.948 | 74 W 183.85 | 75 Re 186.2 | 76 Os 190.2 | 77 Ir 192.2 | 78 Pt 195.09 | |
| | 9 | 79 Au 196.967 | 80 Hg 200.59 | 81 Tl 204.37 | 82 Pb 207.19 | 83 Bi 208.980 | 84 Po [210] | 85 At [210] | | | | 86 Rn [222] |
| 7 | 10 | 87 Fr [223] | 88 Ra [226] | 89 Actinide series[b] | | | | | | | | |

[a] Lanthanide series:

| 57 La 138.91 | 58 Ce 140.12 | 59 Pr 140.907 | 60 Nd 144.24 | 61 Pm [145] | 62 Sm 150.35 | 63 Eu 151.96 | 64 Gd 157.25 | 65 Tb 158.924 | 66 Dy 162.50 | 67 Ho 164.930 | 68 Er 167.26 | 69 Tm 168.934 | 70 Yb 173.04 | 71 Lu 174.97 |
|---|---|---|---|---|---|---|---|---|---|---|---|---|---|---|

[b] Actinide series:

| 89 Ac [227] | 90 Th 232.038 | 91 Pa [231] | 92 U 238.04 | 93 Np [237] | 94 Pu [242] | 95 Am [243] | 96 Cm [245] | 97 Bk [249] | 98 Cf [249] | 99 Es [254] | 100 Fm [252] | 101 Md [256] | 102 No [254] | 103 Lw [257] |
|---|---|---|---|---|---|---|---|---|---|---|---|---|---|---|

# The Particles of Physics[a]

| Family name | Particle name | Symbol | Mass | Spin | Strangeness[b] | Charge | Antiparticle[c] | No. of particles | Averaged[d] lifetime, seconds | Typical decay products |
|---|---|---|---|---|---|---|---|---|---|---|
| | Photon | $\gamma$ (gamma ray) | 0 | 1 | 0 | 0 | Same particle | 1 | Infinite | — |
| Electron family | Electron | $e^-$ | 1 | $\frac{1}{2}$ | — | $-e$ | $e^+$ | 2 | Infinite | — |
| | Electron's neutrino | $\nu_e$ | 0 | $\frac{1}{2}$ | — | 0 | $\overline{\nu}_e$ | 2 | Infinite | — |
| Muon family | Muon | $\mu^-$ | 206.77 | $\frac{1}{2}$ | — | $-e$ | $\mu^+$ | 2 | $2.212 \times 10^{-6}$ | $e^- + \overline{\nu}_e + \nu_\mu$ |
| | Muon's neutrino | $\nu_\mu$ | 0(?) | $\frac{1}{2}$ | — | 0 | $\overline{\nu}_\mu$ | 2 | Infinite | — |
| Mesons | Pion | $\pi^+$ | 273.2 | 0 | 0 | $+e$ | $\pi^-$ | 3 | $2.55 \times 10^{-8}$ | $\mu^+ + \nu_\mu$ |
| | | $\pi^0$ | 264.2 | 0 | 0 | 0 | $\pi^0$ | | $1.9 \times 10^{-16}$ | $\gamma + \gamma$ |
| | Kaon | $K^+$ | 966.6 | 0 | $+1$ | $+e$ | $\overline{K^+}$ | 4 | $1.22 \times 10^{-8}$ | $\pi^+ + \pi^0$ |
| | | $K^0$ | 974 | 0 | $+1$ | 0 | $\overline{K^0}$ | | $1.00 \times 10^{-10}$ and $6 \times 10^{-8}$ | $\pi^+ + \pi^-$ |

| Family name | Particle name | Symbol | Mass | Spin | Strange-ness[b] | Charge | Antiparticle[a] | No. of particles | Average lifetime seconds | Typical decay products |
|---|---|---|---|---|---|---|---|---|---|---|
| Baryons | Nucleon | $p^+$ (proton) | 1836.12 | $\frac{1}{2}$ | 0 | $+e$ | $\overline{p}{}^+$ | 4 | Infinite | $p + e^- + \bar{\nu}_e$ |
| | | $n^0$ (neutron) | 1838.65 | $\frac{1}{2}$ | 0 | 0 | $\overline{n}{}^0$ | | 1013 | |
| | Lambda particle | $\Lambda^0$ | 2182.8 | $\frac{1}{2}$ | $-1$ | 0 | $\overline{\Lambda}{}^0$ | 2 | $2.51 \times 10^{-10}$ | $p + \pi^-$ |
| | Sigma particle | $\Sigma^+$ | 2327.7 | $\frac{1}{2}$ | $-1$ | $+e$ | $\overline{\Sigma}{}^+$ | 6 | $8.1 \times 10^{-11}$ | $n + \pi^+$ |
| | | $\Sigma^-$ | 2340.5 | $\frac{1}{2}$ | $-1$ | $-e$ | $\overline{\Sigma}{}^-$ | | $1.6 \times 10^{-10}$ | $n + \pi^-$ |
| | | $\Sigma^0$ | 2332 | $\frac{1}{2}$ | $-1$ | 0 | $\overline{\Sigma}{}^0$ | | about $10^{-20}$ | $\Lambda^0 + \gamma$ |
| | Xi particle | $\Xi^-$ | 2580 | $\frac{1}{2}$ | $-2$ | $-e$ | $\overline{\Xi}{}^-$ | 4 | $1.3 \times 10^{-10}$ | $\Lambda^0 + \pi^-$ |
| | | $\Xi^0$ | 2570 | $\frac{1}{2}$ | $-2$ | 0 | $\overline{\Xi}{}^0$ | | about $10^{-10}$ | $\Lambda^0 + \pi^0$ |

[a] Adapted and modified from *The World of Elementary Particles*, by Kenneth W. Ford.

[b] This is a "quantum number" whose assignment permits an understanding of the inter-relationships of the particles.

[c] Antiparticles have the same mass and spin as the particles but their charges and strangeness numbers are opposite in sign.

[d] The $K^0$ meson has two different lifetimes; all other particles have only one.

# Symbols, Dimensions, and Units for Physical Quantities

All units and dimensions are in the mksq (rationalized) system. The primary units can be found by reading kilograms for $M$, meters for $L$, seconds for $T$, and coulombs for $Q$. The symbols are those used in the text.

In practice, $Q$ is defined in terms of $M$, $L$, and $T$. However, the addition of $Q$ to the traditional $M$, $L$, and $T$ enables us to avoid the use of fractional exponents in dimensional considerations. The term 'rationalized' simply means that a factor $1/4\pi$ is separated out of Coulomb's law in order to remove the factor $4\pi$ that would otherwise appear in many other formulas in electricity.

| Quantity | Symbol | Dimensions | Derived Units |
|---|---|---|---|
| Acceleration | **a** | $LT^{-2}$ | meters/sec$^2$ |
| Angular acceleration | $\alpha$ | $T^{-2}$ | radians/sec$^2$ |
| Angular displacement | $\theta$ | — | radian |
| Angular frequency and speed | $\omega$ | $T^{-1}$ | radians/sec |
| Angular momentum | **L** | $ML^2T^{-1}$ | kg-m$^2$/sec |
| Angular velocity | $\boldsymbol{\omega}$ | $T^{-1}$ | radians/sec |
| Area | $A, S$ | $L^2$ | meter$^2$ |
| Displacement | **r, d** | $L$ | meter |

| Quantity | Symbol | Dimensions | Derived Units |
|---|---|---|---|
| Energy, total | $E$ | $ML^2T^{-2}$ | joule |
|     kinetic | $K$ | $ML^2T^{-2}$ | joule |
|     potential | $U$ | $ML^2T^{-2}$ | joule |
| Force | $F$ | $MLT^{-2}$ | newton |
| Frequency | $\nu$ | $T^{-1}$ | hertz $\equiv$ cycles/sec |
| Gravitational field strength | $g$ | $LT^{-2}$ | nt/kg |
| Gravitational potential | $V$ | $L^2T^{-2}$ | joules/kg |
| Length | $l$ | $L$ | meter |
| Mass | $m$ | $M$ | kilogram |
| Mass density | $\rho$ | $ML^{-3}$ | kg/m$^3$ |
| Momentum | $p$ | $MLT^{-1}$ | kg-m/sec$^2$ |
| Period | $T$ | $T$ | second |
| Power | $P$ | $ML^2T^{-3}$ | watt |
| Pressure | $p$ | $ML^{-1}T^{-2}$ | nt/m$^2$ |
| Rotational inertia | $I$ | $ML^2$ | kg-m$^2$ |
| Time | $t$ | $T$ | second |
| Torque | $\tau$ | $ML^2T^{-2}$ | nt-m |
| Velocity | $v$ | $LT^{-1}$ | meters/sec |
| Volume | $V$ | $L^3$ | meter$^3$ |
| Wavelength | $\lambda$ | $L$ | meter |
| Work | $W$ | $ML^2T^{-2}$ | joule |
| Entropy | $S$ | $ML^2T^{-2}$ | joules/$K°$ |
| Internal energy | $U$ | $ML^2T^{-2}$ | joule |
| Heat | $Q$ | $ML^2T^{-2}$ | joule |
| Temperature | $T$ | — | Kelvin degree |
| Capacitance | $C$ | $M^{-1}L^{-2}T^2Q^2$ | farad |
| Charge | $q$ | $Q$ | coulomb |
| Conductivity | $\sigma$ | $M^{-1}L^{-3}TQ^2$ | (ohm-meter)$^{-1}$ |
| Current | $i$ | $T^{-1}Q$ | ampere |
| Current density | $j$ | $L^{-2}T^{-1}Q$ | amp/meter$^2$ |
| Electric dipole moment | $p$ | $LQ$ | coul-meter |
| Electric displacement | $D$ | $M^{-2}Q$ | coul/meter$^2$ |
| Electric polarization | $P$ | $M^{-2}Q$ | coul-meter$^2$ |
| Electric field strength | $E$ | $MLT^{-2}Q^{-1}$ | volts/meter |
| Electric flux | $\Phi_E$ | $ML^3T^{-2}Q^{-1}$ | volt-meter |
| Electric potential | $V$ | $ML^2T^{-2}Q^{-1}$ | volt. |
| Electromotive force | $\mathcal{E}$ | $ML^2T^{-2}Q^{-1}$ | volt |
| Inductance | $L$ | $ML^2Q^{-2}$ | henry |
| Magnetic dipole moment | $\mu$ | $L^2T^{-1}Q$ | amp-meter$^2$ |
| Magnetic field strength | $H$ | $MT^{-1}Q$ | amp-meter |
| Magnetic flux | $\Phi_B$ | $ML^2T^{-1}Q^{-1}$ | weber $=$ volt-sec |
| Magnetic induction | $B$ | $MT^{-1}Q^{-1}$ | tesla $\equiv$ webers/meter$^2$ |
| Magnetization | $M$ | $L^{-1}T^{-1}Q$ | amp/meter |
| Permeability | $\mu$ | $MLQ^{-2}$ | henrys/meter |
| Permittivity | $\epsilon$ | $M^{-1}L^{-3}T^2Q^2$ | farads/meter |
| Resistance | $R$ | $ML^2T^{-1}Q^{-2}$ | ohm |
| Resistivity | $\rho$ | $ML^3T^{-1}Q^{-2}$ | ohm-meter |
| Voltage | $V$ | $ML^2T^{-2}Q^{-1}$ | volt |

# Conversion Factors[a]

Conversion factors for common and not-so-common units may be read off directly from the tables below. For example, 1 degree = 2.778 × $10^{-3}$ revolutions, so 16.7° = 16.7 × 2.778 × $10^{-3}$ rev. The mks quantities are capitalized in each table.

PLANE ANGLE

| | ° | ′ | ″ | RADIAN | rev |
|---|---|---|---|---|---|
| 1 degree = | 1 | 60 | 3600 | $1.745 \times 10^{-2}$ | $2.778 \times 10^{-3}$ |
| 1 minute = | $1.667 \times 10^{-2}$ | 1 | 60 | $2.909 \times 10^{-4}$ | $4.630 \times 10^{-5}$ |
| 1 second = | $2.778 \times 10^{-4}$ | $1.667 \times 10^{-2}$ | 1 | $4.848 \times 10^{-6}$ | $7.716 \times 10^{-7}$ |
| 1 RADIAN = | 57.30 | 3438 | $2.063 \times 10^{5}$ | 1 | 0.1592 |
| 1 revolution = | 360 | $2.16 \times 10^{4}$ | $1.296 \times 10^{6}$ | 6.283 | 1 |

1 rev = 2π radians = 360°     1° = 60′ = 3600″

SOLID ANGLE

1 sphere = 4π steradians = 12.57 steradians

[a] Adapted in part from G. Shortley and D. Williams, *Elements of Physics*, Prentice-Hall, Englewood Cliffs, New Jersey, Second Edition, 1955.

# APPENDIX G

## LENGTH

|            | cm | METER | km | in. | ft | mile |
|------------|-----|-------|-----|-----|-----|------|
| 1 centimeter = | 1 | $10^{-2}$ | $10^{-5}$ | 0.3937 | 3.281 $\times 10^{-2}$ | 6.214 $\times 10^{-6}$ |
| 1 METER = | 100 | 1 | $10^{-3}$ | 39.37 | 3.281 | 6.214 $\times 10^{-4}$ |
| 1 kilometer = | $10^5$ | 1000 | 1 | 3.937 $\times 10^4$ | 3281 | 0.6214 |
| 1 inch = | 2.540 | 2.540 $\times 10^{-2}$ | 2.540 $\times 10^{-5}$ | 1 | 8.333 $\times 10^{-2}$ | 1.578 $\times 10^{-5}$ |
| 1 foot = | 30.48 | 0.3048 | 3.048 $\times 10^{-4}$ | 12 | 1 | 1.894 $\times 10^{-4}$ |
| 1 statute mile = | 1.609 $\times 10^5$ | 1609 | 1.609 | 6.336 $\times 10^4$ | 5280 | 1 |

1 angstrom (A) = $10^{-10}$ meter    1 light-year = 9.4600 $\times 10^{12}$ km    1 yard = 3 ft
1 X-unit = $10^{-13}$ meter    1 parsec = 3.084 $\times 10^{13}$ km    1 rod = 16.5 ft
1 micron = $10^{-6}$ meter    1 fathom = 6 ft    1 mil = $10^{-3}$ in.
1 millimicron (m$\mu$) = $10^{-9}$ meter
1 nautical mile = 1852 meters = 1.1508 statute miles = 6076.10 ft

## AREA

|            | METER$^2$ | cm$^2$ | ft$^2$ | in.$^2$ | circ mil |
|------------|-----------|--------|--------|---------|----------|
| 1 SQUARE METER = | 1 | $10^4$ | 10.76 | 1550 | 1.974 $\times 10^9$ |
| 1 square centimeter = | $10^{-4}$ | 1 | 1.076 $\times 10^{-3}$ | 0.1550 | 1.974 $\times 10^5$ |
| 1 square foot = | 9.290 $\times 10^{-2}$ | 929.0 | 1 | 144 | 1.833 $\times 10^8$ |
| 1 square inch = | 6.452 $\times 10^{-4}$ | 6.452 | 6.944 $\times 10^{-3}$ | 1 | 1.273 $\times 10^6$ |
| 1 circular mill = | 5.067 $\times 10^{-10}$ | 5.067 $\times 10^{-6}$ | 5.454 $\times 10^{-9}$ | 7.854 $\times 10^{-7}$ | 1 |

1 square mile = 27,878,400 ft$^2$ = 640 acres    1 acre = 43,560 ft$^2$
1 barn = $10^{-28}$ meter$^2$

## VOLUME

|            | METER$^3$ | cm$^3$ | 1 | ft$^3$ | in.$^3$ |
|------------|-----------|--------|-----|--------|---------|
| 1 CUBIC METER = | 1 | $10^6$ | 1000 | 35.31 | 6.102 $\times 10^4$ |
| 1 cubic centimeter = | $10^{-6}$ | 1 | 1.000 $\times 10^{-3}$ | 3.531 $\times 10^{-5}$ | 6.102 $\times 10^{-2}$ |
| 1 liter = | 1.000 $\times 10^{-3}$ | 1000 | 1 | 3.531 $\times 10^{-2}$ | 61.02 |
| 1 cubic foot = | 2.832 $\times 10^{-2}$ | 2.832 $\times 10^4$ | 28.32 | 1 | 1728 |
| 1 cubic inch = | 1.639 $\times 10^{-5}$ | 16.39 | 1.639 $\times 10^{-2}$ | 5.787 $\times 10^{-4}$ | 1 |

1 U. S. fluid gallon = 4 U. S. fluid quarts = 8 U. S. pints = 128 U. S. fluid ounces = 231 in.$^3$
1 British imperial gallon = the volume of 10 lb of water at 62° F = 277.42 in.$^3$
1 liter = the volume of 1 kg of water at its maximum density = 1000.028 cm$^3$

## MASS

Note: Those quantities to the right of and below the heavy lines are not mass units at all but are often used as such. When we write, for example,

$$1 \text{ kg } `` = " 2.205 \text{ lb}$$

this means that a kilogram is a *mass* that *weighs* 2.205 pounds. Clearly this "equivalence" is approximate (depending on the value of $g$) and is meaningful only for terrestrial measurements. Thus, care must be employed when using the factors in the shaded portion of the table.

| | gm | KG | slug | amu | oz | lb | ton |
|---|---|---|---|---|---|---|---|
| 1 gram = | 1 | 0.001 | $6.852 \times 10^{-5}$ | $6.024 \times 10^{23}$ | $3.527 \times 10^{-2}$ | $2.205 \times 10^{-3}$ | $1.102 \times 10^{-6}$ |
| 1 KILOGRAM = | 1000 | 1 | $6.852 \times 10^{-2}$ | $6.024 \times 10^{26}$ | 35.27 | 2.205 | $1.102 \times 10^{-3}$ |
| 1 slug = | $1.459 \times 10^{4}$ | 14.59 | 1 | $8.789 \times 10^{27}$ | 514.8 | 32.17 | $1.609 \times 10^{-2}$ |
| 1 amu = | $1.660 \times 10^{-24}$ | $1.660 \times 10^{-27}$ | $1.137 \times 10^{-28}$ | 1 | $5.855 \times 10^{-26}$ | $3.660 \times 10^{-27}$ | $1.829 \times 10^{-30}$ |
| 1 ounce (avoirdupois) = | 28.35 | $2.835 \times 10^{-2}$ | $1.943 \times 10^{-3}$ | $1.708 \times 10^{25}$ | 1 | $6.250 \times 10^{-2}$ | $3.125 \times 10^{-5}$ |
| 1 pound (avoirdupois) = | 453.6 | 0.4536 | $3.108 \times 10^{-2}$ | $2.732 \times 10^{26}$ | 16 | 1 | 0.0005 |
| 1 ton = | $9.072 \times 10^{+5}$ | 907.2 | 62.16 | $5.465 \times 10^{29}$ | $3.2 \times 10^{4}$ | 2000 | 1 |

## DENSITY

Note: Those quantities to the right or below the heavy line are weight densities and, as such, are dimensionally different from mass densities. Care must be used. (See note for mass table.)

| | slug/ft$^3$ | KG/METER$^3$ | gm/cm$^3$ | lb/ft$^3$ | lb/in.$^3$ |
|---|---|---|---|---|---|
| 1 slug per ft$^3$ = | 1 | 515.4 | 0.5154 | 32.17 | $1.862 \times 10^{-2}$ |
| 1 KILOGRAM per METER$^3$ = | $1.940 \times 10^{-3}$ | 1 | 0.001 | $6.243 \times 10^{-2}$ | $3.613 \times 10^{-5}$ |
| 1 gram per cm$^3$ = | 1.940 | 1000 | 1 | 62.43 | $3.613 \times 10^{-2}$ |
| 1 pound per ft$^3$ = | $3.108 \times 10^{-2}$ | 16.02 | $1.602 \times 10^{-2}$ | 1 | $5.787 \times 10^{-4}$ |
| 1 pound per in.$^3$ = | 53.71 | $2.768 \times 10^{4}$ | 27.68 | 1728 | 1 |

## TIME

| | yr | day | hr | min | SEC |
|---|---|---|---|---|---|
| 1 year = | 1 | 365.2 | $8.766 \times 10^{3}$ | $5.259 \times 10^{5}$ | $3.156 \times 10^{7}$ |
| 1 day = | $2.738 \times 10^{-3}$ | 1 | 24 | 1440 | $8.640 \times 10^{4}$ |
| 1 hour = | $1.141 \times 10^{-4}$ | $4.167 \times 10^{-2}$ | 1 | 60 | 3600 |
| 1 minute = | $1.901 \times 10^{-6}$ | $6.944 \times 10^{-4}$ | $1.667 \times 10^{-2}$ | 1 | 60 |
| 1 SECOND = | $3.169 \times 10^{-8}$ | $1.157 \times 10^{-5}$ | $2.778 \times 10^{-4}$ | $1.667 \times 10^{-2}$ | 1 |

## APPENDIX G
### SPEED

|  | ft/sec | km/hr | METER/SEC | miles/hr | cm/sec | knot |
|---|---|---|---|---|---|---|
| 1 foot per second = | 1 | 1.097 | 0.3048 | 0.6818 | 30.48 | 0.5925 |
| 1 kilometer per hour = | 0.9113 | 1 | 0.2778 | 0.6214 | 27.78 | 0.5400 |
| 1 METER per SECOND = | 3.281 | 3.6 | 1 | 2.237 | 100 | 1.944 |
| 1 mile per hour = | 1.467 | 1.609 | 0.4470 | 1 | 44.70 | 0.8689 |
| 1 centimeter per second = | $3.281 \times 10^{-2}$ | $3.6 \times 10^{-2}$ | 0.01 | $2.237 \times 10^{-2}$ | 1 | $1.944 \times 10^{-2}$ |
| 1 knot = | 1.688 | 1.852 | 0.5144 | 1.151 | 51.44 | 1 |

1 knot = 1 nautical mile/hr          1 mile/min = 88 ft/sec = 60 miles/hr

### FORCE

Note: Those quantities to the right of and below the heavy lines are not force units at all but are often used as such, especially in chemistry. For instance, if we write

1 gram-force " = " 980.7 dynes,

we mean that a gram-*mass* experiences a *force* of 980.7 dynes in the earth's gravitational field. Thus, care must be employed when using the factors in the shaded portion of the table.

|  | dyne | NT | lb | pdl | gf | kgf |
|---|---|---|---|---|---|---|
| 1 dyne = | 1 | $10^{-5}$ | $2.248 \times 10^{-6}$ | $7.233 \times 10^{-5}$ | $1.020 \times 10^{-3}$ | $1.020 \times 10^{-6}$ |
| 1 NEWTON = | $10^5$ | 1 | 0.2248 | 7.233 | 102.0 | 0.1020 |
| 1 pound = | $4.448 \times 10^5$ | 4.448 | 1 | 32.17 | 453.6 | 0.4536 |
| 1 poundal = | $1.383 \times 10^4$ | 0.1383 | $3.108 \times 10^{-2}$ | 1 | 14.10 | $1.410 \times 10^{-2}$ |
| 1 gram-force = | 980.7 | $9.807 \times 10^{-3}$ | $2.205 \times 10^{-3}$ | $7.093 \times 10^{-2}$ | 1 | 0.001 |
| 1 kilogram-force = | $9.807 \times 10^5$ | 9.807 | 2.205 | 70.93 | 1000 | 1 |

1 kgf = 9.80665 nt          1 lb = 32.17398 pdl

### PRESSURE

|  | atm | dyne/cm$^2$ | inch of water | cm Hg | NT/METER$^2$ | lb/in.$^2$ | lb/ft$^2$ |
|---|---|---|---|---|---|---|---|
| 1 atmosphere = | 1 | $1.013 \times 10^6$ | 406.8 | .76 | $1.013 \times 10^5$ | 14.70 | 2116 |
| 1 dyne per cm$^2$ = | $9.869 \times 10^{-7}$ | 1 | $4.015 \times 10^{-4}$ | $7.501 \times 10^{-5}$ | 0.1 | $1.450 \times 10^{-5}$ | $2.089 \times 10^{-3}$ |
| 1 inch of water at 4° C$^a$ = | $2.458 \times 10^{-3}$ | 2491 | 1 | 0.1868 | 249.1 | $3.613 \times 10^{-2}$ | 5.202 |
| 1 centimeter of mercury at 0° C $^a$ = | $1.316 \times 10^{-2}$ | $1.333 \times 10^4$ | 5.353 | 1 | 1333 | 0.1934 | 27.85 |
| 1 NEWTON per METER$^2$ = | $9.869 \times 10^{-6}$ | 10 | $4.015 \times 10^{-3}$ | $7.501 \times 10^{-4}$ | 1 | $1.450 \times 10^{-4}$ | $2.089 \times 10^{-2}$ |
| 1 pound per in.$^2$ = | $6.805 \times 10^{-2}$ | $6.895 \times 10^4$ | 27.68 | 5.171 | $6.895 \times 10^3$ | 1 | 144 |
| 1 pound per ft$^2$ = | $4.725 \times 10^{-4}$ | 478.8 | 0.1922 | $3.591 \times 10^{-2}$ | 47.88 | $6.944 \times 10^{-3}$ | 1 |

$^a$ Where the acceleration of gravity has the standard value 9.80665 meters/sec$^2$.

1 bar = $10^6$ dyne/cm$^2$          1 millibar = $10^3$ dyne/cm$^2$

## ENERGY, WORK, HEAT

The electron volt (ev) is the kinetic energy an electron gains from being accelerated through the potential difference of one volt in an electric field. The Mev is the kinetic energy it gains from being accelerated through a million-volt potential difference.

The last two items in this table are not properly energy units but are included for convenience. They arise from the relativistic mass-energy equivalence formula $E = mc^2$ and represent the energy released if a kilogram or atomic mass unit (amu) is destroyed completely. Again, care should be used when employing this table.

| | Btu | erg | ft-lb | hp-hr | JOULES | cal | kw-hr | ev | Mev | kg | amu |
|---|---|---|---|---|---|---|---|---|---|---|---|
| 1 British thermal unit = | 1 | $1.055 \times 10^{10}$ | 777.9 | $3.929 \times 10^{-4}$ | 1055 | 252.0 | $2.930 \times 10^{-4}$ | $6.585 \times 10^{21}$ | $6.585 \times 10^{15}$ | $1.174 \times 10^{-14}$ | $7.074 \times 10^{12}$ |
| 1 erg = | $9.481 \times 10^{-11}$ | 1 | $7.376 \times 10^{-8}$ | $3.725 \times 10^{-14}$ | $10^{-7}$ | $2.389 \times 10^{-8}$ | $2.778 \times 10^{-14}$ | $6.242 \times 10^{11}$ | $6.242 \times 10^{5}$ | $1.113 \times 10^{-24}$ | 670.5 |
| 1 foot-pound = | $1.285 \times 10^{-3}$ | $1.356 \times 10^{7}$ | 1 | $5.051 \times 10^{-7}$ | 1.356 | 0.3239 | $3.766 \times 10^{-7}$ | $8.464 \times 10^{18}$ | $8.464 \times 10^{12}$ | $1.509 \times 10^{-17}$ | $9.092 \times 10^{9}$ |
| 1 horsepower-hour = | 2545 | $2.685 \times 10^{13}$ | $1.980 \times 10^{6}$ | 1 | $2.685 \times 10^{6}$ | $6.414 \times 10^{5}$ | 0.7457 | $1.676 \times 10^{25}$ | $1.676 \times 10^{19}$ | $2.988 \times 10^{-11}$ | $1.800 \times 10^{16}$ |
| 1 JOULE = | $9.481 \times 10^{-4}$ | $10^{7}$ | 0.7376 | $3.725 \times 10^{-7}$ | 1 | 0.2389 | $2.778 \times 10^{-7}$ | $6.242 \times 10^{18}$ | $6.242 \times 10^{12}$ | $1.113 \times 10^{-17}$ | $6.705 \times 10^{9}$ |
| 1 calorie = | $3.968 \times 10^{-3}$ | $4.186 \times 10^{7}$ | 3.087 | $1.559 \times 10^{-6}$ | 4.186 | 1 | $1.163 \times 10^{-6}$ | $2.613 \times 10^{19}$ | $2.613 \times 10^{13}$ | $4.659 \times 10^{-17}$ | $2.807 \times 10^{10}$ |
| 1 kilowatt-hour = | 3413 | $3.6 \times 10^{13}$ | $2.655 \times 10^{6}$ | 1.341 | $3.6 \times 10^{6}$ | $8.601 \times 10^{5}$ | 1 | $2.247 \times 10^{25}$ | $2.270 \times 10^{19}$ | $4.007 \times 10^{-11}$ | $2.414 \times 10^{16}$ |
| 1 electron volt = | $1.519 \times 10^{-22}$ | $1.602 \times 10^{-12}$ | $1.182 \times 10^{-19}$ | $5.967 \times 10^{-26}$ | $1.602 \times 10^{-19}$ | $3.827 \times 10^{-20}$ | $4.450 \times 10^{-26}$ | 1 | $10^{-6}$ | $1.783 \times 10^{-35}$ | $1.074 \times 10^{-9}$ |
| 1 million electron volts = | $1.519 \times 10^{-16}$ | $1.602 \times 10^{-6}$ | $1.182 \times 10^{-13}$ | $5.967 \times 10^{-20}$ | $1.602 \times 10^{-13}$ | $3.827 \times 10^{-14}$ | $4.450 \times 10^{-20}$ | $10^{6}$ | 1 | $1.783 \times 10^{-30}$ | $1.074 \times 10^{-3}$ |
| 1 kilogram = | $8.521 \times 10^{13}$ | $8.987 \times 10^{23}$ | $6.629 \times 10^{16}$ | $3.348 \times 10^{10}$ | $8.987 \times 10^{16}$ | $2.147 \times 10^{16}$ | $2.497 \times 10^{10}$ | $5.610 \times 10^{35}$ | $5.610 \times 10^{29}$ | 1 | $6.025 \times 10^{26}$ |
| 1 atomic mass unit = | $1.415 \times 10^{-13}$ | $1.492 \times 10^{-3}$ | $1.100 \times 10^{-10}$ | $5.558 \times 10^{-17}$ | $1.492 \times 10^{-10}$ | $3.564 \times 10^{-11}$ | $4.145 \times 10^{-17}$ | $9.31 \times 10^{8}$ | 931.0 | $1.660 \times 10^{-27}$ | 1 |

1 m-kgf = 9.807 joules     1 watt-sec = 1 joule = 1 nt-m     1 cm-dyne = 1 erg

## POWER

| | Btu/hr | ft-lb/min | ft-lb/sec | hp | cal/sec | kw | WATTS |
|---|---|---|---|---|---|---|---|
| 1 British thermal unit per hour = | 1 | 12.97 | 0.2161 | $3.929 \times 10^{-4}$ | $7.000 \times 10^{-2}$ | $2.930 \times 10^{-4}$ | 0.2930 |
| 1 foot-pound per minute = | $7.713 \times 10^{-2}$ | 1 | $1.667 \times 10^{-2}$ | $3.030 \times 10^{-5}$ | $5.399 \times 10^{-3}$ | $2.260 \times 10^{-5}$ | $2.260 \times 10^{-2}$ |
| 1 foot-pound per second = | 4.628 | 60 | 1 | $1.818 \times 10^{-3}$ | 0.3239 | $1.356 \times 10^{-3}$ | 1.356 |
| 1 horsepower = | 2545 | $3.3 \times 10^4$ | 550 | 1 | 178.2 | 0.7457 | 745.7 |
| 1 calorie per second = | 14.29 | $1.852 \times 10^2$ | 3.087 | $5.613 \times 10^{-3}$ | 1 | $4.186 \times 10^{-3}$ | 4.186 |
| 1 kilowatt = | 3413 | $4.425 \times 10^4$ | 737.6 | 1.341 | 238.9 | 1 | 1000 |
| 1 WATT = | 3.413 | 44.25 | 0.7376 | $1.341 \times 10^{-3}$ | 0.2389 | 0.001 | 1 |

## ELECTRIC CHARGE

| | abcoul | amp-hr | COUL | faraday | statcoul |
|---|---|---|---|---|---|
| 1 abcoulomb (1 emu) = | 1 | $2.778 \times 10^{-3}$ | 10 | $1.036 \times 10^{-4}$ | $2.998 \times 10^{10}$ |
| 1 ampere-hour = | 360 | 1 | 3600 | $3.730 \times 10^{-2}$ | $1.079 \times 10^{13}$ |
| 1 COULOMB = | 0.1 | $2.778 \times 10^{-4}$ | 1 | $1.036 \times 10^{-5}$ | $2.998 \times 10^9$ |
| 1 faraday = | 9652 | 26.81 | $9.652 \times 10^4$ | 1 | $2.893 \times 10^{14}$ |
| 1 statcoulomb (1 esu) = | $3.336 \times 10^{-11}$ | $9.266 \times 10^{-14}$ | $3.336 \times 10^{-10}$ | $3.456 \times 10^{-15}$ | 1 |

1 electronic charge = $1.602 \times 10^{-19}$ coulomb

## ELECTRIC CURRENT

| | abamp | AMP | statamp |
|---|---|---|---|
| 1 abampere (1 emu) = | 1 | 10 | $2.998 \times 10^{10}$ |
| 1 AMPERE = | 0.1 | 1 | $2.998 \times 10^9$ |
| 1 statampere (1 esu) = | $3.336 \times 10^{-11}$ | $3.336 \times 10^{-10}$ | 1 |

## ELECTRIC POTENTIAL, ELECTROMOTIVE FORCE

| | abv | VOLTS | statv |
|---|---|---|---|
| 1 abvolt (1 emu) = | 1 | $10^{-8}$ | $3.336 \times 10^{-11}$ |
| 1 VOLT = | $10^8$ | 1 | $3.336 \times 10^{-3}$ |
| 1 statvolt (1 esu) = | $2.998 \times 10^{10}$ | 299.8 | 1 |

## ELECTRIC RESISTANCE

| | abohm | OHMS | statohm |
|---|---|---|---|
| 1 abohm (1 emu) = | 1 | $10^{-9}$ | $1.113 \times 10^{-21}$ |
| 1 OHM = | $10^9$ | 1 | $1.113 \times 10^{-12}$ |
| 1 statohm (1 esu) = | $8.987 \times 10^{20}$ | $8.987 \times 10^{11}$ | 1 |

### ELECTRIC RESISTIVITY

| | abohm-cm | μohm-cm | ohm-cm | statohm-cm | OHM-M | ohm-circ mil/ft |
|---|---|---|---|---|---|---|
| 1 abohm-centimeter (1 emu) = | 1 | 0.001 | $10^{-9}$ | $1.113 \times 10^{-21}$ | $10^{-11}$ | $6.015 \times 10^{-3}$ |
| 1 micro-ohm-centimeter = | 1000 | 1 | $10^{-6}$ | $1.113 \times 10^{-18}$ | $10^{-8}$ | 6.015 |
| 1 ohm-centimeter = | $10^9$ | $10^6$ | 1 | $1.113 \times 10^{-12}$ | 0.01 | $6.015 \times 10^6$ |
| 1 statohm-centimeter (1 esu) = | $8.987 \times 10^{20}$ | $8.987 \times 10^{17}$ | $8.987 \times 10^{11}$ | 1 | $8.987 \times 10^9$ | $5.406 \times 10^{18}$ |
| 1 OHM-METER = | $10^{11}$ | $10^8$ | 100 | $1.113 \times 10^{-10}$ | 1 | $6.015 \times 10^8$ |
| 1 ohm-circular mil per foot = | 166.2 | 0.1662 | $1.662 \times 10^{-7}$ | $1.850 \times 10^{-19}$ | $1.662 \times 10^{-9}$ | 1 |

### CAPACITANCE

| | abf | FARADS | μf[a] | statf |
|---|---|---|---|---|
| 1 abfarad (1 emu) = | 1 | $10^9$ | $10^{15}$ | $8.987 \times 10^{20}$ |
| 1 FARAD = | $10^{-9}$ | 1 | $10^6$ | $8.987 \times 10^{11}$ |
| 1 microfarad = | $10^{-15}$ | $10^{-6}$ | 1 | $8.987 \times 10^5$ |
| 1 statfarad (1 esu) = | $1.113 \times 10^{-21}$ | $1.113 \times 10^{-12}$ | $1.113 \times 10^{-6}$ | 1 |

[a] This unit is frequently abbreviated as mf.

### INDUCTANCE

| | abhenry | HENRYS | μh | mh | stathenry |
|---|---|---|---|---|---|
| 1 abhenry (1 emu) = | 1 | $10^{-9}$ | 0.001 | $10^{-6}$ | $1.113 \times 10^{-21}$ |
| 1 HENRY = | $10^9$ | 1 | $10^6$ | 1000 | $1.113 \times 10^{-12}$ |
| 1 microhenry = | 1000 | $10^{-6}$ | 1 | 0.001 | $1.113 \times 10^{-18}$ |
| 1 millihenry = | $10^6$ | 0.001 | 1000 | 1 | $1.113 \times 10^{-15}$ |
| 1 stathenry (1 esu) = | $8.987 \times 10^{20}$ | $8.987 \times 10^{11}$ | $8.987 \times 10^{17}$ | $8.987 \times 10^{14}$ | 1 |

### MAGNETIC FLUX

| | maxwell | kiloline | WEBER |
|---|---|---|---|
| 1 maxwell (1 line or 1 emu) = | 1 | 0.001 | $10^{-8}$ |
| 1 kiloline = | 1000 | 1 | $10^{-5}$ |
| 1 WEBER = | $10^8$ | $10^5$ | 1 |

1 esu = 299.8 webers

## APPENDIX G

### MAGNETIC INDUCTION B

|  | gauss | kiloline/in.$^2$ | WEBER/METER$^2$ = TESLA | milligauss |  |
|---|---|---|---|---|---|
| 1 gauss (line per cm$^2$) = | 1 | $6.452 \times 10^{-3}$ | $10^{-4}$ | 1000 | $10^5$ |
| 1 kiloline per in.$^2$ = | 155.0 | 1 | $1.550 \times 10^{-2}$ | $1.550 \times 10^5$ | $1.550 \times 10^7$ |
| 1 WEBER per METER$^2$ = 1 TESLA = | $10^4$ | 64.52 | 1 | $10^7$ | $10^9$ |
| 1 milligauss = | 0.001 | $6.452 \times 10^{-6}$ | $10^{-7}$ | 1 | 100 |
| 1 gamma = | $10^{-5}$ | $6.452 \times 10^{-8}$ | $10^{-9}$ | 0.01 | 1 |

1 esu = $2.998 \times 10^6$ webers/meter$^2$

### MAGNETOMOTIVE FORCE

|  | abamp-turn | AMP-TURN | gilbert |
|---|---|---|---|
| 1 abampere-turn = | 1 | 10 | 12.57 |
| 1 AMPERE-TURN = | 0.1 | 1 | 1.257 |
| 1 gilbert = | $7.958 \times 10^{-2}$ | 0.7958 | 1 |

1 pragilbert = $4\pi$ amp-turn     1 esu = $2.655 \times 10^{-11}$ amp-turn

### MAGNETIC FIELD STRENGTH H

|  | abamp-turn/cm | amp-turn/cm | amp-turn/in. | AMP-TURN/METER | oersted |
|---|---|---|---|---|---|
| 1 abampere-turn per centimeter = | 1 | 10 | 25.40 | 1000 | 12.57 |
| 1 ampere-turn per centimeter = | 0.1 | 1 | 2.540 | 100 | 1.257 |
| 1 ampere-turn per inch = | $3.937 \times 10^{-2}$ | 0.3937 | 1 | 39.37 | 0.4947 |
| 1 AMPERE-TURN per METER = | 0.001 | 0.01 | $2.540 \times 10^{-2}$ | 1 | $1.257 \times 10^{-2}$ |
| 1 oersted = | $7.958 \times 10^{-2}$ | 0.7958 | 2.021 | 79.58 | 1 |

1 oersted = 1 gilbert     1 esu = $2.655 \times 10^{-9}$ amp-turn/meter
1 praoersted = $4\pi$ amp-turn/meter

# Mathematical Symbols and the Greek Alphabet

*Mathematical signs and symbols*

$=$ equals
$\cong$ equals approximately
$\neq$ is not equal to
$\equiv$ is identical to, is defined as
$>$ is greater than ($\gg$ is much greater than)
$<$ is less than ($\ll$ is much less than)
$\geqq$ is more than or equal to (or, is no less than)
$\leqq$ is less than or equal to (or, is no more than)
$\pm$ plus or minus (e.g., $\sqrt{4} = \pm 2$)
$\propto$ is proportional to (e.g., Hooke's law: $F \propto x$, or $F = -kx$)
$\Sigma$ the sum of
$\bar{x}$ the average value of $x$

*The Greek alphabet*

| Alpha | A | $\alpha$ | Nu | N | $\nu$ |
|---|---|---|---|---|---|
| Beta | B | $\beta$ | Xi | $\Xi$ | $\xi$ |
| Gamma | $\Gamma$ | $\gamma$ | Omicron | O | $o$ |
| Delta | $\Delta$ | $\delta$ | Pi | $\Pi$ | $\pi$ |
| Epsilon | E | $\epsilon$ | Rho | P | $\rho$ |
| Zeta | Z | $\zeta$ | Sigma | $\Sigma$ | $\sigma$ |
| Eta | H | $\eta$ | Tau | T | $\tau$ |
| Theta | $\Theta$ | $\theta, \vartheta$ | Upsilon | $\Upsilon$ | $\upsilon$ |
| Iota | I | $\iota$ | Phi | $\Phi$ | $\phi, \varphi$ |
| Kappa | K | $\kappa$ | Chi | X | $\chi$ |
| Lambda | $\Lambda$ | $\lambda$ | Psi | $\Psi$ | $\psi$ |
| Mu | M | $\mu$ | Omega | $\Omega$ | $\omega$ |

# Mathematical Formulas

*Quadratic formula*

If $ax^2 + bx + c = 0$, then $x = \dfrac{-b \pm \sqrt{b^2 - 4ac}}{2a}$.

*Trigonometric functions of angle $\theta$*

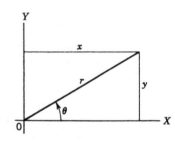

Fig. App. I

$$\sin \theta = \frac{y}{r} \qquad \cos \theta = \frac{x}{r}$$

$$\tan \theta = \frac{y}{x} \qquad \cot \theta = \frac{x}{y}$$

$$\sec \theta = \frac{r}{x} \qquad \csc \theta = \frac{r}{y}$$

*Pythagorean theorem*

$$x^2 + y^2 = r^2$$

*Trigonometric identities*

$$\sin^2 \theta + \cos^2 \theta = 1 \qquad \sec^2 \theta - \tan^2 \theta = 1 \qquad \csc^2 \theta - \cot^2 \theta = 1$$
$$\sin (\alpha \pm \beta) = \sin \alpha \cos \beta \pm \cos \alpha \sin \beta$$
$$\cos (\alpha \pm \beta) = \cos \alpha \cos \beta \mp \sin \alpha \sin \beta$$

$$\tan (\alpha \pm \beta) = \frac{\tan \alpha \pm \tan \beta}{1 \mp \tan \alpha \tan \beta}$$

$$\sin 2\theta = 2 \sin \theta \cos \theta$$
$$\cos 2\theta = \cos^2 \theta - \sin^2 \theta = 2 \cos^2 \theta - 1 = 1 - 2 \sin^2 \theta$$

$$\sin \theta = \frac{e^{i\theta} - e^{-i\theta}}{2i} \qquad \cos \theta = \frac{e^{i\theta} + e^{-i\theta}}{2}$$

$$e^{\pm i\theta} = \cos \theta \pm i \sin \theta$$

*Taylor's series*

$$f(x_0 + x) = f(x_0) + f'(x_0)x + f''(x_0)\frac{x^2}{2!} + f'''(x_0)\frac{x^3}{3!} + \cdots$$

*Series expansions* (these expansions converge for $-1 < x < 1$, except as noted)

$$\frac{1}{1+x} = 1 - x + x^2 - x^3 + \cdots$$

$$\sqrt{1+x} = 1 + \frac{x}{2} - \frac{x^2}{8} + \frac{x^3}{16} - \cdots$$

$$\frac{1}{\sqrt{1+x}} = 1 - \frac{x}{2} + \frac{3x^2}{8} - \frac{5x^3}{16} + \cdots$$

$$e^x = 1 + x + \frac{x^2}{2} + \frac{x^3}{6} + \cdots \qquad (-\infty < x < \infty)$$

*x* in radians
$$\sin x = x - \frac{x^3}{6} + \frac{x^5}{120} - \cdots \qquad (-\infty < x < \infty)$$

$$\cos x = 1 - \frac{x^2}{2} + \frac{x^4}{24} - \cdots \qquad (-\infty < x < \infty)$$

$$\tan x = x + \frac{x^3}{3} + \frac{2x^5}{15} + \cdots \qquad (-\pi/2 < x < \pi/2)$$

$$(x+y)^n = x^n + \frac{n}{1!}x^{n-1}y + \frac{n(n-1)}{2!}x^{n-2}y^2 + \cdots \qquad (x^2 > y^2)$$

#### Derivatives and indefinite integrals

In what follows, the letters $u$ and $v$ stand for any functions of $x$, and $a$ and $m$ are constants. To each of the integrals should be added an arbitrary constant of integration. *A Short Table of Integrals* by Peirce and Foster (Ginn and Co.) gives a more extensive tabulation.

1. $\dfrac{dx}{dx} = 1$

2. $\dfrac{d}{dx}(au) = a\dfrac{du}{dx}$

3. $\dfrac{d}{dx}(u+v) = \dfrac{du}{dx} + \dfrac{dv}{dx}$

4. $\dfrac{d}{dx}x^m = mx^{m-1}$

5. $\dfrac{d}{dx}\ln x = \dfrac{1}{x}$

6. $\dfrac{d}{dx}(uv) = u\dfrac{dv}{dx} + v\dfrac{du}{dx}$

7. $\dfrac{d}{dx}e^x = e^x$

8. $\dfrac{d}{dx}\sinh x = \cosh x$

1. $\int dx = x$

2. $\int au\,dx = a\int u\,dx$

3. $\int (u+v)\,dx = \int u\,dx + \int v\,dx$

4. $\int x^m\,dx = \dfrac{x^{m+1}}{m+1} \qquad (m \neq -1)$

5. $\int \dfrac{dx}{x} = \ln|x|$

6. $\int u\dfrac{dv}{dx}\,dx = uv - \int v\dfrac{du}{dx}\,dx$

7. $\int e^x\,dx = e^x$

8. $\int \cosh x\,dx = \sinh x$

9. $\dfrac{d}{dx}\cosh x = \sinh x$          9. $\int \sinh x\, dx = \cosh x$

10. $\dfrac{d}{dx}\arctan x = \dfrac{1}{1+x^2}$          10. $\int \dfrac{dx}{1+x^2} = \arctan x$

11. $\dfrac{d}{dx}\arcsin x = \dfrac{1}{\sqrt{1-x^2}}$          11. $\int \dfrac{dx}{\sqrt{1-x^2}} = \arcsin x$

12. $\dfrac{d}{dx}\operatorname{arcsec} x = \dfrac{1}{x\sqrt{x^2-1}}$          12. $\int \dfrac{dx}{x\sqrt{x^2-1}} = \operatorname{arcsec} x$

13. $\dfrac{d}{dx}\cos x = -\sin x$          13. $\int \sin x\, dx = -\cos x$

14. $\dfrac{d}{dx}\sin x = \cos x$          14. $\int \cos x\, dx = \sin x$

15. $\dfrac{d}{dx}\tan x = \sec^2 x$          19. $\int \tan x\, dx = \ln|\sec x|$

16. $\dfrac{d}{dx}\cot x = -\csc^2 x$          20. $\int \cot x\, dx = \ln|\sin x|$

17. $\dfrac{d}{dx}\sec x = \tan x \sec x$          21. $\int \sec x\, dx = \ln|\sec x + \tan x|$

18. $\dfrac{d}{dx}\csc x = -\cot x \csc x$          22. $\int \csc x\, dx = \ln|\csc x - \cot x|$

*Vector products*

Let $\mathbf{i}, \mathbf{j}, \mathbf{k}$ be unit vectors in the $x, y, z$ directions. Then

$$\mathbf{i}\cdot\mathbf{i} = \mathbf{j}\cdot\mathbf{j} = \mathbf{k}\cdot\mathbf{k} = 1, \quad \mathbf{i}\cdot\mathbf{j} = \mathbf{j}\cdot\mathbf{k} = \mathbf{k}\cdot\mathbf{i} = 0,$$

$$\mathbf{i}\times\mathbf{i} = \mathbf{j}\times\mathbf{j} = \mathbf{k}\times\mathbf{k} = 0,$$

$$\mathbf{i}\times\mathbf{j} = \mathbf{k}, \quad \mathbf{j}\times\mathbf{k} = \mathbf{i}, \quad \mathbf{k}\times\mathbf{i} = \mathbf{j}.$$

Any vector $\mathbf{a}$ with components $a_x, a_y, a_z$ along the $x, y, z$ axes can be written

$$\mathbf{a} = a_x\mathbf{i} + a_y\mathbf{j} + a_z\mathbf{k}.$$

Let $\mathbf{a}, \mathbf{b}, \mathbf{c}$ be arbitrary vectors with magnitudes $a, b, c$. Then

$$\mathbf{a}\times(\mathbf{b}+\mathbf{c}) = \mathbf{a}\times\mathbf{b} + \mathbf{a}\times\mathbf{c}$$

$$(s\mathbf{a})\times\mathbf{b} = \mathbf{a}\times(s\mathbf{b}) = s(\mathbf{a}\times\mathbf{b}) \quad (s \text{ a scalar}).$$

Let $\theta$ be the smaller of the two angles between $\mathbf{a}$ and $\mathbf{b}$. Then

$$\mathbf{a}\cdot\mathbf{b} = \mathbf{b}\cdot\mathbf{a} = a_xb_x + a_yb_y + a_zb_z = ab\cos\theta$$

$$\mathbf{a}\times\mathbf{b} = -\mathbf{b}\times\mathbf{a} = \begin{vmatrix} \mathbf{i} & \mathbf{j} & \mathbf{k} \\ a_x & a_y & a_z \\ b_x & b_y & b_z \end{vmatrix} = (a_yb_z - b_ya_z)\mathbf{i} + (a_zb_x - b_za_x)\mathbf{j} + (a_xb_y - b_xa_y)\mathbf{k}$$

$$|\mathbf{a}\times\mathbf{b}| = ab\sin\theta$$

$$\mathbf{a}\cdot(\mathbf{b}\times\mathbf{c}) = \mathbf{b}\cdot(\mathbf{c}\times\mathbf{a}) = \mathbf{c}\cdot(\mathbf{a}\times\mathbf{b})$$

$$\mathbf{a}\times(\mathbf{b}\times\mathbf{c}) = (\mathbf{a}\cdot\mathbf{c})\mathbf{b} - (\mathbf{a}\cdot\mathbf{b})\mathbf{c}$$

# Values of Trigonometric Functions

## APPENDIX J

TRIGONOMETRIC FUNCTIONS

| Radians | Degrees | Sines | Cosines | Tangents | Cotangents | | |
|---------|---------|-------|---------|----------|------------|----|--------|
| .0000 | 0 | .0000 | 1.0000 | .0000 | ∞ | 90 | 1.5708 |
| .0175 | 1 | .0175 | .9998 | .0175 | 57.29 | 89 | 1.5533 |
| .0349 | 2 | .0349 | .9994 | .0349 | 28.64 | 88 | 1.5359 |
| .0524 | 3 | .0523 | .9986 | .0524 | 19.08 | 87 | 1.5184 |
| .0698 | 4 | .0698 | .9976 | .0699 | 14.30 | 86 | 1.5010 |
| .0873 | 5 | .0872 | .9962 | .0875 | 11.430 | 85 | 1.4835 |
| .1047 | 6 | .1045 | .9945 | .1051 | 9.514 | 84 | 1.4661 |
| .1222 | 7 | .1219 | .9925 | .1228 | 8.144 | 83 | 1.4486 |
| .1396 | 8 | .1392 | .9903 | .1405 | 7.115 | 82 | 1.4312 |
| .1571 | 9 | .1564 | .9877 | .1584 | 6.314 | 81 | 1.4137 |
| .1745 | 10 | .1736 | .9848 | .1763 | 5.671 | 80 | 1.3963 |
| .1920 | 11 | .1908 | .9816 | .1944 | 5.145 | 79 | 1.3788 |
| .2094 | 12 | .2079 | .9781 | .2126 | 4.705 | 78 | 1.3614 |
| .2269 | 13 | .2250 | .9744 | .2309 | 4.332 | 77 | 1.3439 |
| .2443 | 14 | .2419 | .9703 | .2493 | 4.011 | 76 | 1.3265 |
| .2618 | 15 | .2588 | .9659 | .2679 | 3.732 | 75 | 1.3090 |
| .2793 | 16 | .2756 | .9613 | .2867 | 3.487 | 74 | 1.2915 |
| .2967 | 17 | .2924 | .9563 | .3057 | 3.271 | 73 | 1.2741 |
| .3142 | 18 | .3090 | .9511 | .3249 | 3.078 | 72 | 1.2566 |
| .3316 | 19 | .3256 | .9455 | .3443 | 2.904 | 71 | 1.2392 |
| | | Cosines | Sines | Cotangents | Tangents | Degrees | Radians |

## TRIGONOMETRIC FUNCTIONS (*Continued*)

| Radians | Degrees | Sines | Cosines | Tangents | Cotangents | | |
|---------|---------|-------|---------|----------|------------|------|--------|
| .3491 | 20 | .3420 | .9397 | .3640 | 2.748 | 70 | 1.2217 |
| .3665 | 21 | .3584 | .9336 | .3839 | 2.605 | 69 | 1.2043 |
| .3840 | 22 | .3746 | .9272 | .4040 | 2.475 | 68 | 1.1868 |
| .4014 | 23 | .3907 | .9205 | .4245 | 2.356 | 67 | 1.1694 |
| .4189 | 24 | .4067 | .9135 | .4452 | 2.246 | 66 | 1.1519 |
| | | | | | | | |
| .4363 | 25 | .4226 | .9063 | .4663 | 2.144 | 65 | 1.1345 |
| .4538 | 26 | .4384 | .8988 | .4877 | 2.050 | 64 | 1.1170 |
| .4712 | 27 | .4540 | .8910 | .5095 | 1.963 | 63 | 1.0996 |
| .4887 | 28 | .4695 | .8829 | .5317 | 1.881 | 62 | 1.0821 |
| .5061 | 29 | .4848 | .8746 | .5543 | 1.804 | 61 | 1.0647 |
| | | | | | | | |
| .5236 | 30 | .5000 | .8660 | .5774 | 1.732 | 60 | 1.0472 |
| .5411 | 31 | .5150 | .8572 | .6009 | 1.664 | 59 | 1.0297 |
| .5585 | 32 | .5299 | .8480 | .6249 | 1.600 | 58 | 1.0123 |
| .5760 | 33 | .5446 | .8387 | .6494 | 1.540 | 57 | 0.9948 |
| .5934 | 34 | .5592 | .8290 | .6745 | 1.483 | 56 | 0.9774 |
| | | | | | | | |
| .6109 | 35 | .5736 | .8192 | .7002 | 1.428 | 55 | 0.9599 |
| .6283 | 36 | .5878 | .8090 | .7265 | 1.376 | 54 | 0.9425 |
| .6458 | 37 | .6018 | .7986 | .7536 | 1.327 | 53 | 0.9250 |
| .6632 | 38 | .6157 | .7880 | .7813 | 1.280 | 52 | 0.9076 |
| .6807 | 39 | .6293 | .7771 | .8098 | 1.235 | 51 | 0.8901 |
| | | | | | | | |
| .6981 | 40 | .6428 | .7660 | .8391 | 1.192 | 50 | 0.8727 |
| .7156 | 41 | .6561 | .7547 | .8693 | 1.150 | 49 | 0.8552 |
| .7330 | 42 | .6691 | .7431 | .9004 | 1.111 | 48 | 0.8378 |
| .7505 | 43 | .6820 | .7314 | .9325 | 1.072 | 47 | 0.8203 |
| .7679 | 44 | .6947 | .7193 | .9657 | 1.036 | 46 | 0.8029 |
| .7854 | 45 | .7071 | .7071 | 1.0000 | 1.000 | 45 | 0.7854 |
| | | | | | | | |
| | | Cosines | Sines | Cotangents | Tangents | Degrees | Radians |

# Nobel Prize Winners in Physics<sup>a</sup>

## APPENDIX K

| 1901 | Wilhelm Konrad Röntgen | 1845–1923 | German | Discovery of X-rays. |
|---|---|---|---|---|
| 1902 | Hendrik Antoon Lorentz | 1853–1928 | Dutch | Influence of magnetism on the |
| | Pieter Zeeman | 1865–1943 | Dutch | phenomena of atomic radiation. |
| 1903 | Henri Becquerel | 1852–1908 | French | Discovery of natural radioactivity |
| | Pierre Curie | 1850–1906 | French | and of the radioactive elements |
| | Marie Curie | 1867–1934 | French | radium and polonium. |
| 1904 | Baron Rayleigh | 1842–1919 | English | Discovery of argon. |
| 1905 | Philipp Lenard | 1862–1947 | German | Research in cathode rays. |
| 1906 | Sir Joseph John Thomson | 1856–1940 | English | Conduction of electricity through gases. |
| 1907 | Albert A. Michelson | 1852–1931 | U. S. | Invention of interferometer and spectroscopic and metrological investigations. |
| 1908 | Gabriel Lippmann | 1845–1921 | French | Photographic reproduction of colors. |
| 1909 | Guglielmo Marconi | 1874–1937 | Italian | Development of wireless teleg- |
| | Karl Ferdinand Braun | 1850–1918 | German | raphy. |
| 1910 | Johannes Diderik van der Waals | 1837–1923 | Dutch | Equations of state of gases and fluids. |
| 1911 | Wilhelm Wien | 1864–1928 | German | Laws of heat radiation. |
| 1912 | Nils Gustaf Dalen | 1869–1937 | Swedish | Automatic coastal lighting. |
| 1913 | Heike Kamerlingh-Onnes | 1853–1926 | Dutch | Properties of matter at low temperatures; production of liquid helium. |
| 1914 | Max von Laue | 1879–1960 | German | Diffraction of X-rays in crystals. |
| 1915 | Sir William Henry Bragg | 1862–1942 | English | Study of crystal structure by |
| | Sir William Lawrence Bragg | 1890– | English— his son | means of X-rays. |
| 1916 | (No award) | | | |
| 1917 | Charles Glover Barkla | 1877–1944 | English | Discovery of the characteristic X-rays of elements. |
| 1918 | Max Planck | 1858–1947 | German | Discovery of the elemental quantum. |
| 1919 | Johannes Stark | 1874–1957 | German | Discovery of the Doppler effect in canal rays and the splitting of spectral lines in the electric field. |

| 1920 | Charles Edouard Guillaume | 1861–1938 | Swiss | Discovery of the anomalies of nickel-steel alloys. |
|------|---------------------------|-----------|-------|---------------------------------------------------|
| 1921 | Albert Einstein | 1879–1955 | German | Discovery of the law of the photo-electric effect. |
| 1922 | Niels Bohr | 1885–1963 | Danish | Study of structure and radiations of atoms. |
| 1923 | Robert Andrews Millikan | 1868–1953 | U. S. | Work on elementary electric charge and the photoelectric effect. |
| 1924 | Manne Siegbahn | 1886– | Swedish | Discoveries in the area of X-ray spectra. |
| 1925 | James Franck | 1882–1964 | German | Laws governing collision between electron and atom. |
| | Gustav Hertz | 1887 | German | |
| 1926 | Jean Perrin | 1870–1942 | French | Discovery of the equilibrium of sedimentation. |
| 1927 | Arthur H. Compton | 1892–1962 | U. S. | Discovery of the scattering of X-rays by charged particles |
| | Charles T. R. Wilson | 1869–1959 | English | Invention of the cloud chamber, a device to make visible the paths of charged particles. |
| 1928 | Sir Owen Williams Richardson | 1879–1959 | English | Discovery of the law known by his name (the dependency of the emission of electrons on temperature). |
| 1929 | Louis-Victor de Broglie | 1892– | French | Wave nature of electrons. |
| 1930 | Sir Chandrasekhara Raman | 1888– | Indian | Work on the scattering of light and discovery of the effect known by his name. |
| 1931 | (No award) | | | |
| 1932 | Werner Heisenberg | 1901– | German | Creation of quantum mechanics. |
| 1933 | Paul Adrien Maurice Dirac | 1902– | English | Discovery of new fertile forms of the atomic theory. |
| | Erwin Schrödinger | 1887–1961 | Austrian | |
| 1934 | (No award) | | | |
| 1935 | James Chadwick | 1891– | English | Discovery of the neutron. |
| 1936 | Victor Hess | 1883–1964 | Austrian | Discovery of cosmic radiation. |
| | Carl David Anderson | 1905– | U. S. | Discovery of the positron. |
| 1937 | Clinton Joseph Davisson | 1881–1958 | U. S. | Discovery of diffraction of electrons by crystals. |
| | George P. Thomson | 1892– | English | |
| 1938 | Enrico Fermi | 1901–1954 | Italian | Artificial radioactive elements from neutron irradiation. |
| 1939 | E. O. Lawrence | 1901–1958 | U. S. | Invention of the cyclotron. |
| 1940– | | | | |
| 1942 | (No awards) | | | |
| 1943 | Otto Stern | 1888 | U. S.g | Work with molecular beams and magnetic moment of proton. |
| 1944 | Isidor Isaac Rabi | 1898– | U. S. | Nuclear magnetic resonance. |
| 1945 | Wolfgang Pauli | 1900–1958 | Austrian | Discovery of quantum exclusion principle. |
| 1946 | Percy Williams Bridgman | 1882–1961 | U. S. | High-pressure physics. |
| 1947 | Sir Edward Appleton | 1892– | English | Upper atmosphere physics and discovery of Appleton layer. |
| 1948 | Patrick Maynard Stuart Blackett | 1897– | English | Discoveries in cosmic radiation and nuclear physics. |
| 1949 | Hideki Yukawa | 1907– | Japanese | Prediction of existence of meson. |
| 1950 | Cecil Frank Powell | 1903– | English | Photographic method of studying nuclear processes; discoveries about mesons. |
| 1951 | Sir John Douglas Cockcroft | 1897– | English | Transmutation of atomic nuclei by artificially accelerated atomic particles. |
| | Ernest Thomas Sinton Walton | 1903– | Irish | |
| 1952 | Felix Bloch | 1905– | U. S. | Measure of magnetic fields in atomic nuclei. |
| | Edward Mills Purcell | 1912– | U. S. | |
| 1953 | Frits Zernike | 1888– | Dutch | Invention of phase contrast microscopy. |
| 1954 | Max Born | 1882– | Englishb | Work in quantum mechanics and statistical interpretation of wave function. |

| | | | | |
|---|---|---|---|---|
| | Walther Bothe | 1891–1957 | German | Analysis of cosmic radiation using the coincidence method. |
| 1955 | Willis E. Lamb, Jr. | 1913 | U. S. | Fine structure of hydrogen. |
| | Polykarp Kusch | 1911– | U. S. | Magnetic moment of electron. |
| 1956 | John Bardeen | 1908– | U. S. | Invention and development of |
| | Walter H. Brattain | 1902– | U. S. | transistor. |
| | William B. Shockley | 1910– | U. S.[c] | |
| 1957 | Chen Ning Yang | 1922– | Chinese[d] | Non-conservation of parity and |
| | Tsung Dao Lee | 1926– | Chinese[d] | work in elementary particle theory. |
| 1958 | Pavel A. Čerenkov | 1904– | Russian | Discovery and interpretation of |
| | Ilya M. Frank | 1908– | Russian | Čerenkov effect of radiation by |
| | Igor Y. Tamm | 1895– | Russian | fast charged particles in matter. |
| 1959 | Owen Chamberlain | 1920– | U. S. | Discovery of the antiproton. |
| | Emilio Gino Segré | 1905– | U. S.[e] | |
| 1960 | Donald A. Glaser | 1926– | U. S. | Invention of bubble chamber. |
| 1961 | Robert L. Hofstadter | 1915– | U. S. | Electromagnetic structure of nucleons from high-energy electron scattering. |
| | Rudolf L. Mössbauer | 1929 | German | Discovery of recoilless resonance absorption of gamma rays in nuclei. |
| 1962 | Len D. Landau | 1908– | Russian | Theory of condensed matter; phenomena of superfluidity and superconductivity. |
| 1963 | Eugene B. Wigner | 1902– | U. S.[f] | Contributions to theoretical atomic and nuclear physics. |
| | Maria Goeppert-Mayer | 1906– | U. S.[g] | Shell model theory and magic |
| | J. H. D. Jensen | 1907– | German | numbers for the atomic nucleus. |
| 1964 | C. H. Townes | 1915– | U. S. | Invention of the maser and theory |
| | Nikolai Basov | 1922– | Russian | of coherent atomic radiation. |
| | Aleksandr Prokhorov | 1916– | Russian | |
| 1965 | Richard Feynman | 1918 | U. S. | Development of quantum electro- |
| | Julian Schwinger | 1918 | U. S. | dynamics |
| | Shin-Ichiro Tomonaga | 1906 | Japanese | |

[a] See *Nobel: The Man and His Prizes*, by Schück et al., Elsevier, N. Y.
[b] Born in Germany; naturalized British citizen.
[c] Born in England; naturalized U. S. citizen.
[d] Both have permanent U. S. resident status.
[e] Born in Italy; naturalized U. S. citizen.
[f] Born in Hungary; naturalized U. S. citizen.
[g] Born in Germany; naturalized U. S. citizen.

# The Gaussian System of Units

Much of the literature of physics is written, and continues to be written, in the Gaussian system of units. In electromagnetism many equations have slightly different forms depending on whether it is intended, as in this book, that mks variables be used or that Gaussian variables be used. Equations in this book can be cast in Gaussian form by replacing the symbols listed below under "rationalized mks" by those listed under "Gaussian." For example, Eq. 37–26,

$$\mathbf{B} = \mu_0(\mathbf{H} + \mathbf{M})$$

becomes

$$\frac{\mathbf{B}}{c} = \left(\frac{4\pi}{c^2}\right)\left(\frac{c}{4\pi}\,\mathbf{H} + c\mathbf{M}\right)$$

or

$$\mathbf{B} = \mathbf{H} + 4\pi\mathbf{M}$$

in Gaussian form. Symbols used in this book that are not listed below remain unchanged. The quantity $c$ is the speed of light.

| Quantity | Rationalized mks | Gaussian |
|---|---|---|
| Permittivity constant | $\epsilon_0$ | $1/4\pi$ |
| Permeability constant | $\mu_0$ | $4\pi/c^2$ |
| Electric displacement | $\mathbf{D}$ | $\mathbf{D}/4\pi$ |
| Magnetic induction | $\mathbf{B}$ | $\mathbf{B}/c$ |
| Magnetic flux | $\Phi_B$ | $\Phi_B/c$ |
| Magnetic field strength | $\mathbf{H}$ | $c\mathbf{H}/4\pi$ |
| Magnetization | $\mathbf{M}$ | $c\mathbf{M}$ |
| Magnetic dipole moment | $\boldsymbol{\mu}$ | $c\boldsymbol{\mu}$ |

In addition to casting the equations in the proper form it is of course necessary to use a consistent set of units in those equations. Below we list some equivalent quantities in mks and Gaussian units. This table can be used to transform units from one system to the other.

| Quantity | Symbol | Mks system | Gaussian system |
|----------|--------|------------|-----------------|
| Length | $l$ | 1 meter | $10^2$ cm |
| Mass | $m$ | 1 kg | $10^3$ gm |
| Time | $t$ | 1 sec | 1 sec |
| Force | $\mathbf{F}$ | 1 newton | $10^5$ dynes |
| Work or Energy | $W, E$ | 1 joule | $10^7$ ergs |
| Power | $P$ | 1 watt | $10^7$ ergs/sec |
| Charge | $q$ | 1 coulomb | $3 \times 10^9$ statcoul |
| Current | $i$ | 1 ampere | $3 \times 10^9$ statamp |
| Electric field strength | $\mathbf{E}$ | 1 volt/meter | $\frac{1}{3} \times 10^{-4}$ statvolt/cm |
| Electric potential | $V$ | 1 volt | $\frac{1}{300}$ statvolt |
| Electric polarization | $\mathbf{P}$ | 1 coul/meter$^2$ | $3 \times 10^5$ statcoul/cm$^2$ |
| Electric displacement | $\mathbf{D}$ | 1 coul/meter$^2$ | $12\pi \times 10^5$ statvolt/cm |
| Resistance | $R$ | 1 ohm | $\frac{1}{9} \times 10^{-11}$ sec cm$^{-1}$ |
| Capacitance | $C$ | 1 farad | $9 \times 10^{11}$ cm |
| Magnetic flux | $\Phi_\mathbf{B}$ | 1 weber | $10^8$ maxwells |
| Magnetic induction | $\mathbf{B}$ | 1 tesla $\equiv$ 1 weber/ meter$^2$ | $10^4$ gauss |
| Magnetic field strength | $\mathbf{H}$ | 1 amp-turn/meter | $4\pi \times 10^{-3}$ oersted |
| Magnetization | $\mathbf{M}$ | 1 weber/meter$^2$ | $1/4\pi \times 10^4$ gauss |
| Inductance | $I$ | 1 henry | $\frac{1}{9} \times 10^{-11}$ |

All factors of 3 in the above table, apart from exponents, should be replaced by $(2.997925 \pm 0.000003)$ for accurate work; this arises from the numerical value of the speed of light. For example the mks unit of capacitance ($= 1$ farad) is actually $8.98758 \times 10^{11}$ cm rather than $9$ ($= 3^2$) $\times 10^{11}$ cm as listed above. This example also shows that not only units but also the dimensions of physical quantities may differ between the two systems. In the mks system (see Appendix F) the dimensions of capacitance are $M^{-1}L^{-2}T^2Q^2$; in the Gaussian system they are simply $L$, the Gaussian standard unit of capacitance being 1 cm.

The student should consult *Classical Electromagnetism*, p. 611, by J. D. Jackson (John Wiley and Sons, 1962) for a fuller treatment of units and dimensions.

# Answers to Odd-Numbered Problems (Part I)

## Chapter 1

1. 6.00 ft = 1.83 meters.
3. 186 miles.
5. (a) $d_{sun}/d_{moon} = 400$.
   (b) $V_{sun}/V_{moon} = 6.4 \times 10^9$.
   We assume spherical shapes and precise eclipsing.
7. 2.03 hr.
9. (a) $\sim 10^6$ meters (see Table 1-1).
   (b) $\sim 10$ sec (see Table 1-2).
11. $C, D, A, B, E$ (best to worse). The criteria are first the constancy and second the magnitude of the daily variation.

## Chapter 2

3. The displacements should be:
   (a) parallel, (b) antiparallel,
   (c) perpendicular.
5. The magnitudes are: 5, 10, 11.2, 11.2, 11.2. The angles made with the $x$-axis are: 323°, 53.1°, 26.5°, 79.7°, and 260°.
7. 81.0 miles; 39.5° N of E.
9. (a) $a_x = -2.8$ meters;
   $a_y = -2.8$ meters.
   $b_x = 5.0$ meters; $b_y = 0$.
   $c_x = 3.0$ meters; $c_y = 5.2$ meters.
   (b) $d_x = 5.17$ meters;
   $d_y = 2.37$ meters.

(c) 5.69 meters; 24.6° N of E.
(d) 5.69 meters; 24.6° S of W.
13. $r_x = 2.0$ miles; $r_y = r_z = 4.0$ miles.
15. (a) 21 ft.
   (b) Can be greater but not less.
   (c) $10\mathbf{i} + 12\mathbf{j} + 14\mathbf{k}$ for a particular choice of axes.
17. 6950 miles, pointing through the earth from Washington to Manila.
21. (a) Scalar of magnitude 30 units².
   (b) Vector of magnitude 52 units² perpendicular to the plane formed by $\mathbf{a}$ and $\mathbf{b}$.
31. (a) $d_x = d_y = a^2$; $d_z = -a^2$.
   (b) $\mathbf{b} \cdot \mathbf{c} = a^2$; $\mathbf{d} \cdot \mathbf{c} = \mathbf{d} \cdot \mathbf{b} = 0$.

## Chapter 3

1. (a) 5.7 ft/sec
   (b) 7.0 ft/sec.
3. (a) Infinite number.
   (b) 60 miles.
5. 3000 ft/sec², upwards.
7.    $OA$  $AB$  $BC$  $CD$
   $v_x$  +   0   +  +
   $a_x$  −   0   +   0
   Intervals $OA$ and $BC$
9. $8.0 \times 10^{14}$ meters/sec².
11. 10 cm; no time.
13. (a) 5.0 ft/sec².
   (b) 4.0 sec.

(c)  6.0 sec.

(d)  90 ft.

**15.** (a)  15 ft/sec.

(b)  5.0 ft/sec.

(c)  23 ft.

**17.** No.

**19.** (a)  57 ft/sec.

(b)  3.6 sec.

**21.** 3.41 sec; 187 ft.

**23.** (a)  $3.5 \times 10^5$ ft.

(b)  330 sec.

**25.** 40 ft/sec.

**27.** $\frac{1}{16}$ ft.

**29.** (a)  17 sec.

(b)  290 meters.

**31.** (a)  $a$: $LT^{-2}$; ft/sec$^2$.

$b$: $LT^{-3}$; ft/sec$^3$.

(b)  2.0 sec.

(c)  24 ft.

(d)  $-16$ ft.

(e)  3.0, 0.0, $-9.0$, $-24$ ft/sec.

(f)  0.0, $-6.0$, $-12$, $-18$ ft/sec.$^2$

**Chapter 4**

**3.** The third step.

**7.** 76°.

**9.** 1.9 in.

**11.** Yes.

**13.** (a)  2.0 mm.

(b)  $v_{\text{hor}} = 1.0 \times 10^9$ cm/sec.

$v_{\text{vert}} = -0.20 \times 10^9$ cm/sec.

**15.** Electron    $5.5 \times 10^{-15}$ meter.

Neutron    $1.0 \times 10^{-6}$ meter.

Neon    $1.4 \times 10^{-5}$ meter.

Oxygen    $2.3 \times 10^{-5}$ meter.

Golf ball    $4.9 \times 10^{-4}$ meter (assuming 100 meters/sec).

**19.** (a)  $v_0 \cos \theta_0$.

(b)  $\mathbf{g}$.

(c)  $\mathbf{v} \perp \mathbf{a}$.

(d)  $(v_0{}^2/g) \cos^2 \theta_0$.

**21.** $6.7 \times 10^6$ meters/sec.

**23.** 2400 meters/sec$^2$.

**25.** (a)  4.2 meters at 45°;

5.5 meters at 68°;

6.0 meters at 90°.

(b)  4.2 meters at 135°.

(c)  0.85 meter/sec at 135°.

(d)  0.94 meter/sec at 90°;

0.94 meter/sec at 180°.

(e)  0.27 meter/sec$^2$ at 225°.

(f)  0.30 meter/sec$^2$ at 180°;

0.30 meter/sec$^2$ at 270°.

All angles are measured counter-clockwise from a line extending

horizontally to the right from $O$ in Fig. 4–15.

**27.** $6.0 \times 10^{-3}$ meter/sec$^2$.

**29.** (a)  $\mathbf{r} = \mathbf{i}(r \sin \omega t) + \mathbf{j}(r \cos \omega t)$

**31.** $\mathbf{u}_r = \mathbf{i} \cos \theta + \mathbf{j} \sin \theta$.

$\mathbf{u}_\theta = -\mathbf{i} \sin \theta + \mathbf{j} \cos \theta$.

**33.** 2.2 meters/sec and 1.8 meters/sec.

**35.** (a)  He should head the boat 29° upstream.

(b)  11 min.

**37.** (a)  Wind is blowing *from* a direction 75° E of S.

(b)  30° E of N.

Substituting W for E in the above yields another solution.

**Chapter 5**

**1.** $a_1/a_2 = m_2/m_1$.

**3.** 1.0 meters/sec$^2$, 37° from $\mathbf{F}_2$ toward $\mathbf{F}_1$.

**5.** 1300 lb, 5.5 sec, 50 ft, 2.7 sec.

**7.** $a_{\text{hor}} = 65$ ft/sec$^2$, $a_{\text{down}} = 32$ ft/sec$^2$.

$v_{\text{hor}} = 65t$ ft/sec$^2$,

$v_{\text{down}} = 32t$ ft/sec$^2$.

**9.** (a)  740 nt.

(b)  610 nt.

(c)  Zero.

$H$ is mass is 75 kg at each location.

**13.** Lower it with an acceleration of 4.2 ft/sec$^2$ or greater.

**15.** (a)  3.2 ft/sec$^2$.

(b)  58 lb.

**17.** (a)  2.0 meters/sec$^2$.

(b)  4.0 meters/sec.

(c)  4.0 meters.

**19.** (a)  $g \sin \theta$ down the plane.

(b)  $g \sin \theta$ down the plane.

(c)  $(g - a) \sin \theta$ down the plane.

(d)  $(g + a) \sin \theta$ down the plane.

(e)  Zero.

**21.** (a)  0.50 slugs.

(b)  20 lb.

**23.** (a)  32 lb, 55 lb.

(b)  16 ft/sec$^2$.

**25.** 3.3 meters/sec$^2$, 6.5 nt.

**27.** (a)  19 ft/sec$^2$.

(b)  $(M + m) \times 19$ ft/sec$^2$.

**Chapter 6**

**1.** 110 lb.

**3.** (a)  0.38 ft/sec$^2$, 0.79 ft/sec$^2$.

(b)  0.041, 0.028.

**5.** (a)  0.031 lb.

(b)  0.13.

**7.** 0.75.

**9.** 40 lb.

**11.** (a) 15 lb.

    (b) 6.4 ft/sec$^2$.

**13.** (a) $v_0^2/4g \sin \varphi$.

    (b) No.

**15.** (a) 1.06 nt (in tension).

    (b) 3.62 meters/sec$^2$.

    (c) 1.06 nt (in compression),
    3.62 meters/sec$^2$.

**17.** $g(\sin \theta - \sqrt{2}\, \mu_k \cos \theta)$.

**19.** (a) 2700 ft.

    (b) 5000 lb, upward.

**21.** (a) 0.0338 nt.

    (b) 9.77 nt.

**23.** (a) 15°.

    (b) 0.27.

**25.** $v^2/r = Mg/m$.

**27.** (a) 68 ft.

    (b) 18°.

**29.** $p_{min} = \dfrac{1}{2\pi} \sqrt{\dfrac{g}{r}\left(\dfrac{\sin \theta - \mu \cos \theta}{\cos \theta + \mu \sin \theta}\right)}$

    $p_{max} = \dfrac{1}{2\pi} \sqrt{\dfrac{g}{r}\left(\dfrac{\sin \theta + \mu \cos \theta}{\cos \theta - \mu \sin \theta}\right)}$

## Chapter 7

**1.** (a) 52 lb.

    (b) $-260$ ft-lb.

    (c) $+300$ ft-lb.

  $[(d)$ $-40$ ft-lb.

    (e) Zero.

    (f) Zero.

**3.** (a) 50 lb.

    (b) No.

    (c) Yes; 100 ft-lb.

    (d) No.

**5.** (a) Zero.

    (b) 30.1 joules.

    (c) $-30.1$ joules.

    (d) 0.225.

**9.** Boy: 4.8 meters/sec.
    Man: 2.4 meters/sec.

**11.** (a) $2.9 \times 10^7$ meters/sec.

    (b) $1.3 \times 10^6$ ev.

**15.** (a) 135 nt.

    (b) 60.0 joules.

**17.** 18 ft-lb.

**21.** (a) $5.4 \times 10^{10}$ ft-lb.

    (b) $1.6 \times 10^6$ hp.

**23.** (a) $1.8 \times 10^5$ ft-lb.

    (b) 0.55 hp.

**25.** 0.27 hp.

**27.** (b) $m(v_f/t_f)^2 t$.

    (c) 140 hp.

## Chapter 8

**5.** (a) $v = 2\sqrt{gl}$, $T = 5\, mg$.

    (b) 71°.

**7.** $2d$.

**9.** (a) $v_B = v_0$; $v_C = \sqrt{v_0^2 + gh}$.

    (b) $(v_0^2 + 2gh)/2L$.

    (c) It will never reach $B$.

**11.** (a) $\sqrt{5gR}$.

    (b) $P$ is above the horizontal by
    $\sin^{-1}(\frac{1}{3})$.

**13.** (a) 4.0 meters.

    (b) 4.5 meters/sec.

**15.** (a) $U(x) = -km_1m_2/x$ if $U(\infty) = 0$.

    (b) $\dfrac{km_1m_2d}{x_1(d + x_1)}$.

**17.** (a) $F_x = -kx$, $F_y = -ky$; $\mathbf{F}$ always
    points radially inward.

    (b) $F_r = -kr$, $F_\theta = 0$.

**21.** (a) 31.0 joules.

    (b) 5.33 meters/sec.

    (c) Conservative.

**23.** (a) $\sqrt{2gl(\sin \theta - \mu \cos \theta)}$.

    (b) $l(\sin \theta - \mu \cos \theta)/\mu$.

**25.** 7.2 meters/sec.

**27.** (a) 260 ft-lb.

    (b) 45 ft-lb; 1.7 ft up the plane.

**29.** (a) 6700 ft-lb/sec.

    (b) 2000 ft-lb.

    (c) No.

**31.** (a) $5.8 \times 10^{-13}$ joule.

    (b) 0.08.

**33.** (a) $\cong 0.010$ kg; 0.023 kg.

**35.** 27 Mev.

## Chapter 9

**3.** $6.46 \times 10^{-11}$ meter, along the line of
    symmetry.

**5.** $6.75 \times 10^{-13}$ meter below, on the
    line of symmetry.

**7.** (a) Center of mass remains at rest.

    (b) 0.75 meter.

**9.** 5500 slug-ft/sec; 6.0 miles/hr; 13
    miles/hr.

**11.** 13.6 ft.

**13.** $10\sqrt{2}$ meters/sec, 135° from either.

**15.** $1.1 \times 10^5$ ft.

**17.** (a) The casing and the capsule both
    move forward with speeds of
    24,000 and 27,000 ft/sec respec-
    tively.

    (b) The energy increases from $9.38 \times$
    $10^9$ ft-lb before separation to
    $9.40 \times 10^9$ ft-lb after, the in-

crease coming from energy stored in the spring.

19. $\dfrac{wv_{\text{rel}}}{W + w}$.

21. 220 bullets/min.
25. 5100 lb, 5600 hp.

## Chapter 10

1. 2.5 meters/sec.
3. 8.8 meters/sec.
5. $2mv/t$.
7. Slows down to 3.0 meters/sec.
9. $m_1/3$.
11. 310 meters/sec.
13. Block, 4.0 ft/sec; ball, 8.0 ft/sec.
15. (a) 4.1 ft/sec; $2.4 \times 10^3$ joules.
    (b) $v_{32} = 3.3$ ft/sec; $v_{24} = 5.3$ ft/sec.
17. (a) The left mass comes to rest; the center mass moves to the right with a speed $v_0(m - M)/(m + M)$; the right mass moves to the right with a speed $2v_0m/(m + M)$.
    (b) The left mass moves to the left with a speed $v_0(M - m)/(m + M)$; the center mass comes to rest; the right mass moves to the right with a speed $2v_0m/(m + M)$.
19. 0.25 meter.
21. 12 lb.
23. $v_0 = \left( 2E\,\dfrac{M + m}{Mm} \right)^{\frac{1}{2}}$.
25. (a) $\frac{1}{2}m_1v_{1i}{}^2$.
    (b) $\dfrac{1}{2}\,\dfrac{m_1{}^2v_{1i}{}^2}{(m_1 + m_2)}$.
    (c) $m_2/(m_1 + m_2)$.
    (d) $\frac{1}{2}m_1(v_{1i}{}^2 + v_{1i}v_{\text{cm}} + v_{\text{cm}}{}^2) + \frac{1}{2}m_2v_{\text{cm}}{}^2$; zero; 100%; no.
27. 1.9 meters/sec, 30° to initial direction; no.
29. 117° from final direction of $B$; no.
31. (a) $5.0 \times 10^8$ cm/sec.
    (b) $6.9 \times 10^8$ cm/sec, at 14° to the original direction opposite to the neutron and in the plane defined by the helium nucleus and the neutron.
33. $\pi(r_1 + r_2)^2$
35. $4.2 \times 10^{11}$ transmutations/meter$^2$ sec.
37. 8.12 Mev.

## Chapter 11

1. (a) 1200 in./min.
   (b) 600 in./min.
3. (a) $3.8 \times 10^6$ radians/sec.
   (b) 190 meters/sec.
5. (a) $-0.27$ radians/sec$^2$.
   (b) 20 rev.
7. $0.80\omega_0$.
9. (a) $x^2 + y^2 = R^2$; a circle of radius $R$; $\omega$ is the angular speed of the body.
   (b) $v_x = \omega y$; $v_y = \omega x$; $v = \omega R$; $\mathbf{v}$ is tangential to the circle.
   (c) $a_x = -\omega^2 x$; $a_y = -\omega^2 y$; $a = \omega^2 R$; $\mathbf{a}$ points radially inward.
11. (a) $2.0 \times 10^{-7}$ radians/sec; $3.0 \times 10^4$ meters/sec.
    (b) 6.0 meters/sec$^2$.
13. 5.7.
15. (a) 70 radians/sec.
    (b) $-13$ radians/sec$^2$.
    (c) 240 ft.
17. 0.12 radian/sec.
21. 19 ft/sec$^2$; 7.3 lb; 6.7 lb.
23. $g/2$.
25. (a) 11 ft.
    (b) 1.4 sec.
27. (a) $K = mg(R - r)$; $\frac{5}{7}$ translational; $\frac{2}{7}$ rotational.
    (b) $\frac{17}{7}\,mg$.
29. $F_{\text{hor}} = \dfrac{50mgR}{7(R - r)}$, to the left.
    $F_{\text{vert}} = \frac{5}{7}mg$, downward.
33. (a) $Mg$.
    (b) $MR^2\omega^2/4$.
    (c) $R^2\omega^2/4g$.
37. Axis is $5\sqrt{3}$ ft above ground and 5 ft from the wall.
39. 5.4 meters/sec.

## Chapter 12

1. (a) $\mathbf{i}(yF_z - zF_y) + \mathbf{j}(zF_x - xF_z) + \mathbf{k}(xF_y - yF_x)$.
13. $6.75 \times 10^{12}$ radians/sec.
15. (a) $2.6 \times 10^{29}$ joules.
    (b) $2.4 \times 10^9$ years.
17. 292 ft-lb.
19. (a) $-7.66$ radians/sec$^2$.
    (b) $-11.7$ newton meter.
    (c) $4.58 \times 10^4$ joules.
    (d) 624 revs.
    (e) (c) can be computed and has the same value.

**25.** $\sqrt{2gr/\cos\theta_0}$.

**27.** (a) They rotate about the center of mass (the center of the pole) with $\omega = 6.7$ rad/sec.

    (b) As above, but $\omega = 60$ rad/sec.

    (c) $K_a = 5.0 \times 10^3$ joules; $K_b = 45 \times 10^3$ joules; difference represents work done by the skaters.

## Chapter 13

**1.** 2.0 rad/sec; clockwise as seen from above.

**9.** $\frac{1}{12}ab\omega M$; **L** precesses around the axis of rotation, making an angle $\theta = \tan^{-1} a/b - \tan^{-1} b/a$ with it.

**11.** (a) $L_{\text{spin}}/L_{\text{orbital}} = \frac{2}{5}(R_m/R_{e-m})^2$ in which $R_m$ is the lunar radius and $R_{e-m}$ is the earth-moon distance.

    (b) Increase or decrease by one-half of present value.

**13.** 0.77 rad/sec.

**15.** (a) Linear momentum, angular momentum, and mechanical energy.

    (b) $\dfrac{Ml^2}{12d^2 + l^2}$, where $l$ is the length of the stick.

**19.** 250 rev/min.

**21.** $\dfrac{v_1}{1 + (I/MR^2)}$.

## Chapter 14

**1.** $\dfrac{W[h(2r - k)]^{1/2}}{r - h}$.

**3.** 74.4 gm.

**5.** Along a line extending from the center of the hole through the center of the disk, beyond the latter point by a distance $Rr^2/2(R^2 - r^2)$.

**9.** 7.2 ft.

**13.** Back: 880 lb; front: 630 lb.

**15.** $F_A = 120$ lb; $F_E = 72$ lb; $T = 47$ lb.

**17.** $F_h = 5.0$ lb; $F_v = 30$ lb; $d = 1.0$ ft.

**19.** (a) $W/2 \sin\theta$, tangent to the chain.

    (b) $\frac{1}{2}W \cot\theta$.

## Chapter 15

**1.** 0.28 sec.

**3.** (a) 99 nt.

    (b) 99 nt/meter.

**5.** (a) 4.0 sec.

    (b) $\pi/2$ radians/sec.

    (c) 0.37 cm.

    (d) $0.37 \cos(\pi t/2)$, in cm.

    (c) $-0.58 \sin(\pi t/2)$, in cm/sec.

    (f) 0.58 cm/sec.

    (g) 0.91 cm/sec².

    (h) Zero.

    (i) 0.58 cm/sec.

**7.** 3.1 cm.

**9.** $k_1 = k(1 + n)/n$.
    $k_2 = k(1 + n)$.

**13.** (a) $1.6 \times 10^4$ meters/sec², 2.5 meters/sec.

    (b) 2.2 meters/sec, $7.9 \times 10^3$ meters/sec².

**15.** (a) 6.2 in.

    (b) 1.2%; most of the original energy appears as internal energy in the block.

**17.** 19 lb.

**19.** $\frac{3}{4}$, $\frac{1}{4}$; $A/\sqrt{2}$.

**23.** 9.5 meters/sec².

**27.** $\dfrac{1}{2\pi}\sqrt{\dfrac{(g^2 + r^4/R^2)^{1/2}}{l}}$.

**31.** (a) 0.45 cycles/sec. (Does it matter whether the nail is very smooth or rusty?)

    (b) 4.0 ft.

**33.** (a) 39 radians/sec.

    (b) 34 radians/sec.

    (c) 120 radians/sec².

**37.** (a) $O_2$: 8.0 amu: HCl: 0.97 amu; CO: 6.8 amu.

    (b) 500 nt/meter.

**41.** $K_{\text{trans}} = 6.3 \times 10^{-2}$ joule.
    $K_{\text{rot}} = 3.1 \times 10^{-2}$ joule.

**43.** (b) $\sqrt{k/m}$.

## Chapter 16

**1.** 1600 miles.

**3.** 4.8 sec.

**7.** (b) 3.2 meters.

**9.** (b) 84.2 min.

    (c) No.

**11.** (a) $G(M_1 + M_2)m/a^2$.

    (b) $GM_1m/b^2$.

    (c) Zero.

**13.** (a) $2.6 \times 10^4$ ft/sec.

    (b) 87 min.

**15.** $2.5 \times 10^4$ km.

**17.** (a) $\frac{1}{2}$.

    (b) $\frac{1}{2}$.

    (c) $B$, by $8.5 \times 10^7$ ft-lb.

**19.** (a) $-GmM_e/r$.

    (b) $-2GmM_e/r$.

    (c) Falls directly down.

**21.** 1.88 years.

**23.** (b) $1.0 \times 10^4$ meters/sec.

(c) Moon: $1.9 \times 10^3$ meters/sec.

Sun: $6.2 \times 10^5$ meters/sec.

**25.** (a) $2\pi \sqrt{d^3/3mG}$.

(b) 2.

(c) 2.

**27.** $\sqrt{GM/L}$.

**29.** $a/3$.

**31.** (a) $2.2 \times 10^{-6}$ nt/kg, $\perp$ to line joining centers.

(b) $-5.3 \times 10^{-7}$ joules/kg.

**33.** (a) $-Gm\left(\dfrac{M_e}{R} + \dfrac{M_\mu}{r}\right)$.

(b) Nine-tenths of the way to the moon and at infinity.

(c) Earth: $U = 6.3 \times 10^7$ joules.

$g = 9.8$ nt/kg.

Moon: $U = 3.9 \times 10^6$ joules

$g = 1.6$ nt/kg

## Chapter 17

**1.** (a) 240 lb/in.$^2$

(b) 2.3 lb/in.$^2$

**3.** (b) 6000 lb.

**5.** (a) $\frac{1}{2}\rho g D^2 W$, $\frac{1}{6}\rho g D^3 W$.

(b) $D/3$ up from bottom.

**9.** $\frac{1}{4}\rho A (h_2 - h_1)^2$.

**11.** (a) $fA/a$.

(b) 20 lb.

**13.** 0.20 ft$^3$.

**15.** 0.67 gm/cm$^3$., 0.74 gm/cm$^3$.

**17.** 0.19, no.

**19.** $0.12\left(\dfrac{1}{\rho} - \dfrac{1}{8}\right)$, $\rho$ in gm/cm$^3$.

**21.** (b) $p = \rho g h$ where $h$ is the vertical depth below the surface.

## Chapter 18

**1.** 29 ft/sec.

**3.** $1.1 \times 10^5$ ft-lb.

**7.** $v = 4.1$ meters/sec.

$v' = 21$ meters/sec.

$Av = 8.1 \times 10^{-3}$ meter$^3$/sec.

**11.** (a) $2\sqrt{h(H-h)}$.

(b) Yes, a distance $h$ above the bottom.

**15.** 790 lb; 250 lb (up).

**17.** 410 meters/sec.

## Chapter 19

**3.** (a) 10 cm, 1.0 vib/sec, 200 cm/sec, 200 cm.

(b) 63 cm/sec.

**5.** (a) 12 cm.

(b) 180°.

**7.** 130 meters/sec.

**9.** $v_0$.

**11.** $1/4\pi$ watts/meter$^2$.

**13.** Intensity proportional to $r^{-1}$; amplitude proportional to $r^{-\frac{1}{2}}$.

**15.** $\lambda = 2\sqrt{4(H+h)^2 + d^2} - 2\sqrt{4H^2 + d^2}$.

**19.** (b) Even though the displacement of the string is zero at this instant the transverse velocities are not so that energy is present as kinetic energy.

**21.** $y = 6\cos\dfrac{\pi}{2}(0.005x + 8.00t - 0.57)$.

## Chapter 20

**1.** 17 meters, 0.017 meters.

**3.** $1.0 \times 10^5$ vib/sec.

**7.** (a) $\dfrac{l(V-v)}{Vv}$.

(b) 1600 ft.

**11.** $3.6 \times 10^{-8}$ meter.

**13.** (a) $5.0 \times 10^8$ vib/sec.

(b) $SBD/SAD = \frac{1}{2}$.

**15.** 31 and 94 vib/sec.

**21.** 1130, 1500, and 1880 cycles/sec.

**23.** $L(r-1)r$; 0.13 meter; 0.27 meter.

**25.** (a) 323 vib/sec.

(b) 6.

**27.** 387 vib/sec.

**29.** No.

**31.** (a) 970 vib/sec.

(b) 1030 vib/sec.

(c) Zero.

**33.** (a) 0.90 ft.

(b) 1440 vib/sec.

(c) 1080 ft/sec.

(d) 0.75 ft.

**35.** (a) 42°.

(b) 20 sec.

**37.** 990 meters/sec.

## Chapter 21

**1.** 373.15/273.16.

**3.** Materials, shape, absolute temperature, air currents; dimensions are $T^{-1}$.

**5.** $-40°$; 575°.

**7.** 10.000 ohms, $4.124 \times 10^{-3}/°$C, $-1.780 \times 10^{-6}/°$C$^2$.

**9.** 1.002 in.

**11.** The clock will run about 9 sec slow.

13. 46.4 cm.

19. $+28.9$ cm$^3$.

23. (a) $1.4 \times 10^{-2}$ kg meter$^2$/sec; 0.41 joule.

    (b) $\Delta\omega/\omega = \Delta K/K = -0.32\%$; $\Delta L/L = 0$.

25. $7.44 \times 10^{-4}/$C$°$.

## Chapter 22

1. $1.17$C$°$.

3. 190 watts.

5. 0.13 Btu/lb F$°$.

9. 0.59 cal/gm C$°$.

11. Mean specific heat exceeds that at the midpoint by $B\dfrac{t^2}{12}$.

13. (a) 34 Btu.

    (b) 270 F$°$.

15. (a) 500 C$°$/meter.

    (b) 4.6 cal/sec.

    (c) 75$°$C.

17. 8.6$°$C (Cu-Al) and 57$°$C (Al-brass).

19. $1.4 \times 10^{-5}$ kcal/meter$^2$ sec; $6.2 \times 10^{14}$ kcal.

21. 0.42 cal/meter sec C$°$.

23. (a) 6 cal.

    (b) $-43$ cal.

    (c) 40 cal.

    (d) 18 cal, 18 cal.

25. 8000 cal.

## Chapter 23

1. 76.5% by mass.

3. 100 cm$^3$.

5. 653 joules.

7. 27 lb/in.$^2$

9. The mercury drops 41.7 cm.

11. (a) $565 \times 10^{-23}$ joule, $772 \times 10^{-23}$ joule.

    (b) 3390 joule, 4630 joule.

13. (a) $1.01 \times 10^4°$K, $16.2 \times 10^4°$K;

    (b) 450$°$K, 7200$°$K.

15. He: 1400 meters/sec; A: 440 meters/sec.

17. $6.6 \times 10^4$.

19. (a) Eleven times larger.

    (b) Same size.

25. (a) $6.6 \times 10^{-23}$ gm.

    (b) 40.

27. 4.13 joules/cal.

29. 1910 cal.

35. 1.41.

37. Monatomic.

39. (a) 8.0 atm.

    (b) 600$°$ K.

41. (a) 2.5 atm, 336$°$ K.

    (b) $0.41 \ V_i$.

## Chapter 24

1. $3.2 \times 10^{-8}$ cm.

3. (a) $3.5 \times 10^{10}$ molecules/cm$^3$.

    (b) 160 meters.

9. (a) $7.1 \times 10^3$ meters/sec.

    (b) $2 \times 10^{-8}$ cm.

    (c) $5 \times 10^{10}$ collisions/sec.

11. $\bar{v}, v_{\text{rms}}, v_p$.

13. 1.5 cm/sec.

17. $RT \ln \dfrac{V_f - b}{V_i - b} + a\left(\dfrac{1}{V_f} - \dfrac{1}{V_i}\right)$.

19. (a) $3.2 \times 10^6$ nt/meter$^2$.

    (b) $4.1 \times 10^6$ nt/meter$^2$.

## Chapter 25

1. $5.0 \times 10^4$ joules.

7. (a) 2090 joules.

    (b) 380 cal.

    (c) 1570 joules.

9. 6.5.

11. $1.1 \times 10^6$ joules.

15. $10^{-3}$ $°$N, $10^{-6}$ $°$N, 0 $°$N, $-10^{-6}$ $°$N, $-10^{-3}$ $°$N, for example.

17. $+0.20$ cal/$°$K.

19. $+0.3$ cal/gm $°$K.

21. $+0.1$ cal/$°$K; no.

23. (a) 500 meters/sec.

    (b) N$_2$.

    (c) Positive.

# Answers to Odd-Numbered Problems (Part II)

## Chapter 26

**1.** 0.12 amp.

**5.** $6.0 \times 10^{-8}$ coul.

**9.** (a) $5.7 \times 10^{13}$ coul,
  (b) no,
  (c) 660 tons.

**13.** (b) Along the body diagonal.

**17.** (a) 510 nt,
  (b) $7.7 \times 10^{28}$ meters/sec$^2$.

**3.** $\pm 2.4 \times 10^{-8}$ coul.

**7.** (a) $Q = -2\sqrt{2}q$,
  (b) no.

**11.** $3.8 \times 10^{-5}$ coul, $1.2 \times 10^{-5}$ coul.

**15.** (a) $6.3 \times 10^{11}$,
  (b) $7.3 \times 10^{-13}$.

## Chapter 27

**5.** $5.6 \times 10^{-11}$ coul.

**9.** (a) The larger charge produces a field of $13 \times 10^4$ nt/coul at the site of the small\_
  the smaller charge produces a field of $5.3 \times 10^4$ nt/coul at the site of the larger.
  (b) $1.1 \times 10^{-2}$ nt, repulsive.

**11.** E lies in the median plane and points radially away from the charge axis.

**13.** $1.0 \times 10^5$ nt/coul, pointing up.

**17.** $E = q/8\pi\epsilon_0 a^2$, pointing along the axis of symmetry and away from the hemisphe\_

**21.** (a) $E = \dfrac{1}{4\pi\epsilon_0} \dfrac{qx}{(a^2 + x^2)^{3/2}}$,

  (b) $E = \dfrac{1}{2\pi^2\epsilon_0} \dfrac{(q_1 - q_2)a}{(a^2 + x^2)^{3/2}}$.

**25.** (a) $1.5 \times 10^3$ nt/coul,
  (b) $2.4 \times 10^{-16}$ nt (up),
  (c) $1.6 \times 10^{-26}$ nt,
  (d) $1.5 \times 10^{10}$.

**27.** (a) 7.1 cm,
  (b) $2.9 \times 10^{-8}$ sec,
  (c) 11%.

**29.** $\dfrac{dE}{dz} = -\dfrac{8q}{\pi\epsilon_0 l^3}$, where $l$ is the distance between the charges; yes.

**31.** $1.64 \times 10^{-19}$ coul.

**Chapter 28**

1. $\pi R^2 E$ (an expected result).
7. (a) $4.0 \times 10^6$ nt/coul,
   (b) $E = 0$.

11. $4.9 \times 10^{-10}$ coul.

3. $EA \cos \theta$.
9. (a) $E = \sigma/\epsilon_0$, to the left,
   (b) $E = 0$,
   (c) $E = \sigma/\epsilon_0$, to the right.
13. 0.44 mm.

19. (a) $E = \dfrac{q}{2\pi\epsilon_0 lr}$ (radially inward), where $l$ is the length of the cylinders,

   (b) $-q$ on inner surface and $-q$ on outer surface,

   (c) $E = \dfrac{q}{2\pi\epsilon_0 lr}$ (radially outward).

21. $2.5 \times 10^{-9}$ coul/meter$^2$.

23. $1.9 \times 10^2$ nt,
    $2.9 \times 10^{28}$ meters/sec$^2$.

25. (a) 1.1 nt-meters$^2$/coul,
   (b) $9.3 \times 10^{-12}$ coul.

**Chapter 29**

1. 0.89 mm.
5. (a) Between the charges a distance of 25 cm from $+q$ and outside the charges a distance of 50 cm from $+q$.
   (b) Outside the charges a distance of 140 cm from $+q$.

3. 900 volts.

7. $V_A - V_B = \dfrac{q}{2\pi\epsilon_0}\dfrac{d}{a(a+d)}$.

9. $1.9 \times 10^{-29}$ coul meter; text value ($0.61 \times 10^{-29}$ coul meter) is lower and correct; the assumptions made in this problem are oversimplified.

11. 99 tons.
15. (a) $-0.12$ volt,
   (b) $1.8 \times 10^{-8}$ nt/coul, radially inward.

13. $-6.4 \times 10^{-7}$ joule.
17. 2900 volts.

21. No.

23 (a) $-180$ volts,
   (b) $+2900$ volts and $-9000$ volts.

27. $-0.21q^2/\epsilon_0 a$.
29. (a) $1.1 \times 10^{17}$ volts/meter,
   (b) $4.6 \times 10^{21}$ volts/meter, assuming a nuclear radius of $5 \times 10^{-15}$ meter.
31. (a) $2.6 \times 10^5$ volts,

   (b) $\dfrac{\sqrt{5}}{3}$ c $= 0.745$ c.

33. 9.0 kw.

35. (a) $3.2 \times 10^{-13}$ joule,
   (b) $1.6 \times 10^{-13}$ joule,
   (c) proton.

**Chapter 30**

1. (a) $q_2 = q_8 = 4.8 \times 10^{-4}$ coul,
    $V_2 = 240$ volts,
    $V_8 = 60$ volts;
   (b) $q_2 = 2.0 \times 10^{-4}$ coul,
    $q_8 = 7.7 \times 10^{-4}$ coul,
    $V_2 = V_8 = 96$ volts;
   (c) $q_2 = q_8 = $ zero,
    $V_2 = V_8 = $ zero.

3. 43 $\mu\mu$f.

11. 3.2 $\mu$f.
15. 7.3 $\mu$f.

13. 4 $\mu$f.
21. Mica.

23. Assuming $\kappa = 5.4$:
   (a) $10^4$ volts/meter,
   (b) $+5.0 \times 10^{-9}$ coul, on the positive plate,

(c)  $-4.1 \times 10^{-9}$ coul, next to the positive plate.

**25.** 0.63 meter$^2$.

**27.** 0.11 joule/meter$^3$.

**31.** (a) $1.3 \times 10^{-7}$ joule,
(b) no.

**33.** $7.0 \times 10^{-6}$ coul.

**35.** 7.0¢.

**37.** (a) $q_1 = q_2 = 3.3 \times 10^{-4}$ coul,
$q_3 = 4.0 \times 10^{-4}$ coul;
(b) $V_1 = 33$ volts,
$V_2 = 67$ volts,
$V_3 = 100$ volts;
(c) $U_1 = 5.4 \times 10^{-3}$ joule,
$U_2 = 10.9 \times 10^{-3}$ joule,
$U_3 = 2.0 \times 10^{-2}$ joule.

**Chapter 31**

**1.** (a) 1200 coul,
(b) $7.5 \times 10^{21}$ electrons.

**3.** (a) 2.4, iron being larger;
(b) no.

**5.** $6.7 \times 10^{-6}$ coul/meter$^2$.

**7.** 54 ohms.

**9.** (a) $2.2 \times 10^{-7}$ ohm,
(b) nickel ($\rho = 6.8 \times 10^{-8}$ ohm -meter).

**11.** (a) 260°C,
(b) yes.

**13.** 0.39% ($\rho$),
0.0017% ($l$),
0.0034% ($A$).

**17.** 11 ohms.

**19.** (a) $4.9 \times 10^6$ amp/meter$^2$,
(b) $8.4 \times 10^{-2}$ volt/meter,
(c) 26 volts,
(d) 640 watts.

**21.** 620 watts.

**23.** (a) 8.7%,
(b) smaller.

**Chapter 32**

**1.** $1.1 \times 10^4$ joules.

**3.** $-0.62\%$.

**7.** (a) 990 ohms,
(b) $9.9 \times 10^{-4}$ watt.

**9.** $V_d - V_c = 1.3$ volt.

**11.** (a) 120 ohms,
(b) $i_1 = 0.051$ amp,
$i_2 = i_3 = 0.019$ amp,
$i_4 = 0.013$ amp.

**13.** (a) $R = \frac{1}{2}r$,
(b) $E^2/2r$.

**17.** 38 ohms.

**19.** (a) 10 ohms,
(b) 14 ohms,
(c) 10 ohms.

**21.** series: $i = \dfrac{2}{R + 2r}$.

parallel: $i = \dfrac{2}{2R + r}$.

(a) Put $R_1$ roughly in the middle of its range; adjust current roughly with $R_2$; make fine adjustment with $R_1$.

(b) Relatively large percentage changes in $R_1$ cause only small percentage changes in the resistance of the parallel combination, thus permitting fine adjustment. The ratio is 1 : 21.

**27.** 2.7%.

**29.** 4.6 time constants.

**33.** (a) $9.6 \times 10^{-7}$
(b) $1.1 \times 10^{-6}$ watt,
(c) $2.7 \times 10^{-6}$ watt,
(d) $3.8 \times 10^{-6}$ watt.

**Chapter 33**

1. (a) East,
   (b) $6.3 \times 10^{14}$ meters/sec$^2$,
   (c) 3.0 mm.

3. 7.5 nt, perpendicular to the wire and to **B**.

5. See Appendix.　　　　　　　**7.** 3.8 coul.

9. 520 gauss, normal to plane of tracks.

11. $4.3 \times 10^{-3}$ nt-meter. The torque vector is parallel to the long side of the coil and points down.

15. (a) $1.4 \times 10^{-4}$ meter/sec,　　　　17. (a) $K_p = K_d = \frac{1}{2}K_\alpha$,
    (b) $4.5 \times 10^{-23}$ nt (down),　　　　　　(b) $R_d = 14$ cm.
    (c) $2.8 \times 10^{-4}$ volt/meter (down),　　(c) $R_\alpha = 14$ cm.
    (d) $5.7 \times 10^{-6}$ volt (top +, bottom −),
    (e) same as (b).

19. (a) $2.6 \times 10^7$ meters/sec,
    (b) $1.1 \times 10^{-7}$ sec,
    (c) 14 Mev,
    (d) $7.0 \times 10^6$ volts.

23. $1.6 \times 10^{-8}$ weber/meter$^2$, horizontal and at right angles to the equator.

25. $T = 3.6 \times 10^{-10}$ sec,　　　　　　27. $2.11 \times 10^{-25}$ kg or 127 proton masses.
    $p = 0.17$ mm,
    $r = 1.5$ mm.

29. (a) Increase,　　　　　　　　　31. (a) 8.5 Mev,
    (b) decrease.　　　　　　　　　　　(b) 0.80 weber/meter$^2$,
    　　　　　　　　　　　　　　　　　　(c) 34 Mev,
    　　　　　　　　　　　　　　　　　　(d) 24 mc/sec,
    　　　　　　　　　　　　　　　　　　(e) 34 Mev, 1.6 webers/meter$^2$,
    　　　　　　　　　　　　　　　　　　　　34 Mev, 12 mc/sec.

33. 1.4.　　　　　　　　　　　　35. 3800 meters/sec.

**Chapter 34**

1. $7.9 \times 10^{-3}$ weber/meter$^2$.

3. (a) $3.2 \times 10^{-16}$ nt, parallel to current;
   (b) $3.2 \times 10^{-16}$ nt, radially outward if **v** is parallel to the current;
   (c) zero.

7. $1.0 \times 10^{-6}$ weber/meter.

9. **B** = 0 along a line parallel to the wire and 4.0 mm from it. If the current is horizontal and points toward the observer and the external field points horizontally from left to right, the line is directly above the wire.

11. $8.0 \times 10^{-5}$ weber/meter$^2$, up.　　　13. $3.2 \times 10^{-3}$ nt, toward the long wire.

23. (a) $1.0 \times 10^{-3}$ weber/meter$^2$, out of figure;
    (b) $8.0 \times 10^{-4}$ weber/meter$^2$, out of figure.

27. (a) $9.4 \times 10^{-5}$ weber/meter$^2$,
    (b) $1.5 \times 10^{-6}$ nt-meter.

**Chapter 35**

1. $2.0 \times 10^{-2}$ coul.　　　　　　　3. Zero.

9. $V_m = \pi^2 BR^2 f$,　　　　　　　11. $3.0 \times 10^{-4}$ volt.
   $i_m = \pi^2 BR^2 f / R_M$

13. (a) $3.1 \times 10^{-2}$ webers/sec,　　　17. (a) $3.6 \times 10^7$ meters/sec$^2$, to the right;
    (b) left to right.　　　　　　　　　　　(b) zero;
    　　　　　　　　　　　　　　　　　　　(c) $4.4 \times 10^7$ meters/sec$^2$, to the left.

**Chapter 36**

1. Let the current charge at 10 amp/sec.
9. 12 sec.
15. (a) 10 amp,
   (b) 100 joules.
21. (a) $2.5 \times 10^{-6}$ joule/meter,
   (b) $14 \times 10^{-6}$ joule/meter,
   (c) $0.8 \times 10^{-6}$ joule/meter.

7. $1.0 \times 10^{-7}$ weber.
13. 27 amp/sec.
17. 0.63 joule/meter$^3$.

23. $1.5 \times 10^8$ volt/meter.

**Chapter 37**

1. (a) $5.0 \times 10^7$ amp,
   (b) yes,
   (c) no.
5. (a) 7.6 amp meter$^2$,
   (b) 11 nt-meter.
11. (a) 1.8 webers/meter$^2$,
   (b) $6.5 \times 10^{-23}$ joule.

3. (a) $1.4 \times 10^{11}$ volts/meter,
   (b) $2.8 \times 10^{-3}$ weber/meter$^2$.

9. $7.5 \times 10^{-6}$ weber/meter$^2$.

**Chapter 38**

1. 600, 710, 1100, and 1300 cycles/sec.

15. $\omega = \sqrt{\dfrac{1}{L_1 C_1}} = \sqrt{\dfrac{1}{L_2 C_2}}$.

21. (a) $1.4 \times 10^{14}$ volts/meter-sec,
   (b) $9.9 \times 10^{-6}$ weber/meter$^2$.

13. (a) 35 cycles/sec.
   (b) 38 or 33 cycles/sec.

19. $i_d = \epsilon_0 \pi r^2 \dfrac{dE}{dt}$   $(r \lesssim R)$,

    $i_d = \epsilon_0 \pi R^2 \dfrac{dE}{dt}$   $(r \gtrsim R)$.

**Chapter 39**

3. 4.9 cm, $5.2 \times 10^8$ meters/sec
   $(= 1.7\ c)$.
13. (a) $a^2 EB/\mu_0$
   for faces parallel to $xy$-plane, zero for others;
   (b) zero.
15. 1000 volts/meter,
   $3.4 \times 10^{-6}$ weber/meter$^2$.

9. 18 cm, 12 cm.

**Chapter 40**

1. (a) 5100 A and 6100 A,
   (b) $5.5 \times 10^{14}$ cycles/sec and $1.8 \times 10^{-15}$ sec.
3. $F_{\text{rad}} = 6.0 \times 10^8$ nt,
   $F_{\text{gr}} = 3.6 \times 10^{22}$ nt.
11. 0.13.
15. $3.8 \times 10^{-2}$ A.

7. $1.3 \times 10^{-7}$ nt/meter$^2$.

13. (b) 7.3 (cycles/sec)/(miles/hour).
17. Yellow-orange.

**Chapter 41**

3. $2.05 \times 10^8$ meters/sec.
15. (b) 0.17.
19. Cover the center of each face with a circle of radius 0.33 cm. The fraction covered
   is 0.35.

5. 1.56.

**Chapter 42**

1. (a) 7,
   (b) 5,
   (c) 2.

3. 40 cm.

**6.** Alternate vertical columns:
  (a) $+$, $+40$, $-20$, $+2$, no, yes;
  (c) concave, $+40$, $+60$, $-2$, yes, no;
  (e) convex, $-20$, $+20$, $+0.5$, no, yes;
  (g) $-20$, $-$, $-$, $+5$, $+0.80$, no, yes.

**9.** 4.24 cm.

**7.** Object at center of curvature.

**10.** Alternate vertical columns:
  (a) $-18$, no;
  (c) $+71$, yes;
  (e) $+30$, no;
  (g) $-26$, no.

**11.** Alternate vertical columns:
  (a) $+$, $X$, $X$, $+20$, $X$, $-1$, yes, no;
  (c) converging, $+$, $X$, $X$, $-10$, $X$, no, yes;
  (e) converging, $+30$, $-15$, $+1.5$, no, yes;
  (g) diverging, $-120$, $-9.2$, $+0.92$, no, yes;
  (i) converging, $+3.3$, $X$, $X$, $+5$, $X$, $-$, no.

**17.** 4.5 cm, 9.0 cm.

**19.** Assuming the light is incident from the left, a distance of $-\dfrac{r(n-2)}{2(n-1)^2}$ to the right of the right edge of the sphere.

**21.** (a) $R'$ is negative and $R''$ is positive,
  (b) $i = \dfrac{-2r}{n+1}$,
  (c) virtual and erect.

**23.** (a) Coincides in location with original object and is enlarged 5.0 times,
  (c) virtual and inverted.

## Chapter 43

**1.** Slit separation must be 0.034 mm.

**5.** $6.6 \times 10^{-3}$ mm.

**9.** $I = \dfrac{I_m}{9}\left[1 + 8\cos^2\left(\dfrac{\pi d \sin\theta}{\lambda}\right)\right].$

**13.** 80 million.

**17.** 4800 A (blue).

**23.** 5880 A.

**3.** $0.15°$.

**7.** 3.0 mm.

**11.** $y = 17.4 \sin(\omega t + 13.3°)$.

**15.** 1.21.

**19.** 6700 A.

**25.** 6057.8021 A.

## Chapter 44

**1.** 0.17 mm.

**3.** (a) $\lambda_a = 2\lambda_b$,
  (b) coincidences occur when $m_b = 2m_a$.

**5.** $79.7°$.

**9.** 9100 meters.

**15.** 3.

**7.** (a) $52.9°$,
  (b) $10.2°$,
  (c) $5.1°$.

**11.** (a) 0.16 sec of arc,
  (b) $7.4 \times 10^7$ km,
  (c) $2.2 \times 10^{-4}$ mm.

**17.** (a) Must have $d = 4a$,
  (b) Every fourth fringe is missing.

## Chapter 45

**1.** Three complete orders.

**5.** The intensity would be concentrated near the twentieth order for blue and the eleventh order for red. The orders would overlap to such an extent as to appear almost white.

**7.** All wavelengths shorter than 6300 A.

**9.** $0°$, $\pm10°$, $\pm21°$, $\pm32°$, $\pm45°$, and $\pm62°$.

**11.** 5200 A to 6200 A.

**17.** (a) $0.0032°/A$,
$0.0077°/A$,
$0.024°/A$;
(b) 40,000,
80,000,
120,000.

**19.** 3600 lines.

**21.** (a) $4.6 \times 10^{-2}$ A.
(b) No. The resolution could normally be improved by going to a higher order diffraction, but in this case $m = 3$ is the highest order that can exist (assuming that the light falls on the grating at right angles).

**23.** (a) $6 \times 10^4$ A,
(b) $1.5 \times 10^4$ A,
(c) 0, 1, 2, 3, 5, 6, 7, 9. The tenth order is at $\theta = 90°$.

**25.** $33°$, $20°$, $5.2°$ (all clockwise);
$14°$ (counterclockwise).

**27.** Yes, $n = 3$ for $\lambda = 1.29$ A,
$n = 4$ for $\lambda = 0.97$ A.

### Chapter 46

**1.** (a) $\pm55°$,
(b) $\pm35°$.

**3.** Assuming that a right-handed coordinate system is used,
(a) circular, counterclockwise as seen facing the source;
(b) elliptical, counterclockwise as seen facing the source, major axis of ellipse along $y = x$;
(c) plane, along $y = -x$.

**5.** $55°30'$ to $55°46'$.

**11.** $2.7 \times 10^{-14}$ kg-meter$^2$/sec$^2$,
2.1 hr.

### Chapter 47

**1.** 4.8 A.

**7.** $5.9 \times 10^{-6}$ ev.

**3.** $6.2 \times 10^{23}$ photons/sec.

**9.** (a) 2.0 ev,
(b) zero,
(c) 2.0 volts,
(d) 3000 A.

**11.** 100 years.

**17.** (a) 1,
(b) $5.3 \times 10^{-11}$ meter,
(c) $1.1 \times 10^{-34}$ joule-sec,
(d) $2.0 \times 10^{-24}$ kg-meter/sec,
(e) $4.1 \times 10^{15}$ radians/sec,
(f) $2.2 \times 10^6$ meters/sec,
(g) $8.2 \times 10^{-8}$ nt,
(h) $9.0 \times 10^{22}$ meters/sec$^2$
(i) $+13.6$ ev,
(j) $-27.2$ ev,
(k) $-13.6$ ev.

**19.** $+0.21$ ev.

**21.** 2.6 ev.

**25.** $+54$ ev, assuming the electron to be in its ground state initially.

**27.** (a) $2.6 \times 10^{-13}$ meter,
(b) 2800 ev,
(c) 4.4 A.

**Chapter 48**

1. (a) $1.7 \times 10^{-35}$ meter.

3. (a) $3.3 \times 10^{-24}$ kg-meter/sec, for each;
   (b) 38 ev for the electron and 6200 ev for the photon.

5. (a) Higher orders cannot exist for this accelerating potential and for these planes. (b) 59°; the crystal must be rotated with respect to the incident beam to satisfy Bragg's law for this new wavelength.

7. 1.5 A.

9. (a) 0.20,
   (b) 0.40,
   (c) 0.33,
   (d) 0.33.

11. 0.32.

15. $6.6 \times 10^{-23}$ kg-meter/sec.

# Answers to Odd-Numbered Supplementary Problems

## Chapter 26

1. $-\frac{4}{9}q$, located $\frac{l}{3}$ from $+q$.

3. $\pm 1.0 \times 10^{-6}$ coul, $\mp 3.0 \times 10^{-6}$ coul.

5. $1.61 \times 10^{-9}$ meter.

## Chapter 27

1. $2\pi \sqrt{\dfrac{l}{g - \dfrac{q}{m}E}}$, $2\pi \sqrt{\dfrac{l}{g + \dfrac{q}{m}E}}$.

3. $\dfrac{Q}{\pi^2 \epsilon_0 R^2}$, vertically downward.

5. $2\pi \sqrt{\dfrac{pE}{I}}$.

## Chapter 28

1. $+3.54 \times 10^{-6}$ coul.
3. $1.98 \times 10^7$ meters/sec.

5. $A = \dfrac{Q}{2\pi a^2}$.

## Chapter 29

1. $1.2 \times 10^{-8}$ coul/meter$^2$.

3. (a) $1.0 \times 10^{-8}$ coul from small to large sphere;
   (b) small sphere: $2 \times 10^{-8}$ coul, 3000 volts,
   large sphere: $4 \times 10^{-8}$ coul, 3000 volts.

9. $W = +\dfrac{Q}{8\pi\epsilon_0}\left[\dfrac{1}{r_1} - \dfrac{1}{r_2}\right]$.

11. (a) $\dfrac{qQ}{4\pi\epsilon_0 K}$.

    (b) $\sqrt{\dfrac{K}{m}}$.

13. (a) $\dfrac{\lambda}{4\pi\epsilon_0}\ln\left(\dfrac{y+L}{y}\right)$.

    (b) $\dfrac{-\lambda}{4\pi\epsilon_0}\dfrac{L}{y(y+L)}$.

    (c) Zero.

## Chapter 30

5. $q_1 = \dfrac{C_1 C_2 + C_1 C_3}{C_1 C_2 + C_1 C_3 + C_2 C_3}C_1 V_0$,

   $q_2 = q_3 = \dfrac{C_1 C_2}{C_1 C_2 + C_1 C_3 + C_2 C_3}C_1 V_0$.

7. (a) $10\epsilon_0$ farad,
   (b) $13.6\epsilon_0$ farad,
   (c) $1200\epsilon_0$ coul, $1200\epsilon_0$ coul,
   (d) $10^4$ volts/meter,
   (e) $2.1 \times 10^3$ volts/meter,
   (f) 88 volts,
   (g) $19 \times 10^3\epsilon_0$ joules.

## Chapter 31

1. (a) $2.3 \times 10^{12}$,
   (b) $5.0 \times 10^3$,
   (c) $10^7$ volts.
5. (a) $\rho_A = .10$ ohm-meter, $\rho_B = .05$ ohm-meter,
   (b) $E_A = 1.0$ volt/meter, $E_B = .50$ volts/meter,
   (c) $j_A = j_B = 10$ amp/meter$^2$,
   (d) $V_A = 40$ volts, $V_B = 20$ volts.
7. $T = 130°$ C.

## Chapter 32

1. $R = r_1 - r_2$.
3. (a) $r$,
   (b) $R$.
5. (a) $\frac{7}{12}R$,
   (b) $\frac{3}{4}R$,
   (c) $\frac{5}{6}R$.
7. (a) 85.0 ohm,
   (b) 85.0 ohm.
9. (a) $1.0 \times 10^{-3}$ coul.,
   (b) $1.0 \times 10^{-3}$ amp.,
   (c) $V_C = V_R = 1000e^{-t}$ volts,
   (d) $e^{-2t}$ watt.

## Chapter 33

1. 1 is positively charged, 2 is neutral, and 3 is negatively charged.
3. $2.7 \times 10^{-4}$ weber/meter$^2$.
5. (a) 542 ohms, series,
   (b) 2.52 ohms, parallel.
7. (a) 2.8 Mc/sec,
   (b) 0.34 meter.

## Chapter 34

1. $-10\mu_0 i_0$.
3. $\dfrac{3\sqrt{2}\,\mu_0 i^2}{4\pi a}$, toward center of square.
5. zero.
7. $\dfrac{\mu_0 i}{4}\left(\dfrac{1}{R_1} - \dfrac{1}{R_2}\right)$, into page.
9. (a) $\dfrac{\mu_0 i}{2R}\left(1 + \dfrac{1}{\pi}\right)$, out of page.

(b) $\dfrac{\mu_0 i}{2\pi R}\sqrt{1 + \pi^2}$, out of page at an angle of 18° with page.

## Chapter 35

3. (a) $\dfrac{\mu_0 i \pi r^2 R^2}{2x^3}$,
   (b) $\dfrac{3\mu_0 \pi i r^2 v}{2R^2 N^4}$.
   (c) In the same sense as the current in the larger loop.
5. (a) $q = \dfrac{-1}{R}[\Phi_B(t_2) - \Phi_B(t_1)]$,
   (b) No. $B$ field could still have changed between $t_1$ and $t_2$ inducing currents.

## Chapter 36

3. (a) $i_1 = 3.3$ amp, $i_2 = 3.3$ amp;
   (b) $i_1 = 4.5$ amp, $i_2 = 2.7$ amp;
   (c) $i_1 = 0$, $i_2 = 1.8$ amp;
   (d) $i_1 = 0$, $i_2 = 0$.
5. (a) meter, (b) weber, (c) watt,
   (d) coulomb, (e) ohm.

## Chapter 37

1. $\dfrac{q\omega r^2}{2}$, in direction of $\boldsymbol{\omega}$.
3. (a) $(N \pm 1)\dfrac{eB}{m}$,
   (b) $744 \times 10^{10}$ rad/sec; $759 \times 10^{10}$ rad/sec.
5. 29 amp.

## Chapter 38

1. Let $T_1$ be the period of inductor and 900 $\mu$f capacitor and $T_2$ the period of inductor and 100 $\mu$f capacitor. Then: (a) close $S_2$, wait $T_1/4$; (b) quickly close $S_1$ then open $S_2$; (c) wait $T_2/4$ and then open $S_1$.

## Chapter 39

1. (a) $\dfrac{2\pi\epsilon_0}{\ln(b/a)}$
   (b) $\dfrac{\mu_0 \ln(b/a)}{2\pi}$
5. (a) $6.3 \times 10^{-2}$ volt/meter,
   (b) $2.1 \times 10^{-10}$ weber/meter$^2$,
   (c) $1.3 \times 10^4$ watts.

**7.** (a) $B = \mu_0 \sigma R \omega$.

   (b) $E = \frac{1}{2}\mu_0 \sigma R^2 \alpha$.

   (c) $S = \frac{\mu_0}{2}\sigma^2 R^3 \omega \alpha$.

   (d) They are both $\mu_0 \pi \sigma^2 R^4 l \omega \alpha$.

## Chapter 40

**1.** (a) $1.0 \times 10^8$ cycles/sec,

   (b) $1.0 \times 10^{-6}$ weber/meter$^2$,

   (c) $2.1$ meter$^{-1}$, $6.3 \times 10^8$ rad/sec,

   (d) $120$ watts/meter$^2$,

   (e) $4.0 \times 10^{-7}$ $A$ nt, $4.0 \times 10^{-7}$ nt/meter$^2$.

**3.** (b) About $6 \times 10^{-7}$ meter (comparable with the wavelength of light).

   (c) No.

## Chapter 41

**1.** $1.95 \times 10^8$ meters/sec.

**3.** $180$ cm.

**5.** (a) $\sqrt{1 + \sin^2 \theta_1}$

   (b) $\sqrt{2}$

## Chapter 42

**1.** 6.

**5.** (b) No.

   (c) Rays pass undeviated through system.

## Chapter 43

**1.** .072 mm.

**3.** 8 microns.

**7.** 8400 A.

**9.** 1.89 microns.

## Chapter 44

**1.** (a) The droplets act as diffracting obstacles producing the observed ring.

   (b) .20 mm.

**3.** 71 ft.

## Chapter 45

**3.** (a) 5860 A.

   (b) Since the fourth maximum is missing, the slit width must lie between 1.00 and 1.69 microns.

**5.** (a) One line to each side of the central maximum.

   (b) $1.44 \times 10^{-4}$ rad.

   (c) $\Delta\theta = \dfrac{1}{R}$

## Chapter 46

**1.** 67% polarized, 33% unpolarized.

**3.** Side $A$ has the Polaroid, and the Polaroid axis must be at 45° to the principal axes of the quarter-wave plate.

# Index

# SELECTED NUMERICAL CONSTANTS

---

$\pi = 3.14$      $\pi^2 = 9.87$      $e = 2.72$      $e^{-1} = 1/e = 0.368$

$\ln 2 = 0.693$      $\log e = 0.434$      $\sqrt{2} = 1.41$      $\sqrt{3} = 1.73$

$$\sin 30° = \cos 60° = \tfrac{1}{2} = 0.500$$

$$\cos 30° = \sin 60° = \sqrt{3}/2 = 0.866$$

$$\tan 30° = \cot 60° = \sqrt{3}/3 = 0.577$$

$$\tan 60° = \cot 30° = \sqrt{3} = 1.732$$

$$\sin 45° = \cos 45° = \sqrt{2}/2 = 0.707$$

$$\tan 45° = \cot 45° = 1.00$$